Lt Ralph C. Engel
Jan 1944
San Antonio

Heart of Europe

AN ANTHOLOGY OF
CREATIVE WRITING
IN EUROPE 1920–1940
*EDITED BY KLAUS MANN
AND HERMANN KESTEN*

*WITH AN INTRODUCTION BY
DOROTHY CANFIELD FISHER*

L. B. FISCHER
NEW YORK

CONTENTS

YUGOSLAVIA

POLAND

RUSSIA

GERMANY

BELGIUM

NETHERLANDS

DENMARK

NORWAY

SWEDEN

FINLAND

SWITZERLAND

INTRODUCTION

A RICHLY various anthology such as this one is like the ocean: the chances are that each person who casts his line into it will be rewarded by drawing out something quite other from the catch on the line next to his. All that an introduction can do is to hold up for observation some reflections of one of the first who have looked into the big volume. For those who have not yet opened the book, they may have value as suggesting that its contents will rousingly incite any reader to thought.

The speculations and ideas which it brought to my mind were singularly wider and more far-ranging than they would have been—could have been—before our imaginations, along with our soldiers, were swept away from their ancient regional restrictions by the war-tornado. I could not but see these European writings set, as writings familiar to us have never been set, against the background of world culture, world civilization. And I think many other readers will find, as I did, that thus seeing all of Europe represented in one collection makes us more aware than ever before of the relation of Europe to the rest of the world. It is as though we had stepped back, clear across the studio, from a painting we have long been surveying from close at hand. From the new distance, we see, not so exclusively the familiar details—beautiful, or epic, or vivid, or fascinatingly horrid, or comic or tragic—as their relation to each other and to the whole design. Or as if from a seat so close to an orchestra that our admiring attention is held by the sensuous beauty first of the arpeggios of the harp, then of the singing strings, then of the blare of the trombone, we move back to a place where the details blend together and we hear the great harmony which is the meaning of the music. Just so, the place of Europe in the whole pattern of human existence comes into visibility with such a survey of the literature of the European world.

Or, as the editors and some of the writers in this anthology would put it, the place of the "European-American group." Perhaps this is as good a place as any to call attention to the fact that although the English-

writing peoples are not represented in this anthology, the editor and
some of the writers indicate to us that the collective mind of England
and America is considered by them as a part, an extension of the European mind. English writings, we are told, have been left out of this
collection only because of linguistic-editorial reasons, because writings
not translated would be out of harmony with translations. The assumption of the editor (and one which this introduction accepts) is of a
grouping of the human family in such large masses that one of its divisions is made up of Europe and the New World.

So it is the expression of the European-American mind which is contained in this big volume. And it is with one of the impressions made by
this glimpse of a collective culture that the introduction is concerned.
Like many of the themes in music, the first statement of this impression
was for me of a folk simplicity, evoking the good-humored smile with
which we greet a hearty Haydn theme taken from a folk source. But,
again as in music—and why not, since all the arts are sisters?—that
cadence which seemed so plain, so disarmingly fresh from everyday life,
deepened, developed, bloomed out into a glimpse of a great truth.

It looked very casual, the fancy which came into my mind as I listened
to these brilliant Europeans, brilliantly saying their say about human
life. My smile was at the amusing contrast between the exquisitely sure,
delicate, powerful precision and distinction of their technique, their
dazzling knowingness of their own field, and what might be called the
innocence of their provincial complacency. Before the war, anybody
noting this would certainly have thought it so natural as to be harmless—
their implicit ignoring of the humanness (by definition as complete as
their own) of those huge numbers of the human race who live and
always have lived outside of Europe and the United States. Since such
an ignoring is the manifestation of a trait common to us all, it would,
before 1939, have been taken for granted, scarcely perceived amidst
the excitement and admiration elicited by the disciplined splendor of the
literary gifts of the writers represented in this volume.

But the Germans have shown us, as by a series of shattering strokes
of lightning, what grotesque and obscene idiocy can grow out of this
ignoring of the fact that other people are as wholly human as we. This
limiting of our emotional and intellectual horizon to what we intimately
know is usually, just as we always instinctively felt it to be, a wholesome
recognition of the fact that we can feel and understand only what we
intimately know. Hence, so long as it is kept within reasonable bounds,
it is harmlessly in accordance with the nature of things. It is the war

which has revealed to us that it can, with an appalling speed like that of cancer, transform healthy, natural cells into a horrible sickness. We are shocked into seeing that it is by no means something to be taken for granted. If we disregard it we put ourselves and all the world in danger. It is something to be closely watched from its first manifestations.

Yet to attempt to cut this limited orientation out from our consciousness, in the mild, moderate, picturesque, often amiable, always zest-creating forms in which it is usually encountered, would greatly impoverish human life. For most people it is the very soil in which the love of life is rooted. Any effort to prevent us, as an ordinary proceeding, from keeping in the foreground what happens to us personally or to those known to us, would make life savorless for all but the Einsteins, Newtons, Spinozas and others of our race who have a special genius for the abstract. The enormous importance—to us!—of what is around us is no illusion. It is as concrete an element in human life as a wheelbarrow on a garden path. There is an old story about the Yankee farmer listening to travel-talk of English cathedrals by a fellow-townsman, who said with the heartiest, contented satisfaction, "I bet you didn't see anything that c'd come up to our Town Hall." There is more in that anecdote than a satiric thrust at a yokel's ignorance. There is a truth in it, and a beautiful, living truth. A building viewed by human eyes is not an object of fixed shape and dimension like the original yard-measure or pound-weight, preserved in a vault. Relativity has a thing or two to say about that. For that Yankee, his Town Hall had, in literal reality, a unique quality. To get it built required long patient group-effort by people conquering their narrow self-interests in order to work harmoniously with their fellow-men. By this self-conquest they had collectively achieved something beyond what any one of them could have done, singly. Hence it is, by implication, a constant reminder and celebration of the almost invincible power of action-in-common. Because of its purpose it is also a monument to self-government as a force in human lives, potent as any biologic instinct. Its proportions (whether good or bad) are, as much as those of the Parthenon, the result of the action upon raw material of that creative instinct to produce shapeliness and form from disorganization, which is the greatest in the human heart. The farmer was right. For any of his fellow-townsmen, York Cathedral could not come up to their Town Hall.

This life-giving realization that each scene and event which has become part of human lives really is in those lives unique, literally special, different from other places and other events, no matter how grand or mighty they are, is what gives the throb of vitality to the writings in this collection. Set down by men and women skilled in the arts of expression, they command our attention, because they speak for their less articulate comrades, wordlessly sharing the same mystic certainty that each human life has its own separate and inviolate connection with the whole. This deepening of awareness, this quickening to aroused consciousness of the mystic wonder of human life, is the great, unique, service which the artist, and the artist alone, can render to humanity. The writings in *Heart of Europe,* almost without an exception, faithfully perform this sacred service.

This deepening of our awareness of life's universality—this celebration of the mightiness and importance of personal events—can take, and in this volume does take, almost infinitely various forms. Sometimes it is lovable and heart-warming, like sunshine, as in Sigrid Undset's *Happy Times in Norway,* or poetic as in the brief, exquisite pastel by Pío Baroja, *Angelus.* Sometimes it is funny, as in Hašek's *Good Soldier Schweik.* More often it is tragic, or intolerably pathetic, as in the heart-breaking story by the Portuguese writer Raul Brandão, *The Thief and His Little Daughter,* or as in the anguish of revulsion from the wretchedness of materialism spread before us in Unamuno's essay on Quixotism—and in many other of the compassionate or ironic or rebellious depictions of human destiny in this book. The very life-blood of every one is the passionate, unshakable (and sound) conviction that this scene, this event set down by the author is worth telling, worth spending a lifetime of effort to learn how best to tell, because it is unique, has a special value, a special meaning all its own, because it has happened to a man or a woman or a child.

Nothing could more magically arouse our imaginations from apathy than this noble reminder of the meaningfulness of human life when viewed by the seeing eye. It sets us musing over the unimaginable wealth of human experience all around the globe, now, in the past, in the future. That proud cry of "See! how moving, how interesting, how comic, how tragic, how different, new and special to each person who experiences it, life is, where *I* live," that form of provincial concentration on the writer's own surroundings, is a fertilizing quickener to the spirit of man, so long as its unspoken implication is "That is what it must be also where you are, since you and I and all those around us are human."

But when the implication is provincial and limited, not in this living way, but in the ugly, negative aggressive way, "All this is true where **I** live, but not where *you* live"—? Well, then we are reminded of one of the most masterly satiric scenes ever written:—the half-grown, awkward young bird, who in his radiant white maturity is to enrich the world with beauty and grace, takes refuge from the cold of his first winter in a peasant's hut. A cat and a hen are domiciled there, very much at their ease in a background intimately known to them. To the new arrival, coming from a world they know not, with potentialities they could not even conceive, they put peremptory questions, based on their own ignorance of anything different from themselves: "What are you good for? What can you do?" The cat asks sharply, "Can you purr? Can you give off sparks when stroked?" No, this the newcomer cannot do. "Can you lay eggs?" asks the hen. No, that he cannot do, either. Well then, since he was neither cat nor hen, with their special abilities, he must be good for nothing, reason the provincials.

I take as an especially clear example of the faint disquieting echo of the Hans Christian Andersen fable which struck my ear, Paul Valéry's beautifully written, lucid and eloquent essay, *Homo Europaeus,* and a quotation from Georges Bernanos. By implication, what Valéry does not say, he seems to tell those members of the human race who do not have the European (or, by his own definition the European-American) mind, "Look at the sparks glitteringly cast off from European culture, how they shine!" And what wonderfully nourishing eggs are those produced by European learning! To people outside of Europe and its influence, who cannot lay such eggs, produce such sparks—well, my fellow-European Georges Bernanos, has something to say to you, namely that "Europe will never surrender the privilege she assumes to lead the spiritual life of the world." The cat, proud of the electricity in a cat's fur, does not mention (not because he wishes to hide anything but quite simply because he does not know about them) the useful, beautiful and interesting things no cat can do. The hen, justifiably pleased with her ability to produce one kind of food, ignores in all innocence of ignorance, the many other kinds just as good produced by creatures that are not hens. Paul Valéry rolls out a scroll inscribed in gold and lapis lazuli, whereon is set forth the magnificent achievements of European man. He does not mention any of the hideous failures of European man—the nightmare of his long bloody religious persecutions and wars, compared to the three or four thousand years of China's national life, wholly free from that malignant ulcer. Nor the recurrent breakdowns of European society which shatter all continuity in the civilized arts, compared to the magnificent stability of Chinese society which has given to Chinese painting (one of the greatest schools of art of the world) the proud tradition of fifteen hundred years of unbroken practice.

In one of the most beautifully written passages of this splendid essay, Valéry speaks with natural, to-be-expected pride of geometry as an incomparably fruitful achievement of European learning. He nowhere speaks with natural, to-be-expected humility of the fact that the subtle concept of zero, irreplaceably vital to the advance of mathematics, remained unknown to Europeans, until it was finally brought (via the Arabs) from India where, together with other intricately subtle concepts, it had long been familiar to Brahman intellectuals. Nor does he place beside his claim to a unique flexibility and invincible intellectual curiosity in homo europaeus, the item that for hundreds and hundreds of years after the nimble Arabic numerals had elsewhere opened the door to new mathematical activities, he went on using the clumsy Roman numerals—for no reason that anyone can divine, save that sheer inability to react against senseless tradition, which we think of as the special Chinese weakness.

These instances are of concrete facts familiar to historians. Other possible, useful, beautiful human achievements in fields where the European mind has failed to function are not hinted at—such as, to give one instance, the ways by which peaceful, creative happiness in personal relations might be made the rule instead of the exception. We of the European-American group, so proud of the glitter of our sparks and the food-value of our eggs, are as little abashed by our failures in such aspects of life, as the cat and hen by their ignorance of reading and writing.

That bland assumption that what we have not heard of cannot exist—how laughably we all indulge in it. One of the most curative elements in such a long-range view of the collective whole of our common culture as is made possible by this inclusive collection is to see how universal that assumption is. Shortly after the appearance of Georges Duhamel's acid-etched descriptions of things he had found to detest in the United States of America, he said to me in casual conversation, "One thing in the United States I especially found a desolation—the absence of historical, or literary, or artistic or heroic associations with places. In Europe, when I travel and glance out of the train at the name of a railway station, my mind is instantly flooded with the memories it evokes—of some great (or greatly infamous) deed done there, of some noble, or subtle human soul who lived there, of a crisis in the history of mankind which took place there. But in America—nothing. A meaningless name painted on a board."

Fascinated by this, coming from a man so gifted in the finest psychological analysis, I asked, watching intently the expression of his face as I spoke, "Did you perhaps chance to see among the names painted on boards at American railway stations, the name of Concord, Massachusetts? Or Harpers Ferry? Or Gettysburg? Or Trenton, or Walden Pond? Monticello? Yorktown?" There was not a flicker of recognition in his honest eyes. "No," he answered, evidently wondering a little at the question, "No, I don't remember seeing any of those names."

At first this tiny episode seemed to me as exquisitely full of the essential spirit of comedy as any of Molière's satires. After I had left the Duhamel home that day, I burst into a great fit of laughter—mirth suddenly silenced by the chilling realization that the joke was very much on me also. For I saw myself traveling in Ceylon or China, or Japan, or India, gazing out blankly, my eyes glazed by ignorance, at strange-looking names painted on boards, names which to intelligent people of the country would be bright with triumph after long defeat, like Yorktown, tense with memories of a turning-point in humanity's long pilgrimage, like Lincoln's home town, or radiant—Monticello, Walden Pond, Concord —with immortal brightness from some of the personalities that make one not ashamed to be a member of the human race.

Who was I to taugh at a European's simple-hearted certainty that because he knew none of the memorable associations clustering around place-names, there were none—I, who would gape if I saw the name of K'iuh-Fow, the word as absurd-looking to me as Poughkeepsie to a European. I would be too ignorant even to realize my ignorance, of its resplendent spiritual associations, which have shed light on China for more than two thousand years (two thousand four hundred and twenty-one, to be exact).

And what was happening in Europe at that time, 478 B.C., when a great nation was nobly mourning the death of a never-to-be-forgotten-by-them great, good man, whose whole life had been spent in trying to teach them how to live more peacefully, more honorably, more intelligently together? Mass-murder was going on in Europe, as always, the typically European effort to solve the problem of conflicting human interests and desires by one side's establishing its ability to dominate the other side. The Persians were making a third bloody attempt (or was it the fourth?) to conquer Greece. The still primitive Romans were killing as many Etruscans, Sabines, etc., as possible. The Northern People, the elect of

Destiny, were savage tribes clad in animal skins, gnawing bones in caves (or something of the kind), but already, as the historian divines from their later history, cutting the throats of neighboring tribes as the only way conceivable to them of protecting their own safety.

All this casts a sallow light on the statement of the eminent European of the claim made—now!, still!—that Europe must either be recognized forever as the spiritual leader of civilization or she will certainly destroy it. Little of that "forever" business has proved valid in the history of our race. The Romans of the Empire certainly had the same "forever" graven on their minds. How could they have dreamed what was to come from the barbarians of the British Isles and the savage tribes of the misty North. And the Arabs, a thousand years later, able mathematicians, engineers, doctors, and surrounded as far as they could see by peoples inapt for such intellectual skills, was there not a perfectly natural "forever" in their minds as they looked over the Pyrenees at Charlemagne's empire and reflected that not one person in all that realm was capable of solving quadratic equations? Capable of solving them? Incapable even of guessing at their existence.

The factual observation that these modern Europeans, so magically gifted as this volume of their writings proves, still hold naively to provinciality of the most obvious kind—as do all the rest of us—is as clear as a folk theme in a musical composition. And like the musical theme as it develops, this observation proves to contain meanings of extraordinary depth, breadth and vitality. As one listens and looks and reflects, one sees blooming out of this simple root, warnings for the future, reassurances for the future, hints of where the road into the future must lie—if it is not to be broken off and destroyed.

The warnings are—branded on human hearts in the white-hot hell of a global war—that there can no longer be any hope of solving the essential problem facing men and women—how to live together on the globe peaceably enough at least to survive—by the continued application of the traditional European impulse to protect one's own interests and desires by forcible domination of others.

This idea is a natural, universal human one, of course, but it has especially permeated European life, to its remotest capillaries. Tribes, nations and empires have sought to dominate others by force and have collapsed in desolation. Classes have tried to dominate other classes, men have tried to dominate women, adults children, rich the poor. With consequences of intolerable human misery to high and low, to rich and poor, to young and to old, such as—to their everlasting credit—the sensitive minds and hearts of the European writers in this collection have so clearly seen and so masterfully portrayed. We of the tradition called here the European-American sincerely cannot imagine any other way of managing human existence any more than Charlemagne's great peers could imagine the processes of elementary algebra—which nevertheless have proved so easily grasped by human minds that they are now understood by any normal adolescent of high-school age.

From the dawn of European history the violent method of trying to settle the natural and inevitable conflicts of human interests and desires has been tried and tried, on a bigger and bigger scale, with the result that the ensuing ruin has been bigger and bigger. There can be no more total test of this idea that forcible domination is the way to handle the fact that human interests differ than the Satanic attempt at domination of the Nazis. Human experience is a hard school, but fools will learn in no other! The most foolish human should, after the abysmal failure of this last application of that principle, begin to surmise that something is the matter with the principle, since it always leads to unutterable horrors and ruinous instability.

Yet the Chinese idea that stability can be achieved by walling out others with divergent interests and desires is no longer valid in a world where airplanes fly (literally and metaphorically) over the hugest walls. We all live in the same world now. We cannot wall out any of the difficulties involved. We must somehow solve them, or perish and give way to the insects.

We humans have, in the past, solved problems—we, Hindu, Chinese, Greek, Arabic, European, American. How have we done it? By using our wits in the effort to understand the nature of the problem, of course. Here and there, in this and that nation, to a greater or less degree, all around the globe, the human instinct which tells us that to control and direct we must understand has worked wonders, when turned on the difficulties inherent in bridge-building, in navigation, in medicine, architecture, painting, literature and plumbing. In any field, as soon as the patient, adult effort to understand replaces the raw childish impulse to strike and grab, or to grab and lock the door, we have seen how obstacles can be surmounted. Why should we not hope confidently that if we turn upon our own natures, and upon the relations between human beings, human classes, and nations, that same mighty solvent of the sincere, patient, analytical effort to understand, the difficulties inherent in establishing human harmony, too, may yield. We have never yet really looked at the knot which we must learn how to untie if we are to survive

—more important than surviving, if human life is to become endurable to self-respecting men and women. We have only jerked hard at that knot— or have hidden it away and pretended it was not there.

And in the effort to apply that principle—that the more completely you understand a problem, the more hope you have of solving it—how magnificently Europeans are fitted to serve is shown by the heaped-up treasures in this anthology. It is knowledge of human nature that we need, is it not? What better fellow-workers in the laboratory could there be than Maritain, than Croce, than Gorki, than Silone, than Hugo von Hofmannsthal, than Hašek? They have not, it is true, any more than any of us, revolted from the European (universal, but especially European) fallacy that to dominate or be dominated is the only possible way of human life, no, but to the honor of their hearts and minds, they have profoundly suffered from the effects of this fallacy on human existence, and have depicted those effects with power, accuracy and the deepest sorrow. What wonders they could help accomplish with such gifts if, their imaginations aroused by this last cataclysm, by the violent shoving together under modern conditions of all the children of men, they will lift their eyes from the primitive abacus with which our European-American group has for several thousand years vainly tried to solve human problems too complicated for it, to the moral and social algebra which might make our present wretchedness seem the filth and disease and darkness of mediaeval cities—absurdly, pathetically, unnecessary. Who better than these minds, subtle, disciplined in certain fields, could help in the exploration and surveying of the new field of human co-operation which lies beyond the old way so darkly familiar to us, of beating down, or ignoring the interests and wishes of others?

A fruitful outcome of our human travail is not assured. Life-experienced men and women know better than to laugh joyfully over the birth of a child, while the mother is still writhing in anguish—did any woman of all the untold millions who have given birth since the beginning of our race ever suffer such horrible tortures as those our modern world is undergoing? The child we hope for may be born dead, not alive.

It will take the best that the human race has to give even to start forward on the new attempt to understand ourselves. It will take the best thinking our race has ever done to grasp and hold fast the abstract idea (far more abstract than algebra, and as literally true) that in understanding ourselves we understand others, since in the simplest and most literal way mankind is not only complex and diverse, but also one. We begin to catch vague, fleeting glimpses of an abstraction true, but as strange to us as logarithms to a Hottentot—the idea that there is literally no conflict between differing human interests, because they are identical, since what benefits one benefits all. We are stirring confusedly in our old cave, dark as a womb, conscious as never before of the presence of others around us with as much right as we have to be there. The way out to the sunlit world is open. But steep. So steep that any attempt of one to hold back others, so that he may be in the lead, will hold us all back. Far too steep to be surmounted by anything less than certainty that our destiny is either to slip back into blackness all together, or, all together, emerge into the light of day.

DOROTHY CANFIELD

Arlington, Vermont
1943.

PREFACE

THE FORTRESS OF EUROPE is doomed. The Heart of Europe is immortal.

It may be wounded and weary, this proud and sensitive heart, haunted by sinister memories and even more terrible forebodings. But it still throbs and lives, in the middle of darkness and disintegration. However woeful and fearful, it remains the focus, nay, the dynamic source of vast energies, both creative and devastating.

✿   ✿   ✿

The European genius has often been prone to treachery and corruption. Given to adventures and experiments, the *homo europaeus* is always in danger of going astray, of losing his moral equilibrium. There were periods of confusion and decadence during which Western man forgot his mission and wantonly betrayed the sacred legacy of Hellenic wisdom and Christian faith.

If Europe has been lovable and great, it is by virtue of this twofold heritage. Golgatha and the Acropolis are the tokens of her spiritual survival. She jeopardizes her glory when she distorts or disregards this double source of her substance. The diversity of Europe will inevitably fall into anarchy unless organized and illuminated from this innermost center. A Europe estranged from her own sublime traditions not only forfeits her universal rank but becomes indeed a public enemy—most dangerous to the very civilization that she helped create.

The crisis through which Europe passes now is perhaps the gravest of her history; it certainly involves more frightful perils to the civilized world at large than did any of the previous upheavals and ordeals. This time, two of the most illustratious members of the continental family— the nation of Caesar and Dante and the country of Dürer and Hölderlin —have utterly abandoned whatever was inspiring and constructive in their past, and, moreover, challenge and attack all those who still adhere to the essential laws of Occidental culture.

Of course, it would be absurd to hold a few individuals, however

wicked and however powerful, solely responsible for a calamity of
such apocalyptic dimensions. The disaster called Fascism-Nazism has
its roots not only in the problematic character of two particular nations;
it is derived, not only from the blunders of one particular peace con-
ference or from the social conditions of a chaotic post-war period, but
also from the abysmal depth and complexity of European thought.
Undeniably, the intellectual climate of the continent fostered for many
years the bacillus that has now become so murderously virulent.

The European literature of the nineteenth century—one of the most
fascinating developments of human culture—was charged with ominous,
or ambiguous, potentialities. If the philosophy of Enlightenment had
sapped the authority of religion and feudalism, the pessimistic romanticism and extreme individualism of the following period questioned and
undermined the validity of any hierarchic order—including all accepted
categories of logic, ethics and aesthetics. Jean-Jacques Rousseau and
Immanuel Kant inaugurated an intellectual revolution of staggering
implications and consequences. Man conceived and communicated a
new, daring vision of his own nature and destiny; the basic elements
of the human drama—man's relation to God and society, his physical
impulses and metaphysical aspirations—had to be redefined and
re-evaluated.

The generous illusions of the eighteenth century were refuted, once
and for all, by the psychological discoveries of the nineteenth. How was
it possible to ignore the sinister qualities of modern man, after the bold
and tragic revelations of Nietzsche and Dostoevsky, Stendhal and
Schopenhauer, Freud and Marx, Tolstoi and Kierkegaard? It became
difficult, indeed impossible, to indulge in euphemisms about man's
intrinsic goodness and simplicity, in view of this cruel and admirable
truthfulness.

The very concepts and traditions on which our civilization rests were
affected by the grand intellectual assault. While the material world was
being astoundingly altered by vast technical and scientific discoveries,
man himself seemed to grow and change, to mature, to increase in
glorious and terrible features. The literature of the nineteenth century
echoed and defined these sweeping changes and developments. How
dynamic and colorful the Human Comedy appeared in Balzic's epic
interpretation! How fierce and fascinating was the Human Beast, as
presented by Emile Zola! What unprecedented problems and solutions
were anticipated in Heine's bitter-sweet irony, in Baudelaire's hazardous
cult of vice and ugliness, in Rimbaud's rebellious adventure! The tragedy

of human solitude—both the utter futility and inexplicable grandeur of our struggle—were experienced and formed anew by men like Flaubert and Strindberg. Henrik Ibsen ventured to question such sacred institutions as marriage—one of the moral bases of bourgeois society; Oscar Wilde foolhardily challenged the sex prejudices of the middle class. Karl Marx—infinitely greater as an analyst than as a prophet—discovered the motive powers behind man's collective drama, while Sigmund Freud—equally inspired and equally one-sided—penetrated into the lurid maze of the human subconscious, where he found the tokens and scars of early traumas and incestuous appetites.

Nietzsche-Zarathustra bewitched the intellectual élite with his equivocal catchwords. Prometheus-like, he challenged the gods and defied the moral conventions of two thousand years; whatever had been taught or believed, from Socrates to Pascal, from St. Paul to Kant, was doubted or attacked by this terrific revolutionary.

How thrillingly adventurous life seemed, up there, at glacial height, immeasurably beyond good and evil! An anti-intellectual, anti-humanitarian vogue swept the continent. The commonplace faith in Science, Reason and Progress provoked the new idolatry of Instinct and Intuition. The élan vital—the aimless energy of Life as such—was worshipped, no matter what its purpose or its direction.

But from Nietzsche's power philosophy it is only one step to Sorel's terrible defense of violence and to Spengler's dreary decline of the western world.

*   *   *

With all accepted codes and concepts questioned or destroyed, the moment appeared propitious for the last, decisive blow against Christian, Occidental civilization—the revolution of nihilism.

But Nazism and Fascism, it seems almost needless to say, strikingly failed—or, in fact, never tried—to fulfill the prophecies of those they claim as their literary predecessors. The demagogues of Berlin and Rome simply stole the most dubious ingredients of certain philosophies and mixed them into an obnoxious, indeed deadly, concoction. Is it Nietzsche's fault that his Superman becomes a revolting freak when represented by Hitler, Goering and Goebbels? Can we blame Tolstoi and Dostoevsky for the hackneyed imitation of their ecstasies? Is Schopenhauer's tragic vision responsible for the vulgar nihilism of maniacs and criminals? It might even be unfair to reproach Richard Wagner with Hitler's weakness for Die Meistersinger. . . .

All those European geniuses—being real Europeans and true geniuses —not only were bearers of the diabolic bacillus but also possessed and offered the remedy to render the poison wholesome and stimulating. The European drama proceeds according to complex dialectical rules. Its crucial developments have often, if not always, a twofold impact: they contain the double germ of progress and disaster, of liberation and catastrophe. Each time the European genius challenges the established hierarchy of values and institutions, he threatens, deliberately or unwittingly, the basic structure of Christian civilization. This is true of the Renaissance, of Luther's Reformation, of the French Revolution and of the more recent experiments—both scientific-technical and psychological-artistic. And it is true also of the more fragile literary generation—our contemporaries—succeeding the creative giants of the nineteenth century. Their very weakness is often the source of their potency and persuasion. If some of them appear flippant and cynical, they may be so out of their tonic aversion to bombastic words and beautiful illusions. Some are bitter, out of their relentless truthfulness. Others owe their particular insight to an almost morbid sensitivity of the nervous system. Is there in modern writings a proclivity for the sterile and chaotic? Perhaps so; but there is also an authentic, passionate striving for new, valid concepts and images, the earnest, inspired will to find and formulate a new morality, a new kind of beauty, a new law, a new vision.

*   *   *

The pivotal experience of the first World War intensified and deepened both elements in European letters—on the one hand, the suicidal moods and feverish distortions and, on the other, the constructive will to find new solutions for the vital social and moral issues of our time. European literature emerged from the ordeal richer than ever in colors and contradictions, sublime beauties and dangerous tendencies.

The period from 1920 to 1940 in Europe was perhaps less dynamic and less significant, so far as creative writing is concerned, than were the first two decades of this century. Yet it would be erroneous to believe that literature in Europe stagnated during the years preceding the present disaster. There is a profusion of new, youthful voices—some of them shrill or weak or cheaply sensational, but others candid and powerful. True, this polyphonic concert echoes the anguish of past tribulations and often anticipates the screams and spasms of coming calamities. But at the same time we are struck by unmistakable signs foreshadowing the present fight against evil and even the future epoch of reconstruction and recovery.

*   *   *

It is not the purpose of this anthology to introduce or publicize any particular literary movement. In fact, there are no literary movements in the war-torn, war-weary Europe of 1943; there are only the brave, if secret, opponents, the tragic victims and the venal flunkeys of a totalitarian dictatorship.

The last great boom of literary schools and coteries in Europe existed during the years immediately after the first World War. It was then that Expressionism, Futurism, Dadaism, and the like (all started shortly before or shortly after 1914) became popular and dominated the artistic scene. Their hectic glory, however, utterly failed to last. Yet the influence of those anti-realistic—or surrealist—tendencies is still noticeable and still stimulating, while the products and patterns of the original schools have long become stale and meaningless.

During the following years—from 1925 to 1940—no literary formula was generally accepted by the continental vanguard. Of course, there were groups and cliques, Marxists, neo-Catholics, neo-Conservatives, and so forth, but their slogans and styles were determined by non-literary motives and interests. The leading figures of the European literary scene —men like Rilke and Valéry, Gide and Ortega y Gasset, Thomas Mann and Croce—may have had the authority to launch their own literary programs, but did not choose to do so.

There were no "movements," but there was a rich variety of trends and tastes, promising efforts and superb accomplishments. Novel, criticism, poetry and, in a minor way, also the drama continued to flourish while the continent was drifting towards disaster. No doubt Europe's social and political élites failed signally in their task of leading and enlightening the muddled, malcontent peoples. But the record of the literary men is, on the whole, more impressive and more honorable than is that of politicians and industrialists. The majority of European writers were not unaware of the dangers confronting them, nor were they frightened or paralyzed by their sinister insight. It would be indeed unfair to condemn the creative minds of Europe en bloc as "irresponsible" or even as treacherous. Naturally, there are sad exceptions. But in general the representatives of European letters did their utmost to warn their continent against the imminent catastrophe and, at the same time, to increase its glory by contributing new works and testimonies, some of them of sound and lasting value.

It is, then, the purpose of this anthology to present as comprehensive and as unbiased a survey as possible of what is soundly alive and lastingly valid in the European literary production of the past two decades, in the fields of poetry and of narrative and analytical prose. As for the drama, we decided not to include samples of that particular literary form. The European theater—so vitally creative during the years from 1890 to 1914—somehow lost its spiritual significance during the period covered in this book. Besides, it seemed practically impossible to give an adequate notion of the various theatrical styles by presenting a selection of fragmentary scenes and one-act plays. A special anthology would be necessary to introduce the multitude of recent theatrical developments and tendencies in Europe to the American reader.

*   *   *

Of course, it was impossible to omit in this selection all symptoms of decadence and confusion; they are inherent in the works of the very authors who may turn out to be the heralds of a coming European renaissance. But we made it our policy to exclude from this book all those writers in whose style and ideology fascist elements predominate.

We had at first thought—somewhat apprehensively—that such political discrimination might complicate and corrupt our choice. But the omission of Hitler's and Mussolini's literary champions proved only a minor loss. Nobody will miss Hanns Johst and Marinetti—those ludicrous *poetae laureati* of the Berlin-Rome Axis. And as for those "unpolitical" conservatives who made their peace with the devil—as did Hans Carossa in Germany, Gracia Deledda in Italy—most of them are rather on the boring side. It is indeed possible to present a fairly complete panorama of contemporary European letters without admitting anybody who stained or forfeited his prestige by too intimate a contact with the powers of barbarism.

Yet, there are cases that caused us a little difficulty—Gerhart Hauptmann, for instance, Knut Hamsun and Gabriele d'Annunzio. Their literary rank is beyond any question. Should we do without them because of their political misbehavior? Undeniably, Hauptmann's early dramas are still powerful, regardless of his short-sighted servility toward Hitlerism. But then how long ago is it that he wrote *The Weavers* and *Hannele's Ascension?* The truth is that he produced nothing of real interest after 1918. This anthology, however, covers only the period between the two world wars.

That is why d'Annunzio hardly fits our scheme, quite apart from all political considerations. His poses and vagaries, accents and adventures, are impregnated with the unmistakable flavor of the *fin de siècle;* his theatrical fascination is a phenomenon of the past. It seemed more pertinent to include G. A. Borgese's brilliant analysis of d'Annunzio's character and career than to present a sample from the poet's somewhat over-aged work.

And what about Knut Humsun—that unique old wizard of Norwegian solitudes? True, he lost his genius with his political integrity: the more ardent his panegyrics of Nazism, the more boring his novels. Yet, some of the things he produced between 1919 and 1939 are of compelling beauty and originality. Nevertheless, we decided to renounce his contribution. The influence Knut Hamsun exercised on European literature in general, and on German writers in particular, was exceedingly unfortunate. His fierce, irrational hatred of Western civilization incited the vandalic instincts of many a callow scribbler between Oslo and Rome; his personal style served as a model to the cheapest "blood and soil" romanticists. His place—intellectually and even artistically—is definitely on the other side of the fence.

But, a critical reader might object at this point, if we are so strict in matters of political ethics, how could we admit such equivocal contributors as Stefan George and Paul Claudel, Jean Cocteau and Luigi Pirandello?

It is undeniable that there are suggestions of an anti-democratic, authoritarian philosophy in the work of the great German poet, Stefan George, and of the illustrious French bard and dramatist, Paul Claudel. But in both cases those inimical elements are counterbalanced, or indeed outweighted, by other tendencies of a more approvable nature. If it is true that Claudel, the fervent Catholic and implacable enemy of Enlightenment and Progress, paid embarrassing homage to General Franco and Marshal Pétain, it is also true that his religious feeling is profound and authentic enough to guarantee the innermost purity of his ideas and intentions—far beyond, and quite apart from, his occasional tactical slips. The great European traditions are unquestionably alive in Paul Claudel's prayers and auguries, just as they live in Stefan George's aristocratic ethos. Idolized by German nationalistic youth, wooed by Goebbels and his puny agents, the sacerdotal renovator of German poetry might have become the "Führer" of Nazi literature. But he spurned—proud and

incorruptible—all flattering offers coming to him from Berlin, and died
in exile, disgusted with the blatant vulgarity of the Teutonic "revolution"
which he had, in part, prepared and prophesied. It was his last wish not
to be buried in German soil.

As for Pirandello and Cocteau, they are exceptional, somehow paradoxical cases. But both have to contribute original, and, in a way, indispensable shades to the rich palette we try to present in this volume. Besides,
there is no touch of the fascist bacillus to be traced in their dream worlds.
If Pirandello's psychological fantasies have any relation to Mussolini's
pseudo-Caesarian regime, it can only be a critical, even hostile, one.
Deeply versed in the morbid entanglements of split personalities, the
Italian skeptic and romanticist was certainly not inclined to glorify, or
even to recognize, the hollow greatness of any neurotic duce. If
Pirandello, during the last years of his life, proved unable to resist the
pressure and the temptations of the Fascist Government, his attitude
seems to express a desperate weariness and ambiguous irony rather than
any intellectual or political decision. And if Jean Cocteau—"corroded by
poetry as certain physicists are by X-rays"—yielded to the massive persuasion of the German invaders, he only chose a particularly macabre
form of suicide, which—we think—is hardly apt to depreciate the enthralling authenticity of his previous artistic feats and confessions.

*   *   *

There were other problems and difficulties engaging the editors of
this book. Could we hope to bring about a fairly representative selection
with less than a thousand pages at our disposal? It was a vast profusion
of literature from which we had to pick the most striking, most typical
samples. Every anthology is arbitrary and inadequate, to a certain
extent. Fully aware of this danger, we tried hard not to neglect anything
of real significance—not to admit the mediocre. We excluded, consciously
and deliberately, some of the European names most familiar to the
American literary public—not necessarily because we deemed those
authors second-rate, but because we believe that their works, however
popular, clever and entertaining, are not essential in the particular con-
text of this book.

Another delicate issue arose in the search for an appropriate scheme
according to which the material could be organized. Would the language
be an adequate criterion? But it appeared somehow dubious, if not
outright wrong, to present, say, Ramuz and Maeterlinck as Frenchmen,
just because French happens to be their idiom—Hofmannsthal and Wer-

fel, as Germans, because the German language is their medium of expression. Was it permissible to neglect, or even to deny, the specific qualities of the smaller countries—Switzerland, Belgium, Austria, Czechoslovakia? To claim Franz Kafka and Rainer Maria Rilke as Germans would be almost tantamount to accepting Hitlerian views. Kafka—one of the most extraordinary masters of German prose—is not really a German writer. His incomparable visions are deeply imbued with the mysterious twilight of Prague, a city which is a complex and independent cultural entity, by no means a mere particle of the Greater Reich. As for Rilke, it is particularly difficult to define his nationality: Slavic, French and Nordic elements are fused, intimately and enchantingly, in the iridescent texture of his work and being. Should we present him simply as "a European"? That would have been premature. . . .

The European map, as shaped in 1919, may be imperfect in many ways, but there is no better scheme available as yet. We decided, therefore, to classify our authors according to their respective lands of origin, and to stick to the Versailles Treaty with regard to the various national sovereignties.

A point requiring special explanation is the absence of England's voice in our symphony. It may seem paradoxical, if not provocative, to exclude from a selection of this kind the very nation to which Europe is most profoundly indebted at this historical moment. There were, however, numerous cogent reasons speaking against the admission of English (and Irish) authors.

First, English literature is much more widely and more intimately known to the American reading public than are the European continental writers; consequently, the selection of English material would have had to be made according to principles very different from those applicable to the other national departments. Secondly, it appeared inadvisable, from an artistic, or stylistic, point of view, to include one group of original texts in a book consisting of translations. Thirdly—and this last argument is perhaps the one that brought the final decision—the publishers of this volume are planning a special anthology of writings from the British Commonwealth—conceived as a kind of sequel to "Heart of Europe," just as the latter might not have come into being without the encouraging example of a preceding volume, "American Harvest."

✿   ✿   ✿

It was our ambition to show the vast variety of European landscapes, moods and rhythms. What stirring contrasts! What delicate transitions

and suggestive blends! From the gaudy Balkans—so enchantingly described by Panait Istrati—to the Nordic idyll of Sigrid Undset; from the
almost African colors and contours of Spain's scenery to the mellow
loveliness of Paris resounding through the prose of Marcel Proust and
Jules Romains; from the bleak grandeur of Finland's lakes and forests
to the festival baroque of Salzburg's architecture—solemn and serene as
the style of Austria's great poet, Hugo von Hofmannsthal—what abundance of splendors and memories!

"From richly nourished, old and blood-soaked soil grows all that moves
us," as Richard Beer-Hofmann has said in a remarkable essay on Mozart.
From this ground, the tragic, fertile, sacred soil of Europe, rose the
spiritual heroes whose names we find invoked in certain pages of this
anthology: Goethe and the Romantics, those inspired sons and representatives of a better Germany, now silenced or distorted; Don Quixote
—pathetic and grotesque, yet infinitely moving—an authentic myth, as
conceived and analyzed by Miguel de Unamuno; the great masters, from
Giotto to Picasso, of whom Julien Green speaks to us with so much knowing sensibility; Dostoevsky, the soul and prophet of "Fiery Russia," to
quote Remizov's formula; Balzac, Ibsen, Lenin.

Europe is a continent of nightmares and murderers, the deadly region
where the Age of the Fish begins; it is the realm of antics and mas-
querades, follies and romances, the land of inspired jesters—who could be
funnier, who wiser, than Hašek's Good Soldier Schweik?—What euphoric
weariness in Joseph Roth's reckless and pious drunkard!—Europe, the
land of crusaders and athletes—think of Gustav Regler, Saint Exupéry,
Henry de Montherlant! There is a Europe of martyrs and refugees, a
Europe of madness and disintegration—a continent in ruins.

Europe is a land of terrific changes, sweeping transformations. We
must not visualize Europe as something finished and settled, a monument
of its own glorious past, but, on the contrary, as a dynamic organism,
striving, struggling, sinning and atoning, still pregnant with terrific
dangers, ample promises.

Europe is a continent in the making.

The most illustrious European minds are ardently, primarily concerned
with the future, even when scrutinizing the past, as does the eminent
Dutch scholar, Huizinga. Read Ortega y Gasset's shrewd and humane
reflections! Be moved by André Gide's fervent appeal for Joy and
Progress, for a wider and bolder concept of human life! Respond to the
spirited eloquence of Heinrich Mann's Supernational Manifesto! What

is at stake in all these programs, warnings and discussions? The future of Europe, of our civilization; the future of man himself.

Liberated from its present tyrants and demagogues, Europe may establish herself at last as a political and spiritual unity. Europe is tenacious; she has survived many failures, many horrors, many agonies. She may rise once again from the ashes—Phoenix-like—more deeply experienced than ever, not altered but purified, and sufficiently inspired, perhaps, to conceive and realize a new humanistic ideal—revolutionary, yet conserving what is imperishable in European traditions, sober and realistic, yet with religious perspectives and implications, international—or rather, inter-continental—but proudly maintaining and developing her own specific European character and the individual qualities of the various European nations.

Europe may perish—it was, indeed, on the point of perishing during the past ten years—but it will never stagnate. It will not become a Russian province or a museum for American tourists.

"*Méfiez-vous de l'Europe!*" Thus a great European, Georges Bernanos, admonishes his American friends from his Brazilian exile. "No doubt most of you take it for granted that old Europe will emerge depleted of all constructive forces from this ghastly nightmare. But Europe is not old, to begin with; only its institutions are obsolete. The peoples of Europe are by no means over-aged; only the European élites have to be rejuvenated. The present crisis does not resemble a crisis of senility. . . . Europe has been an incomparable intellectual center; she will never renounce the privilege she assumes—rightly or wrongly so—namely, to stimulate and lead the spiritual life of the world." And, again, with ominous emphasis: "If Europe proves unable to save our civilization, she will certainly destroy it."

●   ●   ●

I do not want to conclude this preface without having expressed my gratitude to those friends who helped me to compile and organize the material contained in this book. The editorial "we" that I have been using in these pages is meant to confirm and stress an intellectual congeniality to which this volume owes its existence and its character. The writers who contributed the introductory pieces are, of course, not responsible for the choice of texts included; yet their suggestions were instrumental in shaping the contents and composition of the various national sections. As for others whose collaboration was particularly useful, I want to mention Miss Lotte Walter, Franz J. Horch, F. C. Weiskopf and with special emphasis, Miss Isabella Athey, of L. B. Fischer's editorial staff.

My warmest thanks, however, are due to my friend, Hermann Kesten, who joined me in the editorial work a few weeks after I had started, and who completed the job when I was no longer able to concentrate on literary things. While I took my basic military training, somewhere in the South of the United States, he was occupied in New York City with adding the last touches to the selection we had planned together.

As this book goes to press, I am on the point of leaving with my unit for an "unknown destination." Wherever I may be when this anthology is published, I shall try to serve the very ideas and values discussed and dramatized in its pages. The Europe we may be destined to see again —God knows under what conditions—will perhaps be a dismal, pitiful place, infested by plagues and poverty, disfigured, humiliated. But we believe—firmly and fervently—that we shall find the Heart of Europe— polluted, bleeding, bitterly insulted, yet lovable, yet strong, yet glowing with the unquenchable flame of pride and protest, faith and fantasy.

KLAUS MANN

U. S. Army
Summer, 1943

HEART OF EUROPE

INTRODUCTION

By Yvan Goll

ONE OF THE charming fantasies of seventeenth-century France was "La Carte du Tendre," drawn for "Les Précieuses" of the Hôtel de Rambouillet, an allegorical map of the heart and mind of France, showing the heights of thought, the rivers of ideas, the valleys of sentiment and the cities inhabited by men. Such a "Map of Tenderness"—defying translation—is both a delightful and an apt simile for French literature today, a literature that is as heart-stirring, diversified and harmonious as the scenery of France and that, like a French landscape, draws and fascinates men from all continents.

The period between the two armistices, from the victory of 1918 to the defeat of 1940—both victory and defeat being equally temporary—was colorful and variegated, feverish and chaotic, open to all generous impulses and to all revolts, to all religions and all nihilisms. In 1930 the centennial of the Romantic movement was commemorated, not without a realization of the fact that another Romantic movement was on. The young were in the throes of a novel "mal du siècle," an ill-being more painful and tragic still, the forerunner of an unescapable catastrophe. Such a catastrophe was indeed forecast by the seismographs of poetry. It was forecast by anathemas, the violent outbursts of language and also of thought, by many a mystical investigation and by all the Freudian discoveries: man's life as a whole, on both the moral and the social plane, was questioned once again.

This entire epoch has been dominated by one writer: André Gide. He gave it its passwords and its leitmotifs. The aesthetic terms most in use and most subject to discussion were his—the gratuitous act, inquietude, escape. His characters are prototypes of several generations and they all obey his directives. He is the "Prodigal Son" of his own capitalistic epoch, the "Immoralist" of sublimated love, the "Mis-chained Prometheus" of an everlasting quest for God. André Gide is the ever youthful man; at 74, he is still the leader of men in their thirties, and his constant rebellion is the very token of his genius.

In contrast to this thinker in action, Marcel Proust is the contemplative painter of a society—a society he typified perfectly. He does not criticize, he does not fight; nevertheless, a super-sensitive being who sickened at the noises of the world, he has the sharpest ear with which to listen to the defective pulsations of the arteries and veins of his contemporaries. His vast fresco,

Memories of Things Past, will serve the centuries to come as a catalogue of our achievements and of our decadence. Armed with a magnifying glass, Proust smiled disarmingly and practised ruthless honesty as he dissected the tissues of our society.

Paul Claudel is a broad river of France, flowing slowly and majestically along the good seasons of life, towards the cosmic objective of all beings— the sea awaits him, eternal security. So he gives himself time to mix with all life, to love the reality of things and the souls of all creatures. A great Catholic poet, he assimilates, beyond the boundaries of the Western world, the "knowledge of the East" and primitive mysticism.

Paul Valéry is like an olive tree sturdily growing in his Mediterranean land; his dry, forceful, nervous verse offers to the ripening sun of philosophy small but perfect fruit, in their essence the unadulterated gold of divine oil.

In the very heart of France, in a comfortable mansion within the walls of one of those innumerable provincial towns living lengthily in the sunshine, Roger Martin du Gard pens the last will and testament of an ancient family, sentenced to disintegration in the social tornado of our day.

In another nook of the country, the Landes (near Bordeaux), François Mauriac applies a stethoscope to characters tormented by an excess of fervor and of love. The conflagrations by which the souls of his impassioned women are laid waste cast a flamboyant, Gothic glare over a whole section of France.

Between the provinces and the capital extends the suburban zone where novel sensations have been found by many a writer. Julien Green had to come all the way from America to discover here in haunted dwellings women obsessed by avarice, girls in the grip of hallucination in the silence of their hearts.

In wild and aroma-laden gardens, Jean Giraudoux's precocious young girls practise the art of loving with a touch of genius.

New unexplored areas are forever discovered by writers on the Map of Tenderness. It would be impossible to name them all, to pin them down. To the richness and variety of French scenery corresponds a variety and richness of writers and poets.

Let us enter Paris, the throbbing heart of the world. The poet Guillaume Apollinaire gives us a new vision: *Shepherdess, O Eiffel Tower, this morning the flock of bridges is bleating* . . . Apollinaire discovered on the face of Paris a few new wrinkles and new smiles, which Villon and Baudelaire did not know; Paris hadn't very much changed, but the eye of man had.

Old provinces of France, which had fallen asleep during the blind realism of the nineteenth century, woke up, discovered by courageous hunters of hidden shadows and hidden goddesses. Surrealism found broken statues of the metaphysical Middle Ages and regenerated them with Freud's sperm-pills. Somber rivers of blood flowed suddenly through the sweet landscapes of the Ile-de-France, and Surrealism built a tremendous power house at the junction of almost exhausted streams, to draft the dream and the unconscious to new life and art.

But at the same time other writers rehabilitated a younger, pink-colored sentimental realism, which they christened populism. In the poor "Hôtels du Nord," they enjoyed very much the "Joyless Streets," and the movies found gold in their gutters.

"Twenty years largely wasted, the years of *l'entre deux guerres*," wrote T. S. Eliot in his newest poem, giving in a French phrase his final judgment on this period, which had such brilliant chances and which made so little of them. So little? Historically speaking, nothing, or less: the ruins of Europe and the loss of all human dignity. But, in art and literature, France gave the world of today, and of tomorrow and forever, dozens of new poets, of new thinkers, of new artists, who changed the world and chiseled new profiles and thoughts which will emerge only later from the shadows and the dusts of history.

Paul Valéry

HOMO EUROPAEUS

THE STORM has died away, and still we are restless, uneasy, as if the storm were about to break. Almost all the affairs of men remain in a terrible uncertainty. We think of what has disappeared, we are almost destroyed by what has been destroyed; we do not know what will be born, and we fear the future, not without reason. We hope vaguely, we dread precisely; our fears are infinitely more precise than our hopes; we confess that the charm of life is behind us, abundance is behind us, but doubt and disorder are in us and with us. There is no thinking man, however shrewd or learned he may be, who can hope to dominate this anxiety, to escape from this impression of darkness, to measure the probable duration of this period when the vital relations of humanity are disturbed profoundly.

We are a very unfortunate generation, whose lot has been to see the moment of our passage through life coincide with the arrival of great and terrifying events, the echo of which will resound through all our lives.

One can say that all the fundamentals of our world have been affected by the war, or more exactly, by the circumstances of the war; something deeper has been worn away than the renewable parts of the machine. You know how greatly the general economic situation has been disturbed, and the policy of states, and the very life of the individual; you are familiar with the universal discomfort, hesitation, apprehension. *But among all these injured things is the Mind.* The Mind has indeed been cruelly wounded; its complaint is heard in the hearts of intellectual men; it passes a mournful judgment on itself. It doubts itself profoundly.

What is this Mind? In what respects can it be touched, injured, diminished humiliated by the present state of the world? Why are intellectual matters in such a miserable state, and whence comes the distress, the anguish, of intellectual men? These are the topics I now propose to discuss.

Man is the separate animal, the curious living creature that is opposed to all others and rises above all others by his . . . *dreams!*—by the intensity, succession, and diversity of his *dreams!*—by their extraordinary effects, which may sometimes even modify his nature, and not his nature only, but that surrounding nature which he tirelessly endeavours to subjugate to his dreams.

I mean to say that man is incessantly and necessarily opposed to *whatever is* by his concern for *what is not!* and that he creates laboriously, or perhaps by genius, whatever is needed to give his dreams the power and precision of reality, and, on the other hand, to force upon this reality the increasing changes which make it resemble his dreams.

Other living creatures are moved and transformed only by exterior variations. They adapt themselves, which is to say that they deform themselves, in order to preserve the essential characteristics of their existence, and in this manner they effect an equilibrium with their environment.

It is not their habit, so far as I know, to break this equilibrium spontaneously. If they are adapted to a certain climate, they do not leave it without some motive, without exterior pressure or necessity. They seek blindly after their own sufficient good, but they do not feel the goad of that *better* which is the enemy of the "good enough," and heartens us to face the worst.

Man, however, has that within him which will break the equilibrium he maintained with his environment. He has that which will render him discontented with everything which satisfied him formerly. At every instant he is something else than he is. He does not form a *closed system* of needs and gratifications for his needs. From such gratification he derives I do not know what excess of power, which destroys his content. Hardly are his body and his appetites appeased when something stirs within him; it torments him, informs him, commands him, goads him on; it directs him secretly. And that something is the Mind, the Mind armed with all its inexhaustible questions. . . .

Eternally it asks within us: Who, what, where, at what time, why, how, by what means? It contrasts the past with the present, the future with the past, the possible with the real, the image with the fact. It is both what precedes and what comes last, what constructs and what destroys, what goes by chance and what proceeds by plan. Thus, it might be called that which is not, and the instrument of that which is not. Finally and principally it is the mysterious author of the dreams I described.

What are the dreams that man has made? . . . Which of these dreams have become reality, and how did they become reality?

Look within us and look about us. Think of the city, or turn the pages of some book at random; or better yet, observe the most instinctive movements of our hearts. . . .

We wish for, we are pleased to imagine, many strange things. These wishes are very ancient, and it seems that man will never resolve not to make them. . . . Read Genesis once more. On the threshold of the sacred book, in the midst of the first steps in the first garden, there appear the dreams of Knowledge and of Immortality; by these fair fruits of the tree of life and the tree of the knowledge of good and evil we have always been tempted. A few pages further, you will find in the same Bible the dream of a completely unified humanity, working together to build a prodigious tower. "And the whole earth was of one language, and of one speech." We dream of this today.

There you will also find the strange story of the prophet who, being swallowed by a great fish, was able to move in the depths of the sea. . . .

Among the Greeks, there are heroes who construct flying-machines. Others can tame wild beasts. Their miraculous words move mountains, cause the stones to walk and temples to spring into being, all by a sort of marvellous telemechanics.

To act on distant objects; to make gold; to transmute metals; to vanquish death and predict the future; to move freely in spheres forbidden to our species; to speak, see, hear from one end of the world to the other; to visit the stars; to realize perpetual motion—we have dreamed so many dreams that the list would be infinite. But all these dreams together form a strange *programme*, the pursuit of which is in some way attached to the very history of mankind.

In this programme all projects of universal conquest and universal dominion, whether material or spiritual, have their place. Everything which we call *civilization, progress, science, art, culture,* relates to this extraordinary creation and depends on it directly. One might say that all these dreams struggle to surmount all the given conditions of our definite existence. *We are a zoölogical species which tends to broaden and diversify its own field of existence;* and one could form a table, a systematic classification of our dreams, by considering each of them as directed against one of the initial conditions of our life. There are dreams against gravity and dreams against the laws of motion. There are dreams against space and dreams against time. Omnipresence, prophecy, and the Fountain of Youth: all these were dreamed of, and still are dreamed of under scientific names.

There are dreams against Mayer's principle, and others against Carnot's principle. There are dreams against physiological laws and dreams against the laws and data of ethnology: the equality of races belongs to the latter class, as does the dream of eternal and universal peace. . . . Let us suppose that we have drawn up this table and are about to consider it. We should be quickly tempted to complete it by the list of realizations. Opposite each dream we should place whatever has been done to make it a fact. If, for example, we have placed the desire to fly in one column, along with the name of Icarus, then, in the column of acquisitions, we should inscribe the famous names of Leonardo da Vinci, Ader, Wright, and their successors. I might easily multiply these examples; it would be a sort of game which we lack the time to play. Moreover, it would also be necessary to construct a table of disappointments, of dreams which have never been realized. A few of these have been finally condemned: the squaring of the circle, for example, and the gratuitous creation of energy. The others still exist in our not unreasonable hopes.

However, we must return to our table of realizations; this is the one to which I wished to call your attention.

If we consider this very honourable list, we can make the following remarks:

Of all these realizations, the most numerous, the most surprising, the most fertile, have been achieved by a fairly limited portion of mankind, in a territory which is very small in relation to the whole mass of habitable lands.

Europe was this privileged place; the European, the European mind, was the author of these marvels.

And what indeed is this Europe? It is a sort of cape of the old continent, an occidental appendage of Asia. By force of nature it looks toward the West. On the south it borders an illustrious sea, the rôle of which (I ought to say the function) has been wonderfully effective in the elaboration of that European mind which is our subject. All the peoples who came to its shores were intermingled; they exchanged blows and merchandise; they founded ports and colonies where not only the objects of ordinary commerce, but beliefs, languages, customs and technical acquisitions were the basis of trade. Even before modern Europe had taken the appearance with which we are familiar, the Mediterranean had seen a sort of pre-Europe established in its eastern basin. Egypt and Phœnicia

were in some sort a prefiguration of the civilization which we have fixed;
afterwards came the Greeks, the Romans, the Arabs, the Iberian peoples.
Around this sparkling water, rich in salt, one imagines a throng of gods
and men, the most imposing in the world. Horus, Isis, and Osiris; Astarte
and the Samothracian deities; Pallas, Poseidon, Minerva, Neptune, and
their like, all reign concurrently over this sea which tossed the strange
thoughts of St. Paul, just as it cradled the plans and dreams of Bonaparte. . . .

To these shores, however, where so many peoples had already mingled and jostled and learned from one another, there came in the course
of ages still other peoples, drawn toward the splendour of Mediterranean
skies, by the beauty and particular intensity of life beneath the sun. The
Celts, the Slavs, the Teutonic peoples, all have felt the enchantment of
this noblest of seas; a sort of invincible tropism, acting throughout the
centuries, has made this admirably formed basin the object of universal
desire and the scene of the greatest human activity. Economic, intellectual, and political activity, religious activity, artistic activity, all centre,
or at least all seem to originate, on the shores of the inland sea. There it
is that one is able to watch the phenomena which preceded the formation
of Europe, and to observe, at a certain time, the division of humanity into
two groups which grow more and more unlike. The first, which occupies
the larger part of the globe, remains in some sort fixed in its customs,
learning, and effective power; it no longer progresses, or progresses only
by imperceptible degrees.

The other is driven ahead by a perpetual disquiet, a perpetual seeking.
The manners and matters of exchange are multiplied; the most varied
problems are discussed in its midst; the means of living, of knowing, of
self-improvement are accumulated from century to century with astonishing rapidity. Soon the difference in power and practical knowledge between Europe and the rest of the world becomes so great that all equilibrium is destroyed. Europe suddenly bursts its own bounds; it sets out to
conquer the world. Modern civilization renews the primitive invasions,
but reverses their direction. And Europe, on its own territory, attains the
maximum of life, of intellectual fertility, of riches and ambition.

This triumphant Europe which arose from the exchange of all spiritual
and material things, from the voluntary and involuntary co-operation of
races, from the rivalry of systems, interests, and religions *in a very limited
territory,* is bustling and animated; it is a sort of marketplace where all
precious things are brought, compared, discussed, and all change hands.
It is a stock exchange where doctrines, ideas, discoveries, and dogmas of

every nature are *registered*, are *quoted*, rise and fall—becoming the object of the blindest enthusiasm and the most pitiless criticism. Soon imports from the most distant lands are arriving abundantly in this market. On the one hand, the new countries of America, Oceania, or Africa, and the ancient empires of the East, send their raw materials to Europe to subject them to the astonishing transformations which Europe alone can accomplish. On the other hand, the knowledges, religions, and philosophies of ancient Asia are brought to nourish the ever-wakeful minds which Europe produces in each generation; and this powerful machine transforms the more or less foreign conceptions of the Orient, tests their depth, and extracts their serviceable elements.

Our Europe, which began as a Mediterranean market, thus became a vast factory—a factory in the strict sense, a mill for converting products, but at the same time an incomparable intellectual factory. This intellectual factory receives all the things of the mind from every part of the world, and distributes them to its innumerable machines. Of these, some seize upon every novelty with hope and avidity, exaggerating its value; others employ the brilliance and solidity of the riches already accumulated to resist every innovation. Between acquisition and conservation a dynamic equilibrium must continually be established; but meanwhile an ever more active critical spirit is attacking one tendency or the other, examining without pity the ideas which are favoured or which hold the field, testing and discussing without pity the tendencies of the adjustment which is always obtained.

Our thought must develop, and our thought must be conserved. It advances only by the extremes, but only by the means does it subsist. Extreme order, which is automatism, would be its ruin; extreme disorder would bring it still more rapidly to the abyss.

Finally, little by little, this Europe takes the shape of a gigantic city, with its museums, gardens, and studios, its salons and its laboratories. Here is its Venice; here its Oxford; here are Rome and Paris and Seville. Here are cities which exist for art, or for science, and others which combine ornaments and instruments. This Europe is small enough to be traversed in a time which is very short, and soon will be insignificant. It is large enough to contain all climates, and sufficiently varied to present cultures and landscapes of every nature. From the physical point of view, it is a masterpiece of moderation, of the conjuncture of all conditions favourable to man. And here man has become the European.

I must apologize for giving the words Europe and European a meaning which is a little more than geographical and a little more than historical, but is in some sort *functional*. I might almost say, my thought deforming my speech, that a *Europe* is a kind of system originally formed by a certain human diversity and a particularly favourable locality, and finally moulded by a singularly eventful and living history. The product of this conjuncture of circumstances is a European.

We must examine this character in relation to more simple types of humanity. He is a kind of monster. His memory is too carefully nourished and charged with too many facts. He has extravagant ambitions. He thirsts for knowledge and illimitable riches. Since he generally belongs to a nation which has dominated the world in its hour, and still dreams of its Cæsar, or Charles V., or Bonaparte, there is a pride in him, a hope, and regrets which are always ready to waken. Since he belongs to an age and a continent which have seen so many astounding inventions, so many successful adventures in every field, there is no enterprise, no scientific conquest of which he cannot dream. He is caught between boundless hopes and glorious memories; and if sometimes he happens to fall into pessimism, he thinks in spite of himself that pessimism has produced a few works of the first order. Instead of plunging into mental annihilation, he draws an elegy from his despair. Sometimes, from the same source, he derives a hard and formidable will, a paradoxical motive for actions, based on his contempt for life and humankind.

But who, then, is European?

Here, with many reserves, with the infinite scruples one should have when attempting provisorily to specify something which is not susceptible of real precision, I will risk an essay at definition. What I wish to develop is not a logical definition, but a manner of seeing, a point of view—it being understood that many others exist which are neither more nor less legitimate.

Well, I shall consider all nations as European which, in the course of history, underwent the three influences of which I am going to speak.

The first is that of Rome. Wherever the Roman Empire held sway, wherever its power made itself felt, and, in a sense, wherever the Empire was the object of fear, envy, or admiration; wherever the nations felt the weight of the Roman sword; wherever the majesty of the laws and institutions, the pomp and dignity of the magistrature, were recognized, copied, sometimes even bizarrely aped—there something European can be said to exist. Rome is the eternal model of organized and stable might.

I do not know the reasons for this great triumph; it is useless to seek them now, as it is idle to ask what Europe would have been had it never been Roman.

But we are concerned only with the fact of the astonishingly durable imprint left on so many races, so many generations, by this power—both superstitious and rational; curiously impregnated with the judicial spirit, the military spirit, the religious spirit, the spirit of formalism; unquestionably the first to impose the benefits of tolerance and good administration on conquered peoples.

Then came Christianity. You know how it spread, little by little, through the whole extent of the Roman conquest. If we except the New World, which was not so much Christianized as peopled by Christians; if we except Russia, the larger part of which was ignorant both of Roman law and the empire of Cæsar, we perceive that the bounds of the Christian church coincide almost exactly, even today, with the former limits of imperial authority. These two conquests, although so different in their nature, bear a sort of resemblance to each other, and this resemblance is important. The policy of the Romans, which became more ingenious and more supple as the central authority declined in power, that is to say, as the Empire grew in extent and heterogeneity, was responsible for a remarkable innovation in the system of the domination of peoples by one people.

Just as the *city par excellence* ended by adopting all beliefs; by naturalizing all faiths, even the most diverse, and all gods, even the most distant and bizarre—in the same way the imperial government, conscious of the prestige which attached to the name of Roman, did not fear to confer the freedom of the Roman city, the privileges and titles of *civis romanus,* on men of every language and every race. Thus, by the existence of the same Rome, gods ceased to be attached to a tribe, a locality, a mountain, or a city, and became universal, in some sort common to all; while, on the other hand, race, language, and the quality of victor or vanquished, of conqueror or conquered, developed into a uniform legal and political condition which was inaccessible to none. The emperor himself might be a Gaul, a Sarmatian, a Syrian, and he might sacrifice to very foreign gods. . . . It was an extraordinary political innovation.

But Christianity also, in accordance with the vision of St. Peter, and although it was one of the very rare religions which were in ill repute at Rome—Christianity, issuing from the Jewish people, spread through the Gentiles of every race; by means of baptism it conferred on them the new dignity of Christian, just as Rome conferred the Roman citizenship on its former enemies. Little by little it spread through the breadth of the Latin power, and assumed the forms of the empire—*civitas* in the fifth century was the name of an episcopal city. It borrowed everything it could from Rome, and fixed its capital there, not at Jerusalem. It adopted Latin as its language. A citizen of Bordeaux could be a Roman citizen, even a magistrate, and at the same time could be a bishop of the new religion. And the same *Gaul* who was an imperial prefect wrote fine hymns in pure *Latin* to glorify the Son of God, who was born a *Jew* and subject to Herod. Here already is an almost perfect European. A common law, a common God; the same law and the same God; a sole judge for time, a sole Judge for eternity.

The Roman conquest had seized only the political man; its control over minds was only through their exterior habitudes. The Christian conquest, however, aimed at and progressively attained the depths of the moral consciousness.

I shall not even try to measure the extraordinary modifications which the religion of Christ imposed on this consciousness. Even the attempt to explain how radically this faith affected the formation of the European is beyond my design. I am forced to move only on the surface of things, and besides, the effects of Christianity are well known.

I shall mention only a few characteristics of its action; and first, Christianity introduced a *subjective* morality, and above all it imposed the unification of morality. This new unity being placed beside the judicial unity created by the Roman law, analysis, on one side and the other, tended to unify the two codes.

Let us go further.

The new religion required that men examine their own hearts. It was in this fashion that occidentals became familiar with that interior life which the Hindus had been practicing in their manner for centuries; the mystics of Alexandria had also, in their manner, recognized, felt, and deepened it.

Christianity proposes the subtlest, the most important, and even the most fertile problems to the mind. Whether the question is one of the value of evidence, the criticism of texts and sources, or the guarantees of knowledge; whether the problems deal with the distinction between reason and faith, with the opposition which develops between them, and with the antagonism of faith and acts and works; whether we reflect on liberty, servitude, or grace; on spiritual and material powers and their mutual conflict; on the equality of men, the condition of women . . . what more need I add?—Christianity has educated and stimulated millions of minds; has made them act and react during a chain of centuries.

Still we are not perfect Europeans. Something is lacking in our pictures; there is lacking that marvellous modification to which we owe not the idea of public order, the cult of the world-city, and the sense of temporal justice; and not the depth of our souls, absolute ideality, and the faith in justice to eternity; but there is lacking that subtle and powerful action to which we owe the best of our intelligence and the delicate solidity of our knowledge—just as we owe the definiteness, purity, and *distinction* of our arts and literature to the same source; it is from Greece that these virtues come.

This time, again, we must admire the rôle of the Roman empire. It conquered to be conquered. Penetrated by Greece, penetrated by Christianity, it offered them both an immense field, organized and pacified; it prepared the site and fashioned the mould into which Greek thought and the Christian idea were later to flow and be so curiously welded.

Our debt to Greece is perhaps what distinguished us most profoundly from the rest of humanity. To her we owe the discipline of the mind, and the extraordinary example of perfection in all fields of activity. We owe her a method of thinking which tends to relate all things to man, to the complete man; he becomes the *system of references* by which all things must finally be measured. Hence he must develop all the parts of his being and maintain them in a harmony as clear, and even as apparent, as is possible. He must develop his body and his mind. As for the mind, he will defend himself from its excesses, its reveries, its vague and purely fantastic productions, by a detailed criticism and analysis of its judgments, by a rational division of its functions, and by the regulation of forms.

Out of this discipline, science was to originate—our science, which is to say the most characteristic product, the most certain and most personal glory of our mind. Europe is first of all the creator of science. There have been arts of all countries; there has been no true science save that of Europe.

Beyond a doubt, a sort of science existed before Greece, in Egypt and Chaldea, and certain of its results may still appear remarkable. This, however, was an *impure* science, sometimes confused with the technique of one trade or another, and at other times permitting of extremely unscientific preoccupation. Observation has always existed. The reason has always been employed. But these essential elements have little value, and do not obtain a regular success, unless no other factors intervene to corrupt their use.

To construct our science, it was necessary that a relatively perfect model be proposed; that a first masterpiece be offered as an ideal presenting all the precisions, all the guarantees, all the beauties, all the solidities, and defining once for all the very concept of *science* as a pure construction separated from all other aims than those of the edifice itself.

Greek geometry was this incorruptible model; not only the model offered to every science which aims at its perfection, but also an incomparable model of the most typical qualities of the European intellect. I never think of classical art without inevitably choosing the monument of Greek geometry as its best example. The construction of this monument demanded all the rarest qualities, and those which ordinarily are most incompatible. The men who built it were hard and penetrating workers, profound thinkers, but also sensitive artists with an exquisite sense of perfection.

Think of the subtlety and force of will which were required of them before they could accomplish such a delicate, such an *improbable* adjustment of common speech to precise reasoning; think how they analyzed extremely complex mechanical and visual operations, and how well they succeeded in making these operations correspond with the properties of speech and grammar. They trusted to words and their combinations to conduct them surely through space. It is true that this space has become a plurality of spaces and has been singularly enriched; it is true that this geometry, which once seemed so perfect, has allowed many flaws to appear in its crystal. We have examined so closely that wherever the Greeks saw one axiom, we count a dozen. For each of the postulates they introduced, we know that we can substitute several others, and thus obtain a coherent geometry which is sometimes physically applicable.

But think what a novelty was this almost solemn form, so pure and lovely in its general design. Think of this magnificent division of the moments of the Mind, of this marvellous order where every act of the reason is separately placed and clearly divided from the others; it calls to mind the structure of a temple, that static mechanism whose every element is visible and declares its function.

The eye considers the load, the support of the load, the parts of the load, the bulk and how it is balanced; the eye divides and arranges without effort the orderly masses whose very shape and vigour are appropriate to their rôle and volume. These columns, capitals, architraves; these entablatures with their subdivisions, and the ornaments deduced therefrom without ever exceeding the limits of their place and harmony, all remind me of those organs of pure science as the Greeks conceived it: definitions, axioms, lemmata, theorems, corollaries, porisms, problems . . . that is, the machinery of the mind made visible, the architecture of the intelligence completely designed—the temple erected to Space by Speech, but a temple which can be heightened to infinity.

Such, I believe, are the three essential conditions which seem to define a true European, a man in whom the European mind can reside in its fullness. Wherever the names of Cæsar, Gaius, Trajan, and Virgil; of Moses and St. Paul; of Aristotle, Plato, and Euclid have possessed a simultaneous meaning and authority, there Europe is. Every race and every land which has been successively Romanized, Christianized, and subjected in intellectual matters to the discipline of the Greeks, is absolutely European.

Some countries have received only one or two of these imprints.

There is, then, some trait quite distinct from race, nationality, or even language, which unites and renders similar the countries of Western and Central Europe. The number of notions and manners of thought which are common to all is much larger than the number of notions which we have in common with a Chinese or an Arab.

I might sum up by saying that there is a region of the world which, in regard to its population, is radically distinguished from all the others. In the realms of power and exact knowledge, the weight of Europe today is still far greater than that of the rest of the world. I am wrong; it is not Europe which excels, but the European mind, of which America is an imposing creation.

Wherever the European spirit dominates, one finds the maximum of *needs,* the maximum of *work,* the maximum of *capital,* the maximum of *returns,* the maximum of *ambition,* the maximum *power,* the maximum of *modification of exterior nature,* the maximum of *exchanges* and *relations.*

This collection of maxima is Europe, or the image of Europe.

On the other hand, the conditions of this formation, and of this astonishing inequality, depend evidently on the quality of the individual, the mean quality of *homo europaeus.* And it is remarkable that the man of Europe is not defined by race, or by language, or by customs, but only by desires and the amplitude of his will. . . .

Translated by MALCOLM COWLEY

Romain Rolland

BETTINA

DURING THE SHORT TIME which has elapsed since the publication, as a serial, of my first studies on Goethe and Beethoven, the biography of Bettina has been enriched by new documents, which shed further light on her interesting and many-sided personality. The principal source has at last been tapped. The private archives of Wiepersdorf, the family home of the Arnims, where Bettina's letters had been collected, were jealously guarded by her second son, Siegmund, a companion of Bismarck in his young days and an ultra-conservative, who would not allow any outsider to see his treasure; they were opened, after his death, to a privileged few who were allowed to make a careful scrutiny of Bettina's correspondence with Goethe. But a vast number of letters, sketches and drafts remained untouched. In 1929 the whole collection was sold. Public opinion in Germany, roused by this dispersal of historic documents, induced private munificence to provide the means of buying up almost immediately and classifying the nucleus of this correspondence, namely all that refers to Goethe; nevertheless many manuscripts were scattered to the four winds. We have been able to discover from the catalogues of antiquaries some of the secrets of the "Goethe-Bettina" enigma. The curtain has been lifted, in part at least, especially on those days in Teplitz, in August, 1810, of which I have written in my first essay, and which must have left on Bettina's mind a far deeper impression than it was wise for Goethe to arouse.

Before quoting here a very intimate letter, over which, as it seems to me, the piety of Goethe's admirers has drawn a veil—a veil which has scarcely been raised—I must recall in a few words to the reader, who may not be so well instructed in this true romance as are the Germans, the principal stages in Bettina's passion for Goethe.

It is indeed a strange and mysterious story, a life's dream, from which the heroine could never free herself, even for a moment. It is a case of invincible auto-suggestion, a destiny ordained, as it were, at birth, and, as Bettina would have told us, a reincarnation of love beyond the grave.

Her mother, Maximilliana La Roche, a beautiful woman, native of the Rhine Provinces, was loved by Goethe when he was twenty-three and she was sixteen (1772–73). This love was not a passing infatuation, but

Maximilliana, obedient to her parents' wish, married a merchant named Brentano and settled in Frankfurt, where Bettina was born on April 4, 1785.

After her mother's premature death in 1793, Bettina was brought up in a convent, where the works of poets were not accessible to her. So she was seventeen before she read Goethe's poems, which at first she did not understand. During the years which followed, however, she came by degrees to appreciate their charm, and her disposition, which was wholesome, fresh, and spontaneous, set her apart from the malevolent prudishness of Cassel society, the people who expressed disgust at *Egmont's* "vulgarities" and at the poet's "platitudes." This innocent attraction for Goethe had, however, no personal character, until that fateful day in June, 1806, when, at her father's house in Offenbach, she discovered by chance eighty-four letters from Goethe to her grandmother, Sophie La Roche, written between 1772 and 1775, full of the young man's adoration of her mother.

This revelation had an overwhelming effect on the young girl. She copied the whole correspondence several times. (One of these copies was sold by auction last year.) She learnt them by heart. And this sensitive dreamer, to whose burning eyes the beauties of nature were an open book, bore henceforth upon her heart the impress of Goethe's young love. This may justly be termed, speaking scientifically, a phenomenon of obsession, which nothing could efface; it was beautiful, it was touching, but it had its dangerous side.

On October 21, 1809, she wrote to Goethe, in a state of melancholy ecstasy:

"I really believe that I have inherited this feeling from my mother. She must have known [erkannt] you intimately. She must have possessed [genossen] you fully when I was coming into the world . . ."

What was her thought? That she was Goethe's daughter ("das Kind")? Perhaps. But she certainly imagined that she was the child of his *love*, and that this love returning from beyond the grave to Goethe the beloved, to Goethe the lover, had taken upon itself her bodily presence.

This love-stricken folly found forthwith the environment in which it could best thrive. In the same month in which she discovered the correspondence she hastened to Goethe's mother, Aja, who when she spoke of her "little boy," was as exaggeratedly sensitive as Bettina. She declared that she was cruelly separated from him by the distance from Frankfurt to Weimar—actually only a few hours—but to her an eternity. . . . The two love-stricken women, the old and the young, both full of fantastic ideas, both warm-hearted, found in the love of their common idol the path to each other's affection.

The old woman poured into the girl's ear a never-ending stream of gossip, her triumphant recollections of the child Goethe, which Bettina drank in like parched soil under a shower. We can imagine how, in such circumstances, the obsession took root and flourished.

In the following spring she paid her first visit to Goethe (April 23, 1807). . . . In those days travel was no easy matter; war was raging throughout the country. In order to accompany her brother-in-law, Jordis, from Cassel to Berlin, whence they proceeded later to Weimar, she and her sister had donned men's clothes. It reminds us of a scene from *As You Like It*. Finally Bettina arrived alone, her heart beating violently, almost fainting with emotion, at Goethe's door. She had a letter of introduction from Wieland, who presented her as the daughter and granddaughter of beloved friends who were no more. Shall I describe this well-known meeting once again? It has been told so well by Fritz Bergmann, who, after a careful scrutiny of the somewhat embellished account of the incident which Bettina gave later, has verified the essential points, and has with delicacy expressed her emotion. Both the old man and the young woman shared it. For him, what a flood of remembrances: it was indeed the beloved dead who came to see him. . . . For her, what a mingled torrent of joy and fear: she stood tongue-tied, at one moment overcome, at another peacefully content. There followed a strange reaction, at which some have foolishly sneered, though it was the most natural in the world; exhausted with emotion, the young girl lost consciousness and fell asleep on Goethe's knees, in his arms. The fainting fit lasted but a few moments. Goethe was very kind to her. He was deeply touched by the elemental force of emotion in his "little Mignon." He spoke to her affectionately, and at length, dismissing impatiently the inquisitive Christiana who had opened the door and asked him to go out with her. With the sweet messenger from the past, he reviewed the days of his boyhood, felt his youth reawaken in the cramped atmosphere of Weimar, and with a symbolic gesture, full of significance for the young dreamer who doubtless saw in it a token of mystic betrothal, he placed a ring upon her finger.

Later Goethe appreciated the danger. When the young enthusiast poured out in a letter to Goethe's mother the longings of her heart—the mother did her best to fan the flame—and when the old lady had sent

him an account of the ardent feeling which he had aroused in Bettina,
Goethe knitted his brows and withdrew in stubborn silence. To Bettina's
first letters there was no single word of reply.

So Bettina went to seek the answer which she could not otherwise
obtain. She returned to Weimar, at the beginning of November, 1807,
this time accompanied by a throng of relatives—Clemens, Arnim, her
sister Gunda, and her brother-in-law Savigny. She stayed in Weimar
for ten days, seeing Goethe almost every day, and Goethe began to enjoy
her company. Bettina noticed this and showed herself at her best; with
her naïve and spring-like charm she elicited friendly smiles; she was
original and alluring and gave free rein to the impulses of her spontaneous fancy. During these familiar talks, these walks on Goethe's arm,
their intimacy had made such progress that when she wrote to him
again, some weeks later, she used the familiar "thou," and henceforth
continued to do so.

Goethe, however, was still on the defensive; another year passed before
he, too, wrote "thou." But his "you" was only a weak defence, and
Bettina knew it. When, on November 10th, they parted, Goethe kissed
her, and soon did more for her than use the intimate "thou" in his
letters. When she wrote him letters, aflame with love, he sent her back
her own words like jewels in the magnificent setting of two sonnets. It
was as if he entered into Bettina's deepest self, till both merged into
one. We know what artists are, how mighty a force for deception lies
in their impressionable nature; it is their peculiar failing, and we are
not the dupes of their florid declarations. But how different must have
been the impression upon Bettina . . . In February, 1808, she told Goethe
that never before had she looked upon a man, and that it hurt her to
think that all her youth was being wasted . . . "But now I have you . . ."

She was intelligent enough not to confine her letters to love; she dealt
with poetry also; she wrote of *Egmont,* which she appreciated and discussed in striking fashion, and a little later of "Wahlverwandtschaften"
("Elective affinities")

Her delight in Goethe's art was like the primitive delight of a child
bathing in the sea. She discussed music with him and showed a virile
taste for Cherubini's *Medea* and for Gluck's *Iphigenie auf Tauris;* following the wise promptings of heart and mind, she constituted herself
the provider of music for Goethe's private choir; she sent him curious
documents and succeeded more than any other woman of his circle in
appealing to his intellect.

After the death of Goethe's mother, Aja (September 13, 1808), the poet's letters to Bettina show a far more affectionate tone. Now that his mother had gone, Bettina was the only one who knew the essential details of his younger days which Goethe himself had forgotten. She was the sole keeper of all those precious memories which she had gathered from the lips of his own mother. He wrote to her a year later: "Your letters give me great pleasure: they remind me of the time when I was perhaps so foolish as you but certainly happier and better than today."

His smile could scarcely hide a feeling of regret and of melancholy. The months which followed showed that his affection increased. Goethe could resist no longer. So much so, that when Bettina interrupted her correspondence for a few weeks, Goethe felt her silence very keenly, and wrote to her on May 10, 1810: "Dear Bettina, I have not heard from you for a very long time; I cannot leave for Karlsbad without sending you greetings, without calling upon you—by letter—and without receiving from you a sign of life. Your letters accompany me. When I am there, they must replace your charming presence . . ." (We feel that Goethe is here restraining his feelings.) "I can say no more, for in truth there is nothing I can give you; it is either you who give everything or you who take everything . . ."

During the following summer months Bettina met Beethoven, and brimming over with the impression which he had made upon her, went to see Goethe in Teplitz and remained with him for three days, from August 9 to 12, 1810.

What happened during those three days? The unusual warmth of Goethe's letter, written to Bettina immediately after her visit, suggests that she had never been more favoured by her idol. I have shown this in my first essay, but there were many gaps in my story. Bettina's long letter of July 6-28, 1810, stopped suddenly in the middle of a sentence in which she spoke of Beethoven. From July 28th to October 18th there was a lull in the correspondence which is all the more difficult to understand, as Goethe in his short letter, written on August 17th, five days after Bettina's departure from Teplitz, spoke with unusual enthusiasm of the many pages (Blätter) which Bettina had left him, and which he "read over and over again"; he spoke also of one which had just arrived . . . What did he do with them, what did they contain, these letters which Bettina did not find in the collection which Councillor von Mueller sent her after Goethe's death, in August, 1832? What is perhaps even more extraordinary is that Bettina, the last person to disguise her feelings—she would much rather have exaggerated them—did not rewrite them. She never wished to disturb the dust of those recollections.

Here, however, are a few grains from the heap, discovered last year, among the drafts of Bettina's letters which were sold under the hammer and which have not been mentioned in any of the books on her:

"The twilight of evening was falling, this hot August day . . . He was sitting at the open window, while I stood before him, my arms round his neck, my eyes piercing his to their depths, like an arrow. Perhaps he could withstand my gaze no longer, for, to break the silence, he asked me whether I felt hot and whether I would not like to be cooler? . . . I nodded assent. He went on, 'Why not open your breast [Mach doch den Busen frei] to the evening breeze?' As I did not object, although I blushed, he undid my bodice, looked at me, and said: 'The glow of the sunset has reddened [eingebrannt] your cheeks.' He kissed my breast and rested his head on it. 'No wonder,' said I, 'for my sun is sinking to rest upon my bosom.' He gazed at me for a long time and we were both silent. He then asked, 'Has anyone ever touched your breast?' 'No,' I replied; 'it is so strange that you should touch me thus.' Then he showered kisses on me, many, many, violent kisses . . . I was frightened . . . He should have let me go; and yet it was so strangely beautiful. In spite of myself I smiled, yet feared that this happiness should not last. His burning lips, his stifled breath—it was like lightning. I was in a whirl of confusion; my curly hair hung in loose strands . . . Then he said, softly: 'You are like a storm; your hair falls like rain, your lips dart lightning, your eyes thunder.' 'And you, like Zeus, knit your brows and Olympus trembles.' 'When you undress at night, in the future, and the stars shine as now upon your breasts, will you remember my kisses?' 'Yes.' 'And will you remember that I should like to cover your bosom with as many kisses as there are stars in heaven?' . . . The memory of it tears me asunder [zerreist mich von allen Seiten], I long to dissolve in tears like a cloudy sky.—Never repeat what I confide to you this lonely night. I have never told it to anyone before . . . !"

These ashes which we have just stirred still burn! What a glow do their embers throw on a letter which Goethe wrote some days later. What a light is shed on those written during the winter 1810–11, which still exist, apart from the letters from Bettina which were destroyed and to which Goethe refers.

"Bettina, dearest of all! [allerliebste] Your letters are such that the latest seems always the most fascinating! Thus it was with the pages which you brought me, and which I read hungrily, again and again, on the morning you left me. But now comes your last letter which surpasses [übertrifft] all the others. If you can go on surpassing yourself [über-bieten], do it! With yourself you have taken away so much, that it is only fair that you should send me back something . . ."

To this letter he pinned a note asking her to sending her reply not to Teplitz, nor to Weimar, but to Dresden, in care of a third person, and he added, "Oh dear, what will your letter tell me? . . ."

We, too, should like to know. What did this letter contain, and those which followed, for more than one was written before October. During that month the correspondence which was saved from destruction began again with a letter from Goethe, who had returned to Weimar on October 25th, in which he says that he should have thanked Bettina long ago "for the dear letters which reached me in due course [nach und nach], and particularly for remembering the 27th of August so kindly . . ." It is lost to us, like all the rest, this souvenir of August 27th. All we know is that Goethe did not reply to the letters after his note of August 17th. He had set a gulf between this memory and himself. And now, instead of reverting to the past, we see the path into which he would direct Bettina's ardent sensibility; he took advantage of her frame of mind—he well knew how to handle loving hearts—to ask her to tell him all the interesting secrets which his mother, Aja, had confided to her, all those stories of his youth which he remembered no longer. He was rather troubled about them; who knows what Juliet's nurse told Romeo of her nursling? . . . It was a great sacrifice which he asked of Bettina, for these stories were her personal treasure, to which no one else had access. How deeply Bettina must have loved him to do what he asked; we feel what it must have meant to her. Goethe, however, could not have chosen a more favourable moment to secure this sacrifice from her.

She complied with his wish. But she was not altogether unaware of his motive, as is shown by her reply of November 4th:

"You have always some good reason for writing to me. But my heart retains nothing of your letter except the last words, 'love me until we meet again' [*Liebe mich bis zum Wiedersehen!*] If you had not added these last words, I should perhaps have taken more careful note of the motive prompting the request which preceded them; but this single proof of affection has defeated me . . . A thousand tender thoughts have held me captive last night, and all today. And now I realize that what you demand [*verlangst*] is so precious to me that I find it worthy of your acceptance."

Thereupon she threw open the sanctuary of her recollections. Is it not as if, in giving them to him, she gave herself again? She expresses a

great deal in the following words, which sound so profoundly sincere:
"*Ich bin ein duftender Garten dieser Erinnerungen*" ("I am a fragrant
garden wherein these reflections flower").

She threw them to him by the armful, these flowers of the past, which
he planted afresh in his *Dichtung und Wahrheit.*

From this moment, however, I find a new tone in Bettina's letters.
There is disturbance, sorrow, a passion imperious and burdensome; there
are spiteful fits in which she inveighs against Goethe's friends and particularly against his "house god," Zelter. There are, indeed, many heavy
clouds in her sky.

"Since we were together in Teplitz I find it impossible to pay you
compliments."

". . . Once I climbed a mountain top . . . What is it that weighs so
heavily on my heart? . . ."

Goethe remained impervious to the allusions in these letters, their cries
of passion, their attacks on Zelter; he was deaf to the passionate dreamer
with her strange soliloquies on music, thoughts like lightning flashes in
the darkness of the night . . . He took good care not to upset her. He
did not waste his time; he gathered all these priceless recollections which
she had inherited from his mother. It was Bettina who gave, gave without end. . . .

But was he, too, not giving, giving in even a larger measure than she?
He was her love! He was her life! Was it not she who wrote: "If you
only knew how often a single word of your delivers me from the horrors
of a crushing dream. Oh, tell me: 'Yes, child, I am within you'! Then all
is well— Tell me!—"

When Goethe needed Bettina no longer he grew tired of her. No doubt
he would. It is no easy matter to feel that one is so indispensable to
another! Did not Bettina's hungry heart ask that Goethe should be "within
her," should belong to her? Such a man as Goethe could belong only
to those who assumed no proprietary rights over his freedom. That is
why he preferred his fat, amiable Christiana to Bettina with the exigencies of her love.

Besides this, there was a deep misunderstanding between them. The
Goethe whom Bettina loved was not the Goethe of her time. The one she
loved was the Goethe of her mother, of the days of the first *Wilhelm
Meister.* . . . Where are the snows—where is the fire—of yesteryear?

Eckermann, asked by Moritz Carrière what Goethe's relations were
with Bettina, replied: 'She always loved him, but she was often a

nuisance; she asked the old man to undertake what he had done long ago, as a young man. She would tell him: 'Art and antiquity, what's that? [*Was Kunst und Altertum?*] You must write a *Götz von Berlichingen;* that's better!' And he would reply: 'I have written it. To each thing its proper time.' "

I shall not refer again to the fatal rupture, which Goethe had determined upon and which took place between him and Bettina in 1811, in spite of her efforts to renew her relations with him. Christiana provided the occasion, but even without Christiana the break would have occurred. In vain did Bettina write to Goethe again in 1817. He did not answer, and her attempts to enter his house by surprise only irritated him the more.

Finally, however, he could not but be moved by the unwavering loyalty of the friend whom he had rebuffed. It was particularly her scheme for a monument to him in Frankfurt which softened his heart and showed his human weakness. He decided that he would let her know how much he was touched. . . .

It was a supreme consolation decreed by fate! Twelve days before his death, on March 10, 1832, a young messenger from Bettina came to see him, Siegmund von Arnim, her second son, who was then eighteen. The mother's letter said, "Embrace me anew in this child" (*"Umfasse mich neu in diesem Kinde"*). Goethe was kind and fatherly. He invited him to his table and saw him daily, until he was stricken by the illness from which he never recovered. Mignon's son was his last visitor, and the lines which he wrote in Siegmund's album were Goethe's farewell to the world. When the young man left him, Goethe was already ailing, and on his arrival in Frankfurt he heard of his death. We still have the letter which he wrote from there to his mother. Bettina was anxious to know if Goethe remembered her, and what he had said. Her son could only tell her that Goethe had praised her talent:

"It will seem little to you, very little, but not to me. If you had seen him, already lost to this world, but turning the pages of life as in a book, you would have thanked him from your heart for his friendly enquiries about all that concerns you. . . ."

Bettina learnt of his death from a short paragraph in a newspaper which she found on the table, late at night when she came back from a reception. There the news was already known, but no one dared to tell her. We can imagine what that night must have been. But we should be wrong in assuming that this strong-willed woman, far stronger than we are apt to think, was plunged in a romantic grief. The blow which struck her could not touch the Goethe whom she had created for herself—the Goethe whom she had enshrined in her heart.

She could say, rather: "You can no longer escape me! Now I hold you for ever. . . ."

Her letter to Councillor von Mueller, written at the beginning of April, 1832, is proof of the nobility of her love, which was in truth stronger than death:

"Goethe's death has indeed made upon me an impression deep and ineffaceable, but in no way sorrowful. If words fail me to express the actual truth of what I feel I can describe the glorious impression to you by a picture. He is risen from the death, he is transfigured, he beholds from Heaven his friends whose souls, to their last breath, are fed by him. . . . I am one of those who have no life except in him! I do not speak *of* him, I speak *to* him, and his replies are my fullest consolation. He leaves no question of mine unanswered, no tender word or prayer without response. How could I be other than happy in the thought that at last he has attained that eternal bliss for which his whole earthly life had been a preparation? And now, here lies the path of my duty: I must cling so close to him that nothing may assume a stronger claim than his. By his side everything that life may bring me henceforth shall but strengthen my communion with him. Thus shall all that is worthy of survival in my earthly existence bear testimony to my love and to his blessing."

She kept her word. And if the remainder of her life was not free from weakness—and why should it have been? She was essentially a woman, and that is why we love her—it remained under the aegis of the two gods to whom from the cradle her life had been dedicated, Love and Dreams, *"Traum und Liebe"*. . . . These words would be a fitting title to her famous correspondence published in 1835, *Goethes Briefwechsel mit einem Kinde,* in which, revising her original letters, she pours forth the flood of that inner consciousness which memory had released. Can we blame her? History, which since then has inquired into what she said, has sifted the dream from the reality. But history must, in the end, testify to the loyalty of her heart. And if a heart so loving has led her sometimes to embroider dreams on the background of her story, she has never knowingly altered the design. Her love and her person were always allied with legend and whatever she touched became legendary. Yet she was real. And if, sometimes, her opinion of others deceived her, she has never deceived others, or herself, about her own nature.

This inner life of Bettina has by no means received the attention which it deserves. Enquiry has been focussed almost exclusively on her relations with Goethe. But no matter how intense this love may have been, we must not think that Bettina had no existence outside it. It is true that her whole outlook was illuminated by the burning flame of remembrance; but its boundaries extend far beyond Goethe's life and even beyond his thoughts.

The abundant harvest of Bettina's literary activity has been studied in part. Without referring to it further here, there is much to be said of her ideas in music, of her voluminous correspondence with the famous men of her day, Alexander von Humboldt, Jacob and Wilhelm Grimm, Schleiermacher, Emanuel Arago, Moritz Carrière, Peter Cornelius, Emanuel Geibel, Friedrich Christoph Foerster, and others. Lastly there is her political activity.

Fortunate circumstances and the authority which she had gained secured her direct access to those in highest authority, the princes and the king of Prussia, and her courage did not fail her. Neither respect for their exalted position nor fear of displeasing them restrained her. She spoke openly and forcibly. She had decided for herself upon the ideal of what a prince should be—the servant of the community—and this ideal she meant to impress upon them. "Everything belongs to the people," she wrote to the *Kronprinz of Wuerttemberg*. "Let the prince go lacking, but the people must be free from want." The princes were both flattered and intimidated by the onslaught of this Deborah, the anointed of Goethe. They dared not protest too much. The year 1848 was coming, and its spirit was already weakening the sovereign power. This power was to return, with a vengeance, later on.

Bettina had a splendid colleague in Berlin, Alexander von Humboldt, the last survivor, with her, of Goethe's great brotherhood. He helped her with all his energy and defended her books against the censor, for whom both had a feeling of utter contempt and hatred, he supported her projects and brought her letters to the notice of the king, who was spared the criticism of neither of them. Acting together, they were a real power, and King Frederick William IV had reason to fear their opinions. Certain interesting and unpublished documents which have been communicated to me by a granddaughter of Bettina, Madame Irène Forbes-Mosse, describe Bettina as a Portia pleading unceasingly the cause of the victims of the social order. "At a time when there was no *Landtag* (state Parliament) in Prussia, nor freedom of the press to ventilate wrongs, it was Bettina who brought them all before the King."

Among the bundles of documents relating to such cases, which passed under the hammer last year, I notice first the case of the poet and professor, Hoffmann von Fallersleben, who was disgraced and dismissed from his post on account of his *Unpolitische Lieder*. Then that of the great manufacturer, F. W. Schlöffel, the spokesman of the miserable Silesian weavers, who had been imprisoned on a charge of communism and high treason. Bettina took up his cause and collected personally the material for an *Armenbuch* (Book of the Poor). In 1846 she appears as the champion of the Polish revolutionary Mieroslawski, who had been imprisoned and condemned to death; he was pardoned, thanks to her vehement intervention. In 1849 it was the case of the revolutionary Kinkel, who was under death sentence. Bettina spent days and nights defending him, writing letter after letter to the king, who replied to her with equal insistence. In my collection are some drafts of unpublished letters by Bettina which are written in her most passionate style:

"You say that Kinkel has been prompted by evil motives. This may be, but the stupidity of putting a man to death because he is a charge on society, and the folly of a law which authorizes such a crime, fills me with revolt. . . . What do his faults matter! It is not this particular man who matters. What matters is that it should no longer be possible for one drop of a man's blood to be shed when that man is in the power of the sovereign."

It must be admitted that the king listened to the arguments of the Angel of Revolution with a respect and a patience which are testimony in favour both of himself and of Bettina. In 1847 he wrote to her, about Mieroslawski:

"You love loyalty and truth and demand it in others; you yourself are an example of both. But loyalty and truth do not cease to be loyalty and truth even when the lips of a king express them."

Bettina, however, became too outspoken in her feverish attempts, and finally wounded the king's pride. A break occurred at the end of 1847. At the same time she was engaged in a struggle with the Municipality of Berlin, was accused of lèse-majesté and sentenced to two months' imprisonment.

"You condemn," she wrote to Pauline Steinhäuser, "my political tendencies. I have never undertaken anything, unless my inner self compelled me to it [*ich habe nie etwas unternommen was nicht ein Muss in mir gewesen wäre*]. Nor have my actions proved without benefit to humanity. There are many whose heads are still on their shoulders, who would have lost them if I had not fought desperately."

She gave her support to the risings of 1848, as did another friend of Beethoven and Goethe, Wilhelmine Schroeter-Devrient. In her letters Bettina lashed the treacherous behaviour of the king and praised the people. But calumny and hatred accumulated forces against her. In April, 1848, she wrote to Pauline Steinhäuser:

"Believe me if they could have thrown me into the ditch it would have been done."

She never flinched from her task: she remained indomitable, facing her foes, even after the ruin of her hopes for democracy. She was "Freiheitsbegeisterte" ("intoxicated with ideas of freedom") to the end of her days. Such was her prestige, such was the glamour which she owed to Goethe, her master, that after 1848 the King of Prussia and the princes, in spite of their bitter feelings, treated her with the highest consideration and interested themselves, in 1851–52, in the realization of her project of a monument to Goethe at Weimar. But the proud Bettina declined the royal offer to carry out the work, saying that "Goethe's monument could only come from the German people [*weil Goethe nur im deutschen Volk ein Denkmal erhalten könne*]."

It was the attitude of one completely aloof. In spite of the king's pressing invitations, she never went to court. Her life became more and more retired; small and frail in her conventual robe of coarse black cloth, she meditated in her room, which she never left except in the evening to hear quartet music in her Pompeian hall—Joachim was first violin. The idols of her youth, Beethoven and Goethe, illuminated the evening of her days. She remained faithful to them, not as the guardian of their graves, but as the ministrant to the immortal flame of their lives. She had two ardent disciples in her eldest daughters, Armgart and Gisela, both artists like their mother; they were painters, especially Gisela, who married Hermann Grimm; they were musicians, Armgart especially, whom Joachim admired; Gisela also wrote for the stage. All three were eager to succour the downtrodden and to welcome the champions of rebellion. Mother and daughters alike bore on their foreheads the trace of the blood which *Berlichingen* and *Egmont* shed for the freedom of the people.

Translated by G. A. PFISTER *and* E. S. KEMP

André Gide

ON JOY AND PROGRESS

*Assuredly, all nature informs us
that man is born for happiness.*

You, who will be here when I shall no longer hear the sounds of the earth and my lips shall no longer drink in its dew—you, who, later perhaps, will read me—it is for you that I am writing these pages; because you are, perhaps, not sufficiently astonished by life; you do not admire, as you should, the overwhelming miracle which is life. It sometimes seems to me that it is with my thirst that you are about to drink and that already it is with my own desire that you are leaning over that other being whom you are caressing.

(I marvel at how vague desire becomes, once it becomes amorous. My love enveloped his whole body so diffusely and so completely that, by Jove, I might have been transformed into a cloud without realizing it.)

An animal is nothing more than a parcel of joy.

Everything loves being, and all beings rejoice in it. It is joy that when it is succulent you call fruit, and when it sings you call bird.

Assuredly, all nature informs us that man is born for happiness. It is the striving for sensual pleasure which germinates the plant, fills the hive with honey and the human heart with kindness.

I am not too certain who put me on this earth. I have been told that it was God; and if it wasn't He, who could it be?

It is true that I find a joy so intense in existing, that, sometimes, I wonder if I didn't already desire being even before I was alive.

But let us put off the theological discussion for some drearier time, because it only causes bad blood.

Love and thought share a subtle confluence.

The white page shines before me.

And just as God makes Himself into man, my idea submits to the laws of rhythm.

Image of my perfect happiness, I spread here, painter-re-creator, the most quivering and vital color.

I shall only seize words by their wings. Is it you, ring-dove of my joy? Ah! do not yet fly off into the sky. Alight here; rest.

I am lying against the earth. Near me, a bough, heavy with bursting fruit, bends to the grass; it touches the grass; it strokes and caresses the most delicate blade. It is balanced by the weight of a coo.

Life cannot be more beautiful than man consents to make it. Wisdom is not in reason but in love. Ah! until today, I have lived too prudently. One must be without law to have ears for the new law. O deliverance! O liberty! Wherever my desire can extend, I shall go. O you, whom I love, come with me; I shall take you thus far, so that you may go even farther.

It is the gratitude of my heart that causes me to invent God each day. From the moment I find myself awake, I am astonished by existence and marvel at it endlessly. Why is there less joy in relief from pain than there is pain in cessation of joy? It is because in affliction you dream of the happiness of which you are being deprived, while at the height of your happiness it never occurs to you to consider the anguish you are being spared; it is because it is natural for you to be happy.

A measure of happiness is due each creature in proportion to whatever capacity his heart and senses have for it. No matter how little of it is denied me, I feel robbed. I really don't know if I required life before I was born, but now that I am alive, all is my due. But my gratitude is so sweet, and it is so compellingly sweet for me to love, that the wind's least caress awakes thanks in my heart. The need for gratitude teaches me to turn all that comes my way to happiness.

It is through abnegation that every affirmation is achieved. All that you deny in yourself will take life. Everything that strives to affirm itself will be negated; everything that is renounced will be affirmed. Complete possession is proven by bestowal. Whatever you do not know how to bestow possesses you. Without sacrifice there is no resurrection. Nothing blooms save in the offering. What you would like to preserve in yourself atrophies. How can you tell that the fruit is ripe? By this: it drops from the bough. Everything ripens for the bestowal and fulfills itself in the offering.

It is in renunciation that all virtue is fulfilled. It is the germination that indicates the final succulence of the fruit.

True eloquence renounces eloquence; the individual never asserts himself more than when he forgets himself. He who thinks of self constricts himself. I never admire beauty more than when it has lost all sense of being beautiful. The most moving line is also the most submissive one. It is in renouncing His divinity that Christ truly becomes God. And, reciprocally, God is created by His renunciation in Christ.

I return to you, Lord Christ, as to God whose living form you are. I am weary of deceiving my heart. It is You I have discovered everywhere, even when I believed I was fleeing You, Divine Friend of my childhood. I well know that it is You only who can content my exacting heart. It is but the demon in me which denies that Your teaching is perfect and that I can renounce all save You, since in complete renunciation I rediscover You.

I have admired, I have never ceased to admire, the superhuman striving for joy in the Gospel. The first word we have of Christ is, "Happy . . ." His first miracle, the metamorphosis of water into wine. (The true Christian is he who is intoxicated by pure water. In him the miracle of Cana is repeated.) It took the degraded interpretation of man to base a cult on the Gospel sanctifying sorrow and pain. Because Christ said: "Come unto me all ye that labor and are heavy-laden and I will give you rest," it was believed that one must labor and be heavy-laden in order to come to Him; and the rest which he bestowed was converted into "indulgences."

It has seemed to me for a long time that joy is more rare, more difficult and more beautiful than sorrow. And when I made this discovery, without doubt the most important one that can be made in this life, joy became for me not only (that which it was) a natural need—but more than that, a moral necessity. It occurred to me that the best and surest way to create happiness around myself was to make myself in its image and I resolved to be happy.

It is towards the sensual that all nature strives. It makes the blade of grass grow, swells the burgeon and brings the bud to bloom. It is nature that arranges the petals of the corolla for the kisses of the sun, invites all things that live to union, turns the thick larva into a pupa and permits the butterfly to escape from the prison of its chrysalis. Guided by her, all things aspire to the greatest well-being, to the highest awareness, to progress. . . . That is why I have learned more from the sensual than from books, why I have found more obscurity in books than in light.

There was neither deliberation nor method to it. I plunged, recklessly, into this ocean of delights, amazed to find myself swimming and to feel that I was not being swallowed up by it. It is in the sensual that the entirety of our being finds awareness.

But what man has made of the promised land—of the earth granted him . . . would cause the gods to blush. No child that breaks a toy, no animal that uproots the pasture that gives him nourishment or muddies the water whence he drinks, no bird that fouls its nest, is more foolish. Oh, the sad outskirts of cities! the ugliness, the disharmony, the stink. . . . With a little sympathy and love, I think of what gardens you might have been, soiled hems of cities, guarding the richest and most tender offerings of nature—instead of checking the least attempt on anyone's part to make anybody happy.

When I think what could have been made of you, leisure! O, the games of the spirit in the blessings of joy! And work, even work, redeemed, liberated from an impious curse.

The fear of ridicule causes our worst cowardice. How many youthful impulses that deemed themselves full of courage have been suddenly deflated by the word "Utopia" applied to their convictions, and by the fear of appearing chimerical in the eyes of sensible people. As if the whole great progress of humanity were not due to a materialized Utopia! As if the reality of tomorrow did not result from yesterday's and today's Utopia—just to contemplate a future which consented to be nothing more than a mere repetition of the past would be the most likely way for me to lose all joy in living. Indeed, without the idea of a possible progress, life would no longer have any value for me—and I take back those words I lent Alissia in my *Porte Etroite:* "Happy though it be, I cannot desire a state without progress . . . and snap my fingers at a joy which would not be progressive."

There are very few monsters who warrant the fear we have of them. Monsters born of fear—fear of darkness, fear of light; fear of death and fear of life; fear of others and fear of self; fear of the devil and fear of God—you will no longer tyrannize over us. But we still live under the reign of bogey-men. Who was it that said the fear of God is the beginning of wisdom? Imprudent wisdom, in truth, you begin where fear ends, and you teach us life.

But the certitude that man has not always been what he is, immediately warrants this hope: he will not always remain thus.

Indeed, I, too, could have smiled or laughed with Flaubert before the idol of Progress; but that is only because progress was presented to us as a ridiculous divinity. The progress of commerce and industry; above all, the progress of the fine arts, what folly! The progress of knowledge, certainly. But what is of importance to me is the progress of Man himself.

That man has not always been what he is; that he has slowly attained his present state, no longer seems even controversial to me, in spite of mythology. Our vision, which, limited to a few centuries, can recognize man as always resembling himself in the past and marvel at his lack of change since the time of the Pharaohs, would no longer find this true of him once it delved into the "gulfs of the prehistoric." And if he has not always been as he is, why think that he will remain as he is forever? Man becomes.

But others imagine and would like to make me believe in a humanity resembling the damned of Dante who cry out in despair at their eternal immoblization: "If only I could move forward one step, every thousand years, I would consider myself well on the way."

This idea of progress has taken its place in my mind, related to all my other ideas and subordinated to them.

(The delusion of the civilized man that he would exchange the whole classic period for the momentary equilibrium it would bring him in return.) The fact that the present state of humanity must necessarily be surpassed is an overwhelming idea, immediately greeted by the hatred of all those who are able to impede this progress (comparable to the hatred of evil among Christians).

It is not only the world which it is a question of changing, but man. Whence shall he emerge, this new man? Not from without. Comrade, try to uncover him in yourself, and like the ore from which pure metal can be extracted without dross, draw him from yourself. Dare to become what you are. Don't let yourself be cheated. There are admirable potentialities in every human being. Believe in your strength and your youth. Learn to repeat endlessly to yourself: "It all depends on me."

The cardinal virtue: patience.

Nothing to do with ordinary waiting. This is a kind of persistence.

Don't be clever. You have seen death; there was nothing very funny about it. You try to joke to conceal your fear; but your voice trembles, and your pseudo-poem is awful.

It happens. . . . I have seen death. . . . Most often, it seems to me, there is, just before dying and just after the agony, a cessation in the goading. Death puts on soft gloves to take us. She does not smother us without first assuaging us; and that from which she cuts us off has already lost its clearness, its presence and, therefore, its reality. A universe become so colorless that to leave it is no longer cause for pain or matter for regret.

Thus I tell myself that it must not be so difficult to die, since in the end death comes to everyone. And, perhaps, after all, it could be a habit to acquire, if only one died more than once.

But death is terrible for him who has not fulfilled his life. To him it is all too easy a trick for religion to say: "Never mind. Your reward is in heaven."

It is here below that we must live.

Comrade, believe in nothing; accept nothing without proof. The blood of martyrs has never proven anything. There is no religion so foolish that it has not made converts and engendered fiery convictions. It is in the name of faith that one dies; and it is in the name of faith that one kills. The appetite for knowledge is born of doubt. Cease to believe and instruct yourself. Belief is only imposed when there is a lack of proof. Do not let yourself be taken in. Do not let yourself be imposed upon.

O, you, for whom I am writing—whom I once called by a name which today seems too mournful, Nathanael; * today, I call you comrade—do not admit the mournful to your heart any longer.

Know how to derive from yourself that which renders lamentation unnecessary. No longer ask of others that which you, yourself, can obtain.

I have lived; now it is your turn. From now on, it is in you that I shall prolong my youth. I pass my power on to you. If I know that you will succeed me, I shall accept death more easily. I turn my hope over to you.

To know that you are courageous enables me to leave this life with-

* Nathanael is the name of an imaginary character to whom Gide addresses himself in his book, *Les Nourritures Terrestres* (1897).

out regret. Take my joy. Make your happiness increase all happiness. Work and struggle and never accept an evil that you can change. Learn to repeat to yourself endlessly: it all depends on me. One does not assume this role without betraying the evil upon which men thrive. Cease to believe, if ever you have believed, that wisdom is in resignation; or cease to aspire to wisdom.

Comrade, do not accept life as men offers it to you. Do not cease telling yourself that life can be more beautiful—your life and the lives of other men, not another life, a future life that will console us for this one and help us accept its misery. Do not accept. The day when you will begin to understand that the responsibility for nearly all of life's ills is not in God but in man, you will no longer share those ills.

Do not sacrifice to false gods.

Translated by CHRISTOPHER LAZARE

Marcel Proust

THE DEATH OF BERGOTTE

I LEARNED THAT a death had occurred during the day which distressed me greatly, that of Bergotte. It was known that he had been ill for a long time past. Not, of course, with the illness from which he had suffered originally and which was natural. Nature hardly seems capable of giving us any but quite short illnesses. But medicine has annexed to itself the art of prolonging them. Remedies, the respite that they procure, the relapses that a temporary cessation of them provokes, compose a sham illness to which the patient grows so accustomed that he ends by making it permanent, just as children continue to give way to fits of coughing long after they have been cured of the whooping cough. Then remedies begin to have less effect, the doses are increased, they cease to do any good, but they have begun to do harm thanks to that lasting indisposition. Nature would not have offered them so long a tenure. It is a great miracle that medicine can almost equal nature in forcing a man to remain in bed, to continue on pain of death the use of some drug. From that moment the illness artificially grafted has taken root, has become a secondary but a genuine illness, with this difference only that natural illnesses are cured, but never those which medicine creates, for it knows not the secret of their cure.

For years past Bergotte had ceased to go out of doors. Anyhow, he had never cared for society, or had cared for it for a day only, to despise it as he despised everything else and in the same fashion, which was his own, namely to despise a thing not because it was beyond his reach but as soon as he had reached it. He lived so simply that nobody suspected how rich he was, and anyone who had known would still have been mistaken, for he would have thought him a miser, whereas no one was ever more generous. He was generous above all towards women—girls, one ought rather to say—who were ashamed to receive so much in return for so little. He excused himself in his own eyes because he knew that he could never produce such good work as in an atmosphere of amorous feelings. Love is too strong a word, pleasure that is at all deeply rooted in the flesh is helpful to literary work because it cancels all other pleasures, for instance the pleasures of society, those which are the same for everyone. And even if this love leads to disillusionment, it does at least stir, even by so doing, the surface of the soul which otherwise would be in danger of becoming stagnant. Desire is therefore not without its value to the writer in detaching him first of all from his fellow men and from conforming to their standards, and afterwards in restoring some degree of movement to a spiritual machine which, after a certain age, tends to become paralysed. We do not succeed in being happy but we make observation of the reasons which prevent us from being happy and which would have remained invisible to us but for these loopholes opened by disappointment. Dreams are not to be converted into reality, that we know; we would not form any, perhaps, were it not for desire, and it is useful to us to form them in order to see them fail and to be instructed by their failure. And so Bergotte said to himself: "I am spending more than a multimillionaire would spend upon girls, but the pleasures or disappointments that they give me make me write a book which brings me money." Economically, this argument was absurd, but no doubt he found some charm in thus transmitting gold into caresses and caresses into gold. We saw, at the time of my grandmother's death, how a weary old age loves repose. Now in society, there is nothing but conversation. It may be stupid, but it has the faculty of suppressing women who are nothing more than questions and answers. Removed from society, women become once more what is so reposeful to a weary old man, an object of contemplation. In any case, it was no longer a question of anything of this sort. I have said that Bergotte never went out of doors, and when he got out of bed for an hour in his room, he would be smothered in shawls, plaids, all the things with which a person covers himself before exposing himself to intense cold or getting into a railway train. He would apologise to the few friends whom he allowed to penetrate to his sanctuary, and, pointing to his tartan plaids, his travelling-rugs, would say merrily: "After all, my dear fellow, life, as Anaxagoras has said, is a journey." Thus he went on growing steadily colder, a tiny planet that offered a prophetic image of the greater, when gradually heat will withdraw from the earth, then life itself. Then the resurrection will have to come to an end, for if, among future generations, the works of men are to shine, there must first of all be men. If certain kinds of animals hold out longer against the invading chill, when there are no longer any men, and if we suppose Bergotte's fame to have lasted so long, suddenly it will be extinguished for all time. It will not be the last animals that will read him, for it is scarcely probable that, like the Apostles on the Day of Pentecost, they will be able to understand the speech of the various races of mankind without having learned it.

In the months that preceded his death, Bergotte suffered from insomnia, and what was worse, whenever he did fall asleep, from nightmares which, if he awoke, made him reluctant to go to sleep again. He had long been a lover of dreams, even of bad dreams, because thanks to them and to the contradiction they present to the reality which we have before us in our waking state, they give us, at the moment of waking if not before, the profound sensation of having slept. But Bergotte's nightmares were not like that. When he spoke of nightmares, he used in the past to mean unpleasant things that passed through his brain. Latterly, it was as though proceeding from somewhere outside himself that he would see a hand armed with a damp cloth which, passed over his face by an evil woman, kept scrubbing him awake, an intolerable itching in his thighs, the rage—because Bergotte had murmured in his sleep that he was driving badly—of a raving lunatic of a cabman who flung himself upon the writer, biting and gnawing his fingers. Finally, as soon as in his sleep it had grown sufficiently dark, nature arranged a sort of undress rehearsal of the apoplectic stroke that was to carry him off: Bergotte arrived in a carriage beneath the porch of Swann's new house, and tried to alight. A stunning giddiness glued him to his seat, the porter came forward to help him out of the carriage, he remained seated, unable to rise, to straighten his legs. He tried to pull himself up with the help of the stone pillar that was by his side, but did not find sufficient support in it to enable him to stand.

He consulted doctors who, flattered at being called in by him, saw in his virtue as an incessant worker (it was twenty years since he had written anything), in his overstrain, the cause of his ailments. They advised him not to read thrilling stories (he never read anything), to benefit more by the sunshine, which was "indispensable to life" (he had owed a few years of comparative health only to his rigorous seclusion indoors), to take nourishment (which made him thinner, and nourished nothing but his nightmares). One of his doctors was blessed with the spirit of contradiction, and whenever Bergotte consulted him in the absence of the others, and, in order not to offend him, suggested to him as his own ideas what the others had advised, this doctor, thinking that Bergotte was seeking to have prescribed for him something that he himself liked, at once forbade it, and often for reasons invented so hurriedly to meet the case that in face of the material objections which Bergotte raised, this argumentative doctor was obliged in the same sentence to contradict himself, but, for fresh reasons, repeated the original prohibition. Bergotte returned to one of the first of these doctors, a man who prided himself on his cleverness, especially in the presence of one of the leading men of letters, and who, if Bergotte insinuated: "I seem to remember, though, that Dr. X—— told me—long ago, of course—that that might congest my kidneys and brain . . ." would smile sardonically, raise his fingers and enounce: "I said use, I did not say abuse. Naturally every remedy, if one takes it in excess, becomes a two-edged sword." There is in the human body a certain instinct for what is beneficial to us, as there is in the heart for what is our moral duty, an instinct which no authorisation by a Doctor of Medicine or Divinity can replace. We know that cold baths are bad for us, we like them, we can always find a doctor to recommend them, not to prevent them from doing us harm. From each of these doctors Bergotte took something which, in his own wisdom, he had forbidden himself for years past. After a few weeks, his old troubles had reappeared, the new had become worse. Maddened by an unintermittent pain, to which was added insomnia broken only by brief spells of nightmare, Bergotte called in no more doctors and tried with success, but to excess, different narcotics, hopefully reading the prospectus that accompanied each of them, a prospectus which proclaimed the necessity of sleep but hinted that all the preparations which induce it (except that contained in the bottle round which the prospectus was wrapped, which never produced any toxic effect) were toxic, and therefore made the remedy worse than the disease. Bergotte tried them all. Some were of a different family from those to which we are accustomed, preparations for instance of amyl and ethyl. When we absorb a new drug, entirely different in composition, it is always with a delicious expectancy of the unknown. Our heart beats as at a first assignation. To what unknown forms of sleep, of dreams, is the newcomer going to lead us? He is inside us now, he has the control of our thoughts. In what fashion are we going to fall asleep? And, once we are asleep, by what strange paths, up to what peaks, into what unfathomed gulfs is he going to lead us? With what new grouping of sensations are we to become acquainted on this journey? Will it bring us to the end of illness? To blissful happiness? To death? Bergotte's death had come to him overnight, when he had thus entrusted himself to one of these friends (a friend? or an enemy, rather?) who proved too strong for him. The circumstances of his death were as follows. An attack of uraemia, by no means serious, had led to his being ordered to rest. But one of the critics having written somewhere that in *Vermeer's Street in Delft* (lent by the Gallery at The Hague for an exhibition of Dutch painting), a picture which he adored and imagined that he knew by heart, a little patch of yellow wall (which he could not remember) was so well painted that it was, if one looked at it by itself, like some priceless specimen of Chinese art, of a beauty that was sufficient in itself, Bergotte ate a few potatoes, left the house, and went to the exhibition. At the first few steps that he had to climb he was overcome by giddiness. He passed in front of several pictures and was struck by the stiffness and futility of so artificial a school, nothing of which equalled the fresh air and sunshine of a Venetian palazzo, or of an ordinary house by the sea. At last he came to the Vermeer which he remembered as more striking, more different from anything else that he knew, but in which, thanks to the critic's article, he remarked for the first time some small figures in blue, that the ground was pink, and finally the precious substance of the tiny patch of yellow wall. His giddiness increased; he fixed his eyes, like a child upon a yellow butterfly which it is trying to catch, upon the precious little patch of wall. "That is how I ought to have written," he said. "My last books are too dry, I ought to have gone over them with several coats of paint, made my language exquisite in itself, like this little patch of yellow wall." Meanwhile he was not unconscious of the gravity of his condition. In a celestial balance there appeared to him, upon one of its scales, his own life, while the other contained the little patch of wall so beautifully painted in yellow. He felt that he had rashly surrendered the former for the latter. "All the same," he said to himself, "I have no wish to provide the 'feature' of this exhibition for the evening papers."

He repeated to himself: "Little patch of yellow wall, with a sloping roof, little patch of yellow wall." While doing so he sank down upon a circular divan; and then at once he ceased to think that his life was in jeopardy and, reverting to his natural optimism, told himself: "It is just an ordinary indigestion from those potatoes; they weren't properly cooked;

it is nothing." A fresh attack beat him down; he rolled from the divan to the floor, as visitors and attendants came hurrying to his assistance. He was dead. Permanently dead? Who shall say? Certainly our experiments in spiritualism prove no more than the dogmas of religion that the soul survives death. All that we can say is that everything is arranged in this life as though we entered it carrying the burden of obligations contracted in a former life; there is no reason inherent in the conditions of life on this earth that can make us consider ourselves obliged to do good, to be fastidious, to be polite even, nor make the talented artist consider himself obliged to begin over again a score of times a piece of work the admiration aroused by which will matter little to his body devoured by worms, like the patch of yellow wall painted with so much knowledge and skill by an artist who must for ever remain unknown and is barely identified under the name Vermeer. All these obligations which have not their sanction in our present life seem to belong to a different world, founded upon kindness, scrupulosity, self-sacrifice, a world entirely different from this, which we leave in order to be born into this world, before perhaps returning to the other to live once again beneath the sway of those unknown laws which we have obeyed because we bore their precepts in our hearts, knowing not whose hand had traced them there—those laws to which every profound work of the intellect brings us nearer and which are invisible only—and still!—to fools. So that the idea that Bergotte was not wholly and permanently dead is by no means improbable.

They buried him, but all through the night of mourning, in the lighted windows, his books arranged three by three kept watch like angels with outspread wings and seemed, for him who was no more, the symbol of his resurrection.

Translated by C. K. SCOTT MONCRIEFF

Roger Martin du Gard

LITANY FOR A HAPPY DEATH

THE FIT OF CHOKING had deprived M. Thibault of the temporary relief which the hot bath might otherwise have given him. Very soon another attack of convulsions came on, and what strength the dying man had drawn from his brief repose served only to enable him to suffer more.

There was an interval of more than half an hour between the first and second attacks. But evidently the visceral pain and neuralgia had set in again with extreme intensity, for all the time he continued groaning and tossing on the bed. The third attack came on a quarter of an hour after the second, and, after that, attacks of varying violence followed in quick succession, at only a few minutes' interval.

Dr. Thérivier had looked in that morning and telephoned several times during the afternoon. When he came again, a little before nine, the paroxysms were of such violence that those who held the patient down were losing control, and the doctor hurried up to help them. But the leg he had grasped wrenched itself free, dealing him a kick that almost knocked him over. How the old man still had such reserves of strength passed their understanding.

When the convulsions had subsided, Antoine led his friend to the far end of the room. He tried to speak, and indeed managed to get out a few words—which the screams coming from the bed prevented Thérivier from hearing—then suddenly stopped short. His lips were quivering, and Thérivier was shocked by the change that had come over his face. With an effort Antoine pulled himself together, and stammered a few phrases in his friend's ear:

"Look here, old man, you can see—see for yourself. It can't go on like— this, this. I can't—stand any more." There was an affectionate insistence in his gaze, as if he were appealing to his friend for some miraculous intervention.

Thérivier dropped his eyes. "Now let's keep calm!" he murmured, adding after a pause: "And let's review the facts. The pulse is weak. No micturition for thirty hours. The uræmic intoxication is getting worse, and the symptoms are becoming masked. I quite understand how you're feeling. But, be patient—the end is near."

His shoulders bent, his eyes fixed vaguely on the bed, Antoine made no reply. The expression of his face had changed completely. He seemed half asleep. "The end is near!" After all, it might be true!

Jacques came in, followed by Adrienne and the old nun. It was the change of shift.

Thérivier went up to Jacques. "I'll spend the night here, so that your brother can get a bit of rest."

Antoine had heard. The temptation of escaping for a while from the sick-room, of rest and silence, of being able to lie down, to sleep perhaps, and to forget, was so strong that he was on the point of accepting Thérivier's offer. But almost at once he pulled himself together.

"No, old man." His voice was firm. "Thanks—but I'd rather not." Something within him had told him—though he could not have accounted for

...ened up, with a movement of annoyance. Another patch of moisture was spreading on the sheet; the kidney had begun working again, copiously.

Dropping his father's arm, Jacques made a rageful gesture. This was the last straw! The only thing keeping him on his feet had been the thought that, owing to the spread of the toxæmia, the end was imminent. What would happen now? Impossible to know. It was as if, during these past two days, death had been persistently setting his trap, and each time the spring was drawn tight, the teeth about to close, the catch had slipped —and all had to begin again.

After that, he did not even try to conceal his mortification. Between the attacks, he flung himself angrily into the nearest chair, and dozed for a few minutes, his elbows on his knees and his fists against his eyes. When a new attack developed, he had to be called, tapped on the shoulder, shaken into wakefulness.

Shortly before midnight, things had come to such a pass that it looked as if the struggle could no longer be kept up. Three exceptionally violent attacks had followed in quick succession, and there were signs of a fourth under way.

It promised to be catastrophic; all the usual symptoms were present, but in a hideously intensified form. The breathing had nearly stopped, the face was congested, the eyes were starting from their sockets, the forearms tensely contracted and flexed so sharply that the hands were hidden and the wrists, folded beneath the beard, had the look of amputated stumps. All the limbs were quivering with the formidable tension, and the sinews seemed on the point of snapping under the strain. Never before had the phrase of rigidity lasted so long; the seconds went by and it showed no sign of easing. Antoine fully believed the end had come.

Then a feeble, gasping breath issued from the mouth, while a frothy saliva formed on the lips. The arms relaxed suddenly, and he passed into the convulsive state. From the very start the paroxysms had a maniacal violence that nothing less than a strait-jacket could have restrained. Helped by Adrienne and the older nun, Antoine and Jacques clung to the old man's arms and legs. He was flinging himself about like a madman, and the four of them were dragged this way and that, hurled against each other, their arms half wrenched from their sockets. Adrienne was the first to let go, and after that, try as she might, could not recapture the leg she had been holding. Then, swept almost off her feet, the nun lost her balance and the other ankle broke free. Out of all constraint, the two legs

it—that it was his ᵈᵘᵗ̶ᵧ̶
confront fatality alone. When ─
added: "Don't insist. I've made up my min─
and fairly fit. Later on, perhaps, I'll call on you."

Thérivier shrugged his shoulders. Still, as he suspected the presen─
of things might last another day or two, and as in any case he had the
habit of always giving in to Antoine, he now made no protest.

"Very well. But tomorrow night, whether you agree or not . . ."

Antoine did not flinch. "Tomorrow night?" Would they still be going on
—these paroxysms and screams of pain? Obviously that was possible. And
the next day, too. Why not? His eyes met his brother's. Jacques alone
guessed his anguish, and shared it.

Hoarse cries were coming from the bed, announcing another attack.
They had to go back to their posts. Antoine held out his hand to Thérivier,
who clasped it warmly, on the point of whispering: "Courage, old man!";
but he dared not, and left without a word. Antoine watched his receding
back. How often had he, too, when leaving the bedside of a patient on the
brink of death—after he had shaken a husband's hand, forcing his mouth
into an optimistic smile, or shunned a mother's eyes—how often had he,
too, once he had turned his back on them, hurried from the room with
the same sense of relief that Thérivier's brisk step betrayed!

At ten that night the attacks, which were now proceeding without intermission, seemed to reach a climax.

Antoine felt that the energies of his helpers were flagging, their endurance weakening; they were getting slower and less careful in their movements. As a general rule such lapses would have spurred him on to greater
personal efforts. But he had reached the stage when his morale could no
longer cope with bodily fatigue. It was his fourth night without sleep
since leaving for Lausanne. He had given up eating; with an effort he had
forced himself to drink a glass of milk earlier in the day, but he had been
living most of the time on cold tea, gulping down a cupful every few
hours. His nerves were getting steadily worse, though their tension gave
him a semblance—but no more—of energy. For what a situation like the
present one called for—never-ending patience, coupled with bursts of
spurious activity sapped by the knowledge of its impotence—was something against which his whole character rebelled. His endurance was being taxed to the breaking-point; yet he must keep on, wear himself out in
never-ending efforts, without an instant's respite.

Towards eleven, when an attack was just ending, and the four of them
were stooping over the bed, watching its last paroxysms, Antoine sud-

beat the air; blood spurted from the heels drumming on the frame of the bed. Panting, streaming with sweat, Antoine and Jacques braced themselves to prevent the huge heaving mass from rolling off the bed.

Then, as suddenly as they had begun, the frenzied paroxysms ceased. After settling his father in the middle of the bed, Antoine stepped back some paces. His nerves were frayed to such a point that his teeth were chattering; he was shivering with cold. Going towards the fire to warm himself, he suddenly caught sight of his reflected self, lit by the firelight, in the mirror. His face was haggard, his hair in disorder, there was blind fury in his eyes. He swung round, dropped into a chair, and, letting his forehead sink between his hands, broke into sobs. No, he could bear no more. . . . What little capacity for reaction yet remained to him centred in a wild desire for it all to end—anything rather than to have another night, another day, and perhaps a second night to pass watching this hellish agony, for which he could do nothing, nothing . . . !

Jacques went up to him. At any other moment he would have flung himself into his brother's arms; but, like his energies, his feelings had been blunted, and the sight of Antoine's prostration, instead of quickening his emotion, numbed it. As he gazed down wonderingly on the twisted, tear-stained cheeks, suddenly it seemed to him he was discovering a picture from the past, the tearful face of a little boy whom he had never known.

Then a thought which had several times already crossed his mind came back.

"Look here, Antoine! Supposing you called someone else in, for a consultation . . . ?"

Antoine merely shrugged his shoulders. Obviously he would have been the first to call in all his colleagues if the case had presented any difficulties. He muttered some impatient remark that his brother could not hear; the screams of pain had started again, indicating that an attack would soon be coming on.

Jacques lost his temper. "But, damn it, Antoine—think of something! There must be *something* you can do."

Antoine clenched his jaws. When he raised his eyes towards his brother, they were tearless, hard.

"Yes. There's always *one* thing can be done."

Jacques understood. He did not flinch.

Antoine threw him a questioning look; then murmured:

"And you, Jacques, haven't you ever thought of that?"

Jacques gave an almost imperceptible nod. As his gaze sank deep into his brother's, he had a fleeting impression that at that moment they must be looking very much alike—with the same crease between the eyebrows, the same expression of reckless despair, the same ruthlessness.

They were in shadow, near the fire, Jacques standing, Antoine seated. The screaming was so loud that the two women kneeling beside the bed, half stunned by fatigue, could not overhear what they were saying.

After a short pause Antoine spoke again:

"What about you, Jacques? Would *you* do it?"

For all the blunt directness of the tone, there was a faint, almost imperceptible quaver in Antoine's voice. Jacques would not meet his brother's eyes. At last he brought himself to mutter:

"Really I don't know. Perhaps not . . ."

Antoine broke at once. "Well *I* would . . . and I will!"

He had sprung hastily from the chair. But now he halted and, making an uncertain gesture, bent towards his brother.

"Do you disapprove, Jacques?"

Quietly, without hesitation, Jacques answered: "No, Antoine."

Again their eyes met, and for the first time since their return from Switzerland they had a feeling that was almost joy.

Antoine went back to the fire. Extending his arms, he gripped the marble mantelpiece with both hands. He bent forward and stared into the flames.

His mind was made up. The only problem was that of ways and means, of when and how. No one except Jacques must be in the room. It was getting on towards midnight. Sister Céline's and Léon's shift would be returning to duty at one. It must be done before they came. Nothing could be simpler. A blood-letting to begin with; it would weaken the patient and induce a state of torpor—a pretext for sending off Adrienne and the old nun to take a rest before their time was up. Once he was alone with Jacques . . .

Patting the inner pocket of his white coat, he felt the little bottle of morphine he had had there since—since when? Since the morning of his return. Yes, he remembered now. When he had gone downstairs with Thérivier to get the laudanum, he had slipped the little bottle under his coat, on the off chance . . . The chance of what? It seemed as if he had had the whole programme mapped out in his mind—all he had now to do was to carry out the details of a long-thought-out plan.

A new attack was coming on. He would have to wait till it was over. Jacques, full of zeal once more, had hastened to his post. "The last attack," Antoine was thinking and, as he went up to the bed and saw

Jacques's eyes fixed on his, he seemed to read the same thought in his brother's gaze.

It happened that the period of rigidity was shorter than usual, but the paroxysms were no less severe.

The suffering man was tossing wildly on the bed, foaming at the mouth. Antoine turned to the nurse.

"It might ease him if we let some blood. When he's calm again, please bring me my instrument-case."

The effects were almost instantaneous. Weakened by the loss of blood, M. Thibault seemed to fall asleep.

The women were so worn out that they were only too glad to go off duty before the next shift came; no sooner had Antoine made the suggestion than they hastened away to snatch a little extra rest.

Antoine and Jacques were alone.

Both were some distance from the bed; Antoine had just gone to shut the door that Adrienne had left ajar, and Jacques, without knowing why he did so, had moved away to the fireplace.

Antoine paid no attention to his brother. Just now he had not the least desire to feel an affectionate presence at his side, and he had no need of an accomplice.

He felt in his pocket for the little nickel box. He allowed himself two seconds' grace. Not that he wished once more to weigh the pros and cons; it was a principle with him, when the time came for action, never to rehearse the arguments that had led up to it. But as his eyes lingered on his father's face reposing on the whiteness of the pillow—the face that the long course of the malady had rendered day by day yet more familiar— he yielded for a moment to the melancholy thrill of a last impulse of compassion.

The two seconds were up.

"It would be less distasteful," he reflected as he walked quickly towards the bed, "to do it during an attack."

He took the bottle from his pocket, shook it, and fitted the needle into the syringe. While he did so, his eyes roved round the room. Then he shrugged his shoulders, ironically; from force of habit he had been looking for the alcohol-lamp on which to sterilize the needle.

Jacques saw nothing from where he stood. His brother's bent back hid the bed from him. So much the better! Then, "No!" he muttered, and took some steps aside. . . .

His father seemed asleep. Antoine had unbuttoned a sleeve of the nightshirt and was rolling it up.

"The right arm, yes, for the injection," Antoine murmured. "It was the left I bled."

Nipping a fold of flesh between his fingers, he raised the hypodermic syringe.

Jacques shuddered, and pressed his hand to his mouth.

A whimper came from the sleeping man, his shoulder twitched. In the silence, Antoine's voice:

"Don't move, Father. It's to ease your pain."

"The last words," Jacques thought, "that any voice will say to him."

The process of expelling the contents of the glass syringe seemed interminably slow. Supposing somebody came in! Finished now? No. Leaving the needle sticking in the skin, with a deft movement Antoine detached the syringe and refilled it. The level of the liquid went down more and more slowly. Supposing somebody came in . . . ! Another eighth of a grain. What a time it took! Only a few drops more.

Quickly Antoine withdrew the needle, then wiped clean the tiny scar from which a small pink drop was oozing. He buttoned up the nightshirt and drew back the counterpane. Surely, had he been alone, he would have bent over the pale forehead; for the first time in twenty years he found himself wanting to kiss his father. But then he straightened up, stepped back, slipped his instruments into an inner pocket, and took a look round to see that all was in order. At last he turned towards his brother; stoically calm, his eyes seemed to be saying simply: "It's done."

Jacques had an impulse to go up to Antoine, grasp his hand, convey his feelings by an affectionate gesture. But Antoine had already turned away; drawing up Sister Céline's chair, he seated himself beside the bed.

The dying man's arm lay outside the bedclothes; the hand was almost as white as the sheets and faintly quivering, like a magnetic needle. As the drug gradually took effect, the features were relaxing, the marks of many days of agony being smoothed away, and the mortal lethargy now settling on the tranquil face might have been the calm of a refreshing sleep.

Unable to fix his mind on any definite thought, Antoine had taken his father's wrist; the pulse was weak and rapid. All his attention was absorbed in counting the beats mechanically: forty-six, forty-seven, forty-eight.

His consciousness of what had just taken place was growing more and more blurred, his notions of reality lapsing into a dark bewilderment. Fifty-nine, sixty, sixty-one. The fingers on the wrist relaxed. He felt himself slipping away into a blissful nonchalance, a backwater of dreams where nothing mattered. Then came a great flood of darkness; oblivion.

Jacques dared not sit down, for fear of waking his brother. Stiff with fatigue, he kept his eyes fixed on the lips of the dying man. They were growing paler and paler, and had all but ceased to flutter with the failing breath.

A sudden fear came over Jacques; he made an abrupt movement.

Waking with a start, Antoine saw the bed, his father; gently he clasped the wrist again.

"Fetch Sister Céline," he said after a short silence.

When Jacques returned, followed by the sister and the cook, the breathing had become a little stronger and more regular, but accompanied by a peculiar rumbling in the throat.

Antoine stood with folded arms. He had lit the ceiling-lamp.

"The pulse is imperceptible," he said when Sister Céline came up to him.

But it was the nun's opinion that the last moments of a life are outside the competence of doctors; experience is needed. Without replying, she sat down on the low chair, felt the pulse, and for a while contemplated the tranquil face. Then, turning, she made a sign of affirmation to Clotilde, who slipped out of the room.

The gasping intensified, with a rattling, nerve-racking undertone; Jacques's face grew convulsed with horror and distress. Antoine, who had noticed this, was going up to him, to say: "You needn't be anxious. He can't feel anything now," when the door opened. There was a sound of whispers and Mademoiselle appeared in her dressing-jacket, leaning on Clotilde's arm, her back bent more than ever. Adrienne followed, and after her came M. Chasle on tip-toe.

Vexed by this intrusion, Antoine signed to them to stand back in the doorway, but already all four were kneeling just inside the door. And suddenly Mademoiselle's piercing voice broke the silence, drowning the gasps of the dying man.

"*O Lord Jesus, I draw nigh to Thee with a con-trite and hum-ble heart . . .*"

Jacques sprang up and ran to his brother. "Stop her! For mercy's sake!" he panted hysterically.

But Antoine's calm, melancholy gaze sobered him at once. "Let her be," he whispered in Jacques's ear. "It's almost over. He can't hear anything."

It had come back to him, that evening when M. Thibault had solemnly charged Mademoiselle to recite, as he breathed his last, the "Litany for a Happy Death"; and the memory touched him.

The two nuns were kneeling now, one on either side of the bed. Sister Céline's hand still rested on the dying man's wrist.

"When my lips, pale and trem-bling, shall utter for the last time Thine adorable name, gentle Jesus, have mercy on me."

The poor old creature had mustered up what little will-power still remained to her after twenty years of servitude to redeem the promise she had made.

"When my face, pale and wan, shall inspire the beholders with pity and dismay, gentle Jesus, have mercy on me.

"When my hair, bathed in the sweat of death and stiffening on my head . . ."

Antoine and Jacques kept their eyes bent on their father. The jaws were opening. The eyelids slowly drew apart, showing the glazing eyes set in a blank stare. Was it the end? Sister Céline, who was still holding the wrist and watching the face, made no sign. Mademoiselle's voice, wheezy as a punctured concertina, squeaked on indefatigably, syllable by syllable.

"When my im-ag-i-na-tion, beset by hor-rid spectres, shall be sunk in an abyss of an-guish, gentle Jesus, have mercy on me.

"When my poor heart, oppressed with suf-fer-ing . . ."

The mouth was still opening. A gold tooth glinted. Half a minute passed. Sister Céline did not move. At last she let go the wrist and looked up at Antoine. The mouth was still gaping. Antoine bent forward at once; the heart had ceased to beat. Then he laid his hand on the tranquil forehead and very gently, with the ball of his thumb, pressed shut the unresisting eyelids, one after the other. Without removing his hand—it was as though he wished its loving pressure to befriend his father on the threshold of eternal rest—he turned to the sister and said in a voice that was almost loud:

"The handkerchief, please."

The two maids burst into tears.

Kneeling beside M. Chasle, her hands resting on the carpet so that she seemed to be crouching on all fours, with her pigtail dangling on the white dressing-jacket, Mademoiselle, unaware of what had taken place, proceeded with her litany:

"When my soul, trembling on my lips, shall bid farewell to the world . . ."

They had to help her to her feet, and lead her away. Only when she had turned her back to the bed did she seem to realize what had happened; and she began sobbing like a child.

M. Chasle, too, was weeping; clawing Jacques's arm, he kept on saying, wagging his head to and fro like a Chinese doll:

"Things like that, M. Jacques, they shouldn't be allowed."

As Antoine shepherded them all out of the room, he was wondering what had become of Gise.

Before leaving the room he gave it a final look round. At last, after so many weeks, silence had returned to it.

And suddenly, grown larger than life, it seemed, propped up on the pillows under the glare of the lamp, with the ends of the handkerchief that swathed his chin standing up in two quaint horns above his head, M. Thibault had taken on the weird, enigmatic aspect of a personage in some fantastic folk-tale.

As he left the flat Antoine found Jacques standing outside the entrance door, and they went down together. The whole house was asleep; the stair-carpet muffled the sound of footsteps. They did not speak; their minds were void of thoughts, and their hearts light, for there was no withstanding the sense of purely physical well-being that had come over them.

Léon, who had gone down earlier, had lit the lamps in the ground-floor flat and, on his own initiative, laid a cold supper in Antoine's study. Then, discreetly, he had retired from view.

Under the bright light, the little table, with the white cloth and the two places laid opposite each other, had quite a festive air—though neither would acknowledge it. They sat down without a word, each abashed at feeling so hearty an appetite, and trying to keep up an appearance of dejection. The white wine was well iced; the cold meat, bread, and butter rapidly disappeared. At one moment their hands went simultaneously towards the cheese-plate.

"Help yourself."

"No, after you."

Antoine cut in half what remained of the gruyère, and helped Jacques to his share.

"It's really in excellent condition, this cheese," he said, as if in self-excuse.

These were the first remarks they had exchanged. Their eyes met.

"Shall we . . . ?" Jacques raised his finger, pointing to the upstairs flat.

"No," Antoine replied. "We'll go to bed now. There's nothing to be done upstairs before morning."

As they were bidding each other good night at the door of Jacques's room, suddenly a pensive look came over Jacques's face.

"Did you notice, Antoine," he murmured, "how, at the end, the mouth keeps on opening wider and wider?"

They gazed at each other in silence. The eyes of both were filled with tears. . . .

At six o'clock Antoine, feeling somewhat rested, returned to his father's flat.

To stretch his legs he went upstairs on foot. "Got to send out the usual notices," he was thinking. "That's obviously right up M. Chasle's street. Then the report at the Registrar's; not before nine, however. Let's see, who exactly should be written to? Not many in the family, luckily. The Jeannereaus will look after our relations on my mother's side; Aunt Casimir will see to the rest. For the cousins at Rouen, a wire. An obituary notice in tomorrow's papers, of course. Must send a line to old Dupré; to Jean, too. Daniel de Fontanin's at Lunéville; I'll write to him this afternoon; his mother and sister are staying on the Riviera—just as well they can't come. Anyhow, I doubt if Jacques will feel like going to the service. Léon can ring up the charitable societies; I'll give him a list. I'll look in at the hospital. Philip. Good Lord, I was forgetting the Institute!"

Adrienne came up. "There's two men been round, sir, from the undertaker's. They're coming back at seven. Oh, and did you know, sir," she added rather awkwardly, "Mlle. Gisèle has been taken ill?"

They knocked at Gise's door. She was in bed; her cheeks were flushed and her eyes fever-bright. It was nothing serious, however. Clotilde's cablegram, coming at a moment when she was already rather out of sorts, had been the first shock; after that, the scramble for the train, and particularly the thrill of seeing Jacques again, had thrown her off her balance. The cumulative effect of these emotions on her young, unstable constitution had been so overwhelming that immediately after leaving the sickroom on the previous night, she had had an attack of violent internal pains and flung herself onto the bed. She had suffered all night, listening to every sound and guessing what was happening, but unable to move.

Her answers to Antoine's questions were so reticent that he desisted. "Thérivier's coming this morning. I'll send him to you."

Gise gave a little jerk of her head in the direction of M. Thibault's room; she felt little grief, and was at a loss for words.

"Then . . . it's over?" she asked timidly.

His only answer was a nod; then suddenly the thought came to him, stark, clean-cut: "And it was I who killed him!"

He who has made the eyes, without eyes shall He behold me?
He who has made the ears, without ears shall He be told me?

I know that where sin abounds, superabounding is your compassion pearled.
I must pray, for it is the hour of the Sovereign of the world.

Translated by JOSEPH T. SHIPLEY

Valéry Larbaud

RACHEL FRUTIGER

IN BYGONE DAYS, when my mother used to tell me about her years at
school, in Geneva, and about her friends there, Penelope Craigie and
Rachel Frutiger, I could only imagine Mother, looking just as I knew her,
strolling with other ladies under the trees of Rousseau's Islet, between the
two big white bridges and the blue water of the Rhône. It was not until
long afterwards—one summer day which happened to be a cantonal fast-
day, as I was going across Plainpalais—that I realized she had been telling me about little girls. Then I imagined them in the likeness of the ones
I had seen, on other days, with their satchels on their backs and two plaits
of hair thrown over each satchel, going in twos and threes and fours, and
locking arms to cross the crowded streets. I knew who "those two little
French girls" were: the two brown plaits, Mother; the two fair plaits,
Aunt Jane. And, going toward the center of town, I followed a course
which must have been their way to school. But is that school still in existence? It was called "The Institution of the Good Shepherd," or perhaps
even "of the good Shepherds." Naturally it was "the best there was," and
the lady who was its principal used to say (speaking of my grandfather):
"The pride of these Frenchmen! This is typical: he takes it into his head
to send his daughters to the most aristocratic school in town, when he
can't even make his monthly payments regularly!"

Such an aristocratic school must, surely, have disappeared, along with
so many other aristocratic things. A real little princess of Germany went
there; and very distinguished and very ugly little English girls, who had
such names as, for example, the Honourable Mildred Taylor. And there
were three red-haired sisters, who spoke some barbarous language, kicked
each other under their seats during class, and wore large golden crosses
round their necks. A footman brought them to school and mounted guard

at the door. Everybody called them "the Prock sisters." At their lessons, when they were not fighting, they were continually sucking their golden crosses, instead of taking notes. One day one of the crosses came loose and fell onto the floor; it was evident then that the cross was hollow: a liquid was coming out of it. The proctor picked it up, and, turning to the teacher, cried:

"Madame, it is ether!"

The Prock sisters had become as red as their hair, and the two women looked at each other for a long moment wtihout saying anything.

I try to imagine what Penelope Craigie looked like. But the first half of her name is a marble bas-relief: Penelope seated in front of her loom, and, beside her, a little flat lamp, with three corners, and lighted, to show that it is late at night. Craigie makes me think of hyperborean mountains. But that is because I know that she was the daughter of the minister of the Scotch chapel at Reikjavik, in Iceland. Little Craigie must have been fair and wiry, with a head no bigger than your fist, two light-grey eyes, and enormous bright-red bows on the tips of her two blond plaits. Even in winter she went without stockings, wearing leather sandals that were too large for her. And it was for all these things, and because she came from so far away and must have felt so completely a stranger in a strange land, and because she spoke slowly, and because all sorts of delightful accidents befell her pronunciation—for these reasons, one of the two little French girls, in the secrecy of her heart, loved Penelope Craigie.

Rachel Frutiger was the daughter of a banker who had a great house on the quai des Bergues. She was just a little native of Geneva like so many others, with the usual accent, and her favorite expletive was: "Oh, my father!"

A few days before Christmas, after class, the principal signaled the two little French girls to come to her:

"It has been two weeks now since your father wrote to me that he was going to send the money for the last two months. You tell him that I say this bill must be settled before Christmas, at the very latest."

My grandfather came of an old family: he had silver platters, knives, forks, spoons, marked with his coat-of-arms, and a fabulous backgammon-board encrusted with several precious materials. He also had certain political opinions, and because of them he had been disinherited by his father, then imprisoned by the Commissions Mixtes, and finally exiled by the government of the Prince-President. And so he was living in Geneva among the rest of the exiles. They were victimized and defeated men; but they were also the men of a great generation. For better or for worse, they

had done extraordinary things—indeed, Europe was still resounding with
the fame of their doings. People whom they did not know were interested
in them, admired them, and loved them. My grandfather's particular
friends were Monsieur Sue and Monsieur Barbès. Once when Monsieur
Sue was coming back from Bath, he had to show his passport at one of
the German customs-houses, and the customs-officer had said:

"Euchane Zue? Yes? The Wandering Chew! La Chouette! The Ripper!" *

As for Monsieur Barbès, one day when he had gone "to have a look at
France" from the border-post on the road to Gex, he came back deeply
moved, with a story that had to be told. He had met a train of two-
wheeled carts loaded with stone, coming from the Jura. Just ahead of him,
one of the carts had got stuck in the mud, bringing the whole train of
them to a standstill. The driver shouted, the horses pulled, but the wagon
would not budge. Finally, speaking to the horse in front, and tenderly
touching its muzzle, the driver had said: "Come on, now, one more tug,
Barbès, old fellow!"

And, too, at Geneva, there used to be saviors of humanity who were
continually going away to found phalansteries in America. And dreamers
with neglected hair, last adherents of Saint-Simonism and first communists, who would describe the beauties of the society of the future in a
voice so gentle—and at such great length—that one dared not lend them
less than twenty francs. And those poor Polish refugees. And the Italian
conspirators who asked only for the means to buy a stiletto!

Again this time, my grandfather declared that Madame Principal could
just wait; and that the money from France would be coming on one of
the earliest days of the next month. And immediately afterwards he went
out to sell his backgammon-board to a dealer in antiques, so that he
might invite a few friends for Christmas dinner, and might make a magnificent donation to the Fund for the Proscribed.

The day before Christmas, after class, all the pupils went up to the
principal's desk to deposit, along with a small bouget, the envelopes
which their parents had entrusted to them. The little French girls would
willingly have waited until the last; but Rachel Frutiger kept arranging
her books and writing-tablets until it seemed that she would never finish.

"Well, now, young ladies——" the principal said.

Her two little French pupils spoke up at the same time:

"Papa said he would get the money from France next month. He
said——"

"So you haven't brought anything? Very well, so long as the fees that

* Titles, and characters, of books by Eugène Sue.

are due have not been paid, you shall not be admitted to school. Tell your papa that is what *I* say."

It was then that Rachel Frutiger went up to the desk:

"Madame," she said, "I haven't brought you anything either."

"What! You, Mademoiselle Frutiger?"

"No, Madame, Papa will send you the money after Christmas. Are you coming, you French girls?"

Outside, Rachel was taken by storm, backed against a tree, held there motionless.

"You did that for us! You had your money!"

"No I didn't. I swear I didn't."

She scuffled with them, and her satchel came open, and out of it (with several note-books) fell an envelope which clinked when it struck the side-walk. Rachel Frutiger cried, "Oh my father!", picked up her note-books and her envelope, and, refusing to listen to a word, and without saying good-bye, ran away.

When the new term began, since the money from France had not come, and since they must not make Papa feel uncomfortable, the two little girls pretended to be going to school. They left home with their satchels on their backs, as usual. Then they would spend an hour in making substantial additions to the snow-man that stood in the Plainpalais square. But after that, what was there to do? They dared not walk in the center of town, for fear of being seen by some fellow-student. One day they tried, by following side-streets, to go all the way to the rue du Rhône, so that they might contemplate at their leisure the Knife-with-twenty-five-blades which was on display there in a window. But Penelope lived within just a very few doors of the cutler's shop. And after a long walk through the narrow streets, the little French girls lost heart.

They could not stay in Plainpalais either: they would be in danger any minute of running into Papa or Mama. And so they resigned themselves to the outskirts of town, following long, sad streets which ran beside the river Arve, or toward Carouge. They walked hand in hand. Fatigue came very quickly. And they felt that they were surrounded by dangers. They had terrifying encounters. Sometimes a workman who had taken his fill of beer would achieve a momentary equilibrium in the middle of the roadway. He would venture to stretch out his arms, and, seeing that he was not falling, would begin to make a speech, in a voice of great gravity and warmth. Women passing by averted their eyes. But the little French girls, for whom this was a novelty, stopped and looked at him. Then he addressed himself directly to them, threatened to come nearer; and his voice followed them for a long way, pointing them out to the notice of passers-by. Farther on, some young hooligans frightened them by shouting out as the girls passed not far from their group. Others came up and spoke to them. One little rowdy even dared to pull one of the fair plaits, as one would pull a bell-rope. That earned him a box on the ear. A very brief moment of triumph: the flight began again at once; a retreat in the snow, like the retreat from Moscow. Surprise and suspicion accompanied these school-girls who were to be seen in the streets during the hours when all the others were at their lessons. And one evening the nurse said to Mama:

"It's funny how dirty the young ladies have been getting themselves, these last few days, at school."

Now they had become accustomed to living through day after day without lessons or exercises; their classes were already forgotten; a new life had begun. The satchels that they carried over their shoulders no longer had any meaning, were now no more than a dead weight added to their fatigue, a mockery added to their feeling of failure. They walked straight ahead without seeing. The time remained their one clear thought in this stupefied state: they must get home at exactly the same time as usual, just as if they were coming back from school.

Once, at the end of an impasse, they discovered a sort of portal, partly open. They crossed a courtyard between abandoned buildings, and found themselves facing an immense door, a folding-door, which gaped upon a shadowy interior. They went in. It was a room of prodigious dimensions. A kind of wharf, like those in harbors, extended along the whole of the room's farther side. A few steps led up to this platform, and at one end there was an inclined plane coming down from it. Up there they felt sheltered, as in a fortress placed on a height, dominating a plain or the sea. By throwing their heads back, they could see the beams and the other pieces of carpentry which ran crosswise up in the shadow where spider's webs hung trembling. As soon as they dared to speak aloud, the children began to explore this newly-discovered domain; and they were afraid, for, suddenly, among some big cases and casks, near the ground, they discovered a pair of eyes fixedly looking at them. It was a cat, and he was afraid in his turn when they clapped their hands at him.

It was a long time before they noticed that there was a little room up above the door by which they had entered, and that a very high ladder, rising aloft from one end of the long wharf, led to the door of this room. It seemed to them that the ladder had been brought in and set up there since they had entered, such was their astonishment at not having seen it before. After hesitating a moment, they gave in to the desire to see what there might be in that little room, and they began to climb the ladder. But they became dizzy from looking down between the rungs into empty space, and, besides, they were, secretly, afraid of the abandoned room. They had not got half-way up the ladder when they saw that darkness was falling, climbed down again, and ran all the way to the first streets of Plainpalais.

For two days after that, they tried to find the impasse again and the big door. It was a place where they could hide and rest; it was also a fine site for having races or playing war. And that unknown little room, up above the larger one, just as heaven is above the earth. . . . On the third day they recognized the impasse. But the big door was closed, and they read a sign: FOR RENT; INQUIRE. . . . And they began once more to trudge about the outskirts. The snow was melting into mud. Disgusting odors, cold and vile, rose from the piles of sweepings and from the gutters, and crept suggestively into their consciousness. They hurried on, and said not another word to each other. For how many months had this existence been going on? To be exact, for eleven days.

At the end of that time, Monsieur Sue came back once again from England. It often happened that he came thus to the Continent; but he left so many things of his in England that everybody knew he was but transiently in any other country. Monsieur Sue had, at his tailor's in London, a mannequin modeled on his own body; he had, at his London bootmaker's, a casting of each of his feet; and he had, at his hatter's, in London, a thing without a name, a thing having the exact shape of his head. Monsieur Sue arrived in Geneva just as he must have left London: with his hair nicely curled and his shirt-frill neatly pleated. He sat (a little stooped) and crossed his fine hands upon his crossed knees. He was shy and did not speak much. He was sad. But it was not because he had, once, been expelled from the Jockey Club, nor because he saw his novels in the hands of middle-class persons with whom he had nothing in common. It was, simply, because he was growing old, and because the shadow that he cast on the sidewalk of Pall Mall was not so slender as it used to be.

Separated from most people as he was by his princely education and by a politeness the secret of which is forever lost, Monsieur Sue was continually astonishing his friends by his interest in small everyday affairs. Now he immediately saw that the children were unhappy; he took them to the garden and made them tell everything. The next day, the little French girls were seen again at the Institution of the excellent Shepherds.

Childhood, so neat, so white, with hair so well combed, little bare feet in sandals, Genevan sweetness, little souls so perfumed with evangelical virtues, often I have thought of you when turning the pages of the Holy Bible that was my mother's and of her Hymn-Book, bound in black and stamped with the federal cross. Often I have wanted to say of you what I have just written. I suppose that, in your deepest, inmost life, the Hymns and their sad music were secretly mingled. Rachel Frutiger, you who loved love, you must have liked best the one which sings so tenderly:

> Nearer, my God, to Thee,
> Nearer . . .

But the most beautiful of all the hymns is the one which has this verse for its burden:

> Lord, with me abide.
>
> *Translated by* HANSELL BAUGH

Jules Romains

THE THREE HUNDRED AND SIXTY-FIVE APARTMENTS

"YOU'VE REALLY never heard it? . . . Perhaps, after all, that's not very surprising, since the persons concerned have naturally kept it a secret. On the other hand, when one thinks of all the people who couldn't help knowing it, it's rather surprising that there has been so little leakage.

"It is difficult to know how far back the business goes. The first thought that comes to one is that it ought to be possible to give a date by finding out the age of the houses concerned. A number of them are, indeed, of almost exactly the same date. But if one presses the investigation, one finds oneself coming up against some that are older, others that are more recent. The thing must have begun a long time ago. Where precisely, and at what date? Some of those who are in the secret may know of some tradition. I don't. Probably during the *ancien régime*. . . . The business must have continued during the Revolution, when it undoubtedly had a particular value. But the probability is that the systematic development of the scheme, the attempt to complete what had been already begun, belongs to the first third of the nineteenth century. True, the person to whom I owe most of my information on the subject is a woman, and women's memory for facts is often erratic; but she told me that her own knowledge was derived from her grandfather, from whom she gathered that the system had been completed between the reign of Louis-Philippe and the middle of the reign of Napoleon III, when Haussmann was busy with his great improvement plans. During those years the work seems to have gone on uninterruptedly, to have functioned perfectly in accordance with the original intention of its inventors, and to have rendered certain important, and at times rather remarkable, services, particularly, as you might guess, during the troubled period which began with the revolution of '48 and continued up to the time of the *coup d'état*. There is nothing especially odd about the fact that in view of changing conditions from age to age and the uncertain state of social life, the conveniences of the system should have been made use of successively by the representatives of different causes. Successively? Who knows? Perhaps simultaneously—to say nothing of the advantages it offered to private persons, which must have remained the same, generally speaking, in all the periods under review. In my own personal opinion it was these private and day-to-day facilities that led to the establishment between the persons concerned of certain bonds bred of familiarity and complicity, so that it would never have occurred to them to refuse the advantages of the system, in cases of urgency, to any one of their number merely because he did not share the opinions of his fellows in the secret, or even because he might belong to some political party which happened to be hostile to them. This is pure supposition on my part. It is natural enough to imagine that in times like those the people concerned developed a sort of clan spirit, as is borne out by certain usages which still hold among them. Where clans such as this are in question, it is a well-known fact that the political views of individuals are less important than the sense of solidarity, the obscure affinities, which bind the members of the group, and that, as a rule, it is the clan itself that decides more or less what political or party loyalties shall be binding on its members.

"I am speaking, of course, of the past. In more recent times the system has been faced with difficulties, mostly of a material nature, which it was incapable of overcoming. What remains of it now is very incomplete.

"But I haven't really explained the thing to you yet, though you must have read a good deal between the lines of what I have been saying. The best thing I can do, I think, is to describe to you how I first stumbled on the secret before I had ever heard any explanation of its intricacies. . . . The explanation and the details which I have given you came to my notice only at a later date. Well, one day I was visiting a certain lady, a very great friend of mine, and a member, as one says, of the very highest social circles. She lives in a handsome apartment in the very middle of Paris, not far from my own home, and situated in one of those quarters which today are no longer very popular, because the streets are too noisy and too dark, the elevators too old, the bathing arrangements too crude, the rooms too high and too big and difficult to heat and furnish. Personally, I am particularly fond of that kind of district. This lady's apartment is very spacious, full of odd corners and unsuspected passages, with a door half lost in a wealth of carved wood—the kind of thing that I adore. She herself is very young, very lovely, and married. Her husband, on this occasion, was not at home—as, thank God, is frequently the case. The only other people in the apartment were the servants, but they were at its far end and would not come unless summoned. At the moment of which I am speaking we were in a small boudoir adjoining the lady's bedroom. She had served, with her own hands and without bothering the staff, a little snack consisting of port and unsweetened cakes which she always kept handy in a cupboard. I had got back into my clothes and was perfectly decent; in fact, except for my hat and my overcoat, which I was not wearing but which were lying at no great distance, I could have gone into the street exactly as I was. She, on the other hand, had merely slipped on a pretty little housegown; her hair was not very tidy, and she was wearing on her feet a pair of bedroom slippers. I can't remember now what we chatted about. She was in a very lively and forthcoming mood. Suddenly, after a moment's apparent hesitation, she said: 'I'm going to show you something!' She took a key from a drawer and motioned me to follow her. At the far end of the boudoir she opened a door which I had already noticed, which was not locked. Passing through it we found ourselves in one of those narrow passages to which I have referred. I had seen it of old, but had never walked down it. It can't have been more then ten yards or so long. At the far end was a large curtain of faded velvet which masked a door. This door my friend opened with the key which she had brought with her. She closed it behind us, though leaving it unlocked. We were in another rather wider, but shorter passage. We crossed a large, ill-lighted room which seemed to be used as a storeroom, and took a third passage which ended in a very dark but very large anteroom. Before reaching it we passed a door behind which we could hear people talking. From the anteroom we could see, through a wide open double door, a very large drawing-room with a heavy hanging lustre. But we did not enter it. I had the impression that we were no longer in my friend's flat, but that the place where we found ourselves was by no means uninhabited. Everything bore evidence of the routine of daily life.

My friend led me out of the anteroom down yet another passage. From this point onwards she seemed to have to think for a moment before getting her bearings and choosing one door in preference to another. She stopped before what I took to be the door of a wardrobe, opened it with the key which she had already used, and, following hard on her heels, I penetrated into a largish room, lit by a window of ground glass, which seemed to be a dressing closet furnished with large cupboards of painted wood. Many little signs indicated that we had crossed over into another flat. My friend went straight over to a small door which stood in the corner of the closet between one of the cupboards and the outer wall. But she changed her mind, and, with a smile, still saying nothing, she approached a larger double door which stood opposite us more in the middle of the wall. She gave two or three discreet little knocks, which appeared to me to be arranged in a definite rhythmic sequence. Then she listened, at the same time readjusting her wrap, which hung very loosely about her, and giving a pat to her hair. When no reply came to her knocking, she very discreetly opened the door and, without crossing the threshold, made a sign to me to look. I saw a large, handsome room filled with rather worn, old-fashioned furniture. The general effect, however, was one of luxury. It contained a huge, low bed, a number of faded silk curtains, some extremely feminine toilet accessories which appeared to have been recently used, a quantity of rugs, upon one of which stood a pair of slippers which I could have sworn were still warm. Although we made no move to enter, there was something about our gazing at this intimate interior in which, as it were, a faint perfume still hung, that seemed rather barefaced, improbable, and exquisitely indecent. I did not dare to question my guide. I was afraid of breaking the charm. A moment later she closed the door as quietly as she had opened it, and turned back towards the smaller door in the corner of the dressing-closet. Passing through it, we found another passage apparently full of odds and ends, which impeded our movement. This we took. Half-way it broadened out into a circular space lit by a window looking onto the street. I glanced out of it and could not help exclaiming: 'But we're no longer in your house at all! We must be a long way from it!' My friend smiled but said nothing and led me a few paces farther. Then, pointing to a long gallery which we had just reached, filled with dark furniture and lit by windows of coloured glass, and to what lay beyond, she spoke the first words she had uttered since leaving the room: 'We could go still farther . . . but at the far end we should have to descend a staircase. . . . You've seen enough, I imagine, to get a pretty fair idea of the place?' We then retraced our steps to her boudoir.

"It was there, behind closed doors, that she began to explain. . . . She told me that we could have gone on a long way, much further than I had any idea . . . opening one door after another . . . always with the same key . . . that from time to time we should have had to go down flights of steps, sometimes to a considerable depth . . . at times also to climb . . . and that if we had gone in the opposite direction—that is to say, leaving her boudoir at the other end—we should have found similar conditions. As you may imagine, I begged her to tell me more. Whither did these two directions lead, and why all these complicated passages? What needs, what secret purposes, did they fulfil? Still smiling, biting her lip in the most charming way, and bringing all her pretty little tricks to bear, she said that it was all a deep secret and that I had no right to know it. I proved to her by certain agreeable if silent arguments that I had, and little by little she imparted to me the key to the mystery. She pretended at first that one could have gone, in either direction, even as lightly dressed as she was, in a mere wrap and slippers, to 'the very end of Paris,' without having to put so much as one's nose out of doors, and without being seen by any passer-by or policeman on duty. I exclaimed that such a thing was impossible. But she obstinately maintained her point, though I was pretty sure that she had never put it to the test. Nor was she wholly consistent. The 'very end of Paris' to which she had referred turned out to be the end of a Paris of bygone days. If I understood her rightly, one of the ends in question would have been somewhere in the neighbourhood of the Place des Vosges or of the Bastille; the other near the old city wall at the rue des Martyrs. . . . This marvellous line of communication between the extremities of the city, this secret way, must, too, have dated from far back. At the time of its completion—if, indeed, it ever had been completed—it must have formed a chain of three hundred and sixty-five links, one for each day in the year. In other words, this subterranean route had been constructed by knocking a way through three hundred and sixty-five apartments, or rather premises, since I imagine that there must have been a number of private houses in the series. It seems a small number, doesn't it? . . . but just think for a moment. There must be plenty of apartments in Paris covering fifteen or twenty yards, sometimes more, especially in the richer residential districts, which were, in fact, those mostly in question, and the distance to be covered could hardly be more, from end to end, than five kilometres measured in a straight line . . . which would leave one with quite a fair margin for necessary detours. . . . Obviously my charming friend was not in a position to answer all my questions, all the inquiries about details which I levelled at her. What she told me was perfectly possible so long as one was dealing with solid blocks of houses, and you will have noticed that in the older parts of Paris these blocks extend for a considerable distance, at least in one direction. But then there was the question of streets. Quite a number of these, some of them fairly wide, would have had to be crossed—though one must admit that seventy years ago they were a good deal narrower. All that my friend could say was the great difficulties had had to be overcome, that ingenious communications had been fashioned up stairs and through cellars, and that it was just where they were concerned that the passage of time had done most damage to the system. She had heard tell, for instance, that the work put in hand by ,Haussmann had been a real disaster which had never been wholly repaired, and that since that time circulation had been possible only by dint of crossing streets at several points, quickly, it is true, by making a dash from one house door to the door opposite, or from one shop to another. For a fugitive from justice or for men who wanted to escape observation, even such partial secrecy was a good deal better than the casual criminal could expect, though it fell far short of the former conditions of almost incredible security—or for those who wanted to move about lightly clad. . . . Sometimes, alas, the breaches made by Haussmann were more serious. Whole islands of houses had disappeared, or been replaced by new buildings. It is not hard to imagine the difficulties of re-establishing communications under such conditions, given the need for secrecy, and the number of workmen who would have had to be trusted. But the final straw seems to have been the new sewage system of Paris and the excavations made during the construction of the Métro. It is easy to see why. My impression is that since then the route exists only in odd patches . . . and that the adepts have more or less given up the struggle. . . . There is nothing to prevent us imagining, in all their details, the strange reasons which made such an enterprise possible, which set it going, brought it to perfection, and maintained it in working order. No need to seek one and one only. No doubt politics entered into it in part. . . . There must have been people who wanted a safe method of communication which could not be interfered with from outside, and safe lines of retreat. . . . Let us imagine, for instance, the case of a man who had got mixed up in some plot or other, who was suspected of murder— political murder, perhaps. He would know that he was being hunted. Assume, for the sake of argument, that he lived near the Châtelet. The approaches to his house would be guarded. The police would be quite sure that he could neither pay nor receive visits without their being aware of the fact. They could decide on making the arrest in their own time.

He would be careful never to go out except, quite deliberately, for an occasional walk down to the quay to look at the caged birds offered for sale there, and on such occasions he would be followed by four cops. But at any time he would be free to meet his friends at, say, the Clichy gate, or nearer still, at some spot in the centre of the city. If the rendezvous was not actually in one of the three hundred and sixty-five, he would merely have to set out from the doorway of some house where he was unknown and unwatched. And if one day he got wind of the fact that men were waiting to arrest him at his own street entrance, he could escape danger by emerging into the open air at some point a long way off, or he could find a new hide-out which no one would ever suspect and which he could reach from some point in the chain. At periods—and there have been many of them—when political plotting was a permanent feature of life, such advantages must have been invaluable and worth every effort to maintain. . . . It would not surprise me to learn that in Lyons, for example, that city of secrets and of plots, there had existed, on a smaller scale no doubt, some similar ingenuity. . . . But I find it hard to believe that plots and political intrigues explain everything. . . . I had a vague but very definite feeling while my fair friend was slipping along those strange passages, with her wrap carelessly fastened and her bare feet tucked into slippers . . . or when, after knocking so discreetly, she made me lean on her shoulder and look into that warm, intimate interior, so that I felt almost as though I were peeping through the interstices of silk underwear. . . . That room had been the scene of many pleasures, I dare swear, of delights and abandonments. I tried to get my friend to admit it. She replied, laughing, that if one were to believe everything one heard, there would be no end to it. She had been told, she said, that at one time the men in the secret had had the 'right of free hunting,' but that of course, or so she maintained, was only a story. 'It must,' she said, with a delicious little gurgle, 'have been something like the *droit du seigneur*. But all that must have stopped a long time ago, even admitting that it ever existed.' She agreed, however, that in view of the facilities presented, and the peculiar freedom of the relations which those in the know must have enjoyed, things almost certainly happened which we should hardly believe nowadays. It was her convinced opinion, however, that such things had occurred only between persons bound by a bond of close relationship, and even then only at certain points in the chain; and that it would be extremely foolish to imagine that there had ever been a time when the spirit of licentious orgy ran like fire-damp through these urban mine-galleries. She assured me that, so far as she knew, nothing of that sort, 'or almost nothing,' now remained. 'I should like,' said I with an anxious glance, 'to be as convinced of that as you are.' My own private opinion is that so extraordinary an institution could have become established, could have flourished for any length of time, only if it guaranteed, in addition to possessing other advantages which I by no means underrate, a certain convenience in the matter of intoxicating promiscuities—and among them a sort of informal adultery, casual adultery, as it were, would rank high— which those in this particular secret had always sought the means of finding and were only too glad to take advantage of. Remember, too, that all this would have been going on during one of those periods in our history when public manners were passing through a phase of rather Puritan austerity. The whole business seems to me to respond to a profound and recurring need in human nature, the need to find means of satisfaction which, if the necessity should arise, can be conveniently camouflaged. . . . No doubt we shall see the same kind of thing happening again. . . . That, I am sure, was what chiefly kept the system going, and, in so far as it still exists, though in an incomplete form, it would surprise me very much to learn that the need itself did not exist too. . . . On another occasion when I had brought the subject up again and was making a number of objections on the ground of improbability, my friend confessed that at the time when the system flourished, the three hundred and sixty-five had had to submit to certain rules. If, for instance, any one of them wished to change his dwelling, this had to be done, so far as might be possible, by effecting an exchange with another person living on the route. In any case, none of them could move until their committee—for they had a sort of committee to run the business of the system—had chosen a new member to fill the vacant place. Naturally, too, mere removal did not release a member from the obligations of secrecy. Still another rule—or I should say, in this case, custom, arising from the very nature of the business—ordained that marriages should take place, so far as might be, within the society, an arrangement which settled a number of problems and lessened or removed a number of practical difficulties resulting naturally from the passage of years, changes among the 'inhabitants,' and the normal process of death and inheritance. . . . I gather that there are still families belonging to the aristocracy of the chain the members of which still observe a tradition of intermarriage. When we read in the papers that a marriage has been arranged between a young lady of the IXth arrondissement and a gentleman of the Marais district, it never occurs to us, does it, that the chain, or what remains of it, is taking on life and substance before our very eyes?"

Quinette had been listening with every sign of thrilled delight.

With shining eyes and a ring in his voice, Claude Vorge finished off his narrative.

"I made a few inquiries—carried out several not very easy tests—and as a result I can prove beyond a shadow of doubt that the whole thing is pure fiction. What a good story it would make, eh? If I only dared publish the confidences which I have just imparted to you, I could write what would be the most magnificent book ever written about Paris. . . . Just think: Paris crossed from end to end by this long, winding, subterranean serpent."

Translated by GERARD HOPKINS

Georges Duhamel

HADJ MAHMOUD HAMAMI

THIS CHAP, the lank, stately one who just greeted you at the door—don't mistake him for a porter, please. He is Hadj Mahmoud Hamami, my benefactor.

You'll meet him frequently while you are here. I tell you: beware of him. He is quite capable of doing you some great service. Saving your life, for instance. And to owe your life to Mahmoud Hamami is bad business. I know—last year he fished me out of the Zafrane. I can tell you the story; it will teach you a few things about the life of these people and perhaps also about the inhabitants of Kamtchatka, whose acquaintance, to my regret, has so far been denied me.

I was returning from a brief ride in the mountains at the time, alone with Maamar, my orderly—and may I say, with less trouble than you meet at night in the alleys of Montmartre. We loafed from village to village, discharged our assignments, were well received and splendidly fed everywhere: the Tunisians are very hospitable people. A week later I was due back at my base in Talla-Ksour, where we were doing some work. On February 23 . . . By the way, I've risked my life on several so-called glorious occasions without remembering the dates. On February 23, however, I met Hadj Mahmoud Hamami, and that was a noteworthy, ineradicable event.

The preceding 22nd has remained in my memory as a rather sluggish day. A ride across the plain in stifling, quite unseasonable weather. The djebel we had left the day before was visible in the distance, full of khaki-colored clouds driven to and fro by the wind. About noon we rested at Sheik Seghir's. A feast, as usual.

"The Captain will cross the Zafrane today?" he asked me after dinner in a soft voice.

"Why?" I replied. "There is no hurry."

Sheik Seghir lowered his eyes and said, softly: "It is raining in the djebel. The Captain ought to cross the Zafrane tonight."

I have known the Sheik for years. He's one of our most valuable collaborators. Let a horse be stolen in Gafsa or a rifle fired in the region of Kef—Seghir knows about the incident within ten minutes. It seemed quite plausible to me that he was informed of certain meteorological disturbances a hundred kilometers further west.

Admittedly, the good advice of others never benefits us; but we might at least be put on guard by personal experience. I knew that the Zafrane was difficult. Seven years earlier it had swept away two of my wagons, complete with animals, cargo and crews. Yet when Sheik Seghir lowered his eyes I dismissed all qualms and smiled. The heat—and the taste of lamb's meat, stuffed grapes, tender artichokes, of all the delicacies Seghir had served up for me—induced inertia. I was napping in utter contentment.

It was late afternoon when I sent for Maamar, who was dining in an adjacent room with the Sheik's horsemen and other retinue. I took a step outside, and was greatly surprised to see an old Ford before the door, looking like a desert spider on its high wheels. A native was busily pouring water from an earthenware jug into the radiator. Seghir, following on my heels, said with an angelic smile that laid rapacious teeth bare: "The Captain will honor me by using this car, to gain time."

My reverie was gone at once.

"And the horses?" I asked.

"Will follow," the Sheik avowed, raising two fingers.

However, at this moment the Ford let go a salvo of uneven detonations and its whole body seemed convulsed by spasms. The idea of starting for home in such a vehicle suddenly outraged me—so much that I called for Maamar. "Thanks," I said. "The horses! Hell, we have time."

The Sheik was still smiling. He asked me to hurry and added a few thoroughly thoughtful words to the effect that the fate of man in general, and mine in particular, rested in God's hand.

We parted. The road was splendidly graded; I put my horse into a trot and Maamar followed at a distance of two lengths—no more and no less. Maamar is a model servant, unable to disturb his master's most profound meditations, even if the result of such meditations should be stark disaster. It was not quite seven, and the evening dew began to fall, when a shudder woke me. I have the bad habit of falling asleep on horseback, especially when a thunderstorm lies in the air. And Maamar has orders never to disturb my siesta. Anyway, night was falling when we reached Enchir Bakhbakha—three huts that stand where the trail to Talla-Ksour enters the river bed.

You know these parts well enough not to think of "river" in terms of a willow-lined embankment. A hardly perceptible indentation—three to four kilometers wide at that point—consisting of rills, holes, boulders, mainly of rubble and sand: a desolate stretch without a blade of grass or a puddle of water. That's the Zafrane. I was still pondering the course we were to take, when a bedouin stepped out from behind some shrubs and called to me in Arabic: "Too late. Sleep here. You can start tomorrow at dawn."

And as I stood, unable to make up my mind, he added: "You cannot find your way at night. But tomorrow—tomorrow. Rain has fallen in the djebel."

Are you from the information center, too? I thought.

He grew quite excited: "Rain has fallen. The water will not be here before six. If the Captain starts early he will get across."

This was the voice of reason. If you have spent ten years in the colonies, as I have, you are not afraid of vermin. I had my blanket spread in one of the deserted huts.

Jove does not smite with blindness all those he will destroy. Sometimes he is content to let them sleep well. I was dreaming of lovely things when Maamar prodded my shoulder, to wake me. I exclaimed, "I'm coming," and relapsed into my gentle slumber. Not till an hour later did the breaking dawn wrest me from it. I jumped up. Maamar was watching me with a rigid attentiveness, in which something like cold feet might have been discerned at close range.

"Mount," I commanded. "Let's go."

In two minutes we were in the saddle. The bedouin of the previous evening waved his camel-driver's staff when he saw us on horseback.

"Too late," he called over. "The Captain should wait here."

I was too incensed at my own thoughtlessness to pay attention to these well-meaning words. I spurred my horse, and we trotted on into the river bed.

The sky was cloudless and looked as if polished, delicately green to my left, shiningly blue like a sapphire to my right. Roundabout, fairy-tale stillness. Neither bird nor insect lived in this inferno of rocks. Far behind in the west, night was retreating. And suddenly I felt absolutely secure.

You can't see much of the road in crossing the river. Frequently it ceases altogether; you just have to keep south. Going wrong was the least of my worries. We had been trotting like that for a good half-hour, and I was looking forward to our imminent exit from the river bed, when the horses suddenly got very restless. At the same instant the sound of their hoof-beats was drowned out by a strange noise, never heard before and comparable neither to the roll of thunder nor to the roar of the ocean. It was a huge, subterranean quake that approached from the right and rose more powerfully by the second.

I looked back at Maamar. He uttered one word: "River." Well, that much was clear to me too. We put our horses into a canter across the rubble, but the water had already reached us.

Imagine a single, steeply arched, yellow wave the height of a wall, roaring at you with the speed of a cavalry attack.

We were lifted up, swept along, whirled about—everything at once. When I regained consciousness I was still sitting in the saddle. My horse held itself over water by a desperate effort; but the whirlpool spun the two of us around like a top. Sometimes I saw Maamar not far away, also on horseback and spun round, with his head barely above water and his burnous trailing, silent and composed. At this moment Hadj Mahmoud Hamami made his appearance. I was drifting off, near suffocation, counting on my imminent demise and helplessly exposed to every trick of the river, when I suddenly heard a yell, a human tally-ho in the roaring flood. At a new turn of this dance into death I perceived, miraculously standing upright above the water, a towering fellow, stark naked, waving his arms and at the same time swinging a rope around, such as the caravan guides use to fasten their loads. In a moment he had thrown it at me. I grabbed at it, first with my teeth, then with my hands, and soon my feet touched bottom. I stood on a sort of water-swept rock pulpit. But I had hardly secured a foothold when the other wrenched the rope away from me, and threw it to Maamar who promptly joined us. How we were to get out of there, of course, was an utter mystery to me. The shore seemed far away. However, the tall one took the reins and by a circuitous route guided us to dry land. The river was crossed.

When I could speak again, our life-saver was just about to don his shirt and burnous with inimitable dignity. He produced a cigarette he had hidden in his garment, lighted it with much circumstance and finally confronted us in the same stately attitude you recently admired about him.

"What's your name?" I asked him.

"Hadj Mahmoud Hamami," he replied with calm assurance.

"Listen," I said. "You have saved my life, Mahmoud. You are my bene-factor. How can I thank you?"

He raised his right hand gravely and replied: "Not at all. Come with me. You will be given to drink, and your clothes will be dried."

We sat in Mahmoud's house for three hours. He had two wives whom he hardly tried to hide and five children. He received us with all sim-plicity, and not without hauteur refused everything I offered him—money, bridle or watch.

"At least give me your address," I said. He named the miserable ham-let: el Aouid. Then he escorted us to the point where the road gets pass-able for vehicles and, when I thanked him once more, he declined again with a polite gesture. Soon he had vanished from sight.

We reached Talla-Ksour the same evening.

Like other Europeans we cannot bear gratitude in patience. The fol-lowing day I bought a horse for considerable money and had it sent to Mahmoud with a few kind lines. And was thereafter quite absorbed in my duties.

A week passed. One morning, a bedouin was announced to me. When I had him sent in it was Mahmoud Hamami.

"I am happy to be able to greet you," I said. "Did you receive my horse?"

"Thank you, I did," he answered darkly.

I shook hands and offered him a cigarette. We smoked. Hamami opened his mouth and said, "May I ask you something?"

I replied unhesitatingly: "You saved my life. You are my benefactor. You are as father and mother to me; I shall do anything you wish."

He lowered his head and said equably: "In that case, give me two lambs."

"You shall have them."

Maamar got his orders. An hour later Hamami wandered back home with his lambs, two well-fed animals which he drove before him. Another week passed—and to my shame, I will confess it, I had all but forgotten Hamami, my benefactor—when he appeared unexpectedly one morning. He generally seems to have considered the morning particularly favorable to the execution of his plans.

"Hello, Mahmoud," I addressed him familiarly. "Are the lambs enjoying good health?"

He nodded his head in the affirmative, settled himself on the rug in my room and remained in this position for two hours. Eventually I asked him: "Is there anything you wish, Mahmoud?"

He moved his head vertically.

"Speak, then."

At which, in his own laconic way, he opined: "We need an ass."

I had him repeat the sentence. No mistake was possible. Hamami needed an ass. After all, you can give an ass to the man who saved your life.

Then, events precipitated each other. On the very next day Hamami reappeared. He was to see the kadi in Sfax on a legal matter. Could I give him the fare?

An hour later he was back, and with gentle urgency asked for a letter of recommendation to the court official concerned.

From that day on, Mahmoud's visits increased frighteningly. Now it was money with which he left, now some animal, now corn. One day he took my phonograph along; and that the sewing machine is still mine is due only to the fact that there are limits to human gratitude.

"Mahmoud," I finally said not without some grimness, "you saved my life—nobody will deny that. When I wished to recompense you for it, you wouldn't take anything. Why does not an hour pass now without your asking something from me?"

He raised his somber eyes, let them rest on me a moment while he twisted his lips into a half-smile and then uttered the not unjustified words: "No, it was not my wish. But you started it."

❁   ❁   ❁

What more shall I say? The harvest was poor. When winter came, Mahmoud arrived with wives, children and cattle. Without much ado he explained: "If you desire it, I shall be your companion."

He has become my companion. I keep his entire kin. Soon my salary will no longer suffice. What of it? Hadj Mahmoud Hamami is my benefactor; he is the man who fished me out of the Zafrane. Yesterday he wanted a cupboard with a mirror.

"Mahmoud," I told him, "I shall wait for the next thunderstorm. I'll jump into the Zafrane and help myself out, if I can. Then we'll be even."

Mahmoud did not bat an eye.

Translated by E. B. Ashton

Henry de Montherlant

THE BULLFIGHTER

"Aı!" . . .

Alcaraz had been bowled over, and he was now clinging to a horn and hanging fast to the muzzle as well, so that the horn should not reach him. Then he was tossed from side to side, let go his hold, and the bull, with the blundering clumsiness of his tribe, charged right and left, everywhere but at the body in front of it. Alban was nearest, so rushing forward he placed his cape under the beast's nose and drew it in his own direction. You may think his action sublime, for he had saved his enemy. But such was not the case; it was a mere automatic reaction. Most acts of self-sacrifice are nothing else.

So far the fight had been both featureless and ridiculous and disgusting. From now on everything down to the very end was to have a well-defined stamp of violence.

As soon as the señorito had risen to his feet, people came out from the corridor and tried to make him return there. But he struggled with them in his desire to continue, and as he did so he turned around. Alban saw that he was wounded in the right leg and that the blood was pouring out. But the señorito kept on struggling violently with the crowd which became more and more numerous as others jumped the barrier and came towards him. They combined altruism with the desire to improve their seats under cover of the confusion. They insisted; the señorito repelled them, and went to get the weapons of death. From every row came the shout: "No! No! Don't do that!" with such violence that a foreigner would have thought they were reviling him. On the contrary they shouted in his interest. The words of his dedication were lost in the uproar.

Limping, he walked across to the bull, and then arose the first roar of applause of the afternoon from the very men who, a moment before, had been trying to dissuade him. Alban heaved a sigh. What would he have thought if he had known that the señorito's merit was less than he believed, since he literally did not know that he was wounded? The horn had simply entered and gone out without tearing anything. All he had felt had been a shock. He had repelled the crowd, not out of bravado, but simply because he did not understand why they should bother him.

Alcaraz had almost reached the middle of the arena, and still one of the areneros, running along with him, pulled him by the arm to make him come back. A real tussle took place between them for a few minutes, and the bull came nearer. The whole amphitheatre saw the danger; they alone did not realize it. A great uproar warned them; three seconds more and it would have been too late. A cape diverted the bull.

The arenero had stayed behind. Alcaraz strode towards the monster all by himself. He had taken only a half dozen steps when he reeled, and the arenero, near at hand, ran up and supported him. Then he let himself be brought back as far as the barrier, over which he was passed by the arms of the people. His sword-boy was already emptying out the water jug as a sign that his master's part was over. At last the audience was awake; they turned their faces towards each other, greatly cheered and unable to conceal the sincere joy that transfigured them. A wound! At last the show was worth the trouble of coming to see it. The prostitutes slapped their thighs; they felt a sort of bestial maternity at the sight of this weakened male, a suitable object for a certain kind of desire which goes under the name of pity.

Then only did Alban realize that since Alcaraz had been wounded he would have to kill the bull instead. He shuddered. As yet he did not perceive clearly that Jesús was running up, his face expressing anxiety, excitement and hope.

"Señó, let me ask the President for leave to kill that bull. . . ." He talked so fast that he could be understood only with difficulty, and in a voice weak from emotion. His glittering bright-green eyes made one think of wet grapes. "I beg you! It doesn't matter to you . . . but I want to be a torero. . . . I am very good at killing you know! If I kill well I shall be noticed immediately. . . ."

"Why, yes," said Alban. "Surely."

What a relief not to have to kill the bull! And then, too, he gratified the boy. Esparraguera came up and pushed Jesús to one side.

"What does this mean? I can kill that bull."

"No," said Alban, "it will be the one who asked first or else I shall do it myself."

Jesús stood below the presidential box and Alban supported his request: "I have been too bad not to want you to see some other performance than mine."

Esparraguera threw his cape violently to the barrier.

"If that thing does the killing, I'm through. I'm a matador as well, I am! I'm not a *mono sabio*."

"You are under my orders and you will do as I tell you."

"I will do nothing at all."

The arena seemed a vat with the ferment rising from the bottom and spilling over the sides. All the spectators rose in their places and the amphitheatre frothed and foamed like a great jar of wine on which the sun beats. There was a violent demonstration on the tiers. As everybody in the ring yelled at his neighbour, somebody shouted: "It's the Chamber of Deputies!" . . . Alban never will know why a whole section of the tiers on the sunny side whistled at Jesús, for it seemed as though the populace ought to be the first to support him. One of the attendants of the plaza even shouted at him right in his face *"Rubio!* Intriguer! Always wanting to show off!" The majority were applauding: the spectators who knew his worth were certainly numerous. There was great confusion, and the next thing that Alban saw was Jesús handing over to a torero in plain clothes his muleta and sword. The torero, José Santa Fé, leaped onto the sand. An expression of disappointment, his dark eyes near to tears, came in the boy's face. Suddenly it became sad as the faces of youthful genii sculptured on shields.

The great majority of the crowd began to whistle the new-comer whose work none had the least desire to see: Santa Fé was a third rate performer. Then Alban took fire in his turn. Like the bull, he needed to be excited to get going. Like his Galgo, the sight of blood had roused him out of lethargy, and then came Jesús' request. Vehemently he called out to the President:

"Presidente! Presidente! I have authorized to kill. If you won't have him, I will kill, as the rule is, and no one else."

Ah! How fine is the inconsequence of man! A few minutes back Alban was shuddering at the thought of having to kill that bull over and above his own. Now he was going out to meet it. One would not call it courage, for that is not what courage is. There are thousands of actions of the sort, both good and evil, done without thinking, and those who achieve them are remembered as heroes or criminals, though they are neither one nor the other. The nearest spectators had heard and applauded. Those who were further away did not hear, but they applauded too, for they had seen Alban intercede for Jesús and had guessed the rôle he was playing. All this was an indication of the politeness and kindliness of the people of Andalusia, who delight in being able to encourage someone of whom they have lately disapproved. Lo and behold, just as the people asks liberty for a *capitalista* who has given it entertainment, by raising its handkerchiefs, in a twinkling the whole amphitheatre flowed into a graceful bloom of fluttering white handkerchiefs, asking permission for Jesús! Just so the populace of Rome, with upturned thumbs, asked for the life of a gladiator to be spared.

"Rubio! Jesúsillo!"
"Presidente! El chiquiyo!"
"Anda, Rubio! Ando, tonto!"

And Jesús, at a motion from the President, took the weapons and made off at full speed towards the bull, which the toreros at the other side of the ring had been distracting throughout this long scene. Alban followed him. As they came near the seats on the sunny side a fresh outburst of hooting from one section greeted Jesús. This endeared him still more to Alban. But could Jesús possibly understand how deeply he himself realized the anxiety which the boy must be feeling? After all that commotion what a mockery it would be if the boy met with disaster, and what a triumph for his opponents! Jesús went up to the bull. Was it of his own free will or through bravado? It seemed that there was a slight reluctance among the toreros to help the interloper. At any rate, whereas Alban and the señorito had had all their men around them, Jesús found himself facing the beast almost entirely alone. Whether he had wished it or whether he had been abandoned, it was equally fine. Alban felt instinctive confidence in the ability of the rapaz, but he thought that he was serving him best by staying a little distance off.

While these incidents had been taking place, the toreros had worked the beast to the best of their ability. It was a great-hearted, easy animal, and they had exhausted it. Jesús did nothing remarkable with the muleta: but what he did do was done between the horns, and showed the inspiration of torero blood. What a wonderful and truly adorable revelation of worth after one of worthlessness! How could anyone fail to recognize it and be roused by it! Alban felt a tremendously keen desire that he might be successful, and many of the spectators shared the same hope. Openly, like a professional, Jesús made a first thrust with the sword, but drew it out again, either because it had struck a bone or because it had not been driven in with sufficient strength; the Andalusian race has more grace than vigour. It was probably the tenth time such a thing had happened during the afternoon. "Is the unlucky series going to begin all over again?" Alban wondered and his face clouded. "It would have been so splendidly satisfying for him to kill better than the rest."

Jesús took a fresh weapon and went to work in magnificent style between the horns. The sword was half buried in the right place in the heart. After such a lot of indifferent work all day, it was a great estocada. Half a minute later the bull collapsed. "Yes," thought Alban, trembling with excitement, "there are only two things in life, love and courage."

Jesús made the round of the ring amid loud applause, save only in the section where he had been hooted a moment before. Alban followed him, taking as much pleasure in the ovation, as though it had been intended for him. Then, too, they knew that he had taken the part of Jesús and out of kindness they applauded him as well. Alban picked up and threw back one of the hats thrown to the conqueror, which is what a subordinate should do. Such simplicity was highly esteemed by the spectators in the sunny seats, it was but those in the shade who judged otherwise. Some saw in the gesture that French demagogy that goes about the world making mischief. They thought that although the boy belonged to their class by birth he must be an enemy.

Now that he was well started, he was a changed man. Impressionable and changeable, always depending upon inspiration, up till that moment he had persisted in a singular apathy. The disappearance of Alcaraz allowed him to breathe. He could do so much more now that there was nobody competing with him, except a human being there by his favor. Besides, the prowess of the youthful killer stimulated his own self-conceit, which now came to life like a beast newly waked and looking about for something to devour. If, as he took up his station to await the entry of his Bad Angel, someone had told him: "You are going to be killed," he would have waved the nuisance aside with: "All right, all right, we'll talk about that presently," and have walked to his death. Yet two hours earlier he had thought of not appearing in the arena!

Esparraguera leaped out of the corridor to take up his post, and all Alban's suppressed desires came to the surface. He was not inspired by passion but by a calculated desire to put his passion to the test. He motioned with his hand towards the presidential box, to hold up the sound of the trumpets, and walked towards Esparraguera.

"You told me a moment ago: 'I do as I like.' You are no longer in my cuadrilla. Kindly leave the ring."

As the man began to protest: "I came here to play the bull," Alban turned once more to the presidential box:

"This man told me a moment ago that he would do as he liked, not as I liked. So he is no longer in my cuadrilla. Will you order him to leave the ring?"

The President looked puzzled. But in the corridor, a fat man whom Alban did not know, but whose very stoutness gave him an air of authority, began waving to Esparraguera to come back. For a moment there was a tumult. Then Esparraguera leaped over the barrier smiling. "All right! So much the less work! You think it makes me mad. . . . On the contrary, I am delighted. Patata, *vámono d'aquí!*"

He poured out water greedily. His lungs were burning.

Patata, who was already at his station, seemed to hesitate, torn between the desire of making common cause with his mate, and of doing his utmost so as to give the lie to his fifty-seven years. This affecting vanity gained the day and he stopped. But Alban did not see the end of this struggle. His eyes were riveted on the bull pen.

A roar hailed the entry of the Bad Angel, together with outbursts of laughter at his singular appearance. The laughter, however, died away immediately the crowd saw the manner in which the animal charged.

Gutiérrez and Jesús challenged right and left, and it faced them alternately by a shift of its hindquarters. It was handsome in its ugliness, with its horns of unequal length, its air as of an angry cat, its head erect, its dewlaps moving. When it stood still two puffs came out of its nostrils in jerks and were outlined against its dull red chest.

"Now is the time when I shall be wounded," thought Alban, "but I don't care, and I don't care if I'm killed, if I can first achieve a few things worthy of myself." That same morning he had said to himself: "I mustn't be wounded. Soledad would be too proud." At present she had no power for or against him. As soon as the bull seemed quiet he went towards it without giving the men time for any fancy tricks.

Quicker than he thought, he had it in his cape, like a sharp blast of wind blowing on him, and he blinked. His feet moved only just enough to let him turn on his toes: a higher power held them fast, independent of his will. He twisted his back and stretched forth his arms, slowly and gently, with marvellous veiled power; the cape, hoisted by the horns, dragged on the shaggy back. He had only to run a few steps and the bull came back of its own accord, butting with its horns and puffing sharply. This time it came so close that the crowd shouted: "*Suicida!*" Alban's face was drawn, his jaws were clenched till they pained, his nostrils dilated, and he was bathed with sweat; he was unable to breathe. He was motionless, alive but unrealizing, chilled and tense to the bursting point. Three times, four times, the pass was made, with the same affecting slowness. Success had given him confidence. Applause was carrying him away as a tide floats a boat. As he made the pass his whole being was without feeling. In the interval between one pass and another, a chill went down his spine, which ceased while he made the next, only to return again immediately.

Now to bring the beast back quicker when it had got past the cape, he hurled himself and knocked against it greedily with his fists and elbow, in the flanks or quarters (satisfying, too, his need of touching it), so that it turned immediately, and henceforward there was not a series of passes, but one continuous pass, one tragic wrestling of two beings confounded in one, one single brutal and continuous embrace. Shortening the cape proportionately, he kept clasping the monster to himself, ever bringing it closer and closer. He rolled the cape around the beast each time, feeling its hot muzzle, wet with slaver, against his hand; for every time that the bull charged, it foamed over him somewhere like a wave breaking against a rock. Without knowing it, he had spoken truth when he said to the Duke: "It is made for me." That body was made for his body. The man answered every movement of the beast with a movement of harmony; man and beast following upon each other's tracks in the empty space each left behind as he moved. The withheld laughter, the eyelids lowered at the culminating point of the too exquisite sensation, the passion animating the gestures—it was the god and his priest constructing their impending communion and transforming it into a nuptial dance.

At last the bull stood still and Alban ceased from his pursuit, for he felt the physical need of taking breath. He breathed and spat, but in breathing, though he cleared his chest he lost his support, for throughout he had been really relying upon his closed lungs, his clenched teeth, and his set face. (Later on, in a two hundred yards' race, compelled to take breath once, he was to collapse on the cinders at the very moment of breathing!) As the beast now stood stock still, he made the cape vanish, and then drew back with short steps.

Once the danger was passed he was so overcome with faintness that he wondered if he was not going to fall. His faintness brutally turned into anger, into jealousy, when he saw Patata showing off with the Bad Angel, instead of leading it to the picador in the shortest possible way:

"Patata! Let it alone! Enough! Go to the barrier!"

The old man, however, kept on doggedly, taking advantage of the opportunity. Here was a fine bull which afforded him the illusion that he was working as he worked twenty years ago, to the accompaniment of the sympathetic laughter of the onlookers, who were pleased to be able to gratify an old fellow who had had his day. But Alban could not take it in that way; every rush that the bull made meant a little more weariness; presently Alban once again approached it. He seized hold of the old man, and, muttering, pushed him aside.

The bull withstood a goad with ease, and liked it. The hurt which the goad inflicted was lost in the pleasure of doing harm to the horses. When it had had its fill, Alban and Jesús together offered it the capes, but it made for Jesús who began to play with it, making light of its simple-

mindedness. Alban allowed the muchacho to go on, in the first place because he liked the boy, and then because he said to himself, "If I order
him to stop and he goes on, I shall have to send him off as I did Esparraguera." So he kept retreating and watching, waiting for Jesús to stop, and
chewing on his chin strap. At last Jesús stopped.

The bull had done its work on three horses without turning a hair.
Now they came to planting the baderillas, and Alban experienced an ordeal. Once already he had suffered in his feelings by taking on Esparraguera who caused him nothing but trouble. And yet, incorrigible, he now
thought it hard not to give this old fool of a Patata his chance, for he kept
looking at him with the eyes of a dog to be allowed to plant a pair. So he
let him. Awful moments! Alban regretted his weakness bitterly. As soon
as he came in front of the horns Patata lost his nerve, and scampered off
as fast as his tottering legs would carry him. The Bad Angel was becoming more and more practised, and more dangerous as he became slower:
he conserved his strength, and grew more wary and cunning. Fortunately
Patata came upon the brute from behind, as it half turned round, and so
succeeded in planting, badly, a couple of banderillas. Swiftly Gutiérrez
planted another pair. And Jesús the third; he had waited for the bull to
charge and deceived it at the last moment by swerving, to a thunder of
applause.

"*Hijo de mi arma,*" a greybeard said to him in the corridor as he clasped
him to his heart. "You plant banderillas *como la Virgen!*"

The Virgin planting banderillas! Splendid! such comparisons indeed
give colour to life.

Alban now took the weapons with which bulls are killed. No, not any
common sword: but his own sword, the sword which he had kissed last
evening. To whom should he dedicate the bull? He loathed the aristocratic and bourgeois crowd in the shade and he was going to show them
so. He walked across the arena with slow steps, enjoying the astonishment
of those whom he loathed. "I will dedicate it to the sun," he thought,
meaning thereby: to the public in the sun. Dedicate the death of the Bad
Angel to the Sun! The whole myth came back to his mind. Was he not
himself almost a shade of Mithras? No doubt the sun had inconvenienced
him a lot, by beating right down in his eyes. Again why had they celebrated the feast on a Saturday, and not on the Sunday which was its
proper day? Alban stopped in the middle of the arena and turned to Him
who towers in the skies above. As he was himself taken a little by surprise he only said in a loud voice the first words which came to his mind:

"I dedicate this bull to the unconquered Sun!" A few people who did not understand clapped their hands.

He called to Gutiérrez:

"Bring the bull here in the middle of the arena."

Gutiérrez went straight to the bull. He worked so close that his cape almost seemed to be covering the beast's head. So he drew it on, stepping backwards, and led it with the cape as a decoy, as you lead a cat with a piece of meat. Olé! Here was a péon who was a man! Here was a fellow who took thirty seconds to do a thing, when the rest took two minutes and only half did it.

The Bad Angel was now standing stock still only five yards away. Gutiérrez slipped behind Alban. Jesús stationed himself behind the bull. Between the tips of the horns Alban could see his delicate and determined face, which pleased as it reassured him.

"If I can get hold of that brute in the first four passes, the rest will come of itself." For one moment he took his eyes off the bull to enlarge his muleta with his sword, "Ah! Got me! I'm done for!" He saw the bull on top of him, and it was too late to do anything except instinctively to protect his belly with both his forearms. A fearful shock tossed him like a straw: everything spun round and he himself spun in the air: he came down with a thud. Lying on the ground, he gathered himself together, tucking in his legs, then, making no more stir which might draw the attention of the bull, he remained there hunched up, at the mercy of God, a long time after Gutiérrez had diverted the bull with his cape. Then he rose with the snap of a spring. "My muleta! My sword!" When he had got them, he looked himself over. His waistcoat was torn and yet he had no wound or pain except from the bruises. But he guessed that there wasn't a drop of blood left in his face.

He ran, shouting with such violence and anger at the top of his voice that it gave way and he could not speak.

"Jesús! Enough! Leave that bull to me alone! Leave that bull to me!"

On, on, tackle it anyhow, or this human machine, his body, would burst! The bull must not see that he was afraid, or all was lost. "*Ha—Ha—toro! Ha —toma!*" The brute took the cloth. He spoke to it as one speaks only to beings when they are about to die. "*Tcha—tcha—toro! Quieto . . . quieto. . . .*" What was all that rubbish in the textbooks that you must play the bull erect? You must bend down when you play it, get close to the brute, force it to your will which shows through your bulging eyes, so that it may see how terrifying you look, with your knitted eyebrows and protruding jaw, and so be panic-stricken. So, too, at the end of the pass, your open left hand must be able to hurl the lightning which brings it to a standstill; you must play the bull so close that you have to fight the impulse to clutch the horn, to touch the muzzle.

Alban's conquering passes were excellent. After the first four he was certain of his power to subdue, a power which a horn thrust dispels in a flash. He stopped short, took a deep breath and filled his lungs.

"Ha embiste ya, malage!"

Once more the cloth enticed the controlled frenzy, and directed it and held it under the muleta, a ferocious mass of sand and blood and slaver and gashes. The beast slipped away like a wave and then—ha!—rose up again like the wave, at the smack of its banderillas. Alban accompanied the leap with his "Ha!" as if he were assisting it, even as one assists his horse with a cry when it is at the top of a jump, and he threw his shoulders back at the same moment as the bull raised his chest. There was a succession of simultaneous dips and rises between man and beast. Now they slackened their rhythm, now speeded it up, at times they were close together, and at others they kept their distance. Time and space fought for and against them: a difference of a couple of inches . . . a difference of half a second. . . . Through the instinct of his sympathy Alban reacted perfectly to the beast's every move. How often in moments of exultation had he identified himself with the bulls! Now, because he knew what it was going to do, he could dominate this beast, as he could not dominate that other bull which he did not like. For a man can really conquer only what he loves, and conquerors are tremendous lovers. Even as a poet in the throes of inspiration, or a composer improvising, Alban *shaped* the bull.

Now the struggle gradually changed its aspect, and ceased to be rough and dramatic. As in all art, mastery in the end begot simplicity. The ritual passes were made composedly and with dignity, appearing as easy as actions in a dream, endowed with the superhuman grandeur and freedom of movement of slow-motion films. It became manifest to all that in the centre of the arena a sovereign power was at work, with an unconcern not untouched by disdain: the sovereignty of the man became manifest to all. The fight had ceased to be a struggle; it was a religious act like an incantation, wrought in chaste gestures, lovelier than those of love itself, subduing men as well as bulls, and bringing tears to the eyes.

So matched were they in the fight, dance, embrace, that bull and man stopped together. They panted hard against each other. Possession had not received its seal, and yet it had been accomplished. Rolling up the muleta, standing sideways, and pointing the sword were all done at such a speed as made them hardly perceptible, because Alban desired that they should all be linked together, that there should be no break in the domination. For one moment he beheld the path of sunlight between his hand and the withers shining in their golden blood; and he saw the sword like that longer beam from the sun which smote the very body of Mithras. Then the shock of his blow made his body swerve to the left and his wrist throbbed with such violence that it seemed broken. He rolled over on the ground and came to his feet still holding his wrist. The sword had struck a bone, and was wavering, but it was in the right place.

"Don't touch that bull! Anybody!"

The beast tossed off the sword. He picked it up without confusion, knowing that it was merely an accident and that the next estacada would be decisive. It was his power to do anything in the realm of the will. He had only to will it for Esparraguera to come back under his orders, for the President to interrupt the fight . . .

Again he pounced on the brute like a falcon, and staggering, drew him-self up, with his hand against his aching heart.

The struggle with the Angel was over. He stood in front of it as he gasped for breath. No matter whatever he might have willed or done, nothing now could prevent his triumph. The life blood flowed like water from the double wound. The brute tottered on its feet, tried to keep its balance and at last collapsed on its side, its destiny fulfilled. For a few seconds more its eyes blinked and they saw its breathing. Then, gradually its legs stretched out as if its body had been blown up with a pump, and its joints cracked with the noise of a hawser wound round a windlass. The culmination of its spasm came violently, and then it rested motionless. The brown and bluish eyes became fixed, wide open on the night.

Alban watched in holy dread, the strain of the struggle still visible upon his face, except in his eyes. Now he knew that he had loved that mon-ster, that his whole life had gone out to it the moment he gave up the young girl, that all the suffering of the senses is the same, and that his terror and his hatred were only forms of love. The supreme thing which he had been waiting for had come at last, and his strength fell as the wind falls.

❖   ❖   ❖

Now people were streaming down from the seats and jumping into the ring, to crowd against the body and take delight in it. A whole swarm of hot little animals thronged about Alban, touching his clothes, taking hold of his hand, placing their arms round his neck, so as to have an equal

share in him who had conquered and was Life. He bent down and drew
out the sword which was three quarters red, and with his arms upraised
stretched it to the sun. Then Jesús, seizing the knife of the *puntillero*, cut
off the genital organs of the beast and with a loud laugh showed them to
the crowd, as he raised them with outstretched arm towards the sun. They
made a thread of blood on his wrist.

Translated by EDWIN GILE RICH

Julien Green

NOTES ON ART

11th JUNE 1930—At the Delacroix Exhibition. It is considered good
taste not to admire the big spectacular pictures. The Massacres of Scio—
rejected. The entry of the Crusaders into Constantinople—rejected. "No,
really, I can't do with that sort of thing!" a lady remarked, as though she
were being asked to allow the Crusaders to gallop through her drawing-
room. On the other hand, she adored the Turkish slippers, a water-colour
lent by J. L. Vaudoyer; she talked about these as though they were something to eat.

There is a strain of savagery in Delacroix. A lion tears to pieces a hare
whose eyes are transfixed with terror. In the Battle of Taillebourg there
are disembowelled horses, a disfigured soldier. Then there is that sort
of obsession of his with abduction and rape (in the Massacres there is
the exquisite young girl bound to the Turkish soldier's saddle), that idea
of feminine beauty now caressed, now roughly handled. That appetite
for suffering is also to be seen, latent, in the painter's own face.

15th JANUARY—An exhibition of Corot drawings and engravings, at
the Nationale. I looked at only fifty of them, but carefully, as I wished
to carry away as much as possible in my memory. The earlier ones seem
to me to be the finest. They have not got that magnificent freedom of
design of the 1840 drawings, but neither have they that appearance of
virtuosity which rather detracts from my pleasure. Occasionally they
are hard and lacking in feeling, and done with a care which recalls the
landscapes of Dürer. My own impression is that, at this period, Corot
must have used the most unfortunate kind of pencil, the type favoured
by architects for their draughts, a pencil which is grey rather than black,
and which tears the paper. However, when it is Corot who is using it,

a single stroke of this pencil is enough to show you a hill, the light on that hill, and almost the colour of the sky. I don't know whether he ever succeeded, in his later work, in utilising that knack of his which has something magical about it. A drawing of his of about the year 1850, done in the manner of his youth, seemed to me stilted, cold. It would be interesting if one could note what he leaves out in his landscapes as well as what he puts into them, for his selection is reduced to the lowest possible minimum, and that, in my opinion, is what makes him so great. As I looked at these marvellous drawings with their depth and breadth of vision such that one feels almost tempted to stretch out one's arm into the paper to see whether it isn't real after all, I wondered what could have been added by colour to such works as these. Nothing, I have no doubt. Colour, in this case, would only be an adornment, what Corot would have called their *charm*.

27th JANUARY—I went to look at Delacroix's Jacob at Saint Sulpice. There is, in the whole of this composition, a kind of speed which enchants me. I was alone in the chapel, and could stay there as long as I wished, till I was in a kind of trance, and the fine dark outline which frames the figures of the two combatants began to *move*. How beautiful Jacob is, and how well one can hear him groaning and panting with fatigue! The angel has the calm and serenity of a dancer, and his attitude suggests something that is almost like affection; he appears to wish to sooth his opponent's agitation, rather than to crush him.

I looked at some bad paintings by Pascin. His women give one the impression that air has been pumped into them through their toes. They would be incapable of standing up, so he lays them out on their back or on their sides.

7th FEBRUARY—An exhibition of Indo-Hellenic art (or supposed to be such). A head of Buddha plunged me into a sort of daydream which robbed me of all consciousness of my surroundings. That haughty, bitter face, indifferent rather than cruel, showed a complete detachment from this world of ours, and above all from the tragic futility of all effort. . . . In those features there was a sort of hypnotic strength which held me fast, and I stayed there for some minutes, beneath the gaze of those mournful eyes.

3rd MAY—Paris and the Revolution. An exhibition at the Carnavalet. I went away very disappointed. Hundreds of trifling memorials fail to revive the thing as a whole. Marat's waistcoat, a glove which belonged to the Dauphin—. The Revolution in glass cases loses all its terror for me. One thinks of an old worm-eaten stuffed wolf which children come and gaze at.

To Saint-Denis of the Holy Sacrament to see Delacroix's Pietà. A large canvas, badly lighted. The colours (particularly the red and the blue) seemed to me unpleasing, dull and violent at the same time. There is a visible effort to give the subject a new treatment. The Holy Virgin is on her knees; her outstretched arms are supported by two other characters, as Moses' arms were upheld by Aaron and Hur during the battle with the Amalekites. This pose is magnificent. It converts the Mother into a cross, and the Son, at her feet, seems detached from this living, human cross.

12th AUGUST—At the Degas exhibition. I looked specially at the painter's portraits of himself. He has a look that is well calculated to intimidate the ninnies, but they, be it said, do not waste much time in front of these portraits, whose expression of guarded hostility they find the reverse of pleasing.

8th OCTOBER—At the Louvre. The Abduction of Europa, by Francesco di Giorgio. As I stand before such a painting as this, the effect it has on me is as though the world were disappearing, or rather, another world were superseding our own. In this picture, we are carried smoothly and without effort into the land of dreams. So far as I am aware, the Siennese School is the only one that is able to accomplish that kind of miracle to such perfection. (I don't speak of Oriental art, to which in any case Siennese art is not entirely unrelated.) The Florentines never bear us away from this earth of ours; rather do they persuade us that it is a pleasant place; while Duccio or Sassetta lead us gently beyond the confines of our earthly life. In the same way, this picture of Giorgio's lies beyond the frontiers of this world. On this beach of mauve sand footsteps leave no trace; hinds, partridges move about near the water's edge, a water of delicate green. Hard by the stream, groups of young girls, joined close together like flowers in a bouquet, are watching the great white bull as he rears up majestically, a crown of plaited flowers resting over his ears. Europa, in a gold-embroidered robe and red stockings, is half reclining on the beast's neck and flanks; she has no fear, she seems almost as unruffled and calm as Peace in the Good Government fresco. But of what avail is it to speak of this? It is as though one tried to describe music. Fifteenth century Siena will always be the native land of those who feel that they are exiles from their own epoch. I left this painting with regret, with strained eyes and rather a heavy heart. I know not whither we are going. I cannot understand the *utility* of the things we do. Everything seems to me empty and false, with the exception of a few pictures, a few pages of music, a few poems. Let me find once again, however far and wide I search for it, that vanished land of which Siena has given me a glimpse today.

15th OCTOBER—At the Louvre, to see the Miletus room. It was closed to the public, but I got in by means of a tip. It was a real joy to see Miletus's great torso once again, and to see it alone. After gazing at it for a few minutes it appeared to me as though that heroic, disdainful figure were gradually increasing in size. In my imagination I saw it filling the room, then the sky, and then the whole universe. In a certain degree it *was* the universe, and I myself had no longer any independent existence, but only by and through its own existence. This strange sensation was only momentary, and the words I am using to describe it can convey no true conception of its nature; for I have no doubt that this would lie beyond the range of human speech.

What a strange place, in the world of reality, is occupied by that world which is its counterfeit! Can I doubt that Miletus's torso is real? But can I say as much for the braided attendant who opened the door for me, and all the element of illusion which he stands for in my eyes—the administration, the authorities? Can I say as much for myself?

23rd OCTOBER—As I was looking at the Mona Lisa, I heard someone remark that the picture created an illusion of life. But it creates far more than this; it creates an illusion of dreams.

25th OCTOBER—I have been going to the Louvre almost every day for several years past; I have never met there any of the people whom I know.

My debt to the Louvre is immense. I feel as though it had fed me and brought me up.

21st JUNE 1932—Saw Gide this afternoon. We had arranged to meet at the Picasso exhibition, and we went through the four rooms full of paintings. Gide was in the state of enthusiasm. "It's astonishing," he kept on saying. "Is there any sort of parallel between this and our literature as it is today? No, indeed there isn't. No one has this daring." He wanted to see everything and went by rather too quickly for my taste, but not a detail escaped him. As we spoke of Picasso's disconcerting facility—nothing seems impossible to him—he quoted, without comment, a saying of Ingres': "The man of talent does what he wants. The man of genius does what he can."

We went on afterwards to the Bonney exhibition—photographs of the 1900 period. Gide seemed to be amused, but ended by finding it depressing. Meanwhile the Comte de B—— had arrived on the scene, and he set out to persuade Gide that nothing was so pretty as the fashions of that period; but Gide would have none of it. "No," he said, with emphasis. "It was not pretty; it was ugly and depressing."

24th JUNE—At the Manet exhibition. A point that hinders me in my admiration of this painter is his facility and brilliance. I have never been able quite to get rid of the idea that a certain awkwardness is a distinguishing mark of sincerity in a work of art. Inwardly, I can't forgive Manet for his elegance, that air of the man about town which he seems to assume when painting, a sort of carelessness redeemed by good taste, and occasionally a lack of seriousness—yes, something approaching frivolity, even in *The Balcony*, a picture whose beauty lies near my heart. I greatly admired the portrait of the young widow with that fixed, mysterious look in her eyes; but the group of beggars seemed to me a mere studio exercise entirely lacking in truth, either in the world of reality (or what claims to be such) or in the world of imagination.

10th JUNE 1933—At the Surrealist exhibition. They were finishing the work of hanging drawings, and arranging places for some quite unbelievable productions; and I wondered whether our presence were not proving a source of great irritation to the people concerned. Suddenly, one of them cried out: "I say, old man, I've just seen a woman run over! She was the third in three days." "Really!" someone else said. "Was she really run over?" "Oh yes! Why, for ten minutes after it happened, people were still hurrying along there to see the blood." Etc. This conversation much amused me. Its object was evidently to drive us out of the Gallery.

NEW YORK, 1st DECEMBER—We went into the Public Library, where there was an exhibition of illuminated books of the ninth to the fifteenth centuries. A page of Girolamo dai Libri's kept me for a long while gazing at it with delight. The style of Mantegna could be seen throughout the whole design, in the petrified draperies, in the little pebbles on the sand, in the curling waves of the rushing stream. In that landscape I felt as though I had found a place of refuge, yes, a refuge from all that overwhelms me in the monstrous beauty of this city. And as I looked at the admirable damsons painted by Jean Bourdichou, my heart beat faster, and it was as though the whole of Europe were displayed for me to see.

5th DECEMBER—At Philadelphia. At the museum, I made a prolonged study of that mysterious portrait of Titian's which represents an ecclesiastic whose face is half hidden by a curtain. Some day I shall be told the meaning of this curtain, but at present, I prefer to know nothing and to leave everything to conjecture. In the same way, I am grateful to Hawthorne for not having told us why his clergyman wore a black veil over his face. Titian's portrait shows us an old man with a beard like that of Jules II. Though the transparent material a large hooked nose and a bitter mouth are faintly seen. The eye has a sort of fixed, stony expression, with a touch of sadness and also of malice in it; but that disturbing curtain leaves only the iris visible; and the longer I examined it, the more sinister did this strange composition appear to me. One actually feels that this curtain, drawn over to the left by some unseen hand, is blotting the man out from the company of the living. (There is a replica of this portrait at New York, but without the curtain interposed.) The portrait is of the Cardinal Filippo Archinto. The curtain must be a symbol of the fall from grace which he suffered.

2nd MAY 1934—At the exhibition of the Passion in French art. I was greatly moved by the large figures of Christ in painted wood, from the Sainte-Chapelle. While pondering over them afterward, it occurred to me that our civilization is indeed a stranger thing than we are accustomed to suppose. That we should find ourselves, from childhood until the day of our death, looking at representations of torture in churches, in houses, and sometimes in the street—does that not seem an odd state of affairs? A man nailed to two pieces of wood—that is what Christianity is incessantly showing us. The Church was born in an orgy of torture. All that a Greek child of the fourth century saw in the temples were statues of men and women ideally beautiful and happy; but what we are offered are effigies of a man in the throes of death. If someone who knew nothing of Christianity were taken to the Louvre, he might, on coming out, feel ill with disgust.

At the Trocadero (where there is a section of this same exhibition),

I looked for a long while at a Philippe de Champaigne, which I had thought uninteresting at first, but which is admirable. It is a *Crucifixion.* To the left there are some lovely blue draperies. There is the body of Christ in an agony of pain, but it is not the Christ of a painter of the Middle Ages; it is an Apollo crucified. Here too, what delight in horror! The weight of the mallets used by the executioners for driving in the nails, the position of the arms poised for the downward stroke, the intent expression on the faces of the torturers (intent, not grimacing as in Bosch's picture), the blood spurting from the feet—all this is portrayed with a touch of calm indifference which detracts from my admiration of the picture.

I am unable to believe that we cannot lift our hearts in prayer without the aid of horrors such as these.

10th MAY—At the exhibition of French painters in Italy. Poussin and Delacroix are men who give us a France we can love, and there are many others too—Racine, Baudelaire. That France remains intact. Try, if you can, to discover her features in the face of France as she is today.

2nd JULY—Carlo B——, who is passing through Paris, wanted to go with me to see the Italian Exhibition. We had a long discussion over Botticelli's *Derelitta,* a picture in which the element of mystery is undoubtedly attractive, but one which I cannot possibly regard as a great painting. It is pretty work, a charming illustration of an anecdote of which the interpretation is not revealed (and it draws an unfair advantage from the fact that a mystery has become attached to it). I would go so far as to say that, for Botticelli, it is an insignificant painting. Carlo B—— was shocked, but managed to hide his feelings pretty well. He looked at me sadly, and said: "Green, let us go back and see the *Derelitta.* I believe I shall be able to show you that you are wrong." But when we looked at the picture again I stuck to my opinion; I even discovered fresh reasons for not admiring it, and Carlo B—— grew more and more depressed. "Don't you see," I said to him, "all the bad painting which has resulted from that picture? It is a Botticelli for a Pre-Raphaelite. Doubtless it would be unfair to hold Botticelli responsible for Burne-Jones, but the bad imitations of a great painter do him poor service when they reveal his weak points . . ." etc. However, I was so unsuccessful in upholding my point of view that I ended by seeing the *Derelitta* through B——'s own enamoured eyes, and it suddenly appeared to me to be a lovely picture; but I am quite sure that the next time I return to look at the disconsolate lady, and he is not with me, I shall feel once more that I am right and fall back into my old heresy. B—— put his arm through mine. He saw that I was hesitating, that I was giving way, and his eyes sparkled with pleasure. That is what I like about him—that deep love of his for colour and design.

UNDATED (1938)—Twice in my life pictures have deceived my eyes to an extent that bordered on hallucination—an effect which the artist had certainly not intended, and for which I fail to find any satisfactory explanation. The first time it happened was at the Pinakothek at Munich, as I was looking at *The Virgin appearing to St. Bernard,* by Perugino. On the second occasion it was at the Georges Petit gallery, when I looked at a still-life by Picasso. In both cases I had to go right up to the canvas to assure myself that the relief had not been conveyed by other than the usual methods. I have since wondered whether this was due to some strange trick played on me by my eyesight. Tactual values will, I have no doubt, be mentioned as an explanation, but it was something quite different and the painter's merits had nothing to do with it.

1st AUGUST 1938—At Copenhagen. I was much struck by the Etruscan collection at the Museum of Sculpture. There are some fine statues on tombs, and copies of paintings. These show us a hardy, cynical race, self-confident, and doubtless free from all illusions except in the matter of its *chances of survival,* as to which it gives an impression of having regarded itself as established in Italy for all time. There is no mystery in these faces, which bespeak nothing but scheming, satisfied greed, insolence, ferocity, and an intelligence of limited range, but vigorous. In those large eyes of theirs there is no hint of any conception of eternity. They were merchants, soldiers, and excellent artists in the manner of Picasso. Their fat women, whom you see with two, three, or four children on their knees looking like huge loaves of bread, their bankers with a cunning, crafty smile, their swaggering horsemen—all this constitutes a civilization of a limited kind, but firmly entrenched. As for ourselves, with our humanitarian sentiments and our instinctive feelings of kindness and affection, they would have thought us tamespirited and effeminate.

30th AUGUST—(In Sweden.) In the Storkyrka, I looked for a long while at the admirable statue of St. George made by an artist at Lübeck in the fifteenth century. The pious knight has round, pink cheeks like those of a young girl, but he is none the less skilful for that in his handling of the long sword with which he is on the point of finishing off the most redoubtable and magnificent Chinese dragon that imagination could ever conceive. There is nothing here of the overgrown lizard in an evil temper which we are accustomed to see in the part of the dragon; what we are shown here is a regular Leviathan, thickly covered with sharp bristles, and with wide-open jaws that threaten to engulf the Perseus of the Christian Church. The monster is lying on its back; its snout with double horn is turned back and upward, and from the depths of its throat a murderous tongue is spurting out like a flame; it is smashing with one of its paws the lance by which it has been wounded, while with another it tries to raise the huge bulk of the knight and his heavy war-horse combined. That the appearance of the dragon is directly influenced by the art of the Far East is a matter which I think leaves no room for doubt; I would go so far as to suggest that it has been borrowed from Chinese teratology, though what connection can there be between Lübeck and Pekin? It is true that one sees in Norway churches of the period of the Vikings which are simply pagodas. . . .

3rd SEPTEMBER—This morning I was at the museum of prehistoric antiquities. There was a little Frenchman explaining these old fragments of stone to some ladies, and I followed him from show-case to show-case, partly out of curiosity to know what he would say, and partly to distract my mind from the bad news in the papers. As we were looking at the axes of carved flint, he declared, in the tone of a professor, that these arms were "a strict imitation of the Bronze Age!"

I noticed, with a certain feeling of emotion, the cross within a circle engraved on flat stones. This is the sign of Atlantis, one of the few intelligible signs which that continent succeeded in handing down to us before it disappeared at the bottom of the sea. I saw also the swastika (which derives from the cross within the circle), but turned in the right direction and blessing whosoever looks at it.

My curiosity was greatly aroused by a mantle of the Bronze Age. This object was actually to be seen in a glass case. Rather, a shred of material was found in a funeral urn, and from it this large cape, dating from a period of remote antiquity, was devised. It is a *tweed* of great elegance with a design of fawn spots on an off-white ground; it would have been drawn together at the neck by a gold brooch. This garment, which is rather reminiscent both of the monk and of the tourist, was doubtless worn by a chieftain; if someone were to appear in it today, he would not cause any great astonishment. . . .

As I looked at all this wreckage of an age so long dead and gone, I had a curious impression—a feeling that the whole of humanity was passing through myself as it might pass along a main road. Humanity was filled with me, and I with it; we were each other. On that day when for the first time humanity raised its eyes to the clouds, I myself existed. I shall be with it to the end, if an end there be; I cannot die. Its heart is mine, and that heart is only now beginning to beat. Life—what I call life—is simply humanity's consciousness of its own existence. This feeling of mine was so vivid that the common fear of death appeared suddenly to me as one of the most tragic of all the misunderstandings from which mankind has ever suffered; it comes no doubt from that disastrous failure to distinguish between ourselves and our bodies. But how can one speak of this? To people who know what I mean, these things appear natural because they have *felt* them. The rest would think me mad. The peculiar quality of these ideas which come into my mind, as they will come gradually into the minds of all of us, for we are no more separated from each other than are the drops of water in the ocean—the peculiar quality of these ideas is that their value is practically nil so long as they are confined to the sphere of the intellect. They must be *lived*.

Translated by JOCELYN GODEFROI

Saint-John Perse

WRITTEN ON THE DOOR

I HONOR the living, among you I have face.
And in the noise of his soul a man speaks at my right
and the other is riding the boats,
the horseman leans on his lance as he drinks,
(Draw into the shade at the threshold the old man's painted chair.)

I honor the living, among you I find grace.
Say to the women they should nourish,
should nourish on the earth that thin thread of smoke. . . .
And the man walks through dreams and goes toward the sea
and the smoke rises at the end of the headlands.

I honor the living, among you I make haste.
Dogs, ho! my dogs, we whistle on you . . .
And the house, heavy with honors and the year yellow among the leaves
Are as nothing to man's heart when he thinks:
all the paths of the world eat out of our hand.

Translated by LOUISE VARÈSE

François Mauriac

THERESE DESQUEYROUX

THE LAWYER opened a door. Thérèse Desqueyroux, as she stood in that remote corridor of the law-courts, felt the fog upon her face and inhaled it deeply. She was afraid some one might be waiting for her, and hesitated to go out. A man with his coat collar turned up appeared from the shadow of a plane tree, and she recognized her father.

"All right," cried the lawyer, "case dismissed"; and, turning to Thérèse, he added, "You can go out now; no one is there."

She went down the damp steps; the little Square seemed indeed deserted. Her father did not kiss her, did not even look at her. He asked a few questions of Duros, the lawyer, who answered in low tones, as though he were afraid of being overheard. She just managed to catch what they were saying.

"I shall get the official notification to-morrow."

"I suppose nothing can go wrong now?"

"No, nothing; it's all over."

"I suppose after my son-in-law's statement, it was a certainty."

"Well, I'm not so sure. . . . You never can tell."

"But after he'd said definitely that he had not counted the drops . . ."

"My dear Larroque, in affairs of this kind the victim's evidence . . ."

Here Thérèse broke in: "But there wasn't any victim."

"I meant by victim, the victim of his own imprudence, Madame."

The two men stared at her for a moment as she stood there motionless, wrapped in her cloak, and looked curiously at her expressionless face. She asked where the carriage was; her father had arranged for it to wait on the Budos road, outside the town, so as not to attract attention.

They crossed the Square, where leaves from the plane trees were sticking to the rain-soaked benches. Fortunately the days had grown much shorter; besides, to get to the Budos road, they could go through

the most unfrequented streets of the little provincial town. Thérèse
walked between the two men (she was nearly half a head taller than
either of them), and they began a further discussion as if she had not
been there; but finding the intervening feminine presence inconvenient
they began unconsciously to elbow her out of the way. She accordingly
dropped a little behind, and took the glove off her left hand so as to be
able to pick the moss off the ancient stone walls at her side. From time
to time a workman on a bicycle, or a trap, came past, and she drew close
in to the houses to avoid being splashed with the mud. But Thérèse
was hidden by the gathering dusk, and no one recognised her. The smell
of fog and baking bread was for her not merely the usual evening smell
of a little town; it was the perfume of the life that had been restored
to her at last. She shut her eyes to savour the moist leafy fragrance of the
sleeping earth, and tried not to listen to the words of the short bandy-
legged gentleman who did not once turn his head towards his daughter.
She might have fallen at the roadside and neither he, nor Duros, would
have noticed it. They were no longer afraid of raising their voices.

"Monsieur Desqueyroux's statement was all that could be desired, but
there was that prescription,—in point of fact, it was a question of forgery.
And it was Doctor Pédemay who had brought the charge . . ."

"But he withdrew it."

"I know; but her explanation—this mysterious individual who handed
her a prescription . . ."

Thérèse walked more slowly, not because she was tired, but to get
out of earshot of these phrases that had been dinned into her brain for
so many weeks; but it was no use. She could not help hearing her father's
raucous accents:

"I told her over and over again that she *must* try to think of something
else."

He was quite right, he had indeed said so very often. But what was he
worrying about now? What he called the honour of the name, was safe:
the whole story would have been forgotten by the time of the Senatorial
elections, Thérèse thought to herself, as she did her best not to catch up
with the two men; but in the heat of the discussion, they stopped, ges-
ticulating at each other, half-way down the street.

"My advice to you, Larroque, is to face the thing out: take the offensive
in next Sunday's *Semeur*: I'll see about it if you like. Get them to put in
a notice headed 'An Infamous Rumour' or something like that."

"I don't agree with you, my dear fellow: as a matter of fact there is
no case to answer, the prosecution obviously had not a leg to stand on;

they did not even consult hand-writing experts. I am sure the best thing
will be to say nothing, and hush it all up. I will do what is necessary
and I won't spare expense: we can't afford to have any scandal, for the
sake of the family."

They had walked on again by this time, and Thérèse did not hear
Duros' answer. She inhaled the damp night air once more as though she
were afraid of choking; and suddenly there came before her mind the
unknown face of her maternal grandmother Julie Bellade: it was indeed
unknown, for neither the Larroque nor the Desqueyroux families possessed a single likeness of her, and nothing was known about her except
that she had one day disappeared. Thérèse realised that she too might
have been wiped out of existence, and later on not even her little
daughter Marie would have been allowed to find in an album the likeness
of one who had brought her into the world. At that moment Marie was
already asleep in a room at Argelouse, where Thérèse would arrive late
that evening: she would listen in the darkness to the murmur of that
childish slumber; she would lean over the bed and her lips would drink
in the sweetness of that sleeping life like a draught of clear water.

The carriage stood waiting by the ditch at the edge of the road; the
hood was raised and the two lamps lit up the skinny hind quarters of the
horses. Beyond it towered two dark walls of forest. The tops of the
lower tiers of pines on either side met overhead, and the road vanished
into the darkness under that dim archway. Above it gleamed the sky,
fretted by a network of myriad branches.

The coachman watched Thérèse with greedy curiosity. When she
asked him if they would get to Nizan station in time to catch the last
train, he said they would if they started at once.

"I shall not need to trouble you again, Gardère."

"Has Madame no more business here, then?"

She shook her head, while the man still devoured her with his eyes.
Would she be looked at like that for the rest of her life?

"Well, are you glad?" asked her father. He seemed at last to have
noticed her presence. Thérèse glanced at that sallow bilious countenance,
those cheeks bristling with a coarse growth of whitish-yellow hair, so
painfully distinct in the light of the carriage lamps.

"I have suffered so much,—I am worn out . . ." she began, in low tones;
but she soon relapsed into silence. It was no use talking; he was not
listening, he was not even looking at her. He cared very little about
Thérèse's feelings. One thing and one thing only mattered to him; his
upward progress to the Senate might be impeded and even endangered

by this wretched daughter of his: all women, in his opinion, were either hysterical or stupid. Fortunately her name was no longer Larroque: she was a Desqueyroux. Now that they had managed to avoid a trial at the Assizes, he breathed again: but it would be difficult to prevent his enemies keeping the wound open. He would go and see the Prefect the very next day. Thank Heaven, he could do what he liked with the Editor of the *Lande Conservatrice*. There was that story about those little girls! . . . He took Thérèse's arm:

"Get in at once, you've no time to lose."

Then the lawyer, perhaps out of malice, or possibly not liking to let Thérèse go without saying a word to her, asked if she was going back to Monsieur Bernard Desqueyroux that very evening. As she replied, "Of course I am; my husband is expecting me," she realised for the first time since she had left the Law Courts that she would, in fact, in a few hours, cross the threshold of the room in which her husband was lying, still rather ill, and that this was the beginning of an indefinite succession of days through which she must live in this man's company.

She had been staying with her father, just outside the little town, while the case had been under investigation, but she had, of course, often made this journey: on the previous occasions, however, she had been intent upon the necessity for giving her husband an exact account of what had happened, and her mind was full of Duros' last words of advice, as they got into the carriage, on the answers Monsieur Desqueyroux was to make when he was again questioned. Thérèse had then felt no distress or awkwardness at finding herself face to face once more with the sick man: what they had to consider was not what had really happened, but what they had better say, or not say. Husband and wife had never been so closely united as they were by the preparation of this defense,—drawn together across the infant body of their little daughter Marie. They concocted, for the judge's benefit, a simple and coherent story, calculated to convince that logical mind. She used to get into the same carriage that was waiting for her this evening: but to-night she dreaded the end of that journey through the darkness which in those days she had found so tedious. She remembered how, the moment she got into the carriage, she longed to be back in that room at Argelouse, and she used to go over in her mind the instructions she was to pass on to her husband: he was to be sure, for instance, to say that she had told him one evening about that prescription which an unknown man had asked her to take to the chemist's, on the pretext that he did not like to go himself because he owed money there,—but Duros did not advise that Bernard should go so far as to pretend that he remembered remonstrating with his wife for doing such a foolish thing.

Now that the nightmare had been exorcised, what would Bernard and Thérèse talk about that evening? She saw in her mind's eye the desolate house in which he was awaiting her: she pictured the bed in the centre of that stone-floored room, and the bed lamp, turned low, standing on a table among a litter of newspapers and medicine bottles. The house-dogs, awakened by the noise of the carriage, bark and are quiet: and then the silence would descend once more, the awful silence of those nights when the wretched Bernard lay racked by frightful paroysms of vomiting. Thérèse tried to imagine the first moment, not far distant now, when their eyes would meet; and then the ensuing night, the next day, the day after, and the weeks to come, in that house at Argelouse, where they would no longer need to compose a presentable version of the drama they had lived. There would be nothing now between them,—except what had really been there, really, and in very truth. Thérèse lost her nerve, and stammered, turning towards the lawyer,—though her words were intended for the older man:

"I expect to stay a few days with Monsieur Desqueyroux, and then, if he goes on improving, I shall come back to my father."

"Not a bit of it, my dear," said Monsieur Larroque, and as Gardère began to fidget on his seat, he added, lowering his voice: "Have you taken leave of your senses? You can't possibly leave your husband at such a time. You must be inseparable,—inseparable, I tell you, for the rest of your lives."

"Of course, father: what could I have been thinking of? Then you will come to Argelouse?"

"But I shall expect you over for the fair on Thursday as usual, Thérèse. You will go on coming as you always did."

She must surely understand that any departure from existing usages would be fatal. She must realise that, once and for all. He felt sure he could depend upon her, she had done the family enough harm already.

"You must do exactly what your husband tells you, and then you won't go far wrong."

And he hurried her into the carriage.

Thérèse noticed the lawyer's outstretched hand, with its coarse dark nails.

"All's well that ends well," said he, and indeed he really meant it. If the case had gone any further he would not have got much out of it.

The family would have called in Maître Peyrecave of the Bordeaux Bar:
so everything was for the best.

Translated by ERIC SUTTON

Louis Aragon

AFTER TWENTY YEARS

TIME HAS refound the old monotonous cart
And harnessed the slow red oxen. Autumn again.
The sky digs hollows through the golden leaves;
Neon October, after the shudder, slumbers.

Carolingian days. We are coward kings,
Whose dreams are bound to the cattle's sluggish tread.
We hardly know there is death at the edge of the field,
The dawn's performance forgotten in the west.

We wander past the desolated dwelling,
No chains, no curtains, no weeping, no ideas,
Wraiths at high noon, revenants from daylight,
Ghosts of a life wherein one spoke of love.

Resume our habits after twenty years
In oblivion's cloak-room. A thousand prisoners
Make the old gestures over in the cells:
Nothing they do can make them hot or cold.

The era of stereotyped phrases starts again,
Man lays aside the ballad and the pride,
Repeating on the lips the idiot tune
Heard too often over the radio.

Twenty years. Scarcely room for childhood, which becomes,
—O does it not?—a bitter penitence
For our seniority, to see again
The little and innocent, setting out with us.

Ironic title: After Twenty Years.
Our life inscribed in full. The dream runs down
In those three mocking words of Dumas *père*,
Gone with the ghosts of those you used to love.

There is only one, most beautiful and kind,
Like russet October, immanent in the air;
The anguish and the hope, only my love—
I wait for her to write. I count the days.

You have had, of living, only the riper half,
O my wife, the deliberate happy years,
Stingily dealt us, but happy, when people we knew,
Who used to talk about us, would say, "Those two."

You have lost nothing of that bad young man
Effaced in darkness, gone like an omen, gone
Like a letter scribbled in sand on the edge of the sea;
You never knew this shadow, this nothingness.

A man will change as the clouds do over the sky;
Your tender hand that used to pass over my face,
Over the anxious frown that the forehead wore,
Lingering where my hair was turning gray,

O my love, O my love, you are all that is left
In existence now in the sad and twilight hour
Where I lose, at once, the thread of the poem I write,
And the thread of life, and the sound of the voice, and joy,

Because I wanted to tell you again, I love you,
And the sentence hurts, unless you are here to hear.
                    Translated by ROLFE HUMPHRIES

André Malraux

PREFACE TO FAULKNER'S *SANCTUARY*

FAULKNER KNOWS perfectly well that detectives do not exist; that the
police depend neither on psychological lore nor on intuitive perspicacity,

but on stool-pigeons; and that it is neither Moustachu nor Tapinois, modest thinkers of the quai des Orfèvres, who apprehend the murderer in his hideout, but the house dicks; for one has only to read the memoirs of chiefs of police to see that psychological insight is not the strong point of these characters, and that a "good cop" is simply one who has a superior organization of informers. Faulkner knows, too, that the gangster is first of all a whiskey merchant. *Sanctuary* is thus, with respect to atmosphere, a detective story without detectives; it is a crime novel whose gangsters are sordid, often cowardly and impotent. But the author gains from this a savagery which the milieu justifies, and is able, without conceding anything to the improbable, to make the reader accept acts of rape, lynching and assassination, the forms of violence which the plot imposes throughout the novel.

Doubtless it is incorrect to regard the plot, the pursuit of the criminal, as the essence of the detective story. In itself, the plot, like a game of chess, is artistically nil. Its importance derives from its being the most effective method of representing a certain ethical or poetic fact in all its intensity. It is worth what it multiplies.

What does it multiply in *Sanctuary?* An uneven, powerful, fiercely personal world, often not without vulgarity. A world in which man exists only to be crushed. There is no concept of "man" in Faulkner's world, there are no values and there is not even a psychology, despite the interior monologues of his first books. But there is a unique Fate working behind all these characters, whatever their psychology, like death behind a room of the incurably sick. An intense obsession flogs them to their collisions; none of them are able to soften it; and it remains behind them, always the same, and calls them instead of being called by them.

Such a world has long been material for fiction: even if rumors from America did not complacently repeat that alcohol plays an important role in Faulkner's personal myth—the relation between his universe and that of Poe or Hoffmann would be evident (similar psychoanalytic material, hates, horses, coffins, like obsessions). But Faulkner is separated from Poe by a different concept of the work of art; more precisely, the work of art was a reality to Poe, and a more important reality than the will to expression—doubtless it is this which at the moment separates him most from us. He created *objects*. The story, told, had for him the independent and limited existence of an easel painting.

I regard the weakening of the importance given to objects as the capital element in the transformation of our art. In painting, it is clear that a picture of Picasso is less and less a "canvas," and more and more the mark of some discovery, a stake left to indicate the place through which a restless genius passed; in literature, the dominance of the novel is significant, for, of all the arts (and I am not forgetting music), the novel is the least governable, in it, the sphere of the will is most limited. We realize how much Doestoyevsky and Balzac were dominated by *The Brothers Karamazov* and *Lost Illusions,* when we read these works after having read the beautiful, paralyzed novels of Flaubert. And the chief point is not that the artist is dominated, but that during the past fifty years he has had more and more freedom to choose what should dominate him and has come to regard the means of his art as a function of this freedom. Some great novels have had this primary meaning for their authors: the creation of the only force able to overwhelm them. And as Lawrence envelops himself in sexuality, Faulkner sinks into the irremediable.

A muffled, sometimes epic power takes hold of him when he brings a character face to face with the irremediable. It may even be that this is his only real subject, that what matters to him is to be able to crush the man. I would not be at all surprised if he were to declare that he often conceives his incidents before imagining his characters, that for him a story is not a process whose unfolding determines tragic situations, but, on the contrary, something produced by the clash and destruction of unknown persons, and that the only function of imagination is to logicize the bringing of these persons to the situation which was conceived first. It is the irremediable, whether symbolized by the deeply felt impotence of a slave (the young girl in the gangsters' hideout), or instanced by absurdities (the rape with a corn cob, an innocent man burnt, Popeye in flight, but stupidly condemned for an offense of which he is not guilty; in *As I Lay Dying,* the farmer who nurses his infected knee by coating it with cement, the astonishing monologue of hatred), which releases the taut exaltation that gives Faulkner his force; and it is their absurdity which gives his minor characters an almost comical intensity (the madame of the brothel with her dogs), comparable to those of Chtchédrine. I shall not compare Faulkner to Dickens, for even the American's minor figures are haunted by the sentiment which gives his work its value: hate. Here it is not a question of that struggle against one's own values, of that lust for fatality through which almost all the great artists, from Baudelaire to the half-blind Nietzsche who sang of light, expressed their deepest experience; it is a question of a psychological *state* on which practically the whole art of tragedy depends, and which has never been studied because it is outside the field of formal aesthetics—fascination. Just as the opium addict can reach his world only after he has taken the drug, so the tragic poet is able to articulate his vision only when in a specific state, of which the invariance indicates necessity. The tragic poet gives form to that which fascinates him, not in order to be delivered from its spell (the object which fascinates him may appear in the next work), but in order to transform it; for, expressing it along with other elements, he forces it to enter the relative universe of things known and already dominated. He does not protect himself against suffering by giving it form, but by giving it form in connection with other things, by reintroducing it into the world. The most profound fascination, that of the artist, derives its power from that which is at once the horror itself and the possibility of its being expressed.

Sanctuary is the intrusion of Greek tragedy into the detective story.

Translated by LIONEL ABEL

Paul Eluard

PABLO PICASSO

THE WEAPONS of slumber have hollowed in the night
Marvelous furrows which separate our heads.
Athwart a diamond every medal is false;
Under the bursting sky the earth is invisible.

The face of the heart has lost its colors
And the sun seeks us and the snow is blind.
If we leave it the horizon has wings
And our gaze from afar dissipates errors.

Translated by CLEMENT GREENBERG

Jean Giraudoux

ORATION IN MASSACHUSETTS

NIGHT IS FALLING.

Amid cheers, old gentlemen with tears in their eyes have led each French naval officer by the hand, impatiently yet without rushing him, till he occupies the center of his lighted circle—for a spotlight follows each of us. We have emerged from our old and somber continent as from a trench, blinded—the commander a little less so, because his spotlight is green—and now, locked in our circles where only men may enter, we live beyond any feminine touch. The attentions which women devise in France are shown to us by men, here, with the oldsters acting like little girls. It is not the banker's wife who wakes me up or the bishop's wife who sits next to me; it is the banker, or the bishop, in person. When we open our door somewhat suddenly, a white-haired professor, caught in the act of nailing a French cockade to it, flees in distress through the window and over the roofs. Every morning the surgeons show us the illustrated newspapers with our portraits as they would present a mirror to their patients, severely criticizing those in which we look thin. Or else an ancient colonel sends us his photographic life history as a sign of friendship, and in one of the pictures, because he was a swimming champion, he is nude. Each of our rooms is dedicated to a graduating class of the University. I happen to live in room 1888; and all those who passed their examination in that summer, just when I was born, have the right to come to see me unannounced, smuggling in their stranded friends.

Evening—every evening—brings a banquet. From the steps, one of our hosts advances toward each of us, bows, and in pairs we go up to the ballroom. The commander gives his arm to the president; for our captain, who stands two meters in his stockings, the tallest member of the Club was brought down by telegram from Canada (since in this country they count in feet and inches, we never get to know which of the two is taller). The third officer, myself, gets the Bostonian who is reputed in the group to be most passionately in love with France—no matter who he is, today this triumph is his due. One is a colossus with a low, stubborn forehead; his arm trembles under my hand. One is a timid, worried little man who has to make a speech; two giant friends find it as he undresses, pick it up and bring it straight to me like a bottle of old whisky, so as not to disturb his ideas and his words. Others are lawyers, geographers, teachers; they see France as perfection in their business—a speech without words, a country spread on four strata of equal thickness, a child showing its soul. One is a jeweller: France to him is a large diamond of sparkling luster.

We go upstairs. The young people withdraw, even from me although I am of the same age; youth in a Frenchman seems an old and stable quality to them, like beauty and goodness in others. Magnesium lights flash at every step; the American air shrivels or blazes under these first bursts of the European war. Fathers and uncles touch our sabers, our medals—everything that is of metal on us, the men from another planet. They touch the iron hand of the commander, and then his other hand which is of flesh; and their eyes grow moist. From the second floor, veterans in uniform throw blue iris at us. Over there, they think the iris is our national flower, and only the dead of the War of Independence offered us the true fleur-de-lys this morning in the cemetery, on their graves; the dead know all. . . . One iris hits the face of my guide. He shudders, as the herald of the Prince of Wales or the King of England would shudder if lightly touched by three true ostrich feathers or a real unicorn; he squeezes my hand, he tells me: "I wish . . . I wish the German planes would finally bomb our cities!"

We reach the hall. The galleries are jammed; the whole town wants to see us dine on our platform in the center. Glasses are set for us alone, for the state is a prohibition one, and heaped at our three places is that bread and wine upon which Frenchmen feed. Every time we raise a glass to our lips, according to whether it is white or red, we reap the smiles—with us, that is a custom, but with them it is instinct—of all blondes or all brunettes.

This being the concert hall, each of the huge bays bears the escutcheon of a German musician. In the bay of Schubert, the most distant, the orchestra has taken refuge. It will play only solo flute pieces tonight, because the flutists of the whole universe are Frenchmen. In Mozart's bay, just before us, at the distace at which millionaires see and hear the world, sit the bankers and their families. Those who have a French name or ancestor wave their hands at us and laugh more often, as if we had to recognize their parentage from their nails and teeth. Others who have names like Schmidt, Mayer, Meyer, are made fun of by their married daughters and draw visiting cards which for this one day they had engraved with their Christian names only: Teddy, Billy. In the Schumann bay shines the face of a young woman who belongs somewhere else, listens instead of looking, is called to from the parterre, understands nothing.

Below, there are family reunions of the students killed in France, with uncles, aunts and the most distant cousins in mourning, but the proud parents in full dress. There is the veteran from Oklahoma who has been to all the wars on foot, to the War of the Secession, to the Spanish War, to the Mexican War—and who arrived early for the German one. There are the Ecuadorean students at Harvard, girded with blue sashes which on holidays float, barely slanting, on the Equator itself. There is the famous author of *Lazy Days in Patagonia,* who bustles about, strides over rows of seats and upsets them, together with the ladies occupying them. There are the ill-bred rich children—the others are in bed—who look without speaking a word, very straight, wise and tender. There—from what bay, from what German despair did it escape?—a bird crosses the hall unhesitatingly, from an old master to a master it knows, and it lightly touches my neighbor who takes the occasion to tell me:

"I wish little American girls were being crucified—little bodies laid out in the coolest dresses. Their pacifist fathers would shake them and understand at last!"

Questions, written and oral, arrive from all sides, for every fold or number or border on our pea-jackets is a mystery. They study the uniforms worn by us who come from the war as the Parisians studied the face of the first soldier come out of a battle. No dog-eared page in a book ever stirred more interest than my falling collar, the only one in the mission. Did I get a bullet in the neck? Did I serve in Egypt? Is it a whim? Am I one to follow my fancies? What have I got on me that has been to the war? All heads are raised, all cigars are put out and lighted anew, at the German bullet that makes the rounds, tamed.

A delegation appears from the town which adopted Péronne. They have maps of Péronne, plans and photographs; but they would like to hear from a Frenchman himself if their godchild (though its sufferings would make up for everything) was loved in France, or detested, or just indifferent. I reassure them; while I am from the Centre, I used to adore Péronne; I even used to believe that Jeanne Hachette was born there. I disclose this to them, and they leave, happy.

There are the hundred, somewhat sad faces of those who vowed to bring back a French officer for the week-end to their wives and children —who are already getting the ancient furniture out and the tame grouse. But they are no longer hopeful. There, smiling at me, is the American pastor who preaches best about Death. When he talks of Death, his words somehow become live butterflies alighting on the mortal listeners, not on their bodies but on their souls. You can feel the soul ripple and bend. He will talk presently, and you will get his speech. He makes signs to me which alight on my eyeballs. . . .

The dinner is drawing to a close. The war journal is handed out, which all the Club members have asked for; from now on, at last, they will know at every moment what the French as a whole have done a year ago, or two years ago. But this is no longer enough for them; they want

to find out what every single Frenchman did at every hour. They question
each of us right to his face and compare the answers. What did we do
on the third of August, on the fifteenth of June? Now and then, without
having the slightest notion, they hit upon one of those sensitive days one
does not speak about; and then they plunge into our very hearts like
customs officers diving into a trunk in which a man is hidden. Sometimes
a day has in all these three years no other anniversary than days of peace
and quiet, and they are a little disappointed. But today they are in luck;
I confess all, and I even have good reasons to remember:

"A year ago?" the jeweller insists.

"A year ago? What day was that? That was the longest day of the year.
My birthday was coming up soon, at the very peak of summer like a portrait nailed below, just below, the frieze. It was a day on which a moon
and a sun went bathing, alone; a long, transparent sun—I'd know it if
I ever saw it again—pierced right through by its own rays. Suddenly a
wind came up, then a squall; an object struck me in the face; there was
no blood—it was no bullet, it was a visiting card. I picked it up and read
the name: it was the card of my lieutenant, missing for two months,
whom for two months we had believed in France, playing his adored
backgammon. Twilight came; with his former orderly I sneaked in front
of our lines and there he was, half buried; the orderly recognized him
by his new leggings. From his pockets, slit by a prowler, fell letters and
another visiting card, all ready to call me at the next strong wind. . . ."

He says nothing.

"Two years ago?"

"That was again my birthday. But this time it was night. Sleeping
near me was Juéry, who had come out to the trenches to see me and
answered, 'Guest,' every time a patrol leader shook him. Small stars
lodged among the big ones and did not move any more. My sentry was
sleeping too, in a shadow bigger than himself; I crawled up to him and
seized him by the shoulders: 'And if I was the Turks, what would you
do now?' He struggled, without being able to free his arms; and he stammered, 'I'd—I'd kill you, sir.' "

He says nothing.

"And three years ago?"

"I was fishing, at Chelles."

"What?"

And suddenly my neighbor remembers, excitedly, that three years ago
there was peace. He upsets the little vase with the flags—unfortunately,

for him, they had poured water into it. He flares up; he hopes that at least a submarine will be able to cruise up the Hudson to Albany and bombard a certain house he knows there, with a portrait of the Kaiser.

But the orchestras cease playing, and the musicians, who in America prefer words even to music—since music is a precise sound while words are a call of strangeness—have thrown their instruments back into the corridor. The cinematographers stop; you see nothing any more but a white square; miraculously, the cinema operator listens. The ceiling opens, and heads bend down through the trap-doors, still far away and prudently, because of dizziness. The entire hall is hypnotized, as every hall and every family in the United States as soon as a speech is made. . . . The president rises. . . . With a gesture, he turns the spotlights away which then direct their beams at the top windows, splashing, dazzling people in the night. . . . He opens his mouth. . . . A second before the miracle, a man who speaks! . . . He speaks!

But why does a president not know more about the perils and rules of speech? Why, in his very first phrase, does he fling a challenge at so many kindly ears? Why, without warning, does he utter the one word which says all, anticipates all:

"France . . ." he says. . . .

He cannot continue, either. All his listeners stand up; all mount their chairs, their tables; at one stroke the thickness of this human tapestry is doubled. They shout. They whistle. In a second the spoken word is written on the caps of children, on the flags, which are waved. Beautiful heads heavy with blonde tresses, from which thoughts evaporate less quickly, are slowly inclined; bald heads wave in delirium. That name, ever present and yet never expected—no other in America could equal it today. Those frenetics will not sit down again until they please, and it will not help to shout other cries at them: "country," "love"—or to seek an antidote at random among the enthusiasms of the past—"Montjoie," "Washington"—or even to shout his secret into the ear of each. The officers rise too; and so does Sir Beltie, the consul of New South Wales, who is deaf and wants to ask his choking neighbor a question. The president has turned to him; he seizes an instant of comparative calm and hurriedly, seeming to want to talk for Sir Beltie alone, to have nothing to say but one single phrase without interest to all the rest but of supreme importance to New South Wales, he resumes—in an almost basso voice, since indeed Sir Beltie will never understand:

"In France, every day . . ."

The same furor grips the hall. They could not stop the president till the fourth word, for he spoke in one breath, but so much the worse, or so much the better, for the words "every" and "day," haphazardly chosen in such a triumph. The doors open, and a packed throng rolls over the Irish ushers, sons and brothers of policemen, who atavistically attempt to resist. The spectators at the ceiling, less rigid now and better balanced, hang down—kept up in the sky by self-sacrificing friends who clutch their feet—and beat boxwood sticks against each other.

Eventually, the president realizes his impotence. These twenty thousand guards will never let him get away with his word, and he makes a sign of resignation: he will start over again, but with another phrase. Suspiciously, the crowd falls silent but remains standing. He soothes them.

"Friends! My dear and true friends . . ."

He is pale; he hesitates; in pity, three or four true friends sit down. Then, in wrongly spaced language, he says:

"Friends, do you—not see that every—day the face of—France grows paler?"

All three of us, caught unawares by this phrase, have paled. There is no glance that does not turn to us, and then, from shame, immediately leave us. Ashamed of their frenzy, all steal back to their places. The blond-tressed heads bow, close their eyelids, see at the inside of their blue ground a France in human shape growing pale, dying. Then the eyes are lifted and return to our faces. Into our faces the blood rises gradually; they turn pink—they turn quite red under these thousands of glances—one of them turns scarlet. Then the applause begins again, without shouts, without whistles this time, joyous, interminable, and our neighbors force us to rise, to salute—still quite strained, bruised by this blood which came back too fast—immortals. . . .

Translated by E. B. ASHTON

Yvan Goll

JOHN LANDLESS LEADS THE CARAVAN

HAVE I a hundred years since or
A hundred thousand tramped these wastes
With a track more vulnerable
Than fire of a sun that hastes?

My camel leads the caravan
Through centuries of rusted sand
To find as might any profane wind
The key to the oblivion land

My great grandparents long since
Have worked this sea and no less
Could their passing shadow have brought
To yoke the ancient nothingness

Although life's mortal light
Would bring their hearts about by day
Still they had a candle lit
For antique love to find the way

In me their ancient skeleton
Of gold calcined by the years
And my new flesh tries as it may
To fill it with heavy cares

I hear the red wolf that howls
On the cavern of my blood
Cracking the bones at nightfall
Of the dream again abroad

Sail on sail on slow dromedaries
And traverse eternity
From the quaternary dawns
To the tomb's near certainty

My kin with limbs of gold and ebony
Die of thirst and of hope the most
At both my wrists I open the veins
That may prove to them a host

O wish that my love would rot
And never see light again
If by this final sacrifice
A young god be born in men

If without Alp to water
From the desert's lifeless skin
The freshness of a rose should rise
And a cloak of sudden green

No bitch will I need to chase
The hunger of a jackal
Enough that my faith revive
And the aurora of my choral

Offering those who covet
Slow camel and proud lion
Salt from my weak moist hand
The strength of my religion
Translated by WILLIAM CARLOS WILLIAMS

Antoine de Saint Exupéry

FLIGHT OVER THE SAHARA

A MOOD OF lethargy and of daydreams came over Bernis. Viewed from such altitude, the earth seemed bound in frozen calm. Yellow Sahara beaches ribboned a blue sea, like an unending pavement. The coastline had a tendency to drift towards the right, slipping athwart him, but Bernis, with a practiced hand corrected the drift and held the due alignment.

At each bend of Africa he canted the plane a little. Dakar was still some fourteen hundred miles away.

Before him lay the disaffected tract, a waste of dazzling whiteness, where, here and there, a naked rock stood out. The wind had winnowed the sand in places into symmetrical hummocks. The plane was wedged in a zone of stagnant air, as in a lode; it neither plunged nor rocked at all and, far below, the landscape too appeared becalmed. Hugged by the wind, the plane advanced in time alone. Port Etienne, his first halt, was a landmark not in space, but time. Bernis glanced at his watch. Six hours remained of immobility and silence; and then he would slough off his chrysalis, the cockpit, and step into a brand-new world.

Bernis observed the watch that worked this miracle, then the rev-counter. If the dial hand, now so steady for the moment, dropped from that figure and a failing engine betrayed him to the sand, time and distance would take on new meanings, meanings beyond his present understanding. Meanwhile, he was a traveler in the fourth dimension.

That queer feeling of oppression was nothing new to him; it visited us all sometimes. In our eyes a horde of pictures came and went; and then one picture dominated all, rendering in their true volume all the dunes and sunlight, and the silence. Another world had settled down upon us. We found that we were weak, our gestures only strong enough, no more, to put the gazelles to flight across the darkness. Our voices carried a bare two hundred yards and could reach no human ear. Some time or other each of us had come down on that unknown planet.

There time became too vast to fit the rhythms of life. At Casablanca we watched the hours advance, thinking of our appointments, and each new hour brought us a change of mood. Flying, we changed our climate every half hour or so, and changed our skins as well. But, fallen in the desert, we reckoned time in weeks.

Our fellow-airmen rescued us. Were we too weak to move, they hauled us up into the cockpit, arms strong as steel withdrew us from the timeless world into their own. "How little of myself I know!" Bernis reflected, poised in mid-air above the vast unknown. For what qualities would thirst and loneliness, or the Arabs' savagery, bring out in him? And his arrival at Port Etienne abruptly retarded for a month or more? "Courage I shall not need," he added inwardly.

For all these things were pure abstractions. So, when a young pilot tries his 'prentice hand at looping, it is no world of solid bodies, the least of which would smash his brains out, that he whirls about his head in perilous proximity; rather a dream-world of phantom trees and fluid walls. Was courage needed, Bernis?

And yet, when he felt the engine give a tremor, something tugged at his heart; the dark unknown might suddenly arise, and oust it.

An hour had passed and now the hostile bay and headland gave place to neutral Africa, discovered, vanquished by wings.

None the less each stage of the tract that lay ahead held its own mystery and menace. Some seven hundred miles still lay in front, like a gigantic blanket that he must roll up, yard by yard, towards him.

Port Etienne to Cape Juby. Mail arrived 4.30 P.M.

Port Etienne to Saint Louis. Mail left 4.45.

Saint Louis to Dakar. Mail left Port Etienne 4.45 will instruct proceed by night.

An easterly wind was blowing from the heart of the Sahara and the sand rose in sallow whirlwinds. At dawn a pale and swollen sun, distorted by the torrid mist, had crouched on the horizon, a pale and flaccid bubble of light. But, as it rose towards the zenith, it gradually condensed and, taking form, grew to a disk of fire, a red-hot goad searing his neck.

An east wind. The air was calm, almost cold, when he took off at Port Etienne but at three hundred feet up he ran into a lava-stream of heat. The readings rose abruptly.

Temperature. Oil. 120°.

Temperature. Water. 110°.

Obviously he must climb, five thousand feet, six thousand maybe, to get above the sandstorm. Obviously! But five minutes' zooming would see his ignition and valves burnt out. And then, to climb—easier said than done. On this springless air the machine floundered, sank as in a quicksand.

An east wind, a blinding wind. The sun was blurred by yellow spirals; only at intervals his wan face fleered and flared across them. Bernis could only see the earth directly beneath him, and even so!

Was he zooming, nose-diving, banking? There was no knowing. He struck the ceiling at three hundred feet or so. Nothing doing there. Better try the ground floor.

On the ground level the windstream came from the north. That was better, anyhow. He trailed an arm outside the cockpit, like a man seated in a swift canoe, who finger-rakes cool river water.

Temperature. Oil. 110°.

Temperature. Water. 95°.

Cool as a river? Well, only by comparison. Each undulation of the soil let fly an aerial fisticuff, setting the plane bumping. Maddening, too, the lack of visibility.

At Cape Timeris, however, the wind came down to the ground level and there was no evading it. A whiff of burning rubber. The magneto? Or was it the packing? The rev-counter flickered, went ten points back. "So you're butting in, too, damn you!"

Temperature. Water. 115°.

Impossible to gain a dozen yards. He spotted a dune approaching, got ready for the bump and glanced at the manometer. Up she goes! The wind eddy caught him above the dune. He steered with the stick right back, but, he knew, it couldn't go on like that for long. His hands were balancing the plane in an unstable equilibrium, like an overflowing cup.

Thirty feet under the wheels North Africa reeled out its beaches, sand and salterns, like the ballast on a permanent way.

Revolutions. 1520.

The next air-pocket landed on the pilot like a boxing-glove. Some fifteen miles ahead was a French outpost, the only one. But—how to get there?

Temperature. Water. 120°.

Dunes, rocks and sandpits were fed into a mangle, flattened out. "More power to them!"

Outlines deployed, dilated and closed up again. Wheels skimmed a world in rags and tatters. A clump of rocks seemed crawling up, black snails; then, presto!, they accelerated; he pounced on them, scattered them to the winds.

Revolutions. 1430.

"Well! If my number's up . . . !" He tapped a steel plate and burnt his finger. The radiator spouted wisps of steam. The airplane seemed heavy as an overladen barge.

Revolutions. 1400.

Only a foot under his wheels the sand was belching up in spadefuls, volleys of gold-dust, for a grand finale. Then suddenly he leapt a dune, the outpost hove in sight. With a sigh of relief Bernis switched off. Just in the nick of time.

The swiftly moving landscape slowed down, stopped dead. A world in dissolution came to itself again.

A French blockhouse in the Sahara. An old sergeant welcomed Bernis in, laughing for sheer delight at meeting a compatriot. Twenty Senegalese presented arms. For a white man meant a sergeant at the lowest estimate; if he were young, a lieutenant.

"Morning, Sergeant!"

"Come in! Come right in! I tell you I'm glad to see you . . . I'm from Tunis."

He poured it all pell-mell into Bernis' ears—his boyhood, the story of his life, his soul. One small table furnished the room; photographs were pinned about the walls.

"My family, yes. I haven't met them all as yet, but next year I mean to go to Tunis. That one? That's my chum's girl friend. It used to stand on this table and he was always gassing away about her. When he died, I took the photo over and stuck it there; I hadn't a girl of my own, you see."

"I'd like a drink, Sergeant."

"Here you are! Glad it's wine for once. When the Captain came, I hadn't any. That must be five months ago, he came. After that I mumped like a sick owl day after day; I just couldn't help it. Why, I even put in for a transfer, I was that sick with myself! . . . How do I pass the time? Well; I write letters every night; I can't sleep and I've got candles. But when the mail comes in every six months, my letters won't do as answers, so I start all over again."

Bernis went on to the parapet, accompanied by the old soldier, for a smoke. Under the moon the desert shamelessly exposed its nakedness. What was the old fellow supposed to be watching out here, in this outpost? The moon, presumably.

"So you're the sergeant in charge of the stars?"

"Look here, don't say no, try my baccy. I've got some now. Hadn't any, though, when the Captain came."

Bernis learnt all about the Captain and Lieutenant. He could have recited the besetting sins and qualities of each; one, for instance, was a gambler, the other too easygoing. And he grew aware that a young lieutenant's visit to an old sergeant at the back of beyond leaves behind it almost the memory of a lovers' meeting.

"He told me all about the stars."

"Yes," said Bernis, "he made them over to you."

Now it was Bernis' turn to tell about them. When the sergeant learnt how far away they are, he thought of Tunis which, likewise, was very far away. After he had been shown the Pole Star, he swore to spot it next time by the cut of his jib; he had only to keep it a little to his left. And then he thought of Tunis, so near at hand.

"And we're dropping towards that cluster over there at a terrific speed."

Whereat the sergeant steadied himself against the wall, just in time!

"Why, you know everything!"

"Don't you believe it, Sergeant! Why, I remember another sergeant saying to me: 'Ain't you ashamed, a gentleman like you, that's had a good education, to muck up your right-turns like that?' "

"Why? That's nothing to be ashamed of; it ain't so easy as all that." Flattering unction.

"Look, Sergeant, look! It's your sentrylamp!"

He pointed to the moon.

"Do you know that song, Sergeant?

"It's raining, pretty shepherdess . . ."

He hummed the tune.

"Don't I know! They sing it at Tunis."

"How does it go on? I want to remember . . ."

"Let's see . . . Wait a bit . . .

> "Take your white sheep home again,
>   Out of the rain, out of the rain."

"Good work, Sergeant! Now I've got it!

> "Listen, listen, in the woods,
>   The rain is coming down in floods.
>   The storm is at your heels. . . ."

"That's the stuff!" observed the sergeant.

They understood the same things.

"Daylight, Sergeant. Let's get on to the job."

"Right, sir!"

"Give us the plug-wrench."

"Sure! Here it is."

"Get a purchase here with the pliers."

"Sure! Just you give the word and I'll do what I'm told."

"You see, Sergeant, it didn't amount to much. Now I'm off."

The sergeant gravely contemplated a young god, fallen out of the blue, preparing to take the air again.

He had come just to remind him of a song, of Tunis, and of himself. From what far paradise beyond the sands did these gay messengers sink soundlessly to earth?

"Good-by, Sergeant."

"Good-by."

The sergeant's lips moved, but he could not construe his thought, or put it into words—that for six months to come a memory of love would fill his heart.

Translated by STUART GILBERT

Jacques Maritain

ON BEAUTY

IF BEAUTY DELIGHTS the mind, it is because beauty is essentially a certain excellence of perfection in the proportion of things to the mind. Hence the three conditions assigned to it by St. Thomas: integrity, because the mind likes being; proportion, because the mind likes order and likes unity; lastly and above all brightness or clarity, because the mind likes light and intelligibility. A certain splendour is indeed according to all the Ancients the essential character of beauty,—*claritas est de ratione pulchritudinis, lux pulchrificat, quia sine luce omnia sunt turpia,*—but it is a splendour of intelligibility: *splendor veri,* said the Platonists, *splendor ordinis,* said St. Augustine, adding that "unity is the form of all beauty"; *splendor formae,* said St. Thomas with a metaphysician's precision of language: for *form,* that is to say the principle determining the peculiar perfection of everything which is, constituting and completing things in their essence and their qualities, the ontological secret, so to speak, of their innermost being, their spiritual essence, their operative mystery, is above all the peculiar principle of intelligibility, the peculiar *clarity* of every thing. Every form, moreover, is a remnant or a ray of the creative Mind impressed upon the heart of the being created. All order and proportion, on the other hand, are the work of the mind. So, to say with the schoolmen that beauty is the *splendour of form shining on the proportioned parts of matter* is to say that it is a lightning of mind on a matter intelligently arranged. The mind rejoices in the beautiful because in the beautiful it finds itself again: recognizes itself, and comes into contact with its very own light. This is so true that they especially perceive and particularly relish the beauty of things who, like St. Francis of Assisi, for example, know that they emanate from a mind and refer them to their Author.

Every sensible beauty, no doubt, implies a certain delight of the eye or the ear or the imagination: but there can be no beauty unless the mind also is in some way rejoiced. A beautiful colour "washes the eye" as a powerful scent dilates the nostrils: but of these two "forms" or qualities only colour is called "beautiful," because being received, as opposed to the perfume, in a sense capable of disinterested knowledge, it can be, even through its purely sensible brilliance, an object of joy to the mind. Again, the more highly developed a man's culture becomes, the more spiritual grows the brilliance of the form which ravishes him.

It is important, however, to observe that in the beauty which has been termed connatural to man and is peculiar to human art this brilliance of form, however purely intelligible it may be in itself, is apprehended *in the sensible and by the sensible,* and not separately from it. The intuition of . artistic beauty so stands at the opposite pole from the abstraction of scientific truth. For in the former case it is precisely through the apprehension of sense that the light of being penetrates to the mind.

The mind then, spared the last effort of abstraction, rejoices without labour and without discussion. It is excused its customary task, it has not to extricate something intelligible from the matter in which it is buried and then step by step go through its various attributes; like the stag at the spring of running water, it has nothing to do but drink, and its drink the clarity of being. Firmly fixed in the intuition of sense, it is irradiated by an intelligible light granted to it of a sudden in the very sensible in which it glitters; and it apprehends this light not *sub ratione veri,* but rather *sub ratione delectabilis,* by the happy exercise it procures for it and the succeeding joy in appetite, which leaps out to every good of the soul as its own peculiar object. Only afterwards will it more or less successfully analyse in reflection the causes of such joy.

Translated by J. F. SCANLAN

Jean Cocteau

THE RUINS OF PARIS

TIME HAS AN elastic quality. Man can stretch it to suit his purpose and, if he so desires, he can change a winter hour into a summer hour. Time is like the instantaneous century of a dream, like the orchestra playing in London, which is carried on the air waves to France so quickly that we hear it before the orchestra leader who is conducting it in England. Time is a system of folds which only death can unfold. How long did Persicaire gaze at the bust? Mornings and evenings, evenings and twilights had come and gone. Twilight was falling. We extricated ourselves from the sticky substance of our dreams. Had I been sleeping on my feet? What was wrong with Persicaire? From one room to the other we heard the iron cock crowing. Persicaire became as pale as death. He caught me by the elbow and dragged me to the window. We drew aside the curtains. Then he said: "I was sure of it!"

The Place de la Madeleine was in ruins. It reminded one of the Forum in Rome in its atrocious disorder of a ransacked house. All the buildings except our own, protected by some magic charm, were stripped of their fronts, wide open to the world, showing the remains of shops, banks, abandoned rooms, apartments. Safes, baths and armchairs hovered over the edges of precipices, and doors by some miracle stood upright without support. A deluge of plaster and jets of flame divided the wreckage between them. Zebra-like stripes on fragments of walls, kiosks and cornices still intact showed the extent of their work of destruction. Where was the source of this destruction? Why, as if under a spell, had we not heard of it? Who or what was responsible? Man? Lightning? The stars? Through my unbroken windows, petrified with fear, we contemplated this profane confusion of weeds, broken columns and drain-pipes. All that could be seen of the Madeleine was this kind of rectangular forum. How deep were its crevasses and how extensive? Should I ever find the invisible room again? Was the Potomak still alive?

In the room behind us strange people had just begun to move about, their faces concealed by sinister looking gas masks. They carried forks attached to electric batteries. Whenever these forks brushed against us, their owners moved aside politely. But one felt that they would have let us die of hunger rather than come to our assistance. They did not speak our language. *We did not interest them.*

We realized that they knew about the heap of golden muck and that we owed our lives to it. Obviously the fears of Persicaire were well founded, and this gold was the cause of the disaster.

A leader was shouting orders. The masked men executed them. Sparks were crackling from their forks.

"Come," I said to Persicaire, "come quickly. There is not a minute to lose. We must find out. Our city! Our streets . . . our friends!"

We descended the stairs.

My stairway turned into a deserted courtyard. Its twisted ironwork was a formidable trap, full of gaps. Pools of dirty water complicated our route. We went up hill and down dale. We got around grottoes, we clambered over piles of stone and trunks of trees.

Quick! Quick! Ours was the speed of dreams. Gradually we plunged deeper and could no longer see the sky.

I was guided by a curious smell. A sickening smell which was growing stronger. After an interminable descent, the smell became so strong that we hesitated. Persicaire struck some matches. We perceived catacombs.

We heard hymns. "These are the Jews," said Persicaire. "Look, they are making designs on the rocks of fish and six-pointed stars. Follow me."

In this labyrinth the monstrous smell spread its tentacles and filled every gallery. From second to second it increased and grew; *it was coming to life.* Suddenly we came into its very midst. The smell came from a crypt and took form on the remains of a platform, infecting the shades. Just as I was beginning to understand (Persicaire already understood), a fearful thing happened. A loud speaker, still functioning, was telling a story. But it was difficult to make out the words. It was a loud voice jabbering from beyond the grave.

The invisible corpse was decomposing between the tangled boards of the old platform where the Potomak had died. This smell almost made him visible and brought him back from the tomb. The filthy smell was only too familiar! It was the smell of gangrene, of dead horses, their bellies swollen with wind, losing their entrails. The smell of dirt and unwashed feet. The smell of powder. The smell of stinking bombs. The smell of rotting flesh.

It was the smell of the field of glory, so dear to heroes.

Translated by ERNEST BOYD

Georges Bernanos

RETURN TO HUMANITY

THOSE WHO DESPAIR for my country should first despair for the world in which they live, for it is this world which is crumbling. France is not responsible for this collapse. No intelligent man would dare seriously to claim that this world is the creation of the French genius. The youngest schoolboy knows that French genius is a genius of logic and balance, at once individual and universal. He knows it not because it has been taught him, but because he can convince himself of it, since my country's legacy has been deeded to the world. French culture is a monument completely realised, a structure balanced from base to pinnacle. It has long since ceased to belong only to those who built it, because it was made for all. It is a home, not a fortress, one of the high places of refuge open to men of good will regardless of their race or color—a meeting-place, a hearth.

We have never tried to make of this hearth the only ideal home for mankind; we could not hope to succeed where the Greeks themselves had failed. But we had the right to think that after having loved and honored it, men would not abandon it save for one more nearly perfect; that this great effort of reason and love would not be lost. Yet that is what appears to be happening. Perhaps it has already happened. Some say that we did not defend our culture. But we did not foresee the need to defend it, since we had never intended to impose it on others. Only a liar or an idiot would pretend that the inconsiderable armies of Louis XIV made Europe submit to French classicism.

Civilised humanity chose it because they found it good; because with it they could breathe more freely. We took no precaution whatsoever to hold it back, our gates were flung wide open. Moreover, this *esprit Gaulois* was no new thing; we never flattered ourselves that we had created it out of "whole cloth." The greatest compliment that could be paid us would be to say that at no time did any man, truly human, feel himself a stranger to that spirit. But men have fallen so low today, have so lost every understanding of eternal verities, that they freely reproach us for not having defended with machine-guns the *Discourse on Method,* the *Thoughts* of Pascal, or the tragedies of Racine.

We used to think that our culture had nothing to fear from anyone, since it was the common property of all. Similarly, we could not foresee that Germanism would attack it in the name of the Viking and his Saxons; that a pagan mythology would inspire misguided unfortunates with the barbarous idea of destroying for no reason (merely to affirm the vigor of their arms and their loins) those precious things, loved by all, that were the masterworks of centuries. That the existence of such monsters was possible, we never doubted. But we thought that there would always be opposed to them the solidarity of wise and free men. A sentry is not stationed on the bank of a clear fresh spring, which is free to all, to slake all thirsts. We had entrusted the better part of our heritage to the protection of Liberty.

I once wrote, "France is silent." Of course she was silent, for to whom could she still talk her language? Our tradition, so rich in humanity, is powerless before inhumanity. They say that France betrayed herself. But she had long since grievously betrayed herself when, during the course of the last century, she tried with such tragic awkwardness to keep her spirit of logic and balance in tune with the new universal rhythm, when she tried desperately to understand a world that did not want to be understood, but overcome. We did what we could. We honestly gave what we had to give. It is true that we, ourselves, had received much in the course of the ages. What we have received, we have magnificently repaid—we owe nothing.

Whatever may be his hope for the future, the man of spirit and intelligence knows that our seventeenth century marked the last great advance made by western civilization. The French spirit has had no legitimate heir, and no really impartial culture has as yet succeeded ours. After us the world spent itself in well-being; it organised itself not to know but to enjoy. The world thought it was being enriched when it was impoverishing itself of everything that made it rich, all the riches really common to men. This hideous logic of "well-being" has brought it to the pitiable and ridiculous condition we now see it in. Incapable of emptying its gigantic warehouses, gorged with wealth which its greed refuses to dispose of without realising from the least crumb a profit, prisoner of an economic system which expands production without limits, yet which shuts off one by one all of its outlets, the world prefers to destroy its stocks with gunfire rather than admit its error and return to humanity.

I despair of this world, or rather, I never hoped for anything from it. I see it throw itself into bondage and I laugh when it tries to prove that it does so by free choice. I have been through much sadness and when I think of these past months it seems to me that I have gone through Hell, itself. But that black night is behind me now. In an excess of humiliation, in a superabundance of shame, I have ended by becoming aware of my country. If, like many others, I had refused to acknowledge this humiliation, parleyed with shame, and rejected the part of dishonor, I would find myself in the midst of an intolerable contradiction. I would be like those unhappy men of Vichy who, in their own vomit, are bound to the wheel by the chain around their necks. To justify one's country is most usually a sly way of justifying one's self. Besides, it is much easier to justify one's country than to save it—the cost is much cheaper. I have not tried to justify my country; my memory of having been one of her soldiers is still too vivid for me to become her pleader, now, in my declining years.

It matters little to me how this may appear, or even how France may actually be today—I want to think, and to think only, of the imperishable value of the trust with which she has been endowed. Who took it from her hands? No one. Therefore, God has not withdrawn Himself. The tradition which has been transmitted, the testimony of which stands, retains its inestimable price. Regardless of her shame, if she still exalts the Spirit with which she has been incarnated, even though she may have betrayed it, she bears its stamp on her features . . . the image and resemblance of Liberty.

Translated by HERMAN G. WEINBERG

SPAIN

INTRODUCTION

By Angel Flores

THE SPANISH WRITERS of the past generation are more or less familiar to the English-reading public. The *opera omnia* of Blasco Ibañez, at least eight works of Unamuno, a dozen or so of Baroja, three or four of Valle Inclán, two of Azorín . . . are available in translation. The creative achievements of these authors belong, for the most part, to the turn of the century. Grouped under the general classification "Generation of 1898," their works naturally reflect the crisis, the setting of the sun on the Spanish domains. Most of their ideology and expression is permeated with political, philosophical or social tendencies: Blasco Ibañez attacking the Church and the Monarchy, Unamuno positing his Unamunism, a sort of Nietzschean-mysticism tinged by Kierkegaard, Baroja raising an anarchic cry, Azorín endeavoring to grasp, in a rather impressionistic manner, the hues and temperature of Spain. Perhaps the one least concerned at first with immediate social problems was Valle Inclán, although in his latest work and in the last decade of his life he proved to be the closest friend of Republican Spain and perhaps the most respected by the younger generation. At all events, the "Generation of 1898" was primarily concerned with ideas and états d'esprit, with themes, rather than with literary methods.

As the twentieth century proceeds, the names become less familiar. Curiously enough, English readers, so avid for knowledge of the latest European utterance, have neglected the expression of the Hispanic Peninsula. A few may know Ramón Pérez de Ayala, who began his career in 1910, and still fewer Gabriel Miró, whose really important creative work began about 1916. Pérez de Ayala is one of the most noteworthy novelists of contemporary Spain, and three of his books have been rendered into English. Gabriel Miró has two books in English, only one of which has been published, with slight circulation, in the United States. Miró died in the Spring of 1930, and it is only now that critics are becoming aware of his influence on the younger prose-writers of Spain. Especially from 1916 till the very year of his death, he worked at developing his style into a magnificently personal instrument, quite distant from the pompous and inane (but still rampantly popular) manner of the nineteenth-century orators and rhetoricians. His choice of words and his careful study of vocabulary have had potent reverberations.

Another influence—Ramón Gómez de la Serna. Born in 1891, Ramón began his literary career at the age of thirteen. His first important novel appeared in 1917. About that same year he discovered a very personal mode of expression, almost a new literary genre, which he baptized *greguerías*, "clamorings," "jab-berings"—a kind of metaphoric maxim or aphorism without any moralizing or academic heaviness. This type of writing is somewhat akin to the Max Jacob of *Le Cornet à Des*, to the Logan Pearsall Smith of *Trivia*, to Chamfort, Cocteau and Chesterton.

Thus Miró and Ramón represent two significant directions in contemporary Spanish prose: Miró's, more traditional, leads to an aesthetic fathoming of vocabulary; Ramón's to a devertebration of the sentence and the paragraph. to an athletic sense of composition—keen observation of details, juxtaposition of images and metaphors and careless but exciting development of pattern.

Then, again, by the gradual obliteration of the Pyrenees, innumerable "isms" and techniques of post-World War I penetrated the Spanish Peninsula. Some writers show the influence of Joseph Conrad, while others resemble Giraudoux, Cocteau, Proust or the ubiquitous James Joyce.

If there are only two books by Miró in English and one by Ramón, the younger men, with the exception of Ramón Sender and Federico García Lorca, are hardly known in English. And yet the between-wars period was unquestion-ably a renaissance in Spanish letters. This period was remarkable for its wide gamut of expression in which the utterly sophisticated rubbed elbows with the utterly proletarian; art-for-art's-sakism alternated with dynamic social forces, and psychological meanderings and aphoristic niceties were frequently cut short by political cries and realistic explosions.

The monthly magazine, *Revista de Occidente*, edited by Ortega y Gasset, was a most influential forum; new writers were discovered and new literary and philosophical values were imported, some extremely significant, others not so much. The outstanding tendencies were the purely literary, represented by consummate stylists such as Benjamín Jarnes in prose and Guillén in poetry; the folkloric, represented by García Lorca in his plays and poems—which evinced many of the preoccupations of the former—and finally the social, which flourished magnificently in the novels of Arconada, Arderíus and Sender, and in the poetry of Alberti and a dozen other gifted poets. Just as the Spanish Republic was wrecked by the Fascist hordes, this splendid literary renaissance was, if not killed, at least uprooted and scattered all over the globe. Some of the finest writers—García Lorca, Antonio Machado—were killed by the Fascist bullets or the torturous aftermath; others found a haven in the Western Hemisphere (Alberti, Jarnes, Sender) or in the Soviet Union (Arconada); and a few, who can hardly be called writers, remained with Franco. With the in-evitable victory of the democratic forces, the great writers of Republican Spain will return to their fatherland to continue their interrupted task, and, then, many of the men in this anthology will become known to English readers. They deserve it.

Miguel de Unamuno

THE RELIGION OF QUIXOTISM

I BECOME more and more convinced that our philosophy, the Spanish philosophy, is liquescent and diffused in our literature, in our life, in our action, above all in our mysticism, and not in philosophical systems. It is concrete. (And is there not perhaps as much philosophy or more in Goethe, for example, as in Hegel?) The poetry of Jorge Manrique, the Romancero, *Don Quijote, La Vida es Sueño, La Subida al Monte Carmelo,* imply an intuition of the world and a concept of life—*Weltanschauung und Lebensansicht.* This philosophy of ours could with difficulty formulate itself in the second half of the nineteenth century, a period that was a-philosophical, positivist, technicist, given up to pure history and the natural sciences, a period essentially materialist and pessimistic.

We shall find the hero of Spanish thought, perhaps, not in any philosopher who lived in flesh and bone, but in an entity of fiction and of action, more real than all the philosophers—in Don Quixote. For there is doubtless a philosophic Quixotism, but there is also a Quixotic philosophy. Was not perhaps the philosophy of the Conquistadores, of the Counter-Reformers, of Loyola, and, above all, the philosophy latent in the abstract but passionate thought of our mystics, in its essence none other than this? What was the mysticism of St. John of the Cross but a knight-errantry of the heart in the divine warfare?

And the feeling that animated Don Quixote cannot strictly be called idealism; he did not fight for ideas. It was spiritualism; he fought for the spirit.

Speculative or meditative Quixotism is, like practical Quixotism, foolishness, a daughter-foolishness to the foolishness of the cross. And therefore it is contemned by reason. Philosophy at bottom abhors Christianity, and well did the gentle Marcus Aurelius prove it.

The tragedy of Christ, the divine tragedy, is the tragedy of the Cross. Pilate, the sceptic, the man of culture, sought by means of ridicule to turn it into comedy and conceived the farce of the king with the reed sceptre and crown of thorns, saying: "Behold the man!" But the people, more human than he, the people that thirsts for tragedy, cried: "Crucify him! crucify him!" And the other tragedy, the human, the intra-human tragedy, is that of Don Quixote with his face lathered for the ducal servants to laugh at, and for the dukes, as much slaves as their servants, to laugh at too. "Behold the fool!"—so they would say. And the comic, the irrational tragedy is suffering beneath ridicule and contempt.

For an individual, as for a people, the highest heroism is being willing to face ridicule—still more, being willing to make oneself ridiculous and not flinching at the ridicule.

Antero de Quental, the tragic Portuguese who committed suicide, wrote as follows, smarting under the ultimatum which England delivered to his country in 1890: "An English statesman of the last century, also certainly a perspicacious observer and a philosopher, Horace Walpole, said that life is a tragedy for those who feel and a comedy for those who think. Very well then, if we have to end tragically, we Portuguese, we who *feel*, we much prefer this terrible, but noble, destiny to that which is reserved, and perhaps at no very remote future date, for England, the country that *thinks* and *calculates*, whose destiny is to end miserably and comically." We may leave on one side the assertion that England thinks and calculates, implying that she does not feel, the injustice of which is explained by the circumstance that provoked it, and also the assertion that the Portuguese feel, implying that they scarcely ever think or calculate—for we sister peoples of the Atlantic have always been distinguished by a certain sentimental pedantry; but there remains the terrible underlying idea, namely, that some, those who put thought above feeling—I should say reason above faith—die comically, and those die tragically who put faith above reason. For it is the ridiculers who die comically, and God laughs at their comic ending, while the portion, the noble portion, of those who are ridiculed is tragedy.

And what we must look out for in the record of Don Quixote is ridicule.

The philosophy in the soul of my people presents itself to me as the expression of an inward tragedy analogous to the tragedy of the soul of Don Quixote, as the expression of a conflict between the world as the reason of science exhibits it to us and the world as we wish it to be, as our religious faith tells us that it is. And in this philosophy is to be found the secret of what is usually said about us, that we are fundamentally irreducible to *Kultur*, that is to say, that we do not resign ourselves to it. No, Don Quixote resigns himself neither to the world nor to its truth, neither to science nor to logic, neither to art nor æsthetic, neither to morality nor to ethics.

"In any case the result of all this," so I have been told more than once and by more than one person, "will simply be to urge people on to the maddest kind of Catholicism." And they have accused me of being a reactionary and even a Jesuit. So be it! And what then?

Yes, I know, I know that it is folly to seek to turn the waters of the river back to their source, and that it is the crowd that seeks the medicine for its ills in the past; but I know too that everyone who fights for any ideal whatsoever, even though it may seem to belong to the past, is urging the world on to the future, and that the only reactionaries are those who find themselves at ease in the present. Every pretended restoration of the past is a creation of the future, and if the past is dream, something not properly known, so much the better. As always, the march is towards the future; he who marches, marches thither, even though he march backwards way—and who knows if that is not the better way?

I feel that I have a mediæval soul and I believe that the soul of my country is mediæval—that it has been forced to traverse the Renaissance, the Reformation and the Revolution, learning from them, yes, but without allowing them to touch the soul, preserving the spiritual heritage of those ages that are called dark. And Quixotism is nothing but the most desperate phase of the struggle of the Middle Ages against their offspring, the Renaissance.

And if some accuse me of furthering the cause of Catholic reaction, perhaps the others, the official Catholics, accuse me of . . . But these, in Spain trouble themselves little about anything and are only interested in their own quarrels and dissensions. And besides, poor folk, they are somewhat dull of understanding.

But the fact is that my work—I was going to say my mission—is to shatter the faith of both these and those and of others besides, faith in affirmation, faith in negation and faith in abstention, and this for the sake of faith in faith itself; it is to war against all those who resign themselves, whether to Catholicism or to rationalism or to agnosticism; it is to make them all live lives of inquietude and passionate desire.

Will this work be efficacious? But did Don Quixote believe in the immediate and visible efficacy of his work? It is greatly to be doubted, and at any rate he did not risk putting the visor he had made to the test by giving it a second blow. And many passages in his history indicate that he did not believe much in the immediate success of his design to restore knight-errantry. And what did it matter so long as he himself thus lived and immortalized himself? And he must have surmised, and did in fact surmise, that his achievement would have another and a higher efficacy —namely, that it would go on working in the minds of all those who in the spirit of devotion read of his exploits.

Don Quixote made himself ridiculous, but did he perchance know the most tragic ridicule of all, the ridicule that is reflected in the eyes of a man's own soul, the ridicule with which a man sees his own self? Transfer Don Quixote's battlefield to his own soul; conceive him to be fighting in his soul to save the Middle Ages from the Renaissance, not to lose the treasure of his infancy; turn him into an inward Don Quixote—with his Sancho, a Sancho equally inward and equally heroically at his side—and then talk to me of the comic tragedy.

And what has Don Quixote left, do you ask? I answer that he has left himself, and a man, a living and eternal man, is worth all theories and all philosophies. Other peoples have left principally institutions, books—we have left souls. St. Teresa is worth any institution, any "Critique of Pure Reason."

Don Quixote was converted? Yes, but only to die. But the other, the real Don Quixote, he who remained on earth and lives among us, breathing his spirit into us, this Don Quixote was never converted, this Don Quixote goes on inciting us to make ourselves ridiculous, this Don Quixote must never die. And the conversion of the other Don Quixote—he who was converted only to die—was possible because he was mad, and it was his madness, not his death or his conversion. that immortalized him and earned for him the forgiveness of the crime of having been born. *Felix culpa!* Neither was his madness cured but only transformed. His death was his last knightly adventure—in dying he stormed heaven, which suffereth violence.

This Don Quixote died and descended into hell, and he entered it lance on rest and freed all the condemned, as he freed the galley-slaves, and he shut the gates of hell, and tore down from them the scroll that Dante saw there, and replaced it by one on which was written "Long live hope!" and escorted by those whom he had freed, and they laughing at him, he went to heaven. And God laughed at him paternally and this divine laughter filled his soul with eternal happiness.

And the other Don Quixote remained here amongst us, fighting with desperation. Is not despair the mainspring of his fighting? How is it that among the words that English has borrowed from our tongue—*siesta, camarilla, guerilla* and the like—there occurs this word *desperado?* This inward Don Quixote that I spoke of, conscious of his own comicness, is he not a man of despair—*desesperado?* A desperado, yes, like Pizarro and like Loyola. But "despair is the master of impossibilities," as Salazar y Torres tells us, and it is despair and despair alone from whence springs heroic hope, absurd hope, mad hope. *Spero quia absurdum,* it ought to be said, rather than *credo.*

And Don Quixote, who lived solitary, sought more solitude still, sought the solitudes of the Peña Pobre in order that there, alone, without witnesses, he might plunge into yet wilder extravagances to the easing of his soul. Yet he was not quite solitary, for Sancho accompanied him, Sancho the good, Sancho the believing, Sancho the simple. If, as some say, in Spain Don Quixote is dead and Sancho lives, then we are saved, for Sancho, his master dead, will become a knight-errant himself. At any rate he is waiting for some other mad knight to follow yet again.

And there is also a tragedy of Sancho. The other Sancho, the Sancho who journeyed with the mortal Don Quixote—it does not appear certain that he died, although some say that he died hopelessly mad, calling for his lance, and believing that all those things which on his death-bed his converted master abominated as lies had been really true. But neither does it appear certain that the bachelor Sanson Carrasco, or the curate, or the barber, or the dukes and canons are dead, and it is with these that the heroic Sancho has to fight.

Don Quixote journeyed alone, alone with Sancho, alone with his solitude. And shall we not also journey alone, we his lovers creating for ourselves a quixotesque Spain which exists only in our imagination?

And again we shall be asked: What has Don Quixote bequeathed to *Kultur?* I answer: Quixotism, and that is no little thing. It is a whole method, a whole epistemology, a whole æsthetic, a whole logic, a whole ethic, above all a whole religion, that is to say, a whole economy of things human and divine, a whole hope in the rationally absurd.

For what did Don Quixote fight? For Dulcinea, for glory, for life, for survival. Not for Iseult, who is the eternal flesh; not for Beatrice, who is theology; not for Margaret, who is the people; not for Helen, who is culture. He fought for Dulcinea, and he won her, for he lives.

And what is greatest in him is his having been ridiculed and overcome, for it is in being overcome that he overcame; he overcame the world by making it laugh at him.

And to-day? To-day he feels his own comicness and the vanity of his efforts so far as temporal issues are concerned; he sees himself from without—culture has taught him to objectify himself, that is to say, to alienate himself from himself instead of to enter into himself, and in seeing himself from without he laughs at himself, but with a bitter laughter. Perhaps the most tragic character would be an inward Margutte, who, like the

Margutte of Pulci, should die bursting with laughter, but with laughter at himself. *E ridera in eterno,* he will laugh for all eternity, said the Angel Gabriel of Margutte. Do you not hear the laughter of God?

The mortal Don Quixote, in dying, understood his own comicness and wept for his sins; but the immortal Don Quixote understands and rises above his comicness and triumphs over it without renouncing it.

But now Don Quixote hears his own laughter, he hears the divine laughter, and since he is not a pessimist, since he believes in eternal life, he has to fight, attacking the modern scientific inquisitorial orthodoxy by adducing a new and impossible Middle Age, dualistic, contradictory, passionate. Like a new Savonarola—an Italian Quixote of the end of the fifteenth century—he fights against this Modern Age which began with Machiavelli and which will end comically. He fights against the rationalism inherited from the eighteenth century. Peace of consciousness, reconciliation between reason and faith, are now, thanks to the providence of God, impossible. The world must be as Don Quixote wishes it to be, and inns must be castles, and he will fight against it and will, to all appearances, be overcome, but he will triumph by making himself ridiculous. He will triumph by laughing at himself and making himself laughed at.

"Reason speaks and feeling bites," said Petrarch; but reason also bites and bites in the heart of hearts. And more light does not make more warmth. "Light, light, more light!" they tell us that the dying Goethe cried. No, warmth, warmth, more warmth, for we die of cold and not of darkness. It is not the night but the frost that kills.

The philosophy of Bergson, which is a spiritualist restoration, in its essence mystical, mediæval, quixotesque, has been called *demi-mondaine* philosophy. Leave out the *demi;* call it *mondaine,* mundane. Mundane— yes, for the world and not for philosophers, just as chemistry ought not to be for chemists alone. The world wishes to be deceived—*mundus vult decipi*—either with the illusion antecedent to reason, which is poetry, or with the illusion subsequent to reason, which is religion. And Machiavelli has said that whosoever wishes to deceive will always find someone who will let himself be deceived. And blessed are those who are made fools of. A Frenchman, Jules de Gaultier, has said that it was the privilege of his countrymen *n'être pas dupe*—not to be taken in. A sorry privilege!

Science does not give Don Quixote what he demands of it. "Then let him not demand it," it will be said, "let him resign himself, let him accept life and truth as they are." But he does not accept them as they are, and he asks for signs, urged thereto by Sancho who stands by his side. And it is not that Don Quixote does not understand what those understand who talk thus to him, those who are able to resign themselves and to accept rational life and rational truth. No, it is that the needs of his heart are greater. Pedantry? Who knows?

And in this critical century Don Quixote, who has contaminated himself with criticism also, has to attack his own self, the victim of intellectualism and sentimentalism, and it is when he wishes to be most spontaneous that he appears most affected. And the poor fellow wishes to rationalize the irrational and irrationalize the rational. And he sinks into the inner despair of the critical century whose two greatest victims were Nietzsche and Tolstoi. And through despair he attains the heroic fury of which Giordano Bruno spoke—that Don Quixote of the mind who escaped from the cloister—and he becomes an awakener of sleeping souls (*dormitantium animorum excubitor*), as the ex-Dominican said of himself. "Heroic love," Bruno wrote, "is the property of those superior natures called insane [*insano*]—not because they do not know [*non sanno*], but because they over-know [*soprasanno*]."

But Bruno believed in the triumph of his doctrines—at any rate they have stated on the inscription at the foot of his statue in the Campo dei Fiori, opposite the Vatican, that it is dedicated to him by the age which he foretold (*il secole da lui divinato*). But our Don Quixote, the Don Quixote who has risen from the dead, the inward Don Quixote, the Don Quixote who is conscious of his own comicness, does not believe that his doctrines will triumph in this world, because they are not of it. And it is better that they should not triumph. And if the world wished to make Don Quixote king, he would retire to the mountain, fleeing from the king-making and king-killing crowds, as Christ retired alone to the mountain when, after the miracle of the loaves and fishes, they sought to proclaim Him king. He left the title of king to be written upon the cross.

What, then, is the new mission of Don Quixote in the world of to-day? To cry aloud, to cry aloud in the wilderness. But the wilderness hears, though men do not hear, and one day it will be transformed into a sounding forest, and this solitary voice that falls upon the wilderness like seed, will yield a gigantic cedar, which with its hundred thousand tongues will sing an eternal hosanna to the Lord of life and of death.

Translated by J. E. CRAWFORD FLITCH

Pío Baroja

ANGELUS

THEY WERE THIRTEEN, thirteen valiant men accustomed to danger, accustomed to struggle with the sea. With them was a woman, the wife of the skipper.

The thirteen, men of the coast, bore the characteristic stamp of the Basque race; the wide head, the aquiline profile, the pupils of the eyes dead from constant contemplation of the sea, that great devourer of men.

They knew the Cantabric; they knew the waves and the wind.

Their long, narrow fishing smack, painted black, was called Arantza, which in Basque means "spine." It had a short mast with a small sail set next to the prow. . . .

It was an autumn afternoon. The wind was slack and the undulating waves were gentle and tranquil. The sail scarcely swelled in the breeze, and the boat slid along smoothly, leaving a silver wake on the green sea.

They had left Montrico with their nets prepared and were going to join other boats for Santa Catalina's day. At that moment they were passing Deva.

The sky was covered with dull, wooly clouds, through whose openings peeped fragments of pale blue. From behind a cloud, in brilliant rays shone the sun, whose red mouth was reflected tremulously over the water.

The thirteen men, serious and impassive, rarely spoke; the old woman sat knitting stockings with coarse needles and a ball of blue wool. Grave and melancholic, the skipper, his cap pulled down to his eyes and his right hand on the oar that served as a rudder, looked impassively at the sea. Sitting on a bench in the stern next to him a dirty water spaniel also looked at the sea, as indifferent as the men. The sun began to set. . . . Overhead, flame reds, copper reds, the color of ashes, leaden clouds, like huge whales. Below, the green surface of the sea, with ruddy, scarlet and purple tones. Now and then the rhythmic trembling of the waves.

As they passed Iciar, the wind brought them the fragrance from the mountains; the coast with all its cliffs and boulders threw its shadow on the surface of the sea.

Suddenly, as day ended, the church clock of Iciar struck the hour, and then the sounds of the Angelus bells floated out over the sea, like lingering voices, majestic and sublime.

The skipper took off his cap and the rest did likewise. The woman laid aside her work, and all prayed gravely, sombrely gazing at the tranquil sea and the rolling waves.

As night began to fall, the wind blew vigorously, bellying the sail, and the boat lost itself in shadow, leaving a wake of silver on the black surface of the water. . . .

They were thirteen, thirteen valiant men, accustomed to danger, accustomed to struggle with the sea.

Translated by PEDRO *and* CLAIRE VILLA FERNANDEZ

Joaquin Arderíus

BATH OF DEATH

PASCUAL WAS in no mood for cutting grapes. For that matter, he was none too concerned over his donkey Mora, who was nibbling at the almond tree which was the pride of the master of the hacienda.

He stood dawdling behind the other grape-pickers, then finally roused himself and began tossing pebbles with intentionally poor aim at the donkey.

"Mora! Go on, beat it! you slut, you!"

Mora turned to her master, threw up her head in the sauciest manner, and continued her ravages on the almond tree. She knew her master too well to mind his threats. Besides, was he not equally guilty in the matter of grapes? Mora had watched him at his work, and of a truth, more grapes went into his paunch than into his saddle-bags.

But that was Pascual's way; on all his jobs he proved himself a most expensive farmhand. On pay-days, for instance, the pay-master very often ran out of small change; but Pascual didn't mind, so long as he did the owing.

"What's the smallest you got there?" he would ask. "A peseta?—a duro? Let's have it; I'll bring you the change in a jiffy."

But he never came back. No one had ever known him to keep his word. It was really absurd, having him for a debtor.

Wherever he worked, there his donkey grazed, devastating every square foot of tilled ground in her path. You might think he had put her up to it, for no sooner was she tied to a post than she expertly snapped her halter, stiffened her tail, thrust her ears back and frisked away to the freshest sprout or the tenderest bud.

As for drink, you couldn't move her with a derrick toward a plebean trough—she was too good for that. So when the girls, with jugs on their hips, came tripping down to a spring, like as not they found the water muddied by Mora's snout and colored with her dung.

Nor was her master any less a rogue. Not only couldn't you get a full day's work out of him, but you could count yourself fortunate indeed if, during the wood-chopping season, he didn't sneak home with a load of brushwood or, at threshing time, with a bundle of shucks. Everything he touched seemed to stick to his fingers.

And yet his greatest skill lay, not in his purloining fingers, but in his matchless tongue. He wheedled his salary out of you, plus interest; he wheedled tips for the most trivial errands; and for his Mora he would have any tidbit you had about.

And if you took it into your head to inspect the accomplishments of this hireling who was so clever with his tongue, in passing over the earth he was to have plowed, you discovered that his tongue was doing double service, and his hands none. That was Pascual, all over. The farmhands just thought him a bit of a fool and let it go at that.

"Mora! Drat you!" For the twentieth time he addressed her, and for the twentieth time threw a stone at her and missed. He stood there, apart from the others, eating his grapes and shaking his head disapprovingly at the beast, whose stout appetite was being appeased at the expense of the master of the hacienda.

The vintagers were pushing up the sun-tinted hill like a flock of ragged sheep. Their leader clambered up ahead, as if he had been hit by a sling-shot; and the rest, swaying heavily from side to side as they followed, looked like those domesticated animals which rear up on their hind legs to eat the figs their master tenders. With one accord, they abandoned their quadrupedal postures and stood upright, stretching and yawning, then dispersed in search of some shelter where they might eat the fruits of their sweat.

"Look, Pascual!" Juan Reina shouted. "Look what your donkey's doing to the almond tree! Hit 'er with something. S'pose Uncle Clemente comes over the hill?"

"My arm's dead already from throwing things. She's the dumbest animal I ever had. She'll be the death of me, yet. Beat it, you!"

He stopped abruptly and burst out into a loud guffaw. He winked his left eye, then the right—grey eyes sparkling like two drops of mercury. Frenziedly, he began scratching himself under the armpits, pawing and stamping like a puppet. He had the itch.

As he danced up and down, the whole crowd gathered around him as around the court jester of some ragamuffin king; and in the centre, resplendent in his gaudy shirt and narrow, blue-striped pants, he cavorted about wildly, making the most grotesque gesticulations.

"Tell us the story of the salt pork in the pot!"

"Say a mass!"

"Bray!"

"Imitate the town-crier!"

"Talk like Don Roque, the master of Fenilla."

They were all clamoring for him to show his tricks.

"Gimme a smoke, an' I'll do anythin' ya want!" he answered in his shrill voice, jumbling his words, pawing, scratching his armpits, winking his tiny mercury eyes, and twitching his nostrils, all at the same time.

"Here!"

"Take mine!"

"Me first!"

"No, me!"

They were shouting, pushing each other out of the way to thrust their tobacco pouches at him.

"You're first!" he decided. "You've got the best tobacco. What'll it be?"

"Show us how Doña Rita, the schoolmarm, walks."

"Sure thing! But hand over the pouch, first. I gotta get paid, if I'm gonna perform."

Thus, on that red-gold hill, with his belly full of grapes, Pascual played the fool and got all the tobacco he needed for a week to come.

The moments of silence during his performance were punctuated by a monotonous *crunch, crunch*. It was Mora, still nibbling on the trunk of the almond tree, pride of the master of the hacienda.

❖   ❖   ❖

When Pascual had done with his antics, his audience broke up into little groups to seek shelter under trees, and opened their lunch-boxes. From above, the sun hurled firebolts at the earth, but the vintagers sat cool as cucumbers, jesting between mouthfuls of bread and ham.

Mora, lying beside her master, slept the deep sleep of the innocent. Pascual and his wife, Andrea, sat eating a vegetable salad, skewering chunks of bread with the points of their knives. Next to them was another couple, Josefa and Jeronimo.

This Andrea was a beauty. Her voice, her smile, the luminous eyes under her broad forehead, all revealed that serene, profoundly human wisdom to be found among peasants. She loved Pascual, and every act of her life, every wish of her being was directed toward his welfare. On market-days, when she went to town to sell her chickens and eggs, she always spent the proceeds in little gifts for him.

On holidays and Sundays Andrea saw to it that Pascual was without exception the most gaudily dressed man at the hermitage. She revelled in this superiority of her husband over the rest. Then, jestingly, she was fond of calling him, before the others, not "my Pascual", nor "my husband", but "my fool."

And you may be sure, she was just the kind of wife to sit him in the tub and scrub his back for him; and to load his dinner-plate and keep plying him throughout the evening with every manner of dainty. The house they lived in, they owned outright; and the many bushels of wheat which the fertile soil around the house yielded, these Andrea herself had sown and reaped.

When they went to town together, Pascual always chose the meandering paths that skirted the steep precipices, and, with Andrea walking ahead, he would sit on Mora, his buttocks buried in a pile of sheepskins —he, humming softly to himself, his pipe between his teeth, she, plaiting a rope or singing as she plowed through the thick dust.

To her, he was no fool. She held her tongue, however, wishing to have him for herself alone, and never revealed his true character to anyone. She was convinced that her "fool" was the wisest man on earth; so she obeyed him implicitly. And if people laughed at him, it was just too bad about them. Watching him act, tell his stories, cut capers in the thick of the crowd, always raising shouts of hilarity about him, she pictured him as the spout of a fountain making a glorious spray with millions of drops of water. Yes, the greater fools, they, for laughing at her fool.

For his physical powers she knew only adoration. His nervous energy, the egoism animating his hasty, incoherent speech and gestures, all these raised the tide of passion in her. Often he would sit in her lap, murmuring nonsensical things in her ear and fixing his passionate glance on her, with his tongue clucking like a male partridge wooing its mate; and she would tremble with excitement, and her breasts would grow hard under her blouse.

"That's enough, silly!" she would protest; but Pascual, with the dexterity of a rustler branding a cow, would push her over and always have his way with her. His ardor, however, was so short-lived that Andrea never knew complete satisfaction. But this she had imputed to her barren womb.

Indeed, Pascual was the archetype of egoism. He loved no one, and everything he could lay his hands on, he retained for himself. He was the king, and Andrea his slave.

And now, finally, after five years of marriage, Andrea was pregnant.

Pascual sat under a tree, eating his salad avidly, to finish it before anyone thought to share it with him.

"God, what heat!" Andrea remarked to Josefa, wiping her moist brow with her apron.

"Well, tomorrow at this time I'll be cooling my body at the seashore with him," Josefa replied, shrugging one shoulder at her husband Jeronimo.

"When are you going?" Andrea asked.

"At daybreak, when it's cool, God willing."

"You're lucky!" Andrea exclaimed.

"Why, aren't you going?"

"I'd love to, but him—" she broke off, sadly pointing to Pascual.

Pascual, however, had no mind for anything but his lunch; silent, insatiable, he went on eating strips of pimento and slices of tomato.

Andrea turned impulsively to her husband. "Don't you wish we were going? Come on, let's go this once."

Pascual raised his head, wiped the tomato seeds from his chin, looked at her indignantly and said nothing.

Jeronimo nudged him with the tip of his sandal. "Don't be stubborn—go on, take her."

"Mind your own business!" Pascual snarled, like a dog disturbed over his bone.

"Well, if he won't go," Josefa urged, "you come with us."

"Don't you worry; if I decide to go, I'll go. When I get something into my head, it sticks there, especially now that I'm getting big." And Andrea patted her swollen belly.

"If I were that way," Josefa replied, "believe me, nobody would stop me from going."

Pascual glowered at her and went on eating.

Andrea knew there was nothing to be gained by making a scene; he always had his own way. Occasionally, however, she could soften him with meekness, cajolery and a few caresses. Motioning to her friends to be quiet, she assumed the most agreeable expression she could muster and leaned toward Pascual. Everyone went on eating in silence.

"Pascual," she wheedled in her softest tone, "let's go with Jeronimo and Josefa."

Pascual merely grunted, twitching like a hog in a tubful of maize who had just got a whack on the snout.

"Come on, let's go with them."

"I'll take you to the bullfight next Sunday." Pascual liked nothing better than a bullfight.

"Oh, Pascual, not a bullfight! You know it always makes me cry."

"All the better! Then you won't wet the bed, nights."

"I wanna go to the beach! Take me there for a dip," she wheedled, tearfully. "I wanna go to the sea, darling."

" 'To the sea thou art going; I shall go there with thee,' " he mocked, singing a snatch from a popular song.

"You can't get out of it by joking. You're gonna take me!"

"Oh, go bathe in the sink!"

"No, I'm going to the sea! I'll get everything ready this afternoon. We can take a couple of rabbits from the hutch—and the big red cock and some tomatoes."

"Nice grub for you and *it!*" he broke out in his high-pitched voice, pointing at her belly with a grotesque gesture.

"Take me for the baby's sake," she pleaded, laying her hands on her belly.

"The kid won't like the water. Babies cry when they're wet."

"I wanna go! If I don't, I'll get upset, and something might happen to the child."

"Suits me! Then we won't have to feed 'im."

"And God only knows what'll happen to me!"

"Bosh! What could happen?—the brat wouldn't come out the right way? Then you'd spit it out, eh?"

Andrea gulped down great sobs, and tears trickled down on her apron.

Jeronimo was moved to indignation. "You're a dog!—Just look at her, crying her eyes out! Listen, you fathead, don't you ever give a thought to anything but yourself and your own belly?"

Pascual had stopped eating and, with his nose in the air, was nervously scratching his head.

"I see it coming—I'll get sick as a dog," Andrea sighed, weeping into her apron.

"What's the sense in that?" Josefa remarked. "You might die from it. Believe me, when I got that way, Jeronimo did everything I wanted— every little thing! That's how all my children were born."

"Just keep it up," Jeronimo warned, "and one of these fine days, the devil will be draggin' you down to hell, sure as your name's Pascual."

"Don't joke, Jerōnimō, please don't joke about such things!" exclaimed Pascual. For he had an overpowering fear of the devil.

"The moment your Andrea shuffles off into the other world, the devil will come along and take you by the ear—and down the kitchen pipe you'll go!" Jeronimo continued, hoping to frighten him into consenting.

"Yeah, an' if she died, do you think I'd just stan' aroun' twiddlin' my thumbs? No, sir! I'd take her down to the sea and bathe her, before I buried her—that's what I'd do. No, sir! I don' wan' no trouble with the other world!" Pascual spoke with all the sincerity of his soul.

"Every decent man around here is taking his wife to the baths this year. And I'm going with Jeronimo, ain't I? Now what's the matter with you?" Josefa interposed.

"He's doin' you a big favor, eh? Well, if I had a mistress the way he has, I'd take Andrea to the baths in a jiffy—and dance the fandango all the way down."

The mention of the mistress had a singular effect on the group: Josefa turned pale, Jeronimo red, and Andrea, toying with her apron-strings, fixed her husband with a glance as if to turn him to stone. There was a moment of embarrassed silence; but Pascual, unperturbed, filled his pipe.

He was right: Jeronimo had a mistress—and Josefa knew it and stood for it because there were certain economic advantages accruing therefrom.

Macaria was a woman of fifty, the widow of an overseer. In men's eyes the slight measure of beauty she retained was undoubtedly enhanced by the knowledge of the acres of land and the plenteous head of cattle she owned. Having fallen in love with Jeronimo, who was young, robust and, in her dazed eyes, handsome, she took him to her and in exchange gave him financial aid.

For a week now, Macaria had been disporting at the beach with Jeronimo. She would go in for a dip and then call to Jeronimo to warm up her fat body for her. And he, like a masseur, would set to work rolling her over in the sand and thumping her with his immense hands, until the exercise had roused in both an appetite for the ham that always comprised their lunch. Then she would stuff him with food and pull him back on the sand for frolicking. This was Macaria.

Pascual suddenly broke the silence he had occasioned by mention of the mistress. "Well, guess that's all I'll have. You'd better run along home, now."

"You, too. It's gettin' late, and the children are all alone," Jeronimo reminded his wife.

The two women got up. "See you later," they both murmured: and with their baskets under their arms, their heads bowed with mortification, they disappeared over the hill.

Pascual and Jeronimo remained seated.

"What a double-crossin' bastard you turned out to be!" Jeronimo exclaimed, turning furiously on Pascual. "You'd trade your soul to the devil if you could get somethin' to pin on God an' his whole outfit—you're just the type! What in hell's got into you, shootin' off your mouth in front of Josefa?"

"Shut up, you snake-in-the-grass! With a wife to keep you warm, an' somebody on the side to shell out money—say, you're a fine one to be talkin'."

"I hope you get pimples on your tongue!" Jeronimo cursed him, throwing a handful of sand at his back and breaking into good-humored laughter.

"Why don't you try it on me? See if I mind. Hand over that dame with all her dough, an' I'll let you tell Andrea any day in the week. How about it?"

Pascual lay on his back, looking into the warm, sea-blue sky, across which four black crows were flying.

                              *   *   *

Andrea could not sleep all night. Racked by the excruciating pain inside her, she had to get out of bed every now and then. In her chemise, by the light of a candle, she sat writhing on the edge of a chair, until the pain had eased and she could return to bed. Between the intervals of the cramped pain that left her stiff and ashen and drenched with sweat, she felt her insides turning over in her.

And Pascual called sleepily, "Squeeze hard and force it out."

Andrea moaned, and he muttered, "Too well hooked, is it? Well, we're in for a pleasant night."

The foetus remained intact, throbbing violently inside her.

When the crisis had passed, she drew the sheets about her, and lay in a pleasant stupor. While Pascual slept to the thunderous accompaniment of his snores, she turned over in her mind the question of the child: Would it all turn out well, or was she going to miscarry?

"God grant I may not lose it!" she prayed. "Holy Virgin, I promise to wear the Franciscan garment if you watch over me. On my knees I'll go to the hermitage on a day of wind and snow. Holy Virgin, make Pascual take me to the sea and ease my troubled mind, which is killing me and my baby. I want just one dip in the sea, just one!"

Again a horrible feeling of nausea seized her, and again she got up and sat writhing in the chair. And when the pain left her, she lay down in peace. So it went, through the night.

When the sun rose and its first rays had pierced her windows, she remembered to pray to the Holy Virgin again for the bath.

Suddenly Pascual woke, with the warm flood of light on his body, and cried out, "Say, why didn't you wake me? Before I turn aroun', it'll be noon already. Do you want me to lose a day's pay?"

"It doesn't matter. Even if you are late, you'll only lose a quarter of a day."

"Ain't that enough?"

They dressed quickly. Pascual, with half a loaf of bread and a slab of bacon wrapped in a newspaper, started out for the vineyard. As he opened the door to go, Andrea begged him again, "Please take me, Pascual, only for one little dip!"

"We're going to the bullfight."

"Look at the awful condition I'm in. Don't leave me this way; it'll kill me. It hurts more and more each time."

"We're going to the bullfight!"

"If the animals were in my condition, you'd do everything for them. If your donkey was like me, it would be a different matter!"

"How you talk!—as if one thing was the same as the other! What the animals give birth to is worth good money, and what you carry aroun' with you is good for nothin' but to eat us out of house and home, an' to bring worry."

Thereupon he strode out, unleashed Mora and was off down the path. At some distance from the house he turned and yelled to Andrea, "Listen! Give the hogs a good feed so they won't be grunting."

Andrea watched him in the distance. She was sick at heart and weak in body, and her eyes were filling with tears. But she would bear this as she had borne everything in the past; for she had all the holy love of a mother for an egotistical, perverse and conscienceless son.

* * *

After his day's work, Pascual kept up an idle chatter with his comrades, till the waning sun robbed him of his audience and left him nothing to do but return home to his lamenting wife. As he went along, the crescent-moon cavorted on tip-toe through the sky in pace with his Mora.

Pascual was in no hurry. Sucking on his pipe and singing out of the corner of his mouth, he let his donkey graze. She ate the vegetables and corn in the little gardens by the knolls which bordered the path, crushed plants under her hooves, and from time to time became preoccupied with sucking her teats, while her tail flew sidewise and up and down with the vigor of a bobbin on a sewing machine.

They went on and came to a little brook splashing its way down the hillside. Twisting in and out between the rosebays and the tamarisks, it crossed the path and continued along on the opposite side. He led the donkey into the stream, brought her to a halt, opened her mouth, and had her rinse it, then splashed water over her flanks and her rump. She reveled in these ablutions, and her loose skin quivered with pleasure. Finally, he washed her nose and ears, ran her up on the bank and proceeded on down the path. Suddenly he stopped, remembering he had a thirst and retraced his footsteps. He crouched, cupped his hands and sucked in the cool water. He wiped his hands on his blouse and rejoined Mora.

The night was warm, and the moon shed its plentiful light over all the land. In the air was a fragrance of ripe wheat and fresh grass, of stalk and seed.

Serenely, contemplatively, Mora plodded on ahead of her master.

A rabbit leaped out from the corn into the middle of the path and crouched a moment in the sand. Pascual flung a stone at it, and the creature scurried off, disappearing into a patch of olive-trees.

As they passed the peasants' cottages, dogs howled; in the distance, a donkey brayed; and standing at a clothes-line unpinning her dry wash, a woman sang melodiously.

Now a shadowy figure was bearing down on Pascual, raising its arm and shouting, "Ain't you got no home?"

"That you, Celestino?" Pascual asked.

"Yeah. Say, gimme a light, eh? I've used up all my flint."

"Here, take it outta my pipe."

"Ain't much to get a light off'n."

"Well, don' use it all, neither."

"Say, you wouldn't give away even a stalk of wheat on Palm Sunday!"

"Yeah? An' it's swell guys like you that come aroun' beggin' off suckers like me. Come on, how about some tobacco?"

"Here y'are, tightwad!"

They separated, each going his own way. After a while Pascual left the road and, climbing a slight rise, viewed his own farmhouse in the distance. On the crest of a hill, with its sides whitewashed, it looked like a pale phantom huddled in a cape, keeping ghostlike watch from the dome of a palace.

❖   ❖   ❖

"Andrea! Andrea! Are you deaf, Andrea?" Pascual cried, as he entered the house.

Silence. He paused in the center of the kitchen, and listened. No answer.

"Andrea! Where the hell are you?" Still no reply.

"Andrea! Andrea!" He lit a candle. "Andrea! Andrea!"

He went into the bedroom. There she lay on the bed, sound asleep.

"Andrea! Andrea!"

Andrea slept on.

A fly hissed, its wings caught by the candle-flame and dropped into the hot tallow.

"Andrea!"

He watched her, puzzled, scratched his head and winked.

A beetle flew serenely in through the window, and brushed his cheek. He swung at it with his open palm, clumsily knocking the candle over with his other hand.

He could see her in the moonlight now, in deep repose.

"Andrea! Andrea! Andrea!" He called more softly, poking her shoulder. Still she did not answer. He shook her roughly by the arms. No response. He seized her by the ankles, lifted her legs and dropped them back on the mattress. Andrea lay still, mute, stiff as a corpse.

"Maybe she's dead," he murmured, scratching his arm-pits. He looked at her blankly for a moment. Lying on the bed, dressed, she was like a confused bundle of clothing.

"She is dead!" he said at length, with some conviction. He thrust his head out of the window and stared at the moon.

"Frera," he thought to himself, "only two hours away. I've got plenty of time—plenty."

Then he turned back to the bed: "Andrea, my girl!" He coughed with embarrassment.

"Dead as a door-nail!" He coughed again.

"Got to bathe her, that's all there's to it. Can't bury her without that bath, or I'll have all the devils on my back. No, sir! Can't afford to fool aroun' with those birds."

And light-hearted once more, he went to saddle Mora.

Across the frames for carrying the water-jugs, Pascual placed the wicker hurdle on which he dried his figs. With a piece of rope he managed to tie it securely around Mora's belly. Then, on top of the frame, he spread a fleecy sheepskin mat, providing a makeshift equestrian bed for his foolish wife, who had gone and died on him.

He carried the corpse of Andrea out, placed her, face-down, on the mat and covered her with a sheet he had got from the trunk. The whole business was carried through with a serenity bordering on unconcern, as though he were taking a bundle of shucks to market. For what did not affect Pascual's own material good was no very great matter to him.

He planned, now, to take her to the ocean and bathe her, so that, when his turn came to die, he might not be dragged below, where all the devils in hell were sure to stamp on his prostrate body. Such was his code of ethics.

As he was about to start, he turned to the moon again and addressed it thus: "I don't like your face tonight, you double-crosser, you!"

He grimaced, calculating the moon's position and finally decided "About eleven—eleven, more or less. I'll be back before sunrise, for certain."

He filled his pipe and lighted it. The smoke poured through his nostrils in two thin streams.

"Gee-up, Mora!"

He did not have to tell Mora where to go; he just faced her in the proper direction, and in her ambling way she got there. The path to Frera was no exception; she knew every inch of the way, for at Frera, Pascual used to buy fish and peddle them to the farmhouses in the district.

When they were almost half-way to Frera, he skirted the foothills of the great chain of mountains whose peaks were outlined in soft curves against the sky. On they moved; Mora, with the dead woman slung across her back, and Pascual behind, serving as the funeral cortege.

It was a gruesome spectacle: the pale-blue sky, empty and fathomless, the hunchbacked mountains, all grey under the moon, the moving blotches of the black beast, the ashen corpse, and the man in his black hat, white shirt and grey pants. The horizon was tinged with the mystery of death, the cold of snow and the mist of all beginnings.

At each step Pascual looked up at the sky and, facing the moon, cried out, "Somethin' bad'll come of a night like this. Somethin' bad! If nothin' happens, it'll be a miracle."

As he climbed higher, he felt his chest contracting, and from his soul came a deep sigh. Bit by bit, fear was creeping into his heart. He stopped suddenly, and grasping Mora by the tail, pulled her up short.

His eyes encompassed a great circle as he scanned the horizons. He saw nothing but Mora and the dead woman, silhouetted against the mountains and the sky.

Pascual dared not continue on to Frera. In a quandary, he stood scratching his head, pawing the ground, and coughing. If only there were a pool nearby in which to bathe her! But the place was drier than chaff! Besides, come to think of it, he had to have salt water for her; and anyway, it was the Frera beach she had asked for. Well, so be it!

He filled his pipe again, lit it, puffed furiously on it, and slapping Mora on the rump, gave the command to proceed. They descended down the slope to a deep ravine, with walls of rock and a sandy floor, through which a tiny stream wound its way. From both walls, rows of poplars and elms, sheaved in their leafy gowns, stood out straight over the ravine.

Mora sensed the need of speeding up her journey along this passage, for such was Pascual's wont here; and she broke into a trot. It was a dangerous spot, and several hair-raising stories were told of it. That deep torrent, flanked with stone, emptied into the sea near Frera. At the top, between the two walls, the sky looked like a river, and the moon a buoy.

At the moment the ravine was dimly illuminated, and the leaves were capped with whiteness. The floor exuded a fresh smell of brine, rosebay and rosemary. In several places the stream split the path, so that Mora had to wade through while Pascual leaped over.

The screeching and hooting of night birds broke the silence. Mora snorted and her hooves went ringing down the canyon. Pascual's heart skipped a beat. The branches of an elm tree shook, and Pascual started back, terrified.

"What's that?" he cried, then recognized it for an owl and moved on. He made as little noise as possible, but the donkey tramped on like a club beating on a skull. Pascual was panicky.

Few persons dared pass through at such an hour. The smugglers of Frera, by perpetrating murders there, had succeeded in giving the place a ghastly reputation.

Before Pascual's eyes, spectres in horrible postures passed, re-enacting the events which he knew had actually taken place here. He saw the fierce, violent faces of men committing crimes—livid faces, pale faces; eyes of fire, and eyes like pools of stagnant water. He saw a man fleeing, with another pursuing him, and heard cries. He was paralyzed with fear at the apparition of a shepherdess, the same that had been found at dawn in this spot, being torn to pieces by two red dogs, while a tiger-colored one defended her from the attacks of a raven which was trying to claw out her eyes. Then there was re-enacted before his eyes the fight between two monsters, who in their attempt to rape a little girl, had ended with murdering her, to deny each other possession.

Pascual felt as if his feet were wrapped in cloth, so noiselessly did he walk. But Mora scampered heedlessly along the path.

After a few moments the phantoms fled, and he perceived again the rows of trees, the rosebays with their red brocades and the black body of the beast, halved by the white mass of the dead woman, plowing through the sand, splashing through the water, like a cross of jet and mother-of-pearl pulled by a string of diamonds along an endless journey over ashes.

Someone was coughing!—Yes, and close to his ear! He leaped back, cowering, seized two rocks in his fists and carefully followed the donkey, prepared for an encounter with a shadow. But no phantom appeared; only, from the rocky walls came low-throated laughter.

"Crack! crack! crack!" sounded Mora's beat along the path, as if her bones were breaking under the weight of her burden. Pascual's breath came now like the beating of a wounded eagle's wings.

The spectres again loomed up from behind rocks and came forth on tiptoe, skulking behind trees, their faces lit with grim expressions of mirth. Once again Pascual's eyes lit up in horror, and his fingers tightened on the rocks he held.

Pascual heard the cough again.

"Heavens!" he muttered. "This canyon is just a great big womb!—everything is alive here, even the rocks! Guess it must be the elms and poplars coughing!"

The mule began to pant.

"So!" thought Pascual. "It was Mora all the time! And I thought somebody was coughing!"

Now, in the distance, the strip of sky had dropped like a curtain to the earth. It was the sea! Pascual breathed freely again: it would soon be over.

"Gee-up, Mora!" he exclaimed, while he intrepidly paused to fill his pipe, light it and blow two streams of smoke from his nostrils.

Soon, they were out of the canyon and headed straight toward the beach, with its waters glistening under the moonlight.

Pascual laid the corpse out on the sand. Mora, thankful for the disburdening, browsed about for giblets.

About a kilometer away, the houses of the village of Frera were visible.

Pascual gazed at the body of Andrea resting in the sand, in her gaudy red dress and her blue kerchief. He stooped, undid her sandals—she wore no stockings—and pulled her dress up over her head, leaving her in her chemise. Then, while her body gleamed in his arms like a mass of foam, he began to wade out into the sea. With the water to his knees, he stopped and looked at his wife. He felt an overpowering desire to possess her.

Dead? Why not? Did it matter? She had always been just as dead as she was now. And he had possessed her every day of their married life. Now he desired her more than ever: she was so still, so defenceless—all his. The greed in him rose as he advanced deeper into the water.

Here?—No, farther on. The deeper the water, the softer the bed. Here, with the water at his elbows? Farther, farther yet. He waded on, halted and looked at her again.

His eager hands itched to rip off her chemise and throw it on the waters like the rent wing of a swan, that he might take her, naked, in his savage embrace, with their bodies fused under the surface in a last feast.

He stood staring down at the length of her, his nerves afire. A little farther on, the water would be taking her from his arms and carrying her off. He advanced one foot, then the other and prepared to launch her, when suddenly, out of the silence, came:

"Ay! ay! ay! ay!"—followed by resounding laughter.

Pascual abandoned the body to the waves, and fled ashore screaming like a madman.

"Don't be scared! I'm not dead! I wasn't dead before, either! Didn't you hear me cough in the canyon? I was afraid you'd find me out then. A mosquito got caught in my throat!" exclaimed Andrea, up to her waist in the water.

Pascual, who had fallen in the sand at the feet of Mora, cried in alarm:

"Don't come near me! Don't come near me!"

"But I'm as much alive as you, Pascual! Come on, let's take a dip. If you only knew how happy the kid is to be here in the water!"

"Don't come near me, Andrea! You're dead, and you know it! The devil himself is inside you, moving and blabbering at me. You can't fool me!"

"Come here! Don't be silly!"

"Only when the devil leaves you and you're dead!"

"But I'm not dead! It was La Cana who put me up to this to save the baby—and me too. Its fatal to be this way and have a wish you can't fulfil—didn't you know that?"

"It's the devil makin' your tongue wag! He's aimin' to catch me, so he can put me in his cauldron to boil. Don't come near me! Just hurry up an' die, like a good girl! Go on, Andrea, die! An' be quick about it!"

"Come, Pascual, let's bathe together!" she exclaimed, beaming happily as she waded toward him. Playfully, she began to splash him.

Pascual, his eyes bulging, took one leap, seized her in his arms and brutally thrust her under the surface. She thrashed about a few moments, sending the water churning, then sank. A few bubbles rose to the surface, indicating her grave; and in a moment, the water resumed its peaceful wash.

"Jeronimo was right," Pascual muttered. "Guess if I'd waited a little longer before bathin' her, they'd sure of got me, those devils!"

Andrea's body rose slowly to the surface. She was dead enough now. He watched the waves a moment, as they cradled the corpse, then turned back to Mora. And together they made their way home again.

Translated by ANGEL FLORES

Antonio Machado

THE CRIME TOOK PLACE IN GRANADA

To Federico García Lorca

I

THE CRIME

HE WAS SEEN, walking among the guns
down a long road
that gave upon the country-side cold
in the dawn, yet beneath the stars.
They killed Federico
as the first light pricked.
The murderous band

dared not look on his face.
They all closed their eyes;
they prayed: . . . Even God shall not save thee . . .
Federico fell dead
—blood on his face, lead in his bowels—
. . . There in Granada the crime took place.
You know— . . . poor Granada . . . —his Granada.

II

THE POET AND DEATH

He was seen walking along with Death
fearless before her scythe.
—Even now the sun from tower to tower
hammers on the anvil,
anvil on anvil in the forges.
Federico spake,
jocund with Death. She gave ear.
'Because yesterday in my verse, companion mine,
crackled the brittle sound of thy palms,
the gleam to my song thou gavest, and to my tragedy
the sharpness of thy silver scythe,
I will sing thy fleshless bones,
thy eyeless holes,
thy windblown hair,
thy rosy lips that were kissed . . .
to-day even as yesterday,
gitane, death of mine,
such friends, along together, thou and I,
the life-breath of Granada? . . . my Granada.'

III

He was seen to fade in air . . .
                    Cut, friends,
in stone and dreams, in Alhambra,
a tomb for the poet,

over a fountain where the water weeps
and eternally cries:
the crime took place in Granada . . . his Granada.

Translated by D. TREVOR

Federico García Lorca

POEMS

SAN MIGUEL

FROM THE rocky shelves they come,
in the mountain, mountain, mountain,
mules and shadows of mules
loaded down with sunflower buds.

Watchful of the craggy drops
they swagger through the infinite night.
Through the corners of the wind
crackle salty threads of dawn.

A sky of white mules
shuts eyes of liquid silver,
finished weeping now across the dark,
the hollows brimming
silent shadow waiting to be tapped.
And the water freezes,
too cold for touch of man.
Mad water known only
in the mountain, mountain, mountain.

In the alcove of his tower,
San Miguel, by lantern light,
covers tight his handsome thighs
from a bolt of rare old lace.
His servant, an archangel,
on the heavy stroke of twelve
becomes a quick soft fury
of nightingales and feathers.

San Miguel sings in the windows;
three thousand Sapphic nights,
fragrance from colonial waters
and misted scent of far off flowers.

The sea dances on the strand,
rippling poem of balconies.
Along the shores of the moon
the rushes swirl to sea,
and voices whisper in their root holes.
Bright shawl draped girls of old Spain come
munching seeds of sunflowers,
their buttocks large, flesh dark
as copper planets.
They come—court gentlemen
and dames of sad demeanor,
swarthy with nostalgia
for a yesterday of nightingales.
Here's the bishop of Manila,
blind from plucking saffron for a living,
with his two sons, saying mass,
for every man and woman.

San Miguel grows silent
in the alcove of his tower,
with his patchwork petticoat
of tiny flaps and mirrors.

King of the globes, San Miguel,
and of the odd numbers,
in the skill of candy making
for the gay squeals of the crowd.

BALLAD OF THE SUMMONING

My solitude without rest!
Small eyes of my body,
large eyes of my horse,
not closing at night

nor seeking the sea,
where melting in silence
are thirteen ships.
So clean and hard
are the watchdogs.
Only the North does my eyes see,
the metals and crags of the North.
My body the stake
in a lonely game
with playing cards of ice.

Thick water bulls
attack the boys
who bathe in the moons
of their curling horns.
And the hammers are singing
on the sleeping anvils
and the cavalier walks
with his sleepless horse.

On the twenty fifth of June
they said to Amargo:
You may cut, if you like,
the rose vines of your garden.
Paint a cross on your door,
put your name beneath it,
for the hemlock and nettle
will spring from your thigh;
wet needles of lye
will bite through your shoes.

In the far night
along the magnetic mountain
drink the water bulls
and the reeds rustle.
Shafts of aurora
crackle in velvet.
Cross yourself and pretend
you enjoy ice bent wind,
born of metals and crags.

In two months, or less,
you will drop enshrouded.
Misty blades
cleave the air of Santiago.
Sword deep silence falls
from the shorn sky.

The twenty fifth of June
opens the eyes of Amargo
and the twenty fifth of August
closes them again.
Men are flung to the street
by the breath of the Summoned;
a fanfare proclaims
her solitude without rest.
And the clean altar sheets
of hard Roman design
lend a balance to death
with the stretch of their breadth.

THE FIRST HISTORICAL BALLAD: A MARTYRDOM OF SANTA EULALIA

1

PANORAMA OF MERIDA

Rearing and trotting along the street
is a horse of sweeping tail,
while the old soldiers of Rome
are gambling or sleeping.
Minerva's half mountain
spreads leafless arms.
The ledges of the rocks
are like water on their sword blades.
A night of sprawled bodies
and splintered stars
is awaiting the threads of dawn
to end it all.

The blasphemies of a cock
shrill redly now and then.
With a groan the saint child
smashes the crystal chalices.
A wheel sharpens knives
and the pointed meat hooks:
The anvil bull bellows
and the tiara of Merida
is a fierce crown of spikenards
and sprouts of blackberry bushes.

. . . .

THE BULLFIGHT

On the handle end
the knives of Albecete,
more handsome in blood to the contrary,
shine as the fish.
Eternal glow from the gambler's spangles,
cut down on the bitter green,
about him angry horses
and profiles of the cavaliers.
High in an olive tree
weep two old women.
The bull, victorious in the gamble,
runs vainly at the walls.
Black angels carry
scarfs and cups of melted snow.
Angels with great wings
of knives of Albecete.
Juan Antonio from Montilla
dead atop the pyre
his body strewn with irises,
a pomegranate on his forehead.
Now he mounts the cross of fire,
highroad of death.

The judge, with Civil Guard,
comes through the olive fields.

Blood slowly dripping
changes the serpent's songs.
Sir Civil Guards:
I come by here often.
There are four dead Romans
and five Carthaginians.

The afternoon, mad with figtrees,
with hot hushed whisperings,
falls pale on its thighs,
wounded by the cavaliers.
And black angels fly
on the west wind.
Angels with long tresses
and hearts of olive oil.

Translated by LLOYD MALLAN

SONG OF THE RIDER

In the black moon,
the spurs of the highwayman
are jingling.

Black horse,
where do you carry
your dead rider?

... the hard spurs
of the motionless bandit
who lost his reins.

Cold horse.
What perfume of flowers
in the knife!

In the black moon
bled the sides
of Sierra Morena.

Black horse,
where do you carry
your dead rider?

Night spurs on
your black flanks,
piercing you with stars.

Cold horse.
What perfume of flowers
in the knife.

In the black moon,
a cry! and the long
horn of the bonfire.

Black horse,
where do you carry
your dead rider?

NIGHT SONG OF THE ANDALUSIAN SAILORS

What a fine little road
from Cadiz to Gibraltar.
The sea recognizes
my step by its sighs.

Ay, maid, maid,
so many ships in Malaga's harbor!

Between Cadiz and Seville
what abundance of lemon trees!
The lemon grove recognizes
me by its sighs.

Ay, maid, maid,
so many ships in Malaga's harbor!

Between Carmona and Seville
not a knife can be found.
The cut-off half-moon will
pass through the air wounded.

Ay, lad, lad,
how the waves carry my horse over!

Through the salt pits' deadness
I forgot you, my love.
He who wants a heart,
let him beg of my forgetfulness.

Ay, lad, lad,
how the waves carry my horse over!

Cadiz, don't come near this spot
lest the sea cover you.
Seville, stand on your toes
lest the river drown you.

Ay, maid,
ay, lad,
what a fine little road!
So many ships in the harbor,
and in the square, how cold!

Translated by EDWIN HONIG

José Ortega y Gasset

THE PRIMITIVE AND THE TECHNICAL

IT IS MUCH to my purpose to recall that we are here engaged in the analysis of a situation—the actual one—which is of its essence ambiguous. Hence I suggested at the start that all the features of the present day, and in particular the rebellion of the masses, offer a double aspect. Any one of them not only admits of, but requires, a double interpretation, favourable and unfavourable. And this ambiguity lies, not in our minds, but in the reality itself. It is not that the present situation may appear to us good from one view-point, and evil from another, but that in itself it contains the twin potencies of triumph or of death.

There is no call to burden this essay with a complete philosophy of history. But it is evident that I am basing it on the underlying foundation of my own philosophical convictions. I do not believe in the absolute determinism of history. On the contrary, I believe that all life, and consequently the life of history, is made up of simple moments, each of them relatively undetermined in respect of the previous one, so that in it reality hesitates, walks up and down, and is uncertain whether to decide for one or other of various possibilities. It is this metaphysical hesitancy which gives to everything living its unmistakable character of tremulous vibration. The rebellion of the masses *may*, in fact, be the transition to some new, unexampled organisation of humanity, but it *may* also be a catastrophe of human destiny. There is no reason to deny the reality of progress, but there is to correct the notion that believes this progress secure. It is more in accordance with facts to hold that there is no certain progress, no evolution, without the threat of "involution," of retrogression. Everything is possible in history; triumphant, indefinite progress equally with periodic retrogression. For life, individual or collective, personal or historic, is the one entity in the universe whose substance is compact of danger, of adventure. It is, in the strict sense of the word, drama.[1]

This, which is true in general, acquires greater force in "moments of crisis" such as the present. And so, the symptoms of new conduct which are appearing under the actual dominion of the masses, and which we have grouped under the term "direct action," *may* also announce future perfections. It is evident that every old civilisation drags with it in its advance worn-out tissues and no small load of callous matter, which form an obstacle to life, mere toxic dregs. There are dead institutions, valuations and estimates which still survive, though now meaningless, unneces-

[1] Needless to say, hardly anyone will take seriously these expressions, and even the best-intentioned will understand them as mere metaphors, though perhaps striking ones. Only an odd reader, ingenuous enough not to believe that he already knows definitively what life is, or at least what it is not, will allow himself to be won over by the primary meaning of these phrases, and will be precisely the one who will *understand* them—be they true or false. Amongst the rest there will reign the most effusive unanimity, with this solitary difference: some will think that, *speaking seriously,* life is the process of existence of a soul, and others that it is a succession of chemical reactions. I do not conceive that it will improve my position with readers so hermetically sealed to resume my whole line of thought by saying that the *primary, radical* meaning of life appears when it is employed in the sense not of biology, but of biography. For the very strong reason that the whole of biology is quite definitely only a chapter in certain biographies, it is what biologists do in the portion of their lives open to biography. Anything else is abstraction, fantasy and myth.

sarily complicated solutions, standards whose lack of substance has been proved. All these constituents of "indirect action," of civilisation, demand a period of feverish simplification. The tall hat and frock-coat of the romantic period are avenged by means of present-day *déshabillé* and "shirt-sleeves." Here, the simplification means hygiene and better taste, consequently a more perfect solution, as always happens when more is obtained by smaller means. The tree of romantic love also was badly in need of pruning in order to shed the abundance of imitation magnolias tacked on to its branches and the riot of creepers, spirals, and tortuous ramifications which deprived it of the sun.

In general, public life and above all politics, urgently needed to be brought back to reality, and European humanity could not turn the somersault which the optimist demands of it, without first taking off its clothes, getting down to its bare essence, returning to its real self. The enthusiasm which I feel for this discipline of stripping oneself bare, of being one's real self, the belief that it is indispensable in order to clear the way to a worthy future, leads me to claim full liberty of thought with regard to everything in the past. It is the future which must prevail over the past, and from it we take our orders regarding our attitude towards what has been.[1]

But it is necessary to avoid the great sin of those who directed the XIXth Century, the lack of recognition of their responsibilities which prevented them from keeping alert and on the watch. To let oneself slide down the easy slope offered by the course of events and to dull one's mind against the extent of the danger, the unpleasant features which characterise even the most joyous hour, that is precisely to fail in one's obligation of responsibility. To-day it has become necessary to stir up an exaggerated sense of responsibility in those capable of feeling it, and it seems of supreme urgency to stress the evidently dangerous aspect of present-day symptoms.

There is no doubt that on striking a balance of our public life the adverse factors far outweigh the favourable ones, if the calculation be made not so much in regard to the present, as to what they announce and promise for the future.

---

[1] This freedom of attitude towards the past is not, then, a peevish revolt, but, on the contrary, an evident obligation, on the part of every "period of criticism." If I defend the liberalism of the XIXth Century against the masses which rudely attack it, this does not mean that I renounce my full freedom of opinion as regards that same liberalism. And vice versa, the primitivism which in this essay appears in its worst aspect is in a certain sense a condition of every great historic advance. Compare what, a few years ago, I said on this matter in the essay "Biología y Pedagogía" (*El Espectador*, III, *La paradoja del salvajismo*).

All the increased material possibilities which life has experienced run the risk of being annulled when they are faced with the staggering problem that has come upon the destiny of Europe, and which I once more formulate: the direction of society has been taken over by a type of man who is not interested in the principles of civilisation. Not of this or that civilisation but—from what we can judge to-day—of any civilisation. Of course, he is interested in anesthetics, motor-cars, and a few other things. But this fact merely confirms his fundamental lack of interest in civilisation. For those things are merely its products, and the fervour with which he greets them only brings into stronger relief his indifference to the principles from which they spring. It is sufficient to bring forward this fact: since the *nuove scienze*, the natural sciences, came into being—from the Renaissance on, that is to say—the enthusiasm for them had gone on increasing through the course of time. To put it more concretely, the proportionate number of people who devoted themselves to pure scientific research was in each generation greater. The first case of retrogression—relative, I repeat—has occurred in the generation of those between twenty and thirty at the present time. It is becoming difficult to attract students to the laboratories of pure science. And this is happening when industry is reaching its highest stage of development, and when people in general are showing still greater appetite for the use of the apparatus and the medicines created by science. If we did not wish to avoid prolixity, similar incongruity could be shown in politics, art, morals, religion, and in the everyday activities of life.

What is the significance to us of so paradoxical a situation? This essay is an attempt to prepare the answer to that question. The meaning is that the type of man dominant to-day is a primitive one, a *Naturmensch* rising up in the midst of a civilised world. The world is a civilised one, its inhabitant is not: he does not see the civilisation of the world around him, but he uses it as if it were a natural force. The new man wants his motorcar, and enjoys it, but he believes that it is the spontaneous fruit of an Edenic tree. In the depths of his soul he is unaware of the artificial, almost incredible, character of civilisation, and does not extend his enthusiasm for the instruments to the principles which make them possible. When some pages back, by a transposition of the words of Rathenau, I said that we are witnessing the "vertical invasion of the barbarians" it might be thought (it generally is) that it was only a matter of a "phrase." It is now clear that the expression may enshrine a truth or an error, but that it is the very opposite of a "phrase," namely: a formal definition which sums up a whole complicated analysis. The actual mass-man is, in fact, a primitive who has slipped through the wings on to the age-old stage of civilisation.

There is continual talk to-day of the fabulous progress of technical knowledge; but I see no signs in this talk, even amongst the best, of a sufficiently dramatic realisation of its future. Spengler himself, so subtle and profound—though so subject to mania—appears to me in this matter far too optimistic. For he believes that "culture" is to be succeeded by an era of "civilisation," by which word he understands more especially technical efficiency. The idea that Spengler has of "culture" and of history in general is so remote from that underlying this essay, that it is not easy, even for the purpose of correction, to comment here upon his conclusions. It is only by taking great leaps and neglecting exact details, in order to bring both view-points under a common denominator, that it is possible to indicate the difference between us. Spengler believes that "technicism" can go on living when interest in the principles underlying culture are dead. I cannot bring myself to believe any such thing. Technicism and science are consubstantial, and science no longer exists when it ceases to interest for itself alone, and it cannot so interest unless men continue to feel enthusiasm for the general principles of culture. If this fervour is deadened—as appears to be happening—technicism can only survive for a time, for the duration of the inertia of the cultural impulse which started it. We live with our technical requirements, but not *by* them. These give neither nourishment nor breath to themselves, they are not *causae sui*, but a useful, practical precipitate of superfluous, unpractical activities.[1] I proceed, then, to the position that the actual interest in technical accomplishment guarantees nothing, less than nothing, for the progress or the duration of such accomplishment. It is quite right that technicism should be considered one of the characteristic features of "modern culture," that is to say, of a culture which comprises a species of science which proves materially profitable. Hence, when describing the newest aspect of the existence implanted by the XIXth Century, I was left with these two features: liberal democracy and technicism. But I repeat that I am astonished at the ease with which when speaking of technicism it is forgotten that its vital centre is pure science, and that the conditions for its continuance involve the same conditions that render possible pure scientific

---

[1] Hence, to my mind, a definition of North America by its "technicism" tells us nothing. One of the things that most seriously confuse the European mind is the mass of puerile judgments that one hears pronounced on North America even by the most cultured persons. This is one particular case of the disproportion which I indicate later on as existing between the complexity of present-day problems and the capacity of present-day minds.

activity. Has any thought been given to the number of things that must remain active in men's souls in order that there may still continue to be "men of science" in real truth? Is it seriously thought that as long as there are dollars there will be science? This notion in which so many find rest is only a further proof of primitivism. As if there were not numberless ingredients, of most disparate nature, to be brought together and shaken up in order to obtain the cock-tail of physico-chemical science! Under even the most perfunctory examination of this subject, the evident fact bursts into view that over the whole extent of space and time, physico-chemistry has succeeded in establishing itself completely only in the small quadrilateral enclosed by London, Berlin, Vienna, and Paris, and that only in the XIXth Century. This proves that experimental science is one of the most unlikely products of history. Seers, priests, warriors and shepherds have abounded in all times and places. But this fauna of experimental man apparently requires for its production a combination of circumstances more exceptional than those that engender the unicorn. Such a bare, sober fact should make us reflect a little on the supervolatile, evaporative character of scientific inspiration.[1] Blissful the man who believes that, were Europe to disappear, the North Americans could *continue* science! It would be of great value to treat the matter thoroughly and to specify in detail what are the historical presuppositions, vital to experimental science and, consequently, to technical accomplishment. But let no one hope that, even when this point was made clear, the mass-man would understand. The mass-man has no attention to spare for reasoning, he learns only in his own flesh.

There is one observation which bars me from deceiving myself as to the efficacy of such preachments, which by the fact of being based on reason would necessarily be subtle. Is it not altogether absurd that, under actual circumstances, the average man does not feel spontaneously, and without being preached at, an ardent enthusiasm for those sciences and the related ones of biology? For, just consider what the actual situation is. While evidently all the other constituents of culture—politics, art, social standards, morality itself—have become problematic, there is one which increasingly demonstrates, in a manner most indisputable and most suitable to impress the mass-man, its marvellous efficiency: and that one is empirical science. Every day furnishes a new invention which this average man utilises. Every day produces a new anesthetic or vaccine from

---

[1] This, without speaking of more internal questions. The majority of the investigators themselves have not to-day the slightest suspicion of the very grave and dangerous internal crisis through which their science is passing.

which this average man benefits. Everyone knows that, if scientific inspiration does not weaken and the laboratories are multiplied three times
or ten times, there will be an automatic multiplication of wealth, comfort, health, prosperity. Can any more formidable, more convincing propaganda be imagined in favour of a vital principle? How is it, nevertheless,
that there is no sign of the masses imposing on themselves any sacrifice
of money or attention in order to endow science more worthily? Far from
this being the case, the post-war period has converted the man of science
into a new social pariah. And note that I am referring to physicists, chemists, biologists, not to philosophers. Philosophy needs neither protection,
attention nor sympathy from the masses. It maintains its character of
complete inutility,[1] and thereby frees itself from all subservience to the
average man. It recognises itself as essentially problematic, and joyously
accepts its free destiny as a bird of the air, without asking anybody to
take it into account, without recommending or defending itself. If it does
really turn out to the advantage of anyone, it rejoices from simple human
sympathy; but does not live on the profit it brings to others, neither an-
ticipating it nor hoping for it. How can it lay claim to being taken seriously by anyone if it starts off by doubting its own existence, if it lives
only in the measure in which it combats itself, deprives itself of life? Let
us, then, leave out of the question philosophy, which is an adventure of
another order. But the experimental sciences do need the co-operation of
the mass-man, just as he needs them, under pain of dissolution, inasmuch
as in a planet without physico-chemistry the number of beings existing
to-day cannot be sustained.

What arguments can bring about something which has not been
brought about by the motor-car in which those men come and go, and
the pantopon injection which destroys, *miraculously,* their pains? The disproportion between the constant, evident benefit which science procures
them and the interest they show in it is such that it is impossible to-day
to deceive oneself with illusory hopes and to expect anything but barbarism from those who so behave. *Especially if, as we shall see, this disregard of science as such appears, with possibly more evidence than
elsewhere, in the mass of technicians themselves—doctors, engineers, etc.,*
who are in the habit of exercising their profession in a state of mind
identical in all essentials to that of the man who is content to use his
motor-car or buy his tube of aspirin—without the slightest intimate solidarity with the future of science, of civilisation.

There may be those who feel more disturbed by other symptoms of

[1] Aristotle, *Metaphysics,* 893a. 10.

emergent barbarism which, being positive in quality, results of action and not of omission, strike the attention more, materialise into a spectacle. For myself, this matter of the disproportion between the profit which the average man draws from science and the gratitude which he returns—or, rather, does not return—to it; this is much more terrifying.[1] I can only succeed in explaining to myself this absence of adequate recognition by recalling that in Central Africa the negroes also ride in motor-cars and dose themselves with aspirin. The European who is beginning to predominate—so runs my hypothesis—must then be, *in relation to the complex civilisation into which he has been born,* a primitive man, a barbarian appearing on the stage through the trap-door, a "vertical invader."

Translator anonymous by request

Gabriel Miró

SEÑOR CUENCA AND HIS SUCCESSOR

THE TRAIN was passing through the flat orchard lands of Orihuela. The landscape slid along, spreading out behind in a panorama of tall, thick, dark hemp plants, luxuriant orange trees, little paths among the green hillocks, rude, patched, white-washed huts with roofs that rested like light cloaks upon the rough-hewn logs which still retained the rugged beauty of living trees, narrow roads, and in the distance, a cart with its burden of sweet-smelling verdure. Under the shadow of an elm, two cows, foul with dung, lay upon the ground, munching tender stalks of maize. Beyond were barren mountain peaks, their naked ribs of living rock penetrating as far as the damp soft earth where terraces of fruit trees stood and then withdrawing blood-stained by the dry plots of ground where fruit was spread to dry in the sun. There were the incidents of a river and an old mill surrounded by ducks, a clump of black poplars and mulberry trees, a solitary palm, a hermitage with a large, black, votive cross nailed to its gable, a patch of blue smoke on the horizon, a narrow canal, two gardeners in overalls breaking the hemp with swingles, orange groves, wheat fields. Then came the river again; in the

---

[1] The monstrosity is increased a hundredfold by the fact that, as I have indicated, all the other vital principles, politics, law, art, morals, religion, are actually passing through a crisis, are at least temporarily bankrupt. Science alone is not bankrupt; rather does it every day pay out, with fabulous interest, all and more than it promises. It is, then, without a competitor; it is impossible to excuse the average man's disregard of it by considering him distracted from it by some other cultural enthusiasm.

background, upon the mountain's back, lay the Seminary, large, desultory, white, and crowned with spires; below, on the side of the mountain, began the city, bristling with the red, white, blue and brown towers and cupolas of parish churches, the cathedral, and the monasteries; on the right, isolated high upon the mountain range, dark, massive and portentous, with gargoyles, windows, and garrets, with its square belfry resembling a tower with a cornice supported on the shoulders of a few monstrous little men, loomed the Jesuit College of Santo Domingo.

Over the orchards, the river and the town spread a tenuous blue cloud. The landscape exhaled the heavy warm odor of dung and stables, the fresh smell of irrigation, the sharp fetid stench of pools of macerated hemp and the unpleasant harsh odor of hemp drying in conical stacks.

Sigüenza sadly contemplated the afternoon. He was sick with sadness, with a sadness so bitter, so intense, that it could not be merely a passing sentiment. It possessed a reality in itself, quite apart from him, larger and stronger than his very soul. It pervaded everything he saw, for the valley with its smoke and its trees, the mountains and the sky, everything was as if fashioned of sadness, curdled thick with it—that same sadness had oppressed him in childhood when, dressed in his schoolboy's uniform, he used to march with the class of smaller boys along those very paths and wait for the train to pass. Now, the train brought him happy memories that made him even more sad than did the landscape and his return to the college of Santo Domingo.

Sigüenza turned to a gentleman, a fellow traveler, who was taking his son to be enrolled in the Jesuit school and began to speak of some of the memories of his own sojourn there as a student.

The gentleman interrupted him, "And wouldn't you like to relive those years? Don't you find that the pain of your school days was really quite delightful? You don't? Why not? Why, if you had sons, wouldn't you send them to the place where you yourself went to school?"

Sigüenza answered that he would not. If that pain, sadness, is pleasant, it must be so only for adults, for the sadness of children is dry and frozen, without the fragrance lent by distance.

When he was at Santo Domingo, he envied the untrameled free life of the village smith, the sound of whose songs and hammer-blows came in gaily at all the windows, breaking the silence of study-hours; he envied a certain Señor Rebollo, a vendor of homemade chocolates, at whom all the boys looked with wonder as they passed by his shop, delighted with the clamor of his rollers and the warm aroma of the cocoa; he envied the men who sat upon the river bank, smoking and watching the bubbles in the stream; he envied the coachman who went to and from the station, cracking his whip until it sounded like the sky rockets of holidays and shouting rude compliments to the peasant women. Sigüenza, when young, fancied this man as the symbol of the holy sentiment of all homes, because in his carriage the parents of fellow students usually arrived at school. They called the driver, "Pine-up-rooter," a marvelous, legendary sobriquet coming from the heavy red lettering and the decorative figure—it might have been a monkey tugging at a branch—which were painted above the door of his coach. At night when Sigüenza translated his fifteen lines of the "Aeneid," marked by the imprint of his fingernail, "Pine-up-rooter" passed gloriously, like an Esplanadian or an Amadis, across the pages of his text-book, transforming it into a grove of ancient pines, sonorous, fragrant and enchanted.

"And what does this all mean? And what does it matter?" the gentleman said. "What have such things to do with the bringing up and the educating of children? Have you any children? Oh, indeed? You have two daughters? Well—I beg your pardon, but I think you ought to enter them in some school. Let them be badly brought up? How can you say that? Good heavens, man!"

Yes, perhaps, Sigüenza was not bringing up his daughters right; at least, it might appear so, according to some points of view. For if they were the least bit ill, he remembered every occasion when, in reproving some one of their whims, he had spoken harshly to the poor little things, and he was repentant, promising himself never again to cause them pain.

"That," shouted the gentleman, "would all be taken care of if you would only send them away to board at a very strict school!"

"To board! Never!"

The schoolboy's father became so indignant that the whole of his round face grew red.

They arrived at Orihuela and went by coach as far as the inn. Later, they dined together and continued chatting on the same subject.

"If only you could have known Señor Cuenca!" said Sigüenza to his companion.

"Why, who is that gentleman?"

"They are very polite in their manner of address at the Jesuit schools. They say 'Señor' to all the students, even to the small boys. I was eight years old when I entered Santo Domingo. So many 'Señors' from the lips of those very serious and learned priests, with their shining spectacles, astonished me, as at home even the servants spoke familiarly to me. But I was still more surprised that they should speak like that to the little fellow standing beside me. I were long trousers, but his trousers were short, and he had stockings. He was much younger than I, delicate, pale and forever dreaming, with his little hands always stained with ink, with the strings of his breeches and the laces of his shoes always untied and hanging down. His name was Cuenca. But, you see, they called him, 'Señor Cuenca.' 'Señor Cuenca,' the Brother Inspector would cry in his dry commanding voice. I would glance at my comrade. His head would be buried in his arms which he had crossed on his desk. The Brother Inspector would mutter, 'Señor Sigüenza, shake Señor Cuenca, he has fallen asleep!' I would wake him. And Señor Cuenca would open his large eyes, misty with sleep and sadness, look at me surprised, stretch himself and then smile forgiveness. The voice of the Brother would thunder. Señor Cuenca would shrug his shoulders, 'What is the Brother saying?' 'He is telling you to get down on your knees!' 'On my knees! Why?'

"Señor Cuenca would kneel. 'Señor Cuenca, Señor Cuenca, I must give you a bad mark in neatness! Don't you see that your stockings are falling down?'

"Almost invariably I had to pull them up for him. They were thick, white woolen stockings, made by Señor Cuenca's nurse at his home in La Mancha. I also had to tie them, since Señor Cuenca did not know how to make his garters hold. Beside Señor Cuenca, I considered myself a grown man and his protector; so I smiled at him paternally.

"Then came the week of Holy Penance. We had to spend it in silence, examining our consciences and listening to sermons on sin, death, hell, purgatory, and salvation. . . . During this time, most of the chapel windows were closed and the entire altar was draped in black. When we sang 'Pardon, oh, my Lord!' we cried out in despair, not because we were inspired to implore grace with such fierce eagerness, but rather to avenge ourselves for the long silence imposed upon us. But Señor Cuenca did not sing. He closed his eyes and dropped his little head, resting it upon my left shoulder. I said to him, 'I'm warning you, they'll punish us both!' Without looking at me, Señor Cuenca smiled. He was very white with two little wrinkles close to his lips, as if he were about to burst into tears. 'My head aches so!' he murmured.

"On the last day of the Penances, instead of Señor Cuenca, there appeared beside me another boy, a fat, red, quiet, and extremely devout boy. I asked him where Cuenca was: 'Where's Cuenca, you?' But the creature did not even answer me. At recess, I asked the Brother for permission to speak with my friend, but he refused. Presently the week of silence came to an end. All the students let out a first free shout, expansive and joyous. I ran to the Inspector and asked for Señor Cuenca. 'Haven't you learned that it is a serious fault to ask questions? Don't do it again!' he warned me.

"Humiliated and depressed, I withdrew, thinking only of Señor Cuenca. Why was that pale boy no longer with us, the sweet, sad, little thing who, when he smiled, seemed more pitiable than when he wept? Where could he be? my little comrade, with his olive-colored breeches and his white, soft, wrinkled stockings which he did not know how to keep up and which seemed to be begging for the hands of a mother, or at least for the hands of Señor Cuenca's nurse.

Two days passed. Then, after the first afternoon recess, we did not go to the study-hall, but to our dormitories. As we entered our rooms the Inspector ordered, 'Holiday uniforms, overcoats and caps.'

Although astonished, we obeyed the command. Where could we be going in such clothes when it was only Wednesday?

We went down to the chapel. What was going to happen? Could it be that the Reverend Father of the Province was coming? Yes, yes, it must be his Reverence. Perhaps, he would give us a holiday, in honor of his visit, a special picnic in the country! Señor Cuenca was not there. What fun we would have! But where was Señor Cuenca?

"We entered the church. I shuddered with fright. My hair and my temples were damp with a cold sweat.

"In the chancel stood a narrow, white coffin, surrounded with candles; inside the box I saw poor Señor Cuenca, very long and very yellow, smiling at me. . . . I swear he smiled at me! . . . And he smiled as if he were showing me the long trousers of his holiday uniform. . . ."

The father of the prospective student lit a cigar, enveloped himself in smoke, and gruffly said, with a slight cough, "It was all due to lack of care. He"—with a movement of his chin, he pointed to his son—"he has never worn laced shoes, but always the other kind, made all in one piece. And socks and garters, and buttons on his drawers. Isn't that so, my child?"

Translated by Angel Flores

Ramón Goméz de la Serna

STRANGE CASES

THE WHITE SMILE

THERE IS a smile I come across rarely in life. When I find it, I know what it means, and I close my lips as though it had warned me not to talk, not to disclose what I see.

"Doctor, why it's nothing!" the patient says with a smile.

I do not feel his pulse. I make no further observations. That patient is not my patient. I take only patients whom I can cure and no others.

"No, really—there is nothing I can do." Let them call in their family doctor. This is not illness for me. I must see on the patient's face that his illness justifies me to undertake a cure. Here, I do not see that. For patients with that kind of a smile—a few words and a short visit.

Even I, who am constantly witnessing human misfortune and disillusionment, though I never attend weddings, am frightened by that smile. How could I describe that white smile to you?

Those people smile blankly, smile whitely, smile with a whiteness of absolute pallor; their eyes, be they black, blue, or tobacco-colored, enter the smile like white eyes—two great cataracts clouding like brandy mixed with too much water, the eyes of a statue. The wrinkles of that smile are not the wrinkles of old age, but those on the face of a youth whom medical students are tickling with tweezers in the operating room. The very clear smile of a person for whom the coming month means a journey is cast by the patient upon the passers-by, upon the furniture, upon everything. It is his farewell smile, the smile which he leaves so as to remain on good terms with them. That smile cannot be confused with the smile of a convalescent, with that of a consumptive or with that of a kind patient. No, that smile is the smile of moonlight on ruins or over graveyards.

Often in order to know how badly infected with death my patient is I say to him like the photographers, "Smile!" The smile that comes from him tells me much about his illness. Some photographs show a smile like a hook, others one like a horseshoe, or perhaps one suffering from an acute pain on the right side. But none show the smile of utter hopelessness. That kind of a smile is already on the face of this sitter.

How painful to have to bid farewell forever to one who always smiles so exquisitely! But it cannot be helped; otherwise, this smile would affect us like the subtle wind that brings pneumonia, and immediately we would catch that very smile, and then—goodbye to all of our plans. . . .

THE IDIOT CHILD

I am often summoned to aristocratic homes to cure an idiot child. Usually there is no way of making oneself understood by an idiot child. When I do not find the spark of reason that sometimes appears in idiots, I give them up as hopeless cases. I go away filled with sadness, because their cries are calling me as if even in their idiocy they realize that the only one who could have cured them has passed them by.

I have been able to cure some by gradually untwining with my long fingers the tight knot that has formed in their brains.

The last patient I cured was an idiot who always stood at the edge of a large pond in the palace garden and never for a single moment stopped throwing stones into the water. The only thing that pleased him a little was the gurgle of the water as it swallowed stones.

I noticed that they scolded him and took him away from the pond as soon as they discovered him, although he would take advantage of their every distraction, with that maliciousness and sagacity peculiar to idiots, in order to go back to throwing stones into the big pond.

"Manolín, stop it! Manolín, behave!"

An idiot is generally misunderstood everywhere. The people who failed to understand this child showed that they were more idiotic than he.

"He has no other occupation than throwing stones into the pond. As soon as our backs are turned, he is out there."

"Well, you see," I said, "the only way to cure him is to let him fill the pond with stones, to let him see his work finished. You'll see how his idiocy will vanish when he sighs that deep sigh that cures idiots."

I went away. It was only after several months had passed that the Count, the boy's father, visited me and said, "You cannot imagine how difficult it has been for him to fill the pond with stones. He has left the garden without a single stone, and sometimes he has used earth to fill it up better. He has worked desperately like a mason working overtime. But a few days ago when a kind of pyramid of stones rose from the dried-up pond the child sat down on the top of it, heaved the deep sigh you mentioned to us and became sane. You do not know how much more sensible the child has been since that day. It seems that, after having fulfilled his mission of idiocy, it was no longer necessary for him to be so. . . ."

GREGUERÍAS

Airplanes were invented to catch the balloons that get loose from children's hands in the parks. They have changed their purpose from the one for which God created them, but originally they were created for that.

❋   ❋   ❋

Zoroaster is a stupendous name that convinces. A man with such a name might have been anything. Thus, I would choose, with great faith, Zoroaster's religion.

❋   ❋   ❋

It is difficult to imagine that a bare, dry skull is that of a woman . . . I am sure that you never have thought that any you had seen was that of a woman. It is hard to forget all of life's passions and come to such a conclusion, so extreme and so a-sexual.

❋   ❋   ❋

Silence is not our silence, that which we must witness nor that in which we must be in order to understand, nor is it the silence Maeterlinck speaks of; these are worthless ideas. Silence is God, and it will be the only thing to last longer than eternity. It will conquer. Silence enjoys the most intense voluptuousness when it is left alone, when we do not disturb or distract it. I have often left silence respectfully alone, so as not to annoy it, left it master of my house and allowed it to kiss the women in the pictures . . . they are its women.

Translated by ANGEL FLORES

Ramón J. Sender

THE DANCING WITCH

OVER THE COUNTRYSIDE spring was beginning, and in the fields covered with the rime of frosty dawns appeared the "cucutes," birds with iridescent breasts and black-and-white wings. Children coveted them for their beauty, but hunters disdained them because their meat was rank. These birds always arrived towards the month of April, and they came singing:

"Cu-cut, cu-cut,
Second of May is Holy Cross."

That was the date of the fiestas. My town had five thousand inhabitants. In the centre, where we lived, there were buildings of two and even three storeys. But as one progressed towards the outskirts, the houses kept getting poorer, and finally became mere cabins; four walls and a hole in the roof for the smoke.

The village was overhung by a mountain with a side as sheer as if it had been cut off by a knife, rising right behind the last houses. It was a natural break two hundred metres high, on the crest of which, presiding over everything, there was a granite platform supporting a huge, iron cross. This cross stood out against the clear sky and protected the township, they said, from thunderbolts and hailstorms. The cliff formed a great step dug out, surely, by the current of the Orna, a river of powerful flow which came down the mountain somersaulting and throwing up blue foam. That great step followed for more than fifteen kilometres parallel to the river, to where it poured into another, larger stream. Between the "Ripas"—as the break was called—and the river was the high-road, which passed through the middle of the village, and between it and the river for a width of some two kilometres, stretched all the fields "under ditch"—orchards, truck gardens, groves—where they raised fruit famous not only roundabout, but in all Spain. The abundance of them allowed us, as children, to fight pitched battles with windfall apples and pears without the farmers' feeling injured. Sometimes, to keep the fruits from being entirely wasted, they collected them afterwards and fed them to the hogs.

In the curtain of sandy rock formed by the cliff, eagles and hawks nested. Their cries carried to my balcony, doubled by the echo which gave them a strange depth. In that echo I used to see the immensity of the night that was coming on. I still remembered, with some of the original feeling, how as a child in my loneliness I talked to the Ripas, to the hawks, and to the black hollows in which I located all the fantasies of my infancy.

But now I was forced to stay shut up in the house, because I had broken my arm and I was kept in for what seemed an eternity so that the bone would knit quickly. A little before that I had returned to the village after an escapade which took me to Saragossa, to Madrid, and to other beautiful cities, in the desire to try the strength of my wings. I was fifteen when I left and sixteen when I came back, I did not return to the village for love of my rustic home, but was brought back by my family and escorted by the king's police. Once in the settlement, I had to do what I could to turn exile into entertainment, and as what interested me most was my grandfather (I had always looked on my father as an enemy, which feeling he reciprocated; we were both quite unconscious of it, but it kept showing in fierce conflicts and delightful armistices) I drew close to my grandfather and lived with him as though no one else existed. He, too, had his quarters on the second floor, with the balcony and back room facing the Ripas. My grandfather loved me greatly (everyone said I looked like him) and I responded to him with that simple respect which the old like so, and which as far as I can remember had gone on increasing throughout my life.

I wanted to go to the farm with him, to irrigate, to prune grapevines in the wasteland (all the land without regular irrigation we called waste). I passed my days, before I broke my arm, helping him in the fields at the light work which he handled himself, and in return by degrees he gave me more and more tasks to carry out alone.

One day after my return, he said to me, "Have you met Ana Launer in the street or on the farm road?"

"No. Why?"

"If you run across her," he warned me mysteriously, "agree with whatever she says. Say yes to everything."

"Is she crazy?"

My grandfather didn't like to say. "In the village they say she's a witch. I don't believe in such superstitions, but . . ." He shrugged his shoulders. "Well, I don't know."

"Do you think she can do harm?"

"Our neighbour Antón," my uncle explained confidentially, "decided to make fun of her one day, and a little later two cows died on him."

"Pure chance," I said.

My grandfather shrugged again. "I tell you I don't believe in it, but it's better to say amen to everything. There's no point in stirring up chance; let it sleep."

After a pause he added, "Ana Launer talks to everyone, she comes and goes. She appears to the workmen and owners at night, in the fields, and says the oddest things to them. One of her whims," he said with a suppressed chuckle, "is to get hold of the most dignified people she can find and make them dance with her in the fields at night."

I burst out laughing.

"All right; laugh as much as you like, but if you meet her don't cross her."

Having read a little in Madrid on hysteria and sexuality (Freud's ideas, which were the fashion), I tried to diagnose her, and questioned my grandfather unwearyingly.

"I don't know what kind of woman she is," he told me. "She laughs all the time. She makes fun of herself. At night they say you can hear her laughing while you sit by the fireside. I think that's the cat on the roof. The old man of the Gonzalo house danced a bolero with her the other night down by the river."

Again I burst out laughing. My grandfather became very serious. You could see that the grotesqueness of that bolero on the river gave him the creeps.

"If you meet her," he insisted, "obey her. That costs nothing. She surely knows you have come back to the village, and she'll have you in mind."

Some days later I met Ana Launer in the street. She was dressed in black. She seemed fifty years old. She said nothing to me, but she looked me over so minutely that I had to smile and nod at her. Then I heard her call after me:

"Chip off the Garcés block! In one year your honesty has gone from you. You're the same make as your father and your grandfather."

Then two weeks passed without my seeing Ana Launer, and I forgot her.

One night we were due to irrigate the truck farm. The water came to us at eleven, and as an hour of irrigation cost a lot of money one had to be there on the dot so as not to waste it. The Irrigation Syndicate had all that well organized and the members irrigated their land by turns, religiously. I suggested to my grandfather that I should go. That seemed good to him, and at half past ten I was ready to start for the farm, which was near the river. I carried a hoe, and had stuck a dagger in my belt, because on nights when the river was running there were sometimes incidents over five minutes more or less of the water. My grandfather ran his hand over my clothes, removed the knife, kept it, and told me:

"The man who needs to use that is no man."

Then he explained that all trouble could be forestalled by going to see the guard who watched over the padlocked gates, and setting my watch with his. That way there would be no misunderstanding.

I set out for the farm. The village slept. The hooting of an owl fell rhythmically from the roof of the church. I passed by the old mill, went down the farm road, and in a few minutes reached our land. The main ditch in which the water would run when they opened the gate half a kilometre above, was on the border of the field, whose rows of rich vegetables stood out in the moonlight. On the other side of the ditch rose an old wall, but between wall and ditch—dry now, awaiting the water—there was a space of a metre, room enough to sit and smoke a cigarette.

Now the hush became less profound because the owl on the church had fallen silent. Far off a frog kept starting to croak, but he could not make up his mind. It began to affect me, and I started singing. But I stopped right away, for at the bottom of the field there appeared a white shape which came between the rows of my vegetables with mechanical, stiff movements. It was a woman. Loose blouse, skirt, and stockings were white. Under the moon, all the whiteness was splashed with blue. She walked on her toes, so that it looked as if she moved on wheels. At the same moment I thought of Ana Launer, and knew it was she. She held her elbows tight against her sides and her hands upraised, and she swayed idiotically from side to side. Dressed in white she seemed bigger, taller, younger. Long before she reached me she lifted her elbows as well, and with her open hands at shoulder height twisted her fingers in grotesque motions. The gravity of her expression was almost religious. It was mad, but there was such certainty in her movements, such lack of self-consciousness, that she began to seem reasonable to me. She stopped in front of me. I got up and tried to smile. She stared at me fixedly.

"Chip off the Garcés block," she said again.

"The chips fall as they may," I said, remembering the proverb.

Ana Launer seemed not to have heard.

"Do you want to dance with me?" she asked.

"I?" I said dubiously. "You can't dance without music."

She turned her back on me and began to go as she had come, dancing, with the same gestures, the same unawareness of me and of herself, like a mechanical doll. The hem of her skirt swept the lettuce leaves, making them rustle. Then from a distance she turned and called back:

"Heir to Garcés, before two o'clock you will dance without music."

Logic breaks down and we laugh or grow angry. This time I did not laugh; when the whole natural order turns upside down, and does it naturally moreover, neither laughter nor anger will serve.

The water came in. With my back to the wall, I opened the side ditches to lead it onto my plantings. The earth received it voluptuously, bubbling and drinking it in with a faint murmur under the wide leaves of the gourds and the melons. Holding your breath, you could hear the plants breathe with pleasure. I sat down, waiting for my full hour. I could not get Ana Launer out of my mind, and my preoccupation with her irritated me. The witch knows her job, I was thinking. She knows how to upset people with her white skirt and her little dances. Five minutes beforehand I got ready to shut off the ditch when the signal should come from the guard's bugle. As soon as I heard it, I shut off, and sat down again under the wall. Midnight, now, I told myself, and the witch isn't coming back nor have I any intention of dancing. Even witches can guess wrong.

Above my head I heard a deep sigh. It was a human sigh, only much stronger. A warm breath enveloped my head. I felt the cold ant-creep of terror up the back of my neck. I looked up and saw nothing. Nor was there anyone on either side. The night became terrifically heavy. It was hard work to make myself move. With an effort I turned, and found in the shadow of the wall—the moon just rested on its top—a mule's head, black, with great, unmoving eyes. Its nostrils were a hand's breadth from mine. That head stuck through a wide crack in the wall with a sort of dumb stubbornness, and stared at me with a total serenity somewhat belied by its ears, which were lying back and close together in the gesture of nervousness. The grotesque again.

Chance had been stirred up, by the look of things. I went around the wall, so as to leave the field. On the other side I met the mule, which studied me with the same rare curiosity. (The moon, which had moved away from the tumbledown wall, showed in the bottom of a pool.) This must be a stray. Perhaps it had got out of the stable because they forgot to tie it or to shut the doors. I gave a friendly pat on the neck. The animal blew its warm breath around me again, but its eyes kept on watching me unblinking. I recovered my nerve, and thought that if I mounted the mule, it would go tamely to its home when it felt me astride. I led it close to the wall and stepping on an outthrust stone, mounted. As I expected, it started travelling immediately, apparently certain of its direction. Now I felt at ease. When it stopped before its owner's door, I planned to call out and return it.

But the mule broke into a trot, and swinging around the church, turned down the old road, leaving the village behind. With open country ahead, I could not hold it in. Every moment its stride became longer and livelier until it worked up to a dead run. The mule straightened out for the cemetery, not for the main gate which gave on the road, but for the back, where the wall was partly broken down. In doing this it crossed two or three fields at a gallop. When it was at the wall, it bunched up to jump, and I let myself fall. My right arm hit the edge of a stone and was broken.

Without looking back, I headed for the road and made for home, holding up my arm as best I could. I thought at moments I saw a white shadow, but with the pain in my arm, fear of the fantastic had vanished.

When I got home and told my grandfather what had happened, he shook his head and said, "Why didn't you dance? We must do the senseless things asked of us, because if we don't, we awaken chance and when chance is awakened, it is to do harm to a man."

On the evening when my story starts, facing the Ripas, in my big, dilapidated, barnlike room, with the old religious pictures the blackened canvases of which were peeling from the frames, I thought over the event which had cost me two months of confinement, and I opened and shut my right hand violently (an exercise prescribed by the doctor), happy because I felt no twinge of pain. Nor had my right arm turned out shorter than my left. Everything was going well, and I was entranced by the promise that I could go hunting with my father the next day (we were having a period of armistice, thanks to the broken arm).

I looked at the Ripas with longing. Since I was a child I had tried to uncover its mysteries, climbing to all but inaccessible spots, peering at times into the eagles' nests. The stated purpose of these expeditions was to get the partridges and rabbits which the eagles caught and carried up to feed their young. With these as prizes we organized footraces for all the small fry of the village, from the children of the great houses down to the poorest. My friends and I, being all of nine years old, acted as judges and assumed enormous importance. The idea that the eagles went hunting for me, kept my father from scolding me too hard when I came in with my clothes shredded and my elbows and knees skinned.

My father was a cold man of few words. I can't remember kissing him save with the rigid formality of a soldier saluting his commander. Some afternoons he would take me hunting. But on the hunt being prepared for tomorrow, I was to be initiated as a grown man, a real hunter. My father had taken me up to the attic where he kept three shotguns. His own was dismounted and kept in a fine leather case. Standing before these he told me with a certain solemnity that all three were centrefire, with a reinforced breech adapted to smokeless powder, and that I should choose one. When I had made my choice he told me to have it clean and oiled for tomorrow, and to come down to watch him load shells, so that I could learn.

Just as I had from our earliest excursions, I deduced where we were going from the type of shell. If he loaded fine shot and number sixes, we were going along the river's edge after woodcock and other marsh birds. The trip was easy, with nothing fatiguing in it; cultivated strips, brooks, reed patches. If on the other hand he loaded with buckshot, ball, and number fives, we were going to the uplands on top of the Ripas, where there were foxes, hares, and in winter it was not unusual to find wolves. The upland was a vast, grey wilderness beginning right at the top of the Ripas, there where the cross had been planted. The fact of the cross guarding the approach made it all the more desolate. To go to the upland was always an adventure.

In that grey, obscure wilderness one ran across occasional plantings of barley or rachitic wheat. The leaden green of the sparse brush was coated half the daytime with dust, and with frost the other half. In this way it took on the most delicate tones. The wind striking from Catalonia or from the Pyrenees froze it or covered it bush by bush. The upland was lost in the horizon without sign of any ending, they said it did not stop in our province, but went on into another. To end "in another province" was as if it reached to another planet. From time to time the plain showed grey undulations. There were no roads save rocky goat-tracks. In each three or four hours of travel one might run across a stone shelter enclosed by a wide corral, a lambing pen, where the shepherds brought their ewes and goats when they were due to give birth. In some of these pens there would be a dwelling, but it was always unoccupied. The owners were almost as wretched as their shepherds, but the latter never used the beds or the rooms, sleeping instead in the shelters on straw.

Climbing the Ripas called for half an hour of hard work, on a path twisting between high, bald rocks. It pleased me to see how, up there, the cross was so much bigger than it seemed from the village, and between its arms was handsome ironwork invisible from below.

On the upland nothing ever happened. My grandfather used to tell the only story there was about that wilderness. In the first Carlist war there were various encounters between Christians and rebels. After the battle the women of the settlement—wives and mothers, full of tender family feelings—climbed to the upland in a long, silent procession, to despoil the dead of their clothes. While they stripped them, they prayed in chorus for the souls of the slain, the oldest conducting the prayers. They brought their booty home, and, shortly after, the countrymen appeared in military jackets and trousers, crudely altered by the old wives who worked them over in the evenings by the fireside. On the upland the men gathered firewood; now the dead, while they remained, gave them clothing as well against the harsh climate. The men brought the wood, the women the garments. All that the villagers knew about the problem of the succession to the throne, was that the dead Christians were better dressed and more worth finding than the Carlists.

I remember one day when, going along the upland with my father, we found partly exposed in the ground, hidden between two twisted bushes, a human skull. My father covered it with earth again, we took off our hats and recited the Lord's Prayer.

Translated by OLIVER LA FARGE

Jorge Guillén

TERRESTRIAL SPHERE

NEITHER THE ravishes of the waves,
Nor the amorous shipwreck
Will alleviate you, wise sea,
That curves between curves?

Incorruptible curves
Over the perfect blue
That denies to desire
The appearance of foam.

Form of the noon,
How universal! The refulgent
Waves unfold
The light in light and breeze.

And the breeze slips
—Infant mariner,
Course, yes, but no weight—
Between a rigor of rays

That gird the noon
With exactitude. Deserted
Refulgence! The sphere,
So abstract is afflicted.

Translated by FRANCES AVERY PLEAK

Rafael Alberti

A SPECTRE IS HAUNTING EUROPE

... AND THE old families close the windows,
bolt the doors,
the father rushes through darkness to the banks,
on the Bourse his pulse stops
... and at night he dreams of fire,
of cattle burning,
that instead of wheat he has bonfires,
instead of grain, sparks,
boxes,
iron boxes filled with embers.

Where are you?
Where?
We are pursued by shots.
Oh!
The peasants pass, trampling our blood.
What is happening?
Bar them!
Hurry! Bar the frontiers!
See him swiftly advancing on the wind from the East,
from the red steppes of ancient hunger.
Let not the toilers hear his voice,
let not his whistle pierce the factories,
let not the men in the fields even glimpse
his sickle borne aloft.
Stop him!
He spans the seas
heedless of all geography,
he hides in the holds of ships,
speaks to the stokers.
lifts them grimy to the deck,
flames their hate and misery to rebellion,
drives the crews to mutiny.
Close,
close the prisons!

His voice will shatter the walls.
What is happening?
But we follow him,
we make him descend from the East wind that carries him,
we ask him of the red steppes of peace and triumph,
we seat him at the poor farmer's table,
we point out the factory owner,
we have him lead our strikes and demonstrations,
speak with the soldiers and the sailors,
we point out the puny officials in their offices
and in the Parliaments shaking their fists while shouting of gold and blood.
A spectre is haunting Europe,
the world.
We call him Comrade.

Translated by IRA JAN WALLACH and
ANGEL FLORES

PORTUGAL

INTRODUCTION

By Lusitano de Castro

"The Portuguese is the greatest literature produced by a small country with the exception of ancient Greece. . . ."
(AUBREY F. BELL, *Fortnightly Review*, London, June, 1922.)

PORTUGUESE LETTERS are ailing. Their ailment is the moral aspect of a complex national crisis of which the culminating point was reached about 1890. After that the struggle for national and personal survival, organic as well as spiritual, went on with its ups and downs until 1926, when the present dictatorship was established to stop the "political unrest" by paralyzing the national soul in the throws of tragic debate.

At about 1890 the writers, as well as the whole people, had a feeling of national impotence, of a destiny that had come to an end. Pessimism and discouragement had come to stay. Most of the great writers of the period 1870–1890 (the highest moment of Portuguese modern letters) turned to the cult of national history, to the past; some resorted to republican Jacobinism; many disowned their former radical views and ideologies; those who survived the nineteenth century died in the course of the following twenty years, bitter and solitary, divorced from the republican regime (established in 1910).

Suicide and premature death were the fate of many poets, novelists, historians and essayists. Their passing left a void which has not yet been filled. On the eve of suicide, Antero de Quental, the greatest poet of that generation, philosopher and man of action, who had founded the Portuguese Socialist Party, said: "Do palácio encantado da Ilusão / desci a passo e passo a escada estreita." [1] A much younger poet of enormous popularity, António Nobre, who died in 1900 at the age of thirty-three, wrote: "Que tristeza, rapazes, ter nascido em Portugal!" [2]

If, after 1900, literary production fell off in quality and significance, at the same time literature became infected with quixotic ideas and systems of reform; the best writers have dealt successfully in polemics, political pamphlets and memoirs, and social problems. The best and most objective writing of the last

---

[1] From the enchanted palace of Illusion
I descended, step by step, the narrow stair.
[2] What a sad thing, my lads, to have been born in Portugal.

forty years is to be found in that field. Meanwhile, poets sang now in low, sad tones; they never achieved the popularity nor the national significance of some of their predecessors, like Junqueiro, Quental, Nobre, Leal, among others. In stories, fools, wretches, failures, bohemians, became the familiar characters, as if the writer were obsessed by his own experience. Escape into aestheticism and exotism, into futility and amiable historical speculation, produced, however, a number of brilliant writers. It was "art for art's sake"—over a swamp. History and erudition developed to great heights, particularly with a view to reinterpreting the national past, the great Portuguese discoveries of the fifteenth and sixteenth centuries.

After the naturalists (above all, Eça de Queiroz, whose shadow extends down to the present day) the novel suffered an eclipse. Reality was now too painful to allow any room for fiction or satire. Dreams of national salvation absorbed all the powers of fiction. However, a short-story writer and pamphleteer of great resource and fecundity, Fialho de Almeida (1857–1911) exerted a deep artistic and moral influence up to World War I days. His sarcasm and bitterness marked the end of the pre-republican era of "demolition." Fialho never achieved a full-length novel, but he was the starting point of the more important trends in the novel, about and after 1910: populism, pity for the humble and the oppressed, the taste for the rare and the decadent, pungent and morbid themes (*Contos, Cidade do Vício, País das Uvas, Os Gatos,* etc.). Literary reviews mushroomed between 1910 and 1926, most of them having a polemic and even a semi-political character.

The republican regime had its great writers, who prevailed as late as the thirties and beyond. Raul Brandão (1867–1930) achieved much recognition in his later years. Placing himself on the side of those who suffer, his novels are strange and misty dramas, out of time and place, impregnated with tragic revolt, profound pity and dolorous humor. His memoirs and historical recreations were noteworthy successes (*A Farsa, Os Pobres, Humus, Memórias, Teatro, El-rei Junot, Os Pescadores,* and many others). M. Teixeira-Gomes (1860–1940), a mixture of Anatolean scepticism and Gidean refinement, survived many generations, to enjoy great success after the twenties, with his short stories, novels and essays. (*Agosto Azul, Inventário de Junho, Cartas sem Moral Nenhuma, Novelas Eróticas, Gente Singular,* etc.) An ambassador of Portugal in London, he later became president of Portugal, and resigned to live and die an exile in Tunisia.

Aquilino Ribeiro (born in 1885) is the outstanding novelist of the Republic. A wholesome populist with a richly flavored style, he possesses an unexcelled capacity to render the rustic and picturesque aspects of peasant life, and has been a dominant figure from the World War days to the present (*Jardim das Tormentas, Estrada de Santiago, Filhas de Babilônia, Terras do Demo, Via Sinuosa,* etc.).

Júlio Dantas (born 1876) has enjoyed great prestige as a dramatist, short story writer, poet and chronicler. Love and historical romance, rendered in a highly polished, drawing-room style, have made him the most widely read of Portuguese writers, after Eça de Queiroz, both in Portugal and Brazil.

In the twenties, another novelist—Ferreira de Castro—came to the fore. His proletarian origins and tendencies, his personal experiences as an emigrant, his professional tenacity, won for him considerable popularity. He is one of the most widely read of living Portuguese writers inside his country and abroad, although artistically he is a long way from his elders (*A Selva, Emigrantes, Eternidade, Terra Fria,* etc.). Manuel Ribeiro (1878–1942), a former revolutionist converted to militant and literary catholicism, reached a wide circle of readers (*A Cathedral, Deserto, Planície Heróica,* etc.).

In the early thirties a timid and short-lived trend toward the "psychological novel" developed, with José Régio, J. G. Simões and J. Rodrigues Miguéis. The orthodoxy of the Portuguese *Estado Novo* discouraged it. As for the novel with a "social significance," it is as strictly forbidden as in Nazi Germany or fascist Italy. . . .

Poetry has remained through the ages the greatest literary instrument of the Portuguese. After Quental, Junqueiro, Leal, Nobre, Verde, and others, Teixeira de Pascoais is today the poet of deep inspiration and lofty tones. A pantheist, he has carried Portuguese lyrism to dramatic heights, and is known as the founder of "saudosismo." [3] He is also a biographer and essayist (*Sempre, As Sombras, Cantos Indecisos, Elegias, Regresso ao Paraíso, Verbo Escuro, São Paulo,* etc.).

The modernists, with their reviews, *Orfeu, Portugal Futurista, Athena, Contemporânea,* although paying heavy tribute to aesthetic and moral uprooting, returned to the purity of the great sources. The leading talent of the so-called futurists was M. de Sá-Carneiro, a bizarre poet and novelist who, still a youth, committed suicide in Paris in 1916. (Among his work were *Indícios de Oiro, Céu em Fogo, Dispersão,* etc.) Fernando Pessoa died in 1935 leaving an extensive, dispersed work. These two are the greatest influences of the period. To the audacious, bizarre and funambulesque attitude of the futurists, the new generations have brought seriousness, professional zest and a taste for the literary essay. However, anxiety remains their deepest note. All modernists have in a way continued the tradition of the "child-poet," dating back from António Nobre, the great "enfant-gaté" of Portuguese contemporary letters. Subjectivism, the search for God, the "eternal," sexual problems, divorce from immediate reality, from the social scene, etc., are their main characteristics. José Régio (*Poemas de Deus e do Diabo, Encruzilhadas de Deus, Biografia,* and a novel, *Jogo da Cabra Cega,* seized by the censors) is the outstanding poet of this group. The reviews *Presença* and *Revista de Portugal* are good documents of Portuguese modernism.

If, before 1926, the economic difficulties, the narrowing down of national horizons, the political strife and the debate for reform and salvation deeply affected creative literary work—since then, the tight prohibitions of censorship, the persecution and exile of writers, the political and intellectual suffocation, have almost succeeded in destroying the life-cells of Portuguese literature. Portuguese culture during these last fifteen years has lived mainly on the remnants of past generations. The present period is one of confused issues and trends; what writers say is, in reality, less important than what they dare not

[3] The cult of the most characteristic expression of the Portuguese soul—"saudade"—which is a mixture of loneliness, longing and nostalgia.

—or are not allowed—to say. Those who did not take refuge in subjectivism have become men of action, a sacrifice which has not yet borne fruit. Of late the government has made efforts to revive literature by offering fat prizes. But these efforts have failed. Aside from economic support, the writer strives for ethical encouragement, contact with historical reality, echo and resonance, and faith in some sort of future. And these are lacking in present-day Portugal.

Raul Brandão

THE THIEF AND HIS LITTLE DAUGHTER

THE DAUGHTER of Death's-Head and the Orphanage Girl grew up in the alley amid the screams of prostitutes and the obscene jests of soldiers and thieves. She was four years old, and she slept in corners or in the arms of the Fat Girl or the Deaf Girl. The Old Man, who had been a ditch-digger, would set her on his knee, and to amuse her would open his enormous mouth that had not a tooth inside it. The Landlady was very good to her, and the "girls" would shower her with frenzied kisses; and then for days at a time she would see nothing of them; they would forget all about her, and she would cry herself to sleep in the beds or on the doorsteps. Her mother was the only one who avoided her always.

"I can't bear the sight of her!"

Yet she grew up. She grew up as chance would have it, in that realm of hallucination in which human beings are transformed as in a dream into figures of truth which, at certain hours only, come to the surface, from out of that world of pain and tragedy to which we all belong. . . .

Death's-Head, the thief, said to his sweetheart:

"Why can't you bear the sight of the child?"

"I can't! That's all. . . ."

"You're worse than the nanny-goats!"

And then he would beat her. She would be silent, her eyes full of malice and of fear.

"You may beat me if you like, but I can't bear to look at her. Take her out of my sight. Leave me alone!"

The thief would cover the child with old rags and draw her to his bosom, and in winter would give her an old overcoat to keep her warm.

"The brat isn't dead yet?" the Orphanage Girl would ask, thinking possibly that Death's-Head would give her a beating.

The brat did not die. With her eyes ever on her father, she would clasp his legs and want to follow him when he left. And so she continued to grow up in that dark alleyway, amid the screams and the insults and the sad little songs that the women sang.

"But why do you beat the little one?" the other women would ask.

"I don't know! I don't know!"

At the beginning of winter, the Orphanage Girl was taken to the hospital, and before she went, she embraced her daughter, weeping desperately. It was all they could do to wrest the child from her arms. The "girls" had to take care of the little one now, and she slept either with them or with the thief. One morning, they said to the latter:

"It's all up with your sweetie now; they're burying her today."

For hours Death's-Head remained alone, lost in thought. Then he heard laughter outside. Lifting the door-curtain, he went directly up to the old ditch-digger, who was sitting there with the little girl on his knees. All the others were silent as he snatched her roughly from the old man's arms, looking him fiercely in the face as the old fellow laughed back with his great toothless mouth, which was like that of a wild beast. Death's-Head left with the child and did not return until afternoon, when he turned her over to the Fat Girl.

"Keep her for me until night."

When night came, he called his daughter and held her closely for a long time. At that moment, it may be, he understood the horror which the Orphanage Girl had felt for her offspring, and the tenderness she displayed just before they took her to the hospital—she had, perhaps, seen the Old Man with the child in his arms and that monstrous gaping mouth of his.

"Come with me."

"Where are we going, Daddy? For a walk?"

"For a walk."

The little one laughed.

"Now?"

"Now."

And taking her by her little hand, he led her down to the river, to the exact spot where he had met the Orphanage Girl for the first time. Climbing into a boat with her, he unmoored it and began rowing.

"Where are we going, Daddy?"

"You'll see. Go to sleep."

The thief now felt the same unconscious horror that had gripped the mother. He did not reason it out. It was not hatred for the alley, which was the only life that awaited the child; it was not seeing her in the ditch-digger's brutal hands or those of the squint-eyed soldier who gazed at her with silent ferocity. There was something that pained him, made it hard for him to breathe. That thing could not go on existing at his side—he had to put an end to it. He felt this, to the very depths of his being, as the mother had felt it without being able to explain it. In the thief's soul was a savage horror at the thought of inflicting all this upon the child. It was necessary to kill her, absolutely necessary.

"Now—"

But the child looked up at him and laughed—and he was afraid.

"Go to sleep!"

The little one began stammering—"O Daddy! Daddy!"—began uttering those disconnected and extraordinary words that children are in the habit of speaking, and along with them, the obscenities which she had heard from the Old Man in the alley as she clung to his neck. The thief was shaken by the profundities of life.

"O Daddy! Daddy!" she cried suddenly, "what is that up there?" And the little one, who had never had a glimpse of stars in that tragic alley-way, pointed to the sky.

"Stars."

"Ah, stars! stars!"— And the childish monologue was resumed. Charming words, words so often repeated, yet always new and fresh on lips the color of roses; it was as if life were always awakening for the first time when a child spoke. Terrible words as well, words that belonged to the tragic life of the alley and which she unconsciously mingled with the others.

At last she fell asleep in the bottom of the boat, gazing up at the sky. But sleeping she inspired as much fear in him as when awake. . . . Very slowly, he put out his hands and fastened a rope about her waist. The little one stirred, awoke, smiled up at him, opened her mouth to say "Daddy," and then dropped back into innocent slumber. The thief for a long time gazed at her quietly. The child could not go on living. Before his eyes always was the toothless mouth of the Old Man, and the women with their obscenities. He knew what fate was in store for her. The child was the thing that was troubling him. He would have peace on this earth only when he had thrown her into the river and had seen her going down there, down, down to the very bottom, far from this life of pain and tragedy.

For the first time he felt that he was committing a crime against something immense and extraordinary, something huge and invisible—felt with horror that he was poisoning the well-springs of life. It was necessary to kill her. . . . Yet even now there came over him another fear, without real existence. . . . Noiselessly, holding his breath, he tried to steal forward, to sink his nails into her throat and strangle her. He could not. . . . He had a mission to fulfill, and he could not fulfill it.

"Am I going to be afraid? Am I going to be afraid?" And he wrung his hands, his enormous hands, his hands that were so cold.

He had come up against a living wall of tenderness. His soul was writhing in the tremendous silence of the night, crushed between two contradictory forces that weighed upon him like mountains. He glanced up at the sky—to the stars of no avail. The child was sleeping in the bottom of the boat. And those two forces, he could almost see them advancing upon him, looming larger all the while. The drama took place in the silence of the night, without his being able to separate his feeling of tenderness from the fierce and necessary act that he meditated.

Finally, he laid his hands upon her and she awoke.

"Daddy! Daddy!"

Thinking that he was playing, she nestled her head against him and exclaimed:

"The stars! The stars! . . . O Rosa! O Rosa! O Rosa! O Rosa! . . . Daddy, you're my friend, yes, you are. . . . How pretty it is up there! . . . Daddy! . . .

*   *   *

Through that pure and innocent mouth the world to which we all belong, we and the thieves of the streets, was speaking. It was too much for him. He could not go through with it. He was paralyzed with pain and horror as he listened to her and felt that little hand in his enormous ones. The thief tried to speak but the words would not come. What he had thought would be easy was impossible. It was better to kill her, but he could not. There was nothing to do but accept her fate: the squint-eyed soldier, the Old Man who waited for her with the joy of the wild beast that scents its prey near at hand and opens its frightful jaws. Slowly, he undid the cord, rowed the boat back to land, and, leaving it adrift, with the child in his arms he returned to deliver her to the life of the alley.

Translated by Samuel Putnam

Aquilino Ribeiro

THE LAST FAUN

ON THAT BRIGHT Sunday, a Sunday given over to the glorious rites of Our Lady of Mercy, Padre Jesuino was about to rise from the confessional, after having absolved Ana Fusca of a hundred small sins, when there at his feet, trembling all over, eyes lowered, cheeks aflame, was the kneeling figure of Maria da Encarnação. Short of temper where the over-zealous devotions of pious ladies were concerned, and all the more so by reason of the fact that the candles for the mass were already lighted, while he still had a baptism to perform, Padre Jesuino received her none too graciously and with a *per signum crucis* that was hastier than the gesture he would have used in shooing a hen from the garden. Having quickly run through the preliminary prayers, he said to her, in an impatient tone of voice:

"Hurry, my daughter, and tell me what it is. Have you a mortal sin on your conscience?"

"I went to confession and received communion one week ago today, at the mission of the Two Churches. I have no mortal sin to confess."

"Well, then!"

"Father," she said, with an air of firm resolve, "every night I hear a voice: 'Maria da Encarnação, thou shalt go up to the Mountain; without stick or stone, thou shalt do away with this fear!' Either I am greatly mistaken, or it is Our Lord who is giving me the task of putting an end to what is happening to the other girls."

The abbot gravely regarded this fair-haired girl of twenty, with the bright eyes and the simplicity of an angel, the only one in his congregation who followed the portions of the holy sacrifice in a prayer book. She had been a dainty, frolicsome little lass until Padre Baldomero came along, mounted on his black mule, as he went from place to place preaching his apostolic mission. He had filled her soul with a vehement contempt for the world and a fondness for all the practices of mystic devotion. Ever since she had listened to the missionary, her merry voice was no longer to be heard at corn-huskings and along the road on pilgrimages, nor was her gaze ever once lifted coquettishly to meet the glance of another. The charming voice which God had given her was now wholly reserved for God's use, in litanies and benedicites, and no one could steal those eyes away from their ineffable vistas of ecstasy and the con-

templation of Jesus, the beloved bridegroom. The latter took on a delicate beauty as he hung there in effigy, in his vermilion-colored tunic, bordered in blue and spangled with gold; to the elect, he held out the
promise of infinite joys beyond the grave. The short of the matter is,
thanks to Maria da Encarnação's persevering efforts, the Society of the
Sacred Heart of Jesus had been installed in the lukewarm town; and as a
result, at that hour of the afternoon when tinkling cowbells were wont
to be heard from the pasture-lands, the slumbering church-bells now rang
out, summoning worshippers for the month of Mary, the month of St.
Joseph, the Christ-Child's novena, and, during Holy Week, the Stations
of the Cross. She went to confession every Sunday and received communion from Padre Jesuino's gnarled, tobacco-stained fingers; that is, providing she was not engaged in seeking sanctification elsewhere, at some
solemn function in a neighboring church, from the long, pale fingers of a
young priest. Padre Jesuino, a preceptor of boys, a huntsman, sower of
grain rather than of souls, was repugnant to her taste for the spiritual;
but he was her ordained pastor, and so she resigned herself to being the
mistress of a house of worship that was very badly kept. Candlesticks,
lamps, vases were now polished until they shone; and Maria da Encarnação's fingers were never more industrious and clever in fitting a dress
than they were, of a Sunday morning, in decking the altars with flowers
from the garden—from the first of the season to the last that were to be
had.

This ascetic passion little by little laid hold of her, to such an extent
that one night she was led to join a pilgrimage to Lamego, in the company of a group of young girls whom Padre Baldomero was conducting
to Spain for a retreat. She left behind her, at home, an aged father and
a paralyzed mother, and the foolish girl grew ashamed of what she had
done and turned back; but this in no way diminished her fervor for the
divine. She had the feeling that she was to be one of the Blessed, like
St. Inez or St. Iria—and she proclaimed it in a voice for all to hear. Meanwhile, she continued to clutch at all the cassocks and to run about to all
the feast-days. As a consequence of this activity, her fine rose-colored skin
began to take on the mummified hue that is common to elderly virgins.

It was in one of her visionary moments that Pedro Jirigodes saw her
and was smitten with her. In a young girl's eyes, he had certain draw-
backs. He was forty years old, for one thing, with a reputation as a
matador—which had enabled him to put by an enviable share of this
world's goods—and an unprepossessing appearance, conferred upon him
by his eyebrows bristling beneath a forehead to match and his heavy,

very black and drooping mustache, which completely hid his mouth. But Pedro Jirigodes was somebody. His costume consisted of a dark-colored cashmere suit, a straw hat slouched down over his eyes, and a watch-chain with big links and a piece of pottery as a charm. Such was the way in which he always appeared at fairs and other functions, kerchief waving, hand affably outstretched— How goes it, friend?—that was Sr. Jirigodes for you. His income was derived from certain church lands, bid in at Viseu behind closed doors, and from money loaned out at a high rate of interest. He did not do a stroke of work; when he was not taking a stroll, he was out hunting, and when he was not hunting, he was down at the river fishing. He was, above all, a great woodsman and an ingenious inventor of traps. He was blamed for heinous misdeeds and was highly respected. He had once creditably fulfilled the duties of administrator of the town of Moimenta, at election time. He was looked upon as an educated man, very well bred, and he subscribed to *O Seculo*. Though close to forty, he was hard as nails, and wanted—so he said—to found a family; and he accordingly proceeded to build a house along the highway, of good masonry and Pampilhosa brick, and, being mad about her, he then asked for the hand of Maria da Encarnação.

So many blemishes should have rendered him odious to her, especially as regarded his age and physique, which is always a matter of moment even to a girl who is saving her charms for a heavenly bridegroom, a bridegroom who is accustomed to plucking the most fragrant of virgin flowers. Nevertheless, she did not repulse him with aversion; no, nothing of the sort; with a melancholy manner, she reminded him of her vows of chastity, and gently sent him about his business.

But Pedro Jirigodes did not give up. Slowly and cleverly he worked his way into the good graces of those whose help he needed, bribing the pious neighbor women and winning the missionary father to his side with the gift of a few legs of veal and a mess of trout. As for the girl's parents, they urged her on to marry him, feeling certain that this would free her from the clutches of the bigots. And with a few maxims having to do with a life that was well provided for and well regulated and none the less virtuous for all of that, the apostle contributed his share by citing examples of holy wedlock—all of which had its due effect in time. Maria da Encarnação was thus left with no one to protect her. Pedro Jirigodes, meanwhile, stubbornly held on; and in the middle of May of that year, just as the fillies were beginning to neigh in the meadows and the feast of Our Lady the Mother of God and Men, of which he had been the major-domo, was drawing to a close, he finally obtained that Yes which he had so stubbornly disputed with the Nazarene. It was at this time that the legal proceedings to establish Jirigodes' free status, which had been dragging along in foreign parts for more than a dozen years, were settled, so that he was in a position to go through with the marriage.

All this ran through Padre Jesuino's mind, which was not devoid of discernment, in the presence of that little blond head in front of him.

"So you heard a voice?" the abbot began, mildly. "And what was it the voice said? Tell me again."

"'Maria da Encarnação, thou shalt go up to the Mountain; without stick or stone, thou shalt do away with this fear!' "

"Ah! And was that when you were asleep or when you were awake?"

"Asleep, Father; but I also heard it one night, just as I had finished saying my beads."

"One must not put too much faith in dreams. In authors who are worthy of all credence I have read that dreams may be the instrument either of angels or of the powers of darkness."

"That is all very well; but I am telling you, I also heard it when I was in possession of my five senses. It was as real as your voice now, Father, and I could hear it just as plainly."

"It would appear, then, that it is sending you up there, on Mount Nave, to put an end to the monster——"

"That is what I make of it."

"From where did the voice come?"

"I don't know; it sounded very distinctly in my ears, but it did not come from any definite direction. I even imagined that it came from above me—but I could not swear to it. And it was a very nice voice; I never heard anything like it before——"

The confessor asked her any number of other questions, all bearing upon the same point; for in his casuistry this case constituted a novelty, and his mind, trained to manual labor, to educating the young and to hunting rabbits, was hardly fitted to deal with so transcendental a problem. He avoided giving a decisive answer by saying:

"My daughter, with regard to something so mysterious as this, I cannot tell you what I think. I know that more than one person has received by such means as this a mandate from heaven to be carried out on earth. But if my memory serves me right, there have also been cases in which such voices proved to be false, having been sent by evil spirits. I shall consult the prelate——"

"The voice is so sweet and tender it could only come from heaven. When I hear it, my whole body is bathed in a joy so marvelous, so delicious, that I forget all about myself and the things of earth!" And as she said this, in a tone of great exaltation, she gave an upward arch to her brows, as if recalling the supreme delight she had experienced.

"Very well, but we cannot take too many precautions. The devil has arts of his own that he masters along with the learned in academies, and each trick of his is more subtle than the ones he has used before. Take my advice; be calm, and let us wait until this question has been settled by those above——"

"And in the meantime, the torture keeps up? Ah, Father——!"

"That is true enough; but the trouble is of so mysterious an origin that in order to be rid of it, the utmost prudence is to be recommended. Go, my daughter, and moderate your thirst for sacrifice, which for the matter of that is not becoming to you. Try to control yourself, and say three Hail Mary's to Our Lady of Good Counsel, that she may tell you what to do." And with these and similar words, he sought to break the spell which lay upon the young soul in his charge.

Two weeks went by, and more rapes were perpetrated in those desolate God-forsaken regions along the border of the old Roman roads, long fallen into disuse. At the monastery mass, Maria da Encarnação appeared once more to ask the abbot to hear her confession.

"Father," she murmured, "the voice still comes to me: 'To the Mountain thou shalt go; thou shalt do away with this fear.' I hear it five or six times a night. The bishop has not answered yet?"

"No, he has not had time."

"Very well, then, Father, I have made up my mind to go up the mountain, up to the very highest peaks, and Our Lord will take care of me."

"The mountain is big, my child; a good horse on the gallop could not make it in a day. It is full of caves—and dens—it will be your undoing!"

"Do not worry about that!"

"If at least you had company!"

"I do not want anyone. Judith went alone to the tent of Holofernes."

"Times are different now, little soul of the Lord! Times are different, and we are not the ancient Hebrews. In the matter of—of copulation, they were none too scrupulous. There was Sarah, wife of the great Abraham, in Egypt——"

"All that I may suffer will be well repaid, if tomorrow it can be said: young girls may now go without fear down those pathways of Christ. . . ."

"That may be. I do not say yes, and I do not say no. Just forget that I have said anything to you."

"The voice is from heaven——"

"Who can tell?"

"It is. I have conjured it night after night, putting my whole soul into the words: If you are divine, speak to me; if you are an angel of darkness, be gone, in the name of the Father, and of the Son, and of the Holy Ghost. And the voice did not stop; it was more melodious than ever——"

"I have observed that you have a tendency to mysticism. In the case of highly sensitive natures, there are sometimes phenomena of auditory, visual and other kinds of hallucination. What I mean to say is, your ears may be deceiving you——"

"So often? God, Our Lord, would not permit a thing like that to happen."

The abbot had no reply to make to this argument of incontrovertible faith.

"My advice to you," he said once more, "was, and shall continue to be: wait!"

"And is *He* to wait, too?"

"You mean to go up in the mountains like that, just as you are?"

"Yes, Father, armed only with the sign of the cross."

"That is a powerful weapon, no doubt of it; but there are occasions when a good rifle is not to be spurned. Judith carried a cutlass——"

"Judith cut off the Philistine's head with the sword of the Philistine. I have read and reread the Book of Kings."

"Joan of Arc went armed——"

"But there was a war then—that was in time of war."

It was not feasible for the abbot to have recourse to his bishop; he felt that the help which the girl looked for from that quarter was a vain illusion. He did not have the heart to continue to deceive her any longer; and much less did he have the courage to keep a promise which called for so much tact and for such care in the matter of style and composition, not to speak of good paper, all of which were indispensable in a correspondence with My Lord, the Bishop, and which in this village monastery were as far removed from the padre as the padre was from his breviary. Years ago—when he still wore his lace rochet in the pulpit and spoke to God with the slow, solemn manner of a minister addressing his monarch —he had enjoyed wide fame as a preacher. Upon succeeding to the chaplaincy of Lama, Friar José had left him a well thumbed volume of sermons, in which he found enough and more than enough to provide a feast for a little rural congregation which hardly could be said to be hungering for spiritual things. And even aside from the book of sermons, inasmuch as the virtues are always exalted and sin irresistibly combatted in the lives of the saints, any panegyric would be in order with a simple substitution of names. The major excellence of rhetoric lay in its adjustability to all the blessed, like kerchiefs to all heads. Padre Jesuino spent more time in the woods looking for a rabbit to tie to his belt than he did at his study table in transforming a sermon on St. Anthony into one on St. Blaise, or the tears of St. Peter into the thorns of Our Lord. The rest could be left to memory, and his memory was very good, thanks to a cerebral economy which afforded room only for the slow, larva-like passage and repassage of thoughts having to do with his duties at the altar.

With age and the vexations caused him by the prodigal sons intrusted to his care, his theological tools had grown rusty from lack of use; and to sit down now and compose a statement for the bishop, laying before him the case of this visionary girl, was a task with which he was in no condition to cope. With scoldings and with maxims of plain common sense, he had done his best to counsel her, as one would a person bent upon butting down a door with his head; but all in vain. Maria da Encarnação, certain that her mission as a redeemer came from on high, was more determined than ever to go through with her plan.

At sunrise the next morning, after having milked the cows, Tomas Pateiro, surprised at not seeing his daughter up and stirring, went to the door of her room.

"Maria da Encarnação! *Oh, lá!* Get up! There's work to be done——"

Receiving no reply and not hearing so much as a sound, he began pounding on her door. Then it occurred to him that she might have had a bad night, addicted as she was to insomnia and nightmares, and he remembered that for some little while she had been given to dropping off into a heavy, death-like slumber shortly before daybreak. Outside, the cock had ceased crowing and the turtledoves were billing and cooing lasciviously and flying in rows over the pine-grove. As he set out with the hired man and his son to plant a field of beans, between a couple of mouthfuls of food he said to his paralyzed wife as she lay in bed:

"A plague on those padres who are putting notions in our lass's head! I called her and she didn't even answer."

The old woman went on saying the rosary of Our Lady, for this was her month, and estimating on her fingers the amount they owed in servant's wages. Time was slipping by; it was mid-morning and still no sign of her daughter.

"Maria da Encarnação!" the old woman shouted at last. "Hey! Maria da Encarnação!"

Frightened at hearing what she thought was a groan, she broke off, listening intently.

"Miaul! Miaul!"

"Plague take the cat! Scat!" she cried, "Scat!" And the puss, which had been foraging on top of the cupboard, gave a leap and scurried out of sight, as the paralytic once more called out:

"Maria da Encarnação! Get up, child; your father will be coming in starved for his breakfast——"

She called and called again, but there was nothing to disturb the deep well of silence that filled the house. It was a silence that seemed to come from the kitchen, from the street, from everywhere. Little by little, she became conscious of its presence about her bed, as hateful as that of certain individuals the very sight of whom filled her with loathing. Oppressed by a feeling of terror which she could not well define, her imagination more halting than a spavined horse, she lay for a time motionless, almost without breathing, withdrawn into herself, as at the bottom of a funnel. It seemed to her that all of human life was fleeing round about her, and that her own life, anguish-ridden, was following close after, to fill like a rising river the emptiness of space. Soon, however, her ear caught the sound, far away, very far away, of a creaking axle. Then, from the threshing-floor, came the merry fanfare of a cock, greeting the light of day with his *Orate, fratres;* and still more distant, like the closing of the missal when the priest has finished saying mass, she could make out the sound of the women beating clothes in the wash-houses. The world continued to revolve about her suspended by invisible cords, but stouter, stronger ones than any that could be fashioned from all the thread that there was.

In harmony with all of this, her anxiety of a moment ago returned to torment her; and once again she called:

"Daughter! Why don't you answer?"

Amid the universal immobility of things, the household utensils—the olive jar at the foot of the bed, the pots and the water jug over there on the shelf—took on the appearance of squatting bronzes, all of them, and seemed to be listening. The very silence itself was putting out unseen hands to stifle her. And then the sounds came back, infinitesimal sounds, the worm gnawing in the wood like a gimlet, the crackle and drip of melting tar on the roof in the heat of the day. And vaguer than the drone of a mosquito in the sun was the far-off rumble of a wagon on the Road of Our Lord.

"Maria da Encarnação! Oh, Maria da Encarnação!"

No answering voice, no sound of breathing was to be heard.

"Oh, Maria da Encarnação!" She was tearful now, like a child in pain.

Everything then grew dark in front of her eyes, and the furniture of the room appeared to be doing a topsy-turvy dance, without making the slightest sound. Mad with fright, as if the mattress that she lay on were afire, she started screaming: "Help! Help!" For a long time the poor woman kept it up, in a voice which at first was as tremulous as tinkling bells, growing hoarser then until it could be heard all over the village, by those at work in their gardens.

They came running up in a swarm; and panting for breath, eyes popping from her head, the paralytic with incoherent speech directed them to her daughter's room—"no sign of her—must be dead——"

The door was locked with a key; but Pedro Jirigodes with a shove had it off the hinges. And when they came back to tell the old lady that there was no Maria da Encarnação there, either dead or alive, her mother's heart was so relieved that she burst into tears upon finding that her immediate and darkest apprehensions were unfounded. As for Pedro Jirigodes, there was a look of amazement on his face and his manner was stern as he came down the stairs and asked all present to aid him in searching for his betrothed; and at his request, either out of sympathy or because they scented a possible scandal, whole groups of them now began hunting along the river banks and the mill-races, among the farms and hamlets, for a trace of the missing girl. Their search proved a fruitless one, and at the end of it, as they gathered to talk matters over, they were inclined in their discouragement to attribute this mysterious disappearance to the monster who had entered from the roof to rape Leopoldina Quaresma. At that very moment, however, just as the sun was tinging with purple the peaks of Caramulo, they caught sight of Maria da Encarnação. She was coming along at an even stride, her head thrown back, as if her soul were inebriated with the holy peace of Heaven.

Jirigodes bounded forward to meet her; but as she saw the anxious look on her lover's face, she drew herself erect with hieratic aplomb.

"Do not touch me, reprobate creature!" she said to him, in a tone of sovereign haughtiness, "do not touch me!"

"What's that?" he barked at her.

"Do not touch me! The Lord's elect has opened to me his amorous bosom and has sanctified me."

On her face was such a glow of light and in her bearing so serene a majesty that they hastened at once, in a body, to conduct her into the abbot's presence.

"Father," she said, "only in God's house is it permitted me to speak of the heavenly messenger."

The abbot was a bit put out by all this, for it was the time of day for him to be watering his onions; but throwing his cassock over his shoulders, he made for the church with Maria da Encarnação at his side. The latter's face was solemn, and she seemed to be walking on air as the two of them made their way through the silent throng. The nave of the church was filled to overflowing with people as she knelt in the confessional, and they all appeared to be deeply immersed in thought and waiting breathlessly, as if the Blessed Sacrament were being exposed on the high altar. Soon, however, Padre Jesuino rose from behind the grating with the gesture of one who has been undeceived.

"This is not a case for auricular confession!" he announced, describing spirals in the air with the palm of his hand, by way of emphasizing his remarks. "She has been seeing visions or something of the sort. I can't listen to it, I can't! If she wants to tell you about it, all right."

And without more ado, the folds of his cassock fluttering in his haste, he took his departure.

Maria da Encarnação, meanwhile, was standing on the first step of the high-altar, her back turned to the Blessed Sacrament; and after letting her gaze roam haughtily over the assembled multitude, she began speaking with the voice of one inspired:

"O people! Men and women, old and young, ye maidens above all, who with foolish tears bewail your maidenhood—I say unto you, rejoice! An angel of Heaven dwelleth among us. I have seen him, I have spoken with him, I have found repose in his arms, more trustingly than an innocent babe at its mother's breast. Oh, but he is beautiful! So beautiful that the beauty of Absalom is as nothing by comparison! And he is strong, stronger than the armies of David when they destroyed those of the six kings! His presence is more inebriating than the wine when it is sweet! He is the Ineffable of whom the Scriptures speak. Just as the Messiah saw the light in the desert of Judea, even so he has elected for the scene of his ministry these desolate backlands of Portugal. Rejoice! His mission it is to regenerate the race, to people the world with comely beings like himself, beings fashioned in the image and the likeness of God. Oh, ye mournful creatures, O piteous creatures, how little ye reckon of the divine Presence! Sin and toil have deformed your bodies, ye poor degenerate ones. But rejoice, for ye shall be exalted in your sons and those that are to come after you; for so hath he revealed it to me with his own sweet mouth. Those born of the Ineffable's embrace shall be beautiful and sound of limb and endowed with a wisdom from on high; but all those founts of life which he toucheth not shall wither and dry up. O ye of little faith, believe me, it is indeed an angel from Heaven that dwelleth among us. Ye maidens whom he shall touch, more lightly than the breeze stirring the canebrake, yet like the lightning's fire striking the earth—I say unto you: give thanks! Ye and your sons shall be of the elect! Let us kneel and pray to God, that God who giveth day and night, joy and sorrow, who one-thousand-nine-hundred years ago sent us a Redeemer for our souls, and who now, today, sends us a Redeemer for our bodies!"

In that great nave, the shadows of twilight appeared to stretch out into infinity, as all hearts felt the gentle wound of these mystic and transcendent words. Ejaculations burst forth from a thousand throats, in celebration of this epiphany of the flesh, a flesh now redeemed from its age-old anathema. And as night fell, it seemed that tongues of living flame, red and glowing from on high, were hovering over all the villages and doorsills, and the people had the feeling that something great was happening in the land.

From that hour forth, the news spread abroad: an angel from heaven had come down to ransom the human race of all its sufferings and deformities, and had selected as the vessel for the divine seed those maidens who were young, virgin and marriageable. His ways were rude and mysterious, until the blind jealousy of man where woman is concerned should at last have been dissipated like the ocular cataract which it was. But nevertheless, the time would come when he would descend to the peoples, and each household would then harbor him as its guest, between the finest of sheets, proffering the embrace of the most sculpturesque of arms. Like a swelling river, spreading afar, the enthusiasm grew. On the trunk of the old religion a new religion of pleasure and delight had now been grafted. Even the old women spoke of the Ineffable with tenderness and deep-bosomed sighs: and few indeed were the men with the murky flames of jealousy still lingering in their eyes. Little by little, all gave in, the women out of passion, the men out of faith and humility.

Simultaneously, the brutal rapes in the silence of the woods and along the equally silent highways now ceased. Stealthily some and others boldly, under the seal of catechumens, the maidens voluntarily went up into the mountains to offer the voluptuous Messiah the flower of their virginity.

In the meantime, pregnancy among the elect was on the increase, and the hour of delivery was drawing near. Much good it did pious-sniffling mothers with their barbarous superstitions to invoke the intervention of the Virgin Saint Euphemia or to have recourse to witches and sorceresses; the pollen possessed the virtue of fecundity. Micas Olaia was the first to feel the pangs of parturition; whereupon all the old midwives came run-

ning up, prepared to make short work of the progeny, if it chanced to be
a werewolf, and ready to conjure it back to hell if it proved to be a monster of Satan. For they were still doubtful, and Padre Jesuino himself
spoke out clearly on the matter.

"If the child is not in our own image and likeness," he said, "strangle
it!" And so saying, he made the gesture which he used in wringing the
necks of partridges brought down on the wing.

It was, however, a bouncing baby boy, perfect in every way, to whom
Micas Olaia gave birth. It at once began to wail, as much as to say, Here
I am; and in less than a jiffy, it was up and at its mother's well stocked
breasts. After Micas, the others in turn were brought to bed, but without
any more exorcisms or dread of monsters. All the offspring, without exception, were healthy, well formed and handsome; there was not a de-
formity or a cross-eye in the entire lot of them.

Compared to these young ones, those born within the bonds of wedlock were ill-favored indeed; they were, one would have said, the rejected
of God. They possessed neither the complexion, the strength and natural
hardihood, nor the delicate beauty of these sons of the Ineffable. Confounded by it all and smitten with compunction, the abbot could only
shake his head and murmur with the apostles: *Judicia divina dum nescin-
tur, non audaci sermone discutienda sunt sed formidoloso silentio vener-
anda.*[1]

                                        Translated by SAMUEL PUTNAM

José Rodrigues Miguéis

PROUD BEAUTY

ALONG THE COAST the storm rages. Livid, furious, the Atlantic sweeps the
deserted beaches, swallows fishing boats, picks up battered ships to fling
them away inland. The tornado uproots trees which saw the landing of
the Pilgrims, rolls before it, as matchboxes, houses, barns, cottages; takes
countless lives. Steel bridges vibrate, bend and snap like reeds. Trains
topple over and the pulled-up rails are contorted into the forms of tetanized
snakes. Telegraph wires whip the air, whistle, entangled as locks of copper hair in the wind. Lifted weightless from the roads, the automobiles
lie as strange scarecrows among the devastated fields, or upturned in the

---

[1] The ways of God being inscrutable, they are not to be the subject of frivolous
conversation, but rather the object of a silent awe and veneration.

ditches. Industrious rivers, now turbid and choleric, leap over the banks, drag dead cattle, houses, stray boats, children's cradles, cries of distress. . . .

Feverish and raucous, the radio talks on without let-up, swelling the anxiety of the people. It is America, the giant of contrasts, struggling! Six o'clock, and it is dark. The bars full, the lights dim, the music languorous. Right here, as if suspended from the sky-scrapers and impelled by the wind, the immense, compact curtain of rain rounds the corner of the hospital, cracking and howling, and breaks on the street below with an angry foam which the wind picks up and dissipates. The asphalt of the pavement is like a dark, oily river running unbridled. No one in the streets. The tall buildings hum musically in the wind, and the frames of the windows chatter like horror-stricken jaws. The city seems hallucinated.

Suddenly, mingled with the cracking whip of the rain and the wind, I hear someone screaming. Instinctively, I look across to the windows of the hospital: closed, serene, incandescent. Enormous, the hospital stands up against the storm. No, it didn't come from there. I listen closer—it's from below, it's from down below. Jesus, what's happened! People are yelling and yelling. Always some trouble brewing—will we never have peace!

I run to the stairs and cock my ear: It's down there, in the depths of the building. I rush back to phone the janitor: "What's happening? I hear screaming down there." And his quiet, slow voice contrasts with the fury of the weather: "Yes, it's here—we're having trouble down here . . ." I drop the phone and shrug my shoulders. But already, from the street, comes the screeching of the police car, weird in the storm. I run to the window: Five men, guns in hand, jump out of a dark, lustrous limousine, and race under the rain toward the door. The homicide squad. My God, what can it be!

In slippers, as I am, I race down the stairs. The screaming has stopped, and a mortal silence rises from the bottom of the building. They won't let me through to the cellar, so I push my way along the hall to the street. The rain pours on me and I have my feet in the water. I should worry! A little way down, an ambulance waits, doors wide open. Near the iron railing on the sidewalk, in front of the house, a small crowd peers and whispers. Through the large window, a little below street level, I see the body of a woman lying on a blue rug, her legs exposed and glowing in the dazzling light of the room. What's going on in there? Now the ambulance doctor and two agents come up the short stair, carrying a man on a stretcher. They take him to the ambulance and leave him there alone, the door open. I come close. He is a young guy, thin and pale, his head soaked in blood, his broken shoes pointing outward. But aren't they going to do anything for him? Just leave him there, like that? Is he dead, then? An arm hangs out, the hand livid and skinny. Of a sudden—he frightened me, I thought he was dead—he lifts his hand and moves it limply as if talking to someone, explaining something. And again the hand falls inanimate. But for Heaven's sake, what happened? Who is he? Nobody answers. The rain beats down. Someone drew the shade, and all I see now are the feet of the woman. But the crowd continues to peer, crouching, almost kneeling in the rain: they gloat on her body.

Soaked to the skin, I make my way back to the hall and down the rear stairs to the cellar. After all, I live here. "Excuse me, sir, I'm a neighbor, a friend. . . . I heard everything." And I walk in through the kitchen door.

The apartment is invaded by people, flooded with light. It looks unreal. It's like a rehearsal in a moving picture studio. All these men standing around. . . . Such a silence! That bald, quiet man walking around slowly in shirtsleeves. . . . Oh, so he's the father! Yes, the janitor of the building —why, didn't you know him? And to think it had to happen on a night like this. A storm as no living man remembers.

Such an education they gave that daughter! . . . She was proud and beautiful, and now, lying on that blue rug, she has a coin of blood right on her forehead. Her perfect, well joined, professional legs have a strange glow in the crude light of the projectors. Just as in a show. (Hell, it's stifling in this place!) Exposed in death, without modesty. Her pride! Miami, Bermuda, Broadway . . . Dead. This time she will make the first page of the *Mirror,* the *News,* the *New York American.* Publicity! Too late. Burnished and cold, those legs will only cause horror. The night clubs will soon forget her, business must go on, there are so many pretty legs, such a thirst for *manhattans* and *cuba-libres,* for swing and oblivion! No more garlands of lubricous gazes climbing up her pure legs (pure, except of ambition and pride). Only worms in procession, creeping silently, without benefit of tips to waiters. (What are you thinking about, mister?)

The detectives look annoyed, their hats on, smoking five-cent cigars, thinking maybe it's getting late for supper, waiting around for God knows what. Such an education her parents gave her. No sacrifice was too great for that daughter. And to have her go like that! Doesn't make sense. And on such a night, too. A storm to knock you silly. Look, they're taking more pictures. Someone carried the youngster to a neighbor's house. Poor child, he saw everything. Oh, so it was he, screaming! The voice sounded like him. It was him. Frightened, hysterical. The one over there is the older son. A very nice boy he is. And the nice little lady near him, that's his wife. Such nice people they are, all of them. I saw the husband carried out to the ambulance. Was he still alive? Of course . . . They threw him in, and left him there alone, with the door open. His head was covered with blood. (A little quiet, please!) Sh! The detectives are getting the mother's story. Poor soul, her eyes are dry from so much crying. She's so dazed, she can't make head or tail of it.

. . . Oh, so she was not living with her husband. No, they'd been separated for months. His parents died when he was only a kid, and left him good money. He spent everything. When she met him, he had no money, no job, no home, nothing. I don't see how any woman would fall for him, such a poor devil! Looked like a bum in those broken shoes. . . . Wouldn't work, said he was sick. Such a bringing up. . . . Wanted his wife to go live with him again. But what a jealous beggar he was. Wouldn't let her work and she had to support him! Her one passion in life was to dance. Since she was a little bit of a thing. They did everything to give her an education. Never let her soil her hands!

So he'd come to see her, beg her to return: No, I've got my life to lead, my career, my future. . . . Poor girl, only twenty-two years old. They had an apartment and everything. She paid the rent. Sorry for him, you know. But that jealousy! A couple of months ago they offered her a contract and she went to Bermuda. It was the beginning of her career, everything. She returned another woman, gay, beaming with health. Look what a beautiful shape she had. When did she come back? Only yesterday, if you please. Her agent wouldn't give her any rest: "Study, work!" What for? She came back full of hope, seems she was in line for another contract. And now look at her, stretched out under the eyes of all these people! Her trunks are still in that corner, see? More than a hundred dresses, not to speak of the rest. A pretty penny they cost. Maybe they can sell them. . . .

But how did it happen? Her agent had invited her to dinner this evening, some place uptown. And the mother insisting with her to go, you need to have a little fun, he's such a nice man, so much interested in you. They argued it for hours: she goes, she doesn't go. And she didn't. Just think, waiting around here for her death! But why didn't she? Didn't want to be seen with a Jew. Said it was bad for her reputation. But I thought *they* were Jews. Oh no, they're Lithuanians. Poor old souls, what they didn't do for that daughter. . . . The agent came to get her, (Mr. Goldstein, I think they called him), and she: "The weather is so bad, I hope you won't mind." He went away in his car: "Some other day, maybe. Don't worry, kid. Take care of yourself." She changed into a gown, put on her dancing sandals. Golden sandals, look at them.

Well, in such bad weather who should show up but the husband! He wanted to see her. They'd see each other now and then, though she avoided him when she could. He'd come down, they'd give him dinner, felt sorry for him. He wasn't a bad sort. . . . They were just sitting down to eat, wouldn't he join them? And he accepted. Very quiet he was. They ate sandwiches and coffee, there in the kitchen. (Look at the dog. Her puppies are just a week old. She howled like anything but never budged from their side.) Well, he started the old story: Please come back to live with him. He'd already found a job (a lie!), why didn't she quit dancing, and those night clubs, and the bad company. Whoever would have thought? Such a natural conversation. . . . They went to the front room and suddenly he says to her: "So you won't come back to me?" Just as natural as that. She smiled: "Please, Bob. Let's remain friends. Let's talk about something else." He pulled out his gun: "If that's how you feel about it, I'll kill you." They thought he was fooling! The girl opened her mouth, and he fired the shot right between her eyes. One shot, to kill. Now you can't see it, they've covered her face with a burlap. (But why don't they cover her legs, the poor thing. It's cruel to make a show of her like that. . . .) She lifted her hands to her face, as if refusing to see death, and dropped without so much as a cry. Nobody could believe it. He began to walk around the house like a loony, the gun in his hand, talking away to himself. He seemed puzzled, as if he couldn't make up his mind. The mother and the youngster began to yell. It was over in a minute. He aimed the gun at his head. . . . Look up there, do you see where the bullet lodged? It went through his brain and landed up there, in the frame of the door. He was crazy, had even been under the doctor's care. Always carrying a gun, that was his mania. And didn't the doctor warn the family? Of course, but who ever listens to such things? They could have saved her, reported him to the police, that would fix him. Once, when they were living together, he shut himself up in the bedroom. She heard a shot and ran to him. He was laughing, revolver in hand: "I knew you'd come running. You expected it!" He'd fired the shot into the pillow. Crazy as a bat, that's what he was. Always talking of killing himself. But he didn't want to go alone. Ever see such selfishness? . . .

Listen, that's the telephone. It's from the hospital. Dead? That's that.

Just a minute ago. Never talked again. The detective who went to his apartment found two more guns, both loaded. He left a note for his sister: "It had to be." And another to the police: "Sorry to bother you, gentlemen." So he had it all figured out, the b——!

* * *

Proud beauty, blonde beauty, one hundred dresses, a future, a career. Stretched out on the rug where she danced silently, looking at the heels of her golden sandals. And the sacrifices of her parents; all their lives spent in the cellars of cheap apartment houses, stoking in coal, lighting fires, emptying garbage, carrying around the bunch of keys for showing the empty apartment, listening to complaints, fixing leaky faucets. And in their hearts, the old country, a hopeless hope. And that daughter with her hard, closed face, beautiful, proud, who never spoke, forever gazing at her golden heels. Professional beauty, dreaming of a future. Dead. The mother never let her soil her hands: "Watch your nails . . ." And there she is now. America, the future, pictures in the papers, a career, her incomparable legs, and such an education as they gave her.

That wind, will it never let up! They say the damage is something awful; and the deaths, and the floods. The rain falls as in the movies. A real American rain . . .

The neighbors are still waiting. What for? The detectives seem relieved now. The reporters finish their notes. The father went out, quiet, cowed, in shirtsleeves: it's time to shake down the ashes, collect the garbage from the dumbwaiter which lets off a gust of putrid wind. "O.K.! Let 'er go!" The janitor goes about his business. Who's dead is dead, life must go on!

Look, I forgot to shut off the radio!

The rain is letting up now, and the air is turning warm. The evening seems tired of the storm.

Gee, we've gotta go to the movies tonight—have a little fun. This place reeks of the crime.

Translated by CAMILA C. CAMPANELLA

ITALY

INTRODUCTION

By Renato Poggioli

SINCE GEORGE BRANDES coined the phrase "literature of exile," literary critics have tried in vain to determine what relationship there may be between this literature and that which continues to exist in the country of origin. The answer to such a problem would help us understand to what extent the works of a Mazzini or a Herzen are the patrimony of European thought, and to what degree they belong to the body of their respective national literature.

In the last twenty years this problem has come to the fore, by force of circumstance, as one of primary importance. Many Russian, Italian, Spanish and French writers, and almost all the first-ranking German writers of the last two generations have followed the road of exile which has led them first to the remaining free corners of continental Europe and finally to the hospitable shores of the two Americas.

The effects of this vast literary migration must be identified with its causes, with the result that the content of this literature is essentially moral, social and political. But an acute student of literature cannot explain away so complex a phenomenon merely in terms of history or geography. It has a thousand ramifications of a psychological and aesthetic nature. We need only remember, for example, that an uprooted language acquires in exile an artificiality of character. Nor can we forget that a writer, weighed down by a feeling of solitude, cannot renounce the traditions in which he has lived, and he sees himself companionless in a strange world where his voice cannot be heard.

It is for such reasons that the literature of exile rarely faces the present, but almost always turns toward the past or the future. The remembrance of things past is shot through more with agony than with nostalgia. The desires or hopes with which it contemplates the future are transformed and become not so much dreams, as ideal Utopias. That is why exile, which the Spanish call so vividly *destierro*, brings forth works in which grief and memory are eased through revelation, acts of faith, visions of transcendency and mystic prophecies. Such is the case of the noblest work ever produced by the grandeur and misery of exile, *The Divine Comedy*.

The passions which inspire emigrant Italian writers have their counterpart in the poetic feelings of the Italians of contemporary Italy, but they function on a different plane and they have a vastly different psychological significance.

It is too often said that the culture of exile is the negation of that culture which is developing contemporaneously, in an atmosphere of tyranny and slavery, in the homeland. At present indigenous Italian literature worthy of the name is not Fascist literature. On the contrary, it is a literature that seems to know of neither the name nor the fact of Fascism. The emigrant writer, naturally, cannot allow himself this luxury. Not for a moment can he forget Fascism. And as for the literature of Fascist Italy, it is one of evasion. Not because of the good or evil of censorship but because of a psychological fatality, it seeks refuge in the lost paradise of childhood, it dotes on itself in a veritable lake of narcissism, and loses itself in the contemplation of death and the passions. It is condemned by its very nature to two forms only, the lyric and the idyl, and spends itself in sighs and songs and wishful dreams.

By an equally mandatory but contrary fatality, the poet exile knows only the voice of enthusiasm and indignation. He sounds only the note of anathema or of prophecy. The exiled writer seeks the cause of his destiny and his suffering. By right of his experience and vision, he can take upon himself the duty of guiding his brother through the wilderness. His march is no evasion of the present or the real. It is a march toward the future, a flight *ad realiora*.

Exile, with the experiences and perspectives peculiar to it, brings into being a kind of author who in other circumstances might never have followed such a calling. Such is the case of Emilio Lussu. Lussu represents a fine blending of legalistic mind and man of action. In his beautiful book, *Sardinian Brigade,* he has evoked his memories of the war. The trenches have inspired many literary works, but this one stands alone. It is more beautiful than the most moving war book ever written in Italy which bore the significant title *Introduzione alla Vita Mediocre*. It is not so hopelessly tendentious, as was *Le Feu* or *Im Westen Nichts Neues*. Lussu can look within himself, within his fellow officers, his superiors, his soldiers, and even within his enemies. The balance between internal and external words, between experience and vision, is admirably sustained.

Although it is the work of a pacifist and a liberal, *Sardinian Brigade* is neither polemic nor sermon. Although it is the work of an Italian (or rather, of a Sardinian), it is a universal book. The conscience of writer and reader alike pronounces against war and the military caste. It is a condemnation dictated by the eloquence of bare fact, by a crystal-like reality of passion. Contrary to what an American critic has written, *Sardinian Brigade* is not concerned with the weaknesses of an army, it is not a routine recital of life at the front. It assails what we can call in contradistinction to military glory, military slavery. Its lesson is addressed to the armies and peoples of all nations.

It is in a very different spirit that Ignazio Silone has re-evoked the moments of moral and political crisis, of injustice and oppression. Conquest and the exercise of power are viewed in the light of action, or seen in the microcosm of an Abruzzi village, or in an heroic pilgrimage in Southern Italy. Everyone knows *Fontamara* and *Bread and Wine*. Of the two books, the former is by far the superior. Silone's case is typical: it reveals how the exiled writer follows and transforms a given national literary tradition. His work is the last fruit produced by a great school of regional writers of the South whose master, admired and translated by D. H. Lawrence, was Giovanni Verga. Verga wrote with solemn, epic grandeur of the misery of the Sicilian peasant. The more objective his style, the more intense the motion it created. One might almost say that the tears of his characters *sunt lacrimae rerum*.

But anguish and fate in *Fontamara* are not cosmic; they are human and social. The author has made the mourning of his women and the imprecations of his men the more intensely tragic through a kind of distorted, multiple echo. This "gnashing of teeth" gives an absurd, grotesque meaning to the powerful characters which Silone etches with the acid, brutal style of a Goya. *Facit indignatio versum:* this formula gives us the key to the work of a writer who is unquestionably one of the most powerful writers, Italian or not, now living in exile.

The literary undertones of Leo Ferrero's *Angelica* are much more complex. *Angelica* is descended from a different tradition, which combines the tendencies of vanguard literature with the exigencies of a vast, highly evolved culture. Ferrero made his first literary appearance in the Florentine group of the *Solaria*. The collaborators on this magazine were oriented toward Joyce and Svevo, Proust and Valéry. In spite of this inheritance, the young author revealed from the first a noble spiritual catholicity which combined naturally with a certain formal and sentimental preciosity. *Angelica* was conceived as a mosaic in which the author stylizes the masks of the Commedia dell'Arte and the characters of the chivalric poems in the form and stature of a puppet theatre. Nevertheless, this imaginative composite rises to a high and powerful dramatic level. In this world of marionettes there appears Orlando, who assumes heroic proportions because he is a real man, and who sacrifices himself in vain for the honor of Angelica and the liberation of her city. Since Pirandello, the Italian theatre has said nothing to surpass the wisdom of this sad "fable."

Italian literature in exile, however, has not produced only memoirs, stories and symbolic dramas. It has given us a great critical work and here criticism must be understood in its highest sense as being a conscious judgment pronounced on history and on culture. It is *Goliath, or the March of Fascism* by G. A. Borgese.

This book constitutes a special case because it was written originally in English, for an American public. It is nonetheless an Italian work. The spiritual position, the intellectual implications of its style are Italian. The very fact that it was written for a foreign reader increases its value for the future Italian reader. Through the mirror of this book he will be better able to judge the glories and the errors of the people to which he belongs. Because no fact or implication is considered as already known or tacitly understood, the message of *Goliath* will be for him all the more telling.

Goliath is a part of the great Italian tradition, to which belong *The Prince* of Machiavelli and the *Storia della letteratura italiana* of de Sanctis. Each of these books speaks to us with the same eloquence and seeks to arouse in us the same emotions. Machiavelli concludes *The Prince* by exhorting Italians to forget their animosities and their factions, and to create together a great national state. De Sanctis counsels his contemporaries to abandon a moribund past and to give to Italy a literature worthy of modern Europe. Borgese pleads the necessity of denying forever the empty dreams of national mysticism, whether it be Roman, Imperial or Fascist. He calls for a new awareness and a new culture that may give Italy the right to exercise an harmonious influence on the human race and on the community of Western civilization.

In a certain sense, *Goliath* is comparable to the famous work in which Gioberti, at the dawn of the Risorgimento, sought to awake the Italian people from a sleep of humiliation and slavery. Actually, in opposition to Gioberti, Borgese does not approach the primacy of the Italians. One of the causes of Fascism, he believes, is precisely that dangerous, indestructible illusion. But thanks to Borgese, there is a superiority that belongs to Italian literature of exile: *Goliath* is the first voice which speaks to the Italian people together with all civilized nations, teaching that there can be no higher ideal for a people than that of becoming, by merit of its contributions to civilization, *primus inter pares.*

Translated by ADRIENNE FOULKE

Benedetto Croce

BALZAC

LITTLE THEORETICAL CERTAINTY is to be found in French literary criticism, because in France, differently from Italy and Germany, the theory of art, understood philosophically, has had little development. Notwithstanding this, I place the French psychological or impressionistic critics before the doctrinaire and systematic critics, Saint-Beuve and Lemaître before Taine and Brunetière. These latter are certainly theoretical, but dominated by that intellectualistic and dogmatic spirit which forms an obstacle to the comprehension of art. One should read Brunetière's volume on Balzac, lately reprinted in an almost popular edition, in order to see how his theories have obscured even those evident truths which are to be found in popular consciousness, and are again to be found, let us say, in Le Breton's modest and diligent study of the same author. Let us pass over (in order not to repeat a criticism which would henceforth be too obvious in Italy) the premiss of the "literary class," certainly not invented by Brunetière, but treated by him with absurd rigidity and in virtue of which the problem of his criticism appears as that of the class of "romance," and of Balzac as of the writer who confers autonomy upon this form, carries out the "true romance" and observes the boundaries which are not to be

crossed. But what has he seen of what is romance, or, to limit ourselves
to what is particularly in question, the "historical" and "social" romance?
And what has he understood of the spiritual disposition of Balzac, both
in regard to "historical romance" and to art?

If Brunetière had not lacked both aesthetic culture and philosophical
training, it would not have been difficult for him to discover that the
"social novel" can indeed be regarded as a form differing from the other
forms of art, as an "autonomous class," not because it is a form of art (in
which case and when it is such, the distinction shows itself to be altogether empirical and arbitrary), but because, on the contrary, in its origin
and proper quality it is not at all a form of art, but simply a didactic
scheme. When in Greece the religious, poetical and mythical impetus
came to an end and gave place to the work of research and criticism,
comedy also, in the imaginative and brilliantly capricious form given to
it by Aristophanes, became converted into the comedy of Menander, upon
which (as Vico was perhaps the first to note and Nietzsche the last to
bring into the sphere of general knowledge) had blown the breath of the
Socratic philosophy. Thereupon playwrights and moralists joined hands,
and comedy availed itself of the characterology of the philosophers, and
the philosophers adopted and developed the discussion of types of character which had been formed in the theatre. It is well known that the
framework of Menander sufficed writers of comedy for centuries, that is
to say, not only the Romans, but also the Italians of the Renaissance and
the French of the Classical period. Its characters became fixed and con-
ventionalized as those of the old man, the lover, the young girl, the astute
slave, the miser, the boaster, and so forth, and if some variety and some
accretions came to be added in course of time, yet it never or hardly ever
broadened beyond the study and representation of man in general and of
human vices and weaknesses.

But between the seventeenth and eighteenth centuries, social struggles
and changes and increased interest in history on the one hand reacted
also upon comedy and caused it to represent definite social and historical
environments, and on the other took possession of the prose of the novels
and turned it in the direction of the "historical" and the "social" novel.
Balzac's preface to the *Comédie humaine* is a good instance of this renovation of the programmes of Menander and Theophrastus: a Menander
who has behind him the French Revolution and before him the rule of
the middle-class, and is himself revolutionary and middle-class in his
own way, or counter-revolutionary and anti-middle-class; a Theophrastus
who has learned something about the new historical philosophy and the

new science of nature. Balzac, in fact, rallied to the doctrine of Geoffroy Saint-Hilaire and to the literary model offered by Buffon. He asked himself, seeing that at every period "des espèces sociales, comme il y a des espèces zoologiques," why something similar should not be done for society to what Buffon had achieved in his magnificent work, "en essayant de représenter dans un livre l'ensemble de la zoologie." The work which he desired to write was to possess a triple content: "les hommes, les femmes et les choses, c'est à dire les personnes, et la représentation matérielle qu'ils donnent de leur pensée: enfin, l'homme et la vie." He did not propose to restrict himself to simple observation, but to rise to the sphere of the reason or law of social facts, and from this to proceed yet further to the principles of judgment or of the ideals of the Good, the True and the Beautiful. The reference to Walter Scott is also noteworthy, and the demand that history should be "social," that is to say, no longer human in general, as in the individualism and pragmatism of the preceding century.

Balzac's proposal, like those of others who both with, before and after him pointed to social and historical romance as the successor of the Graeco-Roman comedy that had disappeared, is not a directly artistic proposal, but is historical, sociological and philosophical, and in so far as those writers wished to avail themselves of the imagination in order to summarize and to expose their observations and theories, they aimed, as I have said, at nothing other than a didactic scheme. But since science and imagination were placed side by side and the fusion of the two turned out to be impossible, two things happened: either the poetical element affirmed itself to be the true centre of the work and enslaved the scientific elements, reducing them to its tones and colours, and a purely poetical work was the result, ascending to the pinnacle of Manzoni's romance-poem, which has been justly described as the concrete historical form of the same author's *Inni sacri;* or the scientific interest declared itself to be the centre of the work, and then the poetical elements were in their turn enslaved and turned to account as supplying the popular and imaginative appeal of the theme in question. This second course had been usually adopted by those of mediocre talents, compilers of books of instruction and vulgarity, because anyone possessing truly original capacity as an observer and a philosopher is not satisfied to compose fables and apologies and to cut up his images into little pieces, but quickly grasps the good sword of scientific, historical and polemical prose. Artists unendowed with certain gifts proper to critics and thinkers, or a certain tendency towards observation and meditation, have never gone beyond a certain point in the development of such capacities, and have either found expression for their thought and conceptions in living representations, cancelling their properly scientific side, or they have left them scattered in notes, diaries and little essays, without subjecting them to truly systematic treatment.

It is not astonishing that Brunetière paid no attention to this difference of relation between the didactic scheme of the novel and art and poetry and to the various solutions to which it gives rise, because, as has been observed, he cultivated an intellectualistic conception both of art itself and of poetry. But what seems to me to be a proof of singular blindness, a result of false theory, is his insistence upon considering Balzac as the incarnation of the very idea of the novel ("Balzac, c'est le roman même"), as creator of the book of objective social observation, which should possess the essential characteristic of "rassemblance avec la vie," and be composed with "l'entière soumission de l'observateur à l'objet de son observation," thus adopting the method "qui a renouvelé la science," and which cannot ever be judged in itself, but only "en le comparant avec la vie." This is tantamount to saying that one set of observations must be controlled by comparing it with new observations and experiments. Now anyone who has examined, I do not say the entire works of Balzac, but has tested some of his novels, has at once seen as obvious that Balzac is by temperament the exact opposite of the scientific observer (the one full of doubts and precautions and a foe to precise affirmations, the other sure of himself and triumphant as Balzac always was in his assertions), and also of the lettered pedagogue, who selects certain concepts and historical points of view for symbolical narrative treatment and compiles instructive works illustrated with examples. And although every reader admires the profound psychological aphorisms to be met with in those novels of Balzac, he is not less sensible of the aphorist's incapacity to demonstrate and systematize, which is clearly manifest in the above-mentioned preface (his principal attempt at theorizing), where his imperfect and trammelled philosophy hastens to crown itself with religion and monarchy, those "deux vérités éternelles: la religion, la monarchie, deux nécessités que les évènements contemporains proclament, etc." And although some of his observations as to social history shine with a very bright light, they are vivid flashes, not diffused and well-distributed light: that is to say, they are rather suggestions as to questions to be asked rather than answers made to questions.

Balzac will, for instance, have clear vision of the power of finance in modern society, and he will make the little old Jew Gobseck say: "Je suis assez riche pour acheter les consciences de cent qui font mouvoir les ministres, depuis leurs garçons jusqu'à leurs maîtresses: n'est-ce pas le Pouvoir? Je puis avoir les plus belles femmes et leurs plus tendres caresses: n'est-ce pas le Plaisir? Le Pouvoir et le Plaisir ne résument-ils pas tout votre ordre social? Nous sommes en Paris une dizaine ainsi, tous rois silencieux et inconnus, les artistes de nos destinées. La vie n'est-elle pas une machine à laquelle l'argent imprime le mouvement? . . . L'or est le spiritualisme de vos sociétés." But this is not science, because science begins when a search is made—I was about to say sceptically—as to whether and to what extent gold dominates society, and by what social ends itself is guided and therefore dominated. The scientific problem has hardly dawned upon Balzac when he already changes it into a feeling of stupefaction and terror. "Je retournais chez moi stupéfié. Ce petit vieillard donc avait grandi. Il s'était changé à mes yeux en une image fantastique où se personnifiait le pouvoir de l'Or. La vie, les hommes me faisaient horreur." . . .

Everyone knows that Balzac as a young man devoured the most extravagant romantic literature both in French and English, adventures, conquests, discoveries of treasure, crimes, ghostly apparitions, hallucinations, and that he himself wrote novels of the same sort, and what he was never able to do without such marvellous tales, introducing them more or less freely and sometimes in profusion into many of the works of his maturity. But Balzac does not do otherwise than give an extraordinary aspect to what is ordinary, middle-class and popular even in those novels and in that series of novels which Brunetière considers to be "objective" and "naturalistic." No portrait of character or surroundings but he exaggerates it to the extent of making it altogether marvellous and fantastic, whether he is telling the story of a former officer of Napoleon like Philippe Brideau, or representing Goriot's paternal affection, or the house of father Grandet of the shop of the *chat qui pelotte*. He takes hold here and there of some bits of reality in order to make of them an object of fascination for himself and to enter by means of them into a dream of the unbridled and immense, through which he progresses, half in admiration, half in terror, as though immersed in an apocalyptic vision. To take this for "a methodical application of natural science" is really somewhat singular, as I observed, excusable only in the non-critical, thoughtless crowd, which takes the history of France to be the same as that told in the novels of the elder Dumas: a writer with whom Balzac has no small resemblance of method, so much so that it might be said, not without truth, that he transports the *Trois mousquetaires* into the world of politics, of speculation,

of invention, of banking, creating Artagnan business men, Athos manu-
facturers, Aramis ministers and Porthos acquiring riches by means of
violence and crime.

Acute writers had already warned people of this vulgar confusion, as,
for example, Baudelaire in one of his essays collected in the *Art roman-
tique:* "J'ai maint fois été étonné que la gloire de Balzac fût de passer
pour un observateur: il m'avait toujours semblé que son principal mérite
était d'être visionnaire et visionnaire passionné. Tous ses personnages sont
doués de l'ardeur vitale dont il était animé lui-même. Toutes ses fictions
sont aussi profondément colorées que les rêves. Depuis le sommet de
l'aristocratie jusqu'aux bas fonds de la plèbe, tous les acteurs de la Comédie sont plus âpres à la vie, plus actifs et rusés dans la lutte, plus patients
dans le malheur, plus goulus dans la jouissance, plus angéliques dans le
dévouement, que la comédie du vrai monde ne nous montre. Bref, chacun,
chez Balzac, même les portières, a du génie. Toutes les âmes sont des
armes chargées de volonté jusqu'à la gueule. C'est Balzac lui-même." . . .

Balzac's ardent imagination not only forbade to him scientific observation, for which Brunetière praised him, but was so violent and voracious
as to disturb his very work as an artist, and this point must be made clear,
as it supplies guidance in the critical reading of his fiction. Here too
Brunetière comes off badly: "C'est la représentation de la vie que l'inté-
resse, et non pas du tout la réalisation de la beauté, comme s'il se rendait
compte un peu confusément, qu'en art la réalisation de la beauté ne
s'obtient guère qu'aux dépens, au détriment de la fidélité de l'imitation de
la vie." These aesthetic perversions, which would put an end both to art
and criticism, show that Brunetière remained calmly reposing upon two
of the worst old rhetorical commonplaces, the idea of the imitation of
reality and of beauty as transcending reality, and did not even suspect
that the representation of reality and beauty is the same thing in art, and
that where we find beauty wanting, there too is wanting nothing else but
the perfection of representation.

How, then, can it be said that the ardour of Balzac's imagination, which
seems to be so favourable to artistic production, yet acted injuriously
upon that art? The reason is that in the delicate process of artistic creation, the imagination which embodies and dominates the impressions and
the passions of reality must be kept clearly distinct from the fancy which
avails itself of the intuitions of the imagination for its own enjoyment,
entertainment or bitter alleviation. Balzac's case was precisely so, for with
him what is described as his imaginative ardour really contained two
diverse activities acting in two different ways under one name, in the one

case inspiring him to artistic creation, in the other deforming the art produced or begun to be produced. One feels that Balzac was a poet in the best sense of the word, from the vigour with which he represents characters, situations and surroundings, from the perfection of the forms that burst forth from his stirred imagination. He has nothing in common with Victor Hugo, even as regards defects, for the latter does not start from poetic motives but from intellectual considerations in his plays and novels, and for this reason always preserves clearness of design in the midst of the revel of images which he groups around the aforesaid considerations, although he possesses very little poetical afflatus and genuine imagination.

Balzac, on the contrary, generally proceeds with energetic genius, like a true artist, but gradually in the course of the work, instead of leaving his creations free to follow the law of their true being and so create the companionship, the surroundings, the kind of action, beginning, middle and end that are implied in their fundamental notion, and consequently to moderate, attemper and take on their proper tone, he compels them to follow the law of his own rapacious temperament, of Honoré de Balzac, whose taste lies in the direction of passions pushed to the extreme, of violent and intransigent conflicts, of colossal undertakings, of astonishing clevernesses and infernal complications, of astounding successes, all of which he enjoys immensely and intensifies, in order to extract from them yet more enjoyment.

It has been said and repeated (and I think Sainte-Beuve is responsible for the statement), that in Balzac the characters are excellent, the action less good and the style vicious. This further empirical utterance of criticism must be corrected by means of the exact theory, namely, that the three things are one, and that one of them cannot be exempt from the defects of the others, and the defects of all must be brought home to a common origin. This common origin is to be found in Balzac's psychological disposition already described, owing to which he capriciously applies movement to his creations, thus making the characters of his personages revolve rapidly and grow vertiginously upon themselves, becoming ever more and more mad about themselves, and then, having attained the summit of this process of expansion, they turn into the opposite of what they were, or reveal other qualities in an unexpected way, which are contradictory or out of harmony with their former qualities. Their actions, owing to this same vertiginous rapidity, either lose all logical consistency, and, in their efforts to develop the characters, assume the customary form of the serial novel, or else they too all of a sudden also collapse and lauguish, and the style, which is all one with those actions and characters, falls from simple and robust plasticity into feebleness and languishment, or assumes the tone of explanation and comment. The characters do not attain to the harmony of discordant concord, and therefore the action does not unfold itself naturally and the style is not rhythmical.

Any one of Balzac's novels selected from among the best offers ready proofs of such inequalities and disharmonies; but I shall limit myself to *Eugénie Grandet,* which is reputed to be the most perfect of all, or one of the most perfect. After the wonderful picture of the country house and of the family surroundings in which flourish the gentle affections of the youthful Eugenia, who is there that does not feel that father and mother Grandet and Eugenia herself are being turned into fixed rhetorical types? Father Grandet is no longer a miser in his humanity, but a madman, and he behaves like a madman in the scene where he finds in his daughter's hands the bag left in her charge by her betrothed:

"Au regard que jeta son mari sur l'or madame Grandet cria:—Mon Dieu, ayez pitié de nous!

"Le bonhomme sauta sur le nécessaire comme un tigre fond sur un enfant endormi.

—Qu'est-ce que c'est que cela? dit-il en emportant le trésor et allant se placer à la fenêtre.—Du bon or! de l'or! s'écria-t-il. Beaucoup d'or! Ça pèse deux livres." . . .

With a maniac of this sort for father and a character without character such as the betrothed cousin, the story of Eugenia, which promised to turn out moving and poetical, loses itself in the insignificant. It seems that the author, who has spent his best strength in forcing characters and oppositions to an extreme, lacks the breadth to represent the drama which he had been preparing. So the story rushes along and what should have been represented is announced as having already happened: "Cinq ans se passèrent"; . . . or: "Pendant que ces choses se passaient à Saumur, Charles faisait fortune aux Indes," etc. Worse still, the style becomes impoverished, and here and there assumes the appearance of a school exercise:

"A trente ans Eugénie ne connaissait encore aucune des félicités de la vie. Sa pâle et triste enfance s'était écoulée auprès d'une mère dont le coeur méconnu, froissé, avait toujours souffert. En quittant avec joie l'existence, cette mère plaignit sa fille d'avoir à vivre, et lui laissa dans l'âme des légers remords et d'éternels regrets. Le premier, le seul amour d'Eugénie était, pour elle, un principe de mélancolie. Après avoir entrevu son amant pendant quelques jours, elle lui avait donné son coeur entre deux baisers furtivement acceptés et rendus; puis il était parti, mettant tout un monde entre elle et lui." . . .

Too often, before Balzac's novels, we experience a feeling of pain as though we had been present at the diminishing of a masterpiece, and our thoughts turn to that story of the same Balzac entitled *Un chef-d'oeuvre inconnu*, where it is a question of a picture that is a confused mass of colours, beneath which some fragment magnificently painted is here and there visible.

What more do you want? we shall be asked:—Balzac was built that way. Certainly, and he was a great man in that way also. Because, notwithstanding deformation, inflation and the abandonment of the end of art, which is very common in him, his art was most vigorous, and is strewn throughout with acute thoughts and observations, which vary its attractiveness. But Balzac never or only on rare occasions attained to aesthetic serenity. I admit that I remained astonished at an Italian comparison between him and Alexander Manzoni (and, in this connection, why should Balzac's unfavourable judgment of the *Promessi Sposi* in a conversation at Milan not be remembered? I read it many years ago in a book of Tullo Dandolo's), between him and Manzoni, as I was saying, where Balzac is held to be audacious and fruitful, Manzoni timid and sterile, astonished above all that anyone could have thought of making such a comparison, but worse than astonished at seeing that not even Manzoni's divine equality of level had been sufficient to throw into a clear light the artistic vice with which was afflicted Honoré de Balzac.

Translated by DOUGLAS AINSLIE

Luigi Pirandello

BETTER THINK TWICE ABOUT IT

FOR THE PAST three days, the home of Professor Agostino Toti had lacked the tranquility and gaiety he had come to look upon as his right.

One could hardly describe the professor as a fine figure of a man for his age. He was about seventy, very small, save for his large bald head, had no neck, and a body quite out of proportion to his two bird-like sticks of legs. Professor Toti had not the faintest illusions about his personal appearance, nor did he for one moment imagine that his pretty little wife, Maddalena, who was not yet twenty-seven, could love him for himself alone.

It is true that he had chosen to marry a poor girl to whom he was able to offer a rise in station. She was only the daughter of a door-keeper at the High School and had become the wife of a Professor of Natural Science, on the permanent staff, who in a few months' time was due to qualify for the full pension. Not only that, but he was a rich man besides, thanks to an unexpected legacy which had come to him two years previously—a windfall of some two-hundred-thousand lire, fallen like manna from heaven after the death of his brother, who had left for Roumania many years before and had never married.

Professor Toti did not, however, consider that all this entitled him to expect cheerfulness and tranquility in his home; being a philosopher, he knew that a pretty young wife needed something more.

Had he come into his fortune before he married, he might perhaps have had the right to ask his little Maddalena to be patient for a while, as it would not be long before his death would enable her to make up for the sacrifice of having married an old man. But alas! those two-hundred-thousand lire had arrived too late—a couple of years after his marriage— by which time Professor Toti had already . . . had already had the philosophy to realise that the trifling pension which he would one day leave his wife was not an adequate compensation for the sacrifice she had made in marrying him.

Having therefore made every concession at an earlier date, Professor Toti considered that he had a better right than ever to expect peace and gaiety in his house now that there was that valuable legacy in addition. All the more so since, as a truly wise and kind-hearted man, he had not rested content with being a benefactor to his wife, but had also been willing to be one to . . . well, yes, to *him* too, to his good Giacomino, who had been one of his most promising pupils at the High School, a well-conducted young fellow, rather shy, but with very nice manners, handsome and with the fair curly hair that one sees in pictures of angels.

Yes indeed, old Professor Agostino Toti had thought of everything. Giacomino Delisi was out of work, he was in a state of deep depression and was losing heart; so he—Professor Toti—had found the young man a post in the Bank of Agriculture where he had invested the two-hundred-thousand lire of inheritance.

There was also a baby now in the household—a little darling, two-and-a-half years old—to whom the professor was utterly devoted, a loving slave. The daily lectures at the High School seemed interminable as he waited for the hour when he could hurry home and satisfy all the whims and fancies of his little tyrant. He could indeed have sent in his resignation when he received his legacy and have retired without waiting for the maximum pension; in this way he would have been free to devote all his time to the baby. But he would not hear of such a thing. True, he had always found his professorship a great worry, but since he had taken it on, he would go through with it to the bitter end. It would be a sin to let slip the right to the full pension. Why, it was for that very reason that he had married—in order that some one might secure a benefit out of what had been a lifelong trial to himself.

Having married with that single aim—to act as benefactor to a poor young girl—his love for his wife was only of a semi-fatherly nature. His feelings towards her became still more paternal after her baby's birth and he would almost have preferred the child to call him 'Grandad' rather than 'Daddy'. It hurt him to hear that false statement uttered all unknowingly by the lips of the innocent baby. He seemed to see in it some insult to his love for the child. But he was helpless in the matter: he had to give Nini a kiss when the child called him 'Daddy', though the use of the name made people smile in no kindly way. How could those evil-minded persons understand the tender love he felt for the little one, or his happiness at the benefits he had conferred and was still conferring on a woman and also on a fine young fellow and on the baby, and lastly on himself too— yes, indeed—on himself, since he was thus able to enjoy the remaining years of his life by spending them in cheerful, loving society and to have a little angel as his close companion during the last stage of his journey to the grave.

Let them laugh to their hearts' content, those malicious onlookers . . . It's easy to laugh in that foolish fashion. Why didn't they put themselves in his place and they would understand. They could only see the comic— the more than comic—the grotesque aspect of the case, because they could not enter into his feelings. Well, what did it matter to him, since he was happy. . . .

Unfortunately, however, for the past three days . . .

What could have happened? His Maddalena's eyes were swollen and red from weeping; she complained of a severe headache and would not leave her room.

"Ah! Youth! . . . youth! . . ." sighed Professor Toti, shaking his head with a knowing look in his eyes, as he smiled sadly. "Some cloud or other . . . a passing storm . . ."

With Nini as companion he wandered round the house, restless, anxious and also rather cross, because—after all—really he didn't deserve to be treated like that by his wife and Giacomino. Young people don't have to

count the days—they have so many more still before them; but to a poor
old man the loss of a single day is a serious blow; and by now it was
already three days since his wife had left him like this, feeling quite lost
in his own home, like a fly that has had its head taken off. It was three
days now since he had heard her sweet voice singing the little airs and
ballads which she knew how to sing so prettily—three days since she had
lavished on him any of the little attentions to which he had become so
accustomed.

Nini too was very solemn, as if he understood that Mummy was not in
the mood to take any interest in him. The professor took him from one
room to another—he was so very short himself that he hardly needed to
stoop at all, as he led the child by the hand. He lifted him up to the piano,
played a few notes, then abandoned the instrument with a yawn and an
impatient little sniff; sat down and took Nini on his knees to play 'Ride-
a-cock-horse' with him and stood up again, feeling utterly miserable. Five
or six times he had tried to induce his little wife to speak of her trouble.

"Feeling bad, are you? . . . Are you feeling very bad?"

But Maddalena still failed to tell him anything. She wept, begged him
to close the balcony shutters and take Nini away—she wished to be left
alone, to lie in the dark.

"Is your head aching?"

Poor girl, she had such a bad headache. . . .

Evidently the quarrel had been a very serious one indeed.

Professor Toti went to the kitchen and tried to approach the servant,
to obtain some information from her. He could not speak at all plainly to
her, for he knew that the maid was by no means a friend of his: outside
the house she let her tongue wag freely, making coarse fun of him, just as
every one else did—the silly fool who ought to have known better.

Failing to discover anything from his talk with the maid, Professor
Toti adopted a heroic resolution. He took Nini to 'Mummy' and asked her
to dress the child up in his best clothes.

"Why?" asked Maddalena.

"I'm taking him out for a little turn," he answered. "It's a holiday to-day
. . . the poor child's getting very bored shut up in the house."

'Mummy' did not like the idea. She knew the unkind way in which
people laughed at the sight of the old professor going hand in hand with
the small child; she knew that at times they had even gone so far as to
say, with shameless irony—"Your son does take after you, Professor. He's
so like you . . ."

Professor Toti, however, insisted.

"Just a little turn—to amuse ourselves."

He then took the child to the house of Giacomino Delisi.

The young man lived with a sister a few years older than himself, who had mothered him in his early days. At first the Signorina Agata had been full of gratitude to Professor Toti for his kindness to her brother. At that time she was in complete ignorance as to the reasons for his conduct. She was an extremely religious woman and accordingly, when she came to learn the truth of the case, she regarded the professor as a fiend in human shape, in that he had tempted her Giacomino and led him into mortal sin.

After ringing at the door, Professor Toti had to wait outside, with the child, for a considerable time. The Signorina Agata had come and peeped through the judas-hole and hurried away. No doubt she had gone to inform her brother that he had called—she would shortly return to tell him that Giacomino was not at home.

At last she appeared—a frosty, sour-faced woman, dressed all in black, with waxy complexion and livid circles round her eyes. The moment she opened the door, she assailed him, all quivering with emotion:—

"I beg your pardon! . . . What does this mean? . . . You even go so far as to look him up in his house, now? . . . And what's this I see . . . You've brought the baby? . . . You've brought the child here too! . . ."

Professor Toti had not expected an attack of this nature. Completely taken aback, he looked first at the Signorina, then at the child, and smiled and stammered.

"Why . . . why? . . . What is it? . . . Can't I . . . can't I come to . . . ?"

"He's not at home," she hastened to answer in a dry, unsympathetic tone. "Giacomino's not at home."

"Very well," said Professor Toti, with a little bow. "But you, Signorina —I hope you won't mind my saying so—you treat me in a way which . . . how shall I put it? . . . I have no recollection of ever behaving towards either your brother or yourself in a way that would justify . . ."

"That's exactly the point, Professor," interrupted Signorina Agata, who had been slightly mollified by his words. "Believe me, we are . . . yes, we are indeed most grateful to you. But surely you must understand that . . ."

Professor Toti smiled again, half closed his eyes, raised his hand and tapped his breast several times with his fingertips to intimate to her that, when it came to understanding anything, she could leave the matter to him.

"I am an old man, Signorina," he said, "and I understand . . . I understand many things. Now here is one of the first of those things—when anyone is in a temper, one must let them cool down; and when misunder-

standings arise, the best course is to clear them up . . . to clear them up,
Signorina, in all frankness, without any subterfuge, without becoming
heated over it . . . Don't you agree?"

"Yes, indeed," replied Signorina Agata, admitting this general proposition.

"Very well then," resumed Professor Toti, "kindly let me come in, and
you go and call Giacomino."

"But if he's not at home?"

"Come, come! You mustn't tell me that he's not at home. Giacomino is
in this house and you ought to go and call him. Say that we shall clear
matters up calmly . . . quite calmly. I am an old man and I understand all
about it, because I was once young myself, Signorina. Quite calmly, tell
him. Please let me come in."

Allowed at last to enter the humble parlour, Professor Toti sat down
and took Nini between his legs. He resigned himself to the prospect of
being kept waiting for a considerable time before Giacomino could be
persuaded by his sister to appear.

"No, don't go over there, Nini . . . behave nicely . . . be a good boy,"
he said every now and then to the child, who wanted to wander off to a
fancy table sparkling with cheap china ornaments. Meanwhile he racked
his brains to discover how the devil such a grave incident could have
taken place in his own house and he not have been aware of it. His Maddalena was such a good little girl. What could she possibly have done to
have aroused such violent, determined resentment in this household, even
in Giacomino's sister?

Up till then, the professor had supposed that there had been only a
temporary estrangement, but he now began to grow quite seriously
worried.

At last Giacomino appeared. Good heavens! how upset he looked, and
what a cross face! And—but no, no that would never do!—there he was
coldly pushing away the child who had run up, holding out his little
hands in greeting, with a cry of "Giami! Giami!"

"Giacomino!" exclaimed Professor Toti in a severe tone, wounded by
such conduct.

"What is it you have to say to me, Professor?" the young man hastened
to enquire and, as he spoke, he avoided looking the professor straight in
the face. "I'm not well . . . I was in bed . . . Really I'm not fit to talk or
even to stand the sight of anyone . . ."

"But the baby?"

"Here's a kiss for him," said Giacomino and stooped down to kiss the child.

"So you're feeling ill?" resumed Professor Toti, slightly pacified by that kiss. "I thought you must be. That's why I've come. Your head bad, eh? Sit down, sit down and let's talk . . . Nini, did you hear that? Giami has the *bua* . . . Yes, he's got the *bua* . . . poor Giami, so you must be very good, Nini. We'll soon be going . . . I wanted to ask you," he continued, turning to Giacomino, "whether the Manager of the Bank of Agriculture said anything to you?"

"No, why?" replied Giacomino, still more upset at these words.

"Because I spoke to him about you yesterday," replied Professor Toti with a little smile of mystery. "Your salary is not very large, my son. And, you know, a little word from myself . . ."

Giacomino shifted uneasily on his chair and clenched his fists so tightly that his nails dug into the palms of his hands.

"I thank you for what you've done, Professor," he said, "but please note that I want you to do me the favour—the great favour—of not putting yourself out in future on my account."

"You really mean it?" answered Professor Toti, with that little smile still on his lips. "Bravo! So we've no longer need of any one, eh? . . . But suppose I should want to help you for my own satisfaction—my own pleasure? My dear boy, if I am not to take an interest in you, whom d'you think I am going to take an interest in? . . . I'm an old man, Giacomino, and old men—mind, I'm not speaking of the selfish ones among us—old men who have worked as hard to make good, as I have done, enjoy seeing deserving young men like yourself make progress in their careers, thanks to the help we can give them. The old find pleasure in the gaiety and hopefulness of the young, in seeing them gradually make their way in the world. And then, as regards yourself—surely you realise that I always look upon you as my son? . . . Good heavens! What's the matter? . . . You're not crying?"

Giacomino had in fact hidden his face in his hands. From his convulsive movements it looked as if he were struggling to avoid breaking into a fit of tears.

Nini looked at him timidly, then turned to the professor and said:—

"Giami . . . *Bua* . . ."

The professor rose and was about to put his hand on Giacomino's shoulder, when the young man sprang up as if in horror at the thought of such contact. His face distorted by a look of fierce determination, he shouted wildly:

"Don't come near me, Professor. Go away—I implore you—go away. You're making me suffer the tortures of the damned. I don't deserve your affection and I don't want it . . . I don't want it, I tell you . . . For goodness sake be off and take the child with you, and forget my very existence."

Professor Toti was dumbfounded.

"What do you mean?" he asked.

"I'll tell you straight out," replied Giacomino. "I'm engaged to be married, Professor. Do you understand? I'm engaged."

Professor Toti tottered as if he had been clubbed on the head. He threw up his hands stammering:—

"You? . . . en . . . en . . . engaged?"

"Yes, Sir. And so you see all is finished . . . it's finished for good . . . Now you'll understand that I can no longer see you . . . see you here . . ."

"You're turning me out?" asked Professor Toti in a voice that was barely audible.

"No," Giacomino hastened to reply, in a tone of grief. "But it is better that you . . . that you should go, Professor . . ."

Go! The professor sank upon his chair. He felt his legs suddenly giving way beneath him. He put his head between his hands and groaned.

"My God! What a disaster . . . So that's the explanation . . . Oh what am I to do—what am I to do . . . But when did this happen? How? Not a word of it to me! Whom are you engaged to?"

"It happened here . . . a short time ago," said Giacomino. "She's like me—an orphan, and poor—and she's a friend of my sister."

Professor Toti looked at him stupefied. His mouth was open, his eyes dull; for several seconds he could not utter a word, then he faltered:—

"And . . . and . . . and so everything is dropped, like that . . . and . . . and no further thought is given to . . . to any one . . . no further account taken of anything . . ."

Giacomino felt the charge of ingratitude which underlay these words; in a gloomy spirit of rebellion he retorted:—

"I beg your pardon, but were you expecting me to become a slave?"

"*I* expect *you* to become a slave?" exclaimed Professor Toti in rising tones. "*I*? You can ask that of *me*, when I have made you the master of my house? Ah! that . . . that really is the basest of ingratitude. What advantage d'you think I have gained? What have I got out of it, except the mockery of those fools who can't enter into my feelings? So *you* don't understand either—you've never understood my feelings? I'm only a poor old man approaching very near the end of my life, but I have been able to derive a tranquil satisfaction from the thought of leaving behind me a happy little family, which was well provided for and had made a good start in life! I am seventy years old, Giacomino, and soon—in a few days perhaps—I shall have left you. What has made you go out of your senses, my son? I am bequeathing my whole estate to the three of you. . . . What more do you want? . . . I don't know yet, I don't want to know who your fiancée is. Since it is you who have chosen her, she's sure to be a decent girl, because you're a fine young fellow. But, consider a moment—consider . . . it isn't possible that you could have found a better girl, Giacomino, when everything is taken into consideration . . . I'm not speaking only of the fact that you would be left in comfortable circumstances, quite well off, in fact; but here you've already got your own little family, with myself only as an extra person in it—I don't count, and anyhow I'm only here for a short time. . . . In what way does my presence worry you? I'm like your father, so to speak . . . I could even, if you wished and if it would make you any happier. . . . But tell me, tell me how it came about? What happened? How did your head come to be turned, all of a sudden, like this? Explain to me, my boy. Tell me all about it. . . ."

Professor Toti went up and was about to put his hand on Giacomino's shoulder, but the young man shrank back, almost with a shudder, and avoided his touch.

"But, Professor," he cried. "Can't you understand? Can't you see that all this kindness of yours . . ."

"Well?"

"Oh! leave me alone. Don't force me to speak out. . . . Oh! my God. How is it that you can't understand that certain things can only be done on the quiet, that it's no longer possible to go on doing them when *you* know all about it, and everybody makes a joke of it?"

"Everybody? I don't care *that* for them," cried the professor. "So you see . . ."

"Oh! do leave me alone," repeated Giacomino, waving his arms wildly, in a frenzy of excitement. "Look, Professor. Look! There are so many other young men in need of help."

These last words wounded Toti deeply: he regarded them as an atrocious and quite uncalled-for insult to his wife. He turned pale; then with a quiver of rage which brought the blood to his cheeks again, he replied:—

"Maddalenina is a young girl, but thank God she is modest and virtuous, as you well know. Maddalenina may die of this blow, because it has stabbed her to the heart . . . how else d'you think she would take it? It is *there*, in the heart that you have stabbed her, ungrateful fellow that you are. And now, in addition, you're insulting her. Aren't you ashamed of yourself? Can you stand there before me and feel no remorse? You can actually say that to my face, Giacomino? D'you think that she can change over from one person to another, as if it were a trifle? You can say that to the mother of this baby? What can you be thinking of? How dare you speak in that way"

Giacomino was so surprised that he found it difficult to answer.

"I?" he said. "But . . . but . . . that question ought to be put to you, Professor. Excuse my saying so, but how can *you* speak in that way? You're not talking seriously?"

Professor Toti threw up his hands and pressed them to his mouth, blinked, shook his head violently to and fro and burst into a flood of tears. At this point, Nini also started crying. The professor heard him, hurried over to him and embraced him, murmuring:—

"Oh! my poor Nini . . . what a terrible blow . . . ruin, complete ruin, poor little Nini . . . What will become of your poor Mummy now? And what will happen to you, my Nini, with a little mother like yours, so inexperienced and with no one to guide her? . . . Oh! God, what a scoundrel!"

He raised his head and peered at Giacomino through his tears, saying:—

"I am weeping because I blame myself so bitterly: I took you up, made you at home in my house and always spoke to her so highly of you—I . . . I removed all the scruples she felt about falling in love with you . . . and . . . and, now that she has come to love you truly . . . now that she is the mother of this darling child . . . you . . . you . . ."

He broke off; then with a sudden savage resolution, he added excitedly:—

"Have a care, Giacomino! You have a care! I am quite capable of presenting myself at your fiancée's house, accompanied by this child."

Giacomino had been in a cold sweat, though he felt at the same time as if he were on hot coals when he heard the professor's reproaches and witnessed his distress. At this concluding threat, he stepped forward and held up his clasped hands with an imploring gesture.

"Professor, Professor," he begged him. "You don't want to make a spectacle of yourself—you don't want to cover yourself with ridicule."

"With ridicule?" shouted the old man. "What d'you think I care about ridicule, when I see the impending ruin of a poor woman, of yourself and of this little innocent one . . . Come along, Nini, let's be off . . . we must go."

Giacomino stepped in front of him.

"Professor, you can't really do that?"

"I most certainly can and will," cried the professor with a look of great determination. "And—what's more—to prevent you from marrying, I am also capable of having you turned out of the Bank . . . I give you three days' time."

Holding the child's hand he turned round at the doorway and added: "You'd better think twice about it, Giacomino!"

Translated by ARTHUR and HENRIE MAYNE

Ignazio Silone

THE REAL STORY OF PEPPINO GORIANO

"I SHALL NOW TELL you the real story of Peppino Goriano," the little old man said to us.

He left Fontamara for Rome the year they murdered King Umberto. How many years ago was that? Easy enough to figure it out: from the death of Umberto up to the comet that came after the war with Tripoli is a little more than ten years; from the comet to the war at Trieste would be around five more and that makes fifteen; the war at Trieste lasted four or five years and that makes twenty; then for five years the labor parliaments were in and that makes twenty-five; then began the period of law and order which had been going on about ten years now with everybody hoping that it will wind up even if we have to get the Turks in but it doesn't seem to wind up and there's no sign of any Turks and so that makes about thirty-five.

"So Peppino Goriano must have left for Rome about thirty-five years ago. He was off in search of his fortune, planning to return to Fontamara as soon as he made it and marry a sixteen-year-old girl he was in love with, who was at that time known as Marietta Sorcettonero."

"And here she is," put in Marietta with a blush.

"That's impossible!" cried the quack doctor, raking Marietta with a glance from head to foot.

We spoke up in corroboration of Marietta and the prophet was dumb with excitement and confusion. After a long pause he commenced again to spin out the life of Peppino Goriano.

"Peppino Goriano counted on making his fortune within a few years. He immediately found work at Rome as kitchen boy in a home called 'The Brothers of Charitable Acts' but he did not make any fortune with them. He worked fourteen hours a day and got his room and board, but no spending money. The priests at the Home were of the opinion that wine degrades man, and they would not allow their subordinates to degrade themselves. The only ones in that Home that had the right to get degraded were the superiors. But the superiors' wine was in the wine-cellar and Peppino Goriano's job was in the winecellar. After two years of faithful service he was fired for habitual drunkenness. For some time he was out of work. Every now and then he would pick up a couple of soldi on odd jobs, but they were hardly enough to tickle his thirst, not nearly enough so that he could really eat or get a room for himself. He slept according to season in the Botanical Gardens, the Colosseum, or under the gates to the Esedra, all of them most magnificent sights by day but difficult to sleep in. One night when Peppino Goriano was asleep he had a dream about San Rocco, who visited him and told him how to get into a nearby butcher shop. Peppino hastened promptly to the butcher shop that had been revealed, but just to make it all perfect for him, he was caught by the police. He was held under arrest and condemned to eight months in prison. During his hearing he tried to do himself some good by bringing in San Rocco, but the judges would not believe him. Judges have a way of never believing people down on their luck. It was in prison that he made his fortune. His eyes got infected. First of all a whitish liquid began to come out of his pupils, then they swelled up and got red as little tomatoes, really heartrending to look at. Once released from prison, thanks to the pitiable state of his eyes, Peppino Goriano succeeded for the first time in his life in getting one arm around Lady Luck; he hired a baby girl from a chap he knew and went into charity. Mornings he used to wander around in churches where they were saying mass for the repose of the dear souls in purgatory, at noon he would get around to two or three convents for a bowl of soup, and afternoons he did miscellaneous pickups in the cemetery and at theater entrances. Although the baby girl he hired was costing him two lire a day, Peppino was still earning enough more to get a room for himself and put something away as well. He had no worries about eating because he got more than enough from convents and he used to have to get rid of part of it at a restaurant near Porta San Giovanni in exchange for wine. Peppino thought he would continue to occupy himself with charity at least a couple of years more, so as to put aside a good round sum and then go back to Fontamara and marry Sorcettonero.

"Why did he ever change his mind, then?" asked Marietta with a sigh.

"Envy, envy was all that ever broke up his plans. One lousy day the police had to go and grab him and they made him go to a hospital to get his eyes fixed. Peppino Goriano tried to show fight. 'They're my eyes,' he said, 'and I can do what I please with them.' But there has never been any real freedom in Italy. So in a few days he had his eyesight back and he was out of a job. The happy days, the days of plenty, were over, and he had fallen upon evil ones. He tried his hands at hard labor as mason's assistant, coachman, hodcarrier at Tevere, but he never used to be able to stick it more than a week. When he had the will for it he didn't have the strength and when he had the strength he didn't have the will. He tried his luck in a thousand other lines. In those days hundreds of country boys used to get into Rome every day, all seeking their fortunes. Those who had small ambitions hired themselves out as streetsweepers, bootblacks, kitchen help, gardeners and stable boys and they worked themselves up into little regular jobs, putting aside a few pennies every day. But Peppino Goriano didn't have the patience to wait ten years to get a thousand lire saved up like other country boys. He was always expecting the door of good luck to come bursting open. But it was the prison door that kept opening for him and he spent a total of four years and five months in jail.

"After so many disappointments Peppino Goriano began to lose courage. He yielded himself up to living the life of the poor people from the Abruzzi who do Rome's humblest tasks. For a while he wandered around among crowds in railroad stations and through barracks with a parrot that for a penny would choose an envelope with the future written in it. But after a few months of this the parrot began to show signs of mental aberration and then one day it died. Making use of the regular influx of Abruzzi people who come to Rome in winter to find work, Peppino went around a little beforehand to get places as nurses and servants for the peasant women and jobs as dishwashers and stone workers for the men.

"At this time Peppino succeeded in making the acquaintance of a holy man, Monsignor Calogero, a barefoot Carmelite, who took him into his service as master of house. The monsignor suffered more from pruriency than he should have at his age, and it was peasant women from the Abruzzi that satisfied him best of all. Peppino was to receive board and lodging free, plus a ten lire bonus for every peasant woman whom he managed to bring into the bed of the holy man. For the first few months Peppino did his work conscientiously and was always wandering up and down the promenades and through the public gardens inducing servant girls to come and confess themselves at Monsignor Calogero's. His takings were scant. Moreover the holy man would not receive the same woman more than two or three times and he always had to be looking for new ones. So as not to lose his job Peppino found himself obliged to call upon the women in Via Panico, who made love professionally. He got them to eat garlic and onions so that the monsignor would think he had a peasant woman fresh down from the Abruzzi. The holy man did not notice what was being palmed off on him until he caught a revolting disease. After that Peppino was discharged. Bad luck was still pursuing him."

"But why didn't he come home at Fontamara?" asked Marietta.

"Come back here like a whipped dog? That was impossible. He remained in Rome where his misery would be more endurable to him. He tried out a thousand trades, dog clipper, bellringer, gravedigger at the cemetery, peddler selling shoelaces and postcards in memory of Guglielmo Oberdan, dishwasher in all kinds of restaurants. The oftener he changed his job, the more he stayed the same thing.

"Thousands of Abruzzians like himself used to live and are still living at Rome, doing what 'the others,' 'the nice people,' are too good to do. They spend their whole lives on a lower level than 'the others.' They stay farmers from habit and wretches from habit. You have only to walk down the street in Rome to recognize them at a glance. They dress, walk, gaze, laugh, and talk in a way different from 'the others.' On Sunday 'the others' go to the Stadium or out to Parioli; they go into some little restaurant or other. Peppino was in Rome while 'the others' were making their demonstrations for and against the war at Trieste, and he was spending his time at a little eating house near the Porta Trionfale. After the war almost all 'the others' used to go to the labor parliaments, and he would spend his time at an eating house in Testaccio. Sometimes he understood how topsy-turvy the whole city was getting and without wanting to he got mixed in with the rest of them. All the worse for him.

"That was how it was that day in Via Cola di Rienzo when he saw a big mob with a red flag plundering stores. He mixed with the crowd and entered a shoestore, but when he got outside he noticed that the shoes he had taken were not mates. He had two women's dancing slippers, both for the left foot, and a big hunting boot for the right foot. What could he do with them? He commenced to hunt for the other person who had taken the shoes corresponding to his, asking on all sides until he met with a very distinguished gentleman who said he would be charmed to be of use to him and invited him to visit his home. But the distinguished gentleman did not take him to his house but to a police station, where he was put under arrest for looting. At the hearing Peppino came up along with many workingmen, all of whom said they had taken part in the attack on stores 'for political reasons,' while Peppino admitted he had done it because he needed shoes. For that he got twice as long as the others.

"In those days it often happened that if a man were killed on the street his assailant was let off or even rewarded if he had done it 'for political reasons,' but he was given a heavy sentence if he had done it on account of poverty. As for himself, after mature reflection Peppino decided that he had been a misfit all his life because he had always done things out of hunger and never 'for political reasons,' and that he would resolve from then on that whatever he did in the future he would do 'for political reasons.'

"Upon leaving prison Peppino was brought to the police station, where he was given this alternative: either you do what we say or to-morrow evening you have to leave Rome and return to Fontamara. Peppino found out that the same proposal was being made these days to all his recently released friends at prison. With great good will Peppino accepted a proposal to work 'for political reasons,' received fifty lire advance wages and orders to go that evening to the Piazza Venezia and shout: 'Hurray for Nitti! Down with Fiume!' "

"Fifty lire just for shouting that?" Michele Zompa asked the fake seer, expressing our common incredulity.

"Don't interrupt me," the wizard went on. "You don't know anything about politics. That evening Peppino Goriano found a lot of people gathered in the Piazza Venezia, among whom was a bunch of old pals of his from the Queen of Heaven Prison. He commenced to shout: 'Hurray for Nitti! Down with Fiume!" Then he saw a group of officials and storm troopers bearing down upon him, while his friends from the Queen of Heaven were breaking up in all directions. But he was right at the outset of his political career and he wanted to keep his job. So he kept on yelling what the police had told him to even though he didn't have any idea what it meant. Peppino was overtaken by the officials and storm troopers. He never really could tell what happened, because he lost consciousness and came to only at the hospital of San Giacomo."

"So there were officials against the police? How could that come about, now?" asked General Baldissera, who had the old ideas about high standards of military discipline.

"Don't keep interrupting me," went on the quack prophet. "You can't understand anything about politics. After he got out of the hospital Peppino kept on working 'politically,' that is, he kept on taking beatings at hours and places fixed by the police. He was beaten half to death once by the streetcar men at Porta Santa Croce, and another time by the gas workers at Porta San Paolo, and then again by the kiln stokers at Porta Trionfale. Whenever he went and yelled what the police told him to he got a beating. Usually he was the only one to take these beatings because the friends with him from the Queen of Heaven would split up and make a getaway whenever danger came too close."

"But why didn't Peppino run away too?" queried the suffering Marietta.

"So's he could earn more money," explained the quack doctor. "He used to get five lire a day from the police, plus twenty-five lire bonus every time he had to go to the hospital. What with the high cost of living and all, five lire was not enough for him and he was absolutely in dire need of being beaten up. Naturally it was not very pleasant, but work has never been a pleasant thing to have to do. Moreover the words he had to shout kept changing constantly; after he had shouted six months, 'Hurray for Nitti!' Peppino Goriano was obliged to shout for a year, 'Down with Nitti!' But the effect was always the same. He always took a beating. After a year and a half of political activity the body of Peppino Goriano resembled that of Jesus against the pillar when Pilate says: 'Behold the man.'

"Peppino Goriano may really be considered a martyr of the political life. No Italian ever suffered so much for political reasons as did Peppino Goriano. He was not one of those who stay shut up in their homes and send the rest out to battle one another. He paid everything in person. Many other Italians were fighting for their theories at that time, but they were not to be compared with Peppino Goriano, who battled for all theories at the same time, who gave his blood for democracy and for nationalism, for socialism and for the church. At bottom there is something good in all theories. Peppino found the good in all theories to be this: that in their service he could earn five lire a day, plus twenty-five lire bonus every time he went to the hospital.

"The beatings got harder for Peppino to endure as he grew older. A desire to retire from the political field began to trouble him. Political clashes were getting more and more dangerous. The participants were not using cobblestones and brickbats so much any more; they were commencing to shoot. Political life was getting deadly. Political life was ceasing to be a way of earning one's living by being beaten up. It was becoming a serious affair, not reconcilable with the character of Peppino Goriano."

"But why were they doing shooting?" Sorcanera asked him.

"I have spent thirty-five years in Rome and I don't know why. So how could you possibly figure it out, an ignorant woman like you who has spent all her life at Fontamara?"—such was the fake doctor's evasive reply. Then he went on again: "It was simply politics. Peppino gave up answering police calls. After awhile he was summoned and a peremptory alternative was laid before him: 'Either you do what we want or you leave Rome to-night for Fontamara. But this isn't a matter of getting beaten up any more. It's a new kind of political life: twenty lire a day and streetcar pass, your duty being to do the beating up yourself and your privilege being not to take any beating.'"

"Don't hand us any more rubbish," broke in Michele Zompa. "Where do you get this about the police giving Peppino Goriano twenty lire a day, plus a free streetcar pass, plus the right to give beatings himself without the risk of taking one? Don't pull any of that on me. I have to make three trips down to Fucino to earn twenty lire."

The fake wizard was silent, as though uncertain whether to continue. But then after a little he went on without making any fuss over Michele's interruption.

It did actually have to do with a new and very attractive kind of political life, an unheard of kind. It had to do with this so-called fascism. Now what did fascism mean to Peppino Goriano? Something simply marvelous! Good wages, three times those of any farmer, the right to hand out beatings and not be beaten, and the protection of the authorities.

"Peppino was taken by a policeman to a big hall behind the printing house of the 'Giornale d'Italia.' Lots of people were already there when he arrived: officials, students, storm troopers, clerks, smart young ladies, merchants and two or three priests including Monsignor Calogero. The walls were decorated with streamers in tricolor. Everybody was talking at the top of his voice. Peppino felt very much frightened being around all these swell people. But then he came upon a group of familiar faces off in a corner, his old friends from the Queen of Heaven, most of them breakers and enterers. Then there fell a great silence. A gentleman appeared on the stage and began to speak. He gave hearty welcome to Peppino Goriano and his friends, the new aristocracy of labor, the most enlightened circle of factory workers, who stood ready to spill the last drop of blood in their veins for the salvation of the motherland. Then he began to give them a lot of deep stuff. When the speech was over the hall emptied itself but Peppino Goriano and his friends were asked to stand by to participate in taking Porto Pia by storm.

"They were given something to eat and drink in a restaurant near by. Thereupon they were loaded onto a truck which took them to Porto Pia, near the monument to Brescia, where they waited about an hour. Waiting there they saw columns of federal troopers and civil guards invade the office of a communist newspaper right across from them, and a little later they saw them taking away as prisoners all men who had been found in the offices. A policeman came up to let Peppino Goriano and his friends know they had nothing more to fear and that they could now attack the offices of the newspaper with all impunity. They did so. The offices were entered, the furniture was carried down into the middle of the street and burned, along with the files and other papers; the windows, doors, typewriters, pictures, stoves and vases were smashed into a thousand bits, ink bottles were slung at the tapestries on the walls; the safe was disemboweled in professional style but found empty.

"Before leaving the wrecked offices the invaders were photographed by a group of newspapermen who had arrived. Peppino was in the middle of the group brandishing a chairleg in the air. Next morning the photograph came out in the 'Piccolo' with the caption. 'The Hero of Porto Pia.'

"Peppino Goriano now enjoyed days of unforgettable glory and fame. He began to hang around the editorial offices of newspapers, where everybody bought drinks for him. He even got a bid from the Marchesa Parucchini, who first introduced him to her lady friends, then took him into her kitchen, and then into her bedroom, where he had to wear himself out a lot more than at the storming of Porto Pia.

"Peppino was able to make use of his newfound glory to the extent of getting himself a post as night watchman in the asylum at Borgo Pio. A friend of his was killed by workmen in the suburb of San Lorenzo and that set him to doing some hard thinking. Whenever he began to hear about more meetings on behalf of fascism he would invariably answer that he wasn't feeling very well. He was not earning much as a night watchman, but he wasn't running many risks, either."

"But when the fascists got the upper hand, why didn't Peppino make use of it and get himself a better job?" Sorcanera wanted to know.

"When the fascists got the upper hand, as you express it, things began to get tough for the old school of fascists. Peppino was summoned before a committee and asked: 'Are you a fascist? How long? Do you have any criminal record?' Result: fascism could no longer shelter in its bosom such delinquents as had been convicted several times for theft. Therefore Peppino Goriano, the Hero of Porto Pia, was expelled from the fascist party. Other friends of Peppino's engaged by the police upon their release from the Queen of Heaven got the same dose, except those who were still very young and were taken into the army. At the same time Peppino was discharged as night watchman at the Borgo Pio asylum and his place was taken by a boy called 'Monsignor Calogero's son.'

"So the lean days began for Peppino all over again. There began again that old hunger that never would be satisfied. Every month life got worse for him. No one would ever have thought the new government could last ten years and still it has gone and lasted ten years.

"Rome got to be unbearable to live in. Every day a new law. Every single day a new law. Of course every government has always made new laws. But this government we have in now makes a new law every day.

"The popes ran things all those centuries with just five precepts of the church. Garibaldi, after the march of the Thousand, brought in only three new laws, the law of the knife, the law of revenge, and the law of the lockup. The present government, on the other hand, has made a law about everything. There's a law to keep you from talking about this or that, from pissing against walls, from keeping to the left, from singing at night, from getting on a trolley by the front door. There's a law for those who don't want to get married, another that handles all the trades, another about employment offices and for settlements between workers and their bosses.

"The more the laws increased, the more poverty increased. The more poverty increased, the more the laws increased. Rome got so that it was really intolerable. The air itself stank. The air of Rome simply stank. Many attempts were made to subdue the stink, but all attempts failed. Someone said: Perhaps the stink comes from mice. The city declared war on mice, gave out poison for the destruction of mice and thousands and thousands of mice were wiped out. But the stink remained. Then someone said: The stink must come from flies. The city declared war on flies and distributed to all citizens of Rome fluids and powders for the destruction of flies. I don't remember how many millions of them were wiped out. But the stink stayed right on. Sometimes during the day it was enough to knock you over."

"What did it come from, filth of some kind?" asked Marietta.

"No one has ever revealed the origin of the Roman stink," replied the doctor. "It isn't quite so strong in residential districts like Trastevere, Testaccio and San Lorenzo. It is more marked at Prati, where the white collar workers live, but you can stand it there. It's absolutely deadly and as foul as it can be downtown, in the suburbs where cabinet ministers live, and in the neighborhood of Saint Peter's. Where does it come from? Nobody knows. You hear them saying it comes from Rome being old. An eternal city cannot help being a stinking city. They say it comes from the dead that are buried away in the cellars of public buildings and police stations. They say too that it comes from the draperies, clothes, plumes, helmets and breastplates that the new government has taken out of the museums to make uniforms for ministers, ambassadors and footmen. They also say that the sewers are choked up. They have many other highly debatable explanations for it. But there is one fact beyond dispute and it is that the stink still remains and gets a little stronger every day.

"The police are discovering new plots every week. Whole suburbs of workmen are invaded every night by thousands of armed men; houses are searched from cellar to garret, hundreds of persons are placed under arrest. No one ever knows why. Everyone knows that the same fate may be waiting for him. Many are afraid.

"Fear in Rome is like a disease, like an epidemic of some kind. There are whole days and weeks of collective panic. To look fixedly at someone on the street or in a restaurant is enough to make him turn pale and leave in a rush. Why? Because of fear."

"Because of fear of whom?" asked Berardo.

"Because of fear."

"But because of fear of whom?" insisted Berardo.

"Because of fear. No one knows why. Because of fear, simply. When fear gets hold of a whole population there's no other way to explain what it is. Fear gets hold of every man from his head to his feet. It's not only the enemies of the government that are afraid; the so-called fascists are more so. Why do they murder their enemies? Out of fear. Why do they keep increasing the numbers of police and soldiers? Because of fear. Why do they send thousands of thousands of persons to prisons? Because of fear. The more their crimes mount, the more their fear mounts. And the more their fear mounts, the more their crimes mount. That sends their fear up again. And that again causes more crimes."

"But isn't the government a strong one?" Michele asked.

"Its fear is very strong," answered the doctor. "And what is the Pope doing about it?" inquired Marietta.

'The Pope is afraid. The Pope has accepted two billions from the new government, he's bought himself automobiles, he's put in a radio sender, he's had a railroad station built just for himself when he never goes traveling, and all kinds of other luxuries, and now all this is making him afraid. The churches and convents of Rome have received a letter from the Pope saying that more soup must be given to the poor. It is the soup of fear. At the home of 'The Brothers of Charitable Acts' a slab of pork has been put in the soup on Thursdays. It is the pork of fear. But they need plenty of bowls of soup with pork in it before that two billion will be forgotten."

"And what is life like in Rome nowadays for people from the country?" I asked.

"The rich Abruzzians are well off and the poor ones are badly off and all of them are afraid. The police have commenced to make an adjustment with the poor. An adjustment of fear. Each week they take a hundred of them and send them back to their native villages. There are some of them who have been living in Rome thirty or forty years, whose villages were destroyed in the 1915 earthquake and none of whose relatives are alive. The police seize them and send them back 'for reasons of public order.' That was how Peppino Goriano was seized, given a ticket of compulsory travel and forced to return to Fontamara, which he had left thirty-five years ago. Why, that's how he happened to come back!"

"Are you Peppino Goriano?" Marietta asked him breathlessly.

"Are you the Hero of Porto Pia?" General Baldissera asked him.

It was indeed he.

Translated by MICHAEL WHARF

Emilio Lussu

IF YOU WANT TO MUTINY

BEFORE TEN O'CLOCK all detachments of the three battalions had gone back to barracks. Order had been re-established. At midnight we officers of the 3rd battalion were still sitting talking in the mess. The major and the adjutant were at regimental headquarters, and the officers on duty for that night were also absent, one from each company. We were discussing, among ourselves, the events of the evening. Avellini was on such a friendly footing with us that the fact that he was a regular officer and that we were of the reserve made no difference to us. I can still remember the conversation, and I can summarize it in this way:

Ottolenghi: My company were all right, or nearly so. Only one idiot wanted to go out with a machine-gun and fire it into the blue. I told him that if he moved, I'd shoot him. One machine-gun indeed! If my machine-guns are taken out, they all have to go together. If one's to fire, they all must. And if my machine-gun section is to take part in a demonstration, it must do it *en bloc,* with officers, noncommissioned officers, and men. In that case I shall be in the mutiny myself. And some fine day I dare say it'll happen. Because I agree entirely with the unit who did protest. They were perfectly right, but they chose a bad moment. To mutiny at night, and without arms! What a blunder!

Avellini: You're mad.

The Commander of the 12th Company: You talk like a lunatic!

Ottolenghi: If you want to mutiny, you ought to do it by day, and with arms, choosing a moment when everyone's with you. All officers of lower rank!

The Commander of the 12th Company: A grand program! But what about the others?

Ottolenghi: What others? Surely you don't want to mutiny side by side with the generals?

The Commander of the 12th Company: If that's what you think, you ought to resign your commission.

Ottolenghi: But whether I'm an officer or in the ranks, I should have to fight just the same. I can't get out of it, so I prefer to serve as an officer.

Avellini: You've taken an oath as an officer. So either you're not speaking seriously, or you don't take the oath seriously.

Ottolenghi: Of course I don't. Whether you're an officer or a soldier, you're forced to swear in, individually or collectively. If I hadn't taken the oath as an officer, I should have to take it as a private. It comes to the same thing. The laws of our country excuse no one but cardinals and bishops from military service. The oath is therefore nothing but a formality which we are obliged to take in the course of our compulsory military service.

Avellini: A man of honour will not give his oath if he doesn't mean to keep it.

The Commander of the 12th Company: You're not only mad, you're disloyal.

Ottolenghi: Can you maintain that if I'm taken against my will, by main force, and compelled to swear, it's dishonourable to make a mental reservation not to keep my oath?

Avellini: Who's going to take you by main force? No one can compel your conscience.

The Commander of the 12th Company: If you've got one.

Ottolenghi: No one, you say? In war-time, if I were called to the colours and refused to take the oath, I'd be handed over to a military tribunal who'd shoot me at the first opportunity. Taking the oath is a necessary lie, a legitimate act of self-defence. That being so, and since there's no escape from it, I prefer to serve as an officer rather than in the ranks.

Avellini: Why?

Ottolenghi: If a favourable occasion were to arise, I want to have a better chance to be able to profit by it.

A Second Lieutenant: Have a drink and turn in.

Ottolenghi: I shan't simply have a rifle and a bayonet, but a hundred rifles and a hundred bayonets and also—here's to you—a couple of machine-guns.

The Commander of the 11th Company: And against whom do you propose to use them?

Ottolenghi: Against our commanders.

The Commander of the 11th Company: And then? Do you aspire to become the commander-in-chief?

Ottolenghi: I aspire merely to direct the fire of my weapons. On that day, whenever it comes, sights down, independent fire! And I'll start with our divisional commander, whoever he may be, because each one of them is always worse than the last.

The Commander of the 11th Company: And then?

Ottolenghi: Then forward! Up the scale! Forward in good order and with discipline. Forward, but only in a manner of speaking, because our true enemies are not in front of us. We must about turn, therefore, first of all, and then we can go ahead.

A Second Lieutenant: That is to the rear?

Ottolenghi: Of course. We must go on, on until we get to Rome. That's where enemy General Headquarters are.

The Commander of the 11th Company: And then?

Ottolenghi: Isn't that enough?

A Second Lieutenant: It'll be a grand outing.

Ottolenghi: The people will seize power.

The Commander of the 10th Company: But if you march our army on Rome, do you think the German and Austrian armies will stay where they are? Or do you imagine that, to please our popular government the Germans will go back to Berlin, and the Austrians and Hungarians to Vienna and Budapest?

Ottolenghi: I don't care what the others'll do. It's enough for me to know what I intend.

The Commander of the 10th Company: That's all very fine, but it doesn't throw much light on the problem. What would your march to the rear really mean? An enemy victory, obviously. Can you believe that a military victory over us wouldn't become a political victory too? In our wars of independence, whenever the enemy was victorious, did they not carry, on their bayonets, the Bourbons to Naples and the Pope to Rome? When the Austrian beat us, at Milan, in Lombardy, and in the Veneto, did they ever allow a popular government to stay in power? If our enemies are victorious now, Italy will again find herself under reactionary foreign domination. Surely that's not what you want?

Ottolenghi: I certainly don't. But all the same I'm against this war, which is nothing but a horrible massacre. Isn't civil war just the same?

The Commander of the 11th Company: To tell the truth, I don't want either.

The Commander of the 10th Company: Ottolenghi doesn't agree with that. He hates the one, but exalts the other. But aren't they both the same?

Ottolenghi: No, they are not. Revolution means progress for the people and all the oppressed. War is nothing but useless slaughter.

The Commander of the 10th Company: Useless, you say? Some of us here were at universities. At mine we burned the speeches of William II, who invoked the war god at every opportunity and who seemed to want to feed his subjects on nothing but guns and bayonets. Useless slaughter indeed! If we hadn't resisted the Central Powers, today in Italy and Europe we'd all be doing the goose-step to the sound of a drum.

Ottolenghi: Each side is as bad as the other.

The Commander of the 12th Company: And democracy? And liberty? What would your country be without them?

Ottolenghi: A fine kind of democracy and liberty we've got!

The Commander of the 10th Company: Still, it's on their account that many of us have been in favour of intervention and have taken up arms and are sacrificing our lives.

Ottolenghi: The slaughter is not worth the sacrifice.

The Commander of the 12th Company: And what of Italy's interest?

Ottolenghi: What of us? Aren't we Italy?

The Commander of the 10th Company: Have the ideals that brought us into the war ceased to exist because war is a massacre? If we are convinced that we must fight, our sacrifices are worthwhile. I agree that we are all tired and the men have loudly proclaimed the fact today. That's only human nature. At a certain moment we grow discouraged and begin to think only of ourselves. The instinct for self-preservation becomes paramount, so that most of us would like to see the war ended, ended in any kind of way, because its end would ensue our physical safety. But is that sufficient justification? If it were, wouldn't a handful of brigands have the power to keep us continually in subjection, with complete impunity, simply because we were afraid of being killed? If injustice and violence were never to meet with resistance, it would be the end of our civilization.

Ottolenghi: I'm prepared to admit that, for the sake of argument.

The Commander of the 10th Company: Then you must admit that it's a duty to defend one's own ideals even at the risk of one's life. The argument that one is tired and has had enough of horrors is not sufficient to condemn war. The men mutinied this evening. Were they right or wrong? They may be either the one or the other; or perhaps both at once. The mass only sees an immediate advantage. But what would happen if their example was generally followed in the army?

Ottolenghi: Their conduct was justified, because the war wouldn't be the ghastly slaughter it is if it weren't for the utter incompetence of our leaders.

The Commander of the 11th Company: That is true.

The Commander of the 12th Company: Yes. Ottolenghi's right there.

A Group of Second Lieutenants: Quite right.

Avellini: I can't deny that, either.

Ottolenghi: You see! You are all forced to admit I've right on my side.

The Commander of the 10th Company: Our political and military leaders were not prepared when we came into the war. But that's no reason why we should lay down our arms.

Ottolenghi: Our generals might have been sent by our enemies to destroy us.

A Group of Second Lieutenants: True enough.

The Commander of the 11th Company: Unfortunately, it is.

Ottolenghi: And a band of speculators who are protected by Rome have grown up round them and are making money out of our lives. We had an example the other day when boots were issued to the battalion. Very fine boots they were, too. They had "Long live Italy" printed on the soles in the national colours. But after a day's wear in the mud, we found that these soles were of paper varnished to look like leather.

A Group of Second Lieutenants: That's true.

Ottolenghi: The boots don't matter. What is terrible is that they have varnished our very lives, stamped the name of our country on us and driven us like sheep to the slaughter.

The door was opened, and the conversation stopped. Major Frangipane came in, followed by Major Melchiorri and their two adjutants. We stood up.

"I am proposing," Major Melchiorri said, "to have ten soldiers in each company shot at once. The position's grave, and it's necessary to make an example."

"Capital punishment cannot be enforced in the case of men who have not had recourse to arms," our major pointed out.

"But the divisional commander agrees with me."

We listened to the two majors without saying a word.

Ottolienghi turned to us and said:

"I'm in favour of the execution of the divisional commander."

Major Frangipane was tired and depressed.

"We'd better turn in," he said. "One officer on duty with each company will be enough. By tomorrow we shall know what decision has been come to tonight by the general in command of the Army Corps."

Translated by MARION RAWSON

Nicola Chiaromonte

LOST ITALIANS

TOULOUSE IS THE capital of the French south west and the south west is the chosen land for Italian peasants coming from the great valley of the Po. In relation to France it is a southern region but, in climate and in the pattern of its culture, it is very like the north of Italy. Men coming from Cremona will think that Saint Sernin, the cathedral at Toulouse, looks like the cathedral in Cremona—except, of course, that their church of Cremona is finer. And so the south west had come to be not only a region for Italian immigration but also the center of exiled Italian social-

ism. It was in the south west that memory lived of the agricultural syndi-
cates of Parma, of Reggio, of Molinella—achievements in civilization to
which could be compared, alone in Europe, the municipality of Vienna.
These men in exile had remained socialist, not as people remain believers
in a religious faith, but simply as people remain honest men. Nothing
could wipe out the memory of the days when the apostles, Prampolini,
Massarenti, Baldini, were primarily the able administrators of prosperous
cooperatives, the days when the ideal had become a tangible achievement and an evident reason for hope, when the normal work of each day
was normally profitable, when there were agencies that would place a
man looking for work, and organizations through which a man could
buy and sell and obtain a loan. All that had been set fire to, destroyed
and pillaged, but to no avail: a peasant never forgets those things that
he knows he has built and paid for himself—with the same pertinacity
and difficulty with which he has made his field and his house and paid
for them. You can make an Italian forget or disown many a theoretical
concept but you cannot make him forget one single good that he has
seen with his eyes, touched with his hands.

And so it came about, at the time of the great disaster which befell
France in June, 1940, that it was toward Toulouse that most of the
Italians who had been living dispersed to the four corners of the country
turned their steps. In Toulouse there were comrades, there were "com-
paesani" who would speak one's dialect, there were the friends of friends:
a man would find a bed there, something to eat. They came from everywhere: from their homes, from the foreign regiments, from labor battalions and from concentration camps; from Lorraine and from Alsace as
well as from the region of Paris, from Belgium, and even from England
—via Dunkirk.

We all met there together in a dilapidated basement round a table and
there was never enough room at the table nor enough chairs. Yet from
out of the abyss of disaster it had been found possible to resurrect
spaghetti. An eating room had been organized. The Secretary of the local
Socialist Section had decided that this was far more economical and
rational than it would be to give out subsidies: to feed men, that is a useful and simple act: but with money, when you hand it out, you can
never tell where it goes, the money. And so those who had no money
could eat without paying, and those who could pay, paid a little extra,
and the Section's treasury made up the difference and made things balance. Furthermore, the basement, at night, could be used for those who

had nowhere to sleep. On the most elementary basis possible—the necessity to eat—a little community had immediately grown into existence, or rather a sort of family had grouped itself together.

Of course, the Belgian refugees and the Poles had their group kitchens too. But it was not at all the same thing: they had big refectories for a hundred or a hundred and fifty people, while with us—apart from the fact that we would not have had the means to establish them—we had never even considered the possibility of the thing growing beyond the proportions of a large family. When occasionally it happened that we were thirty or so at table, there was chaos at once, ill temper, complaints and argument. About twenty was the ideal number: enough for company, enough to feel among friends, and not so many that one would feel, in spite of their numbers, and in their midst, alone. There was, too, a tremendous difference as regards organization between us and the men of the northern countries. Those people had a budget, and directors, and they ran things on a time table. With us it was a question of being able to improvise or rather to reimprovise everything, as each day came. Even at that time, months ago, the problem of getting food to live on was not any too simple in Toulouse—with six hundred thousand refugees in a city of two hundred and fifty thousand inhabitants. The finding of money to purchase food in the market, the finding of something to burn in the stove, the finding of oil for cooking, those were problems which had to be solved anew every other day.

But eventually what we had to find we found, and it was always thanks to a sort of favor of Providence, or thanks to some sort of sleight of hand —but above all it was due to the knowledge of an infinity of little roundabout ways of approach, due, in brief, to that fundamental experience which Italians possess, and by which they know that in the life they lead one never obtains anything by traveling the main and obvious road, but that the little which one can snatch from circumstance is attainable only by following the side roads and the hidden and secret and intertwining lanes. The French know how to find their way about, but it is not the same thing: they are too accustomed to thinking that, all in all, the things you want are delivered to you along the main highway of routine: their resourcefulness lies in finding the right trick at the right time, in ingeniously improvising some perfect little contrivance in a moment of need; but if the necessity to trick and contrive were ever to become a permanent condition and rule of life, that would be indeed exhausting and clearly would no longer be worthwhile. Italian resourcefulness is an instinct, sharpened and distilled, which discovers a track through the jungle of existence, and this path is at once a magical creation and a daily necessity. You understand what it is when you have lived in the land of the Arabs where whenever something or other has become difficult or impossible to find, people say to you: "If you want to find it go and see the Arabs"—just as they would tell you to go and consult the sorcerers. After the disaster which tore their country asunder to its deepest roots, it was extraordinary, and almost irritating, to see the French, surrounded by ruin and chaos, in the immense despair that filled all hearts, intense on one sole aim above all others: that of returning to daily normal life in order to reconstruct, no matter how, that mechanism of normality without which they cannot conceive that life can be possible. But for Italians—for the Italian people—normal life is at best no more than a habit, a hair breadth removed from disaster; and after disaster, as before, endures the necessity for intense resourcefulness.

As for the comrades of whom I speak, a normal life, well, there had been a long time since they had known anything of the sort. Foreigners without papers in France, volunteers in Spain, soldiers once again, in the French Army, or prisoners in French concentration camps—not to mention the years they had spent in Italian prisons—such had been, for almost all of them, the steps in their careers. And this life had left on their faces the imprint of a sort of excessive physical fatigue and of an excessive patience and enduring. Their state was not like that of their Spanish comrades: they had not their nervous despair and their sadness; in their eyes you did not see that look which men have who have seen "the heavens in which nothing shines," and which has remained in the eyes of so many of those who have come alive out of Europe's hells. They were very tired, and especially they were very disappointed; but, when all is said and done, they sought only to forget, if that were still possible.

There was one of them who had come from England. He had been at Dunkirk as a volunteer in a French foreign regiment. Planes, tanks, the Germans at three hundred yards, and cannon from the British vessels, broadside along the beach, shelling them. For three days no one had attempted to cook, and no one had wanted to eat. Ultimately the Italian decided that one could perfectly well make soup out of horse meat, and certainly there were enough dead horses. And he had lighted the stoves. Next day a burst of machine gun fire from a plane had torn the kitchen apart. This made little difference for it was time to go. It was the Italian, too, who managed to find a boat that had been left behind in a hut. At first there were only four of them wanting to leave for England in a row-boat, but when the others saw the four of them going off into the night the four counted themselves and found they were ten. After half an hour of navigation all of them were seasick and he was left alone to row. He had no idea in which direction lay England. A man in the bow, lying on his stomach with his head nearly in the water, kept repeating from time to time: "See that star? That's where you want to go." And he would point at the sky. In point of fact, they rowed for thirty hours and they reached England. They were so exhausted, sprawled on the ground, that women came to them and gently put bits of sugar in their mouths. They were taken to London and in London it was in a jail that they were housed—with all manner of politeness, but locked up just the same, all day, save for two hours of sunlight in the morning and two in the afternoon. After a week their French colonel had come to get them and take them back to France. They landed at Havre, and there were the Germans again, just about to arrive. In spite of that, they were set to work unloading planes from a ship and then loading them back on board again. Quite suddenly no more officers were to be seen. And so they built a raft with gasoline drums and for two days they made their way down the coast. Out of all this adventure there had remained in his mind a decided and dominant impression that people had made a complete fool out of him, for he had volunteered to fight fascism, and all they had done had been to leave him in the lurch on a road to nowhere.

I am convinced that among the volunteers of the International Brigades in Spain, the Italians alone had the courage, between one battle and the next, to take unto themselves a woman and have children: so irresistible among them, in whatever country they may find themselves, is the instinct to take root and to establish a family. For instance, there was Tommasi, the cook at the mess, a workman from Treviso, a serious boy, so serious that he looked like a preacher, who had come from Spain accompanied by a wife and a child. The woman now was in hospital with a sickness of the eyes and he, although without any employment at all, without a penny in his pocket, still somehow managed to keep the child healthy and cleanly dressed. As for Carletti, the case was sadder still: he had had his wife and his child shot down beside him during the retreat of Catalonia. After that, in France, it had been the concentration camp: three thousand square yards, twelve hundred prisoners, iron discipline, for these people were "suspect." A policeman had said one day: "You will never get me to believe that anyone who gets out of here is still a man." During the war, in order precisely to get out of there, Carletti had asked to enlist in one of the militarized labor battalions which had been organized with a view to make these foreigners of some use, somewhere. They had been set to work building roads in the neighborhood of Dunkirk. Caught in the battle, each one had managed as best he could. For two whole weeks Carletti had stayed hidden in a shell hole, with an anti-tank girder above his head to shelter him from bits of steel that were coming at him from every direction. At night he would go out to look for something to eat. Happily there were trucks quite near him which the English had left behind: in them one could find an abundance of first rate provisions. Then the Germans had come and had set him, with the others, at work burying the corpses: they went to work digging pits and filling them with a layer of quicklime, a layer of corpses, quicklime and corpses, corpses and quicklime—for four days. In the end, proclaiming his status as a subject of the Axis powers, he had succeeded in getting his release with a pass to the non-occupied zone. But the Spaniards had been taken away to work in Germany. And that was another commodity found ready-made in France —those thousands of men without a country with whom one could do what one wanted in all tranquillity of mind.

Sometimes sitting in the café, it would happen that Carletti sought to explain to you what was deepest and innermost in his manner of looking at these things. On such occasions he would start reciting in a low voice the poems of Gori. Gori's poetry is not to be found in anthologies, he flourished at the turn of the century, he was the poet of Italian anarchism. Notably he wrote a long poem which is a sort of rhapsody of anarchy— in terza rima, like the "Divine Comedy." In that poem is sung the misery of the proletariat contrasted with the insolent opulence of the rich; the worker's pity for women whom the evil power of money has brought to fall; the sanguinary attempts of obscurantism to put out the Light—and the poem ends with a final vision of Humanity's painful advance toward ultimate Liberation. The whole thing is of a sentimentality so theatrical and so naive that it ends by being poignant. Two generations of Italian proletarians found their nourishment in that poem and its verses were passed on from mouth to mouth. Not that they entirely expressed what these men felt, but, more simply, that they found in them the essential element and character of their faith—which had much in common with the strong emotions men feel at some sudden turn in a play. The surprise element in their drama was the appearance on the horizon of these simple and uneducated men—unsatisfied and resigned—of Hope. And that could also be expressed as their poet expressed it, by the Ideal, written in the skies in great flaming letters. As for the language, it was that of melodrama, the only form with which they had some acquaintance. And then, too, there had been no one else to speak for them in more delicate terms. Gori was the poet of anarchy. But the "Worker's Hymn," written by honest Filippo Turati, the prophet of reformism, expresses in slightly more prosaic words and in slightly worse verse, exactly the same world of feeling—simple, clumsy and dressed for Sunday best.

Of such a nature was the ideal which, for twenty years and all across the world, Francesco Loprete had carried faithfully with him: from his native province of Apulia to Buenos Aires, from Buenos Aires back to the Puglie, and then forward into the trenches of the Carso, and from there into prison, and from prison into civilian life—just long enough to breathe once or twice—and then again to the prison cell and the wardens. That was an Italian Odyssey—complete. It was in Toulouse, as it happened, that I received a postcard from him: it came from the Vernet concentration camp and it said: "I hope that you are all right and that all our friends are all right too. I would like to tell you what it's like here—and some day I hope I will tell you. I am very hungry. All my best wishes to you and to our friends." And then there came another postcard, dated: "Campo di Concentramento di Polizia di Fabriano (Ancona) Italia." When the Italian Armistice Commission passed through Vernet, to ask those detained there whether they wanted to return to Italy, Loprete had opted for Italy, the more readily because they had promised the Italians that in Italy they would not be bothered by the police—a promise in which he probably had placed little trust, but still . . . it was concentration camp for concentration camp—it made little difference.

He had come to see me in Paris in the fall of 1938. He was just out of prison—eight months in France; six months in prison: that was because he had no papers. He had not been able to remain in Milan: they kept arresting him every two weeks for the very simple reason that, having once been convicted as "subversive," he could obtain no work. And since he was not working they arrested him for vagrancy: and if by any chance he found a way to earn a few lire selling fruit or flowers on the streets, he was arrested for violation of police regulations. And so one day he had started off on foot to Switzerland, with, in his pocket, a sample of the bread the Régime gives the population to eat, in Italy, a sample to show to the anti-fascists in Paris who would put something about it in their newspapers. And he did get to France, but only to get arrested no sooner than he set foot in Belfort. After serving his time, things had gone fairly well—from 1938 to 1939—he had even found some work and he began to feel once again at ease with the world. But when war is declared a foreigner without papers risks serious trouble. Someone advised him to go to the authorities and offer his services for the duration. And he had done so: but they arrested him and gave him six months in jail. Always for the same reason. When he came out, more than by anything else he was annoyed at the fact of having made the great mistake of offering to enlist. And this time as before, in his pocket he had brought away "evidence": a little fold of paper in which he had placed three worms, found in the prison bread. All this took place in February, 1940. At the beginning of May, he was offered work in the neighborhood of Versailles as a farm hand, for the French countryside lacked labor. All that he needed now were proper papers, but finally, when he had his contract signed and in order, it seemed certain that he would get them. He applied to the Prefecture at Versailles; they arrested him and sent him off to the concentration camp at Vernet.

All this seems like an entirely exceptional series of misfortunes. But it is exactly the kind of misfortunes provided for poor devils born in southern Italy: fate seems to have settled the pattern once for all.

And now I know, with certainty, that in the concentration camp at Fabriano, Francesco Loprete, obstinate as a stone, is waiting for all this to change. In other words he is awaiting the millennium. Only he would like to have friends write to him. For that would help him think—as he puts it.

Translated by C. G. PAULDING

Italo Svevo

THE SPARROWS

MARIO SAMIGLI was an author, nearly sixty years of age. Forty years ago he had published a novel, which might now be called dead, if what has never been alive can be said to die. But Mario, though somewhat faded and no longer robust, continued to lead a peaceful sort of life, with few business worries and a correspondingly small salary. A life without incident is wholesome enough, but needs some flavour to make it palatable, and Mario's was seasoned with flattering dreams. He still pictured to himself a glorious future, not because of anything he had done or ever hoped to do, but rather because the very inertia which prevented him from rebelling against his lot absolved him from the painful task of destroying a long-cherished illusion. So, in a sense, he triumphed over fate. Life had broken a few bones, it is true, but it had left intact two very important organs, his self-esteem and his respect for the world's opinion, both of which are essential to the enjoyment of fame. A feeling of satisfaction was always present with him, to relieve the dull routine of his life.

Few would have guessed at his cunningly concealed ambition, for Mario had all the dreamer's instinct to protect his dream from contact with the crude realities of life. If ever it peeped through, his friends were careful not to wound his harmless vanity, those strangers might be tempted to laugh a little at those positive judgments of his on authors living and dead, especially when he spoke of himself as an influence in modern literature, or when they saw him even blush, sixty-year-old unsuccessful author though he was. But a little kindly laughter does no one any harm; so they were all at their ease and happy enough together.

Mario wrote very seldom; in fact, for a long time past, the only signs of the writer about him were the pen and blank sheets of paper always lying ready on his desk. Those were the happiest years of his life, given up to dreams, and free from teasing practical problems; a sort of second childhood, more desirable even than the maturity of a successful writer, whose words flow too glibly and with too little effort on to the paper, leaving an empty husk which mistakes itself for the ripe fruit.

That period of happiness could only last so long as the impulse to escape from it remained. And this impulse was always present, though in no disturbing degree; never sufficient to show the way out of his castle of content.

It would have been impossible for him to write another novel like the old one, which had sprung from his admiration for people who were his superiors in rank and fortune, and whom he could only observe through a telescope. He still had a sort of indolent affection for his novel, and because it made some show of having a head and a tail he imagined it to be alive. But when it came to fashioning more of those shadowy beings, and making them live by sheer force of language, he felt a genuine repugnance. Unconscious though he was of it, his sixty-years-old maturity made such a work impossible. And it never occurred to him to describe a humble sort of life like his own, exemplary in conduct and endowed with the kind of strength that came from absolute surrender, a surrender which permeated his whole being and which he would certainly never have thought of as anything remarkable. He did not know how to approach a subject which seemed to him so uninteresting, a weakness common enough among those to whom high life has remained a sealed book. So in the end he gave up writing about human beings and their way of life, be it high or low, and devoted himself exclusively, or so he thought, to animals: he began to write fables. Tiny, rigid mummies—you could not even call them corpses, so quite without odour were they—the crevices of time began to swarm with them. But for him each new one represented a step towards perfection; he rejoiced over them in his childlike way, and felt younger and happier than ever.

At first he repeated the mistake of his youth, and wrote about unfamiliar animals; his fables re-echoed with growls and roarings. Later he became, so to speak, more human, and wrote about the animals he knew. The fly, for instance, supplied him with a number of fables, showing it to be a more useful beast than is generally supposed. In one he marvelled at the speed of the fly, which is, however, wasted, since it neither helps him to capture his prey nor to secure his own safety. And here a tortoise pointed the moral. Another fable was in praise of the fly which destroys the very filth it loves so dearly. In a third, he asked why the fly, which of all beasts is most richly endowed with eyes, should have such bad sight. One was about a man who, having just squashed a troublesome fly, addressed it thus: "I have done you a good turn, for now you have stopped being a fly." So, punctually with his morning coffee appeared his daily fable. It was the war which taught him he might really make use of the fable to express himself: that he might insert his little puppets into the life-machine, and so give them a new organ. And this was how it came about.

When Italy went into the war, Mario was afraid the first act of persecution on the part of the Austrian police would be to summon him, one of the few Italian writers left in Trieste, and possibly to send him to the gallows. He was alternately in a state of hope and terror, now exultant, now pale with fear. He pictured his novel being read by the judges, a Council of War consisting of representatives of the whole military hierarchy from the General downwards; and in order to do justice to it, naturally they would have to study it carefully. Then would come an anxious moment; but unless the Council of War consisted of barbarians, one could only hope that, after reading the novel, they would show their appreciation by sparing his life. So during the war he wrote a great deal, and the knowledge that a censorious public waited to devour his words could not have produced in him a greater agitation. For safety's sake, he wrote only fables of doubtful application, and somehow, between fear and hope, his little puppets came to life. The Council of War could hardly have condemned him for the fable about the powerful giant fighting in a marsh with animals much lighter than himself, and perishing, always victorious, in the mud which was too weak to bear him. What proof had any one that it was about Germany? And what had Germany to do with the lion who was ever victorious because he would never venture far from his fine big lair, till one day they discovered that he might be successfully smoked out?

So Mario gradually got used to going through life accompanied by fables, as a coat is furnished with pockets. His literary progress he owed to the police, who showed no sign of being aware that a native literature existed, and left him in peace during the whole war, reassured but disillusioned.

Another small step forward was his choice of more appropriate heroes for his fables. The exotic elephant, the fly with expressionless eyes—these disappeared, and their place was taken by the familiar little sparrow which he allowed himself the luxury of feeding in his courtyard with crumbs of bread, a great luxury at Trieste in those days. Every day he spent some time watching them hop about, and these were the brightest moments of his day, when his creative faculties were more active than during the actual writing of his fables. His heart overflowed with tenderness for the creatures he wrote about. In the evening, when he heard the sparrows chattering on the neighbouring roofs and on a miserable little tree in the courtyard, he pictured them telling each other the adventures of the day, before they tucked their heads under their wings. In the morning the same loud and lively chirping betokened, no doubt, the telling of their dreams. Like his, their life was passed between two worlds, real life and dreams. Heads like theirs might easily have thoughts in them; so graceful and appealing and of such lovely colouring, their weakness roused one's pity, their wings one's envy: surely these creatures were very like oneself. His fables were still swaddled in moral axioms, but it amused him to write them. Everything contributed to his good humour. One day he wrote: My courtyard is small, but, with practice, one might consume about twenty pounds of bread there a day. It is true this was only a poet's dream, for where was one to find, at such a time, twenty pounds of bread for birds who had no bread ticket? Again: I wish I knew how to end war on the little horse-chestnut in my courtyard, when the sparrows are fighting for the best places for the night; it would be a good omen for the future of humanity.

Mario clothed the poor sparrows in so many ideas that he quite hid their tenuous limbs. His brother Giulio, who lived with him and tried to like what he wrote, could not bring himself to include the birds too. They lacked expression, he said. But Mario explained that they were themselves an expression of Nature, a complement to those parts of her which lie down or walk about; but placed above them like the accent on a word or a sign in music. They are Nature's gladdest expression, he said; not even fear, which makes men green and abject, can spoil the exquisite grace of birds; and this is not because their wings hide it, for it is betrayed in every movement. Probably their tiny brain cannot grasp it; the eye or ear gives the alarm, which is instantly conveyed to the wings. How wonderful for a fugitive in full flight to have a brain that is incapable of fear! If one of the tiny creatures starts and trills, they all take flight, but as if they said: "Here is a good opportunity for being afraid." They never hesitate; it is so easy to flee if you have wings. And their flight is absolutely sure. They skim past obstacles, and yet avoid them; they penetrate the thickest tangle of boughs without ever being caught or injured. They only stop to think when they are already far away, and then they try to grasp the reason of their flight and begin looking about them. They tilt their little heads gracefully from side to side, and patiently await the moment for returning to where they fled from. If they were always conscious of fear, they must all have died. Mario suspected that their agitations were perhaps fictitious. They might have eaten the bread he gave them in perfect peace; but instead, they half shut their malicious eyes and persuade themselves that every mouthful is a theft. And that is how they season their dry bread. Like true thieves, they never eat the bread just where it has been thrown for them; and they know that to fight for it there would be dangerous. So they only begin to quarrel about the crumbs at the end of their flight.

It was this discovery which inspired the following fable:

A generous man had for many years regularly put out food for the birds, and was sure that they were full of gratitude to him. He must have been very unobservant, or he would have noticed that the birds looked on him as an imbecile whose bread they had managed to steal all these years without his having succeeded in capturing one of them.

It seems incredible that a good-natured man like Mario should have been guilty of writing such a fable. Could it be that all his gaiety was only skin-deep? How came he to read such malice, such ingratitude, into the most joyous expression of Nature? It was as good as destroying it outright. Besides, to attribute such insensibility to the winged creation was really a grave insult to humanity; for if that is the language of birds, who cannot talk, what may we expect from creatures who are endowed with human speech?

And all his puppets were really sad at bottom. During the war, horse-traffic grew less and less in the streets of Trieste; moreover, horses were fed only on hay, so that there were no more of those tasty little seeds which the digestion leaves intact. And Mario in fancy asked his little friends: "Are you ruined?" And the birds replied: "No, but there are fewer of us."

Perhaps Mario thought his own failure would be less hard to bear if he could come to regard this too as the result of circumstances outside his own control. We laugh at the fable of the heedless bird which has completely forgotten the ruin that so lately threatened it, merely because it happens to have escaped itself. But when we recall the impassive face of Nature while she makes her experiments, our laughter is turned to gall.

He often wrote fables on the disillusion which follows every human activity. It was as if he sought to console himself for the poverty of his own life by saying: "I am all right. I cannot fail, because I attempt nothing."

A wealthy nobleman was so fond of birds that he reserved for them a whole large estate, in which it was forbidden to snare, or even to frighten them. He built nice warm shelters for them against the long winter months, filled with stores of food. After a while, birds of prey also made their nests there in great numbers, and cats and other cruel animals made war on the little birds. Their benefactor wept, but his kindness of heart was incurable, and he could discover no way of feeding the small birds he loved without providing food for the falcons and all the other beasts.

It was the same rosy, smiling Mario who gave vent to this dry mockery of human goodness. He showed that wherever life flourished by its agency, blood would inevitably flow abundantly soon after; and this did not seem to disturb him.

So, by day, Mario was perfectly happy. It seemed as if all his melancholy found an outlet in his bitter fables, leaving his face without a cloud. But apparently his dreams were less serene. His brother Giulio slept in the next room. He generally snored peacefully, for a gouty digestion may be diseased but is certainly thorough. But if by chance he lay awake, he would hear strange sounds coming from Mario's room; deep and apparently painful sighs, then from time to time a loud, protesting cry. The night resounded with those strange cries, which it hardly seemed possible could have been uttered by the mild and cheerful man one had seen by day. Mario never remembered his dreams, and rising refreshed from a deep sleep, never doubted but that his night had been as serene as his working day.

When Giulio, rather worried, spoke to him about his strange behaviour in his sleep, he only said that he must have invented a new method of snoring. But it happened so regularly that one is forced to think the strange sounds which came from him when asleep were really the expression of his tortured mind. This fact would seem to cast doubt on the most modern theory of dreams, which proclaims them to be the symbol of wish-fulfilment. But it is also possible that the poet's real dream-life is his waking one, and that therefore Mario was right to laugh by day and weep at night. There is, however, another possible interpretation of the dream-theory already alluded to. In Mario's case, the free expression of his grief might well be a wish-fulfilment. At last, in sleep, he was free to throw off the heavy mask he had worn all day to hide his ambitious heart, and proclaim with sighs and exclamations: "I am worth more than they think! I am worth more than they think!" So sleep guarded the issues of his heart.

When day came, Giulio learned with surprise that, for Mario, the restless night had passed in company with some new fable or in complete oblivion. He had been working one out for several days past. The war had brought penury to the sparrows in the courtyard, and poor Mario had invented a way of eking out the few crumbs he had to give them. From time to time he would go out into the yard and frighten them. Their movements are slow unless in flight, and they take a long time to overcome their timidity. Their soul is a little balance, weighted on one side by fear, on the other by hunger. Hunger goes on growing, but if fear is renewed in equal measure they will not touch a morsel. If the method were strictly applied, they would die of hunger with the bread in front of them. But Mario did not carry it to the point of tragedy. The fable, "Your bread would be delicious," said the sparrow to the man, "if only you were not there," was in a light vein, for even during the war the sparrows did not really grow thinner. Even then there was plenty of dirt in the streets of Trieste for them to feed on.

Translated by BERYLE DE ZOETE

Gaetano Salvemini

TWO GOOD EUROPEANS

THE STORY OF THE successes and failures of Rosselli and of his devoted collaborators cannot yet be written. The resounding successes were few. One deserves recording. In May, 1930, an aeroplane flew over Milan and showered down thousands of leaflets denouncing the Fascist regime and

urging Italians to fight against it. The plane was piloted by the young
Giovanni Bassanesi who undertook the venture with only a few hours
experience in flying. His companion on the flight was Dolci, the Dolci
who a year earlier had rescued Carlo and his friends from Lipari. The
Fascist air force on this occasion gave, to use Mussolini's adjective, un-
equivocal ("inequivocabile") proof of inefficiency. After flying for half an
hour over Milan the aeroplane was allowed to return unharmed to Switzerland. There, however, it crashed on landing and a broken leg laid Bassanesi up for six weeks. The trial, by the Swiss authorities, of Bassanesi,
Carlo Rosselli and A. Tarchiani for having organized the venture ended
with their triumphant acquittal.

The most important success—the diffusion all over Italy of the clandestine organization "Giustizia e Libertà" cannot be estimated. Carlo himself did not know its extent. Who can ever tell how far a seed borne by
the wind will travel and what fruit it will bear? Ideas are like seeds. After
years of lying dormant they may suddenly spread with lightning rapidity.
What matters is that they should be kept alive in the minds of the few.
If one can take the number of trials before the Special Tribunals as an
indication of the clandestine movement—and certainly these trials mean
something—it can be stated without fear of contradiction that the secret
organization "Giustizia e Libertà" in Italy has provided, after the Communists, the greatest number of men sentenced by the Fascist Special
Tribunal, practically all of them young and of high intellectual and moral
calibre, boldly professing their political faith despite the knowledge that
heavy sentences will be the result.

But these trials and these sentences are not to be counted as successes.
The true success for a clandestine movement is to elude the spy. Trials
and sentences are failures, sorrowful failures. But no war is carried on
without claiming victims among the best.

The first of these trials deserves mention. In the spring of 1928 Bauer
had been sent back home from the island of Lipari. As soon as he was in
Milan once more he began helping Rossi with the distribution of the
clandestine press. They had stoically calculated in advance all eventuali-
ties, even including death. Neither of them belonged to the generation
that had been deprived by Fascism of honourable and lucrative positions.
Had they adhered to the Mussolinian regime they would have been in
distinguished and highly-paid positions. No self-interest prompted them.
They were representatives of a new generation taking up the struggle
against Fascism, stepping into the shoes of the older men who had been
eliminated by age, blunders and defeats. No sooner was the "Giustizia e

Libertà" movement started than they joined it. But very early a spy wormed his way into their confidence and betrayed their secrets. On October 30, 1930, Bauer, Rossi and twenty-two others in various cities of Italy were arrested on a charge of being members of "a secret organization which was plotting against the regime."

While he was being taken handcuffed to Rome in charge of four carabineers, at 1 A.M., Rossi took advantage of an open window to jump out of the moving train. For six hours in torrents of rain he sought in vain for a refuge among the frightened population. In the end a soldier rearrested him.

Another of the arrested, Umberto Ceva, a liberal, aged thirty, committed suicide in his cell on Christmas Day. In a farewell letter to his wife and two small children, he wrote: "I have faith in three things, my country, my family and liberty, and I cannot live in a country deprived of liberty."

The trial before the Special Tribunal was held on May 29 and 30, 1931. The defendants stood inside an iron cage as do the common criminals in Italy. Calm, dignified, resolute, standing firmly as though ready to repel attack, Bauer vigorously denied the accusation of being a terrorist while declaring himself to be an active agent of "Giustizia e Libertà". He restated the ideals of the organization in sharp, short sentences that rang like pistol shots.

"Our organization," he declared, "bears a revolutionary character because the dictatorship has made every other form of opposition impossible for all who aim at a free, democratic and republican regime for Italy. We summon to action all Italians who feel injured in their national dignity and who are willing to participate actively in the revival. For us revolution is a necessity and a duty, but terrorism is no part of our method."

Rossi, slight of figure with flashing black eyes and a boyish face under a shock of black hair, claimed his full share of responsibility for the activity of "Giustizia e Libertà", and accused the spy, in other words the police who employed the spy, of having at various times urged him to put incendiary bombs in public buildings timed to explode at night, when the buildings would be empty, as a protest against the regime which would not endanger human life. Rossi admitted that such a proposal had appealed to him at first since "ideas are of little value if you are not ready to follow them up with action". But on reflection such methods of action did not commend themselves to him and he began to suspect that the proposer was an *agent provocateur*. He himself in the end frustrated the enterprise. Rossi's evidence against the spy demolished the evidence for the prosecution as far as the accusation of planning incendiarism was concerned. For their clandestine activity he and Bauer were sentenced to twenty years' imprisonment, others to lesser terms; a few were acquitted. After three years of captivity, they were told that if they would sign a form, pledging themselves on their honour to abstain from all political activity, they would be restored to liberty. They all refused to sign and Rossi wrote on the form the words: "If I am set free, I shall begin again."

The statements of Rossi and Bauer about terrorism contradict the charge sometimes levelled against "Giustizia e Libertà" of advocating or resorting to terroristic actions. Carlo and his friends always strongly discountenanced any such action as bomb-throwing which might involve the lives of innocent people, or any attempt which might cause senseless destruction of property.

In these last years things have moved rapidly. Conditions are no longer what they were in 1930, when "Giustizia e Libertà" made its debut.

Hitler has come to power in Germany and the Communists have perceived that the democrats of the Weimar republic were preferable to the Nazis. Soviet Russia has found also that a democratic Germany was more easy to live with than a Nazi Germany. Therefore the Communists have dropped the slogan of "everything or nothing" and are now preaching the popular front, i.e., the alliance of all anti-Fascist parties for the defence or reconquest of democratic institutions. To-day the Italian Communists, while adopting the passwords launched by "Giustizia e Libertà" in 1930, go to the length of offering their alliance to the rank and file of the Fascists, if they will revolt against their chiefs. "The new policy of the Communist Party," Carlo wrote in a letter of January 24, 1937, "is steadily losing its character of a provisional tactical manoeuvre, despite the opposite impression created by too many of the Communist functionaries. It is showing itself effective. I believe we shall have to revise certain judgments on Communist policy or at least take into account the fact that the great bulk of the Italian emigrants fall within the Communist zone of attraction. Perhaps after all our real function is to serve as the yeast with which others will bake bread, both in the intellectual and in the practical field."

At the same time, the world slump which broke over Italy in 1930, after three years of economic difficulty caused by the re-valuation of the lira, the Abyssinian war and the war in Spain have created an entirely new situation. The Italian banks, great and small, are now controlled by the Government and administered by its men of confidence. Most of the large shipping companies have failed and been taken over by the Government. The majority of the larger industrial firms have shared the same fate. The landowners are all ruined; the larger their estates, the worse their financial situation. Mussolini is expropriating all the Italians to maintain a military, bureaucratic and police machine out of all proportion to the economic capacity of the country. Some call this general expropriation "Socialism" and even "Communism". Mussolini is by no means displeased to be called a "Socialist". In actual truth he socializes nothing. He simply destroys the wealth of all but a narrow circle of nabobs whose activities are connected with the preparation of war (steel, rubber, chemicals, certain branches of textiles, etc.). Italy lives to-day under a system of "war capitalism" which places under the control of the Fascist party leaders and the higher civil and military bureaucracy not only the middle and working classes but even the small oligarchy of nabobs. These have to give up part of their profits to the party leaders and the head bureaucrats. Thus these latter also are enriching themselves out of the general distress. The ex-Marxist Mussolini has created in Italy the situation prophesied by Marx, in which wealth is concentrated in an ever diminishing number of hands, the middle classes sink to the level of the proletariat and an impoverished proletariat is left with nothing to lose but its chains. This transformation, however, has not taken place through progress in the methods of production, resulting in an increase of wealth which the growing mass of the proletariat is unable to acquire, as Marx had foretold. What is happening with unheard of rapidity is that a parasitic political and administrative system is concentrating technical progress on war industries paralysing production in all other fields and leaving no wealth to be socialized. Any anti-Fascist revolutionary movement in Italy must take account of this new situation which has been arising between 1930 and 1937. It is no longer simply a question of penalizing with expropriation those responsible for the dictatorship. It is the whole Italian people which must be saved from starvation by the total reorganization of an economic structure ruined by fifteen years of a policy which is as mad as it is wicked.

Carlo's ideas in 1937 were undergoing a thorough process of readjustment. While the Communists had adopted many of the early views of "Giustizia e Libertà", Carlo on the economic field had moved left towards the Communist programme. On one point, however, he remained opposed to the Communists. While they are ready to take over the present Fascist centralized administrative machinery, only grafting on to it the dictatorship of the Communist party, Carlo maintained that the anti-Fascist revolution in Italy must create a new type of federal system, granting a maximum of local autonomy, each district being left free to settle its local problems according to the possibilities of the locality. In this he had come much nearer to the anarchic federalism of Proudhon than to the centralistic Communism of Stalin.

ABYSSINIA AND SPAIN

In September, 1934, even before Mussolini had engineered the Wal Wal incident in Southern Abyssinia, Carlo foretold that Mussolini meant to make war on Abyssinia as a means of reviving his waning prestige in and outside Italy. From week to week in the ensuing year he warned that the British and French Foreign Offices would make no serious effort to avert war or to stop the war once it had begun. This war "Giustizia e Libertà" uncompromisingly opposed from beginning to end, firstly as completely devoid of justification as an act of self-defence, and thus a crime, and secondly because it would bring neither material nor moral benefit to the Italian people.

In December, 1935, there appeared among the Italian *émigrés* in Paris a young man who gave his name as Giuseppe Zanatta and said that he had deserted from the Italian Fleet rather than fight in the Abyssinian war. On March 7, 1936, he "revealed" to Carlo that the wife of a Communist *émigré* had given him a revolver and twenty-five cartridges, and that in the Communist's presence an unknown man had promised him 15,000 lire if he would kill Carlo. The job would be an easy one; all he needed to do was to find Carlo at home early in the morning or late of an evening; the revolver was one which made little noise; one could use it without being heard and escape unobserved. Carlo made the self-styled Zanatta put down his "revelation" in writing. The three sheets of paper, dated March 11, 1936, were found among Carlo's papers after his death.

The following day Zanatta was subjected in Carlo's house to a six hour cross-examination by Carlo and Signor De Vittorio, one of the leaders of the Italian Communists in Paris. At first he repeated from memory what he had written down. But when asked for more details he fell into self-contradiction. He had told Rosselli that he had thrown the revolver into the Seine, but when Carlo and De Vittorio began to search him he put his hand to it hidden in his belt. The revolver was loaded. At this point he lost his head. "Don't be hard on me," he said, "Don't kill me and I'll tell the truth." He then confessed that he was an agent of the Italian Secret Service (OVRA), and that he had been sent to Paris with orders to kill Carlo and had to report to an Italian vice-consul who had suggested to him the story about the giving of the revolver by the Communist's wife and the unknown man giving him orders in the Communist's presence. Entrusted to a man of small intelligence, the attempt in 1936 did not succeed. In more expert hands it did succeed in 1937.

When the Italian Troops occupied Addis Ababa, Carlo wrote in the *Giustizia e Libertà* of May 15, 1936:

"Fascism has had a complete military victory. Fascism will almost certainly have a victory on the diplomatic field as well. We refuse to be taken in by the last act of the Geneva comedy. This complete victory does not mean that history stops there. History goes on. One period in Italy has come to an end. Another is beginning. Nothing would be more foolish than to gloss over the enemy's success. We have to admit that in Italy—which is what concerns us most—Fascism has been strengthened and consolidated by this crisis. Many people will now be converted to Fascism. Others will grow resigned to it. Even the economic and financial difficulties are not such as to threaten the regime. No dictatorship has ever fallen for economic and financial reasons. Economic difficulties may cause it to seek war as an outlet. But when the war is won, the crisis is safely past. We must therefore prepare ourselves for a difficult period whose duration will depend on unpredictable factors. The old anti-Fascism is gone for ever. The organizations which drag after them the dead weight of defeat and the chain of obsolete and equivocal positions are empty shells. We of "Giustizia e Libertà" must also review our position."

Informed by telephone of this article, Mussolini pounced on it and triumphantly announced in the *Popolo d'Italia* of May 16, 1936, that "Giustizia e Libertà" had declared its surrender. In the issue of May 21, Carlo retorted:

"What does Mussolini think to gain by our political decease? If we fall others will take our place. . . . As long as we are there, as long as we fight, his remorse and shame remain. If even only a handful resist, the unanimity is broken. Conscience resumes its rights. We shall never surrender. One period is ended, another begins. But the struggle continues."

The words "If we fall others will take our place" was the only reference that Carlo made in public to the Zanatta episode. He always disliked all allusions to the risks which he incurred.

Mussolini had not long to wait for proofs that neither Carlo nor those around him intended to surrender. When, in July, 1936, it became clear that Mussolini was intervening in Spain in favour of General Franco, Carlo in *Giustizia e Libertà* launched an appeal to Italian exiles of all parties to form a legion of volunteers to fight as an Italian unit at the side of the Spanish popular militias. The world had ignored the 3,000 Italians who had laid down their lives after 1921 fighting against the Fascists in the civil war in Italy, the 3,000 Italians who from 1927 to 1936 were sentenced by the Fascist Special Tribunal to an aggregate of 30,000 years of imprisonment, the thousands of men and women interned on the penal islands for opposition to the regime, the thousands of intellectuals and workers in Italy and in exile who had accepted poverty rather than renounce their dignity as men. The anti-Fascists who went to fight in Spain were not only to give a practical demonstration of solidarity with the Spanish people, but also to show Mussolini and his admirers abroad that Fascism had not destroyed among Italians the tradition of Mazzini and Garibaldi.

Neither the French nor the Spanish Governments were in favour of this undertaking. They objected that Spain's need was for arms, not for men. They did not want to give Mussolini a pretext for intervening, as if he were not already intervening without pretext. Carlo was able to reach Spain with the first group of Italian anti-Fascists only because the Barcelona Government disobeyed the Madrid authorities and welcomed their aid. Through France they had to travel singly to the Spanish frontier.

On August 19, a group, 150 strong, set out for the Aragonese front. Democrats, Socialists, Communists, Anarchists, even a Catholic Democrat follower of Don Sturzo, all of them came together from the most divers countries of exile. Some came from Italy, braving the perils of flight across the closely guarded Italian frontier. Most were men of mature years who had fought in the World War. All were prompted by strong political convictions. They proved very useful to the Spanish militias, then ignorant of the rudiments of modern warfare.

On the morning of August 28, the column had its baptism of fire, before Huesca on the road between Huesca and Saragossa. At 4 a.m. they were attacked by about seven hundred men armed with machine-guns, field-guns and armoured cars. The Italian volunteers had no artillery. The hand-grenades which some of them, creeping up under cover of the rocky ground, threw at the armoured cars did not explode. One of their machine-guns went out of action. Nevertheless they stood their ground for five hours, taking cover behind the rocks and firing their rifles only when certain of their aim. Carlo was the first to be wounded and went back for first aid. As soon as his chest wound, fortunately slight, was bound up, he joined a group of Spanish volunteers behind the lines and led them to the point most threatened by the Fascist attack. The appearance of these reserves and three aeroplanes caused the Fascists to retire, leaving behind a field-gun, several machine-guns and other war material. One of the Fascists left behind was found to have a rope with a running noose for hanging prisoners captured.

Among those who fell in this engagement was the commander of the column, Mario Angeloni. He came of a family in which democratic ideas were traditional. He had fought as a volunteer in the World War with officer's rank, being awarded several medals for valour. He was, from the first, an opponent of Fascism and sacrificed wealth and professional career to the political struggle. His home and his law office were looted several times, and he himself was wounded and banished from his native Perugia. At the end of 1926 he was arrested, and sentenced to five years internment on the Island of Lipari. When he was sent home after five years of internment, in the spring of 1932 he managed to escape across to France. When Franco's revolt broke out, Angeloni was ill. Without waiting for recovery he hastened to Barcelona where his organizing ability marked him out to be the commander of the first Italian unit. He fell while leading the assault on an enemy tank. After Angeloni's death, the Italian column passed under the command of Carlo Rosselli who had been wounded in the same action. The responsibilities of the leader of such a column in such an environment were many: the equipment of his men, trench digging, the making of dug-outs and shelters, the organization of food and ammunition supplies, maintenance of contact with the commanders of neighbouring columns and with the general command of the sector. Behind the fighting lines Catalonia was in a state of revolution. Revolution and war are not easy to run in harness. War demands discipline under a centralized command; revolution necessarily brings with it the breakdown of the old administrative machine. Extreme tenacity of will, endless patience, tireless sympathy with the Spanish people in its struggle to shake off the terrible heritage of the past, all this was necessary if friendly relations were to be maintained between a foreign fighting force, the local population and the Barcelona authorities. Even the maintenance of smooth relations between the different political elements which composed the column was not always an easy matter. Volunteer formations based on the principle of free discipline are superbly dashing in hours of combat but easily disintegrate during the long months of inertia entailed by a war of positions, such as developed in Aragon after August, 1936. The hard realities of life are apt to be disappointing for the idealist who faces them.

At the end of November Carlo was found to be suffering from phlebitis and had to go for treatment to the Swiss ambulance at Castillo de San Luis. While he was tied to his sick bed, the differences between the Anarchists and the other groups which made up the column, became so acute that Carlo and about thirty others, mostly officers, decided to form a new unit bearing the name Italian Matteotti Battalion. Obliged by illness to return to France in January, Carlo was not able to take part in the actions of the new unit. The command of it was given to Libero Battistelli, a barrister of Bologna, who after the advent of Mussolini had emigrated to Brazil and established himself as a farmer. When the war broke out in Spain he returned to Europe to join up as a volunteer. In June he was mortally wounded before Huesca. Transported to Barcelona he died there at the age of forty, full of stoical serenity to the last.

Meanwhile, in October, 1936, it had become evident that Mussolini and Hitler had committed themselves to large scale intervention in Spain. Only then did the Madrid Government cease to offer resistance to the formation of foreign columns. A battalion of Italian anti-Fascists, organized at Albacete, was sent as a unit of the International Brigade to cooperate in the defence of Madrid. It took the name of "Garibaldi Battalion". Its component units were called after the best known martyrs of the anti-Fascist cause. One company took the name of Matteotti, another that of Gastone Sozzi, the young Communist who in 1928 was beaten to death in the prison of Perugia. Another company called itself after Lauro de Bosis, the young Monarchist who in 1931 flew in an aeroplane over Rome, scattering anti-Fascist manifestos calling upon the King to save Italy from Fascist slavery, and was lost on the return flight to Corsica. This variety of names shows that no one political faith had a monopoly in the battalion.

A special correspondent of the *Manchester Guardian,* June 12, 1937, described in the following terms the different national groups of the International Brigade:

"Every nation has shown qualities of its own. The Swiss are formidable for their dour obstinacy and their concentrated, fretful impatience when they are not attacking. The Poles are kind-hearted, romantic, dashing and absolutely fearless. The English seem to treat the war as a kind of job that has to be done—and they do it well. (The pacifists from the English universities are said to be excellent machine-gunners). The Bulgarians have a preference for the hand-grenade; they resemble the Spanish "dynamiteros", who will storm machine-gun positions with home-made grenades. The French have had the largest number of deserters because it was easier for them than for any others both to come and to go. The French who have remained are men of prodigious valour and impetuosity. The Americans are an elite by reason of their sober courage and their simple, keen intelligence. The Germans are the best that Germany can give (and such is saying much). Many of them have been hardened by persecution and have much to avenge. But if there were a vote in the column it would be seen that the Italians are the favourites; they combine a passionate chivalry and devotion with supreme courage, resourcefulness and discipline. There can be no doubt at all that the Italian is a first-rate soldier when he is fighting for the cause he has at heart."

In March, 1937, on the Guadalajara the International Brigade found itself face to face with an Insurgent army, the spearhead of which was an expeditionary force of 16,000 soldiers sent by Mussolini for the conquest of Madrid. The facts are well known. Franco's troops were held and defeated after a week of furious fighting. Mussolini's soldiers left on the field 2,500 dead and a vast booty of heavy guns, machine-guns, motor lorries, rifles, ammunition and foodstuffs. A thousand Italians, officers and men were taken prisoner. Many of these surrendered voluntarily and fraternized with the Republican troops. The decisive factor in the battle was the intervention of the Garibaldi Battalion.

The defeat of the Fascist forces awakened in many newspapers the memory of Caporetto, the reverse suffered by the Italian army in October, 1917. In actual fact, all the belligerent armies had their "Caporetto" during the World War. The French and British armies opened the war with a "Caporetto" on the Belgian frontier, by which the German army almost reached the gates of Paris. The Austrian army in the summer and autumn of 1914 and spring of 1915 experienced a series of "Caporettos". The Russian army at Gorlice in May, 1915, had one of the most colossal "Caporettos" recorded in history. The Italians had their "Caporetto", not at the beginning of the war, like the French and Austrians, but after they had been weakened by over two years of hard fighting and stupid leadership. From March to May, 1918, the British and French had another "Caporetto" in Picardy, losing 28,000 pieces of artillery and 200,000 prisoners.

The battle of Guadalajara brought face to face anti-Fascist Italians, fighting for an ideal to which they had dedicated their lives, and Italians sent to Spain to fight in a cause that was completely unknown to them. Many of these latter had been deliberately tricked. They had signed on thinking they were to be sent to Ethiopia where there would be work for them and a livelihood for their families. The next thing was that they found themselves in Spain. No interest of their country was at stake. They had no reason to fight against the Spanish people, nor to shed their blood for Spanish generals, bishops, and big landowners. The alleged menace of Communism left them indifferent. What had they to lose if Communism triumphed in Spain or even in Italy? Wealth? They had none. Liberty? They had none. The easy victory promised them when they disembarked in Spain had turned into stiff fighting. To crown all they found themselves fighting against Italians whose banner bore the name of Garibaldi. No wonder they listened to their fellow countrymen and refused to fight in a cause that could never be theirs. Italians deceived or forced into serving a political idea that was repugnant to their consciences, surrendered to Italians who were fighting for the liberty of Spain in the hope of fighting one day for the liberty of Italy. The wonder is that they fought for a whole week before disbanding.

Carlo was ill in France when this battle took place. But by his fiery messages and his own example he had started the movement among the Italian exiles that had led to the formation of the Garibaldi Battalion. In Mussolini's eyes Carlo must appear as one of the authors of the moral defeat into which he had plunged. Mussolini tried to conceal the disaster from the Italians. Carlo, in *Giustizia e Libertà*, April 23, published the names and photographs of 227 Italians taken prisoner at Guadalajara and had many copies conveyed into Italy and given to the prisoners' families who were without any news of them.

Thus Carlo sealed his own doom.

Carlo went to the health resort of Bagnoles on May 27 to undergo a cure for phlebitis. Nello came from Florence to join him on June 6. His fourth child had just been born and he meant to return after a few days to his family.

Carlo always spent the morning taking the cure. After lunch he worked in his room until about 5.30 P.M. and then went for a couple of hours drive in his car in the surrounding country. On the homeward run to the hotel in time for dinner, to avoid the heavy traffic of the main road, he used to take a narrow, unfrequented side road through the park of Couterne. This road was eminently suitable for an ambuscade.

It seems that Carlo and his brother, on the return from the usual evening drive, on June 9, 1937, found the narrow road blocked by a car which appeared to have broken down. To go to the help of its occupants, Carlo must have alighted on the off side from his seat at the driving wheel and Nello from the near side. In alighting Carlo was attacked by dagger thrusts, two of which severed the carotid artery. Death must have been instantaneous. The hand which delivered the blows was that of a professional, specialized in this type of operation. Nello, on the near side, was attacked by the other assassins. These were less skillful. They wounded him many times as he struggled to defend himself with his bare hands. When the deed was done the murderers dragged the bodies a few yards into the undergrowth and left them there.

The brothers lie side by side in the cemetery of Père Lachaise in Paris. Their tomb bears the following inscription:

> CARLO AND NELLO ROSSELLI
> murdered together
> June 9, 1937
> await together
> that the sacrifice of their youth
> will hasten
> in Italy
> the victory of their ideals
> Justice and Liberty

Six dots had to be substituted for the words *in Italy* on the tombstone because in 1938 the French Government prohibited them. "Appeasement" was in full swing under Daladier and Bonnet.

G. A. Borgese

D'ANNUNZIO

THE POETS and prophets of the Risorgimento had been Northerners. After the Risorgimento the intellectual leadership returned to the Centre or passed to the South: a good sign, in itself, of the achieved unity. For the first time, in six centuries of national literature, the South came into the foreground.

The greatest master was Francesco de Sanctis, the Neapolitan historian and critic. While the Italian troops were entering Rome he was hurriedly working at his definitive book, *The History of Italian Literature*. It was a summary of the Italian intellectual and ethical experience from Dante to the poets of the Risorgimento, and, in the last page, a very hopeful outline of the future. De Sanctis interpreted the past of Italian literature as a kind of Old Testament of the Italian people, a national Bible crammed with laments, visions, and unsuccessful efforts; the record of long trial and error. Everything became clear under the light of the accomplished fact, the independence and unity of the nation. He had been among the accomplishers of the fact, a teacher, a political prisoner, an exile. His moral authority was matched by the perfection of his literary judgment, by his intimate knowledge of the poetic monuments of Italy, by the candour, if not by the elegance, of his prose. He rendered justice to all the great spirits, from Dante to Manzoni and Leopardi; he drew a sharp, yet not destructive, line of demarcation between the modern and permanent features of Dante's mind and will, and the perishable medieval elements of his belief; he tried to pardon the sin of Machiavelli, upholding against the cynicism of his method the scientific keenness of his mind and the fervour of his patriotism. He mustered all the others, appreciating their results in imagination and beauty, tracing the decadences and the revivals, keeping constantly in mind an ideal picture of Italy as a producer of the beautiful in the frame of the good and the true, such as he would have liked her to have been in the past, such as he wanted her to be in the age to come. His criticism was free and firm, yet filially pious; his new prophecy was courageous, yet considerate and wise. He fully accepted the system of the Risorgimento, combining in a plausible unity its divers tendencies and fusing its contradictions. The realism and modesty of Manzoni were dearest to him, although he, entirely a philosopher and rationalist, was ever far from Catholicism. He could understand the loftiness of Mazzini's plan but could not overcome his dislike for its abstractness and seemingly medieval absolutism. As Manzoni among the poets, so was Cavour among the statesmen the dearest and nearest to him. The future was to him a free, progressive Italy in a commonwealth of free nations. The new Italian literature, of which he affectionately espied the dawn, was to be a New Testament of the Italian people, a continuance as well as a reversal of the Old. To the coming writers he suggested a spirit of truth, science, human faith, honour; a simple popular prose, founded on a sound observation of life; a singing poetic voice, audible in the chorus of a forward-looking and forward-marching mankind. He did not care for world-empire and world primacy. The wish with which he closed his book, namely, that Italy might soon be again among the foremost creative forces of Europe, is quite permissible and honourable, and does not include any concession to the eagerness of nationalistic pride.

The poet of Italy immediately after the Risorgimento was Carducci, a Tuscan scholar and professor. He was the leader, and even the dictator, of Italian literary opinion for about thirty years, until the end of the nineteenth century. Unlike Alfieri, Manzoni, and Leopardi, who were noblemen, he came from a rather low layer of the provincial bourgeoisie: he also lacked the vastness of Foscolo's outer experience and the depth of Parini's introspection. The range of his knowledge and passion was limited; what he really knew (yet he knew it very well) was Italy from Rome to the Alps, Italian history, Italian, Latin, French literature. He spent practically all of his life in Tuscany and, a few miles from Tuscany, in Bologna, and never went abroad. His intellectual career, although reaching, from several points of view, a high standard of respectability, lacked the steadfastness of continuity, except for his triune fundamental love of poetry, virtue, and motherland. From his early youth he was a patriot, but he did not join the armies and the conspiracies, neither did he don the Garibaldian red shirt, prevented as he was from doing so by his bread-earning task; in other words, by the tyranny of the family group in which most Italians are born and brought up, there to learn conformism and obsequiousness, eventually, to any other kind of tyranny. He was a Mazzinian and a republican, but later on he was unable to resist the applause and the blond smile of the queen of Italy, and he bowed to the crown. He was a democrat and a lover of freedom and peace; he had thundered against Napoleon III and the Cavourian statesmen who were not radical enough for him. But, when the test came, he heartily supported Crispi, the would-be dictator of Italy and would-be conqueror of Africa. He loathed Catholicism and the Papacy, but, grown old, he was deeply moved at the sight of a bell-tower in the melancholy countryside; he listened to the ringing of the bells in the dusk, and he too, although in neoclassic strophes, sang an *Ave Maria*.

All these uncertainties were no unpardonable sins, no venal or cowardly about-faces. Carducci was seduced by the softness of the atmosphere which he breathed, and by the ease with which accommodations were made, in Italy as well as all over Europe, between opposite ideas and conflicting interests. He really would have liked to have a drink with the Pope; and his philosophical and religious education was rather thin, in conformity with the collapse of Italian and European culture. He was no match for a Leopardi or Manzoni; yet in spite of all defects his work remains admirable, often stirring, and his moral and political teaching, in its general line, was sound and pure. He worshipped, too much, the French revolution; he hated the phantoms of the Church and Empire; he knew the real worth of Dante's greatness; and his Rome was the Rome of the civil liberties. Tyrants and conquerors were of no use to his imagination; Cæsar himself was to him a usurper and, besides, a degenerate; he sided with Brutus. In the Dark Ages he saw only darkness, and his mind, a product of the positivistic era, never rose to the understanding of Christ and Christianity. He was unable to see any distinction between Catholicism, Papacy, clericalism, the Gospel, Christianity, and Christ: all together a bunch of lies. To the superstition of the Christ—Whom he deemed to be a teacher of devastating sorrow and moral humiliation—he opposed his own, a less vital one: namely, a Neo-Paganism, no less frigid than the neo-classic sculpture of his age. But, again, his Paganism was no sheer voluptuousness, as it was with so many of his contemporary poets and amateurs, neither was it a Titanic escape from the discipline of society and history. He tried, after all, without any offending show of personal ambition, to substitute a religion of the Sun for the religion of the Son; all heroes and citizens were its priests; its laws were rational and liberal, but by no means lax or perverse; and the gods and goddesses were just metaphors. Conclusively centred in what was desirable and possible, he cherished a very cherishable Italy: a fatherland combining the communes of the Middle Ages, by whose improvised armies the German Emperor was driven back to his glaciers and woodlands, and this new Italy of the Risorgimento, a daughter of poetry and innocence. The support given by him to Crispi's aggressive policy was, perhaps, a momentary emotional aberration; but he did not write any poem or hymn for the Ethiopian expedition, neither did he ever care for conquests and territories, except for the two Italian border cities of Trento and Trieste, which, as a consequence of the lame victory of 1866, had remained in the grip of Austria. The military force of Italy was, according to him, an instrument of defence, menacing nobody; within her Alps and seas Italy was a self-sufficient historic personality, in the service of all mankind. An echo, not disturbing, not overemphatic, of the Mazzinian prophecy is in the finale of one of his Roman odes. He sees the arches and columns of the ancient glory in the Italian or third Rome, as Petrarch had seen them in the Papal or second Rome. He too wants new triumphs, yet "no more of kings, no more of Cæsars," with their slaves and spoils,

> Nay, but your triumph, people of Italy,
> Over the black age, over the barbarian age,
> Over the monsters from which ye
> With calm justice shall set peoples free.

In spite of all discrepancies, de Sanctis should have approved both the personality and the work of Carducci.

But the new man, Gabriele d'Annunzio, was of a quite different race.

Carducci could never fully understand him, and wavered between occasional literary praise, mixed with moral warning, and ominous silence. De Sanctis would have stood aghast. All that he had hated in the undercurrents of the Italian tradition, and worse than that, all that he had thought was buried irrevocably in the past, foamed again on the wave of the present.

Nothing ever had been seen like that adolescent who, curly haired, suavely smiling, blond, and azure-eyed, came, after so many conquerors, to the conquest of Rome in the earliest eighties, just one decade or so after the completion of Italian political unity. He had been born in 1863, a Southerner from Pescara in the region of Abruzzi, formerly belonging to the kingdom of Naples. Nobody ever could have foreseen that the literary and intellectual development of Italy, from Alfieri to Carducci, would have borne its ripest fruit in such a poet and such a man.

Apart from any poetical or ethical judgment, d'Annunzio is the one writer since Dante and Machiavelli whose teaching has had a determining effect on the whole of the Italian mind. Through the channel of Fascist Italy he extended the power of his suggestion over Europe and the world. Now a solitary old man, he can rightly think of himself as one of the driving forces in the history of the twentieth century.

His fortune rose while Carducci's sun still stood high on the horizon. Gradually he took the old master's place, and a much broader one, in the heart and imagination of the Italians, especially of the youth. Acknowledged or despised, he was behind all the spiritual movements and modes from the close of the nineteenth century to the years around 1920.

It is still difficult to evaluate which of the two talents of poetry and action was naturally dominant in his personality. Seen at a distance and measured by its effects, it seems more likely that his instinctive trend was rather toward action. He might have been, or have wished to be, both a Casanova and a Napoleon, a combined atavistic revival of the Italian condottiere and adventurer. There is no reason why he should have felt scandalized at the career of Cesare Borgia, except for his failure. Neither could he have found any moral objection to Machiavelli's doctrine, except for the too great part that the Florentine secretary allows to the fox, as compared with the lion-like qualities of the Prince, and for the humility with which the "popular" or bourgeois writer, dreaming of Princes, did not strive to be a Prince himself. As for Dante, d'Annunzio had once read intensely *The Divine Comedy*, sitting under the olive trees in the Greek island of Corfu; there, inspired by the sea and the air, he finally discov-

ered the real meaning of the Dantean poetry. Under the mantle of
medieval theology and Christian piety, Dante had been the singer of the
Titans.

At first d'Annunzio conscientiously thought of himself as the legitimate
heir of Italian poetry. He did not even see any thorough-going contradiction between his creed and Carducci's (although, undoubtedly, Carducci
was the tutor of the hero, a kind of Chiron, and he, d'Annunzio, was
Achilles, the hero himself). Certainly he loved Italy enthusiastically: her
language, her art, her powerful glory from ancient Rome to the Renaissance and further. Still, there is a love which strives toward union in a
spirit of service; this kind of love may deserve the name of charity; and
there is another kind of love which strives toward joy in possession.
D'Annunzio's love was of the latter kind.

From Foscolo and Carducci, even from Leopardi, he borrowed the
Pagan mythology, yet imbuing its fables with a spirit of glamorous primitivism and anarchical revolt. He also borrowed from Carducci his dislike
for Christ and Christianity; but the Antichristian attitude was more sincere and active with the pupil than with the harmless teacher. He did
not borrow from Manzoni or de Sanctis the theory of a popular, plain
Italian prose. On the contrary, he reverted to a, so to speak, Dantean
or aristocratic and lofty—in his case, egotistic—theory of the illustrious
idiom. His Italian, which he ever spoke with a heavy, lush provincial
cadence, was written with an overgrowth of similes, often baroque, on a
constant musical strain, not seldom cheap.

At first his Titanism was aimless, except for literary glory, pleasure of
love, and hunting on horseback in the Roman Campagna with gentlemen
and ladies of the smart set. The Casanovian, rather than the Napoleonic,
features were visible in the early struggles of his ambition. No gossip or
slander, however, affords real evidence that sadism and crime were actually present in his doings. Most of what happened happened in his
imagination and verse. The poet still had the upper hand.

The Italy of the Risorgimento and the liberal era meant little to him.
There is no record that his parents or ancestors might have opposed or
disliked the despotism and obscurantism of the Neapolitan kings; and
many of his leanings, although he was nothing more than a parvenu of
plebeian blood, were toward the black, or reactionary, nobility. He
looked contemptuously at the badly dressed Parliamentarians; and he
soon learned to call the people the Great Beast. When a few hundred
Italian soldiers fell, valiantly and unfortunately fighting, in an African
battle, the autobiographic protagonist of d'Annunzio's first novel very

quietly declared that he kept aloof from the national emotion over the death of a few "brutes."

Nietzsche, almost universally unknown, collapsed into insanity at the beginning of 1889. Immediately thereafter his name and work had begun to spread. D'Annunzio, a couple of years later, stumbled on a French translation. He felt that he was the Superman.

Except for a few scattered boys, nobody heeded him. It was a rather lonesome grandeur, as Zarathustra's had been.

His energy and power needed a community in which to embody themselves, an earth in which to push their roots. Zarathustra had said: "Remain faithful to the earth."

This happened several years later.

At the end of the century d'Annunzio, not yet forty years old, met his motherland, the Italy of the Risorgimento: her body and soul.

Until that time d'Annunzio had staged, in novels and plays, only imaginary heroes. They were quite great in their velleities and ambitions, and quite mean in their behaviour. Andrea Sperelli, in *Voluptuousness*, although a Titan in the circular whirl of his self-conceit, had nothing to tell but languorous love affairs in the setting of baroque Rome. Tullio Hermil, in *The Innocent*, upheld, against the hypocrisy of the social law, the right of the supreme individual to be himself; namely, to enjoy sexual and spiritual disintegration and to commit, when need be, infanticide. Giovanni Episcopo, in the long short story of this title, aped externally the gestures of the Dostoievskian criminals and repentants, while innerly exulting in the fullness of his degradation. Giorgio Aurispa, in *The Triumph of Death*, written or completed when the Nietzschean Superman had already taken hold of the author's mind, ended, after many lengthy speeches and a fit of desperate sensuousness, in a double suicide with his rather reluctant mistress. In the short stories of Abruzzese folk life, collected later under the title *Novelle della Pescara*, the compassionate realism of Verga or Maupassant had been raised to a self-complacent cruelty and glamour; the ignorant and unfortunate people was indeed the Great Beast, very interesting to watch from a good seat above the arena. In his lyric poems, often stylistically and rhythmically fine, d'Annunzio had exhibited himself as a brother of Giorgio Aurispa and all the others, a hungry imagination in a concupiscent flesh. In one of those poems the Chimæra, the alluring monster of desire, addressed Andrea Sperelli, a pseudonym of d'Annunzio himself. She itemized the programme of a full life. "Wilt thou fight? Kill? See streams of blood?

Great heaps of gold? Herds of captive women? Slaves? Other, other spoils? Wilt thou give life to a block of marble? Raise a temple? Compose an immortal hymn? Wilt thou (hear me, young man, hear me), wilt thou divinely love?"

The first two works of d'Annunzio as a playwright, *The Dream of a Spring Morning* and *The Dream of an Autumn Sunset*, were two delightful nightmares of blood and horror. Eleonora Duse liked them. She became the interpreter of d'Annunzio's dramas.

The first great play was *The Dead City*, in 1898. Sarah Bernhardt also liked it, and played it in French. It was an eloquent apology for incest and fratricide. The setting, very illustrious, the dead city of Mycenæ, was borrowed from Æschylus and Schliemann.

Then came *Glory,* in 1899, and in the same year *La Gioconda.* This latter play was another apology for another kind of crime, if the criminal is, or deems himself to be, a great artist.

During all those years d'Annunzio had been secluded, more or less rigorously, in the solitude of the æsthete. Swinburne, Oscar Wilde, and any other kind of English or French decadence had mastered his mind. Italian literature had been to him, more than anything else, a storehouse of phraseology and mythology. There had been no substantial contact between him and the living reality of life.

His approach to politics and Italy was tortuous and slow.

A man is what he does. Until the late nineties d'Annunzio had done poetry and prose, bad, mediocre, and good. He had had women, horses, and debts. He had been a poet and a dandy. But the novelty of his poetry and dandyism is that they were dissatisfied with themselves. His poetry yearned after action, his dandyism after heroism. This is the particular feature which in a way purifies the effrontery of his libido, and accounts for what was to happen a few years later, when his poetical gifts withered and his active personality acquired a national and universal significance.

Except for some moments of melancholy weariness, he did not seek purification in purity; namely, in moral or religious conversion. He wanted to reach another shore by passing through the boiling waters of contamination and boldly avowed sin.

The vision he had of that other shore cannot be explained by suggestions and environments. Perhaps a case of Mendel's law materialized in d'Annunzio; perhaps there was in him the sudden resurgence of an atavistic type. Culture and environment wrapped the individual phenomenon in the forms of the Renaissance; indeed, not the Renaissance of Michelangelo nor even of Machiavelli, but of the secondary, stray forms of men-of-arms and godless dilettanti.

It is, however, doubtful whether he might ever have been a real Borgia. The two personalities in him, the poet and the conqueror, crippled each other. Perhaps even today, even after his wars and medals, he could repeat the confidence which at the dawn of the century he made to his Florentine barber: "I have experienced all, except the joy of killing." A sparkle of poetic innocence—nay, almost of feminine shyness—still glitters, quite unaccountably, in his wasteful nature.

Occasionally, but seldom, he had tried, since his early youth, to endow his imaginary violence with a collective or patriotic meaning. He had celebrated in a kind of prophetic prose—which no Mazzini, no prophet of the Risorgimento, would have liked—the "matchless human joy" with which the victorious Italian sailors of a torpedo-boat might see some day a big enemy ship sinking "into the unfathomable gurge." A few years later he had published a pamphlet of *Naval Odes,* a fiery homage and prophecy to the Italian battleships. There was in the same sequence a salute to the United States of America, echoing—to be sure, not without the shadow of a misunderstanding—the Americanism of Walt Whitman. This country was to him the one where "everybody, free from any yoke or tie, expands the power which he encloses in himself, where everybody is his own sovereign, has in himself his own laws, in himself his strength and his dream." Republican liberty was found equivalent to anarchical lawlessness, where there is no freedom for anybody; the America of the pioneers—eventually of the racketeers—flooded the White House of the Washingtons and Jeffersons.

The last generation of the Risorgimento was not yet old, not all Mazzinians and Garibaldians had died, and Carducci was still vocal. The nation at large did not take very seriously d'Annunzio's ideas of fatherland and liberty; neither did he insist, for a number of years. When, in 1899, his *Glory* was performed—a play in which he represented by means of allusions, the power and failure of Crispi—the crowd hissed loud, and the abortion was hastily buried. No contact had been established between the poet and the national mass.

He had sat for a short time in the Chamber of Deputies, elected by his proud co-citizens of Pescara. At first he had chosen his seat at the extreme Right, a representative of some kind of reactionary and aristocratic feeling; better still, the representative of himself, or, as it was said, the deputy of Beauty. However, it happened one day that the shouts and roars from the Socialist and Radical benches on the opposite side impressed the poet as a manifestation of vigour and life, which his mind opposed to the senescence of his die-hard or conservative neighbours. Then he suddenly rose on his feet and crossed to the extreme Left, exclaiming: "I go toward life." But there was no meaning in the anecdote. Never could he have understood the economic and political backgrounds of Socialists and Leftists. He appreciated in the peasant the gesture by which he, nobly walking, strewed the seeds in the furrow; he loved the workingman, whom he was ever unable to think of except in terms of medieval guilds and craftsmanship, when he bent a handle of wrought iron, or blew a glass of Murano, or studded a brocade with foliage.

After the African defeat and the hardships of the economic depression, the country grew restless, and it came, especially in Milan, to dangerous riots. The poet did not side with the Socialist leaders, who were jailed. He sided with himself. He had settled in the lovely village of Settignano, on a hill above Florence. There everything was quiet. Yet he would grow sometimes uneasy with the restfulness of his abode. Meeting peasants or workingmen of Settignano he would question them: "Why do you not burn the trollies?" Fire, of all things between earth and heaven, ever seemed to him the loveliest.

He was writing his novel *Fire:* no insurrectional or socialist, no actual fire, unless it were the fire of poetic and musical inspiration. The poet, this time under the name of Stelio Effrena, tormented, not quite to death, a great ageing actress, his interpreter and mistress, dreaming at the same time of repeating, indeed of really fulfilling, in Italy the dream which a great barbarian, Richard Wagner, had dreamed only half way. He wanted a national and universal theatre, all for himself, not certainly against the grey-green background of the Bavarian countryside, but on a glorious hill in sight of Rome: there to unite poetry and music, antiquity and future, earth and heaven, in the esctasy of an endless embrace. But the novel which he had published four years earlier, *The Virgins of the Rocks,* had shown the pretension, however preposterously worded, of deeper-going connexions between his personal ambition and an objective world, or Italy. His assumed name was there Claudio Cantelmo: an idle nobleman, a perfect horseman, whose ancestors had been mighty and cruel men-at-arms. Their offspring Claudio had read the ancient and the recent philosophers, and adopted the word of the Superman. The novelty was his plan of transferring the solitary Titanism of the Superman into the brain of an emperor and king. Cantelmo did not think, as yet, of becoming himself the emperor and king, but he quite earnestly thought of breeding him. Through a kind of eugenics of the will, it should have been possible to generate the King of Rome, the man and ruler of the world to come. Three princesses, three virgin sisters, lived in a solitary castle within the frame of an heroic, rocky landscape. Which of the three should be the bride-elect, the Mother? With whose help should Claudio generate the King of Rome? He did not decide.

The real king of the third Rome and of Italy, the heir of Victor Emmanuel and Cavour, Humbert, the husband of the queen whose smile had conquered Carducci, died in 1900 by an anarchist's bullet. It seemed for a few moments as if it were the starting shot of a social and political revolution; but the contrary happened. Apparently the regicide, a sacrificial offer, was the vent which the emotional perturbation of the country required; soon after, the nation began to quiet down. Years of rapid material progress, of growing prosperity, followed in Italy as in the rest of Europe and of the world. The first decade of the century was on the whole the happiest time the Italian people ever lived. A statesman apparently adequate to the situation sat at the helm, the Piedmontese Giovanni Giolitti, a tall, healthy, rosy-cheeked man, never young, never old, endowed with subtlety and humour, a thoroughly prosaic and realistic mind, a modest disciple of Cavour with even a touch of Manzoni. He was at heart a liberal, but he did not think very highly of the Italian people at its present stage of social education (in which feeling a shade of Piedmontese superiority was discreetly visible); thus he felt entitled to use some tricks with liberty and to manage, according to his needs, the Southern electorate and the Parliamentary majorities. Neither did he think very highly of politics, which was to him no science, either Platonic or Machiavellian, no mysticism, but merely administration, a matter of common sense. For the rest, human progress and national improvement, unless hampered by stupidity and revolution, were to him truths as safe as arithmetic and bookkeeping. Those Italians who affected to despise him called him a bookkeeper. He did not fit their Dantean requirements.

Neither was he apt to satisfy Claudio Cantelmo and Gabriele d'Annunzio. It was, however, on that wave of all-embracing optimism that d'Annunzio and the nation, after so many missed dates, finally met. He addressed the new king, when Victor Emmanuel III took the place of the murdered Humbert, with an inflamed poetic epistle in which he praised him, he spurred him, he finally menaced him. If thou wilt not give greatness and glory to the Italian nation—thus he warned—I shall be amongst thine enemies. Everybody enjoyed the monarchical salute—a new sheep in the fold, after Carducci—few if any minded the rhetorical threat. Soon after, a Florentine high school teacher who had read Virgil, Barrès, and d'Annunzio, but mostly d'Annunzio, founded Italian nationalism; in other words, he published a weekly by means of which he wanted to eradicate Giolitti, democracy, and Parliamentarism, to avenge the disgrace of the Ethiopian defeat (whose scar now hardly itched), and to lay the foundations of an Italian Empire under the majestic law of despotism. Never before had the ideal system of the Risorgimento been so crudely opposed or so blindly ignored. But few if any minded the editor or his contributors, who were mostly adolescents either dazzled by the brilliancy of the paradox or misled by a passion of patriotism which seemed to them greater than the greatness of modesty and wisdom; and the circulation of the weekly was not worth counting.

What seemed very good to all the official world and the intellectual élite, and even to the people at large as far as the poor honest people were concerned with such things, was the fact that now, in the era of the new king, there was a national poet again—indeed, the same one whose personal career, whose utterances in things of sex and ethics, had aroused so many misgivings. The old master, Carducci, paralysis-stricken, was now stuttering or silent. The new man took his place. He superabundantly praised any and all the glories of Rome and Italy, from the remotest past to only yesterday; he also adopted the subject matter of the Risorgimento: to be sure, its deeds rather than its ideas, its courage and blood rather than its belief. Among the heroes of the Risorgimento none fitted d'Annunzio's imagination better than Garibaldi. Had he not been a daredevil, a sailor in stormy seas, an adventurer (even in love)?

D'Annunzio wrote an epic song of Garibaldi. He read it in the theatres of the major and minor cities, following his gigantic script through the gleam of his decadent monocle, turning the heavy pages with a hand as white as the shirt, the tie, the face. His stature was small, his voice icy and nasal, but commanding. The crowds, at last his crowds, unanimously applauded.

Then came his years of poetic glory, the first years of the century: three volumes of poems, an untiring pæan to Rome and Greece and Italy and the world and the sea and the sky and all things that were or are or may be, the grandest orgy of optimism and self-satisfaction ever seen; three plays of medieval or modern incest and murders, flames and horrors, equally satisfying; thousands and thousands of pages in all literary genera. One of the plays ended with the line: "The flame is beautiful! The flame is beautiful!" Another play of a few years later (1908), *The*

Ship, a violent and voluptuous celebration of the Venetian Empire, carved into the imagination of the Italians the most comprehensive although rather bewildering suggestion of imperialism and aggression, no matter over what and against whom. The slogan was continued in the line: "Arm the prow and sail toward the world."

He could not yet sail for so far. He left for France. A mediocre collapse, financial in nature, had followed all that glory. His tremendous earnings could not meet his mad, yes, in a way, his heroic squandering. He chose the strangest of exiles, an exile for debts. His refuge was in Arcachon, on the Atlantic shore, not far from Biarritz and Bordeaux.

But he came back to Italy, in spirit, when the Italy of Giolitti declared war on Turkey in 1911 and conquered in 1912 the North African province of Libya. D'Annunzio wrote and sent to Italy his poems and hymns for the war of conquest. They were as loud as gunfire.

Then he came back in person, when Italy was on the eve of her intervention in the World War, in the spring of 1915. He came from France through the Modane tunnel, showing himself at the train window to answer the cheers of his crowds in the station of Turin, stopping in Genoa. There was gossip about women accompanying him and about bills at the hotels. They have no meaning.

There is a meaning in the fact that he chose, for the delivery of one of his most inflammatory war speeches, the same cliff of Quarto, a suburb of Genoa on the Tyrrhenian coast, whence Garibaldi had sailed fifty-five years earlier with a handful of heroes: not toward the world but toward Sicily and the deliverance of his Italian brothers.

From that same cliff d'Annunzio showed to the new Italy the new road to war.

It was to be the war which many Italians gleefully called "Our War."

GREECE

INTRODUCTION

By Demetrios Capetanakis

I HAVE HEARD many impressive things about the Parthenon from Greeks and foreigners, but nothing was as painful to me as the words that Constantin Tsatsos, a young professor of philosophy in the University of Athens, used to repeat in his lectures: "We are interested in the Parthenon, not in the workmen who built it. What matters is the work of art, not human beings." His voice was fiery, his gestures prophetic. It sounded overwhelming, but I was revolted. It was so inhuman that it could not be true. I was very young then, but I was feeling in some obscure way that the Parthenon must be so interesting because it speaks of the interesting people who needed it and made it, and because it can still be mirrored in the eyes of people and affect their lives. What matters is human beings and what becomes of them. That is why, although I want to write something about the modern Greek mind, I am anxious to discuss the people rather than their work. Only if one knows the people, can one understand their works. And in this country, modern Greeks are little known. . . .

Virginia Woolf called one of her essays "On not knowing Greek" because she realised that the Greek of the classical studies had little to do with any Greek historical reality. In this essay she described in a charming way what Greece means to the most cultivated circles in England: "Does not the whole of Greece heap itself behind every line of its literature? They admit us to a vision of the earth unravaged, the sea unpolluted, the maturity, tried but unbroken, of mankind . . . Back and back we are drawn to steep ourselves in what, perhaps, is only an image of the reality, not the reality itself, a summer's day imagined in the heart of a northern winter."

Such dreams can have a tremendous importance in the forming of a civilization—and among them the dream of Greece has been the most effective —but their interference with everyday life can be sometimes misleading. A Greek in England feels often embarrassed when he is introduced to classical scholars. Their eyes accustomed to read Greek texts, do not see clearer for that; instead of seeing the Greek who stands before them as he really is, they fold him in so many verses they know by heart, in so many names of heroes, poets, philosophers or artists they admire, in so many memories from their school or college life, that the poor Greek, who feels himself decked with so much that has but little to do with himself, is overwhelmed. It is still worse when he feels that he is not only associated with the classical studies of the other, but is also compared to the ideal of a Greek the other holds. He feels that the proportions of his body are mentally compared to the proportions of a Greek statue representing a god, a hero or an athlete, and that his nose puzzles the other because it is not as straight as the famous "Greek nose." The modern Greek is very proud of his ancestors, of course, but he does not much like to be considered only in relation to them. He is more or less conscious of being the product of a much longer history than the few centuries of ancient Greece—he is also conscious of belonging to his own age. He is a reality here and now and he may feel uneasy when his questioner tries to place him by transposing him to a world of dream. . . .

Many business men must have met T. S. Eliot's Mr. Eugenides, the rich, vulgar Greek merchant, and they no doubt think of him when they hear of Greece. That is very misleading, as misleading as to think of the age of Pericles when one hears of Greek history. The Greeks of to-day are neither lingering specimens of a race that worked wonders two thousand years ago, nor a Balkan people without any past and without any roots in the history of their land. If one wants to understand them, one must connect them to the whole rather than to some periods of their history, and see them at the same time as modern Europeans. It would be a great pity if the Greeks were still what they were at the time of Pericles. The history of their sensibility would be much too poor. . . .

The Greek through his history has had so many experiences, so many ups and downs—nothing human, neither the lowest nor the highest was refused to him. The only thing that never changed in Greek civilization was its male character. There were times when the Greek could be called effeminate, as during the Hellenistic and Roman periods, but Greece never lost its manliness. In no time of Greek history do we find women setting the tone—as in the France of Louis XIV for instance—unless we go back to prehistoric times in Crete. Historians said that it was a feminine civilization—but it is too long ago, no one can know anything certain about it; besides we are not interested in history whose traces cannot be found in the present.

What matters is not history as history, but human beings. What matters is the Greeks of to-day and what will become of them. What now matters is humanity and what will become of it.

C. P. Cavafy

EXPECTING THE BARBARIANS

> WHAT ARE we all waiting for,
> Gathered together like this on the public square?
>
> The Barbarians are coming to-day.

Why this air of listlessness in the Senate House?
Why have the Senators given up legislating?

The Barbarians are coming to-day.
What would be the good of legislating?
When they come, the Barbarians will make the law.

Why has our Emperor got out of bed so early?
What is he doing at the city gates,
With his crown on his head and such a solemn expression?

The Barbarians are coming to-day.
The Emperor is waiting to receive their leader.
He has even prepared a charter
Granting him honours and titles.

Why are our two consuls and our praetors
All got up in their embroidered scarlet robes?
Why are they covered with bracelets and rings?
What are they going to do with their precious staffs,
Wonderfully filigreed in silver and gold?

The Barbarians are coming to-day.
And such things impress the Barbarians.

Then why are our famous orators not here to make speeches
And display their usual fluency?

The Barbarians are coming to-day.
And the Barbarians do not appreciate fine phrases or long speeches.

Why, now, all of a sudden, this disturbance?
How solemn everybody's face has suddenly become?
Why are the streets and the squares all emptying so quickly?
Why is everybody going home looking so blue?

Because night has fallen and the Barbarians have not come.
And some people have just got back from the frontiers
Who say that there are no more Barbarians.

And now, without the Barbarians, what is to become of us?
After all, they would have been a kind of solution.

                    Translated by MARGUERITE YOURCENAR *and* W. H. AUDEN

Pantelis Prevelakis

TWO POEMS

I

THE BREEZES of freedom blow ail round me!
My body, like the standing harp left
idle in the midst of the moaning orchestra,
trembles quietly,
forgotten by the pains, by suffering,
forgotten by necessity.
I listen to the quiet resound:
resonator of the universe,
secret, imperceptible response,
—O miracle of love!—
top of a high tree
moved by the songs of the birds.

II

THE SUNSET entered the room,
a red lion.
His reflection fell on the mirror
and I felt his tender paw
touching my bare feet.
I stooped under my table,
that was sanctified by the work of the day,
and I saw him, the sun, kissing my feet
with his red tongue.

Translated by DEMETRIOS CAPETANAKIS

Lilika Nakos

MATERNITY

IT WAS MORE THAN a month since they were at Marseilles and the camp
of Armenian refugees on the outskirts of the town already looked like a
small village. They had settled down in any way they could: the richest

under tents; the others in the ruined sheds; but the majority of the refugees, having found nothing better, were sheltered under carpets held up at the four corners by sticks. They thought themselves lucky if they could find a sheet to hang up at the sides and wall them from peering eyes. Then they felt almost at home. The men found work—no matter what—so that in any case they were not racked with hunger and their children had something to eat.

Of all of them, Mikali alone could do nothing. He ate the bread which his neighbors cared to offer and it weighed on him. For he was a big lad of fourteen, healthy and robust. But how could he think of looking for work when he literally bore on his back the burden of a new-born babe? Since its birth, which had caused his mother's death, it had wailed its famine from morn till night. Who would have accepted Mikali's services when his own compatriots had chased him from their quarters because they were unable to bear the uninterrupted howls which kept them awake at night. Mikali himself was dazed by these cries; his head was empty and he wandered about like a lost soul, dying from lack of sleep and weariness, always dragging about with him the deafening burden that had been born for his misfortune—and its own—and that had so badly chosen the moment to appear on this earth. Everybody listened to it with irritation—they had so many troubles of their own—and they all pitifully wished it would die. But that did not happen for the new-born child sought desperately to live and cry louder its famine. The distracted women stuffed their ears and Mikali went hither and yon like a drunken man. He hadn't a penny in his pocket to buy the infant milk and not one woman in the camp was in a position to give it the breast. Enough to drive one mad!

One day, unable to bear it further, Mikali went to the other side of the place where the Anatolians were: they also had fled from the Turkish massacres in Asia Minor. Mikali had been told that there was a nursing mother there who might take pity on his baby. So there he went full of hope. Their camp was like his—the same misery. Old women were crouched on pallets on the ground; barefooted children played about in pools of dirty water. As he approached, several old women rose to ask what he wanted. But he walked on and stopped only at the opening of a tent where an Ikon of the Holy Virgin was hanging; from the interior of the tent came the sound of a wailing infant.

"In the name of the Most Holy Virgin whose Ikon you show," he said in Greek, "have pity on this poor orphan and give him a little milk. I am a poor Armenian . . ."

At his appeal, a lovely, dark woman appeared. She held in her arms an infant blissfully sucking the maternal breast, its eyes half-closed.

"Let's see the kid. Is't a boy or a girl?"

Mikali's heart trembled with joy. Several neighbors had come closer to see and they helped him to take from his shoulders the sack where the baby brother was held; with curiosity they leaned over. He drew back the cover. The women gave vent to various cries of horror. The child had no longer anything human about it. It was a monster! The head had become enormous and the body, of an incredible thinness, was all shrivelled up. As until then it had sucked only its thumb, it was all swollen and could no longer enter the mouth. It was dreadful to see! Mikali himself drew back in fright.

"Holy Mother!" said one of the old women, "but it's a vampire; a real vampire, that child! Even if I had milk I still wouldn't have the courage to feed it."

"A true Anti-Christ!" said another, crossing herself. "A true son of the Turk!"

An old crone came up. "Hou! Hou!" she screamed, seeing the new-born child. "It's the devil himself!" Then turning to Mikali she yelled: "Get out of here, son of mischance, and never set foot again. You'll bring us bad luck!"

And all of them together chased him away, theatening. His eyes filled with tears, he went off, bearing the little child still wailing its hunger.

There was nothing to be done. The child was condemned to die of hunger. Mikali felt himself immensely alone and lost. A chill ran up his spine at the thought that he was carrying such a monster. He slumped down in the shadow of a shed. It was still very warm. The country spread out before him in arid, waste land, covered with refuse. Noon rang out somewhere. The sound reminded him that he had eaten nothing since the day before. He would have to go sneaking about the streets, round café terraces, filching some half-eaten roll left on a plate; or else rake about in the garbage for what a dog would not have eaten. Suddenly life seemed to him so full of horrors that he covered his face with his hands and began to sob desperately.

When he raised his head a man stood before him gazing down upon him. Mikali recognized the Chinaman who often came to the camp to sell paper knick-knacks and charms which no one ever bought from him anyway. Often they mocked him because of his color and his squint eyes; and the children hounded him, shouting: "Lee Link, the stinkin' Chink!"

Mikali saw that he was looking gently down at him and moving his lips

as though to speak. Finally the Chinaman said: "You mustn't cry, boy
. . ." Then, timidly: "Come with me . . ."

Mikali's only answer was to shake his head negatively; he longed to
flee. He had heard so many horrors about the cruelty of the Orientals! At
the camp they even went so far as to say that they had the habit—like
the Jews—of stealing Christian children in order to kill them and drink
their blood!

Yet the man remained there and did not budge. So, being in great
distress, Mikali followed him. What more awful thing could happen to
him? As they walked along he stumbled weakly and almost fell with the
child. The Chinaman came to him and taking the baby in his arms,
tenderly pressed it to him.

They crossed several empty lots and then the man took a little lane
that led them to a sort of wooden cabin surrounded by a very small
garden. He stopped before the door and clapped his hands twice. A few
light steps inside and a tiny person came to open the door. Seeing the
men her face reddened and then a happy smile lit it up. She made a
brief curtsey to them. As Mikali remained there, hesitatingly rooted to the
threshold, the Chinaman said to him: "Come in, then; do not be afraid.
This is my wife."

Mikali went into the room, rather large it seemed, separated in the
middle by a colored paper screen. It was all so clean and neat, though
very poor looking. In the corner he noticed a wicker cradle.

"That is my baby," said the young woman cocking her head graciously
to one side and smiling to him. "He is very tiny and very beautiful; come
and see."

Mikali went up closer and silently admired it. A chubby baby, but
lately out of the darkness of the maternal body, slept peacefully, covered
with a gold-brocade cloth, like a little king.

Then the husband called his wife over, bade her sit on a straw mat,
and without a word set down on her lap the little famished one, bowing
deeply before her. The woman leaned over with astonishment and drew
back the covering in which the child was wrapped. It appeared to her
in all its skeletonic horror. She gave a cry—a cry of immense pity—then
pressed the babe to her heart, giving it the breast. Then with a gesture
of modesty she brought forward a flap of her robe over the milk-swollen
breast and the poor, gluttonous infant suckling there.

                         Translated by ALLAN ROSS MACDOUGALL

RUMANIA

INTRODUCTION

By Saul Colin

VERY LITTLE in Rumanian literature is over a hundred years old. What there is belongs to the long and bitter story of Rumania's emancipation from alien forms of speech and thought. Wedged between the Slavic countries and the Orient, Rumania was for centuries a small island of faltering latinism, with no direct access to western sources of culture. When the center of gravity in that part of the world shifted from the Slavs to the Turks, in political power, and to the Greeks in the field of culture, the Slavic influence, which has left a strong imprint on Rumanian character and vocabulary, started to lose ground. Slavonic, the Latin of the Orient, was to remain the official language of the Rumanian Church until 1710. But, under the impulse of Hussite missionaries, sacred writings were translated from the Slavonic—the first known document printed in Rumanian being a translation of the Gospels in 1561. This movement brought about the unification of the various dialects spoken in the provinces of Moldavia, Wallachia and Transylvania.

The next important step was taken by the great Moldavian chroniclers who wrote their records of local history in the archaic Rumanian tongue of the seventeenth century. From the works of the Italian humanists with which they had become acquainted at the Jesuit colleges in Poland, Grigore Ureche, and Miron Costin picked up the idea of the Latin inheritance of the Rumanian people, which they were the first to bring into focus.

It was only around 1830 that Rumanian literature started to develop as a living organism, and from there on it progressed very rapidly. The same awakening was taking place in every phase of Rumanian life. The echo of Napoleon's victories had reached this remote corner of Europe and planted the idea of France in the consciousness of the Rumanian people at large, thus bringing into play one of the most decisive factors in their history: the influence of France. To the Rumanian people, French culture has proved to be the most readily assimilable culture in the world. Between 1820 and 1840, there was at least one French school in every important city, while Rumanian educators were still hampered in their efforts, principally by the Slavonic alphabet which remained in use until 1864.

Falling as it did on fertile and thirsty ground, the influence of French civilization became an active factor of progress in literature and art as well as in the way of living. The most extensive use was now being made of the Rumanian language. But what the language couldn't assimilate, it adopted, unchanged. When the countless neologisms which the writers had to adopt to do justice to the intricacies of modern thought threatened the language, the latinists stepped in, making a futile, if well-meaning, attempt to eliminate all the foreign infiltrations accumulated through the ages and to replace them with artificial derivations of Latin roots. To the resulting confusion of standards, the discrepancies between this veneer of sophistication and the real self of the people, Rumania owes her greatest satirist, Ion L. Caragiale (1853–1912).

Of the writers who strived to give the youngest of romance literatures a style and magic of its own, first mention should be made of Vasile Alexandri (1821–1890), a poet and playwright, one of whose most important contributions is a collection of folk-poems, published in 1852, that brought for the first time to the attention of the reading public the *doine*, ballads of *dor* or passionate longing, the *horas*, satirical verse, the *basme* or fairy tales.

Only a generation later, the poems of Mihail Eminescu (1850–1889) were to prove that, somewhere between its two sources of inspiration, one spontaneous, the other acquired, Rumanian literature had found its soul. Then, just before World War I, poems of an entirely new tone started to appear in literary magazines. By the time they were published in a volume, in 1927, the poems of Tudor Arghezi (born 1880) had already placed him above the other poets of his time. In "Icons of Wood" and "The Black Gate," the somber and fulgurant poems in prose in which Arghezi has used his first-hand knowledge of both monastic life and political prisons, there is the same extraordinary virtuosity of expression as that which gives his poems explosive power. Yet Arghezi has impressed himself on the style of his time far more than on its soul. With his intellectual, strictly unsentimental approach to life, his high-powered oscillations between revolt at one end and what the mystics called "aridity of soul" at the other, Tudor Arghezi stands out because he is great but also because he is alone of his kind. If only for this reason, his place in Rumanian letters can be compared to that of Paul Claudel in France, with the writer Ion Barbu as a minor Valéry.

As should be expected in a country where, the pattern of society being far from settled, the individual can rise against it but seldom above it, the most significant novels written so far—like Duiliu Zamfirescu's *Life in the Country*, the best-seller of the early 1920's and Liviu Rebreanu's grim, powerful stories—are those dealing with social problems. Younger novelists to whom Proust as well as André Gide have been a revelation, Mircea Eliade, for instance, Camil Petrescu, Hortense Papadat-Bengescu, to name only a few, are now taking the psychological novel out of the experimental stage.

The first source of Rumanian literature being *song*, there are writers who find it difficult to break away from a tradition in which "beautiful" writing is cultivated and loved, as well as painstakingly analyzed in the brilliant, somewhat dogmatic reviews in which the critics indulge. The short stories of Bratescu-Voinesti prove that this tradition does not necessarily entail flamboyance of style. But a novelist as gifted as Ionel Teodoreanu has never quite managed to break through his "talent for writing" and to outgrow his first novel *La Medeleni* (which was the sensation of the late 1920's), a rather enchanting story of adolescence and the breathless discovery of life.

Lyricism is also the keynote, if not the limitation, of Mihail Sadoveanu, the author of more than fifty volumes of novels and short stories and one of the greatest writers of Rumanian prose (*The Land Beyond the Dark, A Mill on the Sereth, etc.*). The magic of his world derives as much from the purely sensorial quality of his *sens de la nature*, which expresses itself best in the simple relationship between nature and "man as God has made him," as from the underlying stress on death as the condition and heightening agent of life.

Of the Rumanian writers or writers of Rumanian descent who have distinguished themselves in foreign literatures, Princess Marthe Bibesco and Panait Istrati may be said to belong to French letters; Valeriu Marcu has written his books in German, while Konrad Bercovici and Peter Neagoe belong to American literature.

Mihail Sadoveanu

THE VESPER BELL

CRICOPOL HAD BEEN chieftain of a Cossack tribe. He had taken part in the Manchurian war. He had crossed many times through the Turkestan. He had camped on the willowy banks of the Amur and the lowlands along the river Ob. He had spent a few years as a colonist under the glorious sky of one of the most enchanting parts of Siberia, amid virgin forests, wild streams and mountain ranges gleaming against the horizon. He had pushed eastwards as far as he could go and returned, this side of the Dniester, to the plains of Bugeac where he was born. He couldn't know that the short trip to the swamps of the Danube would be the last of his wandering career.

I met him, and we became friends, on the shore of a lagoon-island fringed like the banks of the Amur with tall willow-trees. The swamp beyond us lay in a stupor; wild doves crowned the stumps of trees which lightning had struck. Away, somewhere, the world was following its course—its changing faces, its rumors and noise so remote as to be unthinkable. Here the sky looked upon the primeval wilderness of mire and rotting bottoms swarming with minute life, of birds and beasts hidden among the rank grasses, of myriads of fish under the calm surface of the water. The overwhelming peace we felt was a delusion; beneath it stirred a fierce, ruthless, complicated life.

This was the island of Lipan where the first cuckoo is heard in the Spring. The cuckoo will sing, take a look at the wilderness and then fly off into the world of people. Later, the flocks of wild geese make a stop here on their way north from the marshes of Africa. Right on their tail, the spoonbills show up. And the pink flamingoes desert the rest of the Delta for a sheltered nook on Lipan where they hatch and bring up their young.

It was for the snow-white, plumed herons, the precious egrets, that Cricopol had come to this island. He hunted all sorts of rare birds. He stuffed them himself and sold them to museums in Britain and Germany. But his most profitable industry, he told me, was hunting egrets. Their tufts of long, silky feathers were in great demand right then in the cities of the West. Fashionable women would get them from Cricopol and, without knowing he existed, love him for it.

This friend of mine had kept himself in pretty good shape. He could resist loneliness, the mosquitoes and other deadly exhalations of the swamp with the help of what he called an elixir—which referred only to its potency. As I was to find out before we had known each other very long, a friend had as good a right to partake of it as himself.

Hiding a smile in his shaggy beard, he had straightened himself up, tramped in his huge worsted boots to a hut of reeds and brought out from under a heap of Bukhara sheephides and assorted fishing and hunting implements, a bottle of what looked to me like murky water.

"This is it . . ." his low voice said as he came back. "Do as I say and have a drink with me. You'd better, my friend, because the sun is going down and before we know it, dark visions will have stepped out of the reeds and willows. They're sullen and cold. With this to warm them up, we can hear them whisper."

I was still doubtful. He filled a small glass and handed it to me.

"The sun is just about gone now . . ." he urged me again. "In a moment, swarms of mosquitoes will come up and we must be prepared. Drink this elixir, it will make the blood glow in your veins. Then we will light a fire of reeds. These two flames are man's only safeguard in this waste of waters. If you let the swamp have its way, you end in its power, sucked in. . . ."

I swallowed the colorless liquid in one gulp. It hit me like a blast of wind and fire, and knocked my breath out. My hands moved convulsively to clutch my throat. Wild-eyed, I caught one glimpse of death— and then as I started to breathe again, I shuddered. Cricopol was sneering. There was a long scar across his right cheek which pulled down the corner of his mouth and turned his grin into a grimace.

"What on earth . . . ?" I said, aghast.

"It's something very good and useful . . ." my companion said. "I make it myself. I put crushed pepper in a bottle of liquor, any kind provided it's 90% proof, leave it in the sun to clear and then filter it through fine marsh herbs . . ."

He poured himself a drink in the same thick green tumbler and swallowed it as if it had been water. He filled the glass again—handed it out to see me draw myself back with a shudder—and poured the drink down his throat. This time he grunted with contentment. He took the bottle and returned it to its hiding place in the hut. Then he came back to where I was sitting, struck flint against steel, ignited some tinder and set fire to the first pile of reeds.

"How can you drink that elixir of yours?" I asked. I couldn't get over it.

"Can't do without," Cricopol replied soberly. "It keeps the mosquitoes away for one thing. And my face in the water being the only company I have. . . . It helps."

He looked at me, his eyes wide and filled with shadows. Around us the scene had suddenly changed to a fantastic twilight—under a mist of poisonous effluvia. Flights of geese, taking off in rapid succession, were storming through the sky. But in spite of the commotion they created overhead, an ominous stillness was spreading over the lagoon. We could just feel, in the hidden coves, the first visions of night come out: a mournful stork, a swan. . . .

"It helps . . ." Cricopol repeated softly. "I live alone. When I have no company, which is practically always the case, I take as many as three drinks in one evening. . . . Even so, when it comes, I hear it. Don't look at me like this, my head is perfectly clear. I want to tell you what I hear.

"I have been living here since the beginning of Spring, when it's time to start my hunting and other work. I earn quite enough this way. I couldn't be more satisfied. It's far better than Turkestan, for instance, where I hunted the fur-bearing tiger for which the highest prices are paid, or the Amur where malaria and the dengue are out to kill you. In the swamps of the Danube, the sun doesn't hit you on the head like a red-hot hammer, and nature has a delicate and friendly look. Then, as I told you, there is the cuckoo singing first to me. It reminds me of my childhood and of my mother who lived in a village not far from here, in Moldavia. I have come all the way from the wilderness of the yellow people to this place, on the Danube, near my mother's grave. I think this is where I wanted to be.

"I could be happier here than anywhere else. Only something is happening to me and why it should or what it is I can't understand. Maybe another man would go away. But I am staying right here because I want to find out what it means. I drink my potion, light a fire and wait until I hear something no other man can listen to but me.

"It's like this. Late in June, the geese teach their young to fly and start their journey to the northern seas. At about the same time, the flamingoes go up again. And birds fly over my fire that I have never seen by day. I am sure other wild creatures stalk out of the shrub in which they live and stand just beyond this ring of light to peer at me from the dark. I wouldn't know about them. But I can feel them stay there and watch with their unblinking eyes.

"The day of St. Ilie comes and goes and then, one evening, it starts, this thing I am telling you about. The first time, last year, I was sitting by the fire, just as I am sitting now, only I had no company. The ducks had fondled the waters for a while and taken off. The peace of night was setting in. Not a stir of wind and the sky was the color of smoke.

"Two swans came out of a bush. I couldn't see them; I only heard them whisper. Then, an animal stole along the shore, I could hear it snort. A boar, or a wolf, or maybe an otter. . . .

"Finally I was left alone, or at least free to believe I was. It's an illusion I often have inside the narrow circle of my fire; but you are never alone here. The wilderness keeps watching you through unwavering eyes.

"I was taking in the deep quiet of the evening, my ears on the alert as they always are and my eyes, half-closed, turned inwards on some dream, when suddenly, from across the lagoon, I heard a sound.

"It was a clear, vibrant sound, not the cry of a beast. It seemed to come from a great distance, and yet I felt it could have originated right here; and I shivered. It was unlike anything one hears in the swamps. Imagine silence breaking into sound and ringing like a bell. A few strokes come at short intervals and then it stops. I wait, knowing somehow that it will ring again. My heart is beating time, too loud. Then it skips a beat; I hold my breath: the bell is ringing again—and the sound sweeps over the waters and winds through the sedges and reeds.

"It stops. In the dark, the motionless creatures peering through the dark must prick up their ears just as I do. And the slow, even tolling comes to me again.

"That same evening, it rang a third time and, after another pause, a fourth; by then I was really frightened. The only comforting thought was that, in a few hours, I would be able to go and search the lagoon in the daylight. When you live here, you get to know every voice of this wilderness as well as your own. Only an intruder—man—can be the source of unexpected sounds.

"So, the following day, I set out to search the swamp. I went all over this island, through places where I had never set foot before. I paddled through the canals as far as my boat would take me. I even crossed to adjoining islands. There was not a sign of man anywhere. At the end of the day, I was sure there couldn't be a human being living in these parts without my knowledge. I was alone, with the fish, the birds and the willows.

"At nightfall, I was sitting here by the fire. And where you are now, sat fear. No sooner had the ducks sailed overhead—and the swans slipped into their cove for the night—that I heard it again, the tolling bell of my solitude. The sound came and went until a certain hour that I can tell only by the stars, and then it stopped. Altogether, I heard it for twenty days, twenty clear, windless summer evenings which I spent in the open listening and looking at the sky—like the first man—to see when the Great Bear would release me from a wonder and a fear.

"I spent whole days thinking it out and searching my mind for a satisfactory explanation.

"I remembered having heard from other travellers to places where no men live that, somewhere in Sahara, when you stop for the night, you can hear a swift drumming break through the silence—a few, fantastic drops of sound falling from nowhere into that huge expanse of stillness reaching to the skies.

"Scientists ascribe that sound to the different temperatures of the strata of air and the amplification of sound waves. They say that, in the desert, your ears as well as your eyes can be deceived. During the day, the heat produces mirages; at night, due to the sharp drop of equatorial temperatures, the sound of sand grains dropping can be amplified and ring in your ears, maybe hundreds of miles away, like a roll of drums.

"Now the Arabs believe it announces the simoon; they just smile at the white men's explanations. They smile because they don't think, as we seem to do, that the mysteries of nature have to be explained in order to mean something. All that is asked of man is to recognize them as such and then to bow before the power of the great unknown.

"I am no wiser than other white men and I couldn't bear to hear that sound without knowing what made it. Having searched the lagoon, I started to think of a less obvious explanation. Was it the amplification of a faint rustling in the reeds? It couldn't be, with the lagoon in a deadly stupor and not a breath of wind. Or strange birds clapping their beaks in some corner of the bush where they had slipped unnoticed? That was possible. For days after that, I did nothing but look for them. In Sahara, they had their grains of sand; with me, it was the flight of unknown birds coming from a point even farther removed than those sands, like Victoria Nyanza, maybe, or Dahomey.

"You can imagine how I searched for those birds which I have never found. I would see them in my sleep, their shape and colors so real that I almost expected them to dash out of a bush before my eyes. There is nothing like a man's belief in delusions of his own making. I did hang on to those birds that have never existed as long as I could. And when I had to give them up, it was a terrible let-down. I had no other theory.

"That's when I understood what my elixir, which might be poison to others, was doing for me. It was the only way I had to set myself free. Every night, the third drink lifted from my side the fear with glassy eyes and made it vanish into the smoke of my fire of reeds."

We sat a long while without talking. I was lost in the other man's brooding thoughts.

"I know what you're thinking," Cricopol said with his twisted smile.

"Yes . . ." I answered, without intending to. "But tell me, has that unexplained sound stopped since last summer?"

"I am quite sure," he replied, "that I came to hunt on the same spot this year because I wanted a chance to find out. And right after St. Ilie, I heard the tolling come from the same mysterious place. It came and went for twenty days and then it stopped.

"This time it was even more difficult to explain the fact. My tale of birds seemed ridiculous to me now. It didn't stand up to the simplest objections.

"In Sahara, the white people have imagined a theory based on sand grains because sand is the principal element in the desert. Then here, where everything is flooded, I could use the same theory only in regard to water. But how was I to connect with water the sound of a tolling bell? What minute sound, what gurgling or trickle could ring in my ears like churchbells tolling the knell in the village where I was born?

"Will you believe me if I say that, after I gave up these theories, I started to wonder if I wasn't actually hearing the bells of a church? I knew that the nearest village was at a great distance from here. But there was just a chance for the sound to travel through the air to the glowing waters of the Delta—and here glide along their surface and come winding through the wild paths to me.

"I don't need to tell you that I was fool enough to leave the swamps and go to the mainland for a solution to my mystery. The nearest village with a church was over fifty miles away from here. And they don't use the *toaca* any more. I should have remembered that all over the plains of Bugeac, including my native village, it's been years since the last of these vesper bells was heard, the *toaca* which used to ring in the old times to warn the people that their land was invaded. On my way back to Lipan, I could have laughed out loud. If a sound from the mainland could have travelled all this way, I should have been able to hear their churchbells, such as they were. But no matter how I strained my ears after that, I never managed to hear anything I could associate with the ringing of a bell. The stillness has a drone, a crepitation of its own: you can't have perfect silence here any more than real solitude. For one thing, the insects of the earth never stop their buzzing—the more I strained my ears to catch a far-away sound, the louder I heard them. Bells maybe were ringing somewhere in their own world, beyond the wall of the horizon. All I could hear was the silence humming—and at the appointed hour, that clear, ominous peal I couldn't explain.

"Now all considered, maybe I took the trip to the mainland only because I was running short of liquor. Which would prove once more that our sense of realities isn't what it should be.

"So night after night I have listened to the *toaca* and feared the day to come. But nothing has happened to me so far and I am beginning to believe that the toll has no connection with my own life and death. All the same my heart sinks whenever I hear it. Like the birds and the beasts, I open my eyes wide, prick up my ears and listen. . . . But I have a cure for it where they have nothing. And now I am waiting for next year when I shall hear it again. I couldn't stay away."

Cricopol looked at me sadly.

"You wouldn't like another drink, would you? Because I am going to have one. I drink and tell myself that my years of wandering have come to an end right here."

Translated from the Rumanian by S. ALEXANDRIDI

Panait Istrati

JEALOUSY

FOR AN HOUR, in the copse where they had stopped for their midday meal, Stavro refused to tell the story of his childhood which he had touched upon in the hayloft. He didn't really object; he was in a mood for evoking youthful memories, but he wished to be coaxed before he disturbed the long-closed sluices which held back the waters of the past.

The three were lying on the soft moss smoking cigarettes, while the horse nibbled grass, snuffling a good deal and taking little steps around them. Stavro got up and lit a fire with some dry twigs, and when it had burned to embers, he got the coffee things from the cart and boiled the water, throwing the exact amount of coffee and sugar into the copper *ibrik* [kettle]. He knew what good coffee was, and at the right moment poured it, foaming and fragrant, into three cups without saucers, called *félidganes*. He then served it, sat down Turkish fashion and began:

"I remember neither the date nor my exact age, but the event that directly followed my misfortune was the Crimean War. As a tiny child I recall the brutality of my father, who beat my mother continually and for no apparent reason. My mother was often away from the house; he used to beat her before she left and when she returned. I could neither discover whether the former beating was to make her go or stay, nor whether the latter one was given on account of her absence or because she had dared to return.

"In those dimly remembered days my elder brother was in the house. He was just as much of a brute as my father; but I had a deep affection for my sister Kyra, who led a miserable existence with my mother. She was four years older than I.

"Little by little the mist of years clears away. . . . I grew up and began to understand and there were some strange things to be understood. I must have been eight or nine at the time I am thinking of, and my sister twelve or thirteen. She was so lovely that I spent my days looking at her. She spent hers in adorning herself, and so did my mother, for she was as beautiful as her daughter. The two of them would stand for hours before a mirror with a make-up outfit contained in an ebony casket, doing their eyelashes with kinorosse dipped in oil, their eyebrows with charred sticks of sweet-basil wood, and their lips, cheeks and nails with kîrmîz red. When this lengthy operation was over, they kissed each other, murmuring affectionate phrases, and turned their attention to dressing me. When they had done this, we would all join hands and dance a Turkish or a Greek dance intermingled with much kissing. You see we three were a little family to ourselves.

"At that time, my father and brother did not come home every evening. They were the cleverest and busiest wheelwrights in the neighbourhood and they had a house with shop attached at the other end of town in the Karakioï quarter. We lived in the Tchétatzoué district, with the whole town between us and them. The Karakioï house belonged to my father and he had two apprentices, whom he boarded and lodged there, as well as an old woman who did for them all. We never went to my father's house and I can scarcely remember his shop; it always used to frighten me and I kept away from it. My mother's house at Tchétatzoué was quite different; there, we amused ourselves all day long with nothing to bother us. In winter we drank tea; in summer, syrups; and there were always plenty of *cadaifs* * and *sarailiés.* * We smoked hookahs and drank coffee, painted our faces and danced. It was a delightful existence.

"Yes, delightful, except when my father, or my brother, or both of them would burst in upon our revelry to beat my mother and Kyra and break their sticks over my head. I came in for my share, because of my part in the dancing. They called my mother and Kyra *patchaouras,* * * and me *kitchouk pézévengh.* * * * The two wretched women would throw themselves at the feet of their oppressors and clasp their knees, begging them to spare their faces:

" 'Not our faces!' they would scream. 'In the name of Christ and the Holy Virgin, don't strike our faces! Don't touch our eyes! Spare us!' Ah, their faces and their eyes—how could a woman's beauty survive the brutality of those men?

"They both had the loveliest imaginable golden hair reaching below the waist, the whitest skin, and their brows, lashes and pupils were as black as ebony, for though they were Rumanian, the blood of three different races flowed in their veins: Turkish, Russian and Greek.

"My mother's first child was born when she was sixteen, and when I first opened my eyes, no one would have believed her the mother of three. She was made for kisses, but got more beating than anything else. However, if my father did not overwhelm her with caresses, her lovers made it up to her brilliantly, and I have never been able to discover whether it was my mother's unfaithfulness that provoked the beatings or my father's ill treatment of her that caused her to deceive him. In any case there was always something going on; shouts of joy alternated with cries of pain, and it was not long after the last blow had fallen that smiles lit up the tear-stained faces.

"I mounted guard near the window and munched cakes while the lovers, who seemed to have fairly decent manners, sat Turkish fashion on the floor, singing and playing Oriental tunes. There was a guitar, ac-

* Turkish cakes.
** Harlots.
*** Little pimp.

companied by castanets and a tambourine. My mother and Kyra adored
it all and would often do the handkerchief dance which made them dizzy
with its twistings and twirlings. Then with flaming cheeks they would
throw themselves upon the cushions and lie there fanning themselves,
with their legs drawn up under their long silk skirts. Fragrant herbs were
burned and cordials were consumed. The men were young and beautiful
and always dark. They were elegantly turned out, with pointed moustaches, carefully trimmed beards and hair that exhaled a strong scent of
almond oil and musk. There were Turks, Greeks, and sometimes Ruma-
nians. Nationality was of no importance provided they were young, beautiful, refined, discreet, and not too eager.

"My rôle was a thankless one. I have never told anyone until now what
agonies I suffered. My duty was to keep watch, seated on the window-
ledge, and to save the party from sudden interruptions. That pleased me,
for I loathed the two men from Karakioï who beat us, but a terrible
struggle raged in my breast between duty and jealousy.

"There was a high walled court in front of the house, which had windows looking into the court and also out at the back, some distance above
the high ground surrounding the harbour. The house could only be entered through the door from the court, but people seemed less conventional about leaving it. If that strip of sloping ground at the back could
have spoken, what stories of scrambling lovers it would have had to tell!

"I crouched in the window-sill all night, watching the door with the
lamp over it and listening for the grind of rusty hinges. I tried to keep
an eye on the festivities within, too. My mother and Kyra were lovely
enough to drive one mad, with their waists almost small enough to go
through the rings on their fingers, their breasts as round as two melons,
and their marvellous hair falling over their naked shoulders. They wore
scarlet bands about their foreheads, and their long eyelashes fluttered
wickedly as though to feed the flames of desire that darted from their
eyes.

"The efforts of the guests to please their hostesses often led them to
ridiculous extremes. One evening my mother received this doubtful compliment from one of them: 'Good soup is made from old hens.' In a fury,
she threw her fan at him and burst into tears, whereupon another admirer
leapt up in a rage, hurled *tiflas* * in the blunderer's face and spat upon
him. Then they flew at each other, upsetting tables, glasses and hookahs,

---

An offensive Oriental gesture, that of thrusting one's hand at a person's face with
fingers outstretched.

until we were sick with laughing. In order to restore peace, my mother gave her accolade. These kisses were given for many reasons. A beautiful voice, a clever speech, an amusing trick, all these earned their reward from her; and she used them to dispel sulkiness, to soften an ill-considered speech, to pacify the jealousy of a too importunate lover.

"Kyra was, in her way, quite perfect. At the age of fourteen she was so well developed that she passed for sixteen. She was a giddy young thing, but sharp as a steel trap, with her little blunt nose, rather prominent chin and her two dimples symmetrically placed on either cheek. She could not please both her lovers and me with her high spirits and her buffoonery; they wanted more and I thought she gave them too much.

"We called these lovers who came to the house *moussafirs* * and these *moussafirs* kissed her hands and her slippers on the slightest provocation. She pulled their noses and their beards, poured syrup on the burning tobacco in their hookahs, held out her glass and broke it before anyone could drink from it; but a moment afterwards, if any lips had been cut, she would press a strand of her hair against them.

"I was enraged by all this, for I loved Kyra far more than my mother. I adored her and could not endure it if anyone but myself caressed her. One evening I remember something which put the finishing touch to my misery. The lacing of her sandal had come unfastened during a dance and she put her foot on the knees of one of the *moussafirs* and asked him to tie it for her. You can imagine what a chance it was for the fellow. He made as much of it as he could, with me watching him like a hawk all the time, but when he began to stroke her ankle and even her leg, without protest, I lost my head and shouted: 'Here comes father! Be quick!'

"In the twinkling of an eye the two *moussafirs* shot through the window into the outer darkness and rolled over the bank. One of them, a Greek, left his fez and his guitar behind, but my mother threw them after him, while Kyra concealed the two extra hookahs. All this amused me so intensely, when the object of my fury had disappeared, that I almost had hysterics. I fell from the window-sill, rolled on the carpet and became quite purple in the face from lack of breath. My mother thought I had gone mad with fear of my father, and the two poor souls rent the air with their screams of terror, forgetting my father in their despair at my plight.

" 'He's not coming,' I was at last able to say. 'I was angry because Kyra allowed her leg to be stroked. I've had my revenge now.'

"They shouted louder than ever, for joy this time, pounding my behind

* Guests.

and kissing me rapturously. Then we all began to jump about the room;
their troubles were over and I had had only a slight beating and a great
deal of petting."

Translated from the French by JAMES WHITALL

Princess Marthe Bibesco

THEIR SONGS OF SADNESS

WE WERE COMING BACK from Talia in the carriage, Miss Pitts, the doctor
and myself: a Sunday excursion . . .

From an orchard shut in by wooden fencing, a sound of singing rose
up, and fell again, and dies away behind us in the rush of the water on
the stones.

"Nothing but these sad songs hereabouts," remarked the scornful Miss
Pitts. "They sing through their noses in the inns just like in their
churches."

Her reflections are quite accurate, but quite unjust: for Miss Pitts understands nothing at all of the people in the land of willows.

"Sad songs, yes," I granted her. "But there are so many variations that
they never grow monotonous—and besides, one has to understand the
words. It is in the East that the genius of melancholy dwells: the voices
of the marshes, and of the flocks, are breaking voices. And when you hear
nothing else, you drop quite naturally into harmony with solitude. I'm
certain that when King David sang his psalms, he droned them . . ."

Did I convince her? I'm not sure . . . But a little later she asked me if I
did not intend some day to undertake a translation of these folk-songs—
she would *love* to know them.

Poor Miss Pitts! Do you mistake me for a bird-stuffer? Am I really to
stuff and mount the wild dove, the sighing of the evening in the woods?

But none the less, I have put down some versions of the preludes to
their songs. They make my notebooks look as if I were making a collection of wild flowers, every bloom and stem with its name attached. For
these people, you should understand, never pass from ordinary talk or
from silence into song, without warning their listeners by a short ejacula-
tion, a kind of proem which, before they actually say what they are going
to, must always first evoke a flower! A flower, a sprig of leaves, or a plant
of the woods, garden, or sand, or waters. How delicate these overtures

are! The speaker, you see, is still a little afraid his meaning will be obscure: these are his precautions!

What were you thinking of before the singer broke in with his song? Who can tell? Nobody. But perhaps your mood was not quite sympathetically keyed? He will first have to make quite sure of you. And how? Why, with a bunch of flowers, arranged with the quiet skill of an engraver fashioning the initial letter of a book. Before he makes bold to penetrate your memories, he offers you this talisman, a scented plant to sweeten your thoughts as a smouldering perfume sweetens a room . . .

> *A green flower of motherwort,*
> *Oh!*
> *A sprig of mint . . .*
> *A narrow leaf, hyacinths three!*
> *A broad leaf, and poppies three!*

A man will never speak of the woman he loves without quickening a tender emotion in his listener beforehand, by naming first something that has itself tenderness that blossoms and grows green.

I know a great many of these flower preludes: they please me and I collect them. In their brevity of form, they recall those Japanese poems of one verse only, a cry of warning thrown into the darkness where our emotions lie sleeping.

What a force of pent-up love, what a skilled gift of vision, this brevity takes for granted, in one's self and in others! These folk must be quite aware how sensitive and quick to remember are their emotions, that they are satisfied with one hint. This unschooled mode contains the very last of art and its very first secret.

Thus, for example, if a folk-singer wants to convey to his hearers the idea of a beautiful countenance, he starts off with a picked name: *"The peony . . . !"* For he has seen its splendour, and he makes it the emblem for the beauty of men or women, indifferently. He will describe it no farther. What more could he say? Everyone knows what the peony is, its form and colour: a thing of rare completeness!

The lover parted from his beloved will sing names of bitter plants: poppy or wormwood. Before telling that his loved one is dead, he will tell us that she is dark, the blackthorn in flower! If a song of absence speaks of the elder-tree, it means that the man went away in the summer. Or does it name the maize, or the hemp, or the marigold? Then he left the village in autumn.

Flowers are like ghosts, haunting, as each year comes round, the places where we saw them die.

Often before now the phantoms of the narcissus in the Isvor orchards here reappeared to me since I visited them. Sing their name—*"Oh! the narcissus . . ."*—and, if I were at the ends of the earth, I should be back here sitting under those plum-trees!

> *O yellow leaf,*
> *And tree marigolds . . .*
>   *O!*
> *I am no more*
> *The one you love . . .*
> *But I shall be ever*
> *The one you loved! . . .*

The refrain came out to me from the inn as I passed, coming back from a walk.

Translated from the French by HAMISH MILES

Valeriu Marcu

LENIN IN ZURICH

A Memoir

RUSSIA, the Russian Revolution, Siberia, the Peter and Paul Fortress, were magic words to us young revolutionists in Zurich in 1912. We saw the Russian exiles who came to that city in the light of Russian literature. The fact that this most recent generation of refugees from the Tsar was completely different from the heroes of the famous novels did not affect us. What reality can be stronger than a preconceived ideal?

Our Russians were absolutely unsentimental. They used sentiment now and then, as politicians often do. All of them had flight, deportation and a court trial behind them. But it never occurred to them to speak about their past. They would have regarded such talk as childish or as an offense against good taste. They were attractive not only because of their readiness to discuss everything, their willingness to teach without pedantry or didacticism, but, above all, because of their ardent interest in every problem. They were all eternal—and eternally young—students whose thirst for knowledge would never be quenched. In contrast, a French or German Socialist lost his curiosity about mankind as soon as his prudent leaders presented him with a job in the political or administrative machine, or sent him to Parliament.

The Russians we knew in Zurich also displayed the dross in human nature, and sometimes it was as apparent to the beholder as the stains on their clothes. The energy they wasted intriguing against each other would have sufficed to rule a gigantic empire. Yet this must be granted: they were not self-satisfied. Every one of them was in a state of permanent revolution against himself, against his closest party comrades, and against God. These exiles felt the war and the postwar problems directly, concretely, in their own flesh. Politics never left them for a moment. It was like a chronic illness. They dreamed of it, and if they talked in their sleep, surely it was only of things political. Their hope was to track down the germs of war. They worked like bacteriologists to disclose its essential causes. These they hoped to find in books about the recent past.

I clearly recall Karl Radek standing in the middle of his room in front of a hill of books. Radek was the man who, according to all the respectable citizens of Europe, was commissioned by Moscow and the Third International to organize the postwar *putsches* in Germany, Austria, Hungary, Spain and Lithuania. For relaxation Radek read detective stories before going to bed; he once told me that he had to escape the pressure of politics for at least one hour in every twenty-four. The day after each important event of the war he had a pamphlet ready, but only rarely did it find a publisher. Martov, the best stylist among the Russian exiles, nicknamed him "Pamphletovich." The Russians, and particularly Radek, liked to be published in German. Just as Hebrew is a sacred language to the Jews because the Lord of Creation spoke it, so German was sacred to the Russians because it was the language of Karl Marx.

Martov for years had been at the opposite revolutionary pole from Lenin. Since the first year of the twentieth century he had been the leading polemicist of the Socialist tendency called Menshevism. This was rooted in the German and French traditions more than in the Russian. He fought the other Socialist faction, the Bolsheviks, because he felt that they and their leader Lenin harbored dictatorial ambitions.

Delicate in build, sickly, somewhat stooping, with a pale face partly covered by a dishevelled beard, with hollow cheeks and kindly, shining eyes, Martov used to sit surrounded by friends in the Café St. Annahof. Every two or three hours he changed tables. At intervals, he would retire to write, returning later to read an extraordinary essay in German, French,

Russian or English, according to his audience. Sometimes he vanished for days. Worried newcomers to his circle who asked where he had gone would be told that he had buried himself in some library to study the latest happenings in France, Germany or Russia. Lenin said of him: "Martov studies himself into error."

Lenin had no difficulty in defeating an adversary who refused to understand the necessity of unrestrained violence. Less than two years after Lenin's accession to power, Martov was compelled to leave Moscow, to emigrate once more. A few days before that cruel end, during which his nerves died one by one in a long agony, Lenin, scarcely able to speak, murmured to his wife—they were perhaps his last words—"I hear that Martov, too, is dying?" Martov had died of tuberculosis a few months before.

In Zurich, during the first months of war, Lenin and Martov had come close to each other, and both were happy about it. But their accord was short-lived and they soon began a furious battle of ink against each other. Martov told me that, in the last analysis, Lenin was only the brigand chief of a party that had no real existence. These harsh words of course only increased my desire to see Lenin. I met him in a restaurant which served home-cooked meals, run by a Frau Prellog on the second floor of a dilapidated, weather-beaten house in a narrow little street near the Limmat Quai. The restaurant was in reality a dimly lit corridor, long and narrow, vith bare walls and a long, unpainted wooden table that took up most of the space. The place smelled more like a moldy cellar than a restaurant. One door served as the entrance; another, always open, led to the kitchen. Around the table sat six to eight guests on wooden chairs; an equal number of chairs were usually empty. Frau Prellog was extremely busy, as she both cooked the meals and served her customers. She had lived in Vienna for a long time and spoke a peculiar Swiss-Austrian dialect. She was a plump blonde in her early forties, far more appetizing than her thin soups, dried-out roasts and cheap desserts.

When I reached the restaurant Lenin had not yet arrived, and I sat down with Kharitonov, a friend who had undertaken to introduce me to him. The company fascinated me. The men were all young, bold-looking, enigmatic figures. The only lady at the table was not enigmatic at all. She was called Red Maria, not because of her political opinions, but because of her red-blond hair. Maria had a regular, oval face like a Madonna, big blue eyes, long eyelashes and a bass voice which contrasted strangely with her delicate appearance. She immediately asked us, in a voice which drowned out all the men, who we were, what we wanted, who had given us Frau Prellog's address and whether we intended to become regular customers. We could see that the whole group were rather suspicious of us. I explained that I wanted to speak with Mr. Ulyanov—Lenin was known here by his true name. At that Maria became voluble. She said, among other things, that the Ulyanovs were excellent people.

When Lenin arrived with his wife, Nadezhda Konstantinovna Krupskaya, he took a seat near Red Maria. She found in him a willing listener, indeed he listened to her so attentively that it did not occur to me to interrupt. Moreover, her tale of woe interested me. Her troubles were of a worldly, material kind. She said that she had had two lovers; now one was a soldier in Italy, the other in Germany. This war, she continued, was nothing but a robbery of men, a dirty trick invented by the rich. Then she went on to tell the favorite story of ladies of her kind: that she had to support her old mother and younger sisters and brothers. Nadezhda Konstantinovna, too, listened with interest.

Gradually, the other guests left the restaurant. Only Lenin, his wife, Kharitonov, Maria, Frau Prellog and I remained at the long table. Shortly before our arrival Frau Prellog had quarreled with Maria. Lenin tried to effect a reconcilation between them, and succeeded. Frau Prellog was not too stubborn; like Maria, she loved any opportunity of telling her troubles. She complained that some of her guests had failed to pay their bills, that meat was expensive, that soon it would be rationed. This, she said, was a measure directed only against the poor. Wealthy people, of course, would always manage to get their steaks. Oh, this accursed war! She could not understand why the soldiers did not shoot their officers and return home without further ado. Lenin's face shone with pleasure at these words. He looked at us with a satisfied air.

When we left the restaurant it was late in the afternoon. I walked home with Lenin.

"You see," he said, "why I take my meals here. You get to know what people are really thinking about. Nadezhda Konstantinovna is sure that only the Zurich underworld frequents this place, but I think she is mistaken. To be sure, Maria is a prostitute. But she does not like her trade. She has a large family to support—and that is no easy matter. As to Frau Prellog, she is perfectly right. Did you hear what she said? Shoot the officers! A magnificent woman. Such opinions are very important."

In front of their house in the Spiegelgasse I took leave of Lenin and his wife.

"I should like to talk with you about things in greater detail," I said. "We can't do it at Frau Prellog's."

"Yes, with pleasure," he said. "I read an article you wrote about disarmament. That reminds me: Radek told me you were friendly with Martov. Do you sympathize with the Mensheviks?"

"I am neither Menshevik nor Bolshevik," I replied. "We in the Werdstrasse are the most radical group of all and we have our own theory."

"I see, I see," Lenin nodded. "That is very interesting." Then, after a short silence: "Come to see me tomorrow at 4 o'clock; I'll keep that time open for you."

My friend Kharitonov had not walked to the Spiegelgasse with us. The next day when I went to see Lenin there, I asked him to go with me. As soon as we entered the room, I began to speak. After about half an hour I noticed something like an expression of boredom on Lenin's face and stopped.

"What you have just said," he declared, "is false; completely, utterly false. We cannot be against every war. We must instead learn to distinguish the character of each particular war. We admire, for instance, the French revolutionary wars against old Europe, we admire Cromwell's campaigns, we admire Washington's war against London.

"We are against this particular war, which began in August 1914, because its aim is the further enslavement of the five continents, the promotion of the export of capital. This war is the continuation of the policies pursued between 1898 and 1914. Every war is an instrument of politics. This war is an instrument in the hands of the Russian Tsar, the German Kaiser, the Berlin, Paris and London bankers. I am against these people, and for that reason I hope that my country suffers a cruel and crushing defeat. It is my duty to hope so. Do you know the real meaning of this war?"

"What is it?" I asked.

"It is obvious," he replied. "One slaveholder, Germany, who owns one hundred slaves, is fighting another slaveholder, England, who owns two hundred slaves, for a 'fairer' distribution of the slaves."

"How can you expect to foster hatred of this war," I asked at this point, "if you are not, in principle, against all wars? I thought that as a Bolshevik you were really a radical thinker and refused to make any compromise with the idea of war. But by recognizing the validity of some wars, you open the doors for every opportunity. Every group can find some justification for the particular war of which it approves. I see that we young people can count only on ourselves. We refuse to accept a new justification of war even in the name of science."

Lenin listened attentively, his head bent toward me. He moved his chair closer to mine, while Krupskaya, who until this moment had been sitting on her bed like an impassive ghost, broke into a broad smile. She seemed suddenly interested and pleased. This irritated me, because I took it as a sign that she was against me. There was a short silence in the room. Lenin must have wondered whether he should continue to talk with this boy or not. I, somewhat awkwardly, remained silent.

"Your determination to rely upon yourselves," Lenin finally replied, "is very important. Every man must rely on himself. Yet he should also listen to what informed people have to say. I don't know how radical you are or how radical I am. I am certainly not radical enough. One can never be radical enough; that is, one must always try to be as radical as reality itself, and then let the devil and the fools worry about whether one is radical enough. War, however, does not ask me, nor the other Bolsheviks, nor you, whether we accept it."

He looked at me intently, as though trying to read my thoughts, and then went on in a hard voice: "At any rate, one thing is astonishing to me: you and your friends want to transform this entire world which reeks from every pore with baseness, slavery and war, and yet you renounce the use of violence in advance."

"Not at all," I explained, deeply offended. "We do not renounce violence, because that would mean that we renounce the revolution."

"Well, well," said Lenin, "what then is war? What is it but a form of violence? The twentieth century and modern imperialism have mobilized the masses. Every rebellion, every revolution is only a form of war. You can't separate war from revolution or revolution from war. The line of demarcation between them is indefinite and shifting. You cannot say where war ends and revolution begins. Those who expect the revolution to grow out of a peaceful situation, from so-called orderly conditions, do not desire it at all. Revolutions arise in the most complicated situations; most often they result from so-called transitional situations, which contain the sharpest contradictions, I took part in one revolution in Russia, in 1905. It consisted of a number of struggles in which all the discontented classes, groups and elements of the population took part. Among them were large groups who harbored the wildest prejudices and pursued the vaguest and most fantastic aims. There were little groups in the pay of Japan. There were profiteers and adventurers."

I listened with growing curiosity and interest. An hour, perhaps two, went by. Calmly but persistently he tried to convince me. Now and then he raised his finger and pointed at me. He spoke slowly and searchingly, in German with a Russian accent. Sometimes he could not find the word he wanted, and I would suggest one to him. He would nod his head almost imperceptibly and thank me. I became so interested in his ideas that I wanted to ask him not to stop. And my mistrust vanished. This man, who spoke so seriously about the revolution, I thought, was certainly no counter-revolutionary. I felt ready to reconcile myself with him. From an innate inclination to friendship, and also from my fear of being seduced by arguments that I was unable to answer at that moment, I said suddenly, without apparent reason: "Comrade Lenin, will you give me your word of honor never to betray the revolution, like the other leaders of Socialism who are pro-war?"

He had to collect himself before he could understand my question. Kharitonov, who until now had not said a word, burst out laughing, and so did Krupskaya. Their laughter seemed to me an expression of bad taste, and on the part of Kharitonov a direct betrayal, the beginning of an enmity. Lenin did not laugh. My question surprised but did not seem to displease him.

"Distrust," he said, "is a good quality in a revolutionary. I shall always try to do my best. But you must promise me to do the same."

"What must I do?" I asked eagerly.

"Learn," said he. "Stop talking so wildly and vaguely. I say that not only to you but to your friends. You always talk of revolution in general. This is just as false as to talk about war in general. Nothing can be more dangerous for young people than to know the names of things, but not their real meaning. Only a traitor or a stupid person can speak today of revolution without war, or of total disarmament."

"We shall correct our thesis on disarmament," I said, quite shaken.

"There won't be much left of it once it is corrected," he said, "or else our conversation has been in vain."

He rummaged in a drawer for a piece of paper and said: "In my article for your magazine I wrote: 'An oppressed class which does not strive to learn the use of weapons, to practice the use of weapons, to own weapons, deserves only to be mistreated. If the war today creates only fear in the petty bourgeoisie, only reluctance to make use of weapons, only terror before blood and death, we on the contrary say in answer to this feeling: capitalist society has always been terror without end. If an end by terror is not being prepared for this society, we have no reason to despair. The demand for disarmament in the present-day world is nothing but an expression of despair.'"

He was silent for a while and then concluded, with emotion: "Study and re-study war and revolution. Great things are going to happen soon, they are bound to happen. Yes, everything may be changed from top to bottom, overnight."

To be treated as an equal, despite all the sharp criticism, was a new experience for me. The other Russians, with all their patience and friendliness, had always been distant. They contented themselves with expounding their own ideas. They never said: go home, open your mind, try to understand things for yourself, learn. With Lenin I had the impression that I was an important ally, and that I had to study hard to pass the real test of revolution. I did not know then that Lenin spoke seriously to everyone who was interested in serious questions.

"Do you think," I asked him excitedly, dropping my theoretical preoccupations, "that the revolution will break soon?"

"Perhaps in two, perhaps in five, at the latest in ten years."

Lenin's plan was unparalleled in comprehensiveness and boldness, covering all the continents and seas and containing all the elements of the future "total" strategy. He set himself up in opposition to all the warring powers as the representative of another power, and declared relentless war of annihilation against them. He did this not abstractly, not in principle only. He had a definite, concrete strategic scheme according to which he organized the struggle against the warmakers in Berlin, Paris, London and St. Petersburg.

He started from the premise that every war does away with the outworn conventions, shatters the protective shell of a given society, sweeps away everything that has outlived its value, and brings into play the profound drives and forces of that society. He regarded it as his chief task to get into contact with these emerging drives and forces, to organize them in the service of his movement and to direct his action according to their development.

The official strategists of the warring powers used a strategy that may be called horizontal; Lenin had his own "vertical" strategy. Horizontal strategy is in general based on things as they exist, on known facts. A given number of regiments, brigades or divisions move on such and such roads, in such and such directions. They fight such and such engagements, all integrated and directed by the general staff so as to accomplish the broad purpose of the war. Lenin's vertical strategy was based on the powerful forces latent in man. At first these are potential forces; they become actual only as the result of a long political process. Once developed, these forces must be directed by the engineers of revolution, by a small, lucid revolutionary minority. Vertical strategy must cautiously mobilize these changing, still indeterminate, still indefinable forces, and concentrate them for the achievement of its political purposes.

In wartime, political opposition is conceivable only in connection with revolutionary activities. Lenin did not plan invasions from the outside, but from the inside. Every revolutionist must work for the defeat of his own country. To bring about this defeat, the discontented classes in each country must seize the barracks, government offices and other centers of the belligerent imperialists. The main factor was the violence, the force of the attack. The chief task of vertical strategy was to coördinate all the moral, physical, geographical and tactical elements of the universal insurrection, to join together all the hatreds aroused by imperialism on the five continents.

Lenin noted these potential elements of struggle with painstaking exactitude. Every day he commented at length on those little news items published from time to time in obscure sheets, which, to his mind, indicated latent popular unrest. Every day he wrote articles which formed a sort of political diary. He wrote as though thousands awaited his comment, as though a typesetter were standing outside the door. In reality there was only a leaden, echoless silence.

Lenin was always absorbed in the map of the world. He had an extraordinary feeling for the composition of social bodies, for their political specific gravity, so to speak. To him, the little states were an important element in the anti-imperialist fermentation, a means to be utilized in the total strategy. "The little nations," he wrote, "though powerless as independent factors in the struggle against imperialism, can play an important part in it." For that reason, according to the ever-changing requirements of an all-comprehensive strategy, he was for the right of nations to self-determination. Though an internationalist to the marrow of his bones, he could be nationalistic as a means to the end. He was not only for Irish equality in a common parliament with the English, for Czech and Ukrainian representation in the Austrian and Russian parliaments, but for the right of complete separation.

He advocated colonial uprisings as a revolutionary instrument and a strategic requirement, in order to set in motion simultaneously all the anti-imperialist forces. "In the colonies and semi-colonies there live nearly a billion persons, more than half of the population of the planet. Movements of national liberation in these countries are either very strong already, or are continuing to grow and mature." To coördinate all these elements and link them up with the revolutionary upsurges in the cities was for him the prerequisite of the revolution. The uprising of the industrial workers, the peasants and the lower middle class must be merged with the aspirations of the oppressed nations and colonies. Sooner or later, he thought, an international alliance between the oppressed nations and the revolutionary proletariat would take place.

Sooner or later? Yes, for should Lenin not triumph during this war, should his Third Front, which was just coming into being, not be victorious, then one of the two warring coalitions would win the war—Germany's or England's. An imperialist peace of plunder would be concluded, and twenty years later, he wrote on October 1, 1916, a war would break out between Japan and the United States. That war "will mean for Europe a retrogression for several decades. History often makes gigantic leaps backward."

Lenin did not communicate to me his grandiose, complex and many-sided conception of war in one short conversation. I visited him frequently under pretext of asking his advice on lesser matters, but really to create opportunities for drawing him into conversation. I often went with him to meetings of Swiss workers which he sat through silently, listening with interest.

He was completely absorbed in the war. He tried to show its economic necessities, its internal laws, in his book "Imperialism, the Final Stage of Capitalism." Every day he went to the library and brought home statistics and reports of the international cartels. He often spoke of his book. He worried about having to compress a gigantic mass of material into 120 pages. (According to his contract with the publishers his book could not exceed that length.) He was a strange sort of scholar, as nervous as a young student before an examination. He also suffered from not being allowed to use strong language in his book, for his publisher was a neutral, and the contract forbade personal attacks on the "opportunists," as Lenin called them. One day I asked him why he worked so hastily and nervously and spent so much time in the library. He replied: "A work that is not completely checked to the last word, cannot be regarded as even begun."

When Lenin discussed politics, one had the feeling that he spoke not as an individual, but as the leader of a great unknown power, whose very spirit was as strong as territories, armies and bureaucracies. This feeling was correct; he was the unknown Caesar of all the tendencies at work against the world of that time. He was the brain of the inner changes in the social body, the forces and elements set free by the war, the process of remolding and recasting the political structure of the

world. In him these unconscious changes found their conscious expression. "Only from the changes that take place in the soil of the spirit,"
says Hegel, "can the new arise."

These reflections on Lenin are not retrospective. They were not
brought forth by the fact that he finally succeeded in becoming the head
of a Great Power, and that his Russian venture, for better or worse, will
challenge the world for centuries to come. The thing that surprised us
least about Lenin was that he achieved power. The ten to twelve people
who saw him regularly several times a week were convinced of his destiny, firmly convinced that, should there be a revolution in Russia, he
would become the successor of the Tsars.

He himself suffered from depression and felt fettered; all he had was
the prospect of wider horizons. Sometimes, particularly in the last months
of his exile, it seemed to him that his circle was growing smaller and
smaller, the life around him less and less intense. So many tested friends
of his youth, so many old comrades deserted him. The whole Bolshevik
Party at that time consisted of a few friends who corresponded with him
from Stockholm, London, New York and Paris. In addition, he had financial worries and was overworked. In 1914, his wife had inherited 2,000
rubles. They lived on this sum for two years. Lenin made efforts to obtain
work on an encyclopaedia that was being published in Russia. He finally
obtained it toward the end of his exile, but his fee was insignificant.
He was at the end of his resources.

But for all his troubles, he roared like a wounded lion when the Tsar's
emissaries in Switzerland tried to do what he himself was to do at
Brest-Litovsk two years later: negotiate a separate peace. "Russia," he
wrote, "intends, with the help of Japan and that very same Germany
with which she is now at war, to defeat England in Asia, so that she may
annex all of Persia, complete the partition of China and so forth. . . .
In 1904–1905 Japan, with the help of the British, defeated Russia; now
she is cautiously preparing to defeat England with the help of the Russians. . . . There is a Germanophile party in Russian government circles,
among Tsar Nicholas' courtiers, among the nobility and the army."

Lenin knew that if the Russian diplomats succeeded in pulling their
wounded and bleeding country out of the war his chances would vanish
for many years. He now directed all his fury against the Socialists of
the different countries. Every Socialist who spoke of peace was a traitor,
a scoundrel, a charlatan. Just as they had up until now handled all the
war business of their rulers, he said, so they would take care of their
peace business also and save them from bloody catastrophe. "In brief,"

he told me one day, "the rôles are brilliantly distributed. The government and the military clique wage war. The liberals talk about freedom and democracy. The Socialists talk about peace."

Lenin's hidden, yet ever-growing impatience during this period found an outlet in his persistent and stimulating explanations to us. Krupskaya in her memoirs complains of her husband's depression in those trying days and says: "Young people from Germany, Italy and other countries were then in Zurich and Ilich wanted to share his revolutionary experience with them as much as possible."

It is often said that the past is distorted in our minds and turned into a paradise, that everything in it is seen in a softer light. But those impressions of our encounters with people and events which remain alive, which are in profound harmony with our own innate natures and which shape our perceptions and intellects, are not more and not less an idealization of reality than is our appreciation of our daily bread. At a later period, Leninism, raised to the rank of a state religion, thoroughly disgusted and horrified me. The revolution worn as a lackey's livery with Lenin's picture on the buttons seemed to me an absolute negation of life itself. But I have never forgotten Lenin's approach to things and his manner of seeing them, although he later turned his face in a direction completely different from mine.

Translated from the German by NORBERT GUTERMAN

BULGARIA

INTRODUCTION

By Victor Sharenkoff

BULGARIAN LITERATURE up to twenty-five years ago either followed the Vazov tradition or continued along the lines of the individualistic art-for-art's-sake school of Pencho Slaveikov, Peyo Yavorov and Petko Todorov. It took a few years for Bulgarian culture to find a straight way out of the chaotic situation created by World War I. Bulgarian prose writers and poets began then to seek new creative sources and forms; for this they turned both to life at home and to new currents abroad.

The most important trend in post-war Bulgarian literature was Symbolism, which came to Bulgaria rather belatedly. Borrowed either directly from French poetry or by way of the Russian literature of pre-war Russia, Symbolism bore some fruit in Bulgaria. To the circle of the symbolists belong the well-known poets Nikolai Liliev, Teodor Trayanov, Emanuil Dimitrov and Lyudmil Stoyanov. Although Liliev's sphere of emotions and ideas is very limited, he nevertheless brought Bulgarian verse to perfection. His poetry is a combination of words and music, and many a poet fell under his influence.

To this generation of poets belongs Geo Milev, who started as an extreme individualist modernist and ended as a poet of the Bulgarian masses. For his fearlessness in siding with the people in the September uprising of 1923, Milev paid with his life—because of his poem "September," he was abducted by armed officers and never returned home.

Khristo Smirnenski, too, sang of the oppressed and underprivileged class. His themes are drawn from the lives of the working men and their struggle for more bread and for their rights. The Russian Revolution became the theme of several of his poems. Smirnenski introduced new blood into the Bulgarian literature, but he did not use any new forms. He died (1923) rather young, but gave enough to the Bulgarian workers to justify his being called the first Bulgarian proletarian poet.

While the school of symbolists remains today only a memory, their place was filled by new poets who have been making use of the forms created by the symbolists and older poets, although they have followed their own paths. The most talented is Elizabeth Bagryana, author of several volumes of poems. Bagryana is the first woman poet of Bulgaria to break the fetters of the society conventionalities. She sings freely of her own self, without any fear

318

of tradition or prejudice. Bulgarian folk-song is for her a gold mine, which she has utilized masterfully. Her best known book is the collection *The Eternal and the Holy*. In the footsteps of Smirnenski follow several young poets of social themes. The most gifted are Khristo Radevski, Maria Grubeshlieva, Angel Todorov and Kamen Zidarov, poets who have openly declared themselves for democracy, against fascism. They are using conventional forms as well as creating new ones. The folk-song, too, is used very skilfully by Kamen Zidarov. The group is led by the fearless anti-fascist, ex-individualist, Lyudmil Stoyanov, who is author of a number of poems, short stories, novels, plays and essays. The pro-Hitler government of Bulgaria has incessantly persecuted this cultural worker—he has been arrested, imprisoned and interned, and no one now knows his whereabouts. Indeed, the anti-fascist movement in Bulgaria is very well represented in the novel and the short story. The most prominent, besides Lyudmil Stoyanov, are Gyoncho Belev, Krustyu Belev, Orlin Vasilev and Georgi Karaslavov. Some of their work is worth translating into Western European languages.

Bulgaria has been abundant in the recent years in novelists and short-story writers, although, through lack of space, many names must be omitted here. Among the pre-World-War authors that continued to do creative work after the war was Anton Strashimirov, who wrote novels and short stories—first based upon the Bulgarian village and later upon modern city life—plays and essays. His death in 1937 put an end to an extraordinary character and a prolific writer. Elin-Pelin also began to write before the first World War. By the end of the war he was already established as one of the most gifted short-story writers. His work has continued up to the present day, and he enjoys the reputation of being the most popular Bulgarian author and of being translated into many Western European languages. Elin-Pelin draws his themes from the Bulgarian village, which he knows thoroughly. He depicts peasant life with its beauties as well as with its poverty and misery.

The majority of the Bulgarian population live in villages. Most of the prominent men of public life were born in villages, and many of the writers are peasants, too; this explains why the greater part of Bulgarian writers draw material from there. Georgi Stamatov and Dobri Nemirov (the latter with several novels to his credit) were the first to look for themes outside the village.

With some similarity to Elin-Pelin is Yordan Yovkov, whose characters are in most cases drawn from the Dobrudja village. Yovkov is to a great extent a master of the Bulgarian language, in short stories, novels and plays. Both Elin-Pelin and Yovkov are realists. Their works give a true picture of the Bulgarian rural life. They put their finger on the social sores, but do not go further; no remedies are shown for the evils so thoroughly depicted.

Another master of the peasant short story is Angel Karaliichev, whose work reveals a talent of ideas and emotions. Folk-legends and history are also a favorite theme of Karaliichev's.

Of the younger authors there should be mentioned Konstantin Petkanov and Vladimir Polyanov, whose theme is the modern Bulgarian city. To this group too belongs Fanny Popova-Mutafova, author of historical novels and short stories, and Svetoslav Minkov, typical of the extravagant modernists.

In Bulgaria there was much censorship and persecution before the present war, and there are indications that this has been increased. Free thinking and free writing are forbidden. With Bulgarian culture controlled by the Nazis and their Bulgarian puppets, literary development has stopped. Only the political liberation of the Bulgarian people will bring freedom to Bulgarian literature.

Angel Karaliichev

THE STONE BRIDGE OF THE ROSSITSA

"How am I to know, Mother, if I have sinned?"

"Tell me, my son."

"What shall I tell you?"

"You have lain sick for three years. Three summers have passed like a long caravan. They passed in front of your little window and looked through it. Those black cherries have ripened three times. You did not raise your hand to pick them. High ricks of the sheaves have been three times built on the threshing-floor. Was not God's word dear to you? Were you not anxious to be out in the sunshine, to look at the trees and wheat fields and the magnificent bridge—to see how the young girls had bloomed? Three summers—and still you have not got up!"

"I don't know, Mother; somehow I don't miss the world any more."

"Why do you say things like that?"

The candle shed its beneficent radiance upon the face of the sick man. Saint Mary in the icon clasped tight the little Jesus as if she had never seen him before. Sitting on a little bench, the old woman laid her hand gently on the hand of her son. She did not know just how to ask things. A big tear ran quickly down her face. Outside in the white night, it was freezing. Somewhere in the little street above the black hedges, the twisted trees began to whisper as though praying. They besought the heavens softly. The white chimneys pierced the thick branches as if to find out whether the whole world were asleep.

The grey kitten looked up at them and wondered.

"Do you remember, Mother?"

"What?"

"The summer they began to build the bridge over the Rossitsa. Milka had sewed for me a white shirt with red embroidery."

"Yes, I remember it indeed, as if it were to-day. In that summer you finished your twenty-second year—a young man of marriageable age."

"They all laughed at me, saying I could not join the Cherkovo plain to the village, that I could not oppose the river, overcome it, and put a stone girdle on it, subduing it like a young bride. I knew I could. My father and I had wandered seven years in the neighbouring countries building houses for people. I had learned how to build and was very skilful, which pleased my father. Once we went to the river to cut the old poplar-tree—you remember it—we sat by the bank. The swift, violent Rossitsa flowed past, singing. The willows bowed their dark heads, trailing in the water to cool themselves. Father said to me, 'Listen, Manol, I could not do it; you must. Here is the place. It should rest on two banks and connect two worlds. Over there grows the people's bread. Give them a bridge to cross, so they can harvest it.'

"A little bird was singing in the old poplar. I listened to it, listened also to Father, and said, 'Am I the man who could give it to them?'

" 'You are indeed. Remember; this is the best spot. Let it be a large stone bridge with four arches. Summon stone-cutters from Thrace to cut stones. Gather the peasants together and fear nothing. So long as the world lasts they will remember you. There could be no greater deed than this.'

"The little bird that sang had silver wings. Heavenly dews dropped from them. I stood and thought. Even if he had not told me so, I would have built it. There it was, spanning the river—a gigantic bridge—I pictured it, Mother, just as later I built it. It was like a hoop imprisoning within it a cunning yellow viper—the river that twisted and extended its swelling body—darting, untamed and free, to the blue hills. Then I could hear big wagons rumble across, while the hay riggings rattled and the buffaloes from Deli-Orman waved their curved horns.

" 'When you begin to build it,' I heard my father's voice say, 'wall up your dearest one in it.'

" 'Who is my dearest one?'

" 'You know.' "

The sick one was now silent. Christ's Mother nodded her head and her lips formed the words, "Never will I give up my son!"

The moon shone yellow through the little window. The shadows of the cherry-trees along the little white street ran after each other, laughing. The night was a silver blanket. Saint Elias roamed through the dark plain, asking the fields if they were thirsty, that he might water them the next day, and they answered him.

"My father passed into the other world and left me alone to build the bridge. I knew how to do that but did not know if I must sacrifice a human being. Who could tell me? Spring sent the storks to announce its coming. The shaggy stone-cutters arrived. They hammered and hewed and I went on with the work. I was afraid; yet I was glad. It was not easy, Mother, to do away with a human being. How dared I? Whom should I bury? The day approached. We surveyed the two banks. I walked dizzily, thinking I might go mad. . . . One evening I went to his grave, threw myself on it, and tore at the ground.

" 'Tell me whom. You know.' "

The grave was silent. Could a grave speak?

I went home and at dawn, fell asleep and dreamed. My father was coming toward me just as when alive, with his red belt, his coarse woolen cloak on his shoulder, and a white eagle in his hands. He stopped at the high bank of the Rossitsa and said to me:

" 'Watch carefully where the eagle perches when I let him go. It will show whom you must bury. Have courage, my son.' The white eagle clapped its wings and flew toward the sky. It made three big circles above the village and dropped. It sank like a falling stone. I did not see where it perched. My father looked at me, shook his head, and started to the river. Instantly my bridge was spread out before him and he passed over it. He stopped on the bank, looked over the bridge from one end to the other, waved his hand, and said, 'Forward!'

"I jumped startled. You were standing at my bedside, Mother, saying, 'Get up, Manol, it is dawn already. The wagons have been moving for a long time. Wake up! The stone-cutters have already begun to hammer!'

"As I went out I did not go toward the bridge, but took the road to Grandfather Noa's yards. I hoped to see Milka to tell her all and be comforted. When I reached their house, a terrible shock awaited my eyes. Perched on their walnut-tree was a white eagle! The same my father had released!

"Everything became dark to me. My ears were deafened. I rushed to my father's grave, to dig up his bones, to ask him how he could deprive me of her—my own father! Had he no pity for me? Madness—the dead cannot be questioned.

"Down at the bridge the masons were singing. The Rossitsa carried away their words. It murmured. Nothing worried them. They went on with their singing and building. They laid the stones with their large, cracked, trowel-like hands. They would wall up their own beautiful mason's song. Blessed were they! Whom should I bury?

"I sat on the grave and looked toward Milka's walnut-trees. A little white cloud moved in the sky. A white angel's soul bathed in the flame of the morning. I would be unable in the evening, when I met Milka, to utter a single word.

"I bent over the grave's head. Tears were in my eyes. . . .

"Down the Cherkovo road I saw a big yellow cloud. I heard bells and loud cries. Numberless wagons loaded with sheaves began to string themselves out. The bird which had sung on the poplar-tree was now perched on the first wagon, pecking at the grain. When they reached the river they did not unyoke, but waited. Whom were they waiting for? I got up, rubbing my eyes, and put my hand to my forehead. There was no one. Down below the mason's were crying, 'Hey-ha.'

"I made my decision. Let it be!

"In the evening my own Milka came to the well to draw water. When she leaned over I saw her yellow brass ear-rings and measured her long black shadow. Only the moon saw that."

In the branches the little bird began to flutter and warble. The kitten pricked up its ears and in one bound was at the window. The sick man fell into a trance. It was the same little bird, the same sweet bell-like voice which had vibrated from the old poplar-tree before it had been cut down. It had come several nights to sing, and now it came again. It huddled among the kindly leaves of the cherry-tree. The kitten motioned with its little paws, on the window. His mother standing by the bedside listening could not believe her son's words. How could his heart endure her death?

"Cursed be the bridge. Would that the storm might carry it away."

"Why do you curse it, Mother? It was my decision. I built the bridge. I gave her."

"You have committed a great sin, my son!"

The eyes of the master builder became bright.

"Do you remember when we completed it? What a wild and joyous festival it was that Sunday? People from nine villages assembled to celebrate the opening of the bridge over the Rossitsa. A crowd of young men came with them. Two shepherds of the mountains, who spent the summer with us, played bagpipes. Do you remember them? The dark one used to come to our place and proposed to sister Kuna, but you did not give your consent because you thought it wrong to give her to strangers. The old people went around the bridge, knocked with their sticks, touched the cold stone, and said, 'God has given great skill to Manol.' How he gave it to me I alone knew. All rejoiced. They drank healths from bright coloured wine-flasks. I was silent and could not drink, as I watched the gay crowd. And when the bagpipes began to shriek—everyone, old and young, jumped to his feet. They seized each other's hands and began a wild dance. Someone shouted, "Yea, you have forgotten him. Where is the master builder—to dance a little?' He said no more but the bagpipes ceased. The people were confused and suddenly quiet. They made way; I turned, Mother, and—Oh! God!—I saw a dead body! You know whom they carried.

"I went to the cemetery to throw a handful of soil upon the grave. May God give peace to her soul!

"When I came back I still found dancing and merriment. I took a wine-flask, drank and drank till I was drunk. We danced till midnight. Down on the little plain, cauldrons boiled. Nine sheep were killed. Down below, the Cherkovo plain seemed wider. It rejoiced. The swallows played above the corn fields. The soil longed for the men who would come and shout and drive in old Adam's ploughs.

"Bonfires were built to light us. The eyes of the girls gleamed like black fires. My heart was breaking with grief and madness; I thought I would give her up and forget her. I was drunk. God forgive me!

"After midnight when the first cocks crew, all retired dizzily to their homes. I did not go to rest, but sat on a stone meditating. What I thought I don't remember now. As I sat there I heard somebody call me.

" 'Mano-o-ol.'

"I stood up and walked straight toward the voice. The moon was flooding the fields with liquid yellow. How long I walked I don't remember; I was lost in thought. At last I saw, up on the little hill in the middle of the wheat field, a naked woman, her loosened black hair reaching down to the ground.

"She had walked from the left; it was evident from the broken wheat. Who knows where she had come from? The wide field was drunk with the song of the crickets and the gleam of the stars. Who knows, perhaps I was still dizzy. I did not take my eyes from her who was waiting for me.

" 'Man-o-o-ol.'

"Somewhere dogs began to howl. They stretched their heads to the moon and howled, as it seemed to me sadly, not knowing why. I stood and watched her. I quivered. The wheat fields also quivered and began to shrivel. Who was the woman? Where had I seen her? What dark eyes! Oh! Mother, I had never gazed on them, and yet they were familiar to me. They embraced me and she started toward me, white and beautiful. I had never seen a naked woman. Her dark hair rustled, her eyes burned me. Suddenly the wheat fields became dark and she stretched her bare arms toward me.

" 'For a long time I have awaited you.'

"As soon as she uttered these words I knew her. It was Milka. I cried out. No, I did not cry. I was frightened. I ran through the fields, and she, after me.

" 'Why do you run, Manol? We were betrothed to-day. Did you not see how many people from all the villages came to congratulate us?'

"I felt her soft hair suffocating me. . . ."

The little candle before the icon glimmered and went out. The moon was hidden behind the cherry-tree. The old woman laid her hand upon the forehead of the sick man and wept. The kitten chased shadows in the white little street. Farther off in the wheat fields, Saint Elias walked and picked herbs in the moonlight. He asked if he should beg the Lord for water. The wheat stalks answered him.

"Please, Mother, on Saturday when you go to the cemetery, stop at her grave—late, when everyone will have gone. Tell her that the Rossitsa has flown by for three years washing the big stones of my bridge. Has it washed away my sin yet? Ask her, Mother—she will tell you if my sins are forgiven."

Translated by VICTOR SHARENKOFF

Elin-Pelin

GUEST

THE COMPANY OF VOLUNTEERS, in which Uncle Stoyan was serving, followed in the train of the advancing army, doing duty at times as a garrison in the cities, sometimes as patrol at the posts, sometimes as guard of supply trains and railroad tracks, and sometimes as escort for the conveyance of prisoners of war.

From town to town, from village to village, enveloped in his mottled cloak, armed with a rifle, Uncle Stoyan had traversed all of the newly occupied territory and had settled down for a longer period somewhere at the other end of the world as a guard of the bridges on an important highway.

The place was remote and deserted; even during the breathless quietude of an evening, when the river itself was asleep, not even the vigilant barking of a dog or the poor voice of a rooster reached it from the distant hamlets.

Uncle Stoyan remained with the others to guard the bridges. They constructed a warm underground hut, with a chimney and a hearth, hung their clothes and knapsacks inside, made themselves beds of straw, and set about the fulfilment of duty.

Their austere, speechless figures, heavy like rocks, stood guard day and night at the observation point with such faithfulness that not even a bird could pass unnoticed.

On both sides of the muddy road crawled endless caravans of supplies. The oxen gravely and submissively dragged heavily-laden carts, their effortful movements speaking of the common, the great elemental force of the war by which every creature was impelled. During their long co-labour with the people, the animals had felt the hardships of the journey and had instinctively perceived the importance of the goal; so that they hauled the wagon uncomplainingly. They did not wait for the entreating voice of the drivers or the threatening swing of the goad. In the heavy gait of these noble aids and comrades of the peasants, of these beautiful, silent, poetic symbols of duty and labour, there was earnestness and voluntary exertion. Like their masters, they too were fulfilling soldier's duty as if they knew that what they dragged was not a plough.

Uncle Stoyan, covered with his perennial cloak, with his rifle near his feet, followed so closely with his eyes these endless processions of carts that he did not miss a single detail. The oxen, the drivers, the wheels, the racks, the ingenious contrivances which some inventive driver had improvised during the long journeys, all were subjected to the scrutiny of his small eyes, overhung by drooping brows.

At times Uncle Stoyan would make remarks in a loud voice, as if he were speaking to deaf people:

"Hey, boy, are you asleep! . . . Pick up that halter . . . the ox will step on it and tear it to pieces." Or: "Hey, uncle, you'll lose your tar-jug."

Off duty, when he was enjoyably warming himself with his comrades near the fire in the hut, and the conversation revolved about the day's events, Uncle Stoyan would once more reproach unknown, vaguely remembered drivers whom he had caught in negligence: "His wagon wheel loose and crooked like a drunk! . . . Tighten it up, man, tighten it up! . . . Is that the way to drive on a road like this? . . ."

In the political discussions which frequently took place in the hut, Uncle Stoyan did not participate. He sat bent over the fire, smoked his short pipe, listened, and every now and then, stirred the firebrands.

The weather was rainy and foggy. For days the sun did not open its eye. One could not tell when it was dawn and when night was falling. This made the nights seem long and oppressive. No one had a watch. Uncle Stoyan was not inconvenienced, for he had got along without a watch for a great many years, but one of his comrades, a village grocer, could think of nothing but the time and would ask it of every person he met.

Finally Uncle Stoyan said to him: "I'm going to get you not a watch, but a whole alarm-clock!"

And one day, as soon as he was relieved from duty, he went off, got lost somewhere, and did not return until nightfall.

"Here is your alarm-clock, boys," said Uncle Stoyan, smiling to his ears, as he produced from his cloak a big rooster.

They made a place for the rooster in the hut, where they shut him in every evening. This duty was always attended to by Uncle Stoyan, who would say, "Now, let me wind up the clock."

Punctually every evening, and especially at dawn, the clear voice of the rooster resounded through the vicinity, announcing the hour to the old soldiers.

One evening a supply train was unyoked for the night near the hut. Bonfires were built, bagpipes shrieked, and the deserted place was alive with activity.

Uncle Stoyan went to the drivers to ask them the usual questions, where they had come from, where they were going; to hear some news and to look over the oxen and the carts—especially the carts.

"I see," he muttered to himself, "they are not from our part of the country. Strange make—Zagorean. Good make, strong."

He turned around, examined the carts minutely, pulled the draftbars, and patted the racks approvingly, as if he were patting the back of a friend.

When he was examining a beautifully carved and painted yoke, the ox which lay there ruminating sweetly, stretched out his neck and blew at Uncle Stoyan's face.

"Yea! Beltcho! That's our Beltcho!" Uncle Stoyan called out, full of joy and excitement. "He knows me! . . . Hey, he knows me! . . . What do you think of that! My wife wrote that he was requisitioned and I thought to myself, farewell, we shall never see each other again. But . . . Darling Beltcho . . . Go-o-o-d Beltcho!"

Uncle Stoyan squatted in front of the ox and began to caress him gently and to comb his forehead. The animal put his head out and laid his slobbery mouth on the knee of his old friend.

"He knew me! . . . He remembers me," he said to the drivers who had flocked about him. Uncle Stoyan's comrades came too.

"Here's Beltcho that I was telling you about!" he said to them; "Look! I have a guest. And I thought I'd never see him again. Wonderful animal! Isn't he? And how he pulls, how he can pull!"

Uncle Stoyan began to pet the ox: "Dear Beltcho, he too has gone to war. He can do anything! . . ."

"Hey, boy," he turned to the driver. "Take good care of him, do you hear? Give me that curry-comb."

Uncle Stoyan took the iron comb from the driver and began to brush his guest, who had brought him so much joy.

"Get up. Beltcho, rise! That's it. Lift your tail now. Oh, how dirty you are!" And while he was speaking affectionate words, Uncle Stoyan most attentively and painstakingly cleaned him, combing him and dusting him with the broom. After this he looked about for some bran, mixed it with salted warm water, fetched it to Beltcho, and stepped back to look at him. The tired animal ate—ate with enjoyment, licked himself, and directed pleading eyes toward his friend, who clung to him, as it were, unweanably.

"Ha, I understand, you are cold," said Uncle Stoyan, looking at the sky on which quivered cold, frozen stars.

"Here, warm up. . . . You are my guest," he said, as he took off his cloak, "I don't want you to freeze!" and he covered the animal with his garment. "There now! We don't forget goodness, do we?"

It had long ago begun to grow dark and the old soldiers slept near the fire in the hut; but Uncle Stoyan still hovered near his guest.

He came to the hut late and could not sleep all night. In his soul, awakened now by his affectionate meeting with Beltcho, was stirred up every gentle and beautiful memory of home, of the children, of the soil. . . .

In the morning he did not have to be awakened by the rooster, but rose and again went to Beltcho.

When the caravan of ox-carts once more started on its journey, Uncle

Stoyan marched along by Beltcho for a distance. At parting he stopped him, patted him, and kissed him on the forehead.

"Good-bye, my Beltcho!" he said to him. Then turning to the driver, he said: "Boy, look after him, take care of him." And thrusting his hand deep in his bosom he pulled out his money bag, untied it, and took out a grosh which he handed to the boy. "Here. . . . Treat yourself to something. And take care of the ox. Clean him. Feed him."

Then the caravan passed on; Uncle Stoyan looked after it for a long time, and returned to his comrades full of sadness. It was as if he had just parted from his closest friend.

Translated by STOYAN CHRISTOWE

Svetoslav Minkov

THE MAN WHO CAME FROM AMERICA

A FEW MONTHS AGO the mail man brought me a letter from America. He took out of his leather bag a long envelope and handed it to me. Under my name with the modest "Mr." was my unchanged address and above in the right corner of the envelope, on a 15 cent stamp, the skinny face of Abraham Lincoln was smiling.

You can imagine my surprise. A letter from America! But I had no connections with that country. It is true that I received once from a certain Babylonian astrologer in Pennsylvania a detailed horoscope of my life, on account of which I can tell you today with certainty what will happen to me ten years from now. But then I myself was responsible for the honored attention of the famous fortune-teller. I merely read an advertisement in a paper and because I always liked to have my fortune told by coffee grounds and had a particular liking for clairvoyance I became, owing to this old habit of mine, interested in my fortune and I sent to the indicated address all the information required.

Now, of course, this case was altogether different. I have long ago stopped correspondence with the astrologer and therefore the mysterious letter threw me into real perplexity. Thank God, by nature I am a very inquisitive person, so I did not trouble my mind with unnecessary guesses. After some thought, I took the celluloid paper knife, opened the envelope and got out the thick paper with indented edges. Whom do you think this letter was from? But why am I asking you? I don't even suppose you can imagine that I have an aunt in America who, by some strange caprice of fate, had, after a long silence, decided to send me a word. Let me confess that I had forgotten altogether about her existence. Sometimes, on birthdays, at our relatives, when chocolate candies were not yet in style and the guests used to stain their clothes with cherry preserve, an animated gossip about this charming little woman used to go on and on. Then one of my uncles, notary public by profession, wiping his moustaches with a large gay handkerchief, spoke of human fortune, citing the case of my American aunt. She had gone to Zagreb to study pharmacy and there she met a certain millionaire from New Jersey. At first it was just a mere acquaintance: "How do you do"—"How do you do." But by and by some closer relations developed between the two. The American, as my uncle was saying, got hooked by my aunt, who on her side did not remain indifferent to his attention. She quit the studying of pharmacy and became his constant companion. He said something—she: "Ha, ha, ha." She felt happy and did not care to know any more of the chemical tinctures. Finally all this ended with a marriage. They married and left for America. They were happy and were living very prosperously; had an expensive automobile; the Almighty One gave them everything but children. "Well, all happiness cannot be heaped up on one place," concluded the good-natured notary public, and right after that he was interpreting the moral of this short history. "So, as I wanted to say," he added, with the sudden enlightenment of wisdom, "If our Olga had not met the American, she would probably be up to this very present day sweating over the mortars in some drug store and selling pills. Human luck is like a little gold bird. Once in life it perches upon the shoulder of every one of us, and we must keep our eyes wide open so that we may not miss it." At these words full of bitter truth, all of us, close and distant relatives of my lucky American aunt, were silently nodding our heads and were looking at her picture, which appeared to be smiling sneeringly at us from a little seashell frame as if we were Hottentots. When this almost fantastic image passed through all hands and took again its old place on the little table we rose, put our overshoes on, sighing, and headed toward various directions, carrying in us a sad feeling as if we were present at a funeral.

You have seen dry plums strung up on a thread. So looked the little black letters, stuck one after another upon the yellowish paper of the letter. My aunt was reminding me of many forgotten details from the past: of the quiet paternal house with its large shady rooms, upon whose walls fancy mirrors were gleaming and some cruel hunting pictures with innocently smiling hunters who were triumphing between the paws of ferocious bears; of the fire-bugs that flew like green sparks in the darkness of the summer evening; of the old garden amidst whose tall grass beds of fiery cresses were running. "There is not a single trace of that quiet life full of primitive beauty here in New York," my aunt was writing with a nostalgic pathos. "New York is the city of the new era, of the multitudes, gasoline, and the porcelain smiles of Negroes from the boxing-rings. It is the dwelling of millions, with buildings reaching the clouds, upon whose roofs we tango in the evening and in whose basements we drink whisky in coffee cups so that we may evade the law of the dry regime. We live among the steel shafts of an enormous machine and know the value of every single second. In church while the minister is reading Solomon's Proverbs, women are fixing their hair as at home men are shaving; dentists in their cabinets are filling three teeth simultaneously to three different patients, and at last, on going to bed, we place some kind of an apparatus on our head in order to keep our thoughts fresh until the next day and not to exhaust them with foolish dreams." Further on, my aunt was informing me that she is already used to this life and that, notwithstanding her advanced age, she had, not long ago, won a prize in a women's rugby game. At the end she concluded her letter this way: "Maybe you will be surprised that I am writing you, but don't let this look strange to you at all. You will find out in a moment the reason that made me think of you and communicate with you after such a long time. Fancy, my dear, I was passing the other morning in the big banker's street, Wall Street, and imagine what I saw: A little golden haired five- or six-year-old boy was standing on the sidewalk crying. I approached and asked him what was the matter. "Why do you cry, baby?" He looked at me sadly, with eyes full of tears showing me in his rosy little hand a broken lead soldier. And do you know that for a moment your infant image appeared before my eyes, recalling the scene when once you stood exactly like this and were showing me your broken wax jester with a little bell on its hat, which I had bought you for your birthday. Yes, this distant recollection came out through the abyss of time, in the midst of the chaotic experiences in order to brighten my heart with the mirage light of a fairy past.

"I thought of you all day long with such an intensity that I had to swallow pills of compressed air from the Himalayan mountains and to place upon my heart the cooling cone against strong feelings. I am writing you today this letter to inform you that I am making a little present to you. The wax jester of former times with the bell on its hat does not exist any more but you will now get a real man of iron, an automaton-robot who will help you in your house work and will be your good companion in lonely hours. This standard man product of the firm Slaping, Tom, Tone & Co., is a real miracle of the contemporary technology and is recently having a wide application in the practical life of Americans. He is the faithful dog that watches the house as well as a conscientious servant that answers the telephone, opens the door and receives guests. He does not consume anything but machine oil, and here they pay tax for him annually as much as for a bicycle. He is a linguist, too, and understands all the languages on earth, so you can easily converse with him in Bulgarian. With the parcel are to be found directions for use of the automaton. Good luck to you and remember me. Much love from your affectionate aunt Olga."

Tears were running from my eyes. No, blood can't be turned into water. Here it is, after so many years of painful expectation the legendary little gold bird was at last coming to me. It was already perched upon my shoulder, chirping gayly and pecking with its sharp beak at my chin.

He arrived the way all machines come. Well packed in a long wooden case with the inevitable warnings on the cover "Breakable!" "Handle with care."

When at the custom-house the case was opened the custom officer stepped back and on his face a slight fear was noticeable. The standard man was lying inside like a dead knight, his arms crossed over his chest. He was all of iron. Only his head was made of some strange material, similar to rubber, and it had the natural color and shape of a real human head. Closed eyelids, sharp, regular nose, small mouth closed in a sarcastic smile. Curls of blonde hair were falling down carelessly over his forehead, exactly as it is with a traveler after a long and tiresome journey.

"What is this?" the custom officer asked with a professional curiosity. "Automaton," I said embarrassedly.

"What kind of automaton? What is it used for?"

"For everything. It answers the telephone, opens the door, receives guests, boils coffee—in a word, it does every kind of house work. A sort of a servant."

"Uh," murmured the puzzled officer, and he began to turn over the pages of a tariff book absent-mindedly. "It is my first time to tax with duty such an object. Let me call some of my associates."

And he disappeared behind a door.

After a while many custom officers gathered around the standard man. A short official in an unbuttoned jacket, an aluminum medal hanging from his watch chain, looked into the case and, coughing importantly a little, began to inspect the automaton with great care. Then he lifted its arms and at once three buttons glimmered on the iron armour of the robot: yellow, blue and red. The officer pressed hesitatingly the red button and then in a moment an inauspicious humming, as from an infernal machine, filled the air of the big custom-house crowded with bales, cases and packages.

While we were standing with terrified hearts in expectation of an inevitable explosion, the standard man rose from the case, opened his eyes and looked around in wonder. As soon as he saw us, he stood up on his feet and cried aloud:

"Good afternoon!"

"Good afternoon!" I answered and stepped forward. "Let me introduce myself. I am your master."

The automaton looked at me condescendingly from head to feet and said in a perfect Bulgarian:

"Is this the way you meet guests? Why aren't you dressed formally? And what about a bouquet of roses?"

All these questions were put to me so bluntly and with such carelessness that I felt right away like an amoeba.

"Excuse me," I said, smiling guiltily. "I have been running all day long for your release and for this reason I had not much time to prepare myself properly to meet you with all the solemnity needed. On the other hand, I did not want to wait till tomorrow, because, as you see, here in the custom-house is very inconvenient for a gentleman like you to spend the night."

"Oh, I see! I am in a custom-house? What for? What does all this mean?" The robot snapped, as his face grinned maliciously.

"Yes, you are in a custom-house all right!" shouted the custom officers in a choir, lined up in espalier before the empty case. "According to the law you are liable to custom duty."

At the word law the standard man placed his arms upon his chest like an opera singer, bowed politely and said:

"At your disposal, gentlemen. Only hurry up with my taxing because it smells terribly of formalin here and I can hardly bear that odor. It always reminds me of some morgue."

Then a long and quiet consultation among the uniformed officers ensued, which reminded one of a secret trial of the inquisitors of medieval times. The modern descendants of Torquemada and Peter Arbue sank in divining over the holy custom duty and each one of them tried to display as much more pedantism as possible in taxing the robot.

"Let us tax him as a clock," one proposed.

"As a radio," another said.

"As a counting machine," a third one added.

"As a motorcycle!" a fourth one shouted.

"No, let us tax him as a luxurious automobile!" the officer with the aluminum medal intervened and began to babble as if he was tuned up: Studebaker, Buick, Packard, Lincoln, Cadillac, Hispano-Suisse, Alfa-Romeo, Isotta-Fraschini, Rolls Royce . . ."

"Wait a minute! Stop!" I shouted, carried by the stream of the automobile makes. "You are going to ruin me with such a heavy duty. After all, don't forget that this gentleman is not made out of gold but of iron."

"That doesn't matter!" the short officer cut in ferociously. "In a case like this the material is not to be taken into consideration. It is important for us to know the real substance of the object, do you see? The object regarded not as matter but as kinetic energy."

"But . . . but . . ." I objected, without understanding a single sound of this strange terminology of the custom philosophy. "Here before you, gentlemen, is a most ordinary iron automaton, so I beg you to tax it as a kerosene heater."

The standard man who up to this moment was listening with a triumphant satisfaction to the high opinions of the custom officers about him, jumped as if stung and shouted in my ear:

"I forbid you to compare me with a kerosene heater."

"Well, then . . ." I whispered helplessly, "let them tax you, let us say, like a portable fire extinguisher, but by all means not like a luxurious automobile. All this would mean for me to spend all my fortune in order to get you out of this custom-house."

"Quiet, please!" all the officers shouted again in a choir. "In a custom inspection nobody is allowed to make any remarks that may mislead the personnel. We know our job and don't need any advice!"

After this short official confession, the officers gathered again for a consultation. This time still longer and more painful. At length the sentence was read:

"He is to be taxed as a telescope!"

I sighed with relief, took out my pocket book and paid the required sum, which, indeed, was not very small, but, at any rate, was a thousandth of the duty for a Rolls Royce. Then I turned to the automaton and asked:

"Are you pleased with the taxation now?"

"Yes," he said indifferently. "A telescope stands higher in all respects than a kerosene heater or a portable fire extinguisher. It is used for studying the planets and foretelling the cosmic catastrophes. This is not a little."

After I had gone with a pious solemnity through all further rituals of the custom communion, which took off my shoulders a big burden, I approached the standard man, took his hand and asked him to leave.

"And so, if you please, you may lie down again in the case," I said. "It is time to go."

"You are very much mistaken," the robot said, withdrawing his hand. "You objected to their taxing me as a luxurious automobile, so, now you will have to do me the pleasure of hiring a taxi cab to go to your place. Won't you?"

I winked sheepishly and said nothing. I went to the street, called a taxi cab and then I opened its door.

"Go ahead, please."

My dear guest from America got into the car the way noblemen enter: slowly, tired-looking and slightly stooped.

God created man. The Devil in reply created the homunculus. Sometimes the homunculi were born in the sorcerer's kitchens, called into life out of a nightmare fancy and by the long vigilance of the servants of black magic.

Today they are manufactured in factories according to tables of strictly scientific estimations and their evil creators are called engineers.

In 1774, Count Kuffstein and his assistant, Abbot Gillogni, at a Carmelite monastery in Calabria made by an artificial method three human-like beings within six months.

In 1932, the American firm Slaping, Tom, Tone & Co. produces daily 1000 robots. My robot bears on its chest the nickel engraving: "The faithful John. No. 384,991." From morning till evening he and I chat, going into details, and our conversation ends always in a bitter dispute.

"You are a boresome individualist," John says, annoyed. "Is it strange that I hate the cult of the individual and am ready to make all sacrifices for the sake of the collective? Can't you understand, after all, that I am a mass product, a consanguineous twin brother of thousands that think, talk and work exactly like me. We have all not only the same physical qualities but also an exactly equal amount of brains."

"Exactly what I maintain. Just because your brain is weighed on scales and your heads are like lemonade bottles with exactly measured volume, you robots do not represent anything but a grey and impersonal mob," I reply hotly. "It is hardly conceivable that the superman whom you hate so much, and who after all is called genius, will be born from among you. On the other hand remember that the standard production gives always, in compensation of the quantity, a low quality and this undoubtedly reflects upon the mental faculties of the collective. Yes, at the end, in spite of all unbelievable achievements of the contemporary technology, you remain a man-machine. Do you understand? You may be an excellent instrument for somebody else's will but you will never be an independent creative individual."

The automaton looks at me pityingly then crosses its arms behind its back and begins to stride from one to the other end of the room.

"It will remain to be seen who is a tool of somebody else's will," he mumbled through its teeth.

❊   ❊   ❊

Each day brings the most unexpected surprise to me.

John enters my room and says:

"Kindly rub off my feet with a piece of flannel!"

I am staring at him stupifiedly and begin to cross myself.

"You have gone crazy, John! Don't you know how a servant must behave with his master?"

"Ha, ha, ha!" the standard man giggles as his iron body is clanking like a chain. "You are terribly mistaken, sir. I am your servant as much as you are my lackey."

"Lackey!" I exclaim and all the blood rushes up in my head. "John, behave yourself! You don't know me!"

"You don't seem to know me either!" answers daringly the automaton. "I have a right to take care of my attire as much as you do of yours. And if you want me to be more sincere, I will add that although you attribute to yourself a divine origin in fact there is no difference between you and me. Furthermore, is it necessary to remind you that for those of your kind Darwin created a special theory, and that in every zoological garden there is one of your kin who breaks nuts with his teeth and makes his own descendants laugh?"

"This is an unparalleled impudence!" I boil with indignation, clenching my fists.

Through my open window comes the saxophone-like voice of Josephine Baker, played on a distant gramophone record.

The standard man stands, imperturbable, opposite me and repeats the song of the black-skinned doll:

"J'ai deux amou-ou-ours,
mon pay-y-ys est Pari-i-is. . . ."

John has become an absolute master in my house and I tremble in anticipation of each of his actions. Today he slammed the door in the nose of my best friend and did not let him in.

"When somebody comes to see me you are obliged to treat him decently, do you hear me? I forbid you from now on to open the door and to meet guests!"

"Nonsense!" the automaton answers back haughtily. "Your friend has the inexcusable habit of carrying an umbrella when the sun is shining and thus he irritates me extremely. I am a man of modern times and can't stand pedants with poor imagination."

❉   ❉   ❉

I am already neurasthenic. Even the slightest noise is irritating me. My hands shake. My ears buzz. My head is tightened as if bound with hoops. I have lost my appetite and cannot sleep all night long. As I look in the mirror I see in front of me a pale mask with features distorted by suffering.

I cannot stand this cursed robot any more. Imagine, he slapped me today because I refused to read for him the latest number of the *New York Herald Tribune*.

❉   ❉   ❉

I looked once more through the directions for the using of the automaton. Thank God, the officer in the custom-house did not touch the blue button. I am afraid of it as of the pestilence. If I press it the standard man will begin to destroy everything coming his way.

"A good safeguard of our property against burglars," the directions read.

The only salvation is in the yellow button. It brings death to the robot.

But he is clever. For days he has been locked in his room and does not come out at all. Maybe he has a presentiment that I want to get rid of him.

What is this?

I look in the mirror and shudder. My image reminds me of the image of the robot. A strange thought occurs to me: There are dogs that resemble their masters.

❉   ❉   ❉

Yes, something unusual is happening to me, indeed. My similarity with the standard man grows in an inexplicable way. Same face, same lips, closed in a sarcastic smile.

But this is not yet everything.

I begin to do things that were altogether strange to me.

Today, for instance, I went to a football game, and to tell you the truth, I enjoyed immensely the game of the two teams. Score 3:1 in favor of the Gold Calf.

❄   ❄   ❄

It is already a whole week since John has not come out of his room. What is the matter with him?

I approach his room and make efforts to hear. Not a sound inside.

"John."

No answer.

"John, what are you doing in there?"

Silence.

"John, do you hear? Open the door!"

Not a sound.

Then I press the door with all my strength, it cracks under my weight and opens with broken latch.

An icy terror grips my heart.

The robot is lying stretched in the center of the room with arms spread on his sides. In his big glass eyes a devilish smile is gleaming.

I bend timidly over him and make efforts to draw his arms closer to the body. In a moment a low hissing noise of an unwinding spring is heard from under his iron armour. The standard man opens his eyes and his lower jaw shivers.

"Ya, ya, ya-a-a-a!" a long groan comes and dies away as an echo of a clock note.

❄   ❄   ❄

I cannot understand his death.

Suicide?

Or maybe an unexpected touch of the yellow button?

A hard remorse presses upon my conscience and does not give me any peace.

While a few days ago I wanted to kill the automaton myself, now at once I am seized with a terrible torment on account of him.

Before, I considered him machine; today, when he is a soulless iron doll, I love him like a brother.

I try to revive him by pressing the red button but in vain. John does not show any sign of life.

He is dead for ever.

Only his eyes remain the same, open and smiling as if they were the eyes of a living man. May God give peace to his standard soul!

⚬   ⚬   ⚬

This morning I discovered something new in myself. Upon my chest are glittering three buttons: Yellow, blue and red.

A mad joy seizes upon all my being and a triumphant cry is uttered by my mouth. I run to the hall where in a corner is standing the proud knight of the modern time. I throw myself in his arms and cover his cold face with kisses.

"John, look at me. Can't you see? Your eyes are open! I am already your duplicate, your exact likeness. You came from America to reveal to me the intangible secret of transfiguration and to transfuse your immortal spirit into my human body. Thank you, John! Now I begin to understand what it is to become an automaton and to stir up one's own consciousness with the idea that the future belongs to the standard men!"

⚬   ⚬   ⚬

The hour of revenge has come.

Robots! Gather for the great crusade which carries out destruction for the old world! Your endless legions will flood like a torrent the earth; those who believe in the resurrection of the dead and keep on the wall of their rooms mandolins with pink ribbons must be swept away by the hurricane of the machines!

Trumpeters! Blow the tubes and the saxophones. Let all of us swing ourselves into the epileptic rhythm of the holy rumba before we start on our way!

Brothers! Raise your arms and be ready to kindle your noble wrath with the blue buttons of destruction! I am leaving my home to go with you.

The gold bird of happiness will lead us exactly like the ancient biblical dove.

"It is an interesting story," the assistant said to his professor, closing the little green note book. "Well, what became later of your patient?"

"The gold bird of happiness," the professor smiled, "undoubtedly took my patient to the madhouse. He smashed the show windows of a store for toys and began to pick up the dolls, which according to his words were "children of robots." After this occurrence he was brought over to my ward. It is curious to know a little detail. At the searching of the patient's house, the police really found a broken iron robot together with this note book which is something like a diary. Evidently the poor fellow had experienced a great shock, to have reached the absurd thought that he himself was turned into an automaton."

"What an absurd *idée fixe!*" the assistant muttered.

"Ye-e-es, circular deconstruction, maniacal depressive condition," the professor replied to himself, and looked out of the window.

Translated by VICTOR SHARENKOFF

HUNGARY

INTRODUCTION

By Thomas Quinn Curtiss

HUNGARIAN LITERATURE—like Hungary itself—is a curious blending of the Occidental and the Oriental. During the seventeenth century, after nearly two hundred years of occupation, the Magyar at last drove the Turk from Hungary. But the imprint of the Turk remained and remains, culturally as well as architecturally. Buda and Pest, the twin cities divided by the Danube, which compose the capital, are in themselves symbols of the national schizophrenia. Buda, the ancient, brooding Magyar stronghold, and Pest, a modern metropolis, strangely Americanized, suggesting a Continental Detroit or Indianapolis, are in almost grotesque contrast.

The Hungarian writer is likewise divided. Two influences have predominantly played upon him, those of the French, and those of the Russian who, like himself, retains a flavor of the East. Under the Austrian rule the Hungarian, like most invaded and suppressed people, was informed that his past was wild, obscure and barbaric and was encouraged to forget it. It was quite natural, then, that during the nineteenth century the Magyar writer should turn to France rather than to Germany for literary inspiration. For him, as for the Russian, Paris was the international capital of freedom and culture, but his work, unlike the French, bore a lingering melancholy, the fruit of repressed resentment. Count Szechenyi christened Hungary the land of mourning and hope, and the darkest Magyar pessimism is always edged with a silver promise.

The Anglo-American interest in Hungary's political life preceded the Anglo-American discovery of Hungarian literature. During the 1850's Kossuth, the great Hungarian patriot, toured both England and the United States raising large funds for his campaign for independence. Many years afterward Arthur Griffith, the Irish leader, pointed out the striking parallel between the Hungarian struggle and that of Ireland, in his book, "The Resurrection of Hungary". The late years of the nineteenth century brought English translations of Hungarian poets, Petofi and Arany and the novels of Jokai. But the greatest of the Hungarian poets, Ady, remains unaccountably untranslated, as does another major figure of the modern period, Mihaly Babits.

Just before the outbreak of the first World War, English and American theatrical producers discovered, via Berlin and Vienna, the Hungarian drama. This discovery proved doubly valuable for, aside from providing its importers with a gold mine, it brought across the seas many witty and memorable plays and introduced to English-speaking audiences the best work of Molnár, Biro, Herczeg, Lengyal, Vadja and many others. The American movies slowly lured most of these gentlemen to Hollywood, and when the shadow of Hitler first fell across Hungary in the early thirties, the Hungarian drama, which only a few years before had supplied Broadway and Shaftesbury Avenue with its juiciest comedies and its most interesting sex plays, was virtually a thing of the past. The post-war years witnessed the appearance of several serious novels of high rank. Kosztolanyi's "Bloody Poet", Zilahy's "Deserter" and "Two Prisoners", Zsolt's "It Ends In Marriage", Szep's "A Marriage for One" and Heltai's "Csadas" are all available in translation and worthy of the attention of any reader with even a passing interest in the European literary scene.

But the most significant book to have come out of Hungary since the first World War seems to me without any question to be "Black Monastery", the sole work of its author, the late Aladar Kuncz. Kuncz as a young student was on holiday in France at the outbreak of the War in 1914. He was arrested and interned, first in Perigueux, then in Noirmoutier (the Black Monastery) and finally at L'Ile d'Yeu in the region of La Vendée. His book is an autobiography of these years of imprisonment and of the mental, moral and physical decay that attacked his fellow-prisoners. Some die and some survive but all are unrecognizably broken, and freedom finds them burnt out with suffering, hardly human beings; only the charred ashes of their characters remain. It is a relentless tragedy of mortal defeat, overwritten at times and perhaps too long, but filled with a genuine power for all that, because Kuncz has grasped his subject firmly and never lets go. No humor relieves its tension or lights its dark pages, but the strength of the story is binding from the start. It is a sombre and haunting document, a sort of classic of captivity.

Ferencz Molnár is, of course, internationally renowned as a dramatist. But at home his fame by no means rests on his plays alone. Indeed, many believe his novels are superior to his dramas, though this seems incorrect for even in his short stories it is always the dramatic conflict of the situations that interest him principally. The germ of his most celebrated play "Liliom" is found in an early newspaper feuilleton that he later enlarged and dramatized. But that Molnár's prose is as facile as his dialogue is certainly true.

Jenö Heltai, like Molnár, is better known as a playwright than as a short story writer. His play, "The Silent Knight", which proved so popular on the Continent, achieved London production in a translation made by the British poet, Humbert Wolfe. I have already mentioned his novel, "Csadas", a fascinating picture of post-war Budapest; even his most trifling work wears the stamp of his unfailing originality and lively imagination. To the many modern Hungarian authors that a lack of space alone excludes go my profound apologies: Ferencz Herczeg, Sandor Hunyady, Frigyes Karinty, Sandor Mari, Zsigmond Moric, Antal Szerb—the Magyar roll-call of literary honor is a long one.

Today Hungary is again in mourning, shamed once more by a Teutonic conquest, this time a subtler one than that of old, but a no less devastating one to lovers of freedom. But there too is hope, one feels sure, and when the clouds of war have cleared away, perhaps the Hungarian writer as well as the Hungarian patriot will find his place in the sun.

Ferencz Molnár

BORROMEO

I WENT FOR A WALK along the water-front, before dinner, to say goodbye to Lake Geneva, as it were. It was a rarely beautiful June—I was nineteen. After a year at the University of Geneva, I was leaving for my vacation, back home in Budapest. I glanced out over the lake. Two suns were shining: one above in the heavens, and the other below, a dazzling spot of liquid fire on the lake. I wore a scarlet velvet beret and a tricolor of red, white and green across my breast, the regulation dress of Hungarian students at Geneva. A stout cane, clutched tightly in my fist, completed the effect. So I stood at the edge of the narrow jetty that reaches out into Lake Geneva. I saw white sails, flapping golden in the distance, but I was above all that. For my head beneath the scarlet beret was full of penology. Lombroso, Garofalo, Sighele, the popular Italian criminologists of the day. . . . I had studied the Penal Code at the University, and I prided myself on knowing it. Looking out over the great gold and blue lake, I peered through the distant future at the dazzling prospect of becoming an attorney for the defense, or a public prosecutor, if it should turn out that way. For or against, it was all the same to me, just so it had to do with criminal law.

All of a sudden another man started coming down the jetty, a modestly dressed, stocky chap with a tiny black mustache. A couple of stone steps led down to the lake below where I was standing. The fellow sat down on the top of the steps, took off his shoes and socks, rolled up his trousers and began to soak his feet in the lake. He looked around only after that and then took notice of me. He saw the tricolor across my breast, and all at once began to whistle a well-known Hungarian folk song, to let me know that he, too, was Hungarian.

I listened with growing amazement. For this was no ordinary whistle, but the whistling chirp of a canary, with flourishes and full-throated crescendoes. He gave a remarkably true imitation of a canary too, at the same time adapting the melody of the folk song to a canary's scale. When it was all over, he looked up at me, grinning.

"You Hungarian?"

"Yes."

"My name's Borromeo," he said. "That's my stage name. My real name's Boros."

"Stage name?" I asked, taken aback.

"Yes, I used to be on the stage. Now I have a little business renting boats by the hour. I have a partner who's a local boy. We hire out boats and sails to the Sunday trade."

"What did you do on the stage?" I asked.

"I was in variety. Bird and animal imitator."

"What do you mean, bird and animal," I asked. "Aren't birds animals?"

"No sir, not in variety. Bird sounds are a special job. Animals like lions, cows, frogs, cats, dogs or even trains are easier."

"Trains?"

"Yes, we throw that in for good measure. I used a chair and my mouth to do a train. But I quit all that long ago. I'm a business man now. I live here with my two kids. I'm getting married."

"You're a widower?"

"Yes, sir."

"Where do you come from?"

"We used to live in Budapest, but I was on the go all the time. Vienna, Prague, Munich, I was playing the circuit. I don't want to brag, Mister, I don't believe in that. I was always working in second-rate music halls, but I made good money. I even played in the Kursaal, right here in Geneva one time. That's how I met this fellow and invested some of my cash in the boat-renting business. Mind you, Mister, I'm not bragging: this boating business of ours is no Cunard Line. But it's a better living than pretending you're a canary or a train. I've got two kids, two little girls, one eight and the other six. They've been without a mother three years, and we can't go on like that. So I guess I've just got to get married."

"Are you marrying a local girl?"

"No, sir, she's Hungarian. My poor wife's sister. She's been working as a governess for years for some society people. We began thinking about it some time back. But now we've got it all settled in writing, she's here now and I'm going to marry her. Kids need a mother. Specially little girls. Right?"

"Right," I said.

He splashed around with his feet and said nothing for a while. Then he smiled and scratched his head.

"Funny thing, Mister," he said. "Just the same, I have a guilty conscience. I don't mind if I do tell somebody from back home. Specially an educated fellow like yourself, a college man. You studying philosophy?"

"No," I said. "Law."

"That's nice too. Anyhow, you'd know better than a plain tradesman, like myself. Now as I was saying, the kids need a mother. Teri and Bubu. Teri's the eight year old, Bubu's six. My wife died three years ago. Teri'd just turned five. Bubu was three. She died in a hospital in Budapest. It was all so sudden and unexpected. I was here on business in Geneva, talking over the boating deal with my partner. We'd just about come to an agreement, when I got a wire to come right away. I rushed home and a couple of days later the poor soul died in the hospital. The kids were with their Grandma, and they didn't know a thing. All they knew was their Mommy was very sick in the hospital. Well, sir, we let it go at that. I had to come back here right after the funeral, so I brought the kids along. Couldn't leave 'em with their Grandma, she's pretty near blind and deaf and she's got plenty of trouble looking after herself. So I just packed 'em up, rented two rooms here out in the suburbs, and tried to do the best I could. I even put them in a day nursery for a while, as long as I was working. A splendid institution, I tell you. The kids stayed there all day and I went to fetch them home every evening. They're good little girls. They loved their Mommy dearly, and I had to tell 'em about her every evening. Just saying she was still sick, but she was getting better, and soon she'd come by train to join us. Sometimes their Mommy wrote them long letters, and I'd read 'em off a blank sheet on Sundays. And they had to write Mommy too. If you want to call it writing. Anyhow they'd scrawl something on a paper, and their Mommy would answer them. You know what I mean?"

"Certainly."

"Well then, I taught Teri, the older one, to read and write. Afterward Teri wrote long letters to Mommy, and Bubu kept scrawling on the paper with her pencil. I couldn't read 'em their mother's answer off a blank sheet any longer so I used to go to the café every Sunday to write Mommy's letter. I printed it all in capitals, and Teri used to read it out loud to Bubu. They sure loved their mother, and they were looking forward to seeing her. 'When's she coming?' and 'Why doesn't she come?' and so on. If you'll excuse me, Mister, I'll take my feet out of the water, they're getting cold."

He dried his feet with his handkerchief, and pulled on his socks and shoes. After this he offered me a short Vevey cigar.

"I was telling you the kids were growing up and getting smarter, and things were beginning to be tough for me. I'd been thinking for some time I ought to marry my poor wife's sister. She was a little backward at first, in her letters I mean. But she had a good job working for society people. They were mighty nice to her. She had good food and a good bed all her own. Still, after a while she began to like the idea, the two little girls, the beautiful city of Geneva, my prosperous little business, and after all, I'm not so bad myself. She asked for a little time to think it over, but she agreed in principle as they say. Now here's where the trouble begins, Mister. We had a little photo on the wall at home. My poor wife's picture. The kids had a habit of kissing it. I used to have to take it off the wall for them. They'd look at it, one after the other, and give their Mommy's picture big, wet kisses. Now after we'd come to a perfect agreement with my wife's sister, in a manner of speaking, I took the picture off the wall, and put it away in a drawer. For a couple of days the kids didn't know the difference. Then one day, the little one— not the big one, mind you—started to ask, 'Where's Mommy's picture?' I felt as though I had been hit straight in the heart. I said I'd taken the picture to the glazier, to have a new frame put on. The worst of it though was yet to come. The Sunday after that I wrote in Mommy's letter that they should be good little girls, because Mommy was coming soon, she was all right now, except that she still had a lot of things to do back home. Well, you should have seen how happy they were. They asked for the picture again, but I said they didn't need any picture now, because their mother would be with them soon. You're a philosopher, Mister . . . well, anyway, a lawyer. Should I have told those little kids their mother was dead? They wouldn't have known what I was talking about. I would have had to explain what we mean by dying. What for? Just to make 'em cry? I ask you, Mister, why should they cry? God was good to them, taking away their mother while they were still too young to understand. Should I explain just so they'd understand and cry in their beds every night? What should I have done?"

He paused.

"After that," he went on, "it was just one thing after another. Mommy kept writing for three months she was coming, and the kids kept getting worked up. I was stuck with my story, and I just had to keep it up. Sometimes I felt pretty sad when the kids danced around the room because they were so glad about their Mommy, and I had to mimic twice as many birds as usual, they were that happy. Now I told you a while ago, the trouble started with my wife's picture. The fact is, it didn't start there either. It started with what I'm going to tell you now. My sister-in-law, my fiancee, I should say, sent me a picture of herself. I hesitated a week about showing it to the children. Then, seeing that I was stuck anyway, I felt I might as well keep it up. And so, one evening, I showed them my sister-in-law's picture, saying their Mommy had just sent it, it was her latest. I even took care they shouldn't look at it under the light, but further off in the room, where it wasn't so bright."

He grimaced bitterly and scratched his head.

"Mister," he said, "this life's a pretty rotten business. D'you know what happened? Well, *nothing happened.* 'Isn't Mommy pretty!' they said, snatching the picture from each other's hands, and pasting extra big wet kisses all over it. Now, I ask you, Mister. Did it pay the poor woman to bring them into the world in sorrow, to sweat and toil over them, to watch and care for them for years . . . just to be forgotten like that?"

"Does her sister look like her?" I asked.

"I can't say that she does, Mister. It's the same family, of course; they were sisters, after all, but no particular resemblance. She also had a nose in the middle of her face, God rest her. That's how things were. Then, one Sunday, I read them a letter, saying Mommy was on the way, and we were to go to the railroad station to meet her. Well, we went. My fiancee, Anna, got off the train, and kissed the kids. They pretty near tore her clothes off, mommying her every which way. Then, when we got home, they took their presents, fell to playing with all the dolls, and an hour later they'd forgotten their new mommy too. But they worship her, and Anna's just like a real mother to them. We'll be married next week and everything is going to be all right. Mommy's come home, Mommy's here, and that's that. Just the same, though, I didn't tell you the truth a while ago, because here's where the trouble really begins. The whole thing is beginning to get on my nerves. Mind you now what was it I really did? Well, Mister, I'd lied that poor woman, lying in her grave in Budapest, right out of her children's lives. Not that I meant to do it. Believe me. But the way I kept getting in deeper and deeper, there was no other way out. Mommy's come home. Mommy never died. It bothers me, Mister, honest. At least Anna has the excuse they're her sister's kids. But what can I say for myself? Suppose we do go home to Budapest some time. Shouldn't those kids even be allowed to go to their mother's grave? What d'you make of it, Mister? What excuse have I got for faking that poor soul clean out of the world, like a magician in a disappearing act? I ask you, Mister, like an artist talking to a lawyer, have we got a right to steal their memory from the dead? The dead have nothing except the memory they've left, Mister. Have we a right to take even that from them? It's awful, Mister, to think you've deprived a little dead mother of even having her children put a flower on her grave. Suppose I tell 'em all about it some time later. What's Anna going to look like to them in that case? An impostor? You're an educated man, a law student. You tell me if I had a right to do what I did?"

"I think you did," I said.

"What makes you say that?"

"I don't know. But I'm sure you did right."

I had to walk with him as far as the bridge to see his business, the big barge, and the freshly whitewashed rowboats tied to it. They had pretty names, 'Mon amour', 'Pierrette' and 'La Mouette', and he called my attention particularly to two little sailboats, one called 'Teri', and the other 'Bubu.'

"You've made me feel much better, sir," he told me. "But I've been worrying so much lately, I'm afraid I'll start all over again tomorrow. I can't even sleep nights."

Largely because there was no criminal angle, I soon forgot the problem. I only recall it now, thirty-nine years later. If Borromeo were to ask my opinion today, I am afraid I couldn't answer him with nearly as much certainty as I did when I was nineteen.

Translated from the Hungarian

Jenö Heltai

DEATH AND THE PHYSICIAN

ONE MARCH NIGHT a strange and mysterious carriage drew up in the municipal park, in front of Dr. Morbidus's sanatorium. The liveried footman, who sat mutely with folded arms beside the driver, jumped off the box and pressed the electric bell of the iron gate with great violence. The shrill screech of the bell burst mercilessly into the silent, secluded sanatorium, where all the patients were still awake. Only the healthy inmates were asleep—the commissionaire, the nurses, the doctors and, above all, Dr. Morbidus, the director of the sanatorium, a university professor and a world-famous scientist, a wizard in operations relating to the pancreas and the bile.

The footman rang the bell still more violently, still more insistently, and this time the commissionaire rose sleepily and angrily to open the gate. When he saw the liveried footman he was somewhat mollified by the shadow that the prospective tip cast before it.

"Quick, quick!" said the footman agitatedly. "Wake the Professor immediately. His Excellency is dying."

The commissionaire did not attempt to argue. He knew very well that anyone who dared to disturb Dr. Morbidus at this hour must be at least a millionaire. Without the least hesitation he rushed upstairs to the Professor's bedroom and began to tug at the pyjama-jacket of the pancreas and bile wizard. At last Dr. Morbidus woke up. At first he raved a little, but when he heard that the patient was some sort of an Excellency he began gaily and speedily to dress.

Ten minutes later, wrapped in an enormous fur-lined overcoat that appeared to have been made for a whole family, he was already descending the carpeted stairs of the sanatorium. The footman humbly raised his silk hat and opened the door of the carriage.

"Whom are we going to?" asked the Professor as he stepped into the carriage.

"To His Excellency," replied the footman.

"Yes, yes," said the Professor impatiently, "but what's his name? His name."

"Death," returned the footman quietly. Then he slammed the door. A moment later the carriage was on its way.

When Dr. Morbidus heard the familiar and somewhat terrifying name he burst into forced laughter.

"I'm dreaming," he said to himself, "I'm dreaming."

Reaching into his pocket for his silver match-box he struck a match. The interior of the carriage was filled with the flaring light. Dr. Morbidus was alarmed to see a deathly pale, agitated face staring at him—his own face reflected in the small mirror that hung opposite his seat.

"Um," murmured the Professor, "perhaps this isn't a dream after all."

The interior of the carriage was lined with black cloth. The Professor began to feel increasingly uncomfortable. He could not hear the rattle of the wheels or the clatter of the horses' hooves; the carriage rolled along smoothly, noiselessly. That is, if it was rolling at all. For the Professor felt as though it were standing still.

He glanced out of the window. Then he was reassured.

"I'm dreaming after all," he murmured. "This can't be real."

He had only left the sanatorium five minutes ago, and now they were already climbing a steep mountain road, between black cliffs, with dark, bottomless abysses on either side. Here and there, upon the side of the cliffs, shadows glowing in a bluish-white haze appeared, only to disappear rapidly into nothingness.

"This can't be real," repeated the Professor. But this time there was less conviction in his voice. "But if it is not real what is it? However, whether it is real or not, what can happen to me? Nothing. So far as I know, this is the first time since the world began that Death has sent his own carriage for anyone. Up till now he has always paid personal visits, and he always came on foot. It's a great honour, a very great honour."

The Professor lighted a cigar and settled down to await events with a pleasant excitement. After all, he would not be particularly frightened if it turned out that he was going to die. But that did not appear likely. He could have died at home, in his own bed; it would not have been necessary to bring him to this strange, fantastic region for that.

"There's some other reason," he said to himself.

At that moment the carriage-door opened and the footman stood before him again with his silk hat in his hand.

"If you please, sir," he said politely.

The Professor alighted and looked round. He was in a narrow, dark court, very dimly illuminated by a small, flickering oil-lamp. Only the courts of barracks and prisons were as quiet and gloomy as this at night.

The footman hurried ahead up a winding-staircase and the Professor followed him.

"What is it you want of me?" he asked.

But the footman did not reply. He raised his finger to his lips, as the actors in the old romantic tragedies used to do. The Professor sauntered ill-humouredly behind the footman, who finally stopped at the end of a long, narrow corridor and knocked on a door.

"What do you want?" came a voice from within.

"The Professor is here," said the footman humbly.

The double wings of the door burst open and the narrow corridor was filled with a dazzling light.

Dr. Morbidus for a moment covered his eyes with his hand. But he was already walking into the room, attracted by some strange and mighty magnetic force.

At first he thought the room was empty.

"Sit down," said the footman. "His Excellency will be here directly."

Dr. Morbidus sat down on a chair and glanced round him in nervous agitation. His temples were throbbing, his heart was pounding at his ribs. He was a cool, cynical man, but at this moment he felt that something great and terrible was happening to him.

The next instant Death appeared before him.

"It was I who sent for you, Professor," said he in a tired voice. "I trust you'll forgive me for disturbing you at such a late hour."

Dr. Morbidus rose to his feet and bowed deeply. He was now quite calm, even cheerful. He almost burst into laughter. Really, he never imagined that the Great Murderer looked like this. He had not expected to see the traditional skeleton with the scythe and a white sheet thrown over his shoulders, yet he had hoped for something supernatural, something imposing and overwhelming, or at least a very gentle creature. But this . . . A small, wizened figure, a little old man who hardly reached to the Professor's waist. A hundred thousand wrinkles on his face, hands and feet like a child's. "His Excellency" was nothing more than a gigantic germ. Only the heavy purple cloak he wore showed that he was someone of distinction.

Death made a gesture and the Professor sat down again.

"I'm in trouble," said Death plaintively, "I'm very sick. I'm afraid I'm going to die."

Dr. Morbidus stared at him stupidly, uncomprehendingly.

"I beg your pardon, Your Excellency," he stammered, "I didn't quite catch . . ."

"You understand me quite well," said Death with a sad smile, "but, of course, what I said sounded rather queer. But only because I said it. If anyone else had said it . . . Well, I'm afraid I'm going to die."

"Your Excellency is joking . . ."

"I'm not joking. Far from it. If I were joking I shouldn't have sent for you. I know you doctors. Who better than I? You're the only one I trust."

"Your Excellency," said Dr. Morbidus, "I really don't know how to thank you for your flattering confidence in me, but . . ."

"Don't argue. I'm sick. You'll see for yourself when you examine me. How I came to be sick I do not know. I've been sound as a bell all my life. Perhaps I'm getting old and weak, the devil knows. All I know is that I'm not what I used to be. My pancreas hurts, my liver hurts, everything hurts. It's all up with me. If you don't cure me, I'll die."

During this speech Death shrank within himself. The Professor, on the other hand, grew bigger and bigger. An impartial observer of the scene would certainly have regarded the Professor as the more powerful and terrifying creature of the two.

Dr. Morbidus once more became gay, agile and pleasantly excited. Dash it all, what a case. Death was sick! What queer, malignant disease could have invaded the body of this little old man who had been killing,

killing, killing for millions of years? And what an incredible and fantastic
business it would be if Death were to die! On the other hand, what a
sensational, world-shaking event it would be if he, Dr. Morbidus, were
to cure Death!

Dr. Morbidus felt that his skin was getting too tight for him.

"Have patience, Your Excellency, have patience," he said gaily, rubbing his hands with satisfaction. "You must not despair. We'll see in a
moment what's wrong."

Death stared in front of him, dully, hopelessly. The Professor motioned
to the footman, who undressed His diminutive Excellency like a baby.
The desiccated little man looked even more comic in his nakedness than
in the heavy, purple cloak.

Dr. Morbidus fell upon the patient eagerly, feeling and smelling him
all over, looking into every accessible part of his shrunken body. And as
he did so his face became more and more friendly, while his spirits sank.

"Only a trifle," he said gaily, "only a trifle. A slight operation, that is all.
In an hour's time Your Excellency will be as fit as a fiddle."

What he thought was: "He's on his last legs. If I'm to save him I must
cut out his pancreas, liver and bile. Even so the result is doubtful."

Death looked up at the Professor with a gleam of hope in his eyes. But
the Professor avoided his gaze. He busied himself with the instruments
he was taking from his bag and sent the footman hot foot for water and
a clean towel.

"Will I survive the operation?" asked Death anxiously.

"It's child's play, Your Excellency. I've succeeded thirty thousand times
with the same operation. I can do it with my eyes shut. I can do it with
my left hand. My patients call me Velvet Hand."

"Velvet Hand," repeated Death. "I like that name. It's a good name."

"I deserve it, as Your Excellency will see. In any case I'm going to put
you to sleep."

"But can I bear an anaesthetic? Am I going to wake up after it?"

"Really, Your Excellency . . ."

His Excellency regretted and was ashamed of his momentary cowardice and agreed to be put to sleep by Dr. Morbidus. Death slipped into
unconsciousness.

The Professor for a time stood watching the peacefully sleeping Death.

"I've got you in a cleft stick, you scoundrel," he thought. "I can finish
you if I like. I need only err by a thousandth of an inch to free the world
from your ravages. And why shouldn't I err? It would be a crime on my
part if I failed to render this service to humanity."

Then he thought better of it.

"It wouldn't be right after all," he thought. "He's sick, poor fellow. A patient who's placed his life into my hands. I can't be his judge and executioner. I must treat him exactly like any other distinguished patient who pays well. I'm going to save him."

And he raised his lancet. But he did not operate yet. He was seized with a great excitement.

"It would be madness," he said to himself. The blood rushed to his face and his head began to buzz. "It would be madness. I shall never have another opportunity like this. Why should I save this swine so he can come tomorrow and finish me off? Ridiculous! We're going to live, all of us, we're going to live forever as soon as he's dead. And he's going to die!"

And now, with a strong, firm hand, he made two incisions in the body of Death. Then he bent over him, listening. Death did not stir. He was dead.

The Professor calmly washed his hands.

"Unfortunately," he said to the footman, who stood stiffly at the foot of the bed, "unfortunately, we've failed—His Excellency is dead. His pancreas . . . but you don't understand these things. I'm sorry. Perhaps if you'd sent for me earlier."

He spoke calmly, indifferently, though inwardly he was jubilant. Not for a moment did he consider himself a murderer. He felt that what he had done was not a crime but a good deed that would live forever. He heard the jubilation of a world clinging to life; saw himself perpetuated in pictures, statues, interviews and scientific works. He saw himself as the greatest man of all time, fêted by millions of people, giving audiences to kings and popes who had come to kiss his hand.

The footman, too, appeared to be unconcerned. Obsequiously assisting Dr. Morbidus into the fur coat that was big enough for a whole family, he saw him through the corridor, down the winding stairs and to the carriage which, black and motionless, was waiting in the court. The Professor stepped into the carriage, which started off noiselessly down the mountain road.

Dr. Morbidus lighted a cigar with the consciousness of a worthy task well performed and smiled with satisfaction. Fame, riches, immortality—that was what he was bringing back from this nocturnal excursion.

Suddenly the sound of sharp hooting reached his ears. The carriage stopped.

Dr. Morbidus glanced out of the window with disquiet in his mind.

A mighty giant was standing beside the carriage. His shadowy frame glowed in a bluish-white radiance. And there was a blood-stained axe in his hand.

"Excuse me, Professor," said the giant bleakly, "but you forgot to take your fee."

He handed a large envelope to Dr. Morbidus, who broke the seals with excited curiosity. The envelope contained a million kronen.

"Ah," said the Professor, deeply moved, "very kind of you indeed. I thank you."

"I thank you, Professor," replied the giant politely, "for the trouble you've taken. It's a great pity that your efforts should have been wasted."

"A great pity," said Dr. Morbidus, shaking his head. "His Excellency neglected the matter somewhat. He ought to have sent for me sooner. . . ."

"Exactly," said the giant. "I always told father—"

Dr. Morbidus stiffened.

"Ah. Then you're . . ." he stammered, staring at the giant.

"I'm his son," said the latter simply, "and now his successor in the business."

With that he vanished from the cliffs, while the carriage transported Dr. Morbidus back to the sanatorium in the municipal park.

Translated from the Hungarian

Ödön von Horvath

THE AGE OF THE FISH

Some one ought to invent a weapon which should nullify the effectiveness of any other weapon—the opposite of a weapon, in fact. Ah, if only I were an inventor, what wouldn't I invent! What a happy place I'd make the world. So ran my thoughts as I swallowed my sixth schnapps.

But I wasn't an inventor—would this world have missed anything if I'd never seen its light? What would the sun have had to say? And I wondered who would be living in my room now.

Don't wonder such rubbish, I told myself. You're drunk, drunk. If you hadn't been born, how would you know that your room existed? Your bed might still have been a piece of wood or a tree. Shame on you, old fool, asking metaphysical questions like a schoolboy who hasn't digested his first experiences. Don't probe into hidden secrets. You're drunk. Drink down your seventh schnapps.

I drank it, and went on. Ladies and gentlemen, I'm no friend of peace. I'd like to see us all killed off. But not a simple death. An involved death. Torture ought to be introduced again, eh? The rack. Man can't confess to guilt enough, for man is vile.

With the eighth schnapps, I was nodding to the pianist in a very friendly fashion, although his music had struck me as rather curious at the sixth. I was quite unaware that the man standing in front of me had already spoken to me twice. Not until his third attempt did I glance up.

I recognized him at once—our Julius Caesar.

Once a respected colleague—senior language master in a girl's high school—a nasty scandal had lost him his position. The party involved was a girl beneath the age of consent. He was sent to prison. For a long time we saw nothing of him: then I heard that he was hawking cheap goods from door to door. He wore an enormous tie-pin—a death's head in miniature, in which, by means of an electrical device, one solitary eye glowed red whenever he pressed a button in his pocket. Such was the humour of this shipwrecked life.

I'm still rather hazy as to how he suddenly came to be sitting beside me, engaged in a heated argument. I was very drunk, you see: all I can recollect is a few disjointed phrases.

"Everything you're telling me, dear colleague," Julius Caesar was saying, "is a lot of infantile trash. It is high time you fell in with a man who's got nothing left to hope for, and who can therefore view the transition between the generations with a perfectly open mind. Now you and I, colleague, according to Adam Riese, form two generations, and those scummy fellows make another. So altogether, according to Adam Riese, that's three generations. I'm sixty, you're thirty, and those creatures are about fourteen. Now, the experiences of puberty are decisive over the entire course of a lifetime, especially for the male sex . . ."

"You're boring me," I said.

"Even if I am, you'd better listen, if you want me to keep my temper. And so—the one great problem facing my generation in its puberty was the other sex—women—the women we didn't get. For we didn't, in those days. So our outstanding everyday experience was self-gratification, with all that it implied in those times—anxiety over the loss of one's health, etcetera—groundless fears, of course, but we didn't know that then. In other words, women formed our stumbling-block, and we slipped into the world war. But during your puberty, colleague, the war was well under way. There weren't any men, and the ladies weren't so hesitant. You didn't have to waste your time wondering, all the unsatisfied women threw themselves on to your dawning virility. For your generation, women ceased to mean anything sacred and so they'll never mean enough to you and your like, you'll always be hankering after something cleaner, finer, more unattainable: in other words—self-gratification. In this case, we see women finding a stumbling-block in you youngsters, and slipping into masculinity."

"Colleague," I stammered, "you're an ero—an erotomaniac."

"How so?"

"Because you behold all creation from the point of view of sex. It's characteristic of your generation, especially in its old age. But don't spend your days covered up in bed. Get out, pull the curtains aside, let in the light and have a look out. Have a look out."

"And what do we see outside?"

"Nothing very fine, but still—"

"It strikes me you're a romantic in disguise—I beg of you to stop interrupting me. Sit down. We're coming now to the third generation; for them, women simply constitute a problem no longer, for there aren't any women nowadays, all we've got is a lot of monsters who study, row, and march and develop their muscles. Has it ever occurred to you that the charm of women becomes less and less and less?"

"You're biased."

"Who could wax enthusiastic over a Venus with a rucksack? Not I. Ah, yes, the unhappy part of it for the youth of to-day is that they no longer have any puberty, in the right sense—an erotic, political, moral experience—they don't get it, it's all pitched overboard. And besides that, too many defects are celebrated as victories, and too often the innermost feelings of youth are laughed at: while in other ways they're made too comfortable. They've got to take down what the radio bellows out and then they get top marks. But there are still a few here and there, thank God—"

"Who are they?"

He looked mournfully round, crouched closer to me, and very quietly went on:

"I know a woman whose son goes to the high school. His name's Robert, and he's fifteen years old. Lately he's been reading a certain book—in secret. No, it's nothing erotic. Nihilistic. The title's this—*The Worth of Human Life*—and it's strictly forbidden."

We glanced at each other as we raised our drinks.

"So you think some of them put in a bit of secret reading?"

"I'm sure of it. There's quite a little *cénâcle* gathers round at this

woman's house, she's often quite beside herself. The little fellows read
everything. But they only read to criticize and condemn. They live in
their paradise of stupidity and scorn is their ideal. Cold times are coming,
my friend—the Age of the Fish."

"The Fish?"

"I'm only an amateur in astrology, but I know the earth's moving into
the zone of the Fish. The souls of men, my friend, will become as rigid
as the face of a fish."

And that is all that I can recollect of my long argument with Julius
Caesar. I well remember that while I was talking, he would light up his
death's head from time to time to irritate me. But I didn't let him, although I was fearfully drunk—

Then I woke up in a strange room. It wasn't my own bed. In the darkness. I was aware of another person's breathing. A woman, asleep. Was
she blond or a brunette? Red-headed or black? I couldn't remember. I
wanted to see her. Should I turn on the light?

No, I'd just go to sleep.

But I left the bed cautiously and went over to the window.

Still night. And I could see nothing. No streets, no houses. Nothing but
mist. Far off there was a lamp shining and the mist lay like water under
its glimmer. My window might have looked out over the sea.

I didn't wish to see more.

Or the Fish might swim up to the window and gaze in.

Translated from the German by R. WILLS THOMAS

YUGOSLAVIA

INTRODUCTION

By Rastko Petrovich

THE DIVISION of Yugoslav literature, at least between the Serbs and the Croats, is quite artificial, because in the period from the first World War to this, Serb and Croat writers incorporated approximately the same ideas, in the same language, and the same form of expression was used by the Serbs and Croats in Zagreb as well as the Croats and Serbs in Belgrade. Among the most popular of the Belgrade poets was Agustin Ujević, born Dalmatian and Croat. The powerful Croatian writer, Krleža, also edited in Belgrade with a Serb, M. Ristić, a magazine that published Serb writers. Furthermore, in Zagreb one of the most important figures was the editor of *New Europe,* Milan Čurcin, who is a Serb. To separate the works of Serb and Croat writers would make two mutilated parts of Yugoslav literature; only in Slovenia did writers differ in dialect and language, even though they were united in spirit and expression with their Serb and Croat colleagues.

When the war ended, a new generation of young writers made a fight—comparable to that made by the French, Russian, American, German and English writers—for a new expression. They experienced the same lack of comprehension on the part of the public as well as of established writers and critics. They captured their position by a hard struggle and by developing a new public among the young people—even by daily scandals. The best known names in Belgrade at this time were Ujević (Croat), Vinaver (Serbian Jewish), about whom Rebecca West wrote many passages in her *Black Lamb and Grey Falcon;* Manojlovic (Serb), Crnjancki (Serb from Banat), who wrote wonderful poetry; among the most advanced were D. Matić, M. Dedinac, M. Ristić, R. Drainac and many others.

In Zagreb the young writers were Cezarec (a follower of Krleža), and Simić. In Slovenia there was a very pure and sincere lyric poet, Otto Župančić.

The new writers were preoccupied with the crisis in human thought arising from the cataclysm of the first World War, but more than that, they were looking for expression, through their creations, of the mysterious mythological forces of the Slavic race. Soon after, in keeping with social movements, these writers one by one abandoned their purely intellectual creativity for the basic moral exploration of human destiny. Many of them were open admirers of Hegel and Marx and divided their lives between prison and editorial office. The rest made their way in the usual manner, but never compensated for the literary leaders of the previous generation that had produced a few great writers, such as Jovan Ducic (who died recently in the United States, having taken a strong stand in asking that the Serbs separate themselves from the Croats and Slovenes), M. Rakić and S. Pandurović. Only a few, such as Slobodan Yovanović, who was the most representative of all, Bora Stanković, a writer who best expressed the Balkan soul and strength in his novels, Isidora Sekulić and a very popular playwright, Branislav Nusić, were accepted by the younger writers as teachers or friends.

Dragisha Vasić

ON A VISIT

GENTLEMEN, I WAS TERRIBLY NERVOUS. Walking up and down in the room, I rubbed one leg against the other and jerked my shoulders in order to drive away, momentarily, about two million pricks that were crawling on my back under the skin and driving me mad. I had nothing to do. And thus, desperately idle, on that day I tried to think of my nervousness and my strange post-war moods. Before the war, I recall, it was not like this. Then, when I was in a bad mood, it lasted rather long; nevertheless, the same was true, when perchance I was in a good mood. Now, on the contrary: awhile sad and blue, I change in the twinkling of an eye, and here I am gay. Simply unbelievable, isn't it? Therefore, I say, my moods depend upon a strange kind of nervous condition perhaps inexplicable only to me, and produced by whichever object I rest my gaze upon, or by the kind or nature of the sound or noise I perceive about me.

That morning, when I gazed at the bookshelf it was askew as if ready to fall; I dared not even look at the painfully bent little globe, a decoration on the writing desk; and the pendulum of the clock sobbed the seconds, barely stuttering, until all of a sudden, perhaps accidentally and just so as not to crush me completely, it stopped like the heart of a dead man. But when I looked through the window and noticed the large yellow cross on the church, fastened to a ball of the same color, it seemed to me that I beheld an enormous laughing mouth over a terribly swollen neck. And I felt well, looking at the smiling cross, and I gazed at it for a long time, joyfully, almost hilariously, not realizing in the least that there was no reason or sense to such laughter and that it was only one of the irrefutable proofs of my very, very shaken mental condition.

However, I had to move from the window because from a distance the sounds of a funeral march reached me. This plunged me again into sorrow, now caused by the funeral procession of some officer; and it was of no use looking at the cross. Scarcely had the funeral procession passed when the head and the hand of the mail carrier appeared through the door of my room. Although somewhat changed, the handwriting on the letter that was handed me I recognized immediately, and not only the handwriting, for I also guessed in advance the contents of the letter itself. In Vujanovac, a small provincial town somewhere south, I have a best friend of my childhood, a companion of my youth and wars, who has invited me to visit him I don't know how many times. "So much time has passed since our last meeting, we have grown old and I miss you . . . and you know, yourself, that I have no better friend . . ." and so on. I opened the letter and, to be sure, it was just as I expected.

And all of a sudden, now I can't explain how and why, the decision to answer, finally, this cordial invitation flared up in me. And when I had reached that decision I again became happy, and how happy! Only this time it was with much reason, as I was convinced later, for this trip to Vujanovac cured me, at least temporarily, of the unbearable nervousness.

So I suddenly jumped up and rushed to another room and told the maid: "Listen, Maria, get me ready for a trip . . . five days, tonight, please. And do not forget the box with the yellow Imalin, as last time, for God's sake!"

Then I rushed into the room of my mother-in-law and frightened her terribly. She was concentrating deeply on a serial story by Toma Milinović, *Anka Obrenović and the Death of Prince Michael* and particularly on the chapter, "Anka's Son on the Eve of St. Nicholas." She was so frightened that she reprimanded me seriously, stooping over to pick up her pince-nez which had fallen from her nose when I rushed in so suddenly. We made up, of course, after my sweet excuses and flattery, and I begged her to go into town and buy several modest gifts: for a woman twenty-eight years old, a man thirty-seven years old, three children each ten years old, one girl and two boys. Of these children only one was a pre-war child. I do not know why I mentioned the last. When I had arranged everything so nicely and had sent the telegram saying that I was arriving next evening, I went to Moscow to collect there as much authentic news as possible, for I knew, and it was not the first time, that all of them there, and especially the defeated candidate for parliament, would gather around me to ask about the news in Belgrade and especially about the news "that is not to be told."

In the evening everything was ready and in order. Once more repeating the news and the commentaries that I had gathered from men who lied to others, I seized my things and started joyfully to the railroad station. There at the very door of the station Maria caught up with me and handed me the box with the yellow Imalin which she had forgotten again, and which I put into the pocket of my overcoat, and then I went to buy my ticket. I travelled by express, of course, for when a man travels he should travel like a gentleman. Well, I entered one of the cars, met the conductor and looked at him significantly: that is, I simply winked at him and he, understanding me, led me to a dark compartment which he unlocked after flashing his pocket light on the keyhole. He asked me not to light the candle and disappeared.

Thus I entered, locked myself in and awaited the departure of the train. A heavy rain was falling and drops like tears were flowing down the misty window-pane. Through that window-pane I was able to observe, through the dark, the wet rails and cars, and how the porters, stepping into little puddles, hurried with their two-wheeled carts to carry in the passenger baggage which was getting wet. Here and there a late passenger ran quickly by, to take his seat.

After a while we started. . . . I enjoy especially a fast train starting from the station because it starts elegantly, gliding without squeaking and that intolerable screeching, as an ordinary train would start, one on which I disliked to travel, as I said, even as a student.

At another station the conductor entered, inspected the ticket and we settled accounts: that is, I paid him as much as I thought his exceptional attention was worth. And I remained alone to listen to how the windows shook lightly to the pleasant vibration of the train and how the raindrops pattered on the roof of the car, which reminded me of the camp tent and of war, or of the difficulties that had passed.

And thus, comfortably placed, I began to think of my friend whom I was going to visit. We had been friends since childhood and throughout the period of our study we had been the best, inseparable chums. After having completed our studies we parted, and one day before the war he informed me that he was going to get married and asked me to come two days before the wedding. I remember well when I arrived in the province where he lived with his elderly parents. Toward evening he met me at the station with his little sister, and we went to his home where there ruled that solemn pre-wedding silence. Everything was clean, religious, expectant. After a dinner which we spent in talking with his father, a prominent merchant of the old type, severe in appearance and views, and with his mother, a gentle, wrinkled old woman, we went to his room in which I remember very well there flickered a candle before the icon of Archangel Michael. The window was open and the scent of damp earth and moist leaves, that damp freshness full of fragrance, with moonlight after the rain, filled the room with indefinite but dear memories of our early youth. At times there were heard footsteps of late passers-by, otherwise there ruled the complete silence of a provincial town asleep.

I remember very well that I began the conversation in this manner:

"And now, my dear friend, tell me how you decided to get married, and everything else that you wish to entrust to me, but tell me truthfully, above all, which love is it, in order?"

He laughed.

"Is it a real one?"

"Yes, real; very real. . . . Well, to tell you the truth, it is the third."

"And you tell me that it is just as powerful, passionate and true as the first, which I have not forgotten and which did not end very well?"

"It is the most powerful of all, believe me."

"That is possible, and I do not wonder, since I know you."

"Is it difficult to know me? I tell you all that is in my heart. And this is why I know that I love now, as I express myself in the same manner just as senselessly as I did when I loved as a student, and even more. . . . A month ago, in Belgrade, I waited one morning for her to come out of a dental office in that largest house on the Terazije. I was standing on the third floor, leaning over the rail and looking down into the depths and the concrete floor, when she came out. And at once I felt like convincing her how much I loved her, and I said, 'Do you want me to jump down? Please say, just nod with your head.' (I talked fast.) And had she nodded her head, or had I even noticed in her eyes the slightest wish to be convinced of my intention, I knew well that in the twinkling of an eye, I should have lain all bloody and smashed down there on the concrete floor. And you know I was like that, too, five years ago, when I wanted to do the same thing from the second floor of the old University, one morning before the class of Criminal Law, if she had only wished it . . . you know who."

"And you will die like that."

"That I don't know. But I am like that now, and that, since last winter when I strolled with her one evening in the first snow. That snow, I should say, did much. Large flakes were falling in streaks over us and the trees. Covered with them, we looked strangely clean that evening, when the whiteness of the snow covered up all the ugliness of the little shacks of Belgrade, which, in our eyes, all of a sudden became magic palaces. You can laugh at me, for you don't understand much of this, but I cannot express with what enthusiasm, walking after her, I watched the tracks of her little shoes, on the border of which pure snow gathered, and the curls of her black hair, covered with dry snow flakes which did not melt. Had someone asked me that minute, 'Nikola, what more beautiful happiness than yours is there in the world?' I would have answered, 'Man alive, no one has ever felt, nor will ever feel, more wonderful happiness than mine.' And tonight I repeat to you the same."

Then I remember very well how, after this, he struck a match to light a cigarette. His face was shining with health and it was kindly and child-like, and he, strong as if chipped from a mountain, with his curly disheveled hair which fell on his forehead, stretched out as he was, reminded me of a lion.

"And your happiness is not in the least disturbed by the circumstance that her father does not approve of the marriage and that you are going to marry in a somewhat unusual manner, for, as you told me, you are going to elope?"

"No! What do I care about her father!"

"Upon my honor!" I exclaimed enthusiastically and aloud, so that his little sister ran into our room, "I am happy to see a man seize his wife when he chooses her. Why procrastinate? That is the only way I would marry. For real happiness is felt only after a victory, and marriage which is made by general consent resembles those who are not capable of feeling the pleasure of conquest, the joy of gaining by force the favor of battle."

"Right you are. Nor do I beg of anybody."

"And your parents, what do they say?"

He became a little pensive.

"You mean mine? The old people are satisfied to see me married. Everything else is unimportant."

We remained in conversation until morning, and the next day we started to meet the fiancée, for whom we had to wait at a small station on the Niš line. The best man had to go, too, and there in the little village in the parish of one of our priest friends everything was made ready for the wedding.

I was just wishing to remember all the details of the original marriage of my friend—at that moment it was my most pleasant meditation—when I heard steps and some indistinct murmuring in the corridor, and immediately afterwards the conductor appeared with a sleepy gentleman who was mumbling something as if threatening.

I quickly gathered in my legs, which I had comfortably stretched out over the entire seat, and modestly occupied a corner, which I selected as most suitable, not even looking at the man who was entering, when he recognized me and exclaimed with pleasure: "Pardon me for disturbing you."

"Oh, Mr. Deputy," I answered, getting up, "so that is you? I hope that you will graciously leave for me one half of the seat, so that I can continue my dreams, which I love more than your politics. But if you impose upon it also your sacred deputy privilege, then. . . . I submit and will go into the corridor."

The long visage of my old school chum, who extended his hand to me, became serious and forced.

"You know that I, as the people's deputy, whose back is breaking from national worries, must travel undisturbed."

"I fully realize that," said I, turning on the light, "for indeed a deputy must travel undisturbed, in contrast to the rest of us, because he travels gratis."

And during that time, and while we thought in advance how to spend the time in pleasant conversation while traveling, I noticed how a slim figure like an apparition peeked through the door of our compartment and retired, to invade us a little later along with two more figures, one male, and one female with bobbed hair.

"We were just about suffocated in there, excuse us!" . . . and then the baggage was rushed in.

But while they were making themselves comfortable, not paying any attention to our nervousness, confusion and anger, the doors squeaked hoarsely and opened to admit a fat, unbuttoned, perspiring and pimply giant of a man in a threadbare and untidy suit made by a provincial tailor. He entered without greeting or apology, carrying in his hands two brand-new handbags made of fine yellow leather, and with a provocative attitude, after inviting his wife, who was somewhat visible behind his back, to follow him, he mumbled through his teeth:

"We too, perhaps, have paid for our tickets."

"Gentlemen"—my colleague mumbled something, determined to repel the unexpected attack (as for me, I did not mix in it because, in my nervousness, precisely such conflicts were pleasing to me)—"Gentlemen —I am a national deputy and this compartment is reserved for. . . ."

"I know nothing about it. My ticket is here," drawled the giant of a man, hitting his pocket.

"We do not recognize unelected deputies nor the temporary parliament," interrupted the first figure who had discovered us.

"Here we are all equal and everybody is entitled to one seat only," added the man with the new pieces of luggage. And it was clear to me that the newcomers had won the victory very easily. However, my colleague, most probably ashamed and insulted, blew at the candle so hard that he blew it over. But immediately afterward, the figure who had discovered us struck a match and lighted another candle.

Thereupon the man with the new luggage arranged his things and sat down comfortably, taking two seats for himself. Then he took off his shoes, which he placed under a seat, and, untying a package of food, he turned to his wife: "Are you hungry?" The woman, who was moving her lips, with some kind of horrified expression as if she were standing over an abyss, looked at her husband timidly and drawled, "Perhaps I might take a wing." And so, while the chicken bones crackled and the happy couple offered each other wine, we listened silently to the rain striking against the window and the train rattling rhythmically on its way.

After he had dined and wiped his mouth with his sleeve, he carefully tied up the package with the remnants of food and smoked a cigarette, after which we all coughed. The man leaned his head on his wife's shoulder, placed his legs comfortably between that figure who had discovered us and me, and quieted down while the woman struggled heroically to endure dutifully the enormous elephant weight of her husband's body.

Without any desire for conversation, my insulted colleague and I attempted to sleep, but this attempt, at least as far as I was concerned, was in vain, for those three figures who had entered first, and were in all probability students, began a very interesting conversation which they held quietly, and so quietly and confidentially that I had to strain myself to hear it.

The student who had discovered us, toothless, with a large sloping forehead, piercing glance and sarcastic mien, whose fresh behavior, nevertheless, pleased me although at my own expense, turned to the other with a fine, elegantly fatigued and sickly appearance on whose knees were two books which he had just taken from the rack above.

"What is that?"

He answered, "*At the Sign of Queen Pedauque.*"

"Have you read it?"

"No, I haven't finished it yet."

And thereupon, the morose student lifted the book from his knees, and then I noticed that he had only one and a half fingers on his right hand.

"That abbot Coignard," said the first one, "is some kind of relation to Cyrano de Bergerac. Or better, Cyrano and the abbot Coignard are two brothers, the first, about whom Rostand composed verse, and the second, about whom Anatole France in his brilliant style wrote prose. At least, it seems to me like that. Only I don't know whether Rostand invented Cyrano before Anatole France invented abbot Coignard. What do you think?"

The student without fingers modestly shrugged his shoulders and smiled. "I couldn't say. I don't know . . . I don't think so. On the contrary, they are two different men. One a knight, killer, fighter; and the other a bohemian . . . he steals cards while playing. . . . And then, two different fates: one, the hero dies from a blow with a wooden log; and this bum with a sword. . . . At least, according to what I have read so far."

"I couldn't tell you exactly," answered the first. "I haven't concentrated, but that is my impression and I wonder that you are not of the same opinion. However, think it over and you will agree with me. Like Cyrano, Jerome Coignard stands out by the depth of his mind. Both are unruly spirits, noble, witty, intellectual, far above the surroundings in which they lead a turbulent life, and both unrecognized and unhappy. To that extent . . . there is, there is something of Cyrano in abbot Coignard."

"I don't think you are right," said the woman student with the close haircut—a dry, rather ugly and exhausted woman with low breasts—just so as to mix in.

"And this, here—what is this?"

"This is *Morning Shadows* by Artzibashev."

"That is a good thing," remarked the toothless student. "I like Artzibashev especially well." And he flung back his hand and took out of the partition a flat little bottle of brandy which he offered to the woman student. She tipped several swallows and passed it on to the other student, but he refused.

"Comrade"—she leaned toward him and spoke very quietly—"I, too, find that it is a good book. Have you seen how people's spirits were prepared and encouraged? And don't you, yourself, see how today we lack Neznamovs and Korenievs?" And then even more quietly: "Believe me, Comrade, in my serious opinion, things like this should be translated most. We have never had such a great need for them. For among us, too, the spirits must be prepared, for a way out of this chaos and slime cannot even be imagined without terroristic action. You must agree fully with me in this. And you must finally join us."

The morbid student, at first slowly, then ever more lively and with more fire, answered with the following: "Miss, I have told you before that you can't address me like that. I am not a Communist, and even less an Anarchist, nor am I your colleague. That is all I have to tell you, once and for all. I . . . I should like to, but I can't. Excuse me, but you remind me very much of that Dora Barshovska. We are all only imitating, aren't we? Let us speak openly. . . . But nothing can warm me any longer, as it used to before the War. There is no organization, there is no environment that a man can enter without any reservation. And furthermore: I am disappointed, terribly disappointed; I have no faith any more. I sacrificed myself in the War because I believed that liberty was worth more than life, I fought for a better society, that is, I hoped that men would become better. Isn't it so? We all did the same. Who is there who did not believe that evil would be punished? Who doubted justice? Who is there who did not believe in better days? And today, what have we lived to see? The small part which became better has become exhausted. It is only a mute witness to that which is being done today by those whom the War did not change in the least, or better say whom the War has changed to such an extent that it has spoiled their hearts. And what has happened to liberty? . . . And should I, after all that I have seen, experienced and suffered, close my eyes consciously and believe again? Believe in what? Believe in whom? What should I follow? What is it that is supposed now to arouse human hearts, to set aflame, again, that noble disinterested enthusiasm that has become extinguished? What is that word of life, which like a torch of true light, should be carried now by those selected in the midst of this dark and perverted generation? I don't know. I don't know, indeed. And therefore, when you speak to me about your ideal, I am completely cold, because that which you seek does not correspond to objective conditions, and it is not that quite new thing which we sought and imagined indistinctly in the War, bearing our crosses of suffering. And who can say today, after the War, that he is already through with his spiritual orientation and that he knows what he wants and that the thing he wants is the true and greatest justice? And you? You speak for yourself. You want something, and that which you want is not of you, of us, directly. Just say: are you not Russians without a Russian soul? Perhaps you have something of it, but not all of it, and it is not yours. That is why there are no Korenievs and Neznamovs. And there will be none of them, as yet. And in the new order toward which you strive, believe me, in our country those who are not worn out would be the masters again, that is, those who did not suffer; because those who suffer, always become tired of power that is seized by those clever ones in mouse holes. I am not naive; I no longer believe; I do not know whom to trust and what, I have no ideals. Do not call me Comrade."

"And you, Brother, when you have neither will-power nor ideals, you fold your arms, as you have done, suffer, gnash your teeth and watch things being done," answered the toothless student, who during all this listened carefully to him, although he did not look at him once. "If we all were to speak like you, what would happen? Fortunately, not everybody thinks that way. One must make a desperate effort, Brother. One must think what to do. Let there be, of us in the beginning, only a handful of men. That is enough. Better anything than nothing. For today there is no real opposition. And why is there no opposition? Because men think faultily, like you, and they have no ideals. We must create a real opposition, for what is a nation without opposition? Renan said, 'Opposition makes the honor of a country.' As for myself, I have ideals: justice. And I neither can nor want to fold my arms. I have broken my teeth, gnashing, and now I want to break the ribs of somebody else. Well, that is how I am; mad, burning up. I can't look any longer at all that is being done before our eyes. . . . Do you live in Belgrade, Brother? Do you have eyes? You have no arm, I know that. And you are not sorry you gave it. And I, you see, would be sorry. Well, you said yourself; 'When the reactionaries tighten up a little, affairs quiet down and war millionaires crawl out.' Everywhere, on the street, in the theatre, at the races; they are everywhere with their coaches, automobiles, dress, arrogance, squandering immorality, gambling for enormous sums; everywhere behind our backs. Just look at this friend here."

And pointing his finger at the man across:

"How much do you think he is worth? A million like a penny. Just look at his luggage. There is no place on him that a dog could bite. The type of a war millionaire."

The girl student nodded her head and said almost aloud:

"Indeed the type of a newly rich."

During that time I looked stealthily to see whether the man leaning on his wife's shoulder was asleep or just pretending. The woman, I noticed, opened her mouth several times as if she wished to say something. But I was not sure whether she really wanted to say something or just felt like yawning. . . . As for the man, by his short and broken movements made during the course of the last few words referring to him, I had no doubt that he was just pretending to sleep, for earlier I noticed how, from time to time, out of the corner of one eye, he watched whether his luggage of fine leather was there where he had left it. . . . He evidently listened carefully to the last part of the conversation, for after those clear and challenging words that had fallen at his expense, he arose and flared up:

"A Communist, that is, a Bolshevik, that is, a lazy idler, that is, a rebel. Today, everyone can earn if he wants to, and as much as he wants. And you are very impolite and fresh!"

"That is possible," said the student calmly, as if he had expected just these words. "I am a very impolite man. But you are very much a war millionaire, and I a pre-war student. These here, and I. . . . Very much!"

The man made a motion with his arm as if he were getting ready for a physical attack, and we began to fidget.

"Aksentije!" his frightened wife seized him by the sleeve, "Don't forget yourself!— And you, don't you insult him!"

And, I don't know why, she kept looking at the woman student.

This one cut in: "Silence! Why are you meddling in the discussion?"

"Yes, in the discussion!" remarked the toothless student ironically, and he poked with his index finger into the air.

"Look at that!" said the wife who did not take her eyes off the woman student with the mannish haircut and assumed an even more frightened aspect as if she were about to fall into an abyss. "What does this nuisance of a woman want? I never said anything to her; let her be silent!"

"Yes!" added her husband. "How is it that a woman travels alone? If you were mine, I would kill you, you hairless wench!"

And even today, when I am obliged at this point of the story to touch on that unpleasant moment, I don't know through just what mysterious means the whole thing took that turn, or, to use a military term to which I am accustomed, the situation came out so unfortunately; that not the toothless student, who actually provoked the conflict, but the woman student, I repeat, the woman student with the mannish haircut took upon herself the entire weight of that violent attack, that she became the objective, the aim or target, the center of this mad counter-attack of the enemy who was represented in this sad and undesirable case by the man, with the luggage of brand-new, fine yellow leather, and his wife with the frightened expression. I only remember distinctly the details: that the woman student, after the words directed at her by the man, shrieked mortally, so mortally that my friend the deputy, although positively not mixed up in the affair with the new luggage, stretched out his arm instinctively for the bottle of cognac, and handed her that bottle with lightning speed, so to say, sticking it under her nose; that she immediately swallowed a few good swallows—very powerful ones, which, in my opinion, she had solely to thank that after those terrible words she did not faint immediately, as we all, with justified and indescribable terror, expected.

In a moment, however, when the tension of our disturbance was at a climax, the fresh student turned to the maddened man in a very conciliatory tone.

"Don't be angry!" he said, all red with irony. "It was all my fault. I saw the brand-new luggage—and you, here, look as if you came out of a jail or penitentiary."

"You owl!" yelled the merchant. "Now I must let go!"

But fortunately, and to our surprise, he controlled himself and looking the student up and down, said:

"Only suspicious characters dress as well as you."

"The luggage is ours!" shrieked the wife. "And my husband is the elder of his guild."

"Congratulations! Oh, congratulations!" shouted the student as if deeply touched.

"Wife!" said the merchant, all red and after long and silent control as if afraid that the insult which might come would be too heavy, "These are actors, for sure!"

And when this word fell like thunder from a clear sky, the wife became afraid of the artificial excitement of the student who was getting ready to protest.

"Aksentije!" she said scoldingly. "For God's sake, take that word back!"

The woman student gnashed her teeth and looked bloodthirstily at the wife (who after these words of giving in had withdrawn behind the wide back of her husband) and let fly at her various insults in French (such as "rag," "camel," etc.) while the toothless student laughed cynically and the other sat quietly, as one is supposed to sit at a lecture.

But, upon the energetic and sincere intervention of the deputy and myself, the opponents gave in; tense nerves gradually loosened and we spent the time after that, as far as Lapovo, in silence. Only, when the train stopped at Lapovo, the toothless student violently shook the merchant who was snoring as if in a trench.

"Mr. War Millionaire!" he shouted, "you have filed the track-rails!"

"What?" he was frightened awakening,—"What happened?"

"You whistled the alarm and the train stopped."

"No bad feeling, gentlemen," the merchant's wife concluded the 'discussion' and quickly and hastily gathered their things, while the husband, with open and moist mouth, looked at us unconsciously.

And thereupon, all except the toothless student, got up to transfer to the Kragujevac train by which they were to continue their journey.

"My third-class ticket is to Vujinovac," said he, saying good-bye to his colleagues. "Up to here it gave me an honest ride in the second class. It is right, now, to let it go back to its proper place."

And he picked up his things and went into the third class. With the rest who transferred to the Kragujevac train the deputy went too, and I remained alone in that same hot atmosphere in which, for a long time after their leaving, still hummed the turbulent conflict between two worlds, neither guilty nor wrong, however, but which cannot and never will be able to come to an understanding.

Translated from the Serbian by MAE LLOYD PARKER RUZICH

Milan Dedinac

HOW SILENT THEY WHO DIE

How SILENT they who die,
Friend!
Here where man dies alone.

How in gloom they drag themselves away,
Gentle,
Into a woeful day.

Death here is hard,
Friend!
Where the field is too wide,
Where the sky is high, high above.

Here where we are few,
Left so miserably
On the black plain
Under the sky,

Where one is in the field,
Another silent on the threshold;
Where into grass and fields
Weary roads have led us.
Translated from the Serbian by MAE LLOYD PARKER RUZICH

Borivoje Stanković

STANOJE

STANOJE WAS KNOWN all around the business district and the lower town. On market days he would borrow three or four dinars from somebody, buy junk, sell it, return the borrowed money and soak down the net profit.

People said, and he himself boasted of it on occasion, that he used to be well off. As a matter of fact, he once owned a thriving business, had his own shop and a little house, with a crippled sister in it. After my aunt married my uncle, however, he took to drink, neglected his business, finally gave it up altogether and left the house to the sister. He hired himself out here and there, ending up at my uncle's—where he demanded no payment for his services, just bread and a place to sleep in the stable.

Now and then, when he was drunk, he would call my aunt's children and me and take us to a sweets shop, to buy candy and whatever we wanted. Then he sent us to my aunt to show off our presents, while he followed, smiling, and sang his favorite song:

"Wine, fellow, for us!
Schnapps out, and pour us!

I will go and drink like mad,
And forget that I am sad."

"Sure, sing, keep singing—and what about tomorrow?" was my aunt's scolding reception.

He stopped, leaned against the wall and looked at her rather oddly. "Why not? Do you pay for it? It's my money." And as if in defiance he would sit down on the ground, cross his legs, pull a bottle of liquor out of his belt, drink and go on singing.

When sober, he worked like a worm. No matter what kind of a job he was told to do, he did it, toiled and kept still. If we children bothered him too much, teased and finally roiled him, he would drop the work, chase us away and leave. But whoever had annoyed him and however angry he was, when my aunt approached, put her hand on his shoulder and soothingly, gently said, "Stanoje, why are you mad? Stop it; go, do this or that," he resumed his work at once and labored as if he had gone crazy.

My uncle was a violent, brutal man. In the house, his word was law. How often didn't he beat my aunt and kick her out the door! But especially when he was drunk you'd have liked to run away from him into the wide world. I remember once, how he came home drunk, seized my aunt and hit out at her furiously. We children hid in the barn. Stanoje was chopping wood in the courtyard. As long as he did not hear my aunt's voice, he toiled in silence. But when my uncle tore at her hair and dragged her about and struck her, we heard her cry out. Stanoje, hearing the first muffled scream, listened as if to make sure that he had heard right; then he threw the axe away and ran into the house.

"Don't, Stanoje, don't," we yelled at him from our hideout.

"Shut up, you," he told us and his voice was trembling. ˙

He went into the room and stepped between Aunt and Uncle and seized his hands, so Aunt could get away. Then he released Uncle's hands, remained standing before him and begged, "Don't do it, Sir, don't—it's a woman, after all!" My uncle stopped, startled but trembling with rage.

"You? You dare—you dog!" he shouted, picked up his stick and forcefully hit Stanoje's head. Stanoje reeled; he left the room spattered with blood, went to the well, washed his head and face and put tobacco leaves on the wound to still the flow of blood. Then, head lowered and with his hands in his belt, he staggered off the farm. . . .

It may have been the reason why Aunt was attentive toward him. Every evening, with dinner, she gave him a large glass of wine. He got the worn-out clothes, and in winter he got warm woolen blankets to cover himself at night.

Once, Aunt fell sick. Uncle was on a trip, and there was no one in the house to take care of the household and the children. Stanoje took everything upon himself. He kept the house in order, washed and dressed the children and did all the housework, like a woman. And in the evening, when he was finished with everything and had put the children to bed, he sat down outside the room in which Aunt lay abed and watched the whole night on the threshold, to be there in case she needed anything. If he heard from the women who nursed her that the patient had uttered some wish, he ran away and brought her what she wanted. Once, he came with his belt and breast-pockets stuffed full of oranges, lemons and other fruit. He arrived laughing; we leaped at him and begged, but he shook his head: "Go, go; this isn't for you!"

Then he entered Aunt's room and shook it all out in front of her, without saying a word. Aunt was startled, looked at him severely and said, "Are you crazy? What am I to do with that?"

He scratched his head and said nothing.

"Tell me, what is that? Where did you get the money for it? I don't want it." And she pushed the fruits away, so that apples and oranges fell to the ground and rolled away.

He bent down, picked up one piece after the other and handed them all back to her: "Take it and eat," he urged her.

Aunt was angry that the poor fellow had spent so much money. She did not look at him and only said:

"I don't want to. You're not thinking of yourself! How long is that going to go on?"

"As long as I live. . . . It's been willed that way, for me." And his voice trembled.

So as not to reject him altogether, Aunt took a piece and tasted it. At that he jumped out into the kitchen in glee, embraced and kissed us children and lifted us all the way up to the ceiling with his strong arms. . . .

During her illness he did not drink a drop. But as soon as she had recovered he went to the tavern and drank until he was unconscious.— Uncle drank a lot, too. His was a rich house; there was everything aplenty, only love and understanding were lacking. Yes, poor Aunt!

She was tall and slim, had great black eyes and fine brows, a little mouth and thin lips. She was a hard worker—tireless from dawn to dusk. Often when my uncle came home drunk, she fled to us, spent the night in our house and did not dare go home until he had slept off his liquor! In the end she began to be ailing but always kept on with her work, and nobody paid any attention to it. One morning, though, she stayed in bed and did not get up again. . . .

It was on an evening in autumn. The cold had started; a great fire was going in the kitchen. We children were standing about the open fireplace with our feet in the ashes, baking corncobs in the embers. My sick aunt was lying in the adjoining room. She must have been very ill, for my mother and the other women were going in and out on tiptoes and talking to each other in whispers. Stanoje was again huddling silently outside the sickroom. Suddenly the door was opened and Uncle came out.

"Go in, she's calling you," he said to Stanoje. He himself sat on the stool by the fire and hid his face in his hands.

Stanoje went in. The door remained open.

"Stanoje," Aunt was heard to say in a weak, tired voice, "pull your brains together, for I won't be here any more. Pull your brains together, for you have no one in the world. You're standing all alone. Don't drink. Goodbye—and—forgive me!"

I looked at my uncle; his eyes were moist and the lids swollen with tears; his mustache was trembling.

Stanoje's face was bathed in tears as he came out of the room and huddled in the corner by the door again. He covered his hairy face with his hands and sobbed. The tears were running over his hands.

Uncle looked at him darkly.

"What are you crying for? Shut up!" he told him harshly. To us, however, he signaled with his hand that we should go to bed.

"S-i-rr . . ." I still heard Stanoje's choked voice . . .

Two days later we buried my aunt.

The days went by, and Stanoje went more and more to seed. (With my uncle's house, too, it went from bad to worse.) Stanoje was no longer in Uncle's service but went from house to house in the town district and did all sorts of work. He chopped wood, butchered livestock, dug graves in the churchyard.

No matter whether it was summer or winter, he went about in torn pants and a tattered shirt, held together with rags. His hair was matted, the low forehead showed deep creases, the cheek-bones stood out, the strong jaw was covered by a dense, unkempt beard; everything about him was savage, sad and desolate. His whole appearance, with the dull, withered face, the open, hairy chest and unconsciously woeful glance, made a strong but painfully repulsive impression on everyone. If he stood before you with his eyes cast down and his voice toneless, monotonous, you felt tempted to run, just so you would not have to see him any longer. He spent his nights with us; we had given him a tiny room. My mother often gave him bedclothes, but he always carried everything away at once, sold it and bought drinks with what he got for it.

After a few years my mother died. To bury her, we had to open
Aunt's grave. Stanoje was ready at once to dig my mother's grave. He
stood before me with the spade in his hand:

"Shall I go, Mile?"

"Yes, Stanoje, go, but be sure to gather the bones carefully."

"Sure, sure."

"And do you know whose grave you are to open?"

"No."

"Aunt's."

"No, no, then I'm not going!" he called in fright and paled and sat
down on the ground.

"Why not?"

"I'm not going! I'm not going!" he merely called and trembled all
over and held me off with his hands.

"What? Do you want somebody else to do it?"

He rose. I brought him a small glass of brandy.

"No, no, give me a quart. Give me a quart," he said, stepping back.

"Later, Stanoje, or you'll get drunk and won't know . . ."

"No, no—a quart, Mile, a quart—oh, oh . . . !"

I brought a full quart bottle. He took it, held it up against the sun,
shook it; then he drank half of it down. "Oh!" And he shook himself. Then
he took the spade and went.

After dinner they gave me a fine satchel of pure silk, to carry to the
churchyard, where Aunt's remains were carefully to be gathered into it.
Her bones were to be blessed once again, put in my mother's coffin and
buried again together with her.

I went to the churchyard. Even from a distance I saw, next to my
aunt's grave, a pile of earth, and half-rotted boards and remains of clothing
on top of it. On the edge of the grave lay an empty liquor bottle, beside it
the spade and Stanoje's tattered coat. I bent over the grave and immediately
recoiled in horror.

At the bottom of the grave lay Aunt's complete skeleton. Evidently
he had proceeded with care, for the skull, the arm bones, the ribs—everything still was lying next to each other, every limb in its place . . . Above
her earthly remains stood Stanoje, leaning on the rake, smeared with
earth, his forehead contorted, the hair disheveled and full of earth, looking down on the bones. . . .

I had withdrawn and was looking up at the sky. It was blue, cloudless.
The swallows twittered in the clean, dry air, a lark was rising jubilantly.
I took courage and looked down again into the grave. Stanoje stroked his

eyes with the earth-covered hand. Suddenly he fell on his knees and bowed over the skeleton.

"Kato!" he moaned, aloud. "I—this—to you . . ."

"Stanoje!" I called in terror.

He jumped to his feet and threw up a terrible glance. But when he recognized me, he controlled himself quickly, picked up the rake again with his hand and said, in a low tone: "Oh, it's you, Mile."

I handed him the satchel. "Put everything in there," I said, and my voice trembled.

"Yes, right away," he answered humbly. He took the satchel, slowly bent down, crossed himself and reverently, as before touching the sacrament, began to gather her bones. His hands were trembling and from time to time a tear rolled over his face that was dirty with earth.

"Don't cry," I said.

He raised his head and looked at me with a glance in which I could read everything: a buried love, a ruined life and eternal agony for something irretrievably lost.

He died a few years later. It is said that right before his death he ran away from the hospital and the guards found him dead on the way to the churchyard.

Translated from the Serbian

POLAND

INTRODUCTION

By Manfred Kridl

THE CHARACTER of the literature of restored Poland was neither homogeneous nor revolutionary. It was characterized by differing trends, both "old" and "new," thus sharing the fate of all European literatures of that time—yet it possessed a clear face of its own, enabling us to form a new "period" in Polish literature between 1918 and 1939.

The first ten years of this period are distinguished by a predominance of lyric poetry, a predominance not only in literary production but also in consumption. This lyric movement was headed by a group of young poets called after the title of their poetical monthly, *Skamander*. Their first reaction to the recovered political independence was to insist on regaining independence for poetry also, that is, to obtain the liberation of poetry from all the national and social goals which had been a sacred burden of all Polish literature during the enslavement of the nation since the very end of the eighteenth century, and which forced Polish poets to be not only artists but also spiritual leaders and moral teachers. The Skamandrites did indeed realize that their first and most important goal was to be *good poets* and write the *best poems* possible. "We want to be poets of the present day—that is our faith and our entire program. We do not want great words [in the sense of great slogans and programs]— we want a great poetry. Then every word will become great." One of the young poets expressed the same sentiments in a more radical manner: "Since there is spring on the earth let me see the spring and not Poland."

This "program" did not mean, of course, a separation from life in an "ivory tower." The Skamandrites really became what they wished to be, that is, poets of the contemporaneity, "the present day." The main motif of their poetry became the nature of the big, modern city, as was the case in Italian Futurism and Russian "revolutionary" poetry. Their poetic language is enriched by urban elements, the speech of the town-dwellers of all social classes. Consequently their metaphors are handled in new connections, become more courageous and more surprising. Average and common words recover new poetical force. The versification changes no less. The metrical construction becomes more complicated, and, at the same time, more free without approaching the rhythmlessness of the futurists. Stanzas are kept, too, although they undergo different modulation, of course; complete abandonment of stanzas is very infrequent. As

378

to the rhyme, we meet all the acquisitions of contemporary poetry, including difficult and extraordinary rhymes, various kinds of assonance, but not infrequently we find traditional, simple rhymes too.

These general characteristics apply more or less to the main Skamandrites, who nevertheless present very different individualities. The first place in this group was occupied early in his career by Juljan Tuwim (born 1894), whose poems distinguish themselves by an extraordinary lyric eruptiveness, by a conception of the *word* as an elementary, metaphysical being, by a tendency both to the fantastic and to simplicity, by definite and sharp images.

The lyric poetry of the second main figure of the movement, Antoni Slonimski, is more concentrated, intellectual, discursive and rhetorical. It treats both actual and eternal problems with a deep sense of pathos and tragicalness, with a tendency to destroy traditional structures and to employ the most unusual versification.

The youngest of the Skamandrites, Jan Lechon (born 1899), is the most conservative among them, both in versification and in style. Many historical and literary motifs give his poems a rather academic character, increased by a classicism of versification and a poetical crystallization. The representative of a very young and fresh spirit is Kazimierz Wierzynski, the singer of the felicity of existence, the enthusiasm for life, the apotheosis of physical beauty and strength. His collection of poems, *The Olympic Laurel*, won him the first international prize of the Ninth Olympiad in Amsterdam.

In a more casual connection with the Skamander group are: Miss Illakowicz, a very fertile and very unequal poet, inclined to strange fantasies and to a free, unsyllabic versification; Madame Pawlikowska, a master of short, epigrammatic poems, with a tendency toward preciosity; finally, Ladislas Broniewski, an excellent poet devoted to the cause of the proletariat, rather conservative in versification but gifted with an extraordinary invention and emotional force.

A strong opposition to the Skamandrites was represented by various groups of the youngest poets, generally called *Avangarde*. They preached a radical reform of lyric poetry based on such Western and Eastern European trends as futurism, expressionism and surrealism. The result was the destruction of the romantic-impressionistic "emotionalism," of traditional verse forms, of a regular rhythm and the use of a new language full of neologisms, new syntactic structures and abbreviations. The main theoretician of this movement was Thaddeus Peiper; the most talented poets were Przybos, Kurek, Milosz and Czechowicz.

The older generation of poets was represented by John Kasprowicz, the most prominent poet of the former epoch, Leopold Staff who influenced the Skamander movement and was reciprocally influenced by it, and Thaddeus Boy-Zelenski, an excellent translator of hundreds of French works both in poetry and prose, and a prominent literary critic.

Simultaneously with lyric poetry there was a development of the novel which within the second decade of this period even won preponderance. Both older and younger novelists were hard at work. Stephen Zeromski (died 1925), the leading novelist of the former epoch, creator of a new form of novel strongly permeated by lyric elements, continued his work of treating basic social problems in a sharp, ruthless and at the same time pathetic manner, which made him the very social conscience of the contemporary generation. The novels of Andrew Strug (died 1935), a writer less talented than Zeromski but very careful in composition and technique, dealt with the same problems. The novels of Vladimir Perzynski (died 1930), concerned with the life of contemporary Warsaw, possessed a documentary character and considerable narrative value, but Perzynski, contrary to Strug, rather neglected composition and plot. A late echo of the epoch of symbolism was the novel by Waclaw Berent (died 1940), entitled *Living Stones*, containing rather loose pictures of medieval European life presented through an extremely stylized and artificial language. But the last works of Berent turned to a kind of *biographie romancée* created in France and very popular throughout Europe.

The novels of Madame Sophie Nalkowska underwent an interesting evolution. Her early activity was characterized by a series of novels devoted to an entirely new, at least for Polish literature, picture of feminine psychology, a product of the refined bourgeois culture. In this Nalkowska showed already an amazing talent for psychological analysis, planned composition and a style quite in harmony with this somewhat hothouse atmosphere. After the first World War, this world changed. New problems arose, concerning the inherent evil of all war, the evolution of life in Poland (*The Romance of Thérèse Hennert*), criminals and prisoners "who—so to speak—carry on the duty of evil, since its necessary amount in the world must be in some way distributed among people" (*The Walls of the World*). Nalkowska's style also changed completely, became more simple, concentrated, economical. It was connected with the so-called "authenticism" or new reality ("Neue Sachlichkeit") in Western European literature. A "written reality" was now the aim of Nalkowska. It led to an abandonment of many of the traditional techniques for holding the reader's attention, of composition and plot; these were replaced by objective description of simple and common reality (*Choucas*). Her last novel (*Frontiers*), however, marks a harmonization of fascinating plot and "written reality."

The younger generation of Polish novelists tried to discover new means of expression, either within the framework of realism or beyond it. In each case the experiment was concerned chiefly with composition and style, and was only rarely of a revolutionary character. The prevailing method was to achieve a renewal of the traditional realistic technique by abandoning the chronological sequence of events, by flash-backs to earlier moments of the plot, by parallel actions. In addition these writers introduced comments by author or protagonist, mingling of different points of view from which characters and events are presented, synthetic abbreviations in characterization, dramatization of the dialogue, and so on. There were also among the young writers attempts to return to traditional, very slightly complicated novel forms.

Ferdinand Goetel (born 1890) first wrote a series of short stories and a novel *Kar-Chat* (translated into English, with a preface by G. K. Chesterton) very simple in composition and style but undoubtedly fresh in narrative talent. In his next novel *From Day to Day* (also translated into English) he applied a technique of two parallel plots dealing with the past and the present, the analysis of the former from the point of view of the latter, and reciprocally.

Unfortunately, the novel ends rather by a breaking off than a real dénouement.

A much more radical innovator in composition, but still within the framework of "realistic probability," was Michel Choromanski (born 1904) in the novel *Envy and Medicine*. The novel begins with the end, then goes back to the beginning of the story. But this narration is again interrupted by flashbacks. All this creates a very suggestive atmosphere of unrest, unusualness and mystery.

Jaroslav Iwaszkiewicz (born 1894) experimented with different methods and styles, but finished by returning to simple realism. His collection *The Girls from Wilk* shows great ability in short-story composition.

In Helen Boguszewska's novel *Sabina's Whole Life* we find a very expressive picture of memories experienced during a fatal illness and presented within a framework. Mary Kuncewicz did an almost classic novel of character in her *Foreign Women*. Eve Szelburg-Zarembina united realistic and fantastic elements in a provocative manner in *The Wanderings of Joanna*. Sophie Kossak-Szczucka conceived an ambitious presentation of the first Crusade, based on an immense amount of historical material which, unfortunately, was not always artistically digested.

Mary Dombrowska (born 1892) broke with all experimentation in her very popular and voluminous novel *Nights and Days*. It is a novel-*chronicle* of the conventional kind, starting with the genealogy of the main characters and developing the narrative in strict chronological sequence. In this way the structure of the novel approaches real life and acquires a quality of authenticity, especially when, as in the case of Dombrowska, the characters are average people, the narration flows slowly and the language is simple and beautiful.

Another aspect of simplicity was presented by Joseph Wittlin (born 1896), one of the prominent Skamander poets, in *Salt of the Earth*. It is a "war novel" but quite different from others of this kind. The world of war, or at least its inception, is here shown through the eyes of an extremely simple Polish-Ukrainian peasant, in whose eyes everything is unusual and mysterious. Simple facts and events become symbols; the experiences of a very average man assume a universal meaning, become the experiences of all the souls tortured by the cruelties of war. The charm of the narration is strengthened by a delicate lyric element shown in emotion, irony and the author's commentaries and aphorisms. As a result we have a unique *epico-lyric* novel much more effective and expressive than the works of Remarque or Barbusse.

The most representative novels of Julius Kaden-Bandrowski (born 1885), *Dark Wings* and *Meteusz Bigda* stand on the border between experimental realism and an intended anti-realism. Besides a striving for probability and logical motivation, there are some visionary elements, some conscious distortions of real forms, sounds and colors, a crass expressionism—one might say, expression for its own sake. Kaden sometimes obtains strong effects, but in general his method becomes monotonous, though in applying more restrained techniques, the author achieved a work full of touching sentiment in *My Mother's City*.

An entire break with realism is represented by Stanislas Ignace Witkiewicz (born 1885), novelist, dramatist, talented painter and theoretician of "pure form" which he applies especially to drama and painting. His aim is to distort life and the world of fantasy for the purpose of creating a "whole," the meaning of which should be determined exclusively by the dramatic structure and not by the requirements of psychology and real life. He wrote a number of dramas which, unfortunately, are all but "organic wholes." In arbitrarily banning the novel from the realm of art, he wrote many "novels" in which distortion is bound with realistic and even hyper-naturalistic elements. A more serious, concentrated and ripe artist in this trend is Bruno Schulz.

The Polish drama of this period is represented by a number of interesting although not pioneering works. Charles Hubert Rostworowski (born 1877) won a prominent position before the first World War with his drama *Judas*. The essays of the same genre which followed were not successful. But a cycle of dramas dealing with problems of contemporary life (*Surprise*) showed again Rostworowski's dramatic force.

A great literary event was the presentation of Zeromski's drama *The Quail*. Its problem recalled the most touching problems of his former novels and was here presented with an amazing dramatic ability, with concentration and force. The motivation of the dénouement is, however, a weak point in the piece.

Another representative novelist, Madame Nalkowska, produced two very interesting dramas. One of them, *Women's House*, is distinguished by a high dramatic tension, although there is no "action" in the traditional sense of the word. This tension is evoked by means of a very subtle composition of recollections expressed in dialogues among a number of women of different age, revolving around men and erotic experiences. The other drama, *The Day of His Return*, exposes different and complicated ramifications of crime in the moral and emotional lives of persons close to the criminal.

The novelist Perzynski wrote many spirited and witty comedies, unfortunately showing deficiencies in structure. The comedies of the poet Slonimski, *The Negro of Warsaw, Family*, reflect somewhat the spirit of G. B. Shaw. Like the plays of the Englishman, they are based on an intelligent, witty, ironic and sarcastic dialogue by which the whole "action" is created without the necessity of using many "events." A similar character is shown by the plays of Bruno Winawer, one of which, *The Book of Job*, attained the honor of being translated into English by Joseph Conrad. Finally we may note an interesting experiment by Anthony Cwojdzinski in transposing into dramatic form actual scientific problems. The author, a physicist by profession and actor and stagemanager by predilection, wrote one play on the *Theory of Relativity* and another on *Freud's Theory of Dreams*. The explanation of these theories is, of course, very popular, sometimes caricature, but witty and good theater.

We may say that in general, then, the drama, as well as the novel, kept itself in the framework of a largely conceived realism, and, in summing up, that Polish literature of this period carried out its function on a high level, much higher, at any rate, than that of other spheres of Polish life.

Joseph Wittlin

THE EMPEROR AND THE DEVIL

PEACE REIGNED IN THE HEAVENS, and quiet on earth; not a dog barked, not a cock crowed, when the Emperor Francis Joseph called his soldiers. The Emperor's own voice could not reach to the Huzul land, but the Imperial Post could reach it, and where even the Post broke down, the gendarmes and district clerks took over the task.

Sergeant-majors sat in orderly-rooms, side by side with Suppaken; * and they delved into the oldest folios, and found there the lists of the annual conscript classes, back to the very earliest years. They copied out the names of all the men in each class; and they knew of these men one thing only: that they had names. So, to every name they addressed a summons, and the summonses they sent to the municipality. Many of those so summoned had lain for years in the municipal cemetery, or were rotting in foreign soil. But names die less quickly than men, and death keeps his registers more carefully than sergeant-majors. So the Emperor summoned both the living and the dead.

Peter Neviadomski belonged to the class of 1873. He had no idea of that himself, having no head for figures; but the municipality knew it. The municipality knew everything. The municipality kept books and forms on which it wrote down, in ink, and for all times, who was born into the world, and when, and who had left it. Every year, in peace time, the municipality draws up a list, and sets down every man who has completed his twenty-first year; and every man has to report himself to the Army. Blind, lame, deaf, or hunchbacked—it makes no difference. Once in his life every man must report for service. For the Army, as for the Kingdom of Heaven, all are called, but not all are chosen.

In the days of peace Peter had been thrice exempted as being the sole support of his family, which, at the time, included his grey-haired mother and Parashka's illegitimate child. A little later both died, the bastard first and then the old woman. But what had Peter gained? He had gained this: that he was not taken by the Army. He believed they had forgotten him, but he was wrong. The Emperor had not forgotten Peter Neviadomski; he had reserved him for the dark hour.

And now the hour had come. Not dark, but light, being the hour before

* *Suppaken.* The term applied to soldiers who remained in the service after their term had expired, in return for their keep (the soup).

the night falls, the hour when the earth grows still, as though stroked by the hand of her for whom the bells of all the churches were ringing at that moment. A clear sky, blue as the robe of the Blessed Virgin, softly enfolded the earth where noise and strife were dying down. The very insects, weary of endless circling in the warm air, had muffled their buzzing wings. At that hour human hearts, full of turmoil, beat more quietly, and to the most brutal there was granted the blessing of peace.

And this great peace had laid hold of Peter. He had forgotten the war which was raging somewhere far off beyond the dimming horizon, outside the boundaries of his tired senses. Already in the cooling air the whir of the distant sawmill had died down, and smoke was climbing up over the green bank of bushes which hid the village from his view. All the housewives were preparing supper. Over the favored cottages that had real chimneys the smoke went up in straight, tall columns and melted into the blue sky; from the poor mud huts it swirled out, clinging close to the ground, and lay there like a broad and lazy mist. Peter fell to peeling potatoes; the last passenger train of the day had gone past signal-box 86. There was nothing to come now but a freight train due in two hours. Peter sat down in the doorway of his little house and removed his cap. Bass lay beside him, with his nose to the ground and one eye on the ants which were crawling all around him. Wrapped in peace, he would do them no harm. One could hear his placid, regular breathing.

But suddenly the dog threw up his head and pricked his ears. He had heard a suspicious sound below the embankment. A moment later he leaped up and stood on watch. Somebody must have stumbled against the wires connecting Peter's levers with the gates: they twanged softly. They were placed so low, almost touching the ground, that, in the silence, even their quivering was audible. Something was moving in the stillness, some one was coming to the box. Peter paid no attention to the dog's disquiet. He was industriously peeling the potatoes and throwing them into an earthen pot full of water. But Bass had smelled danger and began to growl; and when the noise came nearer, he could bear it no longer; he broke into a loud bark of fear and anger and protest, which nearly choked him. And the danger, like a poisonous snake, wound softly through the bushes, gleamed golden against the grass, disappeared again, and finally slid out into the open.

"Quiet, Bass!" exclaimed Peter Neviadomski, putting his potatoes aside. Intimidated, Bass stopped barking and only growled softly to himself. Down in the bushes a bayonet flashed and glinted, catching and mirroring the rays of the setting sun. Then the brass spike of a helmet appeared.

And suddenly War came over the embankment. It strode along in black hobnailed boots; it climbed the steps with its sword and rifle, and presented itself to Peter Neviadomski in the guise of the corporal of the gendarmerie, Jan Durek.

Peter always felt that there was something sinister about a gendarme. Not that he had anything on his conscience, but because a gendarme always smells of jail and doubtless keeps a pair of handcuffs in his bag. Corporal Durek knew Peter well. He often talked with him at the station, and the railway-man was very proud of the acquaintanceship. In Peter's eyes the gendarme represented the very pinnacle of intelligence and good taste. The unusual smell of a certain shaving-soap that Corporal Durek used never failed to impress Neviadomski. But most of all he was impressed by the shining gold tooth which the gendarme displayed whenever he opened his mouth, whether on public or on private occasions. It was the tooth which set the barrier of class between Peter and the great Jan Durek far more than all the gold on his helmet and uniform, more than the ominous, black chin-strap, more even than his carbine and his sword. It inspired respect *ad personam*, so that even if Corporal Durek had undressed and revealed himself naked, even then the gold tooth would have protected him against familiarity.

This time, it was in his public capacity that Durek opened his mouth, but he condescended to ease the strain of the occasion by smiling like a private individual.

"I've got an invitation for you, Neviadomski!"

"For military service?"

"Oh, no! To a ball!"

The habit of irony was so uncommon in these parts that, just at first, Peter did not catch the point of the gendarme's words. For a moment, fragments of dance music lilted in his head, a Kolomyika * played by a concertina and a fiddle, and heavy, brightly colored skirts swayed before his eyes. Their lovely warmth beat against his face. But the gendarme soon called him back to earth. From the leather bag (the one where he kept the handcuffs) he extracted a paper, folded and sealed.

Gutenberg, Johann Gutenberg, was the name of that man whom the devil made drunk with Rhine wine in Mainz, and who, in the year 1450, invented a new torture for those who knew nothing of letters, for the meek in spirit. Possessed by the devil, Gutenberg, in league with a certain Faust, founded the first printing works. From that time on the devilish business spread like a cholera plague, to bewilder, bewitch, and

* Ukrainian folk dance.

poison, day and night, grasping souls imprisoned by the pride of knowledge. But also since then so much harmless paper has been blackened by the devil's marks that the whole globe might be wrapped in it, yet, in the year 1914, there were still many righteous souls, especially in the district of Snyatin, who had not yielded to temptation. They did not falter, even when confronted by compulsory school attendance, by fines and by imprisonment, preferring to pay, or to languish in jail, rather than to afflict the souls of their children with the Latin or Cyrillian alphabet. It is true that in this triumphant struggle they had a silent but powerful ally: the budget of the Imperial and Royal Ministry of Education. And so it came about that indirectly the Government itself fought against the devil who is present in all written words, even in those of the Holy Books. Wherefore, the righteous man never signs papers; he makes three crosses: + + +. And these are three holy signs, which cast out the devil from all contracts, receipts, and promissory notes.

But the devil is vengeful: on all the ways of man's life—not only at crossroads, but on straight paths—he has set up sign-boards, and warnings, like scarecrows.

Here it is forbidden to spit. There it is forbidden to smoke. And ignorance of the law is no safeguard against punishment. "The use of this water for drinking purposes is forbidden," the devil proclaims from over the great barrel on Topory-Czernielitza station.

"Beware of the train."

"Strzez sie pociagu!"

"Sterehty sia pojizdu!"

"Sama la trenu!"

the devil shrieks from a board set up in the open field, not far from signal-box 86. He apes the devotion of a friend anxious to preserve a man's life, as though it were life he was concerned with, and not death. And death is everywhere, and everywhere, not only in war, one must needs be on guard against it. Wherever railways run, death lurks ready to leap at any moment from the rails. Death lies in wait in the sunshine and falls like sudden lightning on to the heads of the reapers. There is death in the water. And often, in the summer, the bodies of the drowned are taken from the Pruth and the Czeremosz. Death sits in the mushrooms of the fields, it slips into men's bellies with the plums in the sweetness of which lies mortal dysentery. The devil mocks at men's death—the false friend! He talks in words to the dead, in signs to the blind. But there are, of course, means to outwit the devil. For example, the turnpike gates. Horses, and cows, and Huzuls cannot read; but, none the less, God sent them an angel, who couldn't read either, yet preserved them from death on the rails. But for Peter Neviadomski, many a cow, many a Huzul, would have been taken by the devil, and in war-time particularly.

The Corporal knew quite well that Peter couldn't read, but all the same he handed the calling-up order over to him, with an air of not knowing anything of the kind. That Neviadomski should be compelled to ask him to read out the contents of the paper flattered his vanity. In his relations with people who could read, Durek was no more than the executor of a higher power, but in dealing with people who couldn't read, he felt that he was not only the partner of that Power, aware of its intentions, but also the representative of its culture. To such people he personified not only the punishment of guilt, and not only the key to prison cells, but also the key to all the secrets of the written word. So Durek couldn't refrain from enjoying his superiority over Neviadomski, although he hadn't the smallest intention of gloating over the misfortune of the lowly. Quite the contrary. Not an hour ago he had spoken with sympathy of this very misfortune in the hall of a neighboring country house to which he had taken a preliminary notice of a requisition for fodder, and where he had been welcomed with a small glass of vodka, a piece of cake and cigarettes:

"Our people are still very uneducated, gracious Countess—the minimum of illiterates is 80 per cent."

The word "minimum" was intended to show that he himself belonged to the educated.

Neviadomski did not disappoint him. He cast a helpless look at the paper and said:

"Will you do me the favor, Herr Korporal? . . ."

The Corporal was used to this procedure and enjoyed it. He quickly broke the seal, glanced at the date and announced sternly:

"In five days time, punctually at nine o'clock in the morning, before the Tribunal in Snyatin."

He emphasized the word "punctually" in a tone suggesting that he, Corporal Durek, quite agreed with those who had issued the order. But Peter wanted to know what the blue paper contained, and entreated Durek to read it from beginning to end. Durek beamed. He adopted an even sterner expression than before and put on a special voice, like an actor reading the death-sentence in a play. He stressed particularly all words of Latin origin.

"Herr Peter Neviadomski," he intoned, "is to report before the Tribunal."

It can't be so bad if they address me as "Herr," thought Peter, and gave a sigh of relief. His ears took in every word and his imagination struggled to assimilate them. Some words, however, were indigestible. They were as sharp and cruel as bayonets. "The conscript is to appear in a sober and clean condition. . . ." I shall have to take a bath in the Pruth and Magda must wash a shirt. . . . "Non-appearance on the appointed day has as a consequence the taking of coercive measures to bring the culprit before the Tribunal and is punishable with imprisonment and fine, according to Section 324, Clause 12, and Section 161, Clause 13, of the Landsturm Regulations of the year 1861."

What did it all mean? First they said "Herr" to a man, summoned him kindly, put confidence in him; but if he didn't obey them, then it was— "fix bayonets!", and off with him to prison! Already Peter pictured Corporal Durek taking the handcuffs out of his leather bag and holding a bayonet to Peter's throat. Had he not been there when Corporal Durek took the bandit Matwij, alias The Bull, away by train, in chains?

The gendarme, having read to the end, folded the paper carefully, handed it back, looking hard at the conscript to see what impression his recital had created. Peter was silent and seemed unconcerned. The gendarme was displeased, for the whole effect had miscarried. To emphasize the gravity of the situation, and at the same time to call attention to his own powers, he said curtly:

"And do you know how they treat deserters nowadays? Court-martial and a bullet in the head."

"That's as it should be," Neviadomski agreed.

Durek was taken aback. To hide his confusion he smiled, showing his gold tooth, and ostentatiously unslung his rifle. He examined the mushroom head, made sure that it was on the safety-catch, and leaned the weapon against the wall. He took off his helmet, damped his forehead with his handkerchief and sat down in the doorway. Next, he took from his pocket a shining, imitation-silver cigarette case, a present that had been given him by the Countess herself. And with hands which, at any moment, could transform themselves into the hands of justice, he offered the well-filled case to Peter. Peter took a cigarette, and noted that inside the lid of the case there was an enameled picture of a softly pink female body leaning forward roguishly out of a foam of lacy underwear. He felt a sensation of heat creeping up his spine and remembered Magda was due with the milk after sunset. For a time they smoked in silence. The Emperor Francis Joseph looked down at Peter Neviadomski. He looked down from a little cross, a memento of the sixtieth anniversary of his accession, which hung from a red-and-white ribbon on the gendarme's tunic. Just where the arms of the cross met, there glittered the golden bust of the Emperor, encircled by a wreath. For God and the Emperor are always together. The cold, metal eyes of Francis Joseph pierced through Peter's sweaty shirt and stabbed his soul and conscience. Whoever, in such an hour, failed to obey with his whole heart the Emperor who called from the cross would not be pardoned by Jesus Christ on the day of the Last Judgment. Twice Peter had appeared before a judge, but on each occasion as a witness. There had been thefts on the railway. He had taken the oath before a crucifix, placed between two lighted candles on the table. The judge, in a long, black robe and a cap like a priest's biretta, had pronounced judgment. "In the name of His Majesty." And at that every one had to rise, as they do in church during Holy Mass. The judge stood up, and the accused and the witnesses, the just as well as the unjust. But they were not asked to kneel. And above the green table, exactly over the crucifix, hung an immense portrait of the Emperor.

Peter finished his cigarette; and as he threw down the fag end, it suddenly struck him that, with it, he had thrown the Imperial eagle on to the floor. The eagle was painted on the cigarette paper. The cigarette monopoly was the Emperor's.

Everything on this earth belongs either to the Emperor or to God, reflected Peter. Earth and sky, the Pruth, the Czeremosz, and the Carpathians, and cows and dogs, and man belong to God. All the railways, on the other hand, all the cars and engines, all the signal-boxes and gates, down to a rusty bit of wire, down to a rotten tie under the rails, belong to the Emperor. To steal a tie is to injure the Emperor, and for that an Imperial gendarme takes people to an Imperial prison. And quite right. And, of course, the chief thing on this earth is money. And to whom does money belong? It belongs to him whose head is engraved on it. The Emperor gives men money, just as God gives them life. Money and life are just loans. The Emperor is a partner of God. Therefore he has the right to a man's life, which is only lent to him by God.

"Very well, then, I'll go into the Army," Neviadomski said aloud.

The gendarme had again slung his rifle over his shoulder, clapped on his helmet, and settled the black chin-strap.

"Don't be frightened, Neviadomski. You're sure to be taken, there's no getting out of that; they're taking everybody now. If you ask me, the whole show will be over before Christmas."

He said "before Christmas"; but he was really convinced that the war would be over in a month. He saluted and went on his way. Peter forgot that he, too, was wearing an Imperial cap and lifted it civilian-wise. Bass jumped up and began to bark, and Peter silenced him with a kick. The wires twanged again, but the gendarme had already crossed the line and his footsteps were soon lost in the silence. The blue paper lay in Peter's motionless hands, like a pictured saint clasped between the stiff fingers of the dead. And suddenly he grew frightened of the paper which he could not understand. As long as the gendarme had been there, the letters had been alive and human, but now the devil was in them and scared folk with his secrets. Peter's fate depended now on rounded black circles, and fine straight strokes. To be so at the mercy of all these letters, and not even to know what words they represented. He looked at the word "punctual," and it was as though he saw the word "arrest." A dark cell with iron bars across its little window. The written characters seemed to close round his hands like the links of an iron chain. Already he saw red welts around his wrists. There awoke in him some obscure sense of personal freedom, which was his to defend. He couldn't understand how it could be destroyed by a mere piece of blue paper. To be powerless in the face of an enemy he could crumple in his hands, if he would, or tear to pieces without resistance or opposition: it was this which filled him with despair.

Perhaps it was all untrue. Perhaps the gendarme had been lying. How could a lifeless bit of paper dominate a living person? Why are people so silly as to believe in a piece of paper? And then Peter remembered with a sudden shock of horror that railway tickets also were made of paper, and yet that money was paid for them. And, after all, money itself was paper also. Particularly big money, like the ten- and twenty-crown notes, and woe betide the poor wretch who lost one of them! He himself had labored all his life, merely to receive, on the first of each month, a bit of paper and five silver crowns. That was it! The devil had invented all this. And what good would it do if he, Peter Neviadomski, destroyed the calling-up order? At best he would be cheating himself, not the devil. Up till now Neviadomski had believed that man was only made a prisoner when another, stronger than himself, tied his hands, took him by the scruff of the neck and threw him to the ground. But this paper? He knew now that a man could be robbed of his strength and freedom by invisible powers. They dwelt somewhere far off, and they knew everything about a man, and could decide what was to be done with him; they could even send him to his death. Individual intelligence and will power were no longer any use. For invisible threads, like telephone wires, ended in these tiny black living letters, and they came from far, far away, from

Vienna, even from the Emperor himself. That was obvious, for otherwise they would not be so powerful.

So this is how it works? The Emperor knows all about me. He knows that railway-man Peter Neviadomski, the son of Wasylina, lives in the municipality of Topory-Czernielitza, in the district of Snyatin, on the Lemberg-Czernowitz-Itzkàny line, and that he has served him faithfully for twenty years. So the Emperor knows me? He wants me, and so he writes to me and calls me "Herr." "Herr Peter Neviadomski!" How grand it sounds! And Peter pictured the Emperor seated at a great table with gold corners, in his Chancellery in Vienna, writing to all the Huzuls, to the *Herren* Huzuls.

Night was beginning to fall over the Huzul land. Over the two rivers, the Pruth and the Czeremosz, wisps of mist and swirling vapors were rising. Peter got up, straightened his back, sighed heavily, picked up the pot with the still-uncooked potatoes, and turned his back on the sky, the earth and the falling night. Bass he left outside. He went into his room and put the potatoes on the cold hearth. He lay down on his back, still with his boots on. His appetite was gone. Suddenly he got up hastily, strode to the door, and turned the key in the lock. It was a thing he had never done before. Then he threw himself down again on the bed. He lay on his back, trying to see nothing and think of nothing. But, all the same, he saw quite a lot. So he shut his eyes. But that also was useless. Reality stole into his mind through the shut lids and tortured him with pictures. He saw and felt the pawing hands of Corporal Jan Durek, the threatening hands of justice.

It was the hour when the cows, stuffed with green grass and meadow flowers, were returning from pasture. The grave procession halted on its way to the cow-sheds and stood still a while. The cows slid their horns along their backs, and the sound of their lowing was like the blaring call of river boats; they wanted to be rid of the intolerable burden which swelled their udders. In the hymn of the cows there sounded the primeval forces of life and vegetation, of milk and motherhood. There was a bitter break in their voices, as though in anticipation of the slaughter-house. In this rending cry for relief, for rest, for sleep, Peter recognized the voice of his own soul. His soul, too, was heavy and burdened, and fed on grass. With difficulty it now digested its fate, as indigestible as raw meat.

Frogs began their nightly quarrels. The sharp, needle-like chirp of the crickets pierced the stillness. Bass remembered old sorrows, perhaps those of a former existence, but he was not barking at the war, he was

only yowling sadly to the rising moon. Maybe a tooth was aching.
Peter lay with wide-open eyes, staring moodily into the dark.
Over the whole world gendarmes were spoiling people's appetites.

Translated by PAULINE DE CHARY

Juljan Tuwim

PRAYER FOR WILDERNESS

I NO LONGER see the sky,
The stars no longer see my face.
Heavenly Father, let me fly
To the grey desolate wilderness,

That I may lift my eyes with love,
Instead of snarling fear and scorn,
To the bright emptiness above
Where truth shines silver in the dawn;

That Brother Jackal from his lair
May creep nightly to my side,
His breath like steam in the frosty air,
And keep me warm with his beast-hide.

I, with my halo on a hook
Above my head, a happy one,
Shall open the forgotten book
Where for the Father dies the Son.

In this night of starry rain
Brother Jackal at my right hand
Howls sadly toward the homes of men.
He will remember and understand,

And he will lift his gentle head
And meet my eye with his trusting eye,
And from the clear night overhead
A star will fall, but will not die.

PRAYER

LORD, LET the golden bells ring out
Within our hearts, let Poland lie
Open to our weary feet
As lightning opens up the sky.

Let us clean our father's home
Of our guilt and grief and sin,
As we clear the broken stone.
Let the house be poor but clean

That rises where a graveyard stood.
And when she comes to life again,
Our country whom we left for dead,
Let her be ruled by honest men,

By workers. Let the people stand
Triumphant in the clean blue dawn
Of freedom; give into their hand
The harvest they spent labor on.

Let not money multiply
Itself for men who will not share it;
Cast the mighty from their sky
And let the humble man inherit.

Teach us that beneath the sun
There is neither Gentile nor Jew;
Shrivel up the silly crown
Of the boasting, bloated few;

Strike with thunder those who struck
Poland with their shot and shell;
Let their Nazi leader look
Into the eyeholes of a skull.

Give us back our Polish bread
And the taste of Polish wine;
Bury us, when we are dead,
In coffins made of Polish pine,

And give our words their honor back!
Swindlers have changed them overnight
From honest white to bitter black;
Let just mean just, and right mean right.

Lord, your holy name will shine
Brighter in our deeds than our hymns
When the brutal dreams of swine
Yield to men with better dreams.

And we may come to bless the flame
After the fiery waves have rolled
Away, and cleaned us of our shame;
Fire burns the dross and leaves the gold.

Whether the land be great or small
Let her children's hearts be great.
She lies between the German steel
And the hundred-peopled Soviet;

Give her a barrier to the west,
And to the east give her a friend!
Lord, your bleeding hands and breast
Must bleed anew till the war's end,

For we must climb on German bones
And struggle through a crimson sea
Until we reach our ruined homes,
Until we set our Warsaw free.

But we will kneel in hope and grief;
In the bare fields we shall kneel down,
In hope that friends are left alive
Who'll come to meet us from the town;

In grief, and tears that blind the sight,
We kneel upon the ground to pray
That those who stayed behind to fight
Will pardon those who ran away.

Translated by Joy Davidman

Stanislaw Balinski

CHOPIN'S MOTHERLAND

SOMETHING THERE is in her of strange,
Romantic lady: multitudes for her embrace
Destruction gladly, life exultant change
For death, who ne'er behold her face.

For her men died on burnished peaks of Spain,
Consoled by dreams of far Mazovian pool.
For her a black-caped seer one time vain
Journey made to glittering Stamboul.

For her the homesick yearn long
Nights and days on western plain;
Siberia-bound, her lovers raise high song
To her, despite their pain.

The foreigner inquires: Why bleed
So long for her, this phantom star?
But, faithful unto death, they do not heed,
And only for her sake run yet more far.

For her beneath fierce skies the more endure:
The lot of exiles in Mongolian damp.
For her to newer hells advance more sure:
The depths of human woe in German camp.

For her keep fighting in Norwegian snows,
'Mid Egypt's searing winds, in Galilee,
And through the air that over England blows
Wing gallantly aloft, to set her free.

To her they dedicate their very all,
In silence passing each new test of fire,
While she, heart-wounded, makes on them no call,
Nor aught of them demands, nor doth desire.

But only, deep at midnight, when despair
Subsides a while 'neath ghostly Chopin's spell,
They see, in mourning garb, her figure there,
And hear her say she lives—and all is well.

Translated by MARION MOORE COLEMAN

Kazimierz Wierzynski

IN PRAISE OF TREES

"How much I owe thee, O thou trees of home!"—MICKIEWICZ

NOTHING ENTHRALLS me as the soaring trees,
Primeval beings, with a heavenly
Design surcharged, through whom seethes
Ever upward earth's elixir, endlessly.

Slavonic birches, milky white, and tall
Pine masts, thick poplars wherein crows abound,
Larch-maids in vernal green, ye all
Are mine, and mine the breezes murmuring 'round.

Older than any mother, as the veins
Beneath thy hoary bark attest,
I hear in songs of thine my native strains,
And seek but in thyself, my final rest.

E'en as a boy from some Carpathian height
Returned with childish rhymes, I woke
To hear the wood-nymphs call by night,
The maples sing, and all the maple folk!

But this can happen nowhere save in Poland, when
St. Lawrence Night its lustre has unrolled,
When willow sprites enchant the misty fen,
And meteors dart the highway with their gold.

How oft in dank Niefcyrka, 'midst the beechen groves
Of Babiogóra, 'twas the trees that whispered sympathy,
The leaves that bore my soul to far abodes,
Pokucian hazel-shade invited reverie.

Fairest of all, the fir-tree pyramids, each head
Becapped with snow till sudden gust would wreak
Its havoc, lifting snow aloft in smoke, to leave instead
A throng of ladies, velvet-gowned and sleek.

Then from the Gothic darkness of the firs
Into the streaming radiance far below
I'd wander, where the maple's splendor stirs
The fancy like the crimson of Van Gogh.

The harmony remains; for still
Among the trees I walk as one
Of them, knowing my voice will
One day rise with theirs in earth's own song.

The epic of the forest I could spin
Forever in design and hue the mind to overwhelm,
As jungle vines expand, or morning-glories win,
Winding their tendrils 'round the stately elm.

But let us draw aside and gaze
Upon the linden—many a page
I could devote to tell its ways,
From green, full-blooded youth to rusty age.

Its cupola, our country's tree baroque,
How resonant with sound! Flow'r-sprinkled, white
With dust, thick-sown with bees, it woke
Ethereal chords through summer's night.

What dignity within its shade resides!
What pride of race, what utter timelessness!
Within its fancy still King John abides,
And Kochanowski's *dwór* its dreams caress.

For 'twas from thee, O linden, thy refrain,
Our tongue received its earliest poetry,
And Polish song, still rich with thy perfume,
Springs forth today, as then, from thee.

But ah! the giant oaks! In pious Litwa oft
As gods revered, as emperors in all the Crown
Domain! See how each head a halo wears aloft,
Yet deep in pagan soil each root goes down.

Ye Baublises! Ye bibles of the forest, dear
To our Mickiewicz! Three such oaks were found
By Gloger worthy of a *Pan Tadeusz,* one near
My Drohobycz—glory and romance in thee abound!

I sometimes dream—portent of true desire—
That I myself have joined the forest throng,
Yet lost, through taking root, no human fire,
But only sensed more clearly heaven's song.

What wind it was that moved me, from what deity
It came, and how to give it back in Latin phrase,
I learned in fruitful talk with wise Zielinski,
Seer and scholar, very oak tree of our days.

But still, as once in Ovid, trees send forth their lay:
I strain to catch the special song of each,
Of Gorgan firs and Beskid, as in organ tones they pray,
Of Bialowiezian copse, Szwarzewan beech.

Polesia, lone, mysterious, Nowogródek's castled knoll,
Tuchola's grove whence floods enchanted flee,
Strip somehow, by their magic, the evil from my soul,
As worn-out bark falls cleanly from the tree.

Like great tree columns I would grow, deep
Rooted, wreathed in mist, that when the land
Be struck with lightning's sweep,
Still steadfast, though unspeaking, I may stand.

The forest giants thrill me, straight and tall,
Defying all destruction, firm 'gainst every harm,
Refusing, e'en when stricken, e'er to fall,
But raising leafy arms to meet the storm.

And so, more like the trees myself would grow,
Like all the trees, but most—the ones that went
From quaint Kazimierz to Pulawy, row on row,
Deep bruised by lightning, sheathed in stern cement.

> *Translated by* ALBINA KRUSZEWSKA *and*
> MARION MOORE COLEMAN

Antoni Slonimski

ALL

WHEREVER WE are found,
The shattered world around,
In Turkestan, Dakar, by Scottish burn,
In Lisbon, London, still
The tide sweeps on, till
Hope is banished of a swift return.

For what do we contend?
To what our sinews bend?
To win back treasures lost?
No! Not for wealth nor fame,
Nor any worldly game,—
But for a holy cause.

For naught of earthly sway,
But—just to sit one day
Again beneath some plane
Tree, with a book, hear
Village talk, gnats buzzing near,
And horses neigh at twilight in the lane.

'Tis not to force our will
On someone else, but still
At home, with dear ones nigh,
To break bread righteously,
Walk forth in uprightness and free,
Then peacefully retire 'neath starlit sky.

To gaze through shining pane
At chestnut boughs, rain
Silvered, rising tall;
To walk the boulevard, meet
Friends, old by-ways greet,—
It isn't much—but all.

Translated by MARION MOORE COLEMAN

Jan Lechon

FAREWELL, LA MARSEILLAISE

Now, DID these heavy brazen guns, once victorious
Stand motionless in the courtyard of the Invalides,
And did the Maid, with her banner of deeds so glorious
Look down at these troops marching in past her feet,
As detested they come, through the heavy heat of the day?
Well? And nothing? Stillness in the graveyard of the Invalides?
While sunbeams on the Arc de Triomphe still play?
And nothing? Still everyone hurries, busy about his needs?
So—as you once to the first lover bid farewell,
To whom you whispered, and heard a sorrowful reply,
So in this day of June,—why it was so, none can tell—
Through stifled tears I cried: "La Marseillaise—goodbye!"
Song, which always above sin, despair, and all things vile
Raised a triumphant cry, to quicken the heart's beat,
Always above death and suffering was the splendour of your smile,
Goodbye, wonderful song, over-ridden by defeat!
Already your martial music into distance far retires,
Beneath the gates of Paris the last men now go through,
A moment more and your sweet melody expires,
Goodbye, fair freedom, beloved and lover of the true.
Ah, no! Stay! Let me a little longer in your light remain,
I shall sweep aside the opal mists, drifting like sleep,
One moment more let me see the Louvre and the Seine,
And to you, so sinful, I give my thanks to keep.
For I believe that this calm which is growing so intense,
Will bode the coming of a voice whose curses will persist,
The cry of "Shame!" will rise about your monuments,

And though you weep, a branded traitor, you will still exist.
Night falls; let the Gothic cathedrals now in slumber lie,
Those tombs of knights, whose deeds were truly great.
The theatre lights expire, let the voice of Phèdre die,
And turned to stone, in Tragic guise let her so stand and wait.
The moon has twisted shadows into grotesque forms
And darts a silver beam across the castle hall,
While through the sleeping Louvre the Cardinal's huge phantom roams
Hiding his proud head in the red folds of his pall.
It is already time! The "Bellerophon" is below,
Like a ghost in a radiant light, evoking every fear.
But the last of the grenadiers is frozen in the snow;
And someone calls: "Where is he? Save the Emperor!"
Ah, only one more short cry of despair,
And close by, one hears the drumming of a million feet,
While St. Geneviève in tears will at last see there
The victorious barbarians along the city street,
Then when this thy song, O Paris, fades farther from the town,
And to the Place de la Concorde march the endless troops,
Then, behold, drives in the man who shall the House of God break down,
And shall rend the coffins of the saints, to peer in and pollute,
Blaspheming: "What else can stand against my might,
When such a city kneels before the thunder of my guns?"
And now, O song, only thy echo resounds throughout the night,
Calling to the pavements of Paris, a host of phantoms.

Translated by EILEEN BENTLEY

RUSSIA

INTRODUCTION

By Thomas Quinn Curtiss

THE RUSSIAN REVOLUTION did much more than turn Russia inside out politically and economically; it upset Russian literature completely. I use "upset" advisedly, for the Revolution neither remade nor reformed Russian literature. Instead, the Revolution threw it off its rails and set it spinning, scattering its practitioners, obscuring its goals and splitting its objectives. The confusion has been colossal, while Soviet literature as such is still in the process of becoming, as yet a thing neither permanent nor recognizable.

A great portion of the popular pre-World War I writers fled the land in terror after 1917 and died abroad: Andriev in Finland, Artzybashev in Warsaw, Merezhkovsky in Paris and so on. Another group, alarmed by and distrustful of the extremes of the Revolution, also fled but later returned and, having made their peace with the new regime, continued their literary labors more or less unmolested. (Kuprin, Alexei Tolstoi and D. S. Mirsky are perhaps the most representative of these.) A third group, made up for the most part of younger men, remained in Russia throughout the dark and blood-stained years, hailing the Revolution as a cultural as well as a political liberation. Alexander Blok, the symbolistic poet, decried during the twilight of Czarism as a decadent, gave the Revolution its most eloquent pleading in his celebrated masterpiece *The Twelve*, a grim but optimistic picture of Petrograd's last days. Essenin, the peasant poet from Ryazan, whose marriage to Isadora Duncan won him greater notoriety abroad than his poetry, startled the imagination of young Russia with his early verse. He later committed suicide during a fit of depression, while still a mere boy, dramatically writing his last poem in his own blood. Babel and Pilnyak, both of them witnesses of the savagery of the Civil War, captured something of its violence and cruelty in a wild, staccato style of their own. Vladimir Mayakovsky, whom Stalin has singled out as the finest of the Soviet writers, sought Aristophanean stature with his biting and grandiose satires, *The Bed Bug* and *Mystery Bouffe;* while Zamyatin wrote futuristic novels that aroused the censor's ire. These immediate postrevolutionary days were not without their flashing literary color.

During the years that followed, writing of necessity took on a definite political hue, and the novel grew dull, narrow and monomaniacal in its propaganda purposes. The talented Leonov has thus described these lamentable tendencies: "And there you have books of nondescript color and form, without the 'upper story,' without that indispensable hormone which saves them from death for at least a quarter of a century. A standard type has been created for an industrial sketch, a novel, a play (with the inevitable disaster in the middle and the heroism of the masses), for a collective farm epic (with the inevitable cunning peasant who is first 'for' and then 'against'), for a current newspaper or magazine poem (where the revolutionary thought of the poet is replaced by beating on some rather inaudible witch-doctor's tambourine). Titles are prepared in advance just as labels: the birth of a guild, the birth of a hero, the birth of a factory, the birth of an artisan, the birth of a woman: this sounds majestic and saves the author trouble. Many pages of these books are known to the reader before they have been written. A friend of mine, voracious reader, told me while perusing on the counter of a bookshop a well-known book: 'I think I've already paid for it.'"

Fortunately this standardized manner of writing is for the most part a thing of the past. And even during that epoch of literary darkness many a writer in Russia managed to assert himself and to display an original turn of mind and expression. Perhaps no country in Europe can boast of more interesting post-World War I writers than Soviet Russia. The brilliant journalism of Ilya Ehrenburg, together with his memorable novel *Julio Jurenito,* the irresistible humors of Ilf and Petrov with their *Little Golden Calf, Diamonds to Sit On* and their amusing American odyssey, *Little Golden America,* the gigantic structure of Sholokhov's tales of the Don Cossacks and Zostchenko's hilarious sketches of Soviet life, all these were products of a period when intellectual regimentation was supposedly in full force. In only one field have the later-day Russians failed conspicuously and that is in the drama. After two decades, one must sadly relate, only one playwright worthy of serious critical consideration has been revealed, the late Mikhail Bulgakov, the author of *The Days of the Turbins* and of the Moscow Art Theatre's dramatization of Gogol's *Dead Souls.*

Today Russia is in the throes of a titanic struggle for survival, and the heroism of her fight has not left the outside world unmoved. How much more deeply it must have touched the Russian writer! Alexei Tolstoi in a recent speech before the Academy of Science in Moscow, surveying the progress of Soviet literature, has called for a "positive realism." Though the term is more than a little vague, one imagines it to imply a realism based on fact rather than on ideology, which, in turn, will lead to an understanding and interpretation of the Russian people and character that is the heritage of any writer who writes in the language of Dostoievsky and Tolstoi. Alexei Tolstoi has at times achieved this (most notably in his historic pageant *Peter I*) and a handful of other authors represented here as well. In time, then, the Soviet writer will learn that it is more important to create than to manufacture, and Soviet literature as a whole will take on a definite identity of its own.

Maxim Gorki

THE HERMIT

THE FOREST RAVINE slopes gently down to the yellow waters of the Oka; a brook rushes along its bottom, hiding in the grass; above the ravine, unnoticed by day and tremulous by night, flows the blue river of the sky—the stars play in it like golden minnows. Rank, tangled underbrush grows on the southeastern bank of the ravine. Under the steep side of it, in the thicket, a cave is dug out, closed by a door made of branches, ingeniously tied together; before the door is an earthen platform about seven feet square, buttressed by cobbles. From it, heavy boulders descend in a stairway towards the brook. Three young trees grow in front of the cave: a lime, a birch, and a maple.

Everything around the cave is made sturdily and with care, as though it were fashioned to last a life-time. The interior has the same air of sturdiness: the sides and the vault are covered with mats made of willow withies; the mats are plastered with clay mixed with the silt of the brook; a small stove rises to the left of the entrance; in the corner is an altar, covered by heavy matting in place of brocade; on the altar, in an iron sconce, is an oil-burner; its bluish flame flickers in the dusk and is hardly visible.

Three black icons stand behind the altar; bundles of new bast shoes hang on the walls; strips of bast lie about on the floor. The cave is permeated with the sweet smell of dry herbs.

The owner of this abode is an old man of middle height, thick-set, but crumpled and misshapen. His face, red as a brick, is hideous. A deep scar runs across the left cheek from ear to chin, giving a twist to his mouth and lending it an expression of painful scorn. The dark eyes are ravaged by trachoma; they are without lashes and have red scars instead of lids; the hair on the head has fallen out in tufts and there are two bald patches on the bumpy skull, a small one on the crown, and another which has laid bare the left ear. In spite of all this the old man is spry and nimble as a polecat; his naked, disfigured eyes have a kindly look; when he laughs, the blemishes of his face almost vanish in the soft abundance of his wrinkles. He wears a good shirt of unbleached linen, blue calico trousers and slippers made of cord. His legs are wrapped in hareskins instead of leggings.

I came to him on a bright May day and we made friends at once. He had me stay the night, and on my second visit told me the story of his life.

"I was a sawyer," he said, lying under an elder-bush, having pulled off his shirt to warm his chest, muscular as a youngster's, in the sun. "For seventeen years I sawed logs; see the mess a saw made of my face! That's what they called me, Savel the Sawyer. Sawing is no light job, my friend—you stand there, waving your hands about in the sky, a net over your face, logs over your head and the sawdust so thick you can't see, ugh! I was a gay lad, a playful one, and I lived like a tumbler. There is, you know, a certain type of pigeon: they soar as high up as they can into the sky, into the utmost depth and there they fold their wings, tuck their heads under them—and bang! down they come! Some get killed that way, hitting the roofs, or the ground. Well, that's what I was like. Gay and harmless, a blessed one; women, girls were as fond of me as of sugar, 'pon my word! What a life it was! It does one good to remember it. . . ."

And rolling from side to side he laughed the clear laughter of youth, except for a slight rattle in the throat, and the brook echoed his laugh. The wind breathed warmly, golden reflections glided on the velvety surface of the spring foliage.

"Well, let's have a go at it, friend," Savel suggested. "Bring it on!"

I went to the brook, where a bottle of vodka had been put to cool and we each had a glass, following it up with cracknels and fish. The old man chuckled with rapture.

"A fine invention that, drink!" And passing his tongue over his gray, tousled mustache: "A fine thing! Can't do with a lot of it, but in small quantities it's great! They say the devil was first to make vodka. Well, I'll say thanks even to the devil for a good thing."

He half-closed his eyes, remained silent for a moment and then exclaimed, indignantly:

"Yes, they did hurt me to the core, all the same, they did. Ah, friend, how people have grown into the habit of hurting one another, it's a shame! Conscience lives among us like a homeless pup, it does! It isn't welcome anywhere. Well, never mind, I'll go on with my story. I married and all was as it should be; the wife was called Natalia, a beautiful, soft creature. I got on with her all right; she was a bit of a philanderer, but I'm not all too virtuous myself, not exactly a stay at home, and when there is a nicer, kinder woman about, to her I go. That is all only too human, there's no running away from it, and in one's lusty years, what better can one do? At times when I returned home bringing some money or other goods with me, people would laugh! 'Savel, you should tie your wife's skirts before you leave your house!' Jeering, they were. Well, for decency's sake, I'd beat her a bit and then give her a present to make up for it and just scold her gently: 'You fool,' I'd say, 'why do you make people laugh at me? Am I not your pal, instead of your enemy?' She'd cry, of course, and say they were lying. I know, too, that people are fond of lies, but you can't fool me, all the same: the night gives away the truth about a woman—you can feel it, at night, if she's been in another man's arms or not."

Something rustled in the bushes behind him.

"Ps-sh!" the old man shook a branch of the elder. "A hedgehog lives right here, I pricked my foot on it the other day as I went to wash in the brook; I did not see it in the grass and the needle went straight into my toe."

He smiled as he looked at the bush and then, straightening himself out, went on.

"Yes, friend. So I was saying how deeply they had hurt me, yes, how deeply. I had a daughter, Tasha, Tatyana. I may say in a word, without boasting, she was a joy to the whole world, that daughter. A star. I used to dress her up in fine clothes—a heavenly beauty she was when she came out on a holiday. Her gait, her bearing, her eyes . . . Our teacher Kuzmin—Trunk was his nickname, for he was a clumsy-looking chap—called her by some whimsical name, and when he got drunk he would weep and beg me to take care of her. So I did. But luck had always favored me—and that never makes one popular with other men, it just breeds envy. So the rumor was spread, that Tasha and I . . ."

He fidgeted uneasily on the grass, took his shirt from the bush, put it on and carefully buttoned up the collar. His face twitched nervously, he pressed his lips together and the sparse bristles of his gray brows descended on the naked eyes.

Twilight was setting in. There was a freshness in the air. A quail was crying shrilly close by: "Pit-pit . . . wet my lip . . ." The old man was peering down into the ravine.

"Well, so that set the ball rolling. Kuzmin, the priest, the clerk, some of the men and most of the women began wagging their tongues, hissing and hooting and hauling a man over the coals. It is always a treat for us to bait a man; we love it. Tasha sat weeping, unable to leave the house, for fear of the jeering of street urchins—everybody was having the time of their lives. So I said to Tasha: 'Come, let us leave.' "

"And your wife?"

"The wife?" the old man repeated with astonishment. "But she was dead by then. She just gave a sigh and died one night. Yes—yes. That was long before all this happened. Tasha was only twelve. . . . She was my enemy, a bad woman, unfaithful."

"But you were praising her a moment ago," I reminded him. This did not embarrass him at all. He scratched his neck, lifted his beard with his palm and gazing at it, said calmly:

"Well, what if I did praise her? No one remains bad all his life, and even a bad person is often worthy of praise. A human being is not a stone and even a stone changes with time. Do not, however, get any wrong ideas into your head—she died a natural death, all right. It must have been her heart, her heart played tricks on her. Sometimes at night we would be having a bit of fun and she would suddenly go off in a dead faint. Quite terrible it was!"

His soft husky voice had a melodious sound; it mingled tirelessly and intimately in the warm evening air with the smell of grass, the sighs of the wind, the rustle of leaves, the soft patter of the brook on the pebbles. Had he kept still, the night would not have been so complete, so beautiful, so sweet to the soul.

Savel spoke with a remarkable ease, showing no effort in finding the right words, dressing up his thoughts lovingly, as a little girl does her dolls. I had listened to many a Russian talker, men who, intoxicated with flowery words, often, almost always, lose the fine thread of truth in the intricate web of speech. This one spun his yarn with such convincing simplicity, with such limpid sincerity, that I feared to interrupt him with questions. Watching the play of his words, I realized that the old man was the possessor of living gems, able to conceal all filthy and criminal lies with their bewitching power; I realized all that and nevertheless yielded to the magic of his speech.

"The whole dirty business began then, my friend: a doctor was summoned, he examined Tasha thoroughly with his shameless eyes, and he had another fop with him, a baldish man with gold buttons—an investigator, I suppose, asking questions: as to who and when? She just kept silent, she was so ashamed. They arrested me and took me to the district prison. There I sat. The bald one says to me: 'Confess and you'll get off lightly!' So I reply obligingly: 'Let me go to Kiev, Your Honor, to the holy relics, and pray for the forgiveness of my sins!' 'Ah,' he said, 'now you've confessed all right!' Believing he'd caught me, the bald cat! I hadn't confessed anything, of course, just dropped the words from sheer boredom. I was very bored in jail, uncomfortable, too, what with the

thieves and murderers and other foul people around; besides, I couldn't
help wondering what they were doing to Tasha. The whole blasted business lasted over a year before the trial came. And then, behold, Tasha
appeared at it, with gloves and smart little boots and all—very unusual!
A blue frock like a cloud—her soul shining through it. All the jury staring
at her and the crowd and all of it just like a dream, my friend. At Tanya's
side—Madame Antzyferova, our lady of the manor, a woman sharp as
a pike, sly as a fox. Hm, I thought to myself—this one will put me to
the rack and worry me to death."

He laughed with great good humor.

"She had a son, Matvey Alexevich—I always believed him to be a bit
wrong in the head—a dull youth. Not a drop of blood in his face, a pair
of spectacles on his nose, hair down to his shoulders, no beard to speak
of, and all he ever did was to write down songs and fairy-tales in a little
book. A heart of gold—he'd give you anything you asked for. The peasants
around all made use of it: one would ask for a scythe, the other for some
timber, the third for bread, taking anything going whether they wanted
it or not. I would say to him: 'Why do you give everything away,
Alexevich? Your fathers and grandfathers piled it all up, grew rich,
stripped people to the skin regardless of sin, and you give it all away
without rhyme or reason. Aren't you wasting human labor?'—'I feel I must
do it!' he said. Not a very clever lad, but gentle natured, anyway. Later
on the Deputy Governor packed him off to China—he was rude to the
Governor, so to China he had to go.

"Well—then came the trial. My counsel spoke for two hours, waving
his hands about. Tasha stuck up for me, too."

"But was there ever actually anything between you two?"

He thought for a moment as though trying to remember, then said,
unconcernedly watching the flight of a hawk with his naked eyes:

"That happens sometimes—between fathers and daughters. There was
even a saint once who lived with two of them, and the prophets Abraham
and Isaac were born to them. I will not say I did so myself. I played
about with her, that is true, in the long, dreary, winter nights. Dreary
they are indeed, all the more so for one who is used to tramping around
the world—going here and there and everywhere, as was my case. I used
to make up stories for her—I know hundreds of fairy-tales. Well, you
know, a tale is a thing of fancy. And it warms up the blood. And Tasha
. . ." He shut his eyes and sighed, shaking his head.

"An extraordinary beauty she was! And I was extraordinary with
women, mad about them, I was."

The old man became excited and went on with pride and rapture, choking over his words:

"See, friend: I'm now a man of sixty-seven and still I can get all the pleasure I want out of any woman, that's the truth! About five years after all this happened how many a wench would beg me: 'Savel, dear, do let me go, I'm quite played out.' I'd take pity on her and do so and she would come back again in a few days. 'Well, so here you are again, are you?' I would say. A female, my friend, is a great thing, the whole world raves about her—the beast and the bird and the tiny moth—all just live for her alone. What else is there to live for?"

"What, anyway, did your daughter say at the trial?"

"Tasha? She made up a story—or perhaps it was the Antzyferova woman who suggested it to her (I'd once done her a service of sorts)—that she had brought the injury upon herself and that I was not to blame. Well, I was let off. It's all a put-up job with them, a thing of no account, just to show what a watch they keep on the laws. It's all a fraud, all these laws, orders and papers; it's all unnecessary. Let everyone live as he pleases, that would be cheaper and pleasanter. Here am I, living and not getting into anyone's way and not pushing forward."

"And what about murderers?"

"They should be killed," Savel decided. "The man who kills should be done away with on the spot with no nonsense about it! A man is not a mosquito or a fly, he is no worse than you, you scum. . . ."

"And—thieves?"

"That's an odd idea! Why should there be any thieves, if there is nothing to steal? Now, what would you take from me? I haven't any too much, so there is no envy, no greed. Why should there be any thieves? There are thieves where there is a surplus of things; when he sees plenty he just grabs a bit. . . ."

It was dark by now, night had poured into the ravine. An owl hooted three times. The old man hearkened to its eerie cries and said with a smile:

"It lives close by in a hollow tree. Sometimes it gets caught by the sun, can't hide in time, and just stays out in the light. I pass by and stick out my tongue at it. It can't see a thing, just sits quite still. Lucky if the smaller birds don't catch sight of it."

I asked how he had come to be a hermit.

"Just like that: wandered and wandered around and then stopped short. All because of Tasha. The Antzyferova woman played me a trick there—did not let me see Tasha after the trial. 'I know the whole truth,' she said, 'and you should be grateful to me for escaping hard labor, but I won't give you back your daughter.' A fool she was, of course. I hovered around for a time, but no, there was nothing doing! So off I went— to Kiev and Siberia, earned a lot of money there and came home. The Antzyferova woman had been run over and killed by a train, and as for Tasha, she had been married off to a surgeon's assistant in Kursk. To Kursk I went, but the surgeon's assistant had left for Persia, for Uzun. I pushed on to Tzaritzyn, from there by ship to Uzun—but Tasha had died. I saw the man—a red-haired, red-nosed cheerful lad. A drunkard, he turned out to be. 'Are you her father, maybe?' he asked.—'No,' I said, 'nothing like that, but I'd seen her father in Siberia.' I did not wish to confide in a stranger. Well, so then I went to New Mt. Athos, almost stayed there—a fine place! But after a while—I decided I did not like it. The sea roars and rolls the stones about, the Abkhazians come and go, the ground is uneven, mountains all around, and the nights as black as though you'd been drowned in pitch. And the heat! So I came here and here I've been for nine years and they haven't been wasted. I've built all this, planted a birch the first year, after three years a maple, then a lime—see them? And I'm a great consoler to the people round here, my friend—you come and watch me on Sunday!"

He hardly ever mentioned God's name—while as a rule it is always on the lips of people of his kind. I asked whether he prayed a lot.

"No, not too much," he said thoughtfully, shutting his naked eyes. "I did so at first, a lot; for hours would I kneel down and keep on crossing myself. My arms were used to a saw, and so they didn't get tired, or my back either. I can bow down a thousand times without a murmur, but the bones in my knees can't stand it: they ache. And then I thought to myself: what am I praying for, and why? I've got all I want, people respect me—why bother God? He's got His own job to do, why trouble Him? Human rubbish should be kept away from Him. He takes care of us and do we take care of Him? No. And also: He is there for people of importance; where will He get time for small fry like me? So now I just come out of the cave on sleepless nights, sit down somewhere or other, and, gazing into God's heaven, wonder to myself: 'And how is He getting along, up there?' This, friend, is a pleasant occupation; I can't tell you how fine; it's like dreaming awake. And one doesn't grow weary as at prayer. I don't ask Him for anything and I never advise others to do so, but when I see they need it, I tell them: 'Have pity on God!' You come along and see how helpful I can be to Him and to people. . . ."

He did not boast, but spoke with the calm assurance of a craftsman confident of his skill. His naked eyes smiled gaily, toning down the ugliness of his disfigured face.

"How I live in winter? It's all right, my cave is warm even in winter. It's only that in wintertime people find it hard to come because of the snow; sometimes for two or three days I have to go without bread. Once it so happened that I hadn't had a crumb in my mouth for over eight days. I felt so weak that even my memory went. Then a young girl came and helped me out. She was a novice in a convent, but she has got married to a teacher since. It was I who advised her to do so; I said: 'What are you fooling about like this for, Lenka? What good is it to you?'—'I'm an orphan,' she said.—'Well, go and get married and that will be the end of the orphan.' And to the teacher, Pevtzov, a good, kind man, I said: 'Have a good look at that girl, Misha.' Yes. So very soon they got together. And they're getting along fine. Well, in wintertime, I also go to the Sarov or Optina or the Diveyev monastery—there are many of them hereabouts. But the monks don't like me, they all urge me to take the hood—it would be a profit for them, of course, and serve as bait to people, but I have no wish for that. I'm alive, it does not suit me. As though I were a saint! I'm just a quiet man, friend."

Laughing and rubbing his thighs with his hands, he said with exultation:

"But with nuns, I'm always welcome. They just love me, they certainly do! That is no boast, it's the truth. I know women through and through, friend, any sort, whether a lady or a merchant's wife, and as for a peasant woman, she's as clear to me as my own soul. I just look into her eyes and I know everything, all that troubles her. I could tell you such tales about them. . . ."

And again he invited persuasively: "Come and see how I talk to them. And now, let's have another little go."

He drank. Closing his eyes tightly and shaking his head, he said with fresh rapture:

"It does one good, that drink!"

The short spring night was visibly melting away; the air grew cool. I suggested that we light a fire.

"No, what for? Are you cold? I, an old man, don't feel the cold, and you do? That's too bad. Go to the cave, then, and lie down there. You see, friend, if we light a fire, all sorts of small living things will come flying here and will get burnt in the flames. And I don't like that. Fire to them is like a trap, leading them to their death. The sun—the father to all fire, kills no one, but why should we, for the sake of our bones, burn up these little folk? No, no. . . ."

I agreed with him, and went into the cave, while he remained outside fussing about for some time; he went off somewhere, splashed about in the brook, and I could hear his gentle voice:

"Phuit . . . don't be afraid, you little fool. . . . Phueeet. . . ."

Then he broke into a soft tremulous song, as though lulling someone to sleep.

When I woke up and walked out of the cave, Savel, crouching on the ground, was deftly weaving a bast shoe and saying to a chaffinch singing vehemently in the bushes:

"That's it, go on, buzz on, the day is yours! Slept well, friend? Go and have a wash, I've put the kettle to boil for tea and I'm waiting for you."

"Haven't you had any sleep yourself?"

"I'll have time to sleep when I die, friend."

A blue May sky shone over the ravine.

°   °   °

I came to see him again about three weeks later, on a Saturday evening, and was welcomed as an old, close friend.

"I'd been thinking already: why, the man has forgotten all about me! Ah, and you've brought some of that good drink as well. Thanks, many thanks! And some wheat bread? So fresh, too. What a kind lad indeed! People must surely like you; they love kind folk; they know what's good for them! Sausage? No, I have no liking for that, that's dog's food, you can keep it for yourself if you wish; but fish I love. This fish, it's a sweet fish, comes from the Caspian Sea, I know all about it. Why, you must have brought food for more than a ruble, you queer fellow! Well, never mind, many thanks!"

He seemed to me still more alive, more cordially radiant—all burdens seemed to fall away from me; I felt lighthearted and gay, and I thought to myself:

"Devil take it, I believe I actually am in the presence of a happy man!"

Nimble and gentle, he performed little domestic duties, storing away my gifts, while he scattered like sparks those endearing, bewitching Russian words, which act like wine on the soul.

The movements of his sturdy body, swift as the movements of an adder, harmonized beautifully with the precision of his speech. In spite of the mutilated face, the eyes without lashes—torn apart as though on purpose to enable him to see more widely and more boldly—he seemed almost handsome, with the beauty of a life whose confusion was multi-colored and intricate. And his outward disfigurement gave a particular emphasis to that beauty.

Again, almost the whole night through, his gray little beard fluttered and the meager mustache bristled as he burst into uncontrollable laughter, opening wide the crooked mouth, in which gleamed the sharp white teeth of a polecat. At the bottom of the ravine it was still; the wind was stirring above; the tops of the pinetrees rocked; the harsh foliage of the oaks rustled; the blue river of the skies seemed violently disturbed—covered by a gray foam of clouds.

"Sh . . ." he exclaimed, softly raising his hand in warning. I hearkened —all was quiet.

"A fox is prowling about—it has a hole here. Many hunting people have asked me: is there a fox near by, grandfather? And I lie to them! Foxes? What should foxes be doing here? I have no liking for hunters, to the dickens with them!"

I had noticed by then that the old man often wanted to break out into real foul language, but realizing that it was out of character for him to do so, he resorted to milder expressions.

After a glass of cowslip vodka, he said, half-closing his lacerated eyes: "What tasty fish this is—thank you kindly for it—I do love everything tasty. . . ."

His attitude toward God was not very clear to me and cautiously I tried to broach the subject. At first he answered with the hackneyed words of pilgrims, cloister habitués and professional holy-men, but I felt that this manner was in fact irksome to him, and I was not mistaken. Drawing closer to me and lowering his voice, he suddenly began to talk with more animation:

"I'll tell you this, friend, about a little Frenchie, a French priest—a little man, black as a starling, with a spot shaved bare on his head, golden spectacles on his nose, tiny little hands, like a little girl's, and all of him like a toy of God's. I met him at the Pochaev monastery; that is a long way off, over there!"

He waved his hand towards the East, in the direction of India, stretched out his legs more comfortably, and continued, propping his back against some stones:

"Polish people living all around—a foreign soil, not our own. I was palavering with a monk one day, who thought people should get punished more often; so I just smiled and said that if one was to begin punishing rightly, all men would have to go through it, and then there would be time for nothing else, no other work done but just flaying one another. The monk got quite angry with me, called me a fool, and walked away. Then the little priest, who had been sitting in the corner, nestled up to me and started telling me, oh, great things. I tell you, friends, he seemed to me like a kind of John the Baptist. He wasn't quite easy in his speech, for not all our words can be put into a foreign tongue, but his big soul shone through all right. 'I see you do not agree with that monk,' he said, so polite-like, 'and you are right. God is not a fiend; He is a dear friend to people; but this is what has happened, owing to His kindness: He's melted in our tearful life like sugar in water, and the water is filthy and full of dregs, so that we do not feel Him any more; we do not get the taste of Him in our lives. Nevertheless, He is spread over the whole world and lives in every soul as the purest spark; we should seek Him in man, collect Him into a single ball, and when the divine spark of all these living souls is gathered into this powerful whole—the Devil will come and say to the Lord: 'Thou art great, my God, and Thy might is measureless—I didn't know this before, so pray forgive me! I won't struggle with Thee any more now—please take me into Thy service.' "

The old man spoke with emphasis, and his dilated pupils gleamed strangely in his dark face.

"And then the end will come to all evil and wickedness and human strife, and people will return to their God, like rivers flowing into the ocean."

He choked over his words, slapped his knees, and continued joyfully, with a hoarse little laugh:

"All this came as such balm to my heart; it struck a light in my soul—I didn't know how to say it to the Frenchie. 'Might I be allowed to embrace you, you image of Christ?' I said. So we embraced one another and started crying, both of us. And how we cried! Like small children, finding their parents after a long parting. We were both quite old, you know; the bristle round his shaven spot was gray, too. So I told him then and there: 'You're like John the Baptist to me, Christ's image.' Christ's image is what I called him; funny, isn't it, when I told you he resembled a starling! The monk, Vitaly, kept abusing him and saying: 'A nail, that's what you are.' And true it was indeed, he was like a nail, as sharp as one. Of course, friend, you do not understand this sweet joy of mine; you can read and write; you know all about everything; but I, at that time, went about as one blind—I was able to see all right, but just couldn't make out: where *is* God? And all of a sudden this man comes and reveals it all to me—just think, what that meant to me! I told you only a little of what he said to me—we talked until dawn; he went on and on; but I can recall only the kernel of it, I've lost all the shell. . . ."

He stopped speaking and sniffed the air like an animal:

"Guess it's going to rain, eh?"

He sniffed again, and then decided contentedly:

"No, it won't rain, it's just the night's dampness. I'll tell you, friend, all these Frenchmen and inhabitants of other lands, they are people of high intelligence. In the province of Kharkov—or was it Poltava—an Englishman, who managed the estate of a great lord, kept watching me; then he called me into the room one day and said: 'Here's a secret parcel, old man; will you take it to such and such a place, and hand it over to such and such a person—can you do it?' Well—why not? It did not matter to me where I went, and it was about sixty miles to the place indicated. I took the parcel, tied it up with a string, thrust it in my bosom and—off I went. On getting to the place, I begged to be allowed to see the landowner. Of course, they gave it to me in the neck—they beat me up and chased me away. 'Curse you,' I thought to myself, 'may you blow up and burst!' Well, the wrapper of the parcel must have got damp from my sweat, and came apart—and what do you think I saw peeping through it—money! Big money! Maybe three hundred rubles. I got scared; someone might notice it and steal it at night. What was I to do? There I was, sitting in the field, on the road, under a tree—when a carriage comes up with a gentleman sitting in it. Maybe that's the man I want—I thought. So I stood on the road waving my staff. The coachman lashed out at me with the whip, but the gentleman told him to stop and even scolded him a bit. Yes, he was the right man. 'Here is a secret parcel for you,' I said. 'Right,' he replied. 'Sit down next to me and we'll drive back.' He brought me into a luxurious room and asked whether I knew the contents of the parcel. So I told him I thought it was money, as I'd seen it peep through the sweaty paper. 'And who gave it to you?' he asked. I couldn't tell, that would have been against orders. He started shouting and threatening to send me to prison. 'Well,' I said, 'do so, if you think you must.' He went on threatening, but it did not work. I would not be frightened. Suddenly the door opened—and there on the threshold stood the Englishman roaring with laughter! Now, what did that mean? He'd arrived by rail earlier in the day and had sat waiting: would I come or would I not? They both knew all along when I arrived and saw the servants chase me away; they'd given them the orders to do so, not to beat me, but just to throw me out. It was a joke, don't you see, to test whether I would deliver the money or not. Well—they seemed pleased that I'd brought it, told me to go and wash, gave me clean clothes and asked me to come and eat with them. . . . Yes, friend . . . I must say, we did have a meal! The wine too—you just take a sip of it and you can't close your mouth afterwards. It burns all your insides—and has such a flavor, too. They gave me so much of it that I parted with it. The next day again I ate with them, and I told them things that surprised them very much. The Englishman got tight, and tried to prove that the Russian people were the most remarkable in the world and that nobody knew what they'd be up to next. He banged his fist on the table, so excited he got. That money they just handed over to me and I took it, although I've never been greedy for money—it has no interest for me, that's all. But I'm fond of buying things, it's true. One day, for instance, I bought a doll. I was walking along a street and saw a doll in the window: just like a live child, even rolling its eyes, it was. So I bought it. Dragged it about with me for four days—would sit down on the road somewhere, take it out of my sack and look at it. Later on I gave it to a little girl in the village. Her father asked: 'Did you steal it?' 'Yes,' I said —I was ashamed to own I'd bought it. . . ."

"Well, and what about the Englishman?"

"They just let me go, that's all. Shook me by the hand and said they were sorry about the joke, and so on. . . .

"I must go and sleep now, friend, I've got a hard day before me tomorrow. . . ."

Setting down to sleep, he said:

"An odd bird I was. . . . Suddenly joy would seize me, it would flood my innards, my whole heart—I would be ready to dance. And I would dance—much to everybody's amusement. Well—why not? I've got no children—nobody to be ashamed of me. . . .

"That means the soul is at play, friend"—he went on thoughtfully and softly. "A capricious thing, the soul, one never knows what might attract it all of a sudden, something quite funny at times, and just make you cling to it. For instance—just like that doll—one day a little girl bewitched me. I once came across a little girl in a country house. There she was, a child about nine years of age, sitting beside a pond, stirring the water with a twig and shedding tears—her little muzzle bathed in them, like a flower in dew, tears dropping down her breast like pearls. I sat by her side, of course, and asked why she was crying like that on a merry day? An angry little thing she turned out to be, tried to send me away. But I was stubborn, made her speak; so she said to me: 'Don't you come wandering around here; my daddy has a dreadful temper; and so has mammy and also my little brother!' I laughed to myself, but pretended I was really frightened, taking her at her word. Then she buried her little muzzle in my shoulder and just sobbed and sobbed, fairly shook with sobs. Her sorrow proved to be not a very heavy one: her parents had gone to a party near by and had punished her by not taking her, as she'd been naughty and refused to wear the right frock. I played up to her, of course, and soothed her, and said what bad people these parents were. So she begged me to take her away from them; she didn't want to live with them any longer. Take her away with me? Why, of course I would, no trouble about that! So off we went. And I took her to where her parents were having a party—she had a little friend there, Kolya, a curly-headed little sprig—that was the real reason for her sorrow. Well, they all laughed at her, of course, and she stood there blushing worse than a poppy. Her father gave me half a ruble, and I went off. And what do you think, friend? My soul had clung to that little girl, I couldn't tear myself away from the place. I hovered around for a week, waiting to see her, to talk to her; funny, isn't it? I just couldn't help it. She had been taken away to the seaside; she had a weak chest; and there I was roaming about like a lost dog. That's how things happen at times. Yes . . . the soul is a capricious bird—who knows where it may go when it takes its flight?"

The old man paused and yawned as he spoke, as though he were half asleep, or in a trance; then suddenly he brightened up again as though splashed by a cold rain.

"Last autumn a lady from town came to me. She was not very comely, rather weedy and dried-up, I'd say, but when I glanced into her eyes—God Almighty, if only I could have her, if only for one night, I said to myself. After that—cut me to pieces, let horses tear me asunder—I don't care, I'll take any death. So I told her straight away: 'Go. Please go, or I may hurt you, go! I can't talk to you, d'you hear? I beg of you, go!' I don't know if she guessed, or what, but she hurried away, anyhow. How many nights did I not lay awake thinking of her, seeing those eyes in front of me—a real torture. And me an old man, too. . . . Old, yes . . . The soul knows no laws, it takes no account of years. . . ."

He stretched himself out on the ground, twitched the red, scar-like eye-lids, then said, smacking his lips:

"Well, I'm off to sleep now. . . ." And wrapping his head in his cloak he remained still.

He awakened at dawn, looked into the cloudy sky, and hastily ran to the brook where he stripped himself naked, grunting, washed his strong brown body from head to toe, and shouted out to me:

"Hi, friend, hand me over my shirt and trousers; they're in the cave."

Pulling on a long shirt that reached to his knees, and blue trousers, he combed out his wet hair with a wooden comb and, almost handsome, faintly reminding one of an icon, he said:

"I always wash with particular care before receiving people."

While we had our tea he refused vodka:

"No, none of that today. I won't eat anything either, just have a little tea. Nothing should go to one's head; one should keep it light. One needs great lightness of soul in this business. . . ."

People started coming after midday; until then the old man remained silent and dull. His merry, lively eyes had a concentrated look: a grave poise marked all his movements. He looked frequently at the sky and hearkened to the light rustle of the wind. His face was drawn; it seemed more disfigured, and the twitching of the mouth more poignant.

"Someone is coming," he said softly.

I heard nothing.

"Yes. Women. Look here, friend, don't speak to anyone and keep out of the way—or you'll scare them. Sit quietly somewhere nearby."

Two women crawled noiselessly out of the bushes: one, plump, middle-aged, with the meek eyes of a horse; the other, a young woman with a gray, consumptive face; they both stared at me in fear.

I walked away along the slope of the ravine, and heard the old man saying:

"He does not matter; he's not in our way. He's a bit touched in the head; he does not care, does not bother about us. . . ."

The younger woman started to speak in a cracked voice, in hurried and hurt tones, coughing and wheezing, her companion interrupting her speech with short, low, deep notes, while Savel, in a voice that sounded like a stranger's, exclaimed, full of sympathy:

"So—so—so! What people, eh?"

The woman began to whimper plaintively—then the old man drawled melodiously:

"Dear—wait a bit; stop that; listen . . ."

It seemed to me that his voice had lost its hoarseness, sounded more clear and high; and the melody of his words reminded me curiously of the artless song of a goldfinch. I could see, through the net of branches, that he was bending towards the woman, speaking straight into her face;

while she, sitting awkwardly at his side, opened her eyes wide and pressed her hands to her breast. Her friend, holding her head on one side, rocked it to and fro.

"They've hurt you; that means they've hurt God!" the old man said loudly and the brisk, almost cheerful sound of his words was strikingly out of keeping with their meaning. "God—where is He? In your soul, behind your breasts, lives the Holy Ghost; and these witless brothers of yours have injured Him by their foolishness. You should take pity on the fools—they've done the wrong. To hurt God is like hurting a small child of yours. . . ."

And once more he drawled:

"Dee-ear . . ."

I started: never before had I heard this familiar, trivial little word spoken with such triumphant tenderness. Now the old man was talking in a quick whisper; his hand on the woman's shoulder, he pushed her gently, and the woman rocked as though half-asleep. The older woman sat down on the stones at the old man's feet, methodically spreading the hem of her blue skirt around her.

"A pig, a dog, a horse—every beast trusts in human reason; and your brothers are human beings, remember this! And tell the elder one to come to me on Sunday."

"He won't," said the big woman.

"He will!" the old man exclaimed confidently.

Somebody else was descending into the ravine; clots of earth were rolling down; the branches of the bushes rustled.

"He will come," repeated Savel. "Now, go with God's blessing. All will be well."

The consumptive woman rose silently and bowed low to the old man. He raised her head with the palm of his hand and said:

"Remember, you carry God in your soul."

She bowed again and handed him a small bundle.

"May Christ keep you . . ."

"Thanks, friend. . . . And now, go." And he made the sign of the cross over her.

Out of the bushes came a broad-shouldered, black-bearded peasant, in a new pink shirt, that had not yet been washed; it bulged out in stiff folds, protruding from the belt. He was hatless; his disheveled shock of grayish hair stuck out on all sides in unruly locks; his small, bear-like eyes peered sullenly from under frowning brows.

Making way for the women, he followed them with a glance, coughed loudly, and scratched his chest.

"How do, Olesha," said the old man with a smile. "What is it?"

"Here I am," said Olesha dully; "want to sit awhile with you."

"Good, let's do so."

They sat for a moment in silence, earnestly gazing at each other, then started talking simultaneously.

"Working?"

"Father, I'm fed up . . ."

"You're a big peasant, Olesha."

"If only I had your kind heart. . . ."

"You're a strong man."

"What good is my strength to me? It's your soul I want. . . ."

"Well, when your house burned down, another, like an ass, would have lost courage."

"And I?"

"You—no! You've started all over again. . . ."

"My heart is bitter," the man said loudly, and cursed his heart in foul language, while Savel went on with quiet assurance:

"Your heart's just a common, human, anxious heart; it does not want trouble; it longs for peace. . . ."

"It's true, father. . . ."

They went on like that for about half an hour—the peasant telling of a fierce wicked man, whose life was burdened by many failures; while Savel spoke of another man, a strong one, who worked stubbornly, a man who would let nothing slip away from him, nothing escape him, a man with a fine soul.

With a broad smile on his face, the peasant said:

"I've made it up with Peter."

"So I've heard."

"Yes. Made it up. We had a drink together. I said to him: 'What are you up to, you devil? . . .' And he said: 'Well, what about you?' Yes. A fine man, damn his soul. . . ."

"You're both the children of one God."

"A fine man. And clever, too. Father—what about my getting married?"

"Of course. She's the one for you to marry."

"Anfisa?"

"Why, yes. She's a good housewife. What a beauty she is, too, and what strength she has. She's a widow; her first husband was an old man, and she had a bad time with him; but you two will get on well together, take my word for it. . . ."

"I will get married . . . really."

"So you should."

Then the peasant proceeded to relate something unintelligible about a dog, about letting cider out of a barrel; he went on with his stories, guffawing like a wood-sprite. His sullen, brigand's scowl had become completely transformed, and he now had the silly, good-natured look of a domesticated animal.

"Well, Olesha, move on, here's someone else coming."

"More sufferers? All right . . ."

Olesha descended to the brook, drank some water out of the palm of his hand, then sat down for a few moments motionless as a stone, threw himself back on the ground, folded his arms under his head and apparently went to sleep at once. Then there came a crippled girl, in a motley frock, a thick brown plait down her back, and with big blue eyes. Her face was striking and like a picture; but her skirt was annoyingly vivid, covered with green and yellow spots, and there were scarlet spots, the color of blood, on her white blouse.

The old man welcomed her with joy, and tenderly bade her sit down. Then a tall, black old woman, looking like a nun, appeared, and with her a large-headed, tow-haired lad with a congealed smile on his fat face.

Savel hastily led the girl away into the cave, and concealing her there, closed the door—I could hear the wooden hinges screech.

He sat on a stone between the old woman and the boy, his head bent down, and listened to her murmur in silence for a long time.

"Enough!" he suddenly pronounced, sternly and loudly. "So he does not listen to you, you say?"

"No, he doesn't. I tell him this and that . . ."

"Wait. So you don't do as she tells you, lad?"

The lad remained silent, smiling vacantly.

"Well, that's right, don't listen to her.—Understand? And you, woman, you've started a bad job. I tell you frankly; it's against the law. And there couldn't be anything worse than that. Go, there's nothing for us to talk about.—She's out to do you in, lad. . . ."

The lad, with a sneer, said in a high falsetto:

"Oh, I know that, I do-o. . . ."

"Well, go," Savel said, with a disgusted gesture of dismissal. "Go! You will have no success, woman. None!"

Downcast, they bowed to him in silence and went upwards through the thicket, along a hidden path; I could see that having walked up about a hundred feet, they both started talking, standing close together, facing one another; then they sat down at the foot of a pine, waving their arms about, and a quarrelsome drone reached one's ears. Meanwhile from the cave came pouring out an indescribably moving exclamation:

"Dee-ear . . ."

God alone knows how that disfigured old man contrived to put into this word so much enchanting tenderness, so much exultant love.

"It's too early for you to think of it," he said, as though he were uttering an incantation, leading the lame girl out of the cave. He held her by the hand as though she were a child who still walked uncertainly. She staggered as she walked, pushing him with her shoulder, wiping the tears from her eyes, with the movements of a cat—her hands were small and white.

The old man made her sit on the stone by his side, talking uninterruptedly, clearly and melodiously—as though telling a fairy-tale:

"Don't you see you are a flower on earth? God nurtured you to give joy; you can give great happiness; the clear light of your eyes alone is a feast to the soul—dea-ear! . . ."

The capacity of this word was inexhaustible, and truly it seemed to me that it contained in its depth the key to all the mysteries of life, the solution of all the painful muddle of human relationships. Through its fascination it was able to bewitch not only peasant women, but all men, all living things. Savel uttered it in infinitely various ways—with emotion, with solemnity, with a kind of touching sadness. It sounded at times reproachful, at times tender, or else it poured out in a radiant music of joy; and I always felt, whatever the way in which it was said, that its source was a limitless, an inexhaustible love, a love which knows nothing but itself and marvels at itself, seeing in itself alone the meaning and aim of existence, all the beauty of life, capable of enveloping the world in its power.

At that time I had already taught myself to doubt; but in these hours, on this cloudy day, all my unbelief fled like shadows before the sun at the sound of the familiar word, worn threadbare by long usage.

The lame girl gasped happily as she went away, nodding her head to the old man:

"Thank you, grandfather, thank you, dear."

"That's all right. Go, friend, go. And remember—you're going **towards** joy, towards happiness, towards a great task—towards joy! Go!"

She retreated sideways, never tearing her eyes away from Savel's radiant face. Black-haired Olesha, waking up, stood by the brook, shaking his still more disheveled head, and watched the girl with a smile. Suddenly he pushed two fingers into his mouth and gave a shrill whistle. The girl staggered and dived like a fish into the dense waves of the thicket.

"You're crazy, Olesha!" the old man reproved him.

Olesha, playing the buffoon, crouched on the ground, pulled a bottle out of the brook, and brandishing it in the air, suggested:

"Shall we have a drink, father?"

"Have one if you like. I can't, not until tonight."

"Well, I'll wait till evening, too. . . . Ah, father—" and strong curses followed like an avalanche of bricks—"a sorcerer, that's what you are— but a saint, too, 'pon my word! You play with the soul—the human soul, just as a child would. I lay here and thought to myself . . ."

"Don't bawl, Olesha. . . ."

The old woman with the lad came back, and talked to Savel in a low and contrite tone. He shook his head distrustfully, and led them away into the cave, while Olesha, catching sight of me in the thicket, clumsily made his way across to me, breaking the branches as he came.

"A town bird, are you?"

He was in a cheerful and talkative mood, gently quarrelsome, and kept singing Savel's praises:

"A great consoler, Savel. Take me, for instance, I simply live on his soul; my own is overgrown with malice, as with hair. I'm a desperate man, brother. . . ."

He painted himself for a long time in the most sinister colors, but I did not believe him.

The old woman emerged from the cave, and, with a deep bow to Savel, said:

"Don't you be angry with me, father. . . ."

"Very well, friend . . ."

"You yourself know . . ."

"Yes, I know that everybody is afraid of poverty. A pauper is never liked by anyone, I know. But all the same: one should avoid offending God in oneself as well as in others. If we were to keep God in mind always, there would be no poverty in the world. So it is, friend. Now go, with God's blessing. . . ."

The lad kept sniveling, glancing fearfully at the old man, and hiding behind his stepmother. Then a beautiful woman arrived, a woman from the town, to judge by her appearance; she wore a lavender-colored frock

and a blue kerchief, from under which gleamed two large gray-blue eyes
angrily and suspiciously.

And again the enchanting word resounded:

"Dee-ear . . ."

Olesha kept on talking, preventing me from hearing what the old man
was saying:

"He can melt every soul like tin. . . . A great help he is to me. If it
were not for him, Hell alone knows what I'd have done by now. . . .
Siberia . . ."

Savel's words rose from below:

"Every man should be a source of happiness to you, my beauty, and
here you are saying all these malicious things. Chase anger away, dear.
It is goodness we glorify, isn't it, when we glorify our saints on feast days,
not malice. What is it you mistrust? It's yourself you mistrust, your wom-
anly power, your beauty—and what is it that is hidden in beauty? God's
spirit, that's what it is . . . Dee-ear. . . ."

Deeply moved, I was on the verge of weeping for joy, so great is the
magic force of a word vivified by love.

                              *   *   *

Before the ravine had filled with the dense darkness of a cloudy night,
about thirty people came to see Savel—dignified, old villagers carrying
staffs, distressed people overcome with grief; more than half of the visitors were women. I did not listen any more to their uniform complaints,
I only waited impatiently for *the* word to come from Savel. When night
came, he allowed Olesha and me to build a bonfire on the stone platform. We got tea and food ready while he sat by the flames, chasing
away with his cloak all the "living things" attracted by the fire.

"Another day gone in the service of the soul," he murmured, thoughtfully and wearily.

Olesha gave him some practical advice: "A pity you don't take money
from people. . . ."

"It's not suitable for me. . . ."

"Well, you can take from one and give to another. Me, for instance. I'd
buy a horse. . . ."

"You tell the children to come tomorrow, Olesha; I've got some gifts
for them. The women brought a lot of stuff today."

Olesha went over to the brook to wash his hands, and I said to Savel:
"You speak to people so well, grandfather. . . ."

"Ye-es," he agreed calmly. "I told you I did! And people have respect for me. I tell them each the truth they need. That's what it is."

He smiled merrily and went on, with less weariness:

"It's the women I talk best to, isn't it? It just so happens, friend, that when I see a woman, or a girl, who is at all beautiful—my soul soars up and seems to blossom out. I feel a kind of gratitude to them: at the sight of one, I recall all those I have ever known and they are numberless."

Olesha came back, saying:

"Father Savel, will you stand surety for me in the matter of the sixty rubles I'm borrowing from Shakh? . . ."

"Very well."

"Tomorrow, eh?"

"Yes . . ."

"See?" Olesha turned to me triumphantly, stepping on my toe as he did so. "Shakh, my boy, is the kind of man who has only to look at you from a distance and your shirt crawls down of itself from your back, right into his hands. But if Father Savel comes to see him—Shakh squirms before him like a little pup. Look at all the timber he gave to the victims of the fire, for instance." Olesha fussed about noisily and did not allow the old man to relax. One could see that Savel was very tired. He sat wearily by the fire, all crumpled up, his arm waving over the flames, the skirt of his coat reminding one of a broken wing. But nothing could subdue Olesha; he had had two glasses of vodka and had become still more exuberantly cheerful. The old man also had some vodka, ate a baked egg with bread after it; and suddenly he said, quite softly:

"Now go home, Olesha!"

The great black beast rose, made the sign of the cross, and glanced into the black sky.

"Keep well, father, and many thanks!" he said. Then he pushed his hard, heavy paw into my hand and obediently crawled into the thicket, where a narrow path was concealed.

"A good man?" I asked.

"Yes, but he has to be watched carefully; his is a violent nature! He beat his wife so hard that she could not bear any children, kept having miscarriages, and went mad in the end. I would ask him: why do you beat her?—and he would say: I don't know, just want to, that's all. . . ."

He remained silent, let his arm drop, and sat motionless, peering into the flames of the bonfire, his gray eyebrows raised. His face, lit up by the fire, seemed red-hot and became terrible to look at: the dark pupils of the naked, lacerated eyes had changed their shape—it was hard to tell whether they were narrower or more dilated—the whites had grown larger and he seemed to have suddenly become blind.

He moved his lips; the scanty hair of his mustache stirred and bristled —as though he wanted to say something and could not. But when he started to speak again, he did so calmly, thoughtfully, in a peculiar manner:

"It happens to many a man, this, friend; that you suddenly want to beat up a woman, without any fault of her own and—at what a moment, too! You've just been kissing her, marveling at her beauty; and suddenly, at that very moment, the desire overcomes you to beat her! Yes, yes, friend, it happens . . . I can tell you; I am a quiet, gentle man and did love women so much, sometimes to the point of wanting to get deep inside the woman, right to her very heart and hide in it, as a dove does in the sky—that's how wonderful it was. And then, suddenly, would come the desire to hit her, pinch her as hard as one could; and I would do so, yes! She would shriek and cry: what's the matter? And there is no answer— what answer could there be?"

I looked at him in amazement, unable, too, to say anything or ask any question—this strange confession astonished me. After a pause, he went on about Olesha.

"After his wife went mad, Olesha became still more ill-tempered—a fierce mood would come over him, he'd believe himself damned, and beat everyone up. A short while ago the peasants brought him to me tied up; they'd almost thrashed him to death. He was all swollen, covered with blood like bread with crust. 'Tame him, father Savel,' they said, 'or we'll kill him, there's no living with the beast!' Yes, friend. I spent about five days bringing him back to life. I can doctor a bit, too, you know. . . . Yes, it isn't easy for people to live, friend, it isn't. Not always is life sweet, my dear clear-eyed friend. . . . So I try to console people, I do. . . ."

He gave a piteous smile, and his face grew more hideous and terrible.

"Some of them I have to deceive a little; there are, you see, some people who have no comfort left to them at all but deceit. There are some like that, I tell you. . . ."

There were many questions I wanted to put to him, but he had eaten nothing the whole day; fatigue and the glass of vodka were obviously telling on him. He dozed, rocking to and fro, and his red eyelids dropped more frequently over the naked eyes. I could not help asking all the same:

"Grandfather, is there such a thing as hell, do you think?"

He raised his head and said sternly and reproachfully:

"Hell? How can that be? How can you? God—and hell? Is that possible? The two don't go together, friend. It's a fraud. You people who can read invented this to frighten folk, it's all priests' nonsense. Why one should want to frighten people, I cannot see. Besides, no one is really afraid of that hell of yours. . . ."

"And what about the devil? Where does he live, in that case?"

"Don't you joke about that. . . ."

"I'm not joking. . . ."

"Well—well . . ."

He waved the skirts of his coat once more over the fire, and said softly: "Don't sneer at him. To everyone his own burden. The little Frenchie might have been right about the devil bowing down to the Lord in due time. A priest told me the story of the prodigal son from the Scriptures one day—I can remember it well. It seems to me that it is the story of the devil himself. It's he, no other but he, that is the prodigal son. . . ."

He swayed over the fire.

"Hadn't you better go to sleep?" I suggested.

The old man agreed:

"Yes, it's time . . ."

He readily turned on his side, curled himself up, pulled the coat over his head—and was silent. The branches cracked and hissed on the coals, the smoke rose in fanciful streamers into the darkness of the night.

I watched the old man and thought to myself:

"Is he a saint, owning the treasure of limitless love for the world?"

I remembered the lame girl with the sorrowful eyes, in the motley frock, and life itself appeared to me in the image of that girl: she was standing in front of a hideous little god and he, who knew only how to love, put all the enchanting power of that love into one word of consolation:

"Dee-ear. . . ."

1923.

Translated by BARONESS MOURA BUDBERG

Isaak Babel

GEDALI

ON SABBATH EVES I am haunted by the heavy sorrow of memories. At one time my grandfather used to spend these evenings stroking volumes of

Ben-Izra with his yellow beard. My old grandmother, wearing a lace headdress, would perform her rites with knotty fingers over the Sabbath candle and weep sweetly. My child's heart would rock on such evenings like a sailing boat upon enchanted waves.

Oh, the faded Talmuds of my childhood! Oh, the heavy sorrow of memories!

I ramble about Zhitomir, seeking a timid star. By the ancient synagogue, by its yellow, unheeding walls, old Jews are selling chalk, laundry bluing, lampwicks—Jews with the beards of prophets, with the rags of suffering upon their sunken chests.

Behold! Before me is a market and the death of a market. The fatted soul of plenty is dead. Silent padlocks are hanging upon the booths and the granite cobbles of the passages are clean, like the bald heads of the dead. The timid star, it twinkles and goes out. . . .

My success came to me later; it came just before sunset. Gedali's shop was hidden among the rows of locked and barred booths. Oh, Dickens! where was your kindly shade upon that day? In this old curiosity shop you would have seen gilt shoes, a ship's cable, an ancient compass and a stuffed eagle, a Winchester rifle with the date 1810 engraved upon it and a dilapidated saucepan.

Old Gedali potters among his treasures in the rosy void of sunset—the little proprietor in dark glasses and a green surtout reaching down to the ground. He rubs his little white hands, he plucks his little grey beard and, with his head on one side, listens to invisible voices that are fluttering round him.

This shop is like a box belonging to an inquiring and serious boy, who will one day be a professor of botany. There are buttons in this shop and a dead butterfly; and the name of its owner is Gedali. Everyone has left the market place, Gedali remains. And he hovers about the labyrinth of terrestrial globes, skulls and dead flowers, waving a multicolored feather brush and dusty flowers that are dead.

And so we sit upon empty beer-barrels. Gedali twists and untwists his narrow beard. His top-hat rocks above us like a black turret. Warm air flows around us. The sky changes its colors. Kindly blood is flowing from an overturned bottle there, above, and a smell of decay is around me.

'Revolution—to that let us say "Yea!" But surely we will not say "Nay" to the Sabbath!'—thus begins Gedali and enmeshes me with the silken cords of his dim eyes. ' "Yea!" I shout to the revolution, "Yea" I shout: but she hides herself from Gedali and sends naught but bullets ahead of her. . . .'

'The sun enters not into closed eyes, but we will force the closed eyes open. . . .' answered I.

'The Pole closed my eyes'—whispers the old man almost inaudibly— 'that angry dog, the Pole. He beats the Jew, and tears out his beard. Ugh, the cur! And now he is lying beaten, the angry dog. It is splendid, this revolution! And then the one who beats the Pole says to me: "Let me register your gramophone, Gedali" . . . I love music, Pane, I answer to the revolution. "You don't know what you love, Gedali: I shall fire on you, then you will know. I cannot help shooting, because I am the revolution. . . ."

'But the Pole, *he* was shooting, my kindly Pane, because he was the counter-revolution. *You* shoot because you are the revolution. But revolution—why, it is something joyful. And joy cannot bear orphans in the house. Good deeds are done by good men. But good men do not kill. I mean, then, that the revolution is the work of bad men. The Poles are bad men too. Who, then, can tell Gedali where is the revolution and where the counter-revolution? I have studied the Talmud, and I love the commentaries of Rashe and the books of Maymonid. And there are other men of understanding in Zhitomir. And behold, all we learned men, we fall upon our faces and cry out loudly: "Woe unto us, where is the sweet revolution!" '

The old man became silent. We saw the first star come into sight along the Milky Way.

'The Sabbath is coming,' uttered Gedali gravely. 'The Jews must go to the synagogue. . . . Pane, comrade,' he said rising, his top-hat rocking like a black turret, 'bring some good man to Zhitomir. Ah! there is a lack of them in our town; ai! a lack! Bring good men, and we will give them all the gramophones. We are not ignoramuses. The International . . . We know what the International is. And I want an International of good men; I want every soul to be kept on the register and to be given first-category rations. Here, man, pray, eat, and enjoy life. The International, Pane, comrade, you do not know how it should be served. . . .'

'It is served with gunpowder,' I answered, 'and seasoned with the best blood. . . .'

The young Sabbath had ascended its dark blue throne.

'Gedali,' I said, 'it is Friday today and the evening has come; where can one find a Jewish *korzhik*, a Jewish glass of tea and a little of the retired god with my tea?'

'Nowhere,' answers Gedali, hanging a padlock upon his little box, 'no-

where. There is an inn nearby, and good people keep it; but now they
no longer eat there—they weep.'

He buttoned the three bone buttons of his green surtout.

He dusted himself with the feather-brush, threw some water on the
soft palms of his hands and went away—small, lonely, dreaming, in a
black top-hat and a large prayer-book under his arm.

The Sabbath is coming. Gedali—the founder of a fantastic International
—has gone to the synagogue to pray.

Translated from the Russian

Alexei Tolstoi

VASILY SUCHKOV

'I'LL PUT IT THIS WAY: *If only our children had some* understanding, like
we old people have—even that would be something to praise the Lord
for.'

'Mustn't praise the Lord nowadays, Timofey Ivanovich.'

'Well then, praise labour . . . Don't pick holes—I am an old man . . .
Look here—we did fight, didn't we?'

'We did, Timofey Ivanovich. Strictly speaking, mine is a quiet occupation, I didn't fight, but you fought, that's a fact.'

'I like your way of answering, Ivan Ivanovich, you are a straightforward person. The kind of person we need. . . . Waiter, another couple of
bottles and two salmon sandwiches. . . . Well, then, we suffered, didn't
we Ivan Ivanovich?

'No question about that. . . .'

'When the Putilovsky works produced nothing but cigarette-lighters,
do you realize what it was for us, old skilled men, to look on. Who is to
answer? Go on, blame the White Guards, the Allies. . . . Quite, they'll say,
quite. . . . But who started? Did we overthrow everything just to see the
biggest works in the Union grind cigarette-lighters? It is all right now
they are building timber-carriers in the wharves. All the shops working
to full capacity. . . . But in those days one lost hope. . . . Felt like lying
down in the midst of all that destruction and giving up the ghost. . . .
Isn't that suffering? And who set the works running again? See these
hands? Even the bones are saturated with machine oil—see how black
the fingers are. . . . It means that I've got the right to speak. . . . And I
say this: our children are no damn good. . . . Did they fight? No. Did

they suffer? No. They gather in the fruits. And we are an out-of-date lot
for them. My Mishka is a "Young Communist." All right. Mustn't touch
him. Say a word to him—you'll get back ten. All right, all right. Let him
learn, let him try to get into the front ranks, follow the great humanitarian ideal. Though, it would be best to give him an occasional shaking,
but he'll straighten out. . . . Barking impertinently at every word you say
doesn't yet mean his father is a fool. All right, I say, all right. Mishka is
an honest lad. But as for my Kolka . . . Well as for him . . . That's where
I draw the line. He wears loose bags and a hunting knife. Works one day
and spends the next by the sea with the girls . . . And mark you, Ivan
Ivanovich, I mustn't touch him with a stick, or take him by the hair. . . .
What's the matter with his hair? Is it sacred? But he straightway goes off
to complain about me, and at the very best I get a reprimand for tortur-
ing the child. . . . And all the while Kolka's future is obvious—ten years,
with solitary confinement. Do you know what he answers me? "You've
got to prove to me, old cock, why I should work when I want to go out?
In what book is it written, cock, that I should neglect my pleasures? . . ."
And that scamp, Kolka, says it all so confidently as if he's the ruling class.
"And if you hit me," he says, "I'll cut you a hole through the stomach."
And plays with his knife, his eyes burning. . . .'

'Desperate position you are in, Timofey Ivanovich.'

'All right, I won't live to see the final triumph. I am an old man. But
I want my children, my grandchildren to speak three languages, Ivan
Ivanovich. I want them to fly about the earth in airships, as simple as
sitting at home. . . . I want their hands to know fine and brainy work. . . .
I weep, Ivan Ivanovich, because my mother gave me life at the wrong
moment. I was born for knocking brick walls down with my head. . . .
We are the heroic generation, Ivan Ivanovich. . . . Our children and
grandchildren come after us. . . . We have done the dirty work. . . . But
what are they like? That's the tormenting question. For instance. . . .
Down our way, outside the Narva Gate, there are new blocks being built
for working men—houses on foreign lines, with balconies and baths.
Meaning that there is a hint that the workman won't have to live like a
pig now. I come home from the wharf, I wash and sit down to dinner
very orderly. My family is well groomed. We eat in a clean room and our
conversation is about lofty matters, about human progress. That's right,
isn't it? And now—what are the facts? This spring I move into a new
house. Good. And here I am going home from the wharf; and before I
get home—my overcoat is robbed off my shoulders in an alley, for one
thing. . . . I am rushed by people with hunting knives and my belly is

cut open for a bit of sport, for another thing. . . . And, if I escape these
two accidents and come home safe and sound, my neat dining-table is
already occupied by Kolka. . . . His ugly dial just about reeking with
obscenity. No, Ivan Ivanovich, we have expected many misfortunes, but
this misfortune is unexpected.'

Timofey Ivanovich pushed the beer bottles to one side, leant over the
little table close to Ivan Ivanovich's face and raised his finger.

'A secret. Haven't told anyone yet. Even my relations don't know. I am
beginning to fear my son-in-law, Varvara's husband, Vasily Alekseyevich
Suchkov. I don't trust him. He is a suspicious man.'

'Chuck it, Timofey Ivanovich! Really you are beginning to see
things. . . .'

'True. No foundation at all. But I get a bitter taste in my mouth whenever I think of him.'

This conversation took place in June, in a beer-shop on the Peterburgsky Side. Two old friends chatted together: one was Zhavlin, Timofey Ivanovich, a workman on the Putilovsky wharf and the other Ivan
Ivanovich Farafono, employed by the River Conservancy as keeper of
the shallow riverbank by the Petrovsky Island.

It was a windless, sunny day: a Sunday. The beer-shop was almost
empty and filled with a sour smell and stray whiffs of crayfish. The dron-
ing of flies against a plate glass window, which displayed the words
'Stenka Razin Beer' written backwards, suggested a midday languidness.

The friends finished up their beer. Smoked for a while. Paid the bill
and went out. The blue sky with its summer stillness was spread above
the miserable streets of the Peterburgsky Side.

'And yet,' said Timofey Ivanovich, 'and yet, my son-in-law is an inscrutable person.'

After that they walked side by side along the broken pavement strewn
with the pods of sunflower-seeds. An aeroplane floated in the sky above.
So did the clouds, white as the snow. Silence, the monotony of a Sunday.
Flower-pots in the windows. Some children were playing ball on a vacant
site among ruins of brick, and the smallest of them sat amongst pig-
weeds, weeping.

A girl in a light summer frock walked towards the two friends. Her
youthful neck, her shoulders and her slender hands showed a golden sunburn. Fair, curly hair covered her pretty head like a cap.

Wider and wider grinned the friends as they looked at the approaching
girl. The day was fair, the drink had warmed their hearts, and it was a
pleasure to look at Youth browned by the sun.

'Your daughter is first class; meets my approval,' said Timofey Ivanovich.

'Nastya, dear, where are you off to?' asked Ivan Ivanovich, pleased.

She raised her blue eyes and her face became sweeter still. She stopped, sighed slightly.

'I promised to call on Varvara Timofeyevna to-day.'

'I have been over at the daughter's to-day.'--Timofey Ivanovich, with a sudden frown, began to look down under his feet, 'I have been there and could not stand it for an hour. . . . I shan't go again for six months. . . . You've got no business there, either, Nastya. . . . To listen to the discourses of citizen Suchkov? . . . No point. Yes. . . .'

Nastya raised a narrow eyebrow, shrugged a pretty shoulder. She could not see why Timofey Ivanovich had become angry. The three stood silent for a moment. Then Nastya smiled at her father and went her way, so upright that one could see at a glance there was nothing wrong with her.

'A clean girl she is,' said Ivan Ivanovich looking after her. 'That's just it . . . she'd better not visit Varvara; no good will come of it. . . .'

A Sunday afternoon is tedious enough on Peterburgsky Side, in streets where no occasional tram ever appears. It is deserted and miserable. And it seems as though behind the dusty little windows, behind the dilapidated gateways, in little wooden houses built round courtyards overgrown with weeds, in little houses that through a single attic window look through ruined buildings, 'The Side' would like to slumber for ever —leave it alone—that's all.

Here's a pink house with three storeys. It has just been painted; the drain pipes have been repaired; the long blots of plaster have not yet been washed off the windows; it has a blue sign Peterburgsky District Workmen's Co-operative Society. And then right down to the river— weather-beaten walls, fences, ruins; a tobacco stall by the war-cripple who is bored to slumber; a woman with penny sweets; and sun-flower seeds by the side of the drain pipe. . . . Seeds, seeds. . . . Surely the earth and the sun have not given rise to men just in order that he might crack these damned seeds, while shuffling without thought, without passion, along the dreary pavement?

Here's a fence made of rusty corrugated iron. Behind it, on a vacant site, there are a few beds with potatoes, and around them heaps of broken stone overgrown with stinging-nettle. A goat wanders about. A woman sits on a stone, with her chin on her fist, a baby on her lap, and stares vacantly.

Here's another vacant site. By the side of the pavement there are three steps—all that is left of the front entrance. And it seems as though one can walk up these steps into an unseen house. Its outlines can still be seen. On the right a triangle on the wall of the neighbouring house marks the roof that has disappeared; and lower down the remains of blue wallpaper with flowers. On the left, a brick arch still exists, and there is a door leading into the open air.

If you ask the old keeper, who sits by the gateway on the other side of the street, he will tell you that the three steps did in fact lead to a two-storeyed house. It was a good wooden house. Some of the tenants have disappeared, some have died, others live on the Vasilevsky. And the owner of the unseen house is the old man himself, now the keeper.

Thus he sits all day under the gateway opposite, looking back into the past. Higher up a close-cropped girl is reading a book, and sitting on the sill of an open window with her bony knees raised. A citizen in brown knitted trousers crosses the road with a teapot in his hand and leers at the maid in the window. At the sight of Nastya he turns towards her.

'Begging your pardon . . . why are you walking alone?'

'Least of all your concern,' retorts Nastya as she passes with a haughty look at the knitted trousers.

'All matters of skirt are my concern. . . . What's the hurry? You'll come to the same thing in the end, so why not take the bird-in-hand?'

Nastya rounds the corner and enters the courtyard of Varvara Timo-feyevna's house. In one of the open windows of her flat, on the second floor, she could see Suchkov's strong back clad in a grey shirt with a cycling belt. He was playing a guitar and the strong nape of his neck reflected the strain.

❋   ❋   ❋

Varvara met Vasily Suchkov last year at the 'Leshy' cinema. He struck her as an interesting man. He was very polite, cold, neatly dressed. Narrow, clean-shaven face, small eyes, a scar on one cheek, near the mouth. During the interval he fixed his eyes on Varvara (who was dark, round-faced, and somewhat stout) moved to the seat next to her and lent her the programme. Then he said that he did not smoke from hygienic considerations and offered her some fruit drops. Varvara crushed the fruit drops with her ivory teeth and probably a merry, eager smile never left her face—Suchkov looked at her mouth with a cool avidity.

She liked the way he made haste to define his social position: he was an instructor in a school of surveying. His conversational approach indicated the seriousness of his intentions. Varvara told him that she worked as a packer in a chocolate factory; this seemed to please him—it was clean work, and it followed that the girl must also be clean. During the rest of the performance they exchanged impressions—the film shown was 'The Bandits of Paris.' Suchkov saw Varvara as far as the tram, and next Sunday they again met in a Cinema on the Nevsky. After the performance he suggested going to a Caucasian restaurant. Varvara blushed and declined. She yielded to him only after the third visit to a cinema, being under the disturbing influence of the adventures of Mary Pickford.

Suchkov himself offered to have their union legalized at the Registry Office (he insisted on orderliness before everything else in life)—and Varvara moved to his house on the Peterburgsky Side. A year has passed since that time. Varvara told her relations that she lived well and could not wish for anything better. But people began to notice that she was getting thinner, fading, losing her happy disposition. It turned out that she was fiercely jealous because during the year she had lived with him she had not come to know him any better than during the first evening's acquaintance.

*   *   *

The table was laid. Through the open door one could see Varvara in the smoke of the kitchen, busy round a petrol-cooker. Suchkov was half-heartedly playing a guitar. Looking diligent, Andrey Matti, a Finnish subject, fair and well groomed, with bovine eyelashes, sat near him. He was dressed in a new grey suit and wore a pink tie. His straight thin mouth smiled good naturedly. He could sit like this for any length of time—discreetly silent.

Varvara cast piercing glances at her husband and Matti, as she hovered about the kitchen. What are they keeping silent about, I ask you, now? Matti wouldn't be hanging about the house just for a how-d'you-do, if it wasn't with an object; Suchkov wouldn't be playing him the guitar with a smile. That's the umpteenth Sunday the Finn has turned up with a flower or a packet of chocolate for Varvara, and Suchkov has immediately assumed this strange wry smile (it would be good to chuck this saucepan with hot cabbage-soup at his ugly face). Varvara's raging heart knew that they were conspiring, that the Finn was urging her husband, enticing him, leading him away and the husband is willing. . . . No mistake. . . . Would he smile like this otherwise? . . .

Playing a polka with scoundrelly variations, the scoundrel. He's trimmed his nails this morning, so that they should not catch against the strings. Oh, dear, there's no doubt about it; the Finn has found a girl for him. . . .

'I say, Varya,' quietly called Suchkov, 'how are you getting on with the rissoles, or else we'd better sit down to some vodka?'

Varvara thunderously rattled the saucepans, choking with anger. But that was inopportune, because Matti took advantage of the noise in the kitchen to say weightily:

'It is a big inconvenience to be without a cook. Such a decent house should, of course, have a servant. A man with your tastes must have money.'

       ❅   ❅   ❅

Varvara lay in bed with the bedclothes pulled over her head. Suchkov undressed without hurrying, lay down on his back by her side and began to smoke cigarettes. The light of a Northern summer night crept through the dirty glass of the lime-splashed window. Varvara lay as still as a corpse. The clock was ticking on the chest of drawers. Something inside it tripped, groaned, as if existence had become unbearable in this silent bedroom filled with Suchkov's thoughts. It groaned, then recovered and again began to slice off life's seconds, sweeping away their little corpses into the unknown.

. . . Suchkov hopped out of bed, went to the dining-room, angrily treading on the loose strings of his underwear.

He produced out of a drawer in the writing desk a school copybook with the motto 'Grind the granite rock of learning,' and sat down near the window to make an entry:

'17th June. Left the Office this morning, under the pretext of an unendurable toothache. Went to Petrovsky Park. Bathed. Met N. Her constitution comes up to expectations. Spoke to her, very successfully prepared the ground for the next morning. In the evening made final arrangements with M., though I don't yet know what the work will turn out to be like. But I already feel I am spreading my wings. By the way, M. has proposed getting rid of Varvara. Nothing very definite. Perhaps she will understand herself that she should go. . . .'

Having locked the copybook in the drawer and hidden the key in his purse, Suchkov returned to his bedroom. Looking at the pendulum of the clock, he said:

'I am sleepless. Perhaps you will put the kettle on the oil cooker for me?'

Then Varvara tore off the sheet. She sat up in bed in an unbuttoned frock, dishevelled, her stocking dropping down. She did not care—let him look at her swollen, tear-stained face. . . .

'You didn't know I was on the lake to-day, did you? . . . You rotter,' she nodded emphatically, 'rotter.' . . .

'Don't get abusive,' he said icily. 'For your language, the way you have hit me in the face, and for the word "rotter" you have just hurled at me, you might find yourself before the Magistrate in no time. . . . Besides, I made no promises that I would limit my requirements to one woman. . . .'

'I know . . . I know. . . . But there's one thing that's unfortunate for you—the fact that I've got you summed up, Alekseyevich. . . . My eyes are open once and for all. . . . You are a beast. . . . You clean-shaven brute. . . .'

'For the last time: stop it. . . .'

'I shan't stop it, even if you threaten to kill me. Do you think I've a pennyworth of fear for you? You are unclean. . . . Why don't you keep a she-goat instead of a woman? Or this same Nastya under whom you dived this morning! I haven't heard a human word from you during the whole year. You couldn't speak one, my dear, if you tried. . . . Curse these damned rages, your presents. . . .' (She tore open her dress down to the hem). 'I had known men before you. Three men. From our factory. Didn't you know that? Well then, I did. . . . They called me darling, sweetheart . . . dearest comrade. I gave up the third one just before you. He is still pining for me . . .'

'Full stop,' said Suchkov disdainfully—'the details do not interest me.'

Varvara lowered her head and kept silent for a moment. When she looked at her husband again, her face quivered violently.

'If you need more women than one, you'll have to use a different receptacle, my friend. . . . Take care, of course, not to catch any disease. But I must tell you about two secrets.' (Suchkov threw a rapid sidelong glance at her. She noticed it and smiled.) 'I am pregnant, Vasily Alekseyevich, the third month . . . I won't kill the child, I shall bring him into the world and you will pay maintenance. . . .'

'Oh,' Suchkov pulled a wry face and began to pace the room. 'As to that, we shall wait and see. If you really are pregnant it does not follow yet that I am the father. . . . The identity of the father is still an open question. . . .'

He succeeded at last in stepping on the strings, frenziedly jerked his leg, broke them, and shouted: 'And I won't be blackmailed! . . . Don't rely too much on the maintenance . . .'

Then Varvara pulled the torn dress over her breast, covered herself up to the neck, gathered in her bare legs. She seemed now afraid to look at her husband, running about the bedroom in his underwear: she gazed at the window. Wetting her lips she said:

'Now—for the second secret, Vasily Alekseyevich. . . . Since this is the way you look at things . . . I will tell you also. I didn't want to . . . No, no, no . . . After all, you have been my husband . . . but, Vasily Alekseyevich, I am going to denounce you . . .'

Suchkov stopped dead. His long face, with the newly appearing shadows of unshaven cheeks, seemed deathly greenish through the sleeplessness of the twilight summer night. Quietly, sorrowfully Varvara said: 'Vasily Alekseyevich, you are a spy.'

There the conversation ended. Varvara lay down again and covered her head. Suchkov went into the dining-room. Then he made tea for himself. Towards seven o'clock he went into the bathroom for his clothes. He went out soon afterwards.

'18th June—One o'clock at night. Been on the lake. . . . N. has not come to the rendezvous. Waited in vain until seven o'clock. Walked around the bungalow and saw a lock on the door. If that is a challenge on N.'s part, I am not one to give up before the aim is attained. Spoke with M. in the evening and frankly expressed my fears concerning Varya. M. insists. I promised to be a good comrade. Worked out the plan together. Yes, M. is right in saying that one must be modern; see the aim clearly and destroy everything that stands in the way.'

That night Suchkov slept in the dining-room under an old military great-coat. He did not hear how Varvara came quietly near the door and looked at him for a long time. In the black narrow opening of the door her face seemed deathly pale.

On the 10th June, Suchkov returned home from work earlier than usual and grilled the pork chops himself. Varya usually came in from the chocolate factory at half-past five. He opened the front door for her and said with a pleasant smile:

'We must end our rowing, Varya. You have misunderstood me, I have misunderstood you. You have thrown an accusation at me and it has wounded me deeply. But now I understand that we are both guiltless. We must talk it over seriously. . . .Once and for all.'

Varvara repeated, looking into the darkness of the passage: 'Once and for all.' Then Suchkov brought the chops from the kitchen and called out:

'Come and feed! I am the chef to-day.'

He drank several glasses of vodka, groaning good-naturedly. Even told a funny story about a mother-in-law and an inspector of taxes from 'The Rhinoceros.' Varvara sat at the table somewhat on her guard. At last, rolling little balls of bread, he turned to the main theme.

'You have overheard my conversation with Matti. A cinema-like situation develops; the wife finds out that her husband is a spy. Ha, ha, ha! . . . I can understand your feelings . . . But, Varya, my dear. . . . The real explanation is much simpler. Matti is the representative of a certain big firm. And, you see, they tread very warily. They are just collecting preliminary information—to get their bearings, estimates, and so forth . . . But for the present, it is a strict secret . . . That's the sort of spy I am . . . Ha, ha! . . . Yesterday I at last softened Matti's heart and he has allowed me to tell you everything, and put your fears at rest.' (He rubbed Varvara's hand.) 'And as for that girl, Nastya, be reasonable, Varya. . . . It is not even a fleeting attraction . . . Just playing with a kitten . . . I don't like the innocent.'

Varvara had suffered so much during these last days that she was glad to believe anything, and even against her will she believed her husband. What if it really was just her imagination? With the palm of her hand over her eyes, she said:

'But didn't you say yourself that you never promised me you would limit your requirements to one woman? . . .'

'Chuck it, Varya . . . Worse things than that are said in anger.'

'I shall never forget that talk last Sunday at table. . . . Especially Nastya being there and that friend of yours. . . . And it was clear to everybody you were tired of me, ready to throw yourself at the first woman that came your way. . . .'

'Nerves, Varya, nerves. . . . Feminine imagination. . . . I was speaking theoretically, to keep up an interesting conversation at table . . . But you are a fine one as well, aren't you? Slapping me in the face. . . .'

Varvara sighed deeply with her last breath of bitterness. She could not bear to suffer any longer. Leaving the chop unfinished she went into the bedroom. Put on a touch of powder, got her hair in order, thought awhile, then changed her dress. And suddenly a great weight seemed to be removed. No sooner had she left the room than Suchkov seemed to crumple up, lowered his head and began to beat out a tune on the oilcloth. Then he drank three glasses of vodka, one after the other without a snack. Turned round on his chair and stared at the wall behind which Varvara could be heard walking about.

'Varya,' he called faintly and hoarsely; cleared his throat and then loudly: 'Varya, you know, I've got an idea. . . .' She returned to the dining-room. 'Let's go out into the air. We haven't had a walk together for a long time . . .' Varvara suddenly smiled trustingly and readily, just as she did a year ago in the cinema. Suchkov glanced at her and poured out some more vodka . . . 'We'll have a walk and a talk. . . .A man I know has a boat on the Goloday, not far from the Smolensky Cemetery . . . Come on, dress . . . Don't put a hat on . . . better take a shawl . . .'

In the ante-room he began to rub his forehead, waved his hand as though vexed.

'Most vexing, I've quite forgotten. You go on to where No. 6 stops, in the Bolshoy, and wait for me; I'll just call in at the house-committee offices.'

Varvara went away. Suchkov listened at the half-open door as she walked downstairs. It seemed that she had not met or spoken to anyone.

Then he took a long time over putting his cap on in front of a mirror, looked round to see that he had taken everything—cigarettes, matches. On tip-toe, not knowing it—he went out of the flat, noiselessly closing the door behind him. Creeping, he came down to the house-office, and there said to the official very loudly:

'The wife's gone out somewhere, and didn't take the front door key. Please give her the key when she comes back. I am off to work over-time; won't be back until late probably. . . .'

            ❖   ❖   ❖

Behind the Smolensky Cemetery, to the west of it, lay a deserted, barren, low-lying ground, called New Petersburg. Here it was once planned to build a town as beautiful as a dream, all in marble and granite, a new Palmira of the northern seas. But all they had time to build was a small number of five-storey buildings, with their windows looking gloomily at the sea, at the muddy shores with here and there a boat pulled aground, at the abandoned villa of Gregory Gregorevich Ge (who had one night got the fright of his life sitting on the roof during a flood), at the dykes, the piles of broken stone and iron scattered about the island, at the remains of the fountain showing through the grass. The lonely houses are inhabited, but there are few people about, especially in the southwestern part of the island.

That was just where they were going to now: Suchkov, who walked ahead with his hands in his pockets, taking long strides, and Varvara who could not quite keep up with him. In the distance, low over the mirror-like sea, hung the clouds, already coloured by the setting sun.

The red, golden, watery-green light of the sunset spread peacefully behind the Kronstadt fortification, behind the woody shores of Lakhta, that hung as in a mirage over the bay.

'Don't run, Vasya, what's the hurry?' repeated Varvara, gasping for breath. All the way to the Cemetery, Suchkov had stood on the platform of the tram. On getting out he offered Varya his arm. He was walking fast, ever faster. His small eyes jumped about restlessly over the faces of occasional passers-by. Round the corner, when before them spread a mirror-like sea and above them the evening sky, and Varvara hugged close to her husband for a caress, he abruptly disengaged his arm and ran ahead. He stopped on the edge of a small cliff. Below, a thin sheet of water lazily licked the sand, the bits of broken bottles, the stones.

'Curse! there's no boat,' said Suchkov looking at the sea towards the slumbering sails of the becalmed yachts. 'We'll have to wait, curse it. . . .'

He jumped down on to the sand, and, without turning: 'Come on . . . jump. . . . Let's sit down . . .'

Varvara's heart beat furiously. She jumped, sat down on the sand, threw herself back, and leaning on her hands, closed her eyes at the sunset. The action jerked her blue striped frock above her knees. She did not pull it down, left it as it was. She wanted happiness so much this summer evening, that from the moment when she ran off to the bedroom to powder her face and to the very end, she was deluded, guessed nothing.

Suchkov squatted down and smoked. He kept looking round and repeating: 'Presently, presently, wait a moment. . . .' In the distance, in the Goloday Island stadium, a band began to play, but that was a couple of miles away; here the shore was deserted.

'Vasya,' said Varvara, with her eyes still screwed up, 'I don't want a lot, you know. . . . I am not like the others, jealous, tyrannizing . . . So long as I know you pity me, love me . . . What else do I want?'

'Shut up, shut up,' said Suchkov through his teeth. Steps creaked on the cliff above, and Matti's voice said hastily:

'Hurry up and get it over.'

Varvara straightened out, opened her mouth for some air. Cried out. The most terrifying thing of all was her husband's ghastly pale long face. He looked at her with the fierce hatred of the devil incarnate . . . Varvara tried to jump up from the stand, but he grasped her leg, threw her down, briskly leapt on to her chest, put his icy fingers round her throat. He was strangling her, putting the weight of his shoulders into the work. Letting go with one hand, he picked up a brick from the sand and struck Varvara on the head with it several times—struck her till the brick broke. Then he got up from Varvara's chest, glanced back at her blood-covered face and walked away along the edge of the water. Matti was by that time far away, walking across the waste ground towards the cemetery.

Translated from the Russian

Ilya Ehrenburg

THE ZADDIK

WITH DIFFICULTY I have at last succeeded in finding a real Zaddik. He is, perhaps, one of the last. His name is Reb Yosele from Skvernovic. He lives in Warsaw, in the neighborhood of the Jewish paupers. A tiny un-heated room. I am reminded: "Do not forget to cover your head." This is his only request. The Zaddik is a tall, good-looking Jew of about fifty-five years of age, with a long traditional beard and the kind, yet sad eyes of a village dreamer. He is dressed poorly, and everything around him is poor and shabby. The chairs are broken and the tapestry torn. This Zaddik resembles a great poet who is read only by ten or twenty people. His followers are poor workers from the Nalevki.

The Zaddik offers me a cigarette and lights one himself. By the awkward movement of his fingers, and his strenuous puffing, it is obvious that he is not a habitual smoker. Perhaps he only lit the cigarette so as to soften the tension of our strange meeting. However, he soon feels at ease and answers my questions. I ask him about the essence of Hasidism. He answers readily without stopping to think a moment; some-times smiling ironically, sometimes inspired, like a real poet.

"The Misnagdim consider the 'Law' above all. But soldiers are trained differently in different countries. The English soldiers are taught differ-ently from the Polish. However, soldiers of all the world are trained to obey the commands of 'one-two'; the good one forgets everything he has been taught."

The Zaddik caresses his long beard and looks at me questioningly. It seems that he is not certain whether I understood. He adds: "All life is war. . . .

"You ask what is 'Heaven' and 'Hell'? After death a man with strong will power lives his life all over again. The joy from the love and kindness he dispensed through his life is 'Heaven.' And 'Hell'? 'Hell' is shame. . . .

"In order for a man to rise he must first fall. One cannot rise without having fallen. This is the law of life and the law of God. . . .

"Poverty is the path to God. In the book Zohar it is said that God has many attires, but he is always dressed in the prayers of the poor."

My last question: "What is more important, the relation between man to God or between man to man?"

The Zaddik smiles.

"At first it seems that his relation to God is the more important. For God is everything, and man—dust. But when you think about it, especially if you have lived and experienced, you will realize that man's relation to man is the most significant. If a man insults God, he has insulted God alone. But when a man insults a man, he has wronged both, God and man."

Reb Yosele has a score of followers. They always come to him for advice: "What's to be done, the daughter is sick?" or "Soloveichik will not return the ten zlotys he borrowed." His wisdom remains within the four walls, hidden under a faded cap, bent over an old book.

The Zaddik reminds one of an old master who remembers a secret of an ancient craft, but does not know where to apply it. Reb Yosele still remembers the words of the Besht, but his words nobody understands any more. He cures hearts not with his inherited wisdom but with his title of "Zaddik," and with a kind and generous smile.

The rich Jews go to the better-known Zaddikim. There, they too may expect some honor or benefits; the right to sit with the Zaddik, at one table, or with his influential assistants in some commercial scheme. These Hasidim wear silk talletim (prayer-shawls), their beards are neatly trimmed, and on Saturdays, they wear silk caps with borders of yellow fur. They call themselves Hasidim, but if you ask them about the teachings of Besht, they will not be able to answer. For them more important than the joy and ecstasy is—who will sit today next to the Zaddik, Aaron Shmulevich or Hayyim Rosenberg?

There are still other places where Hasidism is yet alive, not its philosophy but spirit—amid the poor of the synagogue of the so-called "Brazlav Hasidim." They have no Zaddik at all. Their Zaddik died long ago—a century and a half ago. His name was "Reb Nachman from Brazlav." He was a great philosopher and poet. His sayings, legends and poetry were recently published in a German translation. This first emergence of historical Hasidism from the borders of the Ghetto was full of belated glory, to the classical astonishment of the descendants. "Whence such daring thoughts? Whence such poetry? From Brazlav? . . . Nobody ever knew about it. . . ."

Yes, only his Hasidim knew it. For them Reb Nachman was a great Zaddik. And when he died, they did not take another one in his place. They have chosen for their adviser the memory of this Zaddik-poet. Among the Brazlav Hasidim there are neither rich nor hypocrites. These have nothing to do here, their place is at the table of the living Zaddik. And here? Here are only the paupers of the Nalevki: peddlers, tailors, cobblers.

I enter the synagogue. It is a small room in a worker's house, dimly lit by a tiny electric lamp. It is crowded to capacity, and with difficulty I manage to elbow my way inside. At first it seems as though it were a trade union meeting. But no, here is a different century, a different chronology. Perhaps it is altogether beyond the concepts of our time. Bearded men in dirty caps who toil the whole week selling rags and herrings, pounding out a monotonous dreary existence. But now is Sabbath Eve. They came here to rejoice. And they are happy, not because it has been prescribed to be happy. No, in them is still alive the belief which is already dead outside of this tiny room. They are meeting the "Sabbath-Queen." They clasp their hands and sing. At first, they say words of prayer. But neither the tongue nor the mind can keep up with the gayness of the soul. Soon, the words are heard no more, only a gay, wide, soul-captivating melody. The feet will not stand in one place any longer, and they begin to jump. And they dance in this tiny and dimly-lit room. Happiness! Life! I observe the faces and wonder. Who changed them? Who erased from their minds the memory of insults, hunger and "Zlotys"? One can speak here even about Catholicism, Freud or "Mass Hypnotism." But is it worth while? These things can be read by everyone in solid books. Would it not be better now to accept the smile of the Brazlav Hasidim as an extraordinary happiness? Even though it is foreign, inaccessible, but human till the end. The joy of losing oneself in a greater joy, the joy of honesty and forgetfulness, the joy of simple and childish souls. Rejoice!!! . . .

Translated by LEON DENNEN

Vladimir Mayakovsky

HANDS OFF CHINA

WAR,
       daughter of imperialism,
stalks,
a spectre through the world.
Workers, roar: Hands off China!—

Hey, Macdonald,
           don't meddle
in leagues and muddle speeches.
Back, dreadnoughts!
Hands off China!

In the embassy quarters
          kings meticulously
sit, weaving a web of intrigues.
We'll brush away the cobweb.
Hands off China!—

Coolie,
enough of dragging them, cool, in ricksaws,
straighten your back.
Hands off China!

They want to pulverize
       you
         with a colony.
400 millions,
      you're no drove.
Louder, Chinese:
       Hands off China!—

Time you drove
      these drivers out.
dropping them off the wall of China.
Pirates of the world,
Hands off China!—

We're glad
          to help
                    all enslaved
to fight,
          teaching
                    and providing.
We're with you, Chinamen!
Hands off China!
Workers,
          rout the robber
night, fire as a rocket
your fiery slogan:
Hands off China!

Translated from the Russian

Boris Pasternak

THE POET

HAD I BUT known of things in store,
How lines with viscous blood can kill,
Can kill and take the throat by storm,
And had, untried, my débuts still,

I'd said a categoric "no"
To jokes with this dread spore of all,
But to begin was far to go,
And timid early passion's call.

But age is Rome again, the same
That in return for gossip fleet
Demands no actor's bid for fame,
But death ungrudging and complete.

And when its feelings lines dictate,
They send a slave upon the stage,
And here breathe only soil and fate,
For art dies consummate with rage.

Translated from the Russian

Mikhail Zostchenko

THE TRAP

A FELLOW I KNOW—he's a poet, by the way—went abroad this year.

He travelled all over Italy and Germany for the purpose of becoming acquainted with bourgeois culture, and to replenish his wardrobe.

He saw many curious things.

"There's a terrible crisis in these foreign countries, of course," he says. "Unemployment, contradictions face you at every step. Plenty of products and manufactured goods for sale but nothing to buy them with."

He dined with a duchess, by the way.

He was sitting in a restaurant with a friend. And the friend said to him:

"I'll call up a duchess if you wish, just for fun. A real duchess, one who owns five houses, a skyscraper, vineyards and so on."

He was laying it on, of course.

But he goes to the phone and calls a number. And soon a beautiful creature appears, aged about twenty. She's dressed gorgeously. Has manners. A nonchalant expression. Three handkerchiefs. Slippers, on bare feet.

She orders a minute steak and says during the course of the conversation:

"It's about a week, you know, since I've tasted meat."

The poet, in broken French and Russian, replies that it can't be true, since she owns à la maison so many houses and so on. She was probably putting it on, hiding behind poverty just to throw dust in their eyes.

She says:

"You know, my tenants haven't paid any rent in six months. The nation has no money."

I relate this little fact for no particular reason. Just to be talking. Just to give a description of the bourgeois crisis. A desperate crisis is looming from all sides there. But their streets, by the way, are clean.

This friend of mine, the poet, praised their European cleanliness and culture. Particularly in Germany, he said, despite their tremendous crisis, they observe remarkable, almost fabulous cleanliness and order.

They clean their streets, the devil take it, with soap powder. Stairs are scrubbed every morning. Cats are not permitted to lie on stairs and windowsills, as they do in our country.

Housewives take their cats out for walks on leashes. The devil knows what it's all about.

Everything, of course, is blindingly clean. One can't even spit anywhere.

Even such secondary places as, excuse me, toilets—even they shine with heavenly spotlessness. It's pleasant, it's inoffensive to human dignity, to enter one of those places.

My friend, by the way, did enter one of those secondary institutions. Just like that, for fun, he looked in—to see whether it really was different from places at home.

He had to admit it was. One could have exclaimed with rapture and amazement, he says. Fabulous cleanliness, sky-blue walls, violets on a shelf. He hated to leave the place. Better than a café.

"What the devil!" he thinks. "Our country leads in the sense of political advancement, but as regards cleanliness we're far behind. When I get back to Moscow," he thinks, "I'll write about it, and hold up Europe as an example. Of course many of our fellows act with great hypocrisy in respect to these questions. They feel embarrassed, you see, to write about such lowly things. But I will cut through their sloth," he thinks. "When I get back I'll write a poem about how there's too much dirt, comrades, and it isn't right . . . especially since we're now waging a campaign for cleanliness—I'll answer my social call."

There our poet stands, behind the closed door. He thinks, he admires the violets, he dreams about the poem he's going to put together. The rhymes and lines even begin taking shape. Something like this:

> Even to enter such a place of theirs is grand.
> Violets nodding and blooming on the shelves!
> Has Attila trampled with a heavy foot our land,
> That we must live for aye in dirt ourselves?

After whistling to himself the newest German foxtrot, "Auf Wiedersehen, My Dear," he wants to go out into the street again.

He wants to open the door, but he realizes that the door doesn't open. He pulled at the door handle. No results. He pushed with his shoulder—no, it doesn't open.

In the first moment he even became a bit confused. "Into what sort of trap," he thought, "have I fallen?"

Then he clapped his hand to his forehead.

"What a fool I am!" he thinks. "I've forgotten where I am—in a capitalist world! Here, at every step, they probably have to pay a pfennig. I probably have to drop a coin and the door will open by itself. Mechanism! The devils! Bloodsuckers! Flay you right to the quick. It's lucky," he thinks, "that I happen to have some change on me. What a fool I'd have been without those coins. I'll buy myself free from those capitalistic sharks," he thinks. "I'll shove a coin or two down their throats."

But he sees it's not so simple as all that. There are no boxes or slits for coins. There's an inscription of some kind, but no figures are indicated. And where to drop the money and how much to drop is unknown.

Here our friend became somewhat scared. He began knocking lightly on the door. No one approached. Then he kicked the door.

He hears—people are gathering around. Germans are approaching. They babble in their own tongue.

The poet says:

"Let me out, do me the favor!"

The Germans whisper, but obviously they don't grasp the acute nature of the situation.

The poet says:

"Genosse, Genosse der Tuer! You rascals, I can't open it."

The Germans are saying:

"Sprechen Sie Deutsch?"

The poet fairly implores:

"Der Tuer," he says, "open der Tuer. May the devil take you all!"

Suddenly a Russian voice sounds behind the door:

"What's going on?" the voice says. "Can't you open the door?"

"That's it," the poet says. "For two hours I've been struggling."

The Russian voice says:

"The scoundrels here have mechanical doors. You probably forgot to press the trigger," he says. "Flush the toilet and the door will open by itself. It's arranged that way expressly for forgetful people."

My friend did as he was told and suddenly, as in a fairy tale, the door opens. And my friend, swaying, emerges into the corridor to the accompaniment of slight smiles and German whispers.

The Russian says:

"Although I am an emigré, I'm sick and tired of these German tricks and fancies. They mock humanity. . . ."

My friend, of course, did not pursue a conversation with an emigré; and raising the collar of his coat, rapidly made for the exit.

At the door the porter brushed him, extracted a sum of money from him and let him go his way.

Only when he had reached the street did my friend breathe freely and pull himself together.

"Aha," he thought, "even this much-praised German cleanliness doesn't work by itself. And the Germans, too, have to impose it by force through the invention of different tricks and fancies to maintain their culture. We should consider something similar."

With these thoughts my friend calmed himself and, singing "Auf Wiedersehen, My Dear," went to visit some friends as if nothing had happened.

> (From "Russia Laughs," copyright 1935 by Helena Clayton, pub'd by Lothrop, Lee & Shepard Co.; by arrangement with the publishers.)

Yury Olesha

THE CHERRY STONE

I WENT INTO THE COUNTRY on Sunday to see Natasha. There were three more guests besides myself: two girls and Boris Mikhailovich. Natasha's brother, Erastus, took the two girls for a sail on the river, while we others—Natasha, Boris Mikhailovich and I—went off into the woods. We sat down to rest in a sunlit clearing. Natasha raised her head and suddenly her face looked to me a shining porcelain saucer.

Natasha treated me as an equal, but with Boris Mikhailovich she behaved as if he was much older; she looked up to him in fact. She knew that I found this very disagreeable, and that I envied Boris Mikhailovich, so, from time to time, she would take me by the hand and, no matter what was said, ask me:

"That's true, Fedya, isn't it?"

As if she was asking my forgiveness in a roundabout way.

We started to talk about birds, because a funny bird-note had rung out just then from the thicket. I remarked that I had never seen a thrush in my life and asked what it looked like.

At that moment a bird flew out across the clearing and perched on a branch over our heads. It did not so much sit as stand, swinging, on the bough. It blinked and I decided that bird's eyes were not in the least pretty, because they had no brows, but the lids were strongly marked.

"What's that?" I asked in a whisper. "Is it a thrush?"

There was no reply. I turned my back to them, so that, my jealous glance removed, they might enjoy their tete-a-tete in peace. I watched the bird. Glancing round suddenly, I caught a glimpse of Boris Mikhailovich stroking Natasha's cheek. The hand seemed to say: let the poor slighted young fellow watch the birds, if he likes. But I no longer saw the bird. I was listening. I caught the sound of a kiss as their lips parted. I did not look around, but they knew they had been caught for they saw me start.

"Is that a thrush?" I asked again.

The bird took flight—up through the tree-tops. It was a difficult flight; the leaves rustled as she flew.

Natasha offered us cherries. Following a childish custom, I kept one cherry-stone in my mouth, rolling it about until I had sucked it clean. When I took it out it looked like wood.

I left the country cottage that day with the stone in my mouth.

I travelled through an invisible country.

I returned from the country to the town. The sun was setting. I went in an easterly direction. I was making a double journey, but only one-half of it was visible. The passers-by could see a man crossing a deserted green common. But what was really happening to this person who walked along, to all appearances, so peacefully? He could see his shadow going before him, sprawling over the ground; the shadow had long, pale legs. I crossed the common and all of a sudden the shadow climbed a brick wall and lost its head. This the passer-by did not see, only I saw it. I entered as it were a corridor between two wings of a building. The corridor was infinitely lofty and shadowy. The ground here was rotten and gave like garden soil under foot. A wild, forlorn looking dog ran towards me, sidling against the wall. We passed each other. Then I glanced round. Far behind me the threshold was bright. For a moment the dog formed a dark protuberance in the brightness. Then it ran off across the common and only then I saw that it was a rusty-coloured animal.

All this happened in an invisible country. What happened in the country visible to the ordinary eye was that a man and a dog passed each other, at sunset, on a green common. . . .

The Invisible Country was the country of attention and imagination. Two sisters walked beside our traveller and led him by the hand. The names of the sisters were Attention and Imagination.

Well, then, what about it? It appeared that, in direct opposition to society and the established order, I was creating a world of my own, subject to no laws but the shadowy laws of my own sensations. But what did that mean? There were two known worlds: the old and the new. But what sort of a world was this? A third world? There were two roads, but what sort of a road was this third one?

Natasha makes an appointment with me but does not keep it.

I am there half-an-hour before time. There is a train-clock at the crossing that reminds me of a barrel. They are really like barrels, aren't they, those street clocks? Two faces. Two ends. Oh, empty barrel of time, I might exclaim.

Natasha made the appointment for half-past three.

I wait. Oh, she isn't coming, of course. Ten minutes past three.

I stand by the train shop. All around me people are bustling about. I tower above the crowd. Those who have lost their way espy me from afar. Now it is beginning. . . . An unknown woman approaches me.

"Would you be so kind," pleads the unknown one, "as to tell me if Number 27 car will take me all the way to Kudrinsk Square?"

No one must know that I am keeping an appointment. Better to let them think: "That young man who is smiling broadly has come to this corner expressly for the convenience of other people. He'll tell you all you want to know, he'll direct you, he'll calm your fears. . . . Go to him."

"Yes," I reply, brimming over with civility. "The 27 will take you to Kudrinsk Square. . . ."

Then suddenly remembering the right number, I fling myself after the woman, calling out:

"No, no! You'll have to take a 16!"

Let us forget about the appointment. I am not a man in love at all. I am the good genius of the street. Come to me! This way, this way!

A quarter past three. The hands of the clock unite and lie horizontal. Looking at them, I think:

"Like a fly twiddling its legs. The restless fly of time."

How silly! As if there was such a thing! She will not come. She will not come. A Red Army soldier comes up to me.

"Can you tell me where the Darwin Museum is?" he asks me.

"I don't know. . . . Over there, I think. . . . Wait a minute, though. . . . Wait . . . a . . . min— No, I'm afraid I don't know."

Next. Who's the next? Don't be shy. A taxi describes a curve and glides up to me. You ought to see how that driver despises me. Not out of strength of mind. No, I should think not. As if he would condescend so far as to waste strength of mind on me. No, no. He shows it by his glove . . . the contempt is conveyed by his glove. Comrade driver, believe

me, I'm only an amateur, I really don't know which way to direct your
car. . . .

I am not standing here for the purpose of directing people. I have
my own business to attend to. . . . My loitering here is enforced, and
rather pathetic. . . . I am not smiling out of sheer good nature. If you
look closer you will see it is a forced, strained smile.

"Which way to Varsonofievski Lane?" the taxi-driver flings over his
shoulder to me.

I hasten to explain: "This way and then that way and then——"

Oh, well, if it comes to that, why should I not stand in the middle of
the road and take up in good earnest the work that is thrust upon me?

A blind man approaches.

He simply shouts at me. He pokes with his stick.

"Is that a Number 10 coming?" he demands. "Eh? Ten, is it?"

"No," I reply, almost stroking him. "It's not a 10. It's a two. But there's
a 10 just coming behind."

Twenty minutes over the appointed hour have passed. Why should I
wait any longer? Perhaps she is hurrying to get here, though, flying as
fast as she can?

"Oh, I'll be late—oh, I'll be late. . . ."

The woman who wanted to get to Kudrinsk Square has caught the 16,
the Red Army soldier is wandering through the cool galleries of the
museum, the taxi-driver is trumpeting in Varsonofievski Lane, the blind
man is climbing in his touchy, egoistic fashion, with his stick held out
before him, up the front steps of the Number 10.

Everyone is satisfied. Everyone is happy. Only I remain there with a
vacant smile on my face.

More people approach me with enquiries: an old woman, a drunken
man, a group of children with a flag. I begin to slash the air with my
arms, I no longer merely indicate the desired direction by a jerk of
my chin as a passer-by casually inquired of might. No, no. I stretch
out my hands, the edge of the palm cutting the air. . . . Another moment
and a baton will appear in my fist.

"Back!" I shall shout. "Stop! That way to Varsonofievski Lane. Turn.
To the right, old lady. Stop!"

Oh, look! here is a whistle clinging to my lips. I whistle. . . . I have
the right to whistle. . . . Children, you may well envy me. Back! Oho . . .
look here! I can stand between two trams going in opposite directions.
I'm standing, you can see, at ease, with my arms crossed behind my back
and the red baton touching my shoulder-blades.

Congratulate me, Natasha. I have turned into a militiaman.

Suddenly I catch sight of Avel standing some way off, watching me. (Avel is my neighbour.)

Natasha is obviously not coming. I beckon to Avel.

I: "Did you see that, Avel?"

Avel: "Yes, I did. You must be crazy."

I: "Oh, so you saw me, Avel? I've turned into a militiaman."

(A pause. I cast another glance at the clock. Ten to four.)

I: "Of course, you cannot understand. My transformation into a militiaman took place in an Invisible Country."

Avel: "Your Invisible Country is all a lot of idealistic nonsense."

I: "And do you know, the most surprising thing about it, Avel, is that I should figure as a militiaman in that enchanted country. . . . By right, I should be marching through it calmly and majestically, as its owner, with the flowering staff of the sage in my hand. . . . And stead of that, look here, this is the militiaman's baton I'm holding. What a curious mixture of two worlds, the everyday and the imaginary."

Avel: (says nothing).

I: "And what is still stranger is that the initial cause of my transformation into a militiaman, is—unrequited love."

Avel: "I can't understand a single thing. It's some sort of Bergsonism, I suppose."

I resolved to plant my cherry-stone in the ground.

I chose a suitable spot and planted it. "Upon this spot," I said to myself, "a cherry tree will grow up, planted by me in memory of my love for Natasha. Perhaps, some day—say five years hence—Natasha will meet me under this new tree in the springtime. We shall stand one on each side of it. Cherry trees never grow very tall; you can touch the topmost leaf if you raise yourself on your tiptoes. There will be bright sunshine and the spring will be a little bare still, for it will be just the time when the running gutters tempt children out to play and the tree is bursting into blossom."

I shall say:

"Natasha, the day is bright and joyous, the breeze blows and fans the light to a brighter radiance. The breeze sways my tree and makes its shining boughs creak. Each of its blossoms will lift and then droop, showing pink and then white. That is a kaleidoscope of spring. Natasha. Five years ago you gave me some cherries, do you remember? Unrequited love has made the memory humble and very clear. I remember even to this day how the palm of your hand was purple from cherry juice and how you made a funnel of it as you poured the cherries into my palm. I took away a cherry stone in my mouth, and I planted it in memory of my unrequited love. It is blossoming now. So you see—I was slighted then. Boris Mikhailovich was more manly than I was and he won you. I was dreamy and puerile. I sought for a thrush, while you two kissed. I was romantic. But you see—a fine, firm, mature tree has grown up from the romantic seed. You know that the Japanese think a cherry blossom is the soul of man. See, this is a short, sturdy Japanese tree. Believe me, Natasha, romance can be manly too, you should not laugh at it. . . . The whole point is how to approach it. If Boris Mikhailovich caught me squatting on the common planting a puerile little cherry stone, he would feel his triumph once more over me, the triumph of the man over the dreamer. And it was just about that time I planted the kernel. It has burst and sprouted into a tree of dazzling beauty. I buried a seed in the soil. This tree is our child, Natasha. Bring me the son that Boris Mikhailovich gave you. Let me see whether he is as healthy, pure and aloof as the tree produced by an infantile person like myself."

As I returned home from the country, Avel appeared from the other side of the wall. He works in a Trade Union. He is small. He wears a Tolstoy blouse made of a cotton imitation of covert coating, sandals, and blue socks. He is clean-shaven but his cheeks look swarthy. He gives the impression of being overgrown with hair. One might almost think that he had not two skins but only one, a black one. He has a hooked nose and a black cheek.

Avel: "What's the matter with you lately? As I was passing in one of the suburban trains to-day, I caught sight of you squatting on your heels somewhere on the permanent way, scraping up the earth with your hands. What was up?"

I: (I make no reply.)

Avel (pacing up and down the room): "A man sits on his heels and digs the earth with his hands. What can he be doing? There's no knowing. Is he making an experiment? Or has he got the colic? There's absolutely no knowing. Are you subject to attacks of colic?"

I (after a pause): "Do you know what I was thinking, Avel? I was thinking that a dreamer should never have children. What does the new world want with a dreamer's children? Better for the dreamers to produce trees for the new world."

Avel: "It's not in the Plan."

The world of attention begins at the head of your bed, with the chair which you draw up to it as you are undressing. You awake early in the morning, while the house is still. The room is flooded with sunshine. Silence reigns. You lie without stirring, for fear of disturbing the immobile light. A pair of socks lie on the chair. They are brown. But in the steady brilliance you suddenly detect among the brown threads tiny wisps of variegated hair—crimson, blue, and orange, stirred by the air.

It is a Rest Day morning. Once more I am taking the familiar route to Natasha's. I ought to write *Travels in an Invisible Country*. Here is a specimen chapter; it might be entitled:

"The Man Who Was in a Hurry to Throw a Stone."

Some shrubs grew under a brick wall. I passed them as I went along the path. I caught sight of a niche in the wall, and wanted to throw some pebbles at it. I stooped. A stone lay at my feet. . . . Then I saw an ant-hill.

The last time I saw an ant-hill was twenty years ago. Oh, of course, I had stepped over ant-hills many a time during those twenty years. And I suppose I had seen them, but had merely thought, "I am walking over ant-hills", and the word "ant-hills" was all that stood out clearly in my consciousness. All the living image was pushed into insignificance by the word that leapt so readily to my service.

Oh, I remembered now: ant-heaps can only be discovered by a casual glance. One. . . . Then . . . here's another. Then—look here—there's another. That was how it happened now. Three ant-hills appeared one after the other.

My height hindered me from seeing the ants properly; all my eye could catch was a certain restlessness in a form that might easily have been taken for immobile. The eye was willing to be deceived. As I looked I was quite ready to think that it was not a multitude of ants swarming round their ant-hills but the ant-hills themselves that were crumbling away like sand dunes.

I stood about four paces from the wall with the stone in my hand. The stone was intended to lodge in the niche. I flung it. The stone flew out and struck the bricks. A spiral of dust arose. I had missed the mark. The stone fell into the bushes at the foot of the wall. Only then did the exclamation uttered by the stone before I opened my palm reach my ears.

"Wait", cried the stone. "Look at me!"

I had been in too much of a hurry. I should have examined the stone first. There was no doubt about it, the stone was a remarkable thing. And now it had disappeared into the shrubs. And I, who had held the

thing in my hand, could not even say what colour it had been. Maybe it
had been of a purplish tint. Possibly it had not been monolithic but made
up of several different bodies. Maybe it had contained the fossilized
skeleton of a flying beetle or a cherry stone; maybe—it had not been a
stone at all, but a bit of mouldy bone.

I encountered an excursion on the way. Twenty persons were walking
across the common where I had planted my cherry stone. They were led
by Avel. I stepped aside. Avel did not see me, or rather, did not understand. He saw me without perceiving me; he gulped me down, so to
speak, like any fanatic, without waiting for either my agreement or
resistance.

Avel detached himself from his flock and turned to face it. His back
was towards me. Flinging out an arm with a powerful gesture, he cried:

"Now here! Here you are! Here!"

A pause. Silence.

"Comrades from Kursk!" bawled Avel, "I hope you have some imagination. Imagine as much as you like, don't be afraid."

So Avel was trying to invade the Country of the Imagination? Would
he even go as far as to show the excursionists the cherry tree planted in
memory of unrequited love? Avel was seeking a way to the Invisible
Country.

He strode along. Then he halted and shook his leg. Then he shook it
again; he was evidently trying to free himself from some twining shrub
which had wound itself around his foot as he was walking. He stamped
his foot and the plant crackled and scattered in little balls of yellow.
(How many plants and trees and shrubs there are in this story!)

"The huge concrete works I was telling you about will be set up here."

"Dear Natasha, I forgot the principal thing: the Plan. I acted without
consulting the Plan. In five years' time a huge concrete works will have
risen on this deserted spot where now you can see nothing but useless
walls and ditches. My sister—Imagination—is an imprudent creature.
They will begin to lay the foundations in the spring-time and then—what
will become of my poor silly little cherry stone? Yes—for a tree planted
in your honour will blossom there in the Invisible Country some day. . . .

"And excursionists will come to see the concrete giant.

"They will not see your tree. Surely the Invisible Country could be
rendered visible . . . ?"

This letter is an imaginary one. I never wrote it. But I might have written it if Avel had not said what he did.

"The building will be laid out in a semi-circle", said Avel. "And the inner side of the semi-circle will be devoted to a garden. Have you any imagination?"

"Yes," I said, "I have. I can see it, Avel. I can see it all quite clearly. There will be a garden just here. And on the very spot where you are standing now, a cherry tree will grow up."

Translated by ANTHONY WIXLEY

Mikhail Sholokhov

THE COSSACKS

THE MELEKHOV FARM was right at the end of Tatarsk village. The gate of the cattle-yard opened northward towards the Don. A steep, sixty-foot slope between chalky, grass-grown banks, and there was the shore. A pearly drift of mussel-shells, a grey, broken edging of shingle, and then —the steely-blue, rippling surface of the Don, seething beneath the wind. To the east, beyond the willow-wattle fence of the threshing-floor, was the Hetman's highway, greyish wormwood scrub, vivid brown, hoof-trodden knotgrass, a shrine standing at the fork of the road, and then the steppe, enveloped in a shifting mirage. To the south a chalky range of hills. On the west the street, crossing the square and running towards the leas.

The Cossack Prokoffey Melekhov returned to the village during the last war with Turkey. He brought back a wife—a little woman wrapped from head to foot in a shawl. She kept her face covered and rarely revealed her yearning eyes. The silken shawl was redolent of strange, aromatic perfumes; its rainbow-hued patterns aroused the jealousy of the peasant women. The captive Turkish woman did not get on well with Prokoffey's relations, and before long old Melekhov gave his son his portion. The old man never got over the disgrace of the separation, and all his life he refused to set foot inside his son's hut.

Prokoffey speedily made shift for himself; carpenters built him a hut, he himself fenced in the cattle-yard, and in the early autumn he took his bowed, foreign wife to her new home. He walked with her through the village, behind the cart laden with their worldly goods. Everybody from the oldest to the youngest rushed into the street. The Cossacks laughed discreetly into their beards, the women passed vociferous remarks to one another, a swarm of unwashed Cossack lads called after Prokoffey. But, with overcoat unbuttoned, he walked slowly along as though over newly ploughed furrows, squeezing his wife's fragile wrist in his own enormous swarthy palm, defiantly bearing his lint-white, unkempt head. Only the wens below his cheekbones swelled and quivered, and the sweat stood out between his stony brows.

Thenceforth he went but rarely into the village and was never to be seen even at the market. He lived a secluded life in his solitary hut by the Don. Strange stories began to be told of him in the village. The boys who pastured the calves beyond the meadow road declared that of an evening, as the light was dying, they had seen Prokoffey carrying his wife in his arms as far as the Tatar mound. He would seat her, with her back to an ancient, weather-beaten, porous rock, on the crest of the mound; he would sit down at her side, and they would gaze fixedly across the steppe. They would gaze until the sunset had faded, and the Prokoffey would wrap his wife in his coat and carry her back home. The village was lost in conjecture, seeking an explanation for such astonishing behaviour. The women gossiped so much that they had no time to hunt for their fleas. Rumour was rife about Prokoffey's wife also; some declared that she was of entrancing beauty; others maintained the contrary. The matter was set at rest when one of the most venturesome of the women, the soldier's wife Maura, ran to Prokoffey on the pretext of getting some leaven; Prokoffey crawled into the cellar for the leaven, and Maura had time to notice that Prokoffey's Turkish conquest was a perfect fright.

A few minutes later Maura, her face flushed and her kerchief awry, was entertaining a crowd of women in a by-lane:

"And what could he have seen in her, my dears? If she'd only been a woman, now, but she's got no bottom or belly; it's a disgrace. We've got better-looking girls going begging for a husband. You could cut through her waist, she's just like a wasp. Little eyes, black and strong, she flashes with them like Satan, God forgive me. She must be near her time. God's truth."

"Near her time?" the women marvelled.

"I'm no babe! I've reared three myself."

"But what's her face like?"

"Her face? Yellow. Unhappy eyes—it's no easy life for a woman in a strange land. And what is more, women, she wears—Prokoffey's trousers!"

"No!" The women drew their breath in abrupt alarm.

"I saw them myself; she wears trousers, only without stripes. It must be his everyday trousers she has. She wears a long shift, and below it you see the trousers, stuffed into socks. When I saw them my blood ran cold."

The whisper went round the village that Prokoffey's wife was a witch. Astakhov's daughter-in-law (the Astakhovs lived in the hut next to Prokoffey's) swore that on the second day of Trinity, before dawn, she saw Prokoffey's wife, straight-haired and barefoot, milking the Astakhovs' cow. From that day the cow's udder withered to the size of a child's fist; she gave no more milk and died soon after.

That year there was unusual mortality among the cattle. By the shallows of the Don the carcasses of cows and young bulls littered the sandy shore every day. Then the horses were affected. The droves grazing on the village pasture-lands melted away. And through the lanes and streets of the village crept an evil rumour.

The Cossacks held a village meeting and went to Prokoffey. He came out on the steps of his hut and bowed.

"What good does your visit bring, worthy elders?" he asked.

Dumbly silent, the crowd drew nearer to the steps. One drunken old man was the first to cry:

"Drag your witch out here! We're going to try her . . ."

Prokoffey flung himself back into the hut, but they caught him in the porch. A sturdy Cossack nicknamed Lushnia knocked Prokoffey's head against the wall and exhorted him:

"Don't make a sound, not a sound, you're all right. We shan't touch you, but we're going to trample your wife into the ground. Better to destroy her than have all the village die for want of cattle. But don't you make a sound, or I'll smash your head against the wall!"

"Drag the bitch into the yard!" came a roar from the steps. A regimental comrade of Prokoffey's wound the Turkish woman's hair around one hand, pressed his other hand over her screaming mouth, dragged her at a run through the porch, and flung her beneath the feet of the crowd. A thin shriek rose above the howl of voices. Prokoffey sent half a dozen Cossacks flying, burst into the hut, and snatched a sabre from the wall. Jostling against one another, the Cossacks rushed out of the porch. Swinging the gleaming, whistling sabre around his head, Prokoffey ran down the steps. The crowd shuddered and scattered over the yard.

Lushnia was heavy of gait, and by the threshing-floor Prokoffey caught up with him; with a diagonal sweep down across the left shoulder from behind he clave the Cossack's body to the belt. Tearing out the stakes of the wattle fence, the crowd poured across the threshing-floor into the steppe.

Some half-hour later the crowd ventured to approach Prokoffey's farm again. Two of them crept cautiously into the porch. On the kitchen threshold, in a pool of blood, her head flung back awkwardly, lay Prokoffey's wife; her lips writhed tormentedly back from her teeth, her gnawed tongue protruded. Prokoffey, with shaking head and glassy stare, was wrapping a squealing, crimson, slippery little ball—the prematurely-born infant—in a sheepskin.

Prokoffey's wife died the same evening. His old mother had pity on the child and took charge of it. They plastered it with bran mash, fed it with mare's milk, and after a month, assured that the swarthy, Turkish-looking boy would survive, they carried him to church and christened him. They named him Pantaleimon after his grandfather. Prokoffey came back from penal servitude twelve years later. With his clipped, ruddy beard streaked with grey and his Russian clothing he did not look like a Cossack. He took his son and returned to his farm.

Pantaleimon grew up darkly swarthy and ungovernable. In face and figure he was like his mother. Prokoffey married him to the daughter of a Cossack neighbour.

Thenceforth Turkish blood began to mingle with that of the Cossacks. That was how the hook-nosed, savagely handsome Cossack family of Melekhovs, nicknamed "Turks", came into the village.

When his father died, Pantaleimon took over the farm; he had the hut rethatched, added an acre of common land to the farmyard, built new barns, and a granary with a sheet-iron roof. He ordered the tinsmith to cut a couple of cocks from the odd remnants and had them fastened to the roof. They brightened the Melekhov farmyard with their carefree air, giving it a self-satisfied and prosperous appearance.

Under the weight of the passing years Pantaleimon Prokoffievich grew stouter; he broadened and stooped somewhat, but still looked a well-built old man. He was dry of bone, and lame (in his youth he had broken his leg while hurdling at an Imperial review of troops), he wore a silver half-moon ear-ring in his left ear, and retained the vivid raven hue of his beard and hair until old age. When angry he completely lost control of himself, and undoubtedly this had prematurely aged his corpulent wife, Ilinichna, whose face, once beautiful, was now a perfect spider-web of furrows.

Piotra, his elder, married son, took after his mother: stocky and snub-nosed, a luxuriant shock of corn-coloured hair, hazel eyes. But the younger, Gregor, was like his father: half a head taller than Piotra, some six years younger, the same hanging hook-nose as his father's, bluish almonds of burning irises in slightly oblique slits, brown, ruddy skin drawn over angular cheekbones. Gregor stooped slightly, just like his father; even in their smile there was a common, rather savage quality.

Dunia—her father's favourite—a long-boned, large-eyed lass, and Piotra's wife, Daria, with her small child, completed the Melekhov household.

Translated by STEPHEN GARRY

Alexei Remisov

FIERY RUSSIA

In memory of Dostoevsky

DOSTOEVSKY IS RUSSIA.

And there is no Russia without Dostoevsky.

And in the last terrible hour, if such a terrible hour be fated, in the last unexpected minute before the last summons and judgement, who, if not he, only he, shall speak alone and for all? For all those suffering and tormented souls, wallowing sinners and yet innocent lovers? For Russia the rebellious, the desperate and hopelessly unhappy (for can a rebel ever be happy?). For the murderer, for the whole Russian people?

"Judge us," he will say to the judge, "if you can, if you dare."

And from his sunken eyes, that have burned to ashes from pain, will, like a spark, flash fire.

What a tired and torn heart—no human heart has beaten so strangely and fast, so impetuously and ecstatically. And the vaster the silence of the Moon—the huge, round, brazen Moon, looking straight in at the window—the more violently beat the heart, and it pained even.

Who is he, and whence did he come?

Traversing what quadrillions of spaces—the response and reflex of what terrible wizard spirit, of what fiery desert spirit-tempter, holding the keys of human happiness?

Whither bent?

Towards what Golgothas without term?

With a word to appall human souls, set fire to the earth and, if such a terrible hour be fated, to answer for all the pain, for all the sin of Man, for Russia the rebellious and hopelessly unhappy.

Under the rolling peal and clang of gogolian bells, through the pushkin azure of Russia the incomparable and inspired, of Russia the enchanted and carolling, of the Russia of Vii—huts black-as-black, and half the huts burned down, with only charred beams protruding. And on the highway, peasant women, a multitude of peasant women, a whole procession of them, and all of them with emaciated, wasted and somehow tanned faces. One especially, there, on the edge of the crowd, so gaunt, so tall, she might be forty, and yet might only be twenty, with that long emaciated face of hers, and in her arms a babe cries, and her breasts must be dried up, with not a drop of milk in them. And the babe cries and cries and holds out its hands, bare, and its tiny fists have turned blue from the cold.

"Why are they crying? What are they crying for?"
"The babe, the babe is crying."
"And why is it crying?"
"The babe is cold, its little clothes are chilled through, and give no warmth."
"And why should that be? Why?"
"The poor, the burnt out . . . go begging for their fire."
"No, no, tell me: why do mothers rendered homeless by fire stand there, why are people poor, why is the babe poor, why is the steppe bare, why are they not embracing, not kissing, not singing glad songs, why have they turned so black from such black misery, why do they not nourish the babe?"
But let all be illumined—
The snow has taken fire in a broad silver field and sparkles in crystal stars—do you hear Gogol pealing?—the frost somehow has flushed warmly, and songs ring out—
No songs, no stars. Everything's covered up, blackened out, muffled. And wherever you look, just one gaunt inseparable bitter joy-spoliator, mother sorrow.
To come into the world on the light and spacious earth of Pushkin and Gogol, and at that very instant have somebody's merciless hand slash at your eyes—so that's what she's like, this light earth!
"No, if I had it within my power not to be born, I would not accept this existence."

Dostoevsky saw man's fate in the world—and more bitter it is than ultimate bitterness—and not only man's. Remember Azorka!—the children were dragging it on the end of a rope to be drowned. Remember also the wretched hack, with eyes that were scarred with whipping, and even the things that have been denied a soul here—Iliushka's little boots, old, worn and patched, standing in the corner there by the bed.

The entire world agonized before his eyes—instantly.

But what can man do for the happiness of man?

Suffering is life, and man's lot confusion and misfortune.

And for man the most unbearable, the most terrible, is freedom: it is terrible to confront one's heart-free decision.

And if there be another way out, it lies only in the renouncement of the will—for is not man, the rebel, weak and incapable of facing his own rebellion? By the renouncement of the will, by fettering authority, by whole-hearted devotion in the beginning, it is still possible to correct and ameliorate something in the world, to make humanity happy.

But would man desire such unrebellious happiness with a stifled "to dare" and an appointed "I wish"?

Or perhaps there is no solution for man?

But to live by rebellion is impossible.

How shall we live then, how love? With what hell in our breast and what hell in our head?

By throbbing inexhaustible memory, by the ecstasy of the heart, by exploit, by the torments of the cross before the cross of the wide world—by these man should live and love.

Dostoevsky is Russia.

Vibrant, moved into eternity, sung by my sorrowful Word, and fresh, ineffable as yet, rising up turbulently from the dust, unrestrainable.

And there is no Russia without Dostoevsky.

Russia the beggar, the hungry and cold, burns with a fiery word.

The fire impetuously gushed from the heart.

I shall ascend a mountain, turn my face to the East—fire,
            turn to the West—fire,
            look to the North—conflagration
            and to the South—conflagration
            fall to the Earth—it burns.

Where and what meeting, who will shape this blazing, unrestrainable fire—

            we-shall-burn-to-ash!

There, on the ancient stones, on the dear graves of Europe, a fiery heart will meet lucid wisdom.

And over Russia, spacious and parched, over the fire-wasted steppe and the menacing forest will light lucid and faithful stars.

Translated from the Russian

Ivan Bunin

NATALIE

THAT SUMMER for the first time I donned the university cap and became filled with the peculiar happiness which comes only at the beginning of a young, free life. I was brought up in the country, in a strict, gentry family, and as a youth, though I dreamed warmly about love, I remained physically and spiritually chaste. I blushed whenever I overheard the loose talk of my schoolmates, who scowled at me and said: "Meshchersky, you should be a monk!" That summer I would not have blushed any longer. When I came home for my summer vacation, I decided that the time had come for me to be like the others, to forget my chastity, and to seek love without sentimentality. This resolution, as well as my desire to display the blue university cap, sent me, in search of amorous adventures, visiting the neighboring estates that belonged to our relatives and friends. That is how I happened to arrive at the estate of my maternal uncle, Cherkassov, a retired cavalryman, a widower for many years, and the father of an only daughter, my cousin Sonia. . . .

I arrived late, and Sonia was the only member of the household to welcome me. When I jumped down from the carriage and, on the run, entered the dark hall, she came to meet me in a flannel bathrobe. Holding high a candle in her left hand, she let me kiss her cheek and, shaking her head, said in her usual mocking manner:

"Ah! The young man who is never on time!"

"For once it is not my fault," I answered. "The train is to blame, and not the young man."

"Not so loud! Everyone is asleep. They almost exploded with impatience waiting for you all evening, but finally they gave up. When papa went to bed he was furious. He called you a popinjay and Yefrem an old fool because he suspected him of remaining at the station to wait for the morning train. Natalie looked offended when she went upstairs, the servants left, and it seems that I am the only patient person who remains faithful to you. . . . . Take off your coat and have something to eat."

Admiring her blue eyes and her raised arm, bared to the shoulder, I answered:

"I find it most gratifying. This new proof of your devotion is very timely—you have become an enticing beauty, and I have serious designs on you. What arms, what a neck, and what a tempting little soft bathrobe, with very little under it, I presume!"

She laughed:

"Very little indeed! . . . But you, too, have improved and matured a great deal. Fiery eyes and a dashing black moustache. . . . What has happened to you? In two years, during which I have not seen you, you have changed from a bashful, eternally blushing boy into a rather fascinating villain. Our grandmothers would have said that this has all the ingredients for a love affair, if it were not for Natalie with whom you will be madly in love from tomorrow morning until your dying day."

"Who is Natalie?" I asked entering the dining room, brightly illuminated by an oil lamp suspended from the ceiling and with its windows opening on the blackness of a warm, quiet summer night.

"My classmate, Natalie Stankevich, who is visiting us. There is a real beauty—not to be mentioned in the same breath with me! Just imagine: a charming head fringed with golden hair, and black eyes which, to borrow a Persian expression, are veritable black suns. To top it all, tremendously long, black eyelashes, and an amazing golden glow in her face, on her shoulders, everywhere."

"Where everywhere?" I asked, more than ever delighted with the turn the conversation was taking.

"Tomorrow morning we are going swimming, and I recommend that you hide in the bushes and see for yourself what I mean. She is built like a young nymph."

"Why are you endangering our affair by singing her praises?"

"That only shows that I am an intelligent person—I always look ahead. . . ."

Cold meats, cheese and a bottle of Crimean red wine were waiting for us on the dining room table.

"Don't look for anything more—that's all there is," she said, taking a seat and filling two glasses with wine. "No vodka. But we can toast our wishes with red wine."

"What wishes?"

"For instance, I wish that I soon would find a man who will be willing to join our 'clan.' I am almost twenty-one and I cannot marry anyone who will take me away from home. If I leave, who will look after papa?"

"Here is hoping!"

We touched glasses, and, having slowly emptied hers, she again with the same peculiar, mocking expression fixed her eyes on me, watching me manipulate the fork. As though talking to herself, she said:

"Not at all bad-looking. You look like a Georgian and you are quite handsome. In the old days you were too scrawny, and your face had a greenish color. You have changed a great deal. Your manner is much lighter and more pleasant, only your eyes are not steady enough."

"That's because they are blinded by your charms. You, too, were very different in the old days. . . ."

Once again I looked at her with admiration. Sitting across the table from me, she was curled up in the chair, her legs folded under her, her plump knees crossed. She was turned so that I could see her almost in profile. The even sunburn on her arms shone in the lamp light, her sapphire, smiling eyes sparkled, and her thick, soft hair, fixed for the night into a large plait, gleamed a chestnut red; the collar of her bathrobe had come open disclosing a round, sunburned neck and the parting between her breasts, also covered with a triangle of sunburn; there was a beauty spot on her left cheek with an appealing tiny curl of black hair.

"How is your father?"

Without changing the mocking expression of the eyes that were fixed on me, she took out of her pocket a small silver cigarette case and a silver match box. In lighting the cigarette, with almost excessive ease she shifted the position of her legs.

"Thank heavens, father is a brick. As straight and firm as ever. He still taps the floor with his crutch, ruffles his grey pompadour, on the sly dyes his whiskers and sideburns with something brown and looks playfully at Christie. . . . Only his head shakes more constantly and more noticeably than before. As though he always disagreed with everyone," she said and laughed. "Would you like a cigarette?"

I lighted one, though at that age I had not yet begun to smoke. She refilled our glasses and sat staring at the darkness beyond the open windows.

"Yes, so far we have no reason to complain, thank heavens! And what a wonderful summer—what a night! Too bad the nightingales have stopped singing. I am really very glad to see you. I sent the horses after you at six o'clock—I was so afraid that Yefrem, who has completely taken leave of his senses, would be too late to meet the train. I was more anxious than anyone to see you. Later, I even was grateful that you were late, that the others had gone to bed and that, if you came, we would be alone. Somehow I felt that you had changed a great deal; it always happens to people like you. Besides, you know it is such a pleasure to be alone in the house on a summer night, waiting for someone to arrive, and finally hearing the tinkling of the bells and the screeching of the wheels as the carriage drives up to the porch. . . ."

I reached across the table and took her hand firmly in mine, instantly feeling the painful longing in my entire body. With gay unconcern she let several smoke rings escape from her lips. I released her hand and, with assumed playfulness, said:

"You keep talking about Natalie. . . . How can Natalie compare with you? . . . Incidentally, who is she, and where is her home?"

"She is one of the local people, from around Voronezh. She comes of a very good family who at one time were extremely wealthy, but who are now virtual paupers. At home they speak English and French and have nothing to eat. . . . She is a very touching girl, very graceful and very brittle. She has a good brain, but she is so secretive that a person meeting her cannot tell whether she is intelligent or stupid. . . . The Stankeviches live not very far from your most charming cousin, Alexey Meshchersky, and Natalie tells me that for some reason or other he has been visiting them frequently of late, and always complaining about his bachelor's lot. But he does not appeal to her. Besides, he is a rich man, people will think that she married him for his money or that she had sacrificed herself for her parents."

"Let's not get too far away from the original subject," I interposed. "Natalie, or no Natalie, how about our affair?"

"Natalie will not interfere with our affair," she answered. "You will be madly in love with her, but you will kiss me. You will cry on my shoulder because she is so cruel to you, and I will try to console you."

"You know very well that I have been in love with you for ages!"

"Yes, but it was the usual affair between cousins, and much too cut-and-dried; besides, in the old days you were terribly ridiculous and boring. But providence is kind, and I am willing to overlook your old stupidity. Regardless of Natalie I am ready to date our affair as of tomorrow. In the meantime we had better go to bed—I have all kinds of things to do around the house in the morning. . . ."

She stood up, wrapped the bathrobe around her, picked up the candle in the hall which was almost out and showed me the way to my room. On the threshold, elated and amazed by the very circumstances that inwardly had elated and amazed me while we were still in the dining room

—the happy ending to my quest for a love affair which I had found in my uncle's household—I kissed her greedily for a long time, pressing her against the door-frame. She closed her eyes somberly and let the dripping candle slip farther and farther down. When with a deep flush on her cheeks she was at last leaving me, she shook her finger at me and said quietly:

"I warn you: tomorrow, when others are present, don't you dare cast 'passionate glances' in my direction! God forbid, if father were to notice anything. He is afraid of me, but I am afraid of him even more. And I don't want Natalie to notice anything. In certain respects I am, actually, very bashful—you should not judge me by the way I behave when I am with you. If you disobey orders, I will have no feeling for you except loathing. . . ."

I undressed and fell into bed. Though my head was in a whirl, I immediately dropped off to sleep, completely exhausted by my new happiness. Never for a moment had I any inkling of the great unhappiness that lay ahead of me, or any reason to take seriously anything Sonia had said.

Much later I frequently thought that I should have recognized one ill omen. When I entered my room and struck a match to light the candle, a large bat brushed past me. It slid so close to my face that even by the light of a match I saw its repulsive, dark velvetiness and its long-eared, pug-nosed, predatory head which looked like death. With a vile flutter it dived into the darkness of the open window, and I instantly forgot about it.

❀   ❀   ❀

Next morning I caught the first fleeting glimpse of Natalie. She peered out of the hall into the dining room: her hair was not combed and she wore a loose-fitting, orange blouse. There was a momentary flash of color, of the golden brightness of her hair, of the blackness of her eyes, and then she disappeared. At that moment I was alone in the dining room. I had finished my coffee and, having risen from the table, I happened to glance over my shoulder. . . .

I awoke early that morning, while the house was still silent. The house had so many rooms that I sometimes became lost in it. I found myself in a far-off room, the windows of which opened on the shady part of the garden. Having rested well I enjoyed the feeling of cold water and of the fresh clothes—especially of the new, red silk shirt which buttoned up the side. After combing more painstakingly than usual my wet black hair, which had been cut the day before in Voronezh, I walked into the hall, made a sharp turn and stopped in front of the door that led into my uncle's study and bedroom. Knowing that in the summer he usually was up at five, I knocked. No one answered; I opened the door, glanced inside and once again experienced the pleasure of reassuring myself about the unchangeable character of this old, spacious room, with its triple French window overlooking the hundred-year-old silver maple. To the left, the entire wall was lined with oak bookcases, and, towering above an empty space between them, hung a mahogany clock with the motionless brass disk of the pendulum underneath; between two other cases several long-stemmed pipes rested against the wall, the bowls richly decorated with beads, and above them hung an immense barometer; a third space was filled with a desk dating back to grandfather's days, its top open and covered with a green cloth showing many brown discolorations and strewn with hammers, pliers, nails and a brass telescope. By the door, over a divan that must have weighed a ton, the wall was hung with a gallery of faded portraits in oval wooden frames. By the window stood a writing table and a deep armchair—both very ancient and of tremendous size. Further to the right, over an unbelievably wide oak bed, the entire wall was occupied by a single painting: its shiny background had turned so dark that only with the greatest difficulty one could distinguish clusters of dim, smoky clouds and of greenish-blue poetic trees; in the foreground, glistening with the fixity of the white of an egg, was a nude, buxom beauty of almost life size—displaying her half turned, proud face and the curves of her full back, of her long flanks and of the calves of her powerful legs, she stood, temptingly covering with the widespread, long fingers of one hand the nipple of her breast and with the other the bottom part of her stomach festooned with folds of fat. No sooner had my eyes had time to take all this in, than I heard behind me the booming voice of my host who, leaning on his crutch, was coming down the hall:

"No, sir! You will not find me in the bedroom at this time of day. It's you who lie in bed until three oaks."

I kissed his wide, dry hand and asked:

"What three oaks, sir?"

"The peasants have a saying," he answered shaking his grey pompadour, and looking me over with keen, intelligent yellow eyes. "The sun is three-oaks high in the skies, but you still have your kisser in the pillow. Come on, let's have some coffee. . . ."

"What a wonderful old man, what a wonderful house!" I thought, following him into the dining room, through the open windows of which came the morning greenery of the garden and the entire well-being of summer in the country. The old nurse, tiny and hunchbacked, waited on the table. My uncle drank strong tea with cream out of a thick glass in a silver holder. Watching him drink and at the same time manipulate with his finger the long, woven stem of an old-fashioned golden spoon, I ate one buttered slice of black bread after another and kept refilling my cup out of a silver coffee pot. Without asking me a single question, the old cavalryman, interested only in himself, told me about his neighbors, cursing and ridiculing them in every conceivable way. Looking at his whiskers, his sideburns and the long hair in his nostrils, I pretended to listen, though I could hardly contain myself waiting impatiently for Sonia and Natalie to appear. What was Natalie like, and how would Sonia and I face each other after last night? I felt a grateful elation about her, I had reprehensible thoughts about her and Natalie's bedrooms and about everything connected with the haphazard morning toilet of a woman. . . . Maybe Sonia had mentioned to Natalie the beginning of our affair last night? If so, I felt already something approaching love for Natalie, not because she was beautiful, but because she shared my secret with Sonia—why couldn't I love two people at the same time? Any moment now, aglow with morning freshness, they would come in, they would see me—my Georgian good looks and my red shirt—they would talk and laugh, they would sit at the table, gracefully filling their cups from the hot coffee pot—young morning appetites, young morning exhilaration, the sparkle of rested eyes, the light coat of powder on the cheeks which would look even more youthful after the sleep, and the laughter—not quite natural and that much more charming—accompanying every word. . . . Before lunch they would walk toward the river through the garden and would undress in the bathhouse, their naked bodies illuminated from above by the blueness of the skies and from below by the reflection of transparent water. . . . My imagination was always lively and I had a mental vision of Sonia and Natalie awkwardly holding the railing leading down from the bathhouse, as they cautiously descended the steps disappearing into the water—the cold, wet boards, slippery with the disgusting green velvet of slime which had covered them; I could see Sonia throw back her thick head of hair and with sudden determination swoop with her high breasts onto the water, suddenly becoming a submerged but clearly distinguishable, chalky-blue figure which, with her arms and legs spreading in every direction, looked exactly like a frog. . . .

"Well, I will see you at dinner! You remember: dinner is at noon," the old cavalryman said rising to his full height, his elderly figure tall and erect in a loose-fitting linen suit and blunt-toed shoes, the crutch held firmly in a broad hand covered with the brown spots of old age, and the cleanly-shaven point of his chin surrounded by brown whiskers which became one with the sideburns. He patted me on the shoulder and quickly marched away. And it was then, as I rose with the intention of walking through the adjoining room out on the porch, that she appeared, twinkled and was gone, instantly capturing my joyous admiration. Amazed, I walked out on the porch: she was really beautiful!—and stood there for a long time, attempting to collect my thoughts. I had been waiting for the two so impatiently, but when at last I heard their voices in the dining room, I rushed down the steps leading into the garden—I was seized by a sudden fear of them: of Sonia with whom I already shared a fascinating secret, and, perhaps, even more of Natalie and of that instant flash of her which had blinded me. I wandered through the garden, which spread along with the rest of the estate over a river bottom. Finally, taking myself in hand, I returned to the house and, affecting innocent surprise, was met by Sonia's gay sauciness and by Natalie's pleasantry. With a smile she raised from underneath the black eyelashes the shining blackness of her eyes, which were so striking in contrast with the color of her hair, and said:

"We have met already!"

Later, standing on the porch, leaning against the stone wall, we were filled with the exalted feeling of the hot summer sun on our bare heads. Natalie stood next to me, while Sonia, embracing her with one arm, stared absent-mindedly into space and in a mocking voice sang: "It happened at a noisy dance. . . ." Suddenly she straightened out:

"It's time for a swim! We will go now, and you can go later. . . ."

Natalie ran to get the towels, while Sonia hung back and whispered:

"From now on you can pretend that you are in love with Natalie. But beware if you should ever go beyond pretending!"

Right then, with a gay recklessness I almost blurted out that already there was no necessity for pretending, but instead I hurriedly and warmly whispered:

"All right, all right, but for God's sake come and see me for at least a moment before you go."

Shaking her head, she answered:

"Evidently I was mistaken—you still are childish. I will see you after dinner."

When they returned, I wandered down to the bathhouse. First I followed a long walk flanked on both sides by rows of birches, then I found myself among old trees which usually line the shores of a river. The air was filled with the warm odor of water, and the starlings were screaming in the tops of the trees. I walked and, with entirely differing sensations, thought about Natalie and about Sonia. I was conscious that in a few seconds I would be in the same water in which they had been swimming. . . .

Amidst everything happy and unhurrying, everything free and calm that penetrated through the open windows from the garden—skies, greenery, sun—I sat through a lengthy dinner of soup, fried chicken and raspberries with cream. I sat in a state of inward suspense from Natalie's nearness and from the anticipation of that hour when everything would be quiet in the house, and Sonia (she had appeared at the table with a dark-red, velvety rose in her hair) would secretly come to me, so we could continue what we had begun the night before, but this time deliberately and without haste. As soon as dinner was over I went to my room, closed the shutters and, stretching out on the divan, lay waiting and listening to the hot stillness of the country and to the moping voices of birds singing in the garden from which the air loaded with the scent of herbs and flowers was wafted inside. Hopelessly I wondered how I could go on with this duplicity: the secret meetings with Sonia, and the proximity of Natalie, the very thought of whom instantly filled me with the pure elation of love, with the passionate desire to look only at her with that joyful devotion with which only a short while ago I had looked at her thin, bent waist and at her sharp, girlish elbows when, leaning forward, she rested them on the old stone of the porch wall, warmed by the sun. Leaning next to her and with one arm around her shoulders, Sonia in her puff-sleeved, satin gown looked like a young, newly married matron, while Natalie in a linen skirt and an embroidered Ukrainian blouse, which gave a hint of the perfection of her body, looked like a girl in her early teens. Perhaps the very essence of my elation depended on the fact that I could not conceive even the possibility of kissing her with the same sensations with which I had kissed Sonia on the preceding night. In the airy, broad sleeve of her blouse, embroidered on the shoulders in red and blue, I could see her thin arm with a hint of reddish hair clinging to the dry, golden skin. I looked at it and wondered: what would I experience, if I were to dare touch it with my lips? Sensing that I was looking at her, she raised her brightly sparkling head, surrounded by a crown of plaited hair. I walked away and, hurriedly dropping my eyes, saw her legs shining in the sun through the hem of her skirt and the thin, firm, thoroughbred ankles clad in grey silk.

With the rose still in her hair, Sonia quickly opened the door, closed it behind her and quietly exclaimed: "So you were asleep!" I jumped to my feet and took both her hands: "How can you say such things? How could I sleep!" "Better lock the door. . . ." I rushed to turn the key in the lock, while she sat down on the divan and closed her eyes. "Now, you can can come to me," and we immediately lost all shame and all reason. During those minutes we did not utter another word. In all the loveliness of her young body, she allowed me to kiss her—kiss her everywhere— while she closed her eyes more somberly than ever, her cheeks aglow with a warm flush. And once again as she was arranging her hair before leaving me, she said in a threatening whisper:

"So far as Natalie goes, I repeat: beware if you should ever go beyond pretending! My disposition is not as sweet as some people imagine!"

The rose was lying on the floor. I hid it in the desk drawer, and toward evening its dark-red velvet turned to a faded purple.

❋   ❋   ❋

Outwardly life went on as usual, but inwardly I had not a moment of peace. I became more and more deeply attached to Sonia and to the sweet habit of our nightly, exhaustingly passionate meetings—now she came to me only at night when the entire household was asleep—and with an ever growing elation I tortured myself by surreptitiously watching Natalie's every move. The days followed the usual summer schedule: the gathering at the breakfast table, swimming before dinner, dinner, the afternoon rest in our rooms and then the garden—sitting in the shade of the birches the girls embroidered and made me read Goncharov aloud to them, or else they were busy making preserves on the shady lawn under the oaks, not far from the house—just to the right of the porch. Around five we had tea on the left lawn, and in the evenings we walked or played croquet in the wide yard in front of the house—Natalie and I against Sonia, or Sonia and Natalie against me. At twilight supper was served in the dining room. . . . After supper the old cavalryman went to bed, while we remained for a long time in the darkness of the porch, Sonia and I joking and smoking cigarettes, and Natalie sitting in silence. At last Sonia would say: "Time for bed!"—and, having said good night, I would go to my room. My hands cold with excitement, I waited there for the magic hour when the entire house became dark and quiet, and listened to the endless thread of sound unwinding in my watch which rested under the candle by my head. I was amazed and horrified: why had God chosen to punish me like this? Why had He given me two such different and passionate loves at the same time—the painful beauty of worshiping Natalie and the physical intoxication with Sonia? And it was not all physical: she was falling in love with me, and I, more and more, was falling in love with her. I felt that any moment we would not be able to endure the incomplete union, that she would give me everything and that then I would lose my mind completely, waiting for our nightly meetings and reliving the sensations in the daytime in the presence of Natalie! Already Sonia was becoming jealous and giving vent to furious explosions, but, when we were alone, she said:

"I am afraid that we are not natural at the table and in Natalie's presence. I believe papa is beginning to notice things, and so is Natalie. Certainly, nurse is convinced by now that we are having an affair and probably has been whispering warnings to papa. Spend more time with Natalie in the garden and read that absurd novel to her, or take her out for a walk in the evenings. . . . The most horrible thing to me is that I already am aware of the idiotic expression with which you stare at her. At times I hate you so much that, like some harlot, I want to pull your hair in everyone's presence. But what can I do?"

To me the most horrible thing was that I began to feel that Natalie was unhappy, or resentful, or at least conscious of the secret between Sonia and me. Always quiet, she grew even more so, and she played croquet and embroidered with an unnecessarily preoccupied air. We seemed closer and more natural with one another, but on one occasion, when we were alone in the drawing-room, where she was reclining on the sofa, leisurely turning over the pages of a music album, I tried to be jovial with her:

"Natalie, I heard that there is a possibility that we will be cousins."

She looked startled:

"What gave you this idea?"

"My cousin, Alexey Meshchersky . . ."

She would not let me finish:

"Oh, that's it! Your cousin is an overfed, snobbish giant, completely covered with shiny black hair, and with red, moist lips. . . . And, besides, who ever gave you the right to talk to me like that?"

I became frightened:

"Natalie, why are you so stern with me? Can't I even tease you? Please, excuse me," I said, taking her hand in mine.

She made no effort to pull away her hand, but merely said:

"I still don't know you. . . . Can't understand you. . . . But enough of this. . . ."

In order not to gaze at her painfully tempting, white tennis shoes, peep-

ing from under the hem of the skirt on the sofa, I rose and walked out
on the porch. A black cloud was enveloping the garden, the light was
growing dim, soft summer noises came nearer and nearer in ever narrowing circles, and a sweet rainy wind was blowing from the fields. Suddenly such a delicious, young, abandoned wave of unreasonable, yielding
happiness took possession of me, that I called:

"Natalie!"

She came to the door.

"Yes?"

"Inhale the wind! How wonderful everything could be!"

She was silent.

"Yes."

"Natalie, you are so stern with me! Have you anything against me?"

She gave me a proud, severe look:

"Why and what should I have against you?"

In the evening, stretched out in the wicker armchairs on the dark porch,
all three of us were silent. A few stars flickered somewhere among the
black clouds, a soft breeze blew gently from the river, and the frogs
croaked lazily.

"Rain in the air makes me sleepy," Sonia said, stifling a yawn. "Nurse
said that a new moon was born and that now it will have to be bathed
for a whole week." After a minute's silence she added: "Natalie, what do
you think about a first love?"

Natalie's voice came firmly out of the darkness:

"I know very little about love, but I am convinced that a first love
means an entirely different thing to a boy and to a girl."

Sonia considered her words in silence.

"Girls, too, can be very different. . . ."

She rose suddenly to her feet:

"Time to go to bed!"

Wanting to hasten my meeting with Sonia, I said hurriedly:

"Yes, we may as well turn in. . . . I am sleepy. . . . The frogs must sense
the rain. . . . I also am going up. . . ."

"I believe I will stay here a while. I am enjoying the night," Natalie
said.

Listening to Sonia's retreating footsteps I whispered:

"Somehow we seem to have been saying the wrong things. You simply
must be more understanding with me!"

She answered:

"Yes, yes, we have been saying the wrong things. We must be more understanding and more natural. . . ."

Outwardly we were perfectly calm when we met next day. A quiet rain had fallen during the night, but in the morning the weather was clear, and after dinner the air again became hot and dry. Just before afternoon tea, while Sonia was working on the household accounts in her father's study, we were sitting under the birches, trying to read aloud Goncharov's *Precipice*. Her small right hand flashed in the air as she bent over her sewing. I read, frequently glancing with sweet yearning at her left arm enclosed in the wide sleeve, at the tiny golden hair hugging the skin above her wrist, and at the back of her neck where it widened into her shoulders. I read with more and more animation without understanding a single word. At last I said:

"Now it is your turn to read. . . ."

As she straightened out, the thin blouse outlined the points of her breasts. She laid the sewing aside, leaned forward once again, dropping her strange, beautiful head, turned to me the nape of her neck and the back of one shoulder, placed the book across her knees and began to read rapidly in a strained voice. I looked at her small hands and at her knees under the book and thought: "She looks like such a young girl because she wears these soft tennis shoes," and was overcome with unbearable love for the sound of her voice. Thrushes flitting through the garden were calling in the twilight; across from us a red-and-grey woodpecker flattened itself high up against the trunk of a solitary pine among the birches. . . .

"Natalie, the color of your hair is beautiful! . . . The plait is just a shade darker—the color of ripe corn. . . ."

She continued to read.

"Natalie, look at the woodpecker!"

She glanced up:

"Yes, I saw it. . . . I saw it today and I saw it last night. . . . Don't interrupt me when I am reading."

I was silent for a minute and then said:

"Look at this! Doesn't it remind you of a dried, grey worm?"

"What? Where?"

I pointed at the white, calcareous bird-dropping on the bench between us.

"Doesn't it?"

I took her hand in mine and, laughing with happiness, kept repeating:

"Natalie, Natalie. . . ."

She looked at me for a long time without uttering a sound, and then in a puzzled voice said:

"I thought you were in love with Sonia!"

The blood rushed to my face as though I had been caught stealing. But I renounced Sonia with such vehemence that her lips involuntarily parted: "Isn't it true?"

"Certainly it is not true! I feel toward her as if she were my sister! We were children together. . . ."

        ✿   ✿   ✿

Next day she did not appear at breakfast or at dinner. "Sonia, what is the matter with Natalie?" my uncle asked, and Sonia, with a disagreeable laugh, answered:

"I don't know. . . . She has been lying in bed without combing her hair since morning. . . . I can tell by her face that she has been crying. We took a cup of coffee to her, but she would not finish it. . . . 'What ails you?' 'A headache.' Perhaps she is in love!"

"Well, that's understandable," my uncle said briskly, giving me an approving glance and at the same time shaking his head.

She put in her appearance just in time for the afternoon tea, but she stepped out on the porch with a light buoyant step and gave me a pleasant though slightly self-conscious smile, surprising me with her cheerfulness, her smile and a peculiar new smartness about her. Her hair, curled gently in front and showing the wavy traces of a curling iron, was wound tightly around her head; she wore a different dress made of something green and transparent—a simple, wholesome dress that fitted gracefully around her waist; on her feet were black, high-heeled slippers; I gasped inwardly with new delight. I had been sitting on the porch, leafing through several old issues of an historical magazine which my uncle had given me, when suddenly she was there in all her loveliness and self-conscious friendliness:

"Good evening. Let's have tea. I am pouring today. Sonia is not well."

"Not well? First you, now she?"

"I merely had a slight headache this morning. I am ashamed to admit it, but I wasn't dressed until just now. . . ."

"How amazing this green dress looks next to your hair and eyes!" I said. And suddenly, feeling the blood rush to my face, asked:

"Did you believe me last night?"

She also blushed—a gentle, bright red—and turned away:

"Not at once, not altogether. . . . Then, suddenly, I realized that I had no reason not to believe you. . . . Why should it concern me how you feel about Sonia? The only reason I was uneasy about it is because she is practically your sister. . . . Let's go. . . ."

Sonia came out for supper and, catching me alone for a minute, said: "I am ill. I always have a difficult time of it—I will be in bed for at least five days. Today I still can get around, but I doubt that I will be up tomorrow. Behave yourself while I am not with you. I love you very much and I am terribly jealous of you."

"You mean you will not come to see me even for a minute?"

"No, no . . ."

This meant both happiness and misfortune: five full, unhampered days with Natalie, and five nights during which I would not see Sonia!

For almost a week Natalie managed the house, gave orders to the servants and, wearing a white apron, walked across the yard to the kitchen. I never had seen her so industrious. Evidently she enjoyed assuming Sonia's duties of a diligent mistress of the household, as though she were anxious to escape the secret tension with which she had been watching Sonia and me talk and exchange glances. Each day, having worried about the arrangement of meals and, later, satisfied that everything had run smoothly and that the old cook and the Ukrainian maid, Christie, had set the table on time, without irritating our host, she retired immediately after dinner to Sonia's room, where I was not admitted, and remained there until the afternoon tea. After supper she disappeared in there again for the entire evening. Apparently she avoided being left alone with me, and, puzzled and bored, I suffered from loneliness. Why should she be pleasant to me and at the same time avoid me? Was she afraid of Sonia, or of herself and of her feeling for me? Passionately I wanted to believe that she was afraid of herself, and I became intoxicated with an ever growing hope: I was not tied to Sonia forever—Natalie, too, was only a guest here—in a week or so I would be on my way—then my tortures would be over. . . . Natalie would go home, and I would find some excuse to meet and visit her family. . . . The parting with Sonia would be painful, especially because I would have to deceive her until the very day of my departure, always secretly dreaming about Natalie and hoping for her love and her hand. As if kissing Sonia were only a transient passion? As if I did not love her? But what else could I do, knowing that the inevitable would come sooner or later. . . . In a constant state of inward turmoil, thinking constantly about my predicament, expecting constantly something to happen, I tried to be pleasant and restrained around Natalie in an effort to attract her by putting my best foot forward. Until the right time all I could do was endure. I was suffering and I was bored. To make matters worse it rained for three days: the raindrops knocked and scampered on the roof with a thousand little paws, the house was dark, and flies dozed on the ceiling and on the lamp in the dining room. I kept myself in check, spending hours in the study listening to my uncle's stories. . . .

Sonia, wrapped in a robe, began to come out for an hour or two at a time. With an indulgent smile for her own weakness, she stretched out on the porch chair and, to my horror, not in the least concerned by Natalie's presence, addressed me in a capricious and unnecessarily tender way.

"Sit close to me, Victor. . . . I am sick, I am sad—tell me something amusing. . . . Nurse was right: the new moon had to be bathed, but I hope the rain is over. . . . The air is clear, and the scent of the flowers so sweet. . . ."

Inwardly infuriated I answered:

"If the flowers smell stronger than usual, it means more rain."

She slapped my hand:

"Don't ever argue with a sick person!"

At last she began to join us for dinner and for tea, but she was still pale and she insisted on having an armchair at her place. But she would not come out on the porch after supper. On one occasion, when she had retired to her room after tea and Christie was carrying the dishes to the kitchen, Natalie said to me:

"Sonia is angry at me, because I always spend my time with her, while you are alone. She is not well yet, and you are lonesome without her."

"I am lonesome without you," I answered. "When you are not with me. . . ."

Her face changed instantly, but she controlled herself and forced a smile:

"We have agreed not to quarrel any more. . . . Look! You have been sitting indoors all day, why don't you take a stroll through the garden? I will join you later. . . . Thank heavens, the predictions about the new moon have not come true—it looks like a beautiful night. . . ."

"Sonia seems to feel sorry for me. . . . Don't you? Not in the least?"

"I am terribly sorry for you," she answered and laughed awkwardly, as she piled the tea dishes on the tray. "But, luckily, Sonia is almost well, and you will not be lonesome much longer. . . ."

As soon as she said: "I will join you later," my heart contracted mysteriously and sweetly, but I at once remonstrated with myself: "No! she simply is trying to be kind to me." I went to my room and for a long time lay on the bed, staring at the ceiling. Finally, I rose, picked up a cap and somebody's stick in the hall and, without knowing where I was going, wandered off away from the yard, among the bare, waste hillocks to a wide ridge which formed the boundary of the estate and overlooked a village. The ridge led toward the empty evening fields. All around, as far as I could see, was spacious, rolling country. On my left was the river bottom, and beyond it other empty fields rose toward the horizon which was aflame with the sunset. On my right, reflecting the red rays, stood an even row of white, peasants' huts in the village, with no sign of life around them. In desolation I looked first at the huts and then at the sunset. When I turned back a warm, almost hot wind was stirring. The new moon, which did not augur anything good, was already in the skies, one half of it lucid like a transparent web, the other half barely perceptible, and the two together shaped like an acorn.

At the supper table—we ate supper on the lawn because it was too hot indoors—I said to my uncle:

"What do you think of the weather, sir? I believe it will rain tomorrow."

"What makes you think so?"

"I just was walking across the fields, and the sad thought occurred to me that soon I shall be leaving you. . . ."

"Why?"

Natalie also fixed her eyes on me:

"Are you planning to leave?"

I made a feeble attempt to laugh:

"After all, I cannot . . ."

This time my uncle shook his head intentionally and with greater vigor than usual:

"Absurd! Absurd! Your father and mother get along nicely without you. I would not dream of letting you leave until two weeks are up. And she would not either."

"I really have no say in the matter," Natalie put in.

In a pleading voice I exclaimed:

"Please, sir, tell her not to be so formal with me!"

My uncle hit the table with the flat of his hand:

"You have your orders, Natalie! And let's forget this nonsense about your departure. But I believe you are right about the rain. It looks as though we are again in for some bad weather."

"The fields seemed much too clear and bright," I said, "and the moon was shiny and looked like an acorn. Besides, it was blowing from the south. Look at the clouds—they are gathering already. . . ."

My uncle turned about and glanced at the garden where at intervals the moonlight faded and grew brighter:

"You have the makings of a Bruce, Victor. . . ."

When he left us I remained at the table, looking at Natalie, who was silently helping Christie with the dishes. Then, with a stupid smile, I recited:

> "Last night by the darkened window
> For a long, long time she sat,
> Watching the gliding moonbeams,
> Playing mischievous games with the clouds. . . ."

"So, besides everything else, you are a poet!" Natalie said with an angry smile and walked across the bright yard to the kitchen.

It was after nine when she came out on the porch where I was sitting, waiting for her and dejectedly thinking: "Ridiculous! Even if she has any feeling for me, there cannot be anything serious or permanent about it— just a passing fancy. . . ." The new moon was playing ever higher and brighter among the masses of banking, smoky-white clouds which were majestically crowding the skies. Whenever its white half, which looked like a bright, deathly-pale human profile, appeared from behind the clouds, everything became aglow and immersed in phosphorescent light. Suddenly I felt the urge to look over my shoulder: with her hands behind her back Natalie was standing on the threshold, studying me in silence. I rose to my feet. Indifferently she asked me:

"Are you still up?"

"You told me . . ."

"I hope you will forgive me—I am so tired tonight. Let's take a quick turn in the garden, and then I will go to bed."

I followed her. She paused on the steps and glanced at the tops of the trees beyond which the clouds now were boiling in stormy throngs, convulsed by silent flashes of lightning. Then she moved through the long, transparent archway of birches, stepping across pools of light and shade. I caught up with her and, to break the silence, said:

"What a magic glow the birches have in the distance! There is nothing stranger or more beautiful than a forest on a moonlit night and the white, silky gloss of birch trunks. . . ."

She stopped and fixed her black eyes on me:

"Is it true that you are leaving?"

"Yes, it's time for me to go."

"But what made you decide so suddenly? I must confess that you took me by surprise when you announced a while ago that you were leaving."

"When you are home, Natalie, may I come and meet your family?"

She remained silent. I took her hands and breathlessly kissed the right one.

"Natalie . . ."

"Yes, yes, I love you," she said hurriedly and without any expression.

I took her around the waist, she threw back her head, and I touched her mouth. Her lips did not respond with the least movement. I dropped my hands, and she immediately started walking toward the house. I followed her as if I were walking in my sleep.

"You must go tomorrow," she said without turning her head. "I shall be home in a few days."

✲   ✲   ✲

As soon as I returned to my room, without lighting the candle, I sat on the divan and remained in a trance, hypnotized by everything marvelous and frightening that so suddenly had entered my life. I sat without being conscious of space or time. The room and the garden were engulfed by the darkness of the clouds. The garden, beyond the open windows, was fluttery and noisy, and again and again I was blinded by the sharp, instantly disappearing, green-blue flame. The strength and the intensity of these silent flashes continued to grow, until for an instant the room was illuminated with incredible brightness. There was a rush of fresh air, and a noise as though the garden was fleeing in panic: the skies and the earth were aflame again! I jumped to my feet, and with difficulty closed the windows, struggling with the wind which was ruffling me, and rushed on tiptoe down the dark hall to the dining room. It seems so strange to me now that at that moment in my life I should have been concerned about the open windows which were likely to be broken by the storm, but I was more earnestly worried about them than I would usually have been. All the windows in the other rooms were already closed. I saw the rooms in a blue-green flash, the color, brightness, and intensity of which had something unearthly about it. Like a flutter of gigantic eyes, it revealed every line, to the furthest corner of the window frame, and made everything appear larger than its normal size, then instantly it plunged the room into a thick darkness, leaving in its wake something red and metallic that blinded the eyes for several seconds. When I hurriedly felt my way back along the wall—strange that I should not have taken a candle to light my way, but probably my behavior was in accord with all the mysterious things that were happening around me—when quickly, as if I were afraid that something would happen in my absence, I entered my room, an angry whisper reached me out of the darkness:

"Where were you? I am frightened. . . . Light a candle. . . ."

I struck a match and on the divan saw Sonia, dressed only in a nightgown and with a pair of slippers on her bare feet.

"No, no, better not," she said quickly. "Come over here, come close to me, I am frightened. . . ."

Obediently I sat down and put an arm around her cold shoulders. She whispered:

"Kiss me! . . . Kiss me! . . . I have not seen you for a whole week!"

With unexpected strength she pulled both of us back against the cushions:

"Take me! I want you to! I cannot endure it any longer!"

At that moment, in her loose blouse and with a candle in her hand, Natalie appeared in the open door. She saw us instantly, but mechanically she spoke the words that were on the tip of her tongue as she had left her bedroom:

"Sonia, where are you? I am terribly frightened. . . ."

Then she was gone, and Sonia rushed out after her.

❖   ❖   ❖

A year later she married Meshchersky. The wedding was solemnized in an empty church on his estate—we, along with other relatives and friends, merely received an announcement. Immediately after the ceremony, without paying the customary calls, the newlyweds left for the Crimea.

On Saint Tatiana's Day, in the following January, the traditional, formal dance was given at the Nobles Club in Voronezh. Having spent Christmas at home, I purposely dallied in the country until that day and arrived in town that evening. The train pulled into the station bringing a whirlwind of snow in its wake. On the way from the station to the hotel, while the sledge was gliding through the streets, I could barely see the lights flickering dimly in the snowstorm, yet after the country solitude the town lights and even the storm held forth the pleasant promise of entering the warm, overheated room of the old-fashioned, provincial hotel, of ordering tea and of beginning to dress and prepare for the long hours of dancing and zestful drinking until dawn. During the time that had elapsed since that terrible night in my uncle's house and since her wedding, I had recovered gradually, or, at least, I had become reconciled to my secretly unbalanced mental state, and outwardly I behaved like everyone else.

When I arrived at the Club the dance was only beginning, but the broad stairway and the coat-rooms were already filled with newly arriving throngs, and from the balcony of the main ballroom, drowning and obliterating all other noises, came the clear, sadly majestic strains of a waltz, played by a military band. My skin still glowing from the frost, my manner more than usually polite and punctilious because of my new uniform, I made my way up the red-carpeted stairway to the upper hall, became hemmed in by the thick, warm mass of humanity crowding in the doors of the ballroom, and then, for no apparent reason, continued on my way inside with such determination that I was probably mistaken for an usher on some urgent errand and was helped by everyone to get through. At last I found myself inside the room, listening to the crash and roll of music over my head and looking at the silvery ripple of chandeliers and of the dozens of couples flickering under them. Suddenly my attention became riveted on a couple that broke away from the whirling throng and with long, graceful glides came directly toward the spot where I was standing. I caught my breath watching how tall and big he was as he stooped over her, how dark with the shining blackness of his hair and of his evening dress, and how light with the incredible lightness that heavy people so frequently display when they are dancing, and I was amazed to see how tall she seemed wearing a formal hairdress, a white evening gown and graceful golden slippers, as she glided with her head slightly thrown back, her eyes lowered, her hand resting on his shoulder and her arm in a white, elbow-length glove curved like the neck of a swan. For a second her black eyelashes flickered at me and the blackness of her eyes came very near, and then, sliding easily in his shining pumps, he turned her sharply, her lips—the lips which I had barely touched—parted with the sudden exertion, the hem of her dress glistened with silver, and with long, even glides they moved in the opposite directions, farther and farther away. Once again I pushed through the crowd and stood in the hall for several minutes. . . . In the cool, empty room across from me I could see two young ladies in Ukrainian costumes waiting idly at the buffet counter: one, a good-looking blonde, the other, a spare, dark-faced Cossack beauty, twice as tall as her companion. I walked in, bowed, and handed them a hundred-rouble bill. Laughing and knocking their heads together behind the counter, they pulled out of a bucket filled with ice a heavy bottle and looked at one another uncertainly—none of the bottles had been opened. I went to their assistance, and a minute later the cork came out with a sharp noise. Forcing myself to smile I offered each one of them a glass—

gaudeamus igitur!—and finished the bottle alone. They watched me first with surprise and later with alarm:

"You look awfully pale!"

As soon as the champagne was gone I left. When I reached the hotel, I ordered to my room a bottle of Caucasian cognac and drank it in teacups, hoping that my heart would not stand it.

Another year-and-a-half went by. One day, toward the end of May, when I again came from Moscow to visit the family, a messenger from the station brought a telegram: "Alexey died this morning after a sudden heart attack." Father made the sign of the cross and said:

"God rest his soul! How horrible! . . . God forgive me, I never liked him very much, but still it is horrible. He was not yet forty. And I am terribly sorry for her—a widow at her age with a child on her hands. . . . I never have seen her—he was so cordial he never brought her to see us—but I have heard that she is charming. What shall we do? At our age it is out of the question for mother or for me to travel a hundred-and-fifty miles. I am afraid you will have to go. . . ."

I could not very well refuse—what possible reason could I have given? Besides, in the unbalanced state into which this unexpected news had plunged me I would not have refused anyway. I thought of only one thing: I would see her again! The occasion for our meeting was tragic, but perfectly plausible.

We sent a telegram, and the following evening the horses which had met me at the railroad station brought me after a thirty-minute ride through the May twilight to her place. As we approached the gates and topped a hill overlooking the river meadows, I saw from a distance that along the west wall of the house, still bright with the sun, all the shutters were tightly closed. Realizing that she and his body were hidden behind them, I shuddered inwardly and wondered why I had agreed to come. In the yard covered with thick young curly grass, two carriages stood in front of a barn, and the silence was broken only by the tinkling of bells whenever a horse shook its head. Except for the two coachmen there was no one in sight—the guests and the servants were in the house, attending the services. The stillness of a May evening in the country was everywhere, and everything exuded the clean spring freshness—the aroma of the fields and the river, the thick young grass in the yard, the rich blooms in the garden that was crowding in on the house from the south. But on the low porch, by the wide-open door leading into the hall, the polished yellow lid of a coffin was resting against the wall. The gentle coolness of the evening air was sweet with the scent of pear blossoms which in the southeastern corner of the garden blended into a milky-white blur against the even and, by contrast dull, background of the skies, dimly illuminated by the pink glow of Jupiter. The youthfulness and beauty of it all, added to my thoughts about her youth and beauty and to my recollections of the past when there was love in her heart for me, suddenly overwhelmed me with such misery, unhappiness and craving for love, that when I stepped down from the carriage in front of the porch I felt as if I were on the edge of an abyss—how, after a separation of three years, could I enter this house and meet her face-to-face? I forced myself to enter the incense-laden darkness of that terrible room, dotted with the yellow flames of candles against the blackness of the people behind the lights, facing the coffin which stood diagonally across the room with its head toward the right corner, illuminated from above by the reddish glow in front of the ikons shining with their golden vestments, and from below by the liquid, silvery glitter of three tall church candles. As I entered to the accompaniment of the funeral chants, the clergy, bowing and swinging the censers, were circling the coffin, and I at once dropped my head in order to avoid looking at the yellow decorations on the coffin and at the face of the dead man, though most of all I feared to see her. Someone handed me a lighted candle. I took it and held it, conscious of its shaking flame which warmed and illuminated my drawn face. Listening with dull resignation to the chanting and the clanking of censers I watched from behind my lowered eyelids the sickeningly sweet-smelling clouds of incense majestically rising to the ceiling. Suddenly I raised my face and saw her. Dressed in deep mourning and holding in her hand a candle which highlighted her cheeks and set off the gold in her hair, she stood a step or two in front of the others. Her appearance had for me the fascination of an ikon, and I could not tear my eyes away from her. When everything became silent, when the air was filled with the odor of extinguished candles and when everyone moved quietly in her direction, I waited to be the last one to approach her. As I stood in front of her I looked with the terror of delight at her black dress, the vestment-like lines of which endowed her with a peculiar air of purity, at the clean, youthful beauty of her face and at her eyelashes and eyes which dropped the instant she saw me. I bowed very, very low over her hand, kissed it, said in a barely audible voice everything a relative is supposed to say under such circumstances and asked her permission to spend the night in the pavilion in the garden—that old-fashioned, round pavilion where I had slept when, as a schoolboy, I had visited my cousin, and where he liked to sleep on hot summer nights. Without raising her eyes she answered:

"I will tell the servants to take your things there and to have supper ready for you."

In the morning I left immediately after the funeral.

As we parted we again exchanged a few polite words and we again avoided each other's eyes.

* * *

Soon after I graduated, I lost my father and my mother within a short time one of the other. I settled in the country, managed the estate and shared my solitude with Gasha, an orphan peasant girl who had grown up in our family and had helped my mother with the house. . . . Now she and Ivan, who had been our overseer—an old man with a yellowing grey beard and enormous shoulder blades—were keeping house for me. There was something childlike about Gasha. She was small, thin, black-haired, with expressionless eyes the color of soot, completely indifferent to her surroundings; she was mysteriously silent, and the fine, dark texture of her skin frequently had elicited from my father the remark: "Hagar must have looked like her." She was infinitely charming, and, kissing her, I loved to carry her around in my arms; I thought: "This is all that is left in life for me!" and, apparently, she could read my thoughts. When she gave birth to a small, dark boy and stopped working, I installed her in the old nursery and wanted to marry her. But she would not consent:

"No, I don't need that. I would feel ashamed in front of the others. I never was made to be a lady! And what difference does it make to you? You will only stop loving me that much sooner. You should pay a visit to Moscow, or else you will become bored here with me. And I have no more time to be bored," she said, glancing down at the child feeding at her breast. "Go, enjoy yourself, but remember one thing: if you fall in love with someone and decide to marry, I will not hesitate for one second: I will drown myself together with him."

I looked at her—it was impossible not to believe her words. I dropped my head: I was only twenty-six years old. . . . To fall in love, to marry— nothing of the sort had ever entered my head, but Gasha's words brought to me forcibly the realization of my ruined life.

Early in the spring I left for Paris, where I spent four months. Toward the end of June, returning home through Moscow I thought: "I will spend the autumn in the country, and in the winter I will go somewhere again." On the train from Moscow to Tula I was depressed: once again I was drifting home without any definite purpose. . . . I remembered Natalie, but immediately dismissed all thought of her: yes, love "until the dying day," about which Sonia had teased me, was a reality, but I was becoming reconciled to it, just as people who have lost an arm or a leg become reconciled to their condition. . . . Waiting to change trains in the station at Tula, I sent a telegram: "Passing through town on way from Moscow will be at station nine this evening hope you will allow me to see you and learn how you are."

She met me on the porch—a maid with a lighted lamp was standing behind her—and with a smile gave me both her hands:

"I am terribly glad to see you!"

"Strange as it may seem, you have grown taller," I said, kissing her hand and instantly feeling a surge of misery. I studied her from head to foot in the light of the lamp which the maid held high above her head, and around which small pinkish butterflies were fluttering in the soft, moist air. Her black eyes were firmer and more confident of themselves; in a green linen dress with a green belt, she was the essence of feminine beauty in full bloom, graceful and unobtrusively smart.

"Yes, I am still growing," she said with a sad smile.

In the large room the red oil lamp was still hanging in front of the old, golden ikons, but now it was not lighted. I hurriedly shifted my eyes from that corner and followed her to the dining room. There, on a brilliant tablecloth, over an alcohol lamp, stood a teapot, surrounded by fragile, shining teacups. The maid brought some cold meats, pickles, a tall decanter of vodka and a bottle of wine. She picked up the teapot:

"I have already had my supper, but I will have some tea with you. But you must have something to eat. . . . You are on your way from Moscow? Why? What were you doing there in the summer?"

"I have been in Paris."

"That explains it! How long were you there? I wish I could go somewhere! But my girl is only three-and-a-half years old. . . . I hear that you are farming?"

Without eating anything I swallowed a glass of vodka and asked her permission to smoke.

"Certainly!"

I lighted a cigarette and said:

"Natalie, you don't have to be on your guard. Just don't pay any attention to me. I have come to look at you once more, and then I will disappear again. Don't feel awkward with me—everything is in the past, and the clock cannot be turned back. I know you are aware of how much you attract me again, but now my admiration should no longer embarrass you —now it is calm and unselfish. . . ."

She lowered her head and her eyelashes—the contrast of color still was as striking as ever—and a pink glow spread slowly over her cheeks.

"It is the truth," I said, feeling that the blood was draining from my face, but speaking firmly in an effort to persuade myself that I was being frank. "Nothing is lasting in this world. So far as my awful crime is concerned, I am certain that it has become a matter of indifference to you a long time ago, and perhaps you can understand and forgive more readily than before. Even then my crime was not altogether of my own making, and I deserved some mercy because of extreme youth and the remarkable combination of circumstances in which I had found myself. Besides I have suffered sufficient punishment for it already—virtual ruin."

"Ruin?"

"What else would you call it? I see that even now you don't know or understand me, just as you didn't then."

She was silent for a long time.

"I saw you at the dance in Voronezh. . . . How young I was then, and how incredibly unhappy! Though how can love be considered unhappiness?" she said, raising her face and calling to me with all the blackness of her eyes and eyelashes. "Doesn't even the saddest music in the world bring happiness? But tell me about yourself. Have you settled in the country for good?"

With an effort I asked:

"So you still loved me then?"

"Yes."

I was silent, feeling my face grow hot.

"Is what I hear about you true, that you have a passion, a child? . . ."

"Not a passion," I said. "Just great pity, tenderness, and nothing more."

I told her everything, including Gasha's admonition to go and enjoy myself. I finished by saying:

"Now you see that I have been ruined in many ways. . . ."

"Don't talk nonsense!" she said, her mind dwelling on thoughts of her own. "Your entire life is ahead of you. But, obviously, marriage is out of the question for you. She is the kind who would not spare the child, not to mention herself."

"Marriage has never entered my mind," I said. "Good Lord! Why should I marry?"

Still absorbed in her thoughts she looked at me:

"Yes, yes. How strange that your prediction should come true and that we should become related after all. Do you realize that you are my cousin?"

Somehow this never had occurred to me and, realizing it for the first time, I looked at her with a passion more sharp and complex than ever. She put her hand on mine:

"You are very tired after your journey and you have not eaten anything. You don't look like yourself. Enough talk for one night. Go to sleep. Your bed is ready for you in the pavilion. . . ."

Obediently I kissed her hand, and she called the maid. Though the moon hanging low over the garden was shining bright, the maid lighted my way with a lamp, as she led me first down the main walk and then somewhere to the side until we were on a wide lawn in front of the old pavilion encircled with wooden columns. I sank into an armchair between the bed and the window and, lighting a cigarette, became lost in thought: I had made a mistake in obeying a sudden silly impulse. I had made a mistake in coming here and counting on my calmness and my strength. . . . The hour was late and the night amazingly still. Very likely it had rained again, because the air was even softer and warmer than it had been. Responding to the tranquil warmth and quiet, the first roosters in the distant village were crowing gently and melodiously. The bright circle of the moon suspended over the garden surrounding the pavilion seemed to remain in one spot, as though waiting breathlessly while it shone on the distant groves and on the apple trees nearby, mixing its light with their shade. Wherever the light penetrated everything was a glassy bright, but in the shade everything was striped and mysterious. And just as quietly and mysteriously, she came to the window, wearing something long, dark and shining in its silkiness. . . .

Later, while we were talking, the moonlight inundated the entire garden and the inside of the pavilion. She was lying on the bed, and I, holding her hand, was kneeling at her side:

"On that terrifying, stormy night, I already loved no one but you. I never have known any passion except the pure exaltation when I am with you."

"Yes, as time went by I understood. And still, whenever I remembered the storm, I remembered what had happened in the garden only an hour before. . . ."

"There is no one in the world like you. When a while ago I was looking at your green dress and at your knees under it, I was willing to die if I could only touch the hem of your skirt with my lips. And now my lips have touched you in a way that I could not have imagined without feeling faint."

"I am all yours now, forever. And during all those years you never forgot me?"

"I forgot you only the way people forget that they are alive and breathing. How right you were when you said that there cannot be unhappiness in love. I can still see the orange blouse and the young girl who flashed before my eyes that morning—that first morning of my love for you! I can see your arm draped in the loose sleeve of the Ukrainian blouse. I can see the turn of your head as you sat reading to me, while I was whispering: 'Natalie, Natalie!' "

"Yes, yes."

"And then at the dance—you were so tall and so frightening in your feminine splendor. That night how I wanted to die, extolling joyously my love and my ruin! And when dressed in mourning, and looking so chaste, you stood with a candle in your hand, I felt that there was something holy about the flame near your face."

"And now you are with me again, and this time forever. But we will see each other so seldom—how can I, your secret wife, become your mistress in everyone's eyes?"

❀   ❀   ❀

That December, on the shores of Lake Geneva, she died, giving premature birth to a child.

Translated by NICHOLAS WREDEN

CZECHOSLOVAKIA

INTRODUCTION

By Christopher Lazare

ALTHOUGH IT HAS BEEN a common observation among historians that the geographical form of Bohemia "marks her out for an independent and homogeneous state," history has rather consistently violated that generalization and covered its Czech pages with a shocking record of invasion, oppression and foreign domination. 1526 is the date of the ascension of the first Hapsburg to the throne of Bohemia; the pretext was the union of Austria, Hungary and Bohemia against the Turk who was invading Europe and had already besieged Vienna; it might well mark the beginning of the long Czech struggle for self-assertion. In less than a hundred years—a short interval in terms of independence—the Hapsburgs had suppressed the ancient free constitution of Bohemia, and as a result of the Thirty Years' War—so familiar in its contemporary parallels—created a precedent for intolerance and restriction from which the Czechs never quite recovered, although they resisted and even thwarted many of its subsequent repetitions and variations.

Czech literature exists as a testimonial to that struggle and as the stubborn and courageous affirmation of a national identity which has not only survived the ravages of history, but which has, to a logical extent, resulted from them. It is the literature of a challenged language, of a subjugated culture and also of an indomitable individuality; its traits are the metaphoric and poetic equivalents of those conditions: a racially proud preoccupation with self, with native legend and lore; a tragi-mystic interpretation of destiny; a ritualistic interest in human defeat, in death and its paraphernalia of derangement and disease; a compensatory system of satire and fantasy which is, in fact, the bitter awareness of incongruity and inequality; and finally, the mythology of persecution, the hero inverted and cast in the role of a victim. As a movement to achieve independence, it contains a convincing dialectical contradiction: on one hand, the tendency toward insulation and subjectivism, and on the other, an emphasis on cosmopolitanism and the assimilation of external influences.

The earliest known example of Czech literature (the use of Slovak is comparatively recent) is a hymn, sung in churches and at coronations during the eleventh century to which its origin is usually assigned. The output of the next several hundred years is characteristic of the formative period of any literature —it consisted of saints' legends, of allegories, fables and the poetry of troubadours. By the end of the fourteenth century Jan Hus had succeeded in establishing a standard, written Czech language, which was employed by his disciple, Petr Chelćický, with a distinction which caused Tolstoy to describe him as one of the world's greatest philosophers; indeed, he is frequently regarded as the forerunner of many of Tolstoy's theories. Chelčický's important work, "The Net of True Faith," was later incorporated into the tenets of the Moravian Brethren.

The cultural rebirth which swept Europe in the sixteenth century found its corresponding Golden Age in Bohemia, which during that era produced its famous Králice Bible, its dictionaries, historical works and the organized printing of books. In 1621 the Czechs were deprived of their independence and, although writers of the stature of Comenius continued their work in exile, the Czech language, which was resented by the Hapsburgs, fell into disuse, while, thanks to the efforts of the Jesuits who celebrated a campaign against heresy with the burning of all available Czech books, Czech literature was abandoned entirely until the latter half of the eighteenth century. At that time, Joseph II, who had little love for either the Vatican or the Society of Jesus, instigated a series of liberal reforms that served to mitigate some of the more obvious abuses of the Counter-Reformation.

The subsequent Czech revival concerned itself chiefly with the problems of language. Josef Dobrovský (1753–1829) and Josef Jungmann (1773–1847) were instrumental in the founding of modern Slavonic philology, and it was the latter who translated Milton's "Paradise Lost" and Chateaubriand's "Atala" into the new idiom, thus broadening its scope and literary frame of reference. The poetry of the Slovak, Jan Kollár, belongs to this period, with its nostalgia for unity and its idealized version of Slavonic brotherhood; one may well contrast Kollár with Havlíček, a nineteenth-century satirist, disillusioned with patriotism, the author of the "Tyrolese Elegies" and the translator of Voltaire and Gogol. The poetry of Havlíček's contemporaries is, for the most part, simple and romantic, influenced by the folk-song.

Havlíček may perhaps be regarded as the instigator of a movement that, in the eighties and nineties, became an open conflict between the writers who were motivated by a desire to consolidate the national spirit, Neruda and Čech, and those who were attracted by the achievements of Western Europe, Zeyer and Vrchlický. Neruda, who has been called the "Czech Dickens," concerned himself with the pathetic and ludicrous aspects of lower middle-class life. Vrchlický and Zeyer might be described as exotics—the former, who was as prolific and romantic as Lope de Vega, produced over seventy volumes of his own and almost as many translations, ranging from Dante and Ariosto to Whitman and Calderon; the latter attempted, like the Pre-Raphaelites in England, to revive the Gothic spirit.

The reaction to this foreign movement was led by T. G. Masaryk, one of the most vital forces in Czech literary criticism as well as in politics, who launched a new realism and opposed the literature of personality with that of social consciousness. The novel in the hands of Holeček returned to the soil and to the Czech peasant of idealized virtues, but, at the same time, Neruda's descendants, Ignát Hermann and K. Čapek-Chod, devoted themselves to novels of the city, in which life in Prague was treated with derision and harshness. In poetry, Neruda's tradition was continued in the social satires of J. S. Machár (1864–1942), while the opposing individualistic and subjective trend was resumed by Antonín Sova (1864–1928) and Otakar Březina (1868–1929); Březina, in particular, made distinguished deviations from the nationalistic pattern in poetry of a mystical and metaphysical character of which the relation to religion is as strange as that of superstition.

The anthology that follows has been selected from material written in the extremely brief interval between the two World Wars, the lull during which Czechoslovakia enjoyed momentary freedom from external domination. It is no more comprehensive or complete than the resumé which has preceded it, but it does attempt to make a fairly representative collection of contemporary Czech letters—representative, that is, of what has already been described as the Czech spirit, not in the literal, chauvinistic sense which breathes Fascist odium, but as a synthesis of native and assimilated traditions which relate to the general character and identity of the nation.

Thus the work of those authors who wrote in German, Franz Kafka and Rainer Maria Rilke, has been included. Their independence of literary nationalism is as typical of Czech letters as their preoccupation with human inferiority, death and ultimate restitution. More specifically, Kafka's systematized persecutions, his "fantasies" in which heroes or heroines retain their human characteristics but inhabit such minor and underprivileged organisms as birds and insects, may be related to the work of such traditional masters of Czech vernacular as Jaroslav Hašek, the inventor of that Chaplinesque hero-victim, "The Good Soldier Schweik", or to the author of "The Manufacture of the Absolute" and "War with the Newts", Karel Čapek. In the same sense, Rilke may be associated with Otakar Březina.

Recently another Bohemian author writing in German, F. C. Weiskopf, has used Slovak motifs in his writings in addition to Czech ones; his work may be regarded as somewhat associated with that of the Czech writer, Ivan Olbracht.

Slovakia and her people have, up to the present time, been very little known, and hardly recognized at all, as part of European literature. Slovak was first established as a written language only in the middle of the nineteenth century. Since then it has been subjected to various upheavals and disorders which are, for all their opposition to Czech domination, a minor variation of the essential Czech problems of language and identity. It would only confuse the reader to enumerate these problems here, and we must content ourselves with the observation that, considering its span, Slovak literature has been surprisingly precocious. We must also mention the contemporary Slovak writers Novomeský, Kráľ, Lukáč, whose work equals in interest the output of the Czech poetic revival of the twenties and thirties, Nezval, Wolker, Seifert, Halas. Modern Slovak prose contains the familiar name, Milo Urban, who is the author of the first Slovak novel to achieve acclaim abroad, "The Living Whip", and Peter Jilemnický.

Ivan Olbracht, one of the prominent post-war Czech novelists, was the author of a penetrating psychological novel, "The Strange Friendship of Jesenius the Actor," which offers a curious contrast to his later work, chiefly pastoral and concerned with the Carpathian peasantry. Vančura was one of the most vital influences in modern Czech prose, and his work varied from studies of proletarian life and nationalist problems to baroque, romantic novels. The third member of this group is Egon Hostovský, whose *Vertigo*, published here, is a distinguished example of Czech literature since the beginning of the second World War, although its emotional impact would seem no less forceful or genuine had it been written after the first Hapsburg suppression of the Bohemian charter; the narrator's consolatory "We shall wake up when it comes to the worst" might well be the legend of an entire category of Czech characters who somnambulate towards some moral, poetic or historic disaster, of which the resolution has been a recurrent Czech problem, but which, more recently, has become the universal problem of our time.

Karel Čapek

ON LITERATURE

FORGIVE ME if I start off with something quite other than literature, something from the days when I was a small boy. Your city boy is a kind of super-boy, a born sceptic, lord of the streets; and it is quite natural that he should have a huge contempt for hobble-dehoys, nincompoops, bumpkins, and clodhoppers, as he nicknames country boys. Your country boy looks down immeasurably and with justice on the city boys; for he is lord of the fields and forests; he knows all about horses, and is on friendly terms with the beasts of the field; he can crack a whip and has under his dominion all the treasures of the earth, from willow-switches to ripe poppy-heads. And even your boy from a small country town is by no means the least among worldly princes; for he includes in his circle more than any other mortal creature: he can watch all human activities at close quarters.

When I was a boy in a little country town I saw at home how a doctor's business is run, and at my grandfather's I could inspect the business of a miller and baker, which is ever so jolly and fine. And at my uncle's I saw what a farmer has to do; but if I once started on that I should never stop telling you all I learnt there, and all the things I got to know. Our nearest neighbour was the painter who stencilled the walls, and that is a tremendously interesting job. Sometimes he used to let me mix him the colours in their little pots; and once, almost bursting with pride, I was allowed to smear one stencil pattern with the brush; it came out crooked, but otherwise most successfully. I shall never forget how that painter used to stride up and down the planks whistling, gloriously splashed with all the colours of the rainbow; and he stencilled in such miraculously straight lines, sometimes even painting in something freehand—it might be an amazingly well-nourished rose the colour of stale liver, on the ceiling. It was my first revelation of the painter's art, and I lost my heart to it then, and have been in love with it ever since. And then I used to go every day and have a look at how the innkeeper runs his job, and see how they roll the casks down into the cellar and how they draw the beer and blow off the froth, and hear the wise tales the old gossips tell as they wipe the froth from their whiskers with the backs of their hands. Every day I used to look in on neighbour cobbler and watch in silence how he cut the leather and hammered it on his last and then put on the heel, and all manner of other things; for shoemaking is an intricate and delicate work, and if you have not seen leather in the cobbler's hands you know nothing about it at all, though you may wear shoes of Cordovan or even of celestial leather. Then there was neighbour hurdy-gurdy man, and I went to see him too, when he was at home, and was so surprised that he did not play his hurdy-gurdy at home, but sat and stared at one corner of the room till I felt quite uncomfortable. There was the mournful stone-mason who carved crosses and queer, short, dumpy angels on the grave-stones; he would tap away all day and never say a single word, and I stood watching for perhaps an hour while he chipped away at the un-seeing eye of a weeping angel. And then, ha ha! yes! there was the wheel-wright with his beautiful wood throwing off sparks and his yard full of hastening wheels, as Homer says, and a wheel, you know, is a wonder in itself. Then there was the smith in his black smithy: I burst with pride when I was sometimes allowed to work the bellows for him while he heated the iron bar red-hot and hammered it, looking like a black Cy-clops, till it sent out a shower of sparks; and when he put the shoe on the horse it smelt of burnt horn, and the horse would turn his wise eyes on the smith as much as to say, "All right, go on, I shan't make a fuss."

A little farther on lived Tonča, the prostitute; I did not understand her business very well, and I used to pass her little house with a queer, dry feeling in my throat. Once I looked in through the window, but it was all empty—just striped feather beds, and some consecrated willow catkins above the bed. I had a look at the mill owner's business, and watched them hurrying through their counting-houses, and collected foreign stamps out of their waste-paper baskets; and I watched the mill hands at the vats full of tow, and the weavers at the mysterious mechanical looms: I went into the red-hot hell of the jute-drying kilns and scorched myself beside the stokers at the boilers, wondering at their long shovels, which I could hardly lift. I would visit the butcher, eyeing him with interest to see if he would cut off a finger. I would have a look in at the shopkeeper as he weighed and measured; stop at the tinsmith's, and go into the carpenter's yard where everything was a-whirr and a-clatter. I went to the poor-house to see what the poor do with themselves, and went with them to their fair in the city on a Friday to learn how the business of begging was carried on.

Now I have got a profession of my own, and I work at it the livelong day. But even if I were to sit in the porch with my work I don't think a single boy would come and watch my fingers—standing on one bare foot and rubbing his calf with the other—to see how a writer's business is done. I don't say that it is a bad or useless profession: but it is not one of the superlatively fine and striking ones, and the material used is of a strange sort—you don't even see it. But I should like all the things that I used to see to be in it: the ringing hammer-strokes of the smith and the colours of the whistling house painter, the patience of the tailor, and the careful chipping of the stone-mason, the bustling of the baker, the humility of the poor, and all the lusty strength and skill which men of towering stature put into their work before the astonished and fascinated eyes of a child.

Translated from the Czech by DORA ROUND

Jaroslav Hašek

SCHWEIK, THE GOOD SOLDIER, INTERVENES IN THE GREAT WAR

"So THEY'VE KILLED FERDINAND," said the charwoman to Mr. Schweik who, having left the army many years before, when a military medical board had declared him to be chronically feeble-minded, earned a livelihood by the sale of dogs—repulsive mongrel monstrosities for whom he forged pedigrees. Apart from this occupation, he was afflicted with rheumatism, and was just rubbing his knees with embrocation.

"Which Ferdinand, Mrs. Müller?" asked Schweik, continuing to massage his knees. "I know two Ferdinands. One of them does jobs for Prusa the chemist, and one day he drank a bottle of hair oil by mistake; and then there's Ferdinand Kokoska who goes round collecting manure. They wouldn't be any great loss, either of 'em."

"No, it's the Archduke Ferdinand, the one from Konopiste, you know, Mr. Schweik, the fat, pious one."

"Good Lord!" exclaimed Schweik, "that's a fine thing. And where did this happen?"

"They shot him at Sarajevo with a revolver, you know. He was riding there with his Archduchess in a motor car."

"Just fancy that now, Mrs. Müller, in a motor car. Ah, a gentleman like him can afford it and he never thinks how a ride in a motor car like that can end up badly. And at Sarajevo in the bargain, that's in Bosnia, Mrs. Müller. I expect the Turks did it. I reckon we never ought to have taken Bosnia and Herzegovina away from them. And there you are, Mrs. Müller. Now the Archduke's in a better land. Did he suffer long?"

"The Archduke was done for on the spot. You know, people didn't ought to mess about with revolvers. They're dangerous things, that they are. Not long ago there was another gentleman down our way larking about with a revolver and he shot a whole family as well as the house porter, who went to see who was shooting on the third floor."

"There's some revolvers, Mrs. Müller, that won't go off, even if you tried till you was dotty. There's lots like that. But they're sure to have bought something better than that for the Archduke, and I wouldn't mind betting, Mrs. Müller, that the man who did it put on his best clothes for the job. You know, it wants a bit of doing to shoot an archduke; it's not like when a poacher shoots a gamekeeper. You have to find out how to get at him; you can't reach an important man like that if you're dressed just anyhow. You have to wear a top hat or else the police'd run you in before you knew where you were."

"I hear there was a whole lot of 'em, Mr. Schweik."

"Why, of course there was, Mrs. Müller," said Schweik, now concluding the massage of his knees. "If you wanted to kill an archduke or the Emperor, for instance, you'd naturally talk it over with somebody. Two heads are better than one. One gives one bit of advice, another gives another, and so the good work prospers, as the hymn says. The chief thing is to keep on the watch till the gentleman you're after rides past. . . . But there's plenty more of them waiting their turn for it. You mark my words, Mrs. Müller, they'll get the Czar and Czarina yet, and maybe, though let's hope not, the Emperor himself, now that they've started with his uncle. The old chap's got a lot of enemies. More than Ferdinand had. A little while ago a gentleman in the saloon bar was saying that there'd come a time when all the emperors would get done in one after another, and that not all their bigwigs and such-like would save them."

"The newspaper says, Mr. Schweik, that the Archduke was riddled with bullets. He emptied the whole lot into him."

"That was mighty quick work, Mrs. Müller, mighty quick. I'd buy a Browning for a job like that. It looks like a toy, but in a couple of minutes you could shoot twenty archdukes with it, thin or fat. Although between ourselves, Mrs. Müller, it's easier to hit a fat archduke than a thin one. You may remember the time they shot their king in Portugal. He was a fat fellow. Of course, you don't expect a king to be thin. Well, now I'm going to call round at The Flagon and if anybody comes for that little terrier I took the advance for, you can tell 'em I've got him at my dog farm in the country. I just cropped his ears and now he mustn't be taken away till his ears heal up or else he'd catch cold in them. Give the key to the house porter."

There was only one customer at The Flagon. This was Bretschneider, a plainclothes policeman who was on secret service work. Palivec, the landlord, was washing glasses and Bretschneider vainly endeavoured to engage him in a serious conversation.

"We're having a fine summer," was Bretschneider's overture to a serious conversation.

"Damn rotten," replied Palivec, putting the glasses away into a cupboard.

"That's a fine thing they've done for us at Sarajevo," Bretschneider observed, with his hopes rather dashed.

"I never shove my nose into that sort of thing, I'm hanged if I do," primly replied Mr. Palivec, lighting his pipe. "Nowadays, it's as much as your life's worth to get mixed up in them. I've got my business to see to. When a customer comes in and orders beer, why I just serve him his drink. But Sarajevo or politics or a dead archduke, that's not for the likes of us, unless we want to end up doing time."

Bretschneider said no more, but stared disappointedly round the empty bar.

"You used to have a picture of the Emperor hanging here," he began again presently, "just at the place where you've got a mirror now."

"Yes, that's right," replied Mr. Palivec, "it used to hang there and the flies left their trade-mark on it, so I put it away into the lumber room. You see, somebody might pass a remark about it and then there might be trouble. What use is it to me?"

"That business at Sarajevo," Bretschneider resumed, "was done by the Serbs."

"You're wrong there," replied Schweik, "it was done by the Turks, because of Bosnia and Herzegovina."

And Schweik expounded his views of Austrian international policy in the Balkans. The Turks were the losers in 1912 against Serbia, Bulgaria, and Greece. They had wanted Austria to help them and when this was not done, they had shot Ferdinand.

"Do you like the Turks?" said Schweik, turning to Palivec. "Do you like that heathen pack of dogs? You don't, do you?"

"One customer's the same as another customer," said Palivec, "even if he's a Turk. People like us who've got their business to look after can't be bothered with politics. Pay for your drink and sit down and say what you like. That's my principle. It's all the same to me whether our Ferdinand was done in by a Serb or a Turk, a Catholic or a Moslem, an Anarchist or a young Czech Liberal."

"That's all well and good, Mr. Palivec," remarked Bretschneider, who had regained hope that one or other of these two could be caught out, "but you'll admit that it's a great loss to Austria."

Schweik replied for the landlord:

"Yes, there's no denying it. A shocking loss. You can't replace Ferdinand by any sort of tomfool. If war was to break out to-day, I'd go of my own accord and serve the Emperor to my last breath."

Schweik took a deep gulp and continued:

"Do you think the Emperor's going to put up with that sort of thing? Little do you know him. You mark my words, there's got to be war with the Turks. Kill my uncle, would you? Then take this smack in the jaw for a start. Oh, there's bound to be war. Serbia and Russia'll help us. There won't half be a bust-up."

At this prophetic moment Schweik was really good to look upon. His artless countenance, smiling like the full moon, beamed with enthusiasm. The whole thing was so utterly clear to him.

"Maybe," he continued his delineation of the future of Austria, "if we have war with the Turks, the Germans'll attack us, because the Germans and the Turks stand by each other. They're a low lot, the scum of the earth. Still, we can join France, because they've had a grudge against Germany ever since '71. And then there'll be lively doings. There's going to be war. I can't tell you more than that."

Bretschneider stood up and said solemnly:

"You needn't say any more. Follow me into the passage and there I'll say something to you."

Schweik followed the plainclothes policeman into the passage where a

slight surprise awaited him when his fellow-toper showed him his badge
and announced that he was now arresting him and would at once convey
him to the police headquarters. Schweik endeavoured to explain that
there must be some mistake; that he was entirely innocent; that he hadn't
uttered a single word capable of offending anyone.

But Bretschneider told him that he had actually committed several
penal offences, among them being high treason.

Then they returned to the saloon bar and Schweik said to Mr. Palivec:
"I've had five beers and a couple of sausages with a roll. Now let me
have a cherry brandy and I must be off, as I'm arrested."

Bretschneider showed Mr. Palivec his badge, looked at Mr. Palivec for
a moment and then asked:

"Are you married?"

"Yes."

"And can your wife carry on the business during your absence?"

"Yes."

"That's all right, then, Mr. Palivec," said Bretschneider breezily. "Tell
your wife to step this way; hand the business over to her, and we'll come
for you in the evening."

"Don't you worry about that," Schweik comforted him. "I'm only being
run in for high treason."

"But what about me?" lamented Mr. Palivec. "I've been so careful what
I said."

Bretschneider smiled and said triumphantly:

"I've got you for saying that the flies left their trade-mark on the
Emperor. You'll have all that stuff knocked out of your head."

And Schweik left The Flagon in the company of the plainclothes
policeman.

And thus Schweik, the good soldier, intervened in the Great War in
that pleasant, amiable manner which was so peculiarly his. It will be of
interest to historians to know that he saw far into the future. If the situation subsequently developed otherwise than he expounded it at The
Flagon, we must take into account the fact that he lacked a preliminary
diplomatic training.

SCHWEIK, THE GOOD SOLDIER, AT THE POLICE HEADQUARTERS

The Sarajevo assassination had filled the police headquarters with
numerous victims. They were brought in, one after the other, and the
old inspector in the reception bureau said in his good-humored voice:

"This Ferdinand business is going to cost you dear." When they had shut Schweik up in one of the numerous dens on the first floor, he found six persons already assembled there. Five of them were sitting round the table, and in a corner a middle-aged man was sitting on a mattress as if he were holding aloof from the rest.

Schweik began to ask one after the other why they had been arrested.

From the five sitting at the table he received practically the same reply:

"That Sarajevo business." "That Ferdinand business." "It's all through that murder of the Archduke." "That Ferdinand affair." "Because they did the Archduke in at Sarajevo."

The sixth man who was holding aloof from the other five said that he didn't want to have anything to do with them because he didn't want any suspicion to fall on him. He was there only for attempted robbery with violence.

Schweik joined the company of conspirators at the table, who were telling each other for at least the tenth time how they had got there.

All, except one, had been caught either in a public house, a wineshop or a café. The exception consisted of an extremely fat gentleman with spectacles and tear-stained eyes who had been arrested in his own home because two days before the Sarajevo outrage he had stood drinks to two Serbian students, and had been observed by Detective Brix drunk in their company at the Montmartre night club where, as he had already confirmed by his signature in the report, he had again stood them drinks.

When Schweik had heard all these dreadful tales of conspiracy he thought fit to make clear to them the complete hopelessness of their situation.

"We're all in the deuce of a mess," he began his words of comfort. "You say that nothing can happen to you, or to any of us, but you're wrong. What have we got the police for except to punish us for letting our tongues wag? If the times are so dangerous that archdukes get shot, the likes of us mustn't be surprised if we're taken up before the beak. They're doing all this to make a bit of a splash, so that Ferdinand'll be in the limelight before his funeral. The more of us there are, the better it'll be for us, because we'll feel all the jollier."

Whereupon Schweik stretched himself out on the mattress and fell asleep contentedly.

In the meanwhile, two new arrivals were brought in. One of them was a Bosnian. He walked up and down gnashing his teeth. The other new guest was Palivec who, on seeing his acquaintance Schweik, woke him up and exclaimed in a voice full of tragedy:

"Now I'm here, too!"

Schweik shook hands with him cordially and said:

"I'm glad of that, really I am. I felt sure that gentleman'd keep his word when he told you they'd come and fetch you. It's nice to know you can rely on people."

Mr. Palivec, however, remarked that he didn't care a damn whether he could rely on people or not, and he asked Schweik on the quiet whether the other prisoners were thieves who might do harm to his business reputation.

Schweik explained to him that all except one, who had been arrested for attempted robbery with violence, were there on account of the Archduke.

Schweik went back to sleep, but not for long, because they soon came to take him away to be cross-examined.

And so, mounting the staircase to Section 3 for his cross-examination, and beaming with good nature, he entered the bureau, saying:

"Good evening, gentlemen, I hope you're all well."

Instead of a reply, someone pummelled him in the ribs and stood him in front of a table, behind which sat a gentleman with a cold official face and features of such brutish savagery that he looked as if he had just tumbled out of Lombroso's book on criminal types.

He hurled a bloodthirsty glance at Schweik and said:

"Take that idiotic expression off your face."

"I can't help it," replied Schweik solemnly. "I was discharged from the army on account of being weak-minded and a special board reported me officially as weak-minded. I'm officially weak-minded—a chronic case."

The gentleman with the criminal countenance grated his teeth as he said:

"The offence you're accused of and that you've committed shows you've got all your wits about you."

And he now proceeded to enumerate to Schweik a long list of crimes, beginning with high treason and ending with insulting language toward His Royal Highness and members of the Royal Family. The central gem of this collection constituted approval of the murder of the Archduke Ferdinand, and from this again branched off a string of fresh offences, amongst which sparkled incitement to rebellion, as the whole business had happened in a public place.

"What have you got to say for yourself?" triumphantly asked the gentleman with the features of brutish savagery.

"There's a lot of it," replied Schweik innocently. "You can have too much of a good thing."

"So you admit it's true?"

"I admit everything. You've got to be strict. If you ain't strict, why, where would you be? It's like when I was in the army—"

"Hold your tongue!" shouted the police commissioner. "And don't say a word unless you're asked a question. Do you understand?"

"Begging your pardon, sir, I do, and I've properly got the hang of every word you utter."

"Who do you keep company with?"

"The charwoman, sir."

"And you don't know anybody in political circles here?"

"Yes, sir, I take in the afternoon edition of the *Narodni Politika,* you know, sir, the paper they call the puppy's delight."

"Get out of here!" roared the gentleman with the brutish appearance. When they were taking him out of the bureau, Schweik said:

"Good night, sir."

Having been deposited in his cell again, Schweik informed all the prisoners that the cross-examination was great fun. "They yell at you a bit and then kick you out." He paused a moment. "In olden times," continued Schweik, "it used to be much worse. I once read a book where it said that people charged with anything had to walk on red-hot iron and drink molten lead to see whether they was innocent or not. There was lots who was treated like that and then on top of it all they was quartered or put in the pillory somewhere near the Natural History Museum."

"Nowadays, it's great fun being run in," continued Schweik with relish. "There's no quartering or anything of that kind. We've got a mattress, we've got a table, we've got a seat, we ain't packed together like sardines, we'll get soup, they'll give us bread, they'll bring a pitcher of water, there's a closet right under our noses. It all shows you what progress there's been. Ah, yes, nowadays things have improved for our benefit."

He had just concluded his vindication of the modern imprisonment of citizens when the warder opened the door and shouted:

"Schweik, you've got to get dressed and go to be cross-examined."

Schweik again stood in the presence of the criminal-faced gentleman who, without any preliminaries, asked him in a harsh and relentless tone:

"Do you admit everything?"

Schweik fixed his kindly blue eyes upon the pitiless person and said mildly:

"If you want me to admit it, sir, then I will. It can't do me any harm."

The severe gentleman wrote something on his documents and, handing Schweik a pen, told him to sign.

And Schweik signed Bretschneider's depositions, with the following addition:

All the above-mentioned accusations against me are based upon truth.

JOSEF SCHWEIK.

When he had signed, he turned to the severe gentleman:

"Is there anything else for me to sign? Or am I to come back in the morning?"

"You'll be taken to the criminal court in the morning," was the answer.

"What time, sir? You see, I wouldn't like to oversleep myself, whatever happens."

"Get out!" came a roar for the second time that day from the other side of the table before which Schweik had stood.

As soon as the door had closed behind him, his fellow-prisoners overwhelmed him with all sorts of questions, to which Schweik replied brightly:

"I've just admitted I probably murdered the Archduke Ferdinand."

And as he lay down on the mattress, he said:

"It's a pity we haven't got an alarm clock here."

But in the morning they woke him up without an alarm clock, and precisely at six Schweik was taken away in the Black Maria to the county criminal court.

"The early bird catches the worm," said Schweik to his fellow-travellers, as the Black Maria was passing out through the gates of the police headquarters.

SCHWEIK BEFORE THE MEDICAL AUTHORITIES

The clean, cosy cubicles of the county criminal court produced a very favourable impression upon Schweik. And the examining justices, the Pilates of the new epoch, instead of honourably washing their hands, sent out for stew and Pilsen beer, and kept on transmitting new charges to the public prosecutor.

It was to one of these gentlemen that Schweik was conducted for cross-examination. When Schweik was led before him, he asked him with his inborn courtesy to sit down, and then said:

"So you're this Mr. Schweik?"

"I think I must be," replied Schweik, "because my dad was called Schweik and my mother was Mrs. Schweik. I couldn't disgrace them by denying my name."

A bland smile flitted across the face of the examining counsel.

"This is a fine business you've been up to. You've got plenty on your conscience."

"I've always got plenty on my conscience," said Schweik, smiling even more blandly than the counsel himself. "I bet I've got more on my conscience than what you have, sir."

"I can see that from the statement you signed," said the legal dignitary, in the same kindly tone. "Did they bring any pressure to bear upon you at the police headquarters?"

"Not a bit of it, sir. I myself asked them whether I had to sign it and when they said I had to, why, I just did what they told me. It's not likely that I'm going to quarrel with them over my own signature. I shouldn't be doing myself any good that way. Things have got to be done in proper order."

"Do you feel quite well, Mr. Schweik?"

"I wouldn't say quite well, your worship. I've got rheumatism and I'm using embrocation for it."

The old gentleman again gave a kindly smile. "Suppose we were to have you examined by the medical authorities."

"I don't think there's much the matter with me and it wouldn't be fair to waste the gentlemen's time. There was one doctor examined me at the police headquarters."

"All the same, Mr. Schweik, we'll have a try with the medical authorities. We'll appoint a little commission, we'll have you placed under observation, and in the meanwhile you'll have a nice rest. Just one more question: According to the statement you're supposed to have said that now a war's going to break out soon."

"Yes, your worship, it'll break out at any moment now."

That concluded the cross-examination. Schweik shook hands with the legal dignitary, and on his return to the cell he said to his neighbours:

"Now they're going to have me examined by the medical authorities on account of this murder of Archduke Ferdinand."

"I don't trust the medical authorities," remarked a man of intelligent appearance. "Once when I forged some bills of exchange I went to a lecture by Dr. Heveroch, and when they nabbed me I pretended to have an epileptic fit, just like Dr. Heveroch described it. I bit the leg of one of the medical authorities on the commission and drank the ink out of the inkpot. But just because I bit a man in the calf they reported I was quite well, and so I was done for."

"I think," said Schweik, "that we ought to look at everything fair and square. Anybody can make a mistake, and the more he thinks about a thing, the more mistakes he's bound to make. Why, even cabinet ministers can make mistakes."

The commission of medical authorities which had to decide whether Schweik's standard of intelligence did, or did not, conform to all the crimes with which he was charged, consisted of three extremely serious gentlemen with views which were such that the view of each separate one of them differed considerably from the views of the other two.

They represented three distinct schools of thought with regard to mental disorders.

If in the case of Schweik a complete agreement was reached between these diametrically opposed scientific camps, this can be explained simply and solely by the overwhelming impression produced upon them by Schweik who, on entering the room where his state of mind was to be examined and observing a picture of the Austrian ruler hanging on the wall, shouted: "Gentlemen, long live our Emperor, Franz Josef the First."

The matter was completely clear. Schweik's spontaneous utterance made it unnecessary to ask a whole lot of questions, and there remained only some of the most important ones, the answers to which were to corroborate Schweik's real opinion, thus:

"Is radium heavier than lead?"

"I've never weighed it, sir," answered Schweik with his sweet smile.

"Do you believe in the end of the world?"

"I'd have to see the end of the world first," replied Schweik in an off-hand manner, "but I'm sure it won't come my way to-morrow."

"Could you measure the diameter of the globe?"

"No, that I couldn't, sir," answered Schweik, "but now I'll ask you a riddle, gentlemen. There's a three-storied house with eight windows on each story. On the roof there are two gables and two chimneys. There are two tenants on each story. And now, gentlemen, I want you to tell me in what year the house porter's grandmother died?"

The medical authorities looked at each other meaningly, but nevertheless one of them asked one more question:

"Do you know the maximum depth of the Pacific Ocean?"

"I'm afraid I don't, sir," was the answer, "but it's pretty sure to be deeper than what the river is just below Prague."

The chairman of the commission curtly asked: "Is that enough?" But one member inquired further:

"How much is 12897 times 13863?"

"729," answered Schweik without moving an eyelash.

"I think that's quite enough," said the chairman of the commission. "You can take this prisoner back to where he came from."

"Thank you, gentlemen," said Schweik respectfully, "it's quite enough for me, too."

After his departure the three experts agreed that Schweik was an obvious imbecile in accordance with all the natural laws discovered by mental specialists.

SCHWEIK IS EJECTED FROM THE LUNATIC ASYLUM

When Schweik later on described life in the lunatic asylum, he did so in terms of exceptional eulogy: "The life there was a fair treat. You can bawl, or yelp, or sing, or blub, or moo, or boo, or jump, say your prayers or turn somersaults, or walk on all fours, or hop about on one foot, run around in a circle, or dance, or skip, or squat on your haunches all day long, and climb up the walls. I liked being in the asylum, I can tell you, and while I was there I had the time of my life."

And, in good sooth, the mere welcome which awaited Schweik in the asylum, when they took him there from the central criminal court for observation, far exceeded anything he had expected. First of all they took him to have a bath. In the bathroom they immersed him in a tub of warm water and then pulled him out and placed him under a cold douche. They repeated this three times and then asked him whether he liked it. Schweik said that it was better than the public baths near the Charles Bridge and that he was very fond of bathing. "If you'll only just clip my nails and hair, I'll be as happy as can be," he added, smiling affably.

They complied with this request, and when they had thoroughly rubbed him down with a sponge, they wrapped him up in a sheet and carried him off into ward No. 1 to bed, where they laid him down, covered him over with a quilt, and told him to go to sleep.

And so he blissfully fell asleep on the bed. Then they woke him up to give him a basin of milk and a roll. The roll was already cut up into little pieces and while one of the keepers held Schweik's hands, the other dipped the bits of roll into milk and fed him as poultry is fed with clots of dough for fattening. After he had gone to sleep again, they woke him up and took him to the observation ward where Schweik, standing stark naked before two doctors, was reminded of the glorious time when he joined the army.

"Take five paces forward and five paces to the rear," remarked one of the doctors.

Schweik took ten paces.

"I told you," said the doctor, "to take five."

"A few paces more or less don't matter to me," said Schweik.

Thereupon the doctors ordered him to sit on a chair and one of them tapped him on the knee. He then told the other one that the reflexes were quite normal, whereat the other wagged his head and he in his turn began to tap Schweik on the knee, while the first one lifted Schweik's eyelids and examined his pupils. Then they went off to a table and bandied some Latin phrases.

One of them asked Schweik:

"Has the state of your mind ever been examined?"

"In the army," replied Schweik solemnly and proudly, "the military doctors officially reported me as feeble-minded."

"It strikes me that you're a malingerer," shouted one of the doctors.

"Me, gentlemen?" said Schweik deprecatingly. "No, I'm no malingerer, I'm feeble-minded, fair and square. You ask them in the orderly room of the 91st regiment or at the reserve headquarters in Karlin."

The elder of the two doctors waved his hand with a gesture of despair and pointing to Schweik said to the keepers: "Let this man have his clothes again and put him into Section 3 in the first passage. Then one of you can come back and take all his papers into the office. And tell them there to settle it quickly, because we don't want to have him on our hands for long."

The doctors cast another crushing glance at Schweik, who deferentially retreated backward to the door, bowing with unction all the while. From the moment when the keepers received orders to return Schweik's clothes to him, they no longer showed the slightest concern for him. They told him to get dressed, and one of them took him to Ward No. 3 where, for the few days it took to complete his written ejection in the office, he had an opportunity of carrying on his agreeable observations. The disappointed doctors reported that he was "a malingerer of weak intellect," and as they discharged him before lunch, it caused quite a little scene. Schweik declared that a man cannot be ejected from a lunatic asylum without having been given his lunch first. This disorderly behaviour was stopped by a police officer who had been summoned by the asylum porter and who conveyed Schweik to the commissariat of police.

Translated from the Czech by PAUL SELVER

Egon Hostovský

VERTIGO

28th March, 1949.

ALL OF US, my dear friend, are suffering so acutely from vertigo that you could tell it at once by our eyes, which have seen so many things that had hitherto seemed secure, crumble so quickly to dust.

I was looking for Mr. Albe in the café yesterday.

"Mr. Albe?" pondered the waiter.

"He wears glasses; he is bald . . ."

"The one who always orders chocolate?"

"He wears a blue suit."

"I know whom you mean; he drinks mineral water with his coffee. Or, wait a minute, it must be the one who drinks no brandy but Raphael."

Believe me, the waiter was not jesting; he really knows the guests by what they eat or wear. Why do I feel uneasy? Because I don't know how I can recognize people, and how they can recognize me. I just don't know; I just don't know.

"You are Müller, of course," said an eccentrically dressed young man, with a waxed moustache under an enormously large nose, who accosted me in the street.

"I'm not Müller."

"Stop kidding, man, of course you are Müller! My name is Colt, I want to work with you. Forty per cent for me and sixty for you. Shall we shake on it?"

"Sorry, I'm not Müller!"

"Then seventy for you—all right? . . . Then who *are* you? It's as plain as the nose on your face that you're not a native here. Keep your incognito and take a chance on me. Surely you must have heard of me? Colt—

diamonds. Gentleman of the first water. Listen here, Müller, I have a grand new system, sure to make eighty per cent profit . . ."

He was a hundred per cent thief. It was a long while before he was convinced that I was not Müller. That didn't worry him; it was enough that I am an emigré. His offer was some crooked deal with stolen or smuggled diamonds. I confessed regretfully that I had never been guilty of any kind of fraud, and he said I was a mug. That we did not speak the same language. That he had been in prison here for three months, and that many emigrés were in jail. Not that they had ever stolen anything; but no one treats emigrés any better than thieves. What, they do treat them better? Everything in this world is a hundred per cent ramp. Useless to tell him that I earn my living in a respectable way, he knows I am an emigré, and emigrés are not allowed to earn a sensible living. Suppose I give him my address?—He will come to see me, and learn how his proposition has struck me.

How can we recognize the people we seek? By what they eat and drink? How distinguish a thief from an honest man when everything in this world is a ramp. No, everything is not a ramp. Mr. Thief, if only for the reason that you have held my arm for the past ten minutes and have stolen nothing from me! Mr. Albe, my good waiter, is an exceedingly good man; you would know that at once if you looked into his eyes. You may be up against it some day, waiter, and then you won't know to whom you can turn, if you cannot tell people by their faces.

I repeat, my dear friend, we all suffer from vertigo. So swift is time in its phantasmal flight that our senses reel; one rushes off somewhere, one collapses somewhere, and still one remains in the same place; one's hopes fly away and return with the coming of the birds; we grow old, we become grey, but we go on defying death and the devil. To them we refuse to yield. They circle and circle around us, they plague us with nightmares, but we do not give in to them. "We shall wake up when it comes to the worst," we whisper in a faint, small voice through the nightmare. Sometimes those two, the devil and death, all but hold us by the collar. "You poor fool," they grin, "from what do you expect to wake? You're not asleep, you *are* awake. This is no dream, this is the truth! All this is reality!"

No, no, we are not yet in their clutches, and please God we shan't be. You say we are not dreaming. Perhaps not; I don't know.

Now it's your turn, poets and bards; give ear to the tale of Jeronimo, the fiery Spaniard.

It was just before the end of their civil war. He was taken prisoner. For three days they let him starve in some sort of a hole, some deep cellar. He carried a small bag of gold slung round his neck. I forget how he had come by this gold. "Why suffer?" asked the grisly one, tenderly, "come, let's be betrothed!" He let himself be persuaded, although she was ugly, and her breath freezing. He began lustily, to shout awful obscenities, and to kick in the door. He was ready to hurl himself at the first guard who entered the dungeon, and to bite off his nose, so that he might be shot on the spot. And as he kicked and banged upon the door, he turned the knob—and behold, a miracle!—the door opened. Either it had not been closed, or it had been insecurely locked. He tottered out, stumbled up the stairs, and suddenly ran into a soldier who was armed to the teeth. He was about to grab the soldier by the throat and bite off his nose, but before he could raise his hands, the soldier asked, in a matter of fact way:

"Have you got the bowl already?"

"I haven't it," whispered Jeronimo, in astonishment.

"Then go quickly!"

Jeronimo will never know for whom the soldier mistook him, nor of what bowl he spoke. Perhaps the soldier was drunk, perhaps he was walking and talking in his sleep. It was night, Jeronimo walked out of the cellar and out of the prison and disappeared in the darkness. With the gold he had with him he bought people. They helped him to get to the frontier. In France he was imprisoned again. Then . . . Is all this true? Or is it a lie? . . .

My pale-faced countryman goes about like a somnambulist, whispering something unintelligible.

"What are you muttering about?"

He lifts his head and looks at me, stupidly, as if he were seeing me for the first time. He swallows, and then he says:

"I must go to France!"

"We must all of us go there; have patience!"

"But I want to get to the front right away!"

"Why?"

"Because . . . I saw them die . . ."

"Saw whom die?"

"Our people . . . Those five . . . Back home . . . I alone escaped!"

This is the incident of the six who were staying at a certain Italian nobleman's castle near Prague. A true incident? How can I tell! A kind-hearted stranger took pity upon the six; they were five men

and one woman, and their names were on the Germans' black list. While
the usurpers were marching upon Prague a small car brought the six,
one by one, to the castle. The Italian saved them from torture. They
stayed with him for four months and six days (exiles in their own country); they huddled together in the library, and were only allowed to go
into the garden at night. From the adjoining rooms they could hear
voices, music, the ring of glasses, and laughter, but that had nothing to
do with them. They were underlings. The pale-faced youth wanted to run
away; he begged the others to let him go; he declared that he could get
to Poland. They would not let him go, since his capture might reveal
their hiding-place. They were allowed to play cards, to eat and drink, to
talk in whispers—they had permission to exist. One night the pale-faced
youth succeeded in climbing over the fence, but they pulled him back,
beat him, and imprisoned him in the empty attic. One of them, a red-
bearded man, had brought a yellow box to the castle with him; he
guarded it constantly, and kept it hidden. No one had the slightest inkling
of what was in the box, until the evening when the Italian, pale as death,
burst into the library and blurted out: "They're here; you must give
yourselves up!"

Thereupon the red-bearded man is said to have pounded upon the
table until the windows rattled, while the others began to laugh boister-
ously and to sing some rollicking song. The Italian ran away from them,
weeping; the pale-faced youth clasped his hands, knelt, and pleaded:
"Let me go, please let me go! I can crawl through the drain under the
garden wall!"

"You can go to hell now, you coward!"

He was still able to see the red-bearded man open the box with hammer and pincers. The box held weapons. They pounced upon the weapons as upon some prey; they were laughing no longer, only smiling,
they were no longer singing, no longer talking, they only fondled the
weapons. It was night when they ran out into the garden, but there
was a full moon. And it started immediately. The Germans opened fire
from three sides. The fourth side, that side of the garden under which
the drain ran, was unguarded; so the pale-faced youth was able to escape.
He got into Poland, and after a time, to us. But before he ran away he
saw the red-bearded man fall. He fell slowly, holding himself erect, facing forward, and firing twice as he fell. He saw the woman fall, too;
she was barely twenty-three, and very beautiful, just like a story-book
princess. The Italian was said to be in love with her (give ear, ye bards
and poets!). The pale-faced boy saw a strand of her golden hair blend

in tender union with a stream of living crimson on her brow. Shot in the forehead, she fell upon her knees, and thus remained, as if in prayer.

Hearken, all ye poets and all ye bards, hearken well to the outlaws, and then inscribe, on some eternal memorial, how our people died at home, and how, of six who saw death in a castle garden, somewhere near Prague, only one was afraid to die.

Vertigo is the disease in which we are writhing; vertigo, from the dizzying whirl of too many deeds compressed within too short a time; vertigo from the necromantic procession of facts and impressions.

Sometimes, at close of day, when I sit before my fire in the deepening dusk and listen to the lamentations of the widows, the orphans, the hungry, the lost and the wandering—familiar cries, which are akin to the wailing lament of a lost soul—the door seems to open noiselessly, and friends and kinsfolk from my home tiptoe in to see me. They seat themselves round about me on the chairs, on the edge of the bed, and even on the floor; they bow their heads and are silent. They have come from prisons, from confiscated homes, from plundered estates, from burned synagogues. When I fled from my native land I was not able to clasp their hands in farewell. What shall I say to them now? What shall I say? Why are they all silent? Are they reproaching me?

We sit in the dark. Outdoors the elements are raging. Terrifying stories flood the world; somewhere the bells are ringing an alarm; the laws in all the statute-books are topsy-turvy; nobody understands them; woe unto all men! A great storm is gathering, the most terrible storm that has ever come to pass, a storm such as is only visited upon a sinful land when the people thereof have burned and crucified the saints. My friends and relatives, my dearest ones, the hungry, the half frozen, the sick, the tortured, the demented, now lift their heads as in question and raise their eyes from the floor. The wind has ceased its wailing lament; it is I who am weeping now. What shall I say to them? What shall I say to my dearest ones?

When our frontier vanished they celebrated a shabby peace in this little country. When droves of humanity came flocking from our sunny hills into the weeping valleys they were dancing here and singing; our lamentations were shouted down by drunkards; there was no one to whom we could appeal, our desolate hearts found no confessor. And now this small country is hard hit; fear has beset it; the good fortune they sought to build upon our misfortune is passing away. The stuffed shirts are still sitting at laden tables, but the food sticks in their throats; the false prophets cry out in their sleep, the traitors seek alibis; who has given warning of the impending storm? Ah, those dissensions! Do you hear them, my dearest ones? They say the Ministers are to blame. The nations which did not defend themselves are to blame. Russia is to blame. They say England is to blame. The priests are to blame. Unfaithful wives, who broke the commandments, are to blame. Who is to blame? Who is guilty?

My dearest ones, why are you rising to your feet? Must you go? I know, you living dead, you are going forth to a battle in which poverty is your only weapon. You go without fear, without ignominy; I know, I know everything. See, I am no longer weeping, I am smiling now, for he who is your leader has never yet lost a battle.

Decay has hardly touched the fallen autumn leaves, and behold the spring is here again, with its blue sky. Now green whistles can be made of willow bark, and the primroses are in bloom. The silver snows of the worst winter known have at last melted away; forgotten is the silver in our hair, and spent, too, is the silver saved up for a final tip.

"You resemble my grandson, sir," says the old man who has been pushed into the doctor's waiting-room in a wheeled chair. "I am a Pole, sir; my grandson fell on the very first day of the war. My son died some time ago; I am the only man left of our whole family. I'm eighty-five; that's a good many years. I didn't want to leave my country, sir, but the women gave me no peace. There are too many women around me all the time. I find them a trial; they won't let me drink vodka; I mustn't eat this, I mustn't eat that; besides, they're always keeping things away from me. But now, sir, I'm glad I came away. I could never have survived what has happened back home, and I don't want to die yet; I still go on waiting, for it isn't possible that I left home never to see it again. Whatever should I say to Stanislaus then? That was my grandson's name. Do you think there's no reason for my outliving him? No, sir, there's reason for everything in this world; nothing happens by chance. I want to wait a little longer, perhaps a year or two, perhaps five. Since the good Lord has seen fit to visit me with so many afflictions, it is surely because I am to remember this and that, because I am to brood upon it, so that I may be able to say to Stanislaus: 'You had to go before your grandfather, my darling, so that you might not see the things that left the rest of us drained of tears. You see, my boy, I did not die of grief only because it has been decreed that I should live to see, like Job . . .' Well, sir, here they come to carry me to the doctor. This is my niece, sir, and this my daughter-in-law, both no longer chickens. Well, good-bye. No, indeed, I'm going to wait a bit longer, I don't want to die yet! Good-bye!"

His name is unknown to me. He did tell it to me, but I think he did not give me his right name. He comes from Vienna, and by the merest chance he left his country a few days before the occupation of Austria. I suspect that he is a poet, although he denied it. He has been ill for a long while here, and he was practically starving; and moreover, the police were always harassing him until recently. I think he has even been arrested. He volunteered for the Foreign Legion, but was turned down. I have shared my money with him, the money which you have sent me. He is getting along better now; he no longer goes about in rags, and even shaves occasionally.

We go walking along a country road not far from the city. Myriads of brooks are trickling all around us; the sky is one vast smile; our hearts are enamoured of its heavenly azure. He walks with a stick, and has a habit of gazing far into the distance when he is telling one anything.

"I cannot understand how people can be so irresponsible. Have you met a single person who has been anxious and terrified, even for a moment, at the thought that he himself, he alone, is the accomplice of the catastrophe that has befallen the world?"

"I could not have met such a person, because I meet no dictators or other rulers of the world."

He stopped, thrusting his stick into the ground with a quick, angry jerk, but did not take his eyes off the horizon.

"You don't really think that dictators, ministers, and generals rule the world?"

"Who then?"

He pulled his stick out of the ground and strode on. Quietly, but seriously, he answered: "Perhaps you or I."

Now it was I who stopped abruptly. Poor fellow! Why hadn't I noticed it before? I ought to see about getting him home as quickly as possible. Obviously one would have to be very careful in talking to him. When could this have begun?

"That's really a very interesting idea of yours."

"Don't think I'm joking!"

"God forbid! Then you believe that you or I may be to blame for all that has befallen the world? H'm! wouldn't you like to elucidate that a little farther?"

"That is very difficult to explain to anyone who believes that he lives for and by himself alone. I have never believed that; ever since I was a child I have felt . . . Listen . . . No, I don't care to talk about this; there's no sense in doing so. I should only seem very ridiculous to you."

"Go ahead, and tell me about it. Nothing seems ridiculous or impossible to me any more. You evidently think—if I understand you correctly —that you are somehow to blame for the collapse of Europe."

"To tell you the truth . . . yes! Look at it this way: I am guilty too, and it may be that my guilt is the last link in a chain of casual events. At the same time, my whole personal history does not coincide with politics in the least. Now, consider this; you must be familiar enough with the myths of the religious fanatics, according to whom there are upon this earth, a very small number of apparently ordinary people for whom alone the world exists, and upon whose shoulders the whole arch of heaven is supported. If a single one of these chosen people should stumble on his allotted path, the results would be terrible. I don't in the least believe that it is possible to discover the tracks of these chosen ones in the events of which we read through which we are living. I am firmly convinced that the real causes of the appalling complex of events are concealed from us; that Napoleon and his wars need never have been, had it not been for some—well, let us say—some unknown barmaid in a tavern somewhere, and for some incident in her life, some incident even less known to the world than she herself. Do you understand?"

"Not a bit. About what barmaid are you talking?"

"It might not have been a barmaid; it might have been a chimney-sweep, or a miller; how do I know? Do you think that He who makes the world revolve and directs the fate of humanity cares about emperors and generals? Nonsense! He is more likely to be concerned about a country schoolteacher, the hunchbacked child of drunken parents, or some crazy poet. Believe me, the world still revolves upon its axis for the chosen unknown, and it is because of their sins that States are shattered and cities burned, and it will only be because of their repentance that in due time there will be peace upon earth once more to men of good will."

"Then you . . . If you'll forgive me . . . then you think of yourself as . . . you think you are one of the chosen ones?"

"Yes. You need not be afraid of me (and a sad smile flitted over his face). I'm otherwise perfectly harmless. My life has been a very happy one; whatever I have touched has prospered. I was dependent upon good fortune; I depended on luck as every spoiled darling depends upon the indulgence of his benefactors. I was forgiven much; far more than others, for my many little knaveries, lies, and deceptions were hard to prove.

But I also committed a crime, and that likewise was hard to prove. Even while I was contemplating this crime I knew that I should be punished. I had been warned, I had been admonished; every time I opened a newspaper or a book the first words that met my eyes cautioned me. But I did it in spite of everything. I wanted to get rid of my wife and marry a younger and prettier woman. Weeks and months went by, and still my wife and I were living together, living together like a murderer and his chosen victim. Surely every time she looked into my eyes she must have seen that I wanted to kill her! Nevertheless, I managed to keep on friendly terms with her; I smiled at her now and then, I seemed to be anxious and attentive when she was ill. It would have been better if I had killed her and had atoned for the crime in jail. But I was too great a coward; besides, I knew that the world would come to an end if I touched even a hair of her head. I did not ask her to divorce me; I only hinted, half in jest and wholly in earnest, that she was standing in the way of my happiness. She was such a small, shy, good woman; she never lied, she was always pottering about in the kitchen, or straightening out the linen cupboard. Although we had a servant, she washed up the dishes, mended my socks, and never wanted to go the theatre; for, as she said, we are not out to squander our money. She used to help me on with my coat, poor thing; she did all that she could to hold me. As a girl she had had many admirers, and I had striven hard to win her for myself—why had I wronged her so? How did it happen? One day I came home drunk. I tripped over the rug in the hall; I switched on the light and looked into the mirror—my hat was on askew, my mouth twisted. How well I remember it; the white door of the bathroom was half open; the water from the shower was dripping into the bath. I went into our room; on the right was a bookcase, on the left a sofa, made up as a bed. My wife was sitting on the sofa, fully dressed; she was waiting for me. 'I'll tell her now,' flashed through my brain. She understood, and quietly said: 'Tell me!'

"'See here, you must go away; I simply can't stand you, we can't go on like this . . .'"

"She rose and walked out of the room, like a mechanical doll. Her cheeks were bloodless, her mouth wide open, but she did not cry until she got into the bathroom. She forgot to close the door. I could hear her sobbing; I heard her strike her head against the wall. Something within me cried out, desperately: 'There is still time. Hurry after her, crush her in your arms, beg her forgiveness! There's still time!' But I didn't stir. She went away that night, and I have never seen her again;

I have never known where or how she is living. I didn't ask the lawyer who arranged the divorce. She refused to accept alimony.

"I was very unhappy in my second marriage; my new wife deceived me from the very beginning. I said to myself: This is your punishment. But I had a premonition that something worse was coming, that the world would be shaken to its depths for what I had done.

"Just think, man! Three years later, chance brought me to this country, where I didn't know a soul. I came here to see a sick friend about something; his relatives here persuaded me to stay with them in their country house while I was here. They themselves lived on the ground floor; I was to have the first floor. Splendid! And now just listen to this! They gave me a key. I went upstairs, opened the door, tripped over the rug, and looked about me. Overcome with horror, my feet gave way under me, for I was standing in my former home, in the same rooms from which I had driven my wife. A round mirror, just like the one we had at home, hung in the hall. My eyes stared back at me from the mirror; I could see that my hat was askew, and my mouth twisted, just as then. I turned round—the white door of the bathroom was half open, and water from the shower was dripping into the bath. Still carrying my bag, I staggered across the threshold into the room; yes—a bookcase on the right, a sofa on the left, but no one was sitting on the sofa. I let my bag fall to the floor with a thud; I staggered on; I sat down on the bed; and at that moment the invisible radio announcer was shouting from somewhere: ALL TELEPHONE CONNECTIONS DOWN! GERMAN SOLDIERS ARE ENTERING VIENNA!

"My first thought was: I cannot go home!

"I got up; I was gasping, and pale as death, and I went, as she had gone, into the bathroom, not closing the door behind me. There I beat my head against the wall and wailed; but no one heard me, no one came to help me. I called my wife's name again and again, but in vain, a thousand times in vain. The world is collapsing, the world is tottering, and I know that I am a fellow accomplice."

The rain beating across the windows again. Here I sit, writing to you, my friend. This may be my last letter to you, or the last but one. I think I shall soon be leaving this country; and for that matter, you will soon be leaving your native land. Shall we still be able to write to each other? Shall we ever see each other again?

I looked out of the window a little while ago and watched the passers-by. I found them ugly. I did not like their ears. The ear is really a very ugly appendage, don't you think so? It seems to me, sometimes, that people are actually uglier than rats. No doubt this is because of the vertigo in which we are writhing, and because it is so long since I have kissed anyone, so long since anyone has embraced me. The distance between my dearest ones and myself is continually increasing. There are so many words in the vocabulary of love and beauty that we have never yet used in speaking to one another.

Shall we not forget these words before we meet again, before this vertigo passes? We must not forget them; we dare not . . . for these are the words that alone can redeem the world.

Translated from the Czech by ANN KRIIL

Vítězslav Nezval

NIGHT OF ACACIAS

TWO OR THREE days of love has life: then this withered tree hangs full
  of a thousand bees and blossoms,
Like the one night in June when the acacias bloom and die.
The river is wearing a chaplet of lights and is fragrant with embalmed
  bathers,
The streets are suddenly wide and sparkling like beauty shops
From beyond the river over hanging bridges, with a rosary of lights,
Invisible gardens are on the march, colliding with walkers;
They're off to their rendezvous with the parks and the alleys of the
  central squares and main streets.
Benumbed I do not recognise the old streets of the New City
Whose plain and graceless walls are to-day majestic as palace courts.

O night of acacias, of fountains and of that treacherous pianissimo, stay,
Make me for ever yearn for love and for Prague;
O night at the end of June, short-lived as passionate love, as sensual
  delight.

O night of acacias, do not pass before I have crossed all the bridges of
  Prague
In my search for no one, not a friend, not a woman, not even myself.

O night with summer in your wake, I long to breathe unendingly your
  ebon hair;

Your diamonds have bewitched me, I want to look for them in the waters,
  poor fisherman that I am.

Oh, if at least I could say au revoir to you,
O night in June,
If I were never to see you again,
Let me dissolve in your embrace, my evil fate, my love.

PANORAMA OF PRAGUE

LIKE BERETS thrown into the air,
Berets of boys, cocottes and cardinals,
Turned into stone by the sorcerer Zito
At the great feast;
Berets with Chinese lanterns
On the eve of St. John's Day
When fireworks are let off—

Yet also like a town of umbrellas opened skyward as shields against
  rockets:

All this is Prague.

Leaning over a wall
I want to break this twig of wonderful blossoms.

My eyes drink in the lights of the great merry-go-round
Whose ringing chimes are calling homeward
All its barges and stray horses,
Whose ringing chimes are calling homeward
All sparks of light.

Translated from the Czech by EWALD OSERS

Ivan Olbracht

NIKOLAI ŠUHAJ, THE BRIGAND

WHEN THE WRITER of this book was collecting stories in the home of
Nikola Šuhaj about this *invulnerable* man who used to take from the rich

and give to the poor, and who never killed anybody, except in self-defence, or out of righteous revenge, the testimony of so many respectable and trustworthy people gave him no reason to doubt but that Šuhaj's invulnerability was caused by a green twig, by waving which he drove away the policemen's bullets as a farmer drives away swarming bees on a July day.

For in this country of woods, crinkled up by mountains like a piece of paper which we are about to throw into the fire, things still happen at which we smile foolishly only because for centuries they have ceased to happen with us. In this country of hills upon hills, and ravines within ravines, where in the decay and dusk of the forests the springs are being born and the ancient maples die, there are still enchanted places from which no stag, no bear, no man has ever got away. The streamers of the morning mists dragging their way wearily over the crowns of the fir trees upwards into the mountains are processions of frozen men, and the clouds floating above the gullies are evil curs with gaping mouths which will drop down beyond the mountain to do harm to someone. And below, in the narrow valleys of the rivers, in the villages which are green with maize and yellow with the sunflowers, werewolves live which after having rolled over a log in the evening, after nightfall, change from men into wolves, and towards morning from wolves back into men; here on moonlight nights young witches chase about on horses into which they have changed their sleeping husbands, and you need not search for hags in windy valleys, beyond seven hills and seven rivers, but you can easily meet the evil ones on pasture lands while they are dropping salt into three cattle footmarks to make the cows go dry, and the good ones you can visit at any time in their cottages and call them from breaking hemp to charm away a snake bite, or, in a bath made from an infusion of nine herbs, to make a sickly child into a strong one.

Here God is still alive. In the oppressive silence of the forests the old God of the earth still lives who embraces the hills and dales, who plays with bears in the thickets, fondles the heifers which have fled from their herds, and who loves the horn of the herdsmen, calling the cattle in the evening. He breathes into the crowns of the old trees, he drinks water from the springs out of the hollow of his hand, he shines from the night fires on the pastures, he sways the rustling leaves of the maize fields and nods the yellow discs of the sunflowers. The ancient pagan God, master of woods and of the herds, who refuses to have anything to do with that other proudly pompous God who lives in gold and silk behind the multi-coloured screens of the iconostases, nor with that sulky old man who hides behind the shabby little curtains of the puryoches in the synagogues.

＊　　＊　　＊

In the narrow valleys, on the slopes where the woods have left a tiny bit of space for the meadows, or above on the tableland men are living. They live in huts similar to the houses perched on chickens' feet,＊ or, if grouped together, to a family of mushrooms under the birch trees. The men smell of the wind, and the women of the smoke of their huts. They are shepherds and woodsmen, for they have still not reached the farming stage, and a plough has not yet been seen in these parts. The descendants of shepherds who had fled into these inaccessible hills before the inroads of the Tartar khans into the Ukrainian plain, the great-grandsons of the rebellious serfs who had fled from the whips and the gallows of the sheriffs and the atamans of Master Josef Potocky, the great-grandsons of men who had rebelled against the exploitation of the Roumanian bojars, Turkish pashas and Hungarian magnates, fathers, brothers and sons of the men killed in the slaughterhouses of the Austrian emperors. And all of them at the bottom of their hearts brigands. For this is the only kind of defence they know. A defence which is helpful: for a week, for a month, for a year; for two years as with Nikola Šuhaj, for seven as with Oleksa Dovbuš. What does it matter that it is dear, costing nothing less than a life? Is life eternal after all? Only once did your mother bear you; once only do you die. And in every little blood cell of their veins there is a dim recollection of past injuries and a burning consciousness of present wrongs, and in every one of their nerves is a wild desire for liberty. It is Dovbuš's desire. Šuhaj's desire. For that they are loved.

Translated from the Czech by M. WEATHERALL

Vladislav Vančura

IN MY END IS MY BEGINNING

THE OLD THINGS are coming to an end. All that was big is made small, fires are larceny, the executioner's axe is a laughing stock, bread is eaten up, and the bruised head of nations is leaning to one side.

The working day is coming, the star and the new era, for from the end of the war, as from the creation of the world, the years will be numbered.

＊ A conception taken from a Slav fairy tale.

The first, the second, the third, and so unto thousands!

Wars will drop through the spider's web. The time of dominion is broken up, and the time of the workers begins. Fires and blood, like mountains and seas, will divide the two periods. You hastened as you turned up the soil, sowed and reaped, you built towns like God, and made silk like the silkworm, but the work was ravaged, and wailing for bread never ceased for a minute. Well then, from here, from this chasm, from the mountains of war, a new campaign is beginning, the vast and most glorious expedition of labour.

The wars are lost. A trumpet is a braggart's sound, voice of revolt, and the pressing of rebellion make themselves heard in every man. Once in the middle of summer, with cursed zeal you were beating up rags for the winter camp. You stood the men drinks, and you called them by their Christian names. You yourselves pressed army caps upon their heads, but now you have grown wise, and the times are different. You know what to say to people who search for deserters in the attics. You have learned loyalty, and nothing is now in the way for you to start the age from the beginning, except for one thing. Except for the jargon of the rabble.

The worker's tongue is labour.

The soil which barely covers the porphyry, gneiss, and quartz in the regions of the Middle Vltava, the shallow arable soil and the pinch of clay on the western slopes which have no name, the rock bottom of dullness, the floor of misery, is by far not so mean for the woods not to spring from it. They will rise just as speech originates during long silence before it breaks out in sound.

The old generation of workers and the newcomers will rebel under the blows and the lashes, the coppery cloud of silence will be split by lightning.

The bars of misery are broken, and the cramped range is opening into space. It will be pierced by cheerful roads from North to South and from East to West. Time, oscillating and returning like a clock pendulum, was pulled down by the terrible movement of the war. The veil of the temple is rent in twain, and the epoch of the Old Testament is at an end.

Except for the nations of workers the world would be a waste. Let the songs shouted from the deep be silent; the jeering, curses, and terrible jests. Let the ruffled mane of the world lie down; let Golgotha reaching to the icebergs be swept away, let nothing of the past step into the new year.

The last soldier of the World War, the murderer who was not tried, is listening. His face striped by the worms like a tiger's, and his weeping wound, are gazing up, waiting for the glorious mound over his grave to be swept away.

Translated from the Czech by M. WEATHERALL

Jiří Wolker

DYING

WHEN I SHALL die there'll be no sign in all this world, and nothing changed,
Only the hearts of some will quiver like flowers at morning in the dew.
Thousands are dead and thousands are dying, thousands are longing for death to come,
For in dying as in birth no one has ever been alone.
Death does not fright me, death is not evil, death's but a harder fragment of life,
The thing which is so dread, so evil, that is dying.
When the senses, shot on the wing, are falling, falling, falling,
And in rusting veins of the body time rots as it dies away,
Hands are relaxed, and eyes, and nerves, and every sinew
Wherewith the world in your arms you caught and clasped and loved.
Death does not fright me, death is not evil, in death I am not alone.
Dying is what I fear, when each is abandoned—and I am dying.

Translated from the Czech by DORA ROUND

František Halas

DEAD SOLDIER

UPON THE MANTLE of his blood he lies;
His face—that mask—has been torn off by fear;
A magic key has opened his lifeless eyes.

He's held in bondage by mysterious chains
And of the stars he drinks the adder's milk;
For food he eats the grass his own blood stains.

Around him helpless souls by storms are driven
And fall like scattered chaff upon his brow;
Wingless and crippled they are seeking heaven.

Into a fold of God his own soul slips;
From time to time it flies down, deep in thought;
He smiles at it, a worm between his lips.

IT IS TIME

SILENT AND STERN your lips together press.
Our faith is well-nigh spent and from the world
We're drawn apart by dreams of loveliness.

In swooning sweetness all our words must end
In this dim age of wavering indecision;
Our lives in words too often yet we spend.

If only could come crashing down in thunder
The grief of masses piled up to the stars,
And all my hapless race lie buried under.

Translated from the Czech by EWALD OSERS

Josef Hora

AUTUMN

THE SILVER EVENING in the coolness woke;
The maidens' voices on the wind it threw.
The sickle of the moon stooped down to stroke
Hair that the darkness lightly touched with dew.

The lapping waves, the voices in the night,
A shadow thrown behind a screen of light,

A mirror on whose surface Autumn seems
To breathe the silver ashes of my dreams.

Translated from the Czech by EWALD OSERS

Ernst Weiss

CARDIAC SUTURE

THE MEDICAL STUDENT Friedrich von B. was a tall, blond young man passionately in love with Major Surgery—but not at all loath to love others too, among whom a certain Hildegard Anneliese had played a large, if recently not always pleasant part. Early in December he became an unpaid assistant in the Surgical Department of Geheimrat O., whom the students, because of his military bearing and imposing presence, called "the General"—an appointment aided by the fact that the professor and the student's father were fraternity brothers.

In the university clinic, without getting much attention from his father's friend at first, Friedrich von B. performed many small but indispensable and responsible services, such as general anesthesia, dressings, minor operations. Often, of course, he just stood idly about awaiting orders, or he presented patients at the lectures which took place between 9:15 and 11 A.M., weekdays.

On one such occasion, on January 17, the professor lectured on malignant tumors. He proudly pointed out his permanent successes: cases on which he had operated three and five years since; even that of a patient from the start of his teaching and operating career in town, not less than seven-and-a-half years ago, who like the rest had remained in good health, without recurrence of symptoms. The operations had been serious ones, and it was a surgical triumph that the cures had lasted so long—the blessing of quick, radical measures.

The old patients had been recalled to the clinic by mail, and those who lived out of town received a mileage fee for travel expenses.

Now they were perched on a bench in the broad corridor leading from the wards to the auditorium. Five were men, three were women; four came from the city and as many from the flat countryside. Although the First Associate had forbidden them to talk of their diseases (a general prohibition for all patients in the hospital) they had now talked of nothing else for an hour. Some had pulled their shirts up to show off their scars, while others merely indicated the place and length of the incisions from outside—exaggerating the length. Then, smoothing their clothes, they proudly followed the student into the auditorium and one of the women broke out in a sweat, because in the hurry she could not get her gloves on fast enough.

The General reveled in surgical optimism. He compared the recovered patients' fate with that of others stricken with the same disease and now long resting in the cool earth, while he held the shoulders of a frail, elderly woman between his huge arms and moved her about, right and left, like a little doll. Then he quickly turned away from the woman, and with simple lines drew the diagram of the operation on a blackboard for the students, holding the piece of chalk in his right hand and the chart, on which all required data were listed and which the Associate had handed him, in his left. Then, with impeccable delivery, he described the advances in operational technique, critically illuminated the good and bad sides of each method, calcuated the prognosis with the aid of careful statistics and forgot entirely that the eight people concerned were standing in the auditorium—which also served as operating room, by the way.

He was still deeply absorbed by his surgical observations when suddenly the old Associate, Professor E., rushed in and whispered something into his ear. The excitement spread at once to the surgeon and appeared in his face, which looked as if bathed in vermilion with only the old duelling scars of his youth standing out more brightly, cherry-red. A steep crease formed on the General's forehead, a sign of acute reflection, while the Associate herded the eight healed ones out of the hall like a small flock of poultry.

The professor immediately turned on the water at a basin reserved for his use; he turned upside down the hour-glass that stood on a glass shelf. The brown sands started trickling, to indicate ten minutes: the prescribed duration of hand-washing and personal asepsis.

The student helped to dress the General for the operation. The General was talking and washing by turns, while a big, yellow waterproof apron was tied with a brass chain round the bull-neck that was as vermilion as his face; without looking, he stepped into black galoshes that came up above his ankles.

Instantly, the academic instructor had become a different person. His voice, his bearing, his very glance were different. With the hard brush he scrubbed his fingers, palms and the backs of his hands, and his forearms up to the elbow. By foot pressure he took soap from an automatic container, and soon the arms were covered with white lather. Then everything was rinsed off; the skin, of an increasingly vivid red, reappeared, only to vanish again in the froth.

By his side, the assistants did exactly likewise.

Now the General turned to the audience:

"Lucky, unfortunately rare, coincidence. Suicide attempt near the hospital. A young woman, a young girl. Stab into the heart. A cardiac suture, I expect. Modern operation. Antiquated suicide instrument: an old-fashioned penholder with a common steel pen. Office girl. One relatively favorable circumstance, gentlemen—the ominous object has remained in the wound and so kept her from bleeding to death. Luck in disaster.

"Quite an achievement, by the way, to hit the heart with such a primitive weapon. The method which I now hope that all of you, and that includes the gentlemen in the top rows (I only urgently request everyone to remain seated, the dust is terrible and highly dangerous) —anyway, the method which I now hope to demonstrate is new, and remains one of the many, extraordinarily great merits of the late Professor Rehn in Frankfurt. First assistantship to you, Mr. Associate E., as usual; second, Mr. Glicker, with the third going to Mr. Schillerling; anesthesia might be given by the young man here—one of your colleagues, gentlemen, who already anesthetizes quite nicely. In cases like this we need a very good anesthesia—nota bene: hyper-pressure anesthesia, because after all, the thing happens within the chest cavity.

"As I said, for some years now we are no longer helpless against heart injuries. Since Rehn, we can attack punctured—in fact, though of course only in the rarest cases, even shot wounds of the heart—we can attack anything of the kind, provided, gentlemen, that the patient gets onto our table here alive. Out of five cases operated on in time, no less than three will recover. No doubt but that the Archduke, the Austrian heir-presumptive, if his heart injury in Sarajevo at the time—well, let's drop this painful chapter; Head Nurse, have sodium chloride solution heated, prepare adrenalin, solution 1:1000—yes, I just wanted to say we have methods against any kind of injury, but we have no method yet against the murderers. We stitch up the wound, but we don't heal the heart. Pulse to be checked by the anesthetist. Don't forget to bring the rib dilator; in fact, all bone instruments.

"The indication is simple in such cases: you start operating as soon as you've got the patient. Prompt aid is decisive. Although there isn't a second to be lost, where have you got our patient? Bring her right in to us; formalities and red tape are unnecessary; I operate even without the consent of the patients—often dazed in such cases—or relatives who haven't the faintest notion. All that doesn't matter here. Up and at 'em—but not without strictest observance of the rules of asepsis. We ask no quarter; we must and we shall stick exactly to the rules of asepsis, for we are about to open one of the most sensitive parts of the body, always prone to suppuration: the thorax and the pericardium. Well, here she is. Come on! Careful! Gently!"

The tall, light-blond, somewhat light-minded student of medicine, Friedrich von B., saw again Hildegard Anneliese who had played a large, if not always pleasant part in his most recent past.

Instruments were being sterilized on several electrically-heated little stoves. Thick steam rose from the small kettles and evaporated in the amphitheater. Though it was close to noon, the auditorium was gloomy. "Light," said the General. Lamps, set in rows beneath the ceiling, hissed up and a shadowless, all but pure white light fell on the operating table, the professor and his aides, and on the bottom rows of seats in the audience. A clock, the dial of which had been only indistinctly visible, now showed not quite two minutes after eleven. The General was silent. No sound was heard except the bubble of the seething water, the silvery tinkle of the instruments moving about in it and the murmuring breath of the listeners.

The would-be suicide moaned dully. She did not scream; she seemed to hold her breath back, as every movement of her chest was painful. In the depths before them, brightly illuminated by the lamps on the ceiling, the students saw her face—framed in tumbled, moist, dark-blond hair, the upper lip drawn far over the lower, moist too. The light-grey eyes were shut tightly, then torn open again; the lids trembled, the irises shifted restlessly from one corner of the eye to the other. Scissors had already cut the clothes from the upper part of the body and a light gauze veil was spread over it; in one place the veil rose to a sharp point, and this place moved rhythmically.

Silence reigned. The General and the assistants had ceased scrubbing arms and hands with their brushes and were looking at the patient.

It seemed as though it were midnight. Stillness. Nothing but the hiss of the water, the gurgling of the sterilizers, the hiss of the lamps and the muffled moans recurring with each exhalation.

The General had signaled to the head nurse. Gently, as if afraid to hurt the other woman, she removed the gauze veil with a sterile forceps. One saw the penholder under the patient's left breast; it bobbed with every heartbeat, as if depressed to a downstroke by an invisible force and rising again so as to trace a hairstroke.

"Above all," said the General, resuming the brush treatment of his already lobster-red arms with particular intensity, "above all you see that consciousness remains quite unaffected. Aside from shock—only too natural in such cases. And: no hemorrhage. External bleeding has ceased. Ought to have been inappreciable, anyway."

His muscular male arm, gleaming like polished metal in the glare, waved the student Friedrich von B. closer to the sufferer.

"All right. Go ahead. Anesthesia."

The student shrugged his shoulders. He was trembling all over with horror and had to strain every nerve to control himself. For hyper-pressure anesthesia he needed a special apparatus which should have been there long ago. It had been moved to another room, however, for a small adjustment, and now that every second counted it was missing, and nobody dared tell the chief.

Large drums of nickel-plate with coats, caps, towels, rubber gloves and dressings were swiftly opened by nurses. Working in pairs, they took out white, square sheets, opened them and spread them under the patient whom the head nurse lifted up with infinite tenderness. Below the waist, the body was covered with sheets; only the upper part of the torso remained free, and the face, growing paler by the second. The hands were strapped down. A broad belt was drawn over the thighs.

Nine minutes had run off in the hour glass. The rustling big sieves with the instruments were taken from the seething water. Vapor steamed up in huge clouds. On small wheel-tables, the head nurse deftly sorted the metal gear in systematic, orderly rows: similar instruments next to each other, larger ones to the right, smaller ones to the left. Scissors, straight and curved, four-fingered hooks, bone forceps, clamps, small pincers, needle-holders, boxes with sickle-shaped needles and others with straight needles, silk and catgut thread rolled onto glass spools and arranged according to thickness.

The sands had all but run out of the upper glass; the student gazed about the room but as yet the anesthesia apparatus hadn't arrived. The gurgle of the water ceased abruptly.

"Iodine," said the surgeon.

Now, in the last second, the contrivance rolled in—a complicated contrivance. The rust-colored tank with the rust-colored faucet was the oxygen tank; the blue one with the blue faucet held carbon dioxide and the green faucet adduced the narcotic. Gleaming pressure-gauges and clear glass cylinders filled with liquids served to check every breath.

While the professor was helped into his surgical whites—white coat, white cap, white mask—the student held the reddish, closely adhering rubber mask over the young girl's nose and mouth. Great pearls of the narcotic, mixed with air, trickled through a transparent glass vessel.

"Breathe deeply. Breathe deeply," the student told the girl in a toneless voice. The girl shook her head silently, stubbornly. With feeble motions she pushed the mask away from her as best she could. The mask followed her, but the pale face squirmed and sought to get away from it. She opened her mouth, she wanted to scream, she wanted to fight. But not a word, never anything but the same long drawn-out dull moan came from the bloodless, skin-colored lips.

"Iodine," the General repeated, donning rubber gloves. A metallic purplish brown, daubed on the operating field with a broad piece of gauze, now covered the two breasts, the entire skin as high as the region of the throat and down to the navel.

In the center of the brown field bobbed the penholder—wearier now, faster and weaker, as if scribbling—driven by the helplessly trembling heart. The breath, distinct until now, became shallower. The eyes were wide open, despairingly but clearly roving through space.

Incredible, that a human being so badly hurt was still clear in its mind, that it knew what it was doing, what it was suffering.

Already the General's face showed the peculiar, almost gay, virtually relaxed expression indicating that he had thought the course of the operation through to the last detail, taking into consideration all possible complications, so that nothing remained but the technical execution—but why was the patient still awake?

She was really almost livelier now than before, with her eyes seeking and at last finding those of her former lover.

Not a second to be lost, the student thought; it must be. But what should he tell her; how was he to make her understand, how to make her see reason, what could he remind her of? Whose fault was it? Who can make up for it—two minutes before death? Eleven o'clock and twelve minutes.

"And the pulse?" the General asked.

The medical student groped at the girl's soft, beautiful throat, the lines of which were familiar to him from times long past. Gently, with the tips of his index and second fingers, he touched the moist, soft, lukewarm skin.

"Nothing at the carotid. I can feel nothing at the carotid."

But the girl had felt his hand. Did she love him still? Did she want to live again? Did she repent? Was she still the one she had been a few minutes ago?

Her eyelids suddenly closed; the long lashes came close together and formed a dense, dark-blond line all but brass-colored in the glaring light.

The lips opened softly; milk-white teeth, set in gums of a pale coral red, appeared as the student lifted the mask an instant. She was breathing toward him, drawing in the ether air in hurried, shallow breaths. Thirteen minutes past eleven.

"All right, we'll start anyway. Is she asleep? Not yet? Doesn't matter. Life is primary, anesthesia secondary. War is war. Up and at 'em. Keep the head quite low—avoid cerebral anemia, above all supply the respiration center, medulla oblongata. The blood issuing from the wound presses on the heart from outside and congests in the pericardium. Heart tamponade, this was called by our genius Ernst Bergmann. Still a little lower—good, enough."

The table had been lowered soundlessly by a hydraulic mechanism. The student felt the girl's head, covered with moist, silken hair, descend on his knees. Was she alive? Did she suffer? She was no longer moaning. Was she asleep? Was she awake? Was she dead?

"All right now, please."

From a gleaming, alcohol-filled crystal bowl the First Associate took a thin nickel scalpel bent like the fin of a fish, with a blue-glistening steel blade. The General seized the upper end almost as a painter grips his brush, and with the blade, as though merely experimenting with the design of an arabesque, he drew a curved line starting between the two breasts and circling the left one at its lower rim. The line was drawn in a pale red, as if breathed onto the skin. No real drop of blood. The assistants gripped the wound edges with their hooks from above and below, and pulled them far apart. The patient moaned, then fell silent. The student gave ether. The knife disappeared from the surgeon's hand—you did not see how—and now the instruments in his right alternated between large and small, sharp and blunt, cutting and solving, grasping and releasing ones.

The hands of the surgeon and his aides were stuck into tight, reddish gloves of thinnest rubber, so tightly clinging to the fingers that the nail contours were visible through them. In the operating field nothing was seen but the one big, long-fingered hand of the General, whose every move seemed lax and casual but was in fact made with exact, methodical precision. The other hands were busy holding the wound edges, passing instruments or sponges and carrying out all sorts of supporting measures which the General directed mostly with his eyes, using his voice only for the most important commands. What he was saying was rather addressed to the listeners and intended to make them understand the course of his operation.

"You notice that there is virtually no hemorrhage. Unfortunately. Blood pressure is infinitesimal. Careful with the anesthesia. Better let her moan —just as much as is absolutely necessary, so she won't wake up. She's still under the influence of shock, will hardly feel pain. We hear a rustle in the subcutaneous tissue: air emanates, squeezed out of the injured thorax. What to do? We shall remove a piece of the breast-bone here; here we'll fold up the ribs. We make a gateway to the heart, a sort of a door. That means we must sever two, three, in fact a good four ribs—handling the periosteum with care, because later all this must grow together again. It does that quite easily. Keep your heads away—no germ must get in! Now more pressure for the anesthesia, please. Just a trace of ether and plenty of oxygen. Now we're engaging the enemy. Grip the suicide instrument from outside, with a forceps—just hold it like that. And here we go after it—this is the way the pen went, you can still see the ink marks. Now we mobilize it—twist a little from outside, good! Now, pull—gently, stronger, more energetically—good! It's out. Good, take it away to the collection. There's idiocy for you; a desperate person takes anything that happens to be handy. Now for the ribs; look out now; rib scissors—yes, put it there, cautiously—first a finger underneath, now I press through, and now we pass on to the next. Finger underneath, and hold the whole skin-and-bone flap upward, cautiously, without force. One, two, and another one— one, two, ruck-ruck, keep going but don't slip—hold the flap quite still, damn it, take it easy, so, easy, ea-sy—good!"

The student von B. held his hand over the girl's mouth; he could scarcely feel her breath.

"Don't lift the mask! Hyper-pressure must stay. She's breathing all right, don't worry; we know better up here, we can see the lungs expand. Just check the anesthesia; we have to take it as it comes. Watch it! Here's the pericardium. All right, forward! Sharp clamp. Clamp. Larger one. Smaller one! Medium size, damn it—pay attention and twist the thing outward a little! Another, and another, and so forth without a lot of talk! Here is the wound in the pericardium, serrated, zig-zag—that's the way it must have gone through; not a simple cut, of course, because at the moment of the injury the pericardium tightened and turned, as at every heart-beat. Hollow probe—we want to get inside, we want to get deeper and deeper!"

The probe, a finger-like instrument of nickeled steel, ribbed lengthwise, slipped smoothly through the wound into the dark, bloody depths.

"All right. Hold the probe down, please. Now the scissors on top of it, please—straight ones are best—yes, and support it below; hold the probe exactly below the scissors. One cut! That's good. And now first of all a clear view! All full of blood clots. That must be removed. We'll clean it out. Wipe off, lightly—don't rub on the pericardium, it doesn't like that. Now we have a clear view but it won't last long; we must see the wound without delay. It may be right before our eyes, but it doesn't have to be there, either. Where does it bleed? Where does it bleed from? Pretty gory, that. Sponge, please. Head up—only I must see; get out of my way! Sponge, don't touch it with your hand, just sponge with the forceps— gently—more energetically—gently, I said; gently and energetically at the same time, and don't rub, don't scrub! Watch it! Go on! Soon we'll see daylight. How's the pulse? Anything there? Nothing? Well, give her sodium chloride solution, as much as possible—blood would be better, a blood transfusion; would take too long, though; we'd have to have the blood group first, takes too long—inject physiological sodium chloride solution into the cubital vein at the elbow, as much as will go in! Life substitute, blood illusion! And one of the gentlemen determines the blood group in the laboratory—have we got a donor, then? You gave us blood once, Mr. B., what's your blood group? Watch it—just for another hundred seconds. Quiet! Forward, fixation of the heart. With the heart leaping around like that we can't do anything. It has to be kept still. It must come out of its lair. Out, I say, you coward! We have to hold it quite still, and we must have it accessible if we want to stitch it up. So; sutures up for fixation. Yes, a thread like that will do—thin silk, curved needle, this size will do. Give it to me, why the fooling around, don't thread it too short after the eye and give me the needle-holder right away and you hold the pericardium clear and you take up the end of the thread, so it doesn't drag. Here, you see, I puncture the serous peri- and epi-cardium —left ventricle, apex—going in, and here I come right out again; now we have a loop, the brother here will hold it for us; and the same again a little higher up and a bit to the right, and one more loop over to the side—like this, you see, I catch the cardiac muscle with the needle, in, through, out, needle away, ends together, and it's all done. Pick the thread up—and now out with the heart, cautiously, from its cave. It bleeds? Let it bleed. Of course it bleeds. Lift it up. Faster, higher—more gently! Still a little more, perhaps. Don't be scared—over to the side, like this. On this heart wall: nothing. Nothing here, either. All right, now the other side. Lift it up a little, please, and over to the right. Hold it—and sponge again, very lightly, without pressure. Stop! Stop!

"Here we are. Here's the wound. Finger in the wound, you—finger *at* the wound, I mean. Hold the wound edges together, very gently, yield with your hand as the heart beats! Like this; good. But we want to see something, too! Don't press. Enough. It's good, it's all right. Well, and now on to the heart suture. Same silk as before. First suture crosswise. Left wound edge, right wound edge, out with the thread, make a knot, hang the thread on a clamp to be held off, like that. In order. Caught the top layers. Doctor, you take over the suture and hold the heart wall a bit toward me—no, a bit over to the right, and always yield to the heart movements. Good. Second suture. A little deeper, to be on the safe side. In, out, make a knot, pull it tight slowly, equally from both sides, and hang the thread up again. Hemorrhage is fading, but that isn't enough. Anything stir at the pulse? Not yet? How's the breath? Wretched? Just keep calm. Keep your hand away. Third suture. Got it. Hemorrhage has stopped. The heart wound is closed. Scissors—cut the threads of the three sutures. Not too short. But no tail, either! No. Good. A fourth? No, that will do. Leave it alone. The suture is solid enough; it will hold even when the blood pressure rises and the vessels fill up normally. Pulse? No? It'll come. It'll come all right. Man lives if the heart lives. You can see how the heart muscle recovers evidently, beats get more marked, it contracts and dilates properly—not like the hysterical trembling and fluttering of a while ago. That was in extremis, you might well say. Good—just keep giving sodium chloride into the arm vein, but don't disturb us up here and don't come too close to us with the filthy stuff. Relax the heart rein, pull the threads out, everything in its proper order. You see how the heart muscle tears at the three reins, like a fresh colt; it is gaining strength before our eyes. Good, and the pulse? Hardly tangible. We'll fix that all right! Hand us the adrenalin now, we'll shoot her the injection right into the heart. Good. Got it. Well?"

"The pulse is—back. I think."

"We think so too. Respiration?"

In a glass tube of the anesthesia apparatus the student saw pearls of exhaled air rising in a silvery, increasingly vivid stream.

"Going all right," he said.

"Now to close the pericardium. We'll take catgut for that. For the heart we didn't dare; silk is safer. But the pericardium doesn't have to stand that enormous pressure. It'll work, it'll be all right. Now we put the ribs back into their old position; the periosteum we sew up quickly with a few stitches. Glass tube under the skin; here, down at the bottom. Muscle—fascial closure of the wound, that is to say: skin suture, fine silk, just a few stitches. Anesthesia?"

"Off for some time."

"Good. From now on pure oxygen, three and a half, four liters—by and by. And camphor for safety's sake. Keep the head low, up in the ward too. Blood transfusion only if required. Rather yes than no. Which blood group? A? And you, Mr. B.?"

"Also A."

"Couldn't be better. Associate E. and Mr. B. stay with her. When did we start?"

"11:13."

"Operating time: seven minutes and a half. A hundred years ago Napoleon's personal physician could amputate a leg in that time, including everything, blood-stilling, etc. But those were other masters than we are. Well, pick the patient up carefully and lift her into the bed—or rather, let me do it. That's it—that's the way. Hot water bottles ready? Cover her. Cover her! Everything all right. Everything else we'll leave to —luck. Good morning, gentlemen, good morning."

Translated from the German by E. B. ASHTON

F. C. Weiskopf

THE LITTLE GOLDEN APPLE

WHEN Marina Kmetko, woman day-laborer in Nižné Vrútky in Slovakia, heard that her son Laco had quit the good job in the Kremnitz paper-mill to travel to the far and unknown country of Spain, to a war, more-over, of which as yet she had heard nothing at all, she thought quite seriously that the boy had lost his mind. But then Laco sent a letter: a paper with writing on it, and two pictures. On the pictures there were dead children to be seen and weeping women before burned-out shacks. The writing said:

"The peasants here used to be as poor as ours in the rock district of Kysúce. They got land from the Republic but the counts won't let them keep it and that's why there is war. They burn the villages and kill the children, but the peasants fight back all right. The workers from the cities help them, and from other countries many come and help too. Now you know why I came here. . . ."

When Rifkele Berschkowitz, the trader's daughter in Vrútky whom Marina got to read her the letter, had come this far, she interrupted herself and said: "But that doesn't make any sense. He's meschugge, your Laco. Or, do you know what that's got to do with him?"

"Yes," Marina replied and her eyes grew strangely dark and flickering, "he's thinking of his father." Rifkele ran upstairs with an uncanny feeling which she did not want to do harm to the child within her. "She's either running a fever or I don't know what," she told her husband, Hirsch, and sent him down into the store. He weighed out the two pounds of salt that Marina wanted and advised her to put on a mustard plaster. "That takes the heat out of the blood and puts the brain in order," he said.

Marina's brain, however, was in perfect order. She thought of Laco's father, her dead husband. He had gone to fight the counts in the year 'nineteen, over in Hungary, but they had caught him and strung him up. At the time, fourteen-year-old Laco wanted to avenge his father. He ran away and hadn't come back until a month later, all starved and ragged.

It was immediately settled for Marina that she had to send the boy something. Something special. Something he would enjoy.

She thought it over. What had you sent the men in the great war? Tobacco and woolen socks. But Laco didn't smoke, and in his letters he reported that it was so hot in Spain that they were all going without stockings, in straw shoes. She tried to recall Laco's wishes. She did not succeed. Thinking about such things was difficult anyway. Laco had been born as the fifth of ten children. Ten children in the house; the man off in the woods timbering, and later to the war; and the field so barren that the potato harvest would last for nine months in the year at best—where was Marina to have found the time to bother with her children's dreams and wishes?

And after returning from the abortive tour of vengeance against the Hungarian counts, Laco had gone to a *gazda*, a peasant from the neighborhood who took tinker's apprentices along on the "big trip." The boy had lived his own life ever since, coming home infrequently and never for more than very short periods, each time a little bigger and more masculine, each time a little more like his dead father and therefore dearer to his mother's heart but stranger to her eyes and ears. Oh, well.

At long last, however, she did think of something. In Vrútky she saw a few village children stand before the Berschkowitz store and admire the two oranges in the window. And she remembered that when Laco was in town with her for the first time he had stood just as entranced before the store of Leib Berschkowitz and for a long time afterwards had talked longingly of the little golden apples never seen before.

Her mind was made up at once. She went into the store and asked for an orange.

"What's that you want?" asked Rifkele who had reached automatically for the salt shovel at Marina's appearance. Then she recalled Marina's recent strange demeanor, and merely remarked: "And you know what that costs?"

"I have money," Marina replied, getting the nickels out of a knotted end of her petticoat. "How much do I pay?"

Shaking her head Rifkele brought the fruit.

"I'd like to have it wrapped," said Marina, "in paper and in a strong box and well tied."

"Wrapped and tied—did you ever hear of anything like it? What for? You want to send it away, perhaps?"

"Yes."

"Really? Where to?"

"Far."

She paid no further attention to Rifkele Berschkowitz's questions, counted twelve twenty-heller pieces on the counter, took the sugar box with the orange carefully under one arm and left.

"Meschugge, positively meschugge," Rifkele murmured, looking after her from the threshold of the store. The child moved in her and she spat out three times, in order to protect it, "Toj, toj, toj." Then she quickly turned and slammed the door.

❃   ❃   ❃

"Crazy," the post-office girl too thought when Marina stepped up to her window and asked to have the box prepared for shipment.

"To Spain."

"What? To Spain? What's in it? Fruit? Not acceptable for delivery. And anyway, who's think of sending oranges to Spain? That's where they grow, isn't it?"

She pushed the box back, closed the window and lost interest in Marina who remained standing before it for quite a while. It was not easy to sort out all that the post-office girl had said. But in the end she had thought it through and understood it and knew what she wanted to do.

She knocked once more at the window.

"What do you want now?" hissed the post-office girl. "I've told you that we don't accept fruit for mail delivery abroad." She slammed the window again.

Marina waited a little longer and then went back to the store of Leib Berschkowitz. Rifkele first wanted to run when she saw her, but then curiosity held her in her place behind the counter. Why was Marina coming back? She wanted to ask a favor. Could Rifkele write her a letter? To Laco, to the boy in Spain.

Once more curiosity conquered an urge to refuse. Rifkele produced paper and pencil and wrote down what Marina had to tell the boy:

"Dear son Laco!

"I wanted to send you one of the little golden apples you wanted to have, remember? I bought it at Berschkowitz's but they would not take it at the post-office. They also say it is unnecessary because the little apples grow where you are now. So I send only the letter, because you do not smoke either and woolen socks are no use when it is hot.

"With kisses and blessings I am your mother, Marina Kmetko of Nižné Vrútky."

"You can exchange it for salt, or for kerosene," Rifkele announced generously when she had finished writing. "I'll take it back."

But Marina wanted to keep the little golden apple: "Because it comes from where he is."

She expressed thanks for the writing of the letter and took her leave, having wrapped the box with the orange in her shawl like a baby.

*   *   *

The letter to Laco came back. It was in a new envelope, together with another letter, in which the commissar of the Masaryk Battalion wrote that during the defense of an advanced position against greatly superior enemy forces Corporal Laco Kmetko had died for liberty. "He was killed on the very day when your letter arrived, and we buried him under a tree which bears golden apples twice a year."

Rifkele could read only slowly, her eyes were all wet. "And what for did he have to go to war?" she exclaimed, gulping excitedly. "It wasn't his business. But that's how they always are, your men; never think of the women and mothers."

Marina stroked her shoulder. One might have thought the other's son had died, not hers. "Don't cry," she told Rifkele, "you don't understand that. He went because he was thinking of the women and children."

She bought a candle. Rifkele gave her another one, as a present. Hirsch gaped when he saw it. Over the open mouth, like a small invisible cloud, hung the silent wail at Rifkele's extravagance. His wife was as if changed, though. She turned to him: "Shut your mouth, there isn't any manna from heaven and I'm not meschugge . . . it's just that you don't understand anything, understand?"

Marina glued the candles on top of the chest, to the right and left of her painted wedding plate with the golden apple. Evenings, coming back from work, she would stand before the chest for a while, and in the gathering dusk the fruit assumed the form of a little child's head. It was strange: from the time when Marina learned of Laco's death she remembered quite plainly how he had looked as a child. Moreover, he who had been just one of ten children now became the best loved.

She began collecting keepsakes: his top, a whip he had as a herd-boy, the leather bag which he had taken on the tinker's journeys. Each time when she came to Vrútky, to Berschkowitz's, she asked for news from the country of Spain where Laco lay buried. Rifkele always had put the old papers aside for her. (She sometimes wondered: What the devil was she bothering with now? It was all Marina's fault and that of her Laco. Or was it not all theirs?) She would read to Marina: "There was bitter fighting on all fronts. Yesterday Barcelona underwent its seventieth air raid. Among the dead are more than a hundred children. The Non-Intervention Committee . . ."

She looked up from the paper into Marina's face and said with a strangely rough voice: "Do you know what that is, the Non-Intervention Committee? That's the English gentlemen who see to it that the others get all the guns and your people get nothing. Do you understand?"

"Yes," Marina replied. She understood also that Rifkele had only said, "your people," not "our people," because she was still ashamed. "Yes," she replied, "but in the end it still won't do them any good, the gentlemen, against us. Read on."

Once when Marina came into the store Rifkele had special news for her: "They're getting the children out of Spain. They send them to France, to houses that they're buying specially for them. It takes a lot of money and they're collecting everywhere now, in Prague too. Those who have no money can send things." She lowered her voice, lest she be heard by her husband who was busy in the storeroom next door. "I've sent a sugarloaf already." She laughed, bashfully. "And you, won't you send something too?"

Of course Marina would. But what? She had no money, the pig was to be fattened only in three months, and of her things . . . ? Then she thought of something: "I know."

She went and returned on the next day. In her shawl she brought Laco's top, whip and tinker's bag. "That's what I'll send them."

Rifkele asked, "Shouldn't we put something in the bag?"

"No need. Get pen and paper, I want to tell them something with it

... Ready? ... All right, write this: 'I, Marina Kmetko of Nižné Vrútky, am sending you children the things of my son Laco who is buried in your country, under a tree which bears golden apples twice a year.' Have you got it all down? Yes? Then give it to me, I want to make my crosses under it."

Rifkele handed her the paper. Accidentally she nudged the bag. It slipped, broke open. Rolling out came a brown, dried, wholly shriveled fruit.

Marina quickly caught it and put it back into the tinker's bag.

"It's just so they'll have something from home," she said softly.

Translated from the German by E. B. ASHTON

Franz Kafka

FIVE PARABLES

MY NEIGHBOUR

MY BUSINESS RESTS ENTIRELY on my own shoulders. Two girl clerks with typewriters and ledgers in the front office, my own room with writing-desk, safe, consulting-table, easy chair and telephone: such is my entire working apparatus. So simple to control, so easy to direct. I'm quite young, and lots of business comes my way. I don't complain, I don't complain.

At the beginning of the year a young man snapped up the empty premises next to mine, which very foolishly I hesitated to close with until too late. They also consist of a room and a front room, with a kitchen, however, thrown in—a room and a front room I would certainly have found some use for, my two girl clerks feel somewhat overdriven as it is—but what use would a kitchen have been to me? This petty consideration was solely responsible for my allowing the premises to be snatched from under my nose. Now that young man sits there. Harras, his name is. What he actually does there I have no idea. On the door there is a plate: "Harras Bureau." I have made enquiries and I am told it is a business similar to mine. One can't exactly warn people against giving the fellow credit, for after all he is a young and pushing man who probably has a future; yet one can't advise people to trust him either, for by all appearance he has no assets so far. The usual thing said by people who don't know.

Sometimes I meet Harras on the stairs; he seems always to be in an extraordinary hurry, for he literally shoots past me. I have never got a good look at him yet, for his office key is always in his hand when he passes me. In a tick he has the door open. Like the tail of a rat he has slipped through and I'm left standing again before the plate "Harras Bureau," which I have read already far oftener than it deserves.

The wretchedly thin walls betray the honourable and capable man, but shield the dishonest. My telephone is fixed to the wall that separates me from my neighbour. But I single that out merely as a particularly ironical circumstance. For even if it hung on the opposite wall, everything could be heard in the next room. I have accustomed myself to refrain from naming the names of my customers when speaking on the telephone to them. But of course it does not need much skill to guess the names from characteristic but unavoidable turns of the conversation. Sometimes I absolutely dance with apprehension round the telephone, the receiver at my ear, and yet can't help divulging the secret.

Because of all this my business decisions have naturally become unsure, my voice nervous, What is Harras doing while I am telephoning? If I wanted to exaggerate—and one must often do that so as to make things clear in one's mind—I might assert that Harras does not require a telephone, he uses mine, he pushes his sofa against the wall and listens while I at the other side must fly to the telephone, listen to all the requests of my customers, come to difficult and grave decisions, carry out long calculations—but worst of all, during all this time, involuntarily give Harras valuable information through the wall.

Perhaps he doesn't wait even for the end of the conversation, but gets up at the point where the matter has become clear to him, flies through the town with his usual haste and, before I have hung up the receiver, is already at his goal working against me.

A COMMON CONFUSION

A common experience, resulting in a common confusion. A has to transact important business with B in H. He goes to H for a preliminary interview, accomplishes the journey there in ten minutes, and the journey back in the same time, and on returning boasts to his family of his expedition. Next day he goes again to H, this time to settle his business finally. As that by all appearances will require several hours, A leaves very early in the morning. But although all the accessory circumstances,

at least in A's estimation, are exactly the same as the day before, it takes
him ten hours this time to reach H. When he arrives there quite exhausted in the evening he is informed that B, annoyed at his absence,
had left half an hour before to go to A's village, and that they must have
passed each other on the road. A is advised to wait. But in his anxiety
about his business he sets off at once and hurries home.

This time he achieves the journey, without paying any particular attention to the fact, exactly in a second. At home he learns that B had arrived
quite early, immediately after A's departure, indeed that he had met A
on the threshold and reminded him of his business; but A had replied
that he had no time to spare, he must go at once.

In spite of this incomprehensible behaviour of A, however, B had
stayed on to wait for A's return. It is true, he had asked several times
whether A was not back yet, but he was still sitting up in A's room. Overjoyed at the opportunity of seeing B at once and explaining everything
to him, A rushes upstairs. He is almost at the top, when he stumbles,
twists a sinew, and almost fainting with the pain, incapable even of
uttering a cry, only able to moan faintly in the darkness, he hears B—
impossible to tell whether at a great distance or quite near him—stamping down the stairs in a violent rage and vanishing for good.

THE BRIDGE

I was stiff and cold, I was a bridge, I lay over a ravine. My toes on one
side, my fingers clutching the other, I had clamped myself fast into the
crumbling clay. The tails of my coat fluttered at my sides. Far below
brawled the icy trout stream. No tourist strayed to this impassable
height, the bridge was not yet traced on any map. So I lay and waited;
I could only wait. Without falling, no bridge, once spanned, can cease to
be a bridge.

It was towards evening one day—was it the first, was it the thousandth?
I cannot tell—my thoughts were always in confusion and perpetually
moving in a circle. It was towards evening in summer, the roar of the
stream had grown deeper, when I heard the sound of a human step! To
me, to me. Straighten yourself, bridge, make ready, railless beams, to
hold up the passenger entrusted to you. If his steps are uncertain steady
them unobtrusively, but if he stumbles show what you are made of and
like a mountain god hurl him across to land.

He came, he tapped me with the iron point of his stick, then he lifted my coat-tails with it and put them in order upon me. He plunged the point of his stick into my bushy hair and let it lie there for a long time, forgetting me no doubt while he wildly gazed round him. But then—I was just following him in thought over mountain and valley—he jumped with both feet on the middle of my body. I shuddered with wild pain, not knowing what was happening. Who was it? A child? A dream? A wayfarer? A suicide? A tempter? A destroyer? And I turned round so as to see him. A bridge to turn round! I had not yet turned quite round when I already began to fall, I fell and in a moment I was torn and transpierced by the sharp rocks which had always gazed up at me so peacefully from the rushing water.

THE BUCKET RIDER

Coal all spent; the bucket empty; the shovel useless; the stove breathing out cold; the room freezing; the leaves outside the window rigid, covered with rime; the sky a silver shield against any one who looks for help from it. I must have coal; I cannot freeze to death; behind me is the pitiless stove, before me the pitiless sky, so I must ride out between them and on my journey seek aid from the coal-dealer. But he has already grown deaf to ordinary appeals; I must prove irrefutably to him that I have not a single grain of coal left, and that he means to me the very sun in the firmament. I must approach like a beggar, who, with the death-rattle already in his throat, insists on dying on the doorstep, and to whom the grand people's cook accordingly decides to give the dregs of the coffee-pot; just so much the coal-dealer, filled with rage, but acknowledging the command, "Thou shalt not kill," fling a shovelful of coal into my bucket.

My mode of arrival must decide the matter; so I ride off on the bucket. Seated on the bucket, my hands on the handle, the simplest kind of bridle, I propel myself with difficulty down the stairs; but once down below my bucket ascends, superbly, superbly; camels humbly squatting on the ground do not rise with more dignity, shaking themselves under the sticks of their drivers. Through the hard frozen streets we go at a regular canter; often I am upraised as high as the first storey of a house; never do I sink as low as the house doors. And at last I float at an extraordinary height above the vaulted cellar of the dealer, whom I see far below crouching over his table, where he is writing; he has opened the door to let out the excessive heat.

"Coal-dealer!" I cry in a voice burned hollow by the frost and muffled in the cloud made by my breath, "please, coal-dealer, give me a little coal. My bucket is so light that I can ride on it. Be kind. When I can I'll pay you."

The dealer puts his hand to his ear. "Do I hear rightly?" he throws the question over his shoulder to his wife. "Do I hear rightly? A customer."

"I hear nothing," says his wife, breathing in and out peacefully while she knits on, her back pleasantly warmed by the heat.

"Oh, yes, you must hear," I cry. "It's me; an old customer; faithful and true; only without means at the moment."

"Wife," says the dealer, "it's some one, it must be; my ears can't have deceived me so much as that; it must be an old, a very old customer, that can move me so deeply."

"What ails you, man?" says his wife, ceasing from her work for a moment and pressing her knitting to her bosom. "It's nobody, the street is empty, all our customers are provided for; we could close down the shop for several days and take a rest."

"But I'm sitting up here on the bucket," I cry, and unfeeling frozen tears dim my eyes, "please look up here, just once; you'll see me directly; I beg you, just a shovelful; and if you give me more it'll make me so happy that I won't know what to do. All the other customers are provided for. Oh, if I could only hear the coal clattering into the bucket!"

"I'm coming," says the coal-dealer, and on his short legs he makes to climb the steps of the cellar, but his wife is already beside him, holds him back by the arm and says: "You stay here; seeing you persist in your fancies I'll go myself. Think of the bad fit of coughing you had during the night. But for a piece of business, even if it's one you've only fancied in your head, you're prepared to forget your wife and child and sacrifice your lungs. I'll go."

"Then be sure to tell him all the kinds of coal we have in stock; I'll shout out the prices after you."

"Right," says his wife, climbing up to the street. Naturally she sees me at once. "Frau Coal-dealer," I cry, "my humblest greetings; just one shovelful of coal; here in my bucket; I'll carry it home myself. One shovelful of the worst you have. I'll pay you in full for it, of course, but not just now, not just now." What a knell-like sound the words "not just now" have, and how bewilderingly they mingle with the evening chimes that fall from the church steeple near by!

"Well, what does he want?" shouts the dealer. "Nothing," his wife shouts back, "there's nothing here; I see nothing, I hear nothing; only six striking, and now we must shut up the shop. The cold is terrible; tomorrow we'll likely have lots to do again."

She sees nothing and hears nothing; but all the same she loosens her apron-strings and waves her apron to waft me away. She succeeds, un-luckily. My bucket has all the virtues of a good steed except powers of resistance, which it has not; it is too light; a woman's apron can make it fly through the air.

"You bad woman!" I shout back, while she, turning into the shop, half-contemptuous, half-reassured, flourishes her fist in the air. "You bad woman! I begged you for a shovelful of the worst coal and you would not give it me." And with that I ascend into the regions of the ice moun-tains and am lost for ever.

THE SILENCE OF THE SIRENS

Proof that inadequate, even childish measures, may serve to rescue one from peril. To protect himself from the Sirens Ulysses stopped his ears with wax and had himself bound to the mast of his ship. Naturally any and every traveller before him could have done the same, except those whom the Sirens allured even from a great distance; but it was known to all the world that such things were of no help whatever. The song of the Sirens could pierce through everything, and the longing of those they seduced would have broken far stronger bonds than chains and masts. But Ulysses did not think of that, although he had probably heard of it. He trusted absolutely to his handful of wax and his fathom of chain, and in innocent elation over his little stratagem sailed out to meet the Sirens.

Now the Sirens have a still more fatal weapon than their song, namely their silence. And though admittedly such a thing has never happened, still it is conceivable that some one might possibly have escaped from their singing; but from their silence certainly never. Against the feeling of having triumphed over them by one's own strength, and the conse-quent exaltation that bears down everything before it, no earthly powers could have remained intact.

And when Ulysses approached them the potent songstresses actually did not sing, whether because they thought that this enemy could be vanquished only by their silence, or because the look of bliss on the face of Ulysses, who was thinking of nothing but his wax and his chains, made them forget their singing.

But Ulysses, if one may so express it, did not hear their silence; he thought they were singing and that he alone did not hear them. For a fleeting moment he saw their throats rising and falling, their breasts lifting, their eyes filled with tears, their lips half-parted, but believed that these were accompaniments to the airs which died unheard around him. Soon, however, all this faded from his sight as he fixed his gaze on the distance, the Sirens literally vanished before his resolution, and at the very moment when they were nearest to him he knew of them no longer.

But they—lovelier than ever—stretched their necks and turned, let their cold hair flutter free in the wind, and forgetting everything clung with their claws to the rocks. They no longer had any desire to allure; all that they wanted was to hold as long as they could the radiance that fell from Ulysses's great eyes.

If the Sirens had possessed consciousness they would have been annihilated at that moment. But they remained as they had been; all that had happened was that Ulysses had escaped them.

A codicil to the foregoing has also been handed down. Ulysses, it is said, was so full of guile, was such a fox, that not even the goddess of fate could pierce his armour. Perhaps he had really noticed, although here the human understanding is beyond its depths, that the Sirens were silent, and opposed the afore-mentioned pretence to them and the gods merely as a sort of shield.

Translated from the German by EDWIN MUIR

Rainer Maria Rilke

A LETTER ABOUT GERMANY

To Lisa Heise

Chateau de Muzot sur Sierre/Valais,
Switzerland, February 2, 1923

THE SAME FEARS and inexpressible upheavals that make you suffer so, render me more and more silent. How often have I intended to answer your next-to-the-last troubled letter, dear friend, and have postponed it for a better and happier hour: so that you could know fully how (with its large four-leaf clover) it was taken to my heart. But my summer, and particularly my autumn were troubled by many uncertainties, and if I am now trying, solitary in my old tower, to make this winter resemble its good predecessor as much as possible, that too has its difficulties; partly because my health is less stable, partly because of those same intrusive disturbances which with general conditions going from bad to worse, intrude on everything one may begin (exactly as it was in the War!). As far as that is concerned, I can apply literally to myself many sentences that you write; the "already during the day, half my thoughts are no longer my own; and the nights are filled with feverish visions." That and others. . . . For it is no different with me. *What* is happening? And what are *we* in this happening?—Now, as in the War, it is obtrusive and withal hardly concerns us, an alien misfortune in which one becomes involved—. Isn't it often as if in *one* breath one could rise above it? Often too, as in walking through summer fields one brushes against some small blossom that answers with a liberated scent, one comes upon some modest measure of consolation which at once communicates itself as if it emanated from a reserve of abundance. . . . Your letter itself is full of such surprises, full of those pure fragrances of the heart with which only one who has experienced the utmost deprivation becomes acquainted.

For me, as I see everything and must experience it according to my nature and ability, no doubt exists that it is Germany which, because she does not know herself, is holding back the world. The manifold composition and broad training of my blood afford me a special perspective for seeing this. Germany, in the year 1918, at the moment of collapse, could have shamed and shaken the whole world through an act of deep sincerity and conversion. Through a visible, determined renunciation of her falsely developed prosperity—, in a word: through that humility which would have been so completely in character with her spirit, and an element of her dignity and which would have forestalled everything one could have dictated to her in the way of alien humiliation. At that time—so I hoped for a moment—the lost trait of that humility which strikes one as so constructive in the drawings of Dürer should again have been entered, added to the German face, grown so one-sided and obstinate! Perhaps there were a few people there who felt that, whose wishes, whose hopes were directed toward such a correction,—now the fact that it did *not* happen is beginning to show and already to take vengeance.— Something has been left out which would have established a due measure for everything; Germany has failed to give her purest best, that moderation based once more on the oldest tradition—, she has not fundamentally renewed herself and searched her heart, she has not created for herself that dignity which has as its root the most profound humility; she was intent only on salvation in a superficial, hasty, distrustful and greedy sense; she wanted to act and to come out clear and on top instead, according to her inmost nature, of bearing and enduring and being ready for her miracle. She wanted to persist instead of changing. And so one feels now—something has been left out. A date is lacking from which to take one's bearings. A rung is missing in the ladder, hence the indescribable anxiety, the fear, the "premonition of a sudden and violent calamity" . . . What is one to do? Let us remain each on his *still* quiet, *still* trustworthy little island of life, doing our own work on it, suffering and feeling what truly concerns us. . . .

Translated from the German by CHRISTL RITTER

SONNETS TO ORPHEUS

FIRST PART

VI

DOES HE BELONG here? No, out of both
realms his wide nature grew.
More knowing would he bend the willow's branches
who has experienced the willow's roots.

Going to bed, leave on the table
no bread and no milk; it draws the dead—.
But he, the conjurer, let him
under the eyelid's mildness

mix their appearance into everything seen;
and may the magic of earthsmoke and rue
be to him as true as the clearest relation.

Nothing can harm for him the valid symbol;
be it from graves, be it from rooms,
let him praise finger-ring, clasp and jug.

IX

Only one who has lifted the lyre
among shadows too,
may divining render
the infinite praise.

Only who with the dead has eaten
of the poppy that is theirs,
will never again lose
the most delicate tone.

Though the reflection in the pool
often swims before our eyes:
Know the image.

Only in the dual realm
do voices become
eternal and mild.

XV

O fountain-mouth, O giving, O mouth that speaks
exhaustlessly one single, one pure thing,—
before the water's flowing face,
you marble mask. And in the background

coming of aqueducts. From far away
passing by graves, from the slope of the Appenines
they bring to you your speaking, that then falls
past the blackened aging of your chin

into the basin there before it.
This is the ear laid sleeping down,
the marble ear in which you always speak.

An ear of earth's. So that she is only talking
with herself. If a pitcher slips between
it seems to her that you are interrupting.

XXVI

How the cry of a bird can stir us . . .
Any once created crying.
But even children, at play in the open,
cry past real cries.

Cry chance. Into interstices
of this world-space, (into which the unbroken
bird-cry passes, as people do into dreams—)
they drive their wedges, wedges of shrieking.

O woe, where are we? More and more free
like kites torn loose
we chase in mid-air, with edges of laughter,

windily tattered.—Array the criers,
singing god! that they waken resounding,
a current bearing the head and the lyre.

XXIX

Silent friend of many distances
feel how your breath is still increasing space.
Among the beams of the dark belfries let
yourself ring out. What feeds on you

will grow strong upon this nourishment.
Be conversant with transformation.
From what experience have you suffered most?
Is drinking bitter to you, turn to wine.

Be, in this immeasurable night,
magic power at your senses' crossroad,
be the meaning of the strange encounter.

And if the earthly has forgotten you,
say to the still earth: I flow.
To the rapid water speak: I am.

Translated from the German by M. D. HERTER NORTON

THE SECOND DUINO ELEGY

EVERY ANGEL is terrible. Still, though, alas!
I invoke you, almost deadly birds of the soul,
knowing what you are. Oh, where are the days of Tobias,
when one of the shining-most stood on the simple threshold,
a little disguised for the journey, no longer appalling,
(a youth to the youth as he curiously peered outside).
Let the archangel perilous now, from behind the stars,
step but a step down hitherwards: high up-beating,
our heart would out-beat us. Who are you?

Early successes, Creation's pampered darlings,
ranges, summits, dawn-red ridges
of all beginning,—pollen of blossoming godhead,
hinges of light, corridors, stairways, thrcnes,
spaces of being, shields of felicity, tumults
of stormily rapturous feeling, and suddenly, separate,
mirrors: drawing up their own
outstreamed beauty into their faces again.

For we, when we feel, evaporate; oh, we
breathe ourselves out and away; from ember to ember
yielding a fainter scent. True, someone may tell us:
'You've got in my blood, the room, the Spring's
growing full of you' . . . What's the use? He cannot retain us.
We vanish within and around him. And those that have beauty
oh, who shall hold them back? Incessant appearance
comes and goes in their faces. Like dew from the morning grass
exhales from us that which is ours, like heat
from a smoking dish. O smile, whither? O upturned glance:
new, warm, vanishing wave of the heart—alas,
but we *are* all that. Does the cosmic space
we dissolve into taste of us, then? Do the angels really
only catch up what is theirs, what has streamed from them, or at times,
as though through an oversight, is a little of our
existence in it as well? Is there just so much of us
mixed with their features as that vague look in the faces
of pregnant women? Unmarked by them in the whirling
return to themselves. (How should they remark it?)

Lovers, if Angels could understand them, might utter
strange things in the midnight air. For it seems that everything's
trying to hide us . . . Look, the trees exist; the houses
we live in still stand where they were. We only
pass everything by like a transposition of air.
And all combines to suppress us, partly as shame,
perhaps, and partly as inexpressible hope.

Lovers, to you, each satisfied in the other,
I turn with my question about us. You grasp yourselves. Have you proofs?

Look, with me it may happen at times that my hands
grow aware of each other, or else that my hard-worn face
seeks refuge within them. That gives me a little
sensation. But who, just for that, could presume to exist?
You, though, that go on growing
in the other's rapture till, overwhelmed, he implores
'No more'; you that under each other's hands
grow more abundant like vintage grapes;
sinking at times, but only because the other
has so completely emerged; I ask you about us. I know
why you so blissfully touch; because the caress persists,
because it does not vanish, the place that you
so tenderly cover; because you perceive thereunder
pure duration. Until your embraces almost
promise eternity. Yet, when you've once withstood
the startled first encounter, the window-longing,
and that first walk, just once, through the garden together:
Lovers, are you the same? When you lift yourselves
up to each other's lips—drink unto drink:
oh, how strangely the drinker eludes his part!

On Attic stelès, did not the circumspection
of human gesture amaze you? Were not love and farewell
so lightly laid upon shoulders, they seemed to be made
of other stuff than with us? Remember the hands,
how they rest without pressure, though power is there in the torsos.
The wisdom of those self-masters was this: we have got so far;
ours is to touch one another like this; the gods
may press more strongly upon us. But that is the gods' affair.
If only we could discover some pure, contained,
narrow, human, own little strip of orchard
in between river and rock! For our heart transcends us
just as it did those others. And we can no longer
gaze after it into figures that soothe it, or godlike
bodies, wherein it achieves a grander restraint.

Translated from the German by J. B. LEISHMAN *and*
STEPHEN SPENDER

AUSTRIA

INTRODUCTION

By Robert Pick

IT HAS FREQUENTLY been remarked that Austrian writers—who wrote in German—had practically no part in the classical epoch of German literature. In fact, Austria's contributions to world literature, during the eighteenth and nineteenth centuries, did not live up to the high level of her general culture. The true expression of Austria's culture was her music. Not by coincidence were the great composers of the world at home in Austria. Music, the supra-national medium of understanding between men, was the natural art of a country a-national in its origin, and avowedly supra-national in its structure.

German-speaking Austrians did not constitute simply another German stock among many. Their civilization, determined first of all by tradition, formed part of a pattern common, in a great many respects, to all racial groups in the wider realm of Hapsburg. Their local regionalism found its higher outlet in universalistic feelings rather than in narrow national concepts.

Perhaps these are oversimplified afterthoughts. But the fact remains that Austrian arts and letters were nurtured by a peculiar form of universalistic thinking. Both centered in Vienna—that curious German-speaking city which, besides Germanic blood, had amalgamated the most widely differing strains of Europe. Vienna was not only the political focus of a world power, and for centuries the seat of the legitimate heir of the Roman Empire; it also was—contrary to German cities big and small—a European metropolis. Embedded in one of the loveliest landscapes of the Continent, it remained provincial in its easy-going mode of life; but it was cosmopolitan in its spirit.

This, briefly, was the climate in which Austrian literature came of age in the course of the nineteenth century—the period that, at the same time, gave rise to the general European hypertrophy of nationalism. While Austrians by and large could enjoy the beauties of their country and the urbane tolerance of their paternalistic tradition, Austrian writers, though not always aloof from their fellow-citizens' Southern *joie de vivre,* soon realized how doubtful was the survival of what more and more appeared as a political anomaly. To the thoughtful among them, ever since 1848 the impending end of their multinational island was a certainty.

Austria's non-German provinces were gaining strength in looking forward to her dismemberment, and their own literature came only into fuller flower through these centrifugal forces. German-writing Austrians could but watch the growth of nationalistic trends within Austria's frontiers and abroad—an ideology that finally began even to take hold, as pan-Germanism, of their own national environment. Thus, their supra-national concepts gradually lost any political meaning, and more and more dissolved in a nameless and, as it were, purely personal sentiment. Nostalgic love for everything these vague feelings stood for could not prevent Austrian writers from admitting to themselves that the *raison d'être* of Austrian letters, as distinct from German literature, was doomed.

These forebodings gave Austrian writing its specific quality—a blending of melancholy and skepticism. The outer world saw only the waltzing playground of Vienna, and had but little eye for the somber background of that voluble merriment. The great spirits of Austria knew better. Franz Grillparzer, the nineteenth century classic, who had so passionately tried to believe in the Hapsburgs' historical mission, died disillusioned and embittered; Ferdinand Raimund, the romantic of the Viennese stage, committed suicide, bewildered and yet touched by the sophisticated cynicism of his greater successor, Johann Nestroy; and Adalbert Stifter, one of the very few great epic writers in the German language—whose novels, by the way, are imbued with the atmosphere of neighboring Slav lands—followed Raimund on his voluntary road into darkness.

With even stronger accents, the conflict between nostalgic love and skepticism impregnates the writings of the "Young Viennese" who made their appearance around the turn of the century. They were born when Francis Joseph was already an aged man—the emperor who, as all his subjects knew, was the last bond holding the country together. And although these writers had their spurts of romantic hope and even frivolity, they all seemed to feel how little time was left to them. Nothing is more revealing, in this respect, than the precocity of their talent; Hugo von Hofmannsthal, their foremost representative—foremost also in his deep attachment to music—was a great poet at seventeen. But equally significant is the almost continuous preoccupation with death in Arthur Schnitzler's plays and stories, or Richard Beer-Hofmann's early flight into the timeless landscape of the Bible.

Already at that time, a group of minor literati—minor, to be' sure, as writers —began to join arms with radical pan-Germanism. Austria's best men of letters, however, at any time tried to understand the spirit and the longings of their non-German compatriots. Hermann Bahr, for a short period a kind of literary *magister Austriae,* was second to none in his praise for the hidden treasures of Slavic and Latin culture in Austria's confines. Franz Werfel, who later chose his grandiose subjects from the four corners of the world, is nowhere so moving as in the rare pages of devotion to his native Prague—that Czech town which still holds vestiges of its medieval existence as a center of cosmopolitan learning.

Nor did Austrian writers turn their back on the social problems of their days. Their skeptical restraint never decayed into nihilism. But the mellowness of their mood somewhat weakened the *élan* of their moral demands—at least in its effects upon a world which had grown accustomed to ruder means of approach. Even Alfons Petzold, the poet of Austria's forceful labor movement, was not revolutionary in his artistic means. Karl Kraus, Vienna's great and implacable moralist, was at the same time one of the finest purists of the German language. True, traditional elements give to Austrian twentieth century writing a certain poise; yet opposition to prejudice and obscurantism is ever-present as a definite sense of justice and human dignity, and a deep-rooted mistrust of obsolete formulae. It was Vienna that produced psycho-analysis, one of the most far-reaching intellectual revolutions of the past decades.

The closer old Austria drew to her political end, the more Austrian writing detached itself from that Swinburnean quest for subtle beauty which had so misleadingly marked the neo-romantic beginnings of the "Young Viennese." Even Stefan Zweig's life-long search for the neutralized humanism of belles lettres appears different, today, in the light of his tragic death. Love of humanity and skepticism gained new and clearer accents in Robert Musil's Proustean novels, and in the handful of poems young Georg Trakl left. He died in 1914.

The centripetal forces of Austria outlasted her downfall as an empire. Joseph Roth was born in what now is Poland—and still his work contains all the basic elements of Austrian writing and, in its struggle for the absolute values of faith, all its intrinsic conflicts. In an Austrian peasant novel, Hermann Broch, so universalistic in his philosophy, bade farewell to the country of his birth.

Indeed, they all were lovers of Austria. As Austria failed them, she was, in the end, alive only in her letters. But Austria's creative minds—their ranks had become thin—knew that Austrian literature as such had ceased with the disappearance of its spiritual hinterland, the multi-national realm of old Austria. They became what they had long been anonymously—world citizens.

When the hour struck which destroyed the small country that had borne the name of Austria for twenty crucial years, they left their native soil. As citizens of the world, they had but little to learn and nothing to forget. Their inherited supra-national spirit, seemingly so anachronistic in Europe's world of yesterday, is akin to the spirit of the future as all men of good will perceive it.

Franz Werfel

THE BULLETPROOF HIDALGO

I

THAT THE JUST fare ill on earth, while evil-doers often live to enjoy the "wages of sin"—this is a sorry truth on which not even the Bible can keep silent. It is a hard truth to swallow for the faithful; for does it not prove that higher justice seems to be slower, more involved and indifferent, and less reliable than its earthly counterpart? Clearly, our zealous picture of a moral world order does not agree with the super-human (or call it inhuman) order actually inherent in the universe.

On occasion things can try the patience of even the most brazen blasphemer. Are there not signs and miracles, clear and unmistakable, which serve to snatch the evil-doer from perdition, to exempt the sinner from his well-deserved punishment by the nimble intercession of Heaven itself? Providence may, however, be credited with a certain logic, since its benevolence toward petty evil-doers does not conflict in the slightest with its similar attitude toward big criminals. Just recently someone related such an exemplary heavenly miracle on behalf of the Devil. The teller had a few weeks before returned from the Civil War in Spain to our little inquisitive town.

II

The last columns of the hard-pressed Loyalist militia left the city of Malaga toward noon. The advance guard of the Rebels entered the following morning. Not even a full day intervened between departure and entry. Just as there is a No-Man's-Land between the fronts, there is a No-Man's-Time between hostile armies in motion. Cities and towns that have had the misfortune of becoming the theatre of war well know this No-Man's-Time, which is never so oppressive as in a Civil War.

The Commandant of the Loyalist Garrison had not left the population in doubt as to its fate. Those who were in danger had had plenty of time to reach safety, and many of them had taken advantage of the opportunity. At the last moment a considerable number of those who had previously been unable to make up their minds joined the retreating militia with wives and children, with all their earthly goods. Upon many others good advice remained ineffective. They refused to leave the city where their entire life was rooted. The reason for their staying behind had nothing to do with stubborn heroism; it was, for the most part, carelessness and laziness—that unfortunate lack of imagination, as far as the power of evil is concerned, which so often threatens worthwhile people with danger. Time and again they and their like give voice to certain stereotyped phrases that are eloquent testimony of the fact that people will not learn:

"It will soon be over." "It can't be as bad as all that." "Nothing can happen to me personally." "Why should they do anything to me? I have never been politically active nor have I ever done harm to anyone."

It was not over quickly. It is not even over today. It was worse than the most anxious forebodings could have anticipated. Things happened to the very people to whom "nothing could happen." Precisely they were harmed who had never harmed any one.

The new penal institution lay on the outskirts of the city. It consisted of several well-equipped buildings and tree-shaded courts—the latter the object of much pride by humanitarians as evidence of progressive tendencies. This sad, yet, in its way, estimable institution now became the center of events. During the very first hours after the Rebel troops had marched in, the above-mentioned harmless idealists were pulled in from all sides and assembled at the prison. With incredible speed the denizens of the lovely city had changed from unquestioning partisans of the Government into equally fanatical partisans of the Rebellion. It was far more than a mere artificial show of enthusiasm that flooded the streets, even though this species had not heretofore been much in evidence. Engendered by the Civil War, hatched during No-Man's-Time, it had not come out into the open until the pause was ended. Still, it was not only the victims who marveled how many well-known and old familiar faces stood revealed as traitors, informers, conspirators, denouncers, vengeful pace-makers of the victor; how many openly boasted of their unexceptionable sentiments, of how they had long been in Rebel pay.

In front of the high iron prison gates there had been a large crowd which in chorus demanded the liberation of the political prisoners the Government had left behind. The prisoners had been led out in triumph even before the noon bell was rung. In their place ten times the number of new prisoners were now quartered in the recently vacated cells. The very first day there were more than a thousand, the first batch consisting of the harmless idealists as well as of a large number of marauders and stragglers who had been picked up during the advance in the vineyards, fields, farms and barns. The space was wholly insufficient. Twelve and fifteen men were herded into cells meant for three prisoners. Solitary confinement was restricted to a few of the most important prizes. There was no more distinction between political and criminal prisoners. But the crowding was soon to be reduced. Toward eleven o'clock in the evening several trucks lumbered up to the other prison court. They accommodated about ninety men.

The terror began . . .

III

Among the criminal inmates of the model prison—there had been hardly two dozen at the time—there was a certain Esteban Ahimundo y

Abreojos. The bearer of this name must be imagined as a splendidly sinister hidalgo, a grandee with a mad sense of honor, straight out of a sword-and-costume play by Lope de Vega. Esteban Ahimundo y Abreojos, however, was a murderer. He was not a common murderer, but a murderer out of the book, indeed, out of the picture book. Nature had not tried to hide her handiwork in his face. He had been properly picked for the role of monster. Indeed, his mask, if anything, was exaggerated. His brows beetled on heavy ridges. His mouse-grey eyes underneath were tiny and almost hidden, with the shiftless gaze of the restless who are forever watching for an opening. His low forehead receded under frizzy, matted hair. His nutcracker mouth was set in a craggy, challenging chin. His square underset figure was stoop-shouldered and bull-necked, almost hunchbacked with humiliation, viciousness and discomfort. His torso was shaped like an iron money chest. By his sides hung the hairy, strangling paws of a gorilla. The whole man was a perfect specimen for a museum of criminal pathology, the classic criminal type, eminently suitable for presentation to a seminar. There was no mitigating feature, no childlike remnant, no merciful weakness such as is found in almost every evil-doer. No, Estaban Ahimundo y Abreojos was the incarnate nightmare of lonely widows who start from sleep at night with a cry of terror.

The crimes he was expiating could no longer be counted on the fingers of both hands. Two sex murders and three murders committed during the course of robberies were the chief items. To shorten the trial, he had been charged only with his "selected works," while mere trifles like simple burglary and theft were ignored. There had been a long-drawn-out investigation, but the trial itself had been before a court-martial on the last two days of the siege. At the start of the Civil War the legitimate authorities were greatly concerned with conducting public business in the normal way. Theaters and motion pictures played and the courts continued their sessions.

The Malaga court-martial, as may be imagined, condemned the mass murderer to death by garroting. But the strange intercession of higher powers on behalf of the evil-doer at once came into miraculous play. The sentence could not be executed, since there came No-Man's-Time. The old legal authority disappeared and was seized by the victorious generals and their well-drilled hordes.

The new Commandant of the city had taken personal charge of the business of vengeance. Every day for several hours he held forth in the prison office, examining the most important victims himself and enjoying their complete helplessness. He was a youngish colonel whom hatred seemed to have emaciated. A monocle was frozen into his face after the Prussian model, while he was splendidly booted and spurred after the Italian. When his kind, instead of disciplining others, is itself curbed for a while, as had been the case under the Spanish Government, it becomes surcharged with high-tension currents of wrath and cruelty. The seared features of the Colonel revealed his regret that he was unable to deal out anything worse than death.

In the due course of events the case of Esteban Ahimundo y Abreojos came before the Commandant. He sat in his office, his two legs, encased in resplendent riding boots of yellow leather, stretched far out where they were zealously worked over with polish and brushes by two lackeys. Amid the piles of official papers on his desk, each deciding the life and death of a human being, stood an aperitif, colored a poisonous green. Thoughtfully the Colonel sucked at the cool drink through a straw, while reading the sentence that had been passed on the murderer. Throwing out a half-muttered word to the servile group of officers and officials that surrounded him, he ordered the wretch whose life had been spared by the advent of No-Man's-Time brought before him. The sight of this incredible monster who put the most sensational pictures of criminals in the shade seemed to fill the Commandant with satisfaction. A brilliant idea flashed into his mind—an idea that was immediately translated into an order indifferently dictated into the typewriter and addressed to the technical director of the work of vengeance. In the Colonel's opinion death by shooting was far too mild a punishment for pacifists, democrats, Socialists, Communists, and other humanitarian fighters for freedom. Now this death was to be sweetened, for the first batch of these weak-kneed idealistic dogs, by giving them the honorable company of a five-fold sex and hold-up murderer.

Just after midnight the trucks were loaded with their freight in the prison yard. Among the notables caught up in the general vengeance— nearly all of them dignified figures with fine heads—sat the hairy monster and blinked with his shifty killer's eyes. The others, most of them older men, looked as though they had been torn from slumber and seemed wholly unaware of what was in store for them. The motors were started up and roared through the oppressive quiet and deceptive desertedness of the night. To the municipal cemetery went the wild ride. There more trucks awaited them with a battery of military searchlights. The dreadful light of the giant reflectors hissed and stabbed into the darkness, clearing a broad spot of strangling brightness, at the borders of which dense night reared into the sky. In the spared-out space of unnatural and fateful light three squadrons of soldiers stood at ease, guns at rest. A little farther on coarse voices were heard from the ground and heavy shovelfuls of dark clods rolled down a broad mound which temporarily hid the hurriedly dug mass grave. It was some thirty feet long, twenty wide and ten deep.

The massacre took place without haste, but also without the slightest trace of ceremony. It was performed with utter efficiency—no muffled drums, macabre commands and signals as of old, but casually, skillfully, offhand, as it were.

An officer called out the names of the first ten. They were the best that had fallen to the enemy. They were wrenched off the trucks. Two physicians who had had nothing to do with politics, the newspaper editor with three members of his staff, a writer, a famous painter and three minor officials of the fallen regime. Their faces were not deathly pale but chalkwhite in the glare of the searchlights through which the figures moved as though in the shooting of a film. The ten were not even shackled, but offered no resistance as they were herded up the embankment. Nor did they utter a word. Guards moved close to them and barked out the order: "Take off your coats!" The victims obeyed.

Not until now, when they saw each other in the exaggerated white of their shirt-sleeves, did they seem to grasp the hopeless truth. With high choking voices rising in confusion they cried out to their utterly indifferent executioners, sought to convey quick and decisive information. But the armed band had meanwhile quietly and still without a single word of command closed in the brightly lighted spot. The ten on the mound had no way of escape except through the great mass grave—a possibility which occurred to none of them. Their talk grew faster and louder. Then the rattattat began—a machine gun at close range, hardly noticed before. A single cartridge belt, no more, dusted up and down the row a few times. The dry rattle took only a few seconds. The dignified gray-heads burst like eggs. The sound of cracking skulls could be heard through the rattle. In the glare of the searchlights, intolerant of color, black rivulets of blood flowed, lapping down the clods and merging into streams.

Regulares and Moros stepped up to the fallen and whipped a few bullets into their bodies from Mauser pistols—utterly indifferently, casually, as one grinds out the stubbornly glowing stub of a cigarette. Then they seized the bodies by feet and shoulders and flung them in a high arc into the ditch. The first layer of vanquished fighters for freedom lay where it fell. A few shovelfuls of earth and of slaked lime were tossed after them.

When this procedure was repeated for the eighth time, the noble

Esteban Ahimundo y Abreojos stood at the left wing of the row of death —its eleventh and last man. The other ten who had witnessed their fate seven times hardly seemed alive any more. There was no more confusion of high-pitched male voices, only an occasional moan, as of a man who wants to vomit. Abreojos alone seemed to be in possession of his senses. He stood quietly upright without swaying, a hero. His eyes flickered back and forth attentively as usual. Every now and then he lifted his heavy paw up high and cried "Arriba España!" the slogan of Nationalist Spain. Did he do so to inveigle himself into the good graces of Death, who seemed so completely on the side of the Nationalists?

The moment the machine gun set up its rattle, Esteban Abreojos fell to the ground. To this extent it was his work, and not that of providence, that the bullet spared him. He had watched the machine gun crew, his senses on the alert. But what followed surely was not his own work. For who could have anticipated that two of the Falangists—members of that half-military, half-civilian group that had heretofore been satisfied with the role of spectators—suddenly felt the irresistible desire to take part in this pleasant business of "laying them out"? Since, however, all the victims were already laid out, the two happened to step up to the only guilty man in the lot, who lay with outstretched limbs hugging the dirt, without a doubt as dead as a dormouse. The Falangists were not taken seriously by the Army. Thus they were equipped not with Mausers, but with ancient rifles, veterans of at least twenty colonial campaigns, that had not had to fire a single shot during the Civil War up to this hour.

Now the two barrels almost touched the pathologically malformed cranium of the murderer, to do their first job of the campaign. The trigger trip mechanism of one of the guns could certainly not have been called a marvel of mechanical ingenuity. But that the other one also failed to function—can that too be attributed solely to chance? The two youths looked at their guns and at each other in perplexity. Both were under twenty, came from rich families and had the white, well-kept hands of sheltered children. Perhaps their stomachs turned and their spirits fell in the sight of blood and spattered brain. They were suddenly ashamed to have meddled with this ghastly business, and without success at that. The others seemed to be too passionately immersed in their slaughter to notice the failure of the old guns and tender minds. Abreojos did not stir a fiber. At his side the last shots of the Moros and Tertios whipped into the victims' writhing flesh. The huge body of the murderer seemed to cover his own pool of blood. No one saw the flushed faces of the two courageous Falangists. They returned to the ranks of the Regulares, as though they had done their job and everything were in best order. The searchlights flared up like fountains and suddenly died into black. There was wild shouting and cursing. A few flares were quickly improvised. The Moros seized the corpses, swung them rhythmically to and fro and tossed them into the yawning ditch. Esteban Ahimundo y Abreojos was also swung back and forth and tossed into the grave—the last to go, since he lay on the outside wing. He fell soft. He broke no bones. He was saved.

IV

By six o'clock the next morning Esteban Ahimundo y Abreojos had already been brought back to the prison. His good fortune seemed to be concerned solely with preserving him from bloody death; for the rest it by no means smiled upon the shedder of blood. The guard had picked him up near the great cemetery, just as he was attempting to pawn a few golden wedding rings in a thieves' den. More rings were found in his pocket, together with a few gold spectacle frames, cigarette cases and cuff links. He presented an even more hideous aspect than usual. His shirt and trousers were smeared with blood and eaten by lime. His hands showed large abrasions. Yet his shifty mouse-grey eyes revealed no trace of fear, torment or mortal anguish suffered in the course of the past night. The Commandant before whom Abreojos was later led gazed over his head. The monocle frozen between the officer's nose and brow seemed to cloud over with his painful thoughts. The Señor was in all likelihood trying to get to the bottom of the mysterious event. At last he shook off his irksome thoughts, lifted his wrist with an inimitably elegant gesture and glanced at his wrist watch with an expression of boredom. The glass with the poisonously green aperitif sparkled in the sunlight. A passing trace of revulsion curled his mouth.

"Too good for a bullet," he muttered, dictating a new order of whose execution he demanded to be notified early the next morning. That notification, however, was precluded, because a higher Providence at once began to intervene again on behalf of the murderer.

No garrote seemed to have been made to the measurement of Esteban Ahimundo y Abreojos. The store-rooms of the prison were ransacked in vain. During the years preceding the rebellion the garrote had fallen into disuse. Thus there seemed to be no legal means to expedite the evildoer from life to death. Yet, since the entry of the victors there was no other law or precept but the passing whims of the new overlords. The civil administration of the prison had at once turned over its affairs to the military and was anxiously hovering in the background. The Colonello had to be bothered with the Abreojos Case once more. "String him up in the prison yard, to one of the trees there," he hissed, showing the immaculate white of his teeth.

Execution of this order was taken over by an old sergeant in the Foreign Legion, of which two squadrons had been assigned to the prison. The sergeant was a giant of a man, towering half a head above the mighty Abreojos. He was a Scipetar from the region of Scutari, and he was called Mehmed. Mehmed, armed to the teeth even when off duty, strode down the inner prison yard looking out for a suitable point of support.

In the court of the political prison two old sycamore trees eked out an existence, their poorly leaved branches stretched wide. A few prisoners of the Rebels who were enjoying the special favor of walking in the fresh air suddenly stood rooted to the spot. They saw Sergeant Mehmed climbing a ladder held by a laughing Legionnaire and carefully tying a stout rope to one of the muscular sycamore branches. Horror glazed the eyes of the doomed. Mehmed held on to the rope with both hands, kicked away the ladder, remained suspended a few seconds three feet above the ground, to test the strength of rope and branch; Mehmed was a conscientious practitioner of his craft.

The branch did not pass the test. Its outward soundness concealed inward rottenness. It snapped under the load and broke with a loud crack. Mehmed fell to his knees. The prisoners had turned away.

The branch had broken, giving the executioner a hint to seek out a stronger one; but the rope had remained whole. These two facts, as we shall see, constituted another stroke on the part of those benevolent powers who so favored the common murderer.

v

Esteban Ahimundo y Abreojos himself seemed to have grasped that he enjoyed some mysterious form of protection. Even his mouse-grey eyes had given up their flickering motion. The moon had set and a few carbide lamps burnt oppressively and spread a nauseating stench, as a guard of Tertios led him to the sycamore that was to be his gallows tree. Behind the bars of the cells all around over-large eyes appeared, shining like the eyes of beasts. This time it appeared as though everything would come off according to plan. Even the prescribed cleric was present, superfluously trying to keep up the courage of the insensate colossus and poor sinner. Despite his handcuffs, Abreojos smoked one cigarette after the other. Mehmed, his easy-going executioner, placed them in his mouth. (At this very moment seventy innocents were "laid out" by machine guns in the Malaga cemetery, without trial, without spiritual comfort, like mad dogs.) Standing on the ladder, Esteban Ahimundo y Abreojos spat his last cigarette stub high into the air, as Sergeant Mehmed placed the well-oiled noose around his neck. The prisoner could now no longer raise his hands, since they had been finally tied behind his back. As had been the case yesterday, his ropy voice broke out into the enthusiastic call: "Arriba España!" There can be no doubt that this incantation carried magic, for five seconds later he lay on the ground. The branch had withstood the strain; but the noose had parted. The strangled man had lost consciousness—or perhaps he was merely feigning unconsciousness.

The sergeant and his men were more than perplexed. Had the victim been a "Red" they would have quickly finished him off with knife and gun after such a fiasco. This, however, was no mere case of political opposition but a lawfully condemned man, a judicial item to be accounted for. They went for the prison doctor who, ridiculously enough, undertook vigorous efforts at resuscitating the victim who had so stubbornly resisted all attempts to kill him. Abreojos, at any rate, had enough sense to take his time about regaining consciousness. Pitiful moans emanated from his iron torso—moans that cleverly played for time. The inadequately executed man did not open his eyes until the officers themselves appeared on the scene. Mehmed had dispatched an orderly to the Grand Hotel where the Commandant had his quarters. The Colonel was still up. He had been drinking in the bar of the hotel with a few younger gentlemen. among whom were two stiffly smart German aviators. The news that Esteban Ahimundo y Abreojos had again escaped execution aroused amazement, admiration and cynical merriment. With steps more or less firm, the entire company, some dozen gentlemen, followed the Colonel into the prison. Abreojos was gently reclining against the old sycamore, which seemed to shield him like a mother. The carbide lamps hissed and stank. The naked walls with the square, barred little windows lay in the darkness. The eyes of the murderer at once began to wander observantly back and forth between the officers. A heavy sigh of "Arriba España"—the well-tested slogan—escaped his lips, as though, despite all exhortation, he were unable to relinquish his patriotism.

The Colonel approached him and fixed him with emaciated eyes.

"You goddam ape," he said in soft monotone, "why do you make so much trouble for me? Why don't you want to die?"

Esteban Ahimundo y Abreojos lifted his already unshackled hands up
to the officers. His voice still sounded choked. It creaked in astonishment, as thought it had to be dragged in from afar.

"I die gladly . . . But I die for the Señores . . . Arriba España . . ."

It cannot be denied that a certain movement went through the group
following these words. Why should this man die, who had, by a spectacular miracle, already won two tussles with death, who had actually
arisen sound in body and limbs from the mass grave? It would be a pity
to challenge Death a third time and thereby jeopardize the two precious
victories. War is war. Let the enemy die, the red dog, the corrupter of
the people who wishes to abolish property and to destroy the better
people, the gentlemen. It is this weak-kneed, soft-hearted enemy, this
whining equalitarian who knows nothing of the dangerous life—it is
upon him that all hatred must be concentrated. This man here is a murderer. All right! Who of us standing here is not a murderer? The old
order cannot be restored without murder. The thoughts of the slightly
inebriate officers rose to a dangerous degree of honesty. The Colonel was
staring straight ahead, smoking his cigarette, and keeping silence. His inscrutable features wore a sneer.

A captain, his breast decorated to the limit with medals and orders,
suddenly stepped forward. He wore a patch over his left eye, while he
carried his right arm in a sling. This imposing image of warrior-like terror
now tossed away his cigarette with a determined gesture, drew himself
up before the Commandant in careless elegance and broke out into a
rumbling bass voice:

"My Colonel, kindly leave this man to me!"

In some surprise the Commandant regarded Captain Sanrubio. This
Sanrubio of the Tertios was an important figure in the Nationalist Army,
a reckless hero who had been specially mentioned in many dispatches,
a ruthless heaven-stormer whom the generals put in the most dangerous
spot in every offensive and important action. The shock troop under this
wild battle crier was the terror of friend and foe alike. In contrast to
this bully the smart young Colonel's talent lay more in the field of
strategy and diplomacy. He did not feel at home in the front-line trenches
or in hand-to-hand combat, nor was bloody business of this sort among
his duties. Yet he was seized with a slight feeling of uncertainty in the
face of this hero. He put it off as the good-natured indulgence of a superior teacher for a reckless and amusing student of no special intelligence.
Truly, no superior officer could very well afford to deny this hero a
request. The Colonel smiled questioningly:

"What do you propose to do with this dangerous caveman, my dear Sanrubio?"

The Captain seemed surprised at this obtuse question of the Commandant.

"My dear Colonello," he growled indulgently, "this is the very type of which I can never get enough."

A remnant of legalistic formalism compelled the Colonel to a few lightning calculations. Two sex murders, three holdup murders, a sentence of death! But judgment had been pronounced by a court-martial of a controversial, deposed and thus illegal government. Accordingly it was wholly null and void. A new trial would have to be set for Esteban Ahimundo y Abreojos. But we have other things to do than to enjoy juicy criminal trials. Properly seen this anthropoid ape must now, until convicted by our own courts, be regarded in the light of an accused (if, indeed, he will be re-indicted), but by no means as a convict. As Commandant it is my right to take the case, as it were, into my own custody, and to decide his fate later, after military operations have been concluded.

Thus ran the subtle thought process of a man who night after night, without the slightest trace of thoughts of this kind, sacrificed hecatombs of men whose sole guilt consisted in holding another political opinion. But before the Colonel had a chance to make his decision, it so happened that the monster returned to life, rose from beneath the sycamore tree. Pressing his monstrous paw—whose spatulate fingers still strangely wore three or four wedding rings—to his mighty chest, he performed an irreproachable bow in the direction of the Commandant—every inch a proud Andalusian. The man who even during his own trial had hardly uttered a word, rarely more than an indifferent and contemptuous grunt, now proved that he played the gorilla only for outward show, that he was quite capable of a well-turned little speech, delivered with good manners:

"Señor Colonello," he said, neither audacity nor humility in his tone, "be good enough to fulfill the request of this high-born gentleman. The victorious Army shall not have to rue it. I have been picked up because of stupid chance, just as I was about to get together the money to cross the lines of the red murderers to join the brave troops of the generalissimo. That alone is the reason for the unjust treatment I have suffered. God himself did not desire that I should succumb to such injustice—let the noble Señores consider that. I am descended from an ancient and honored family which a bitter fate has brought down in life. Let me die for Spain, rather than die for nothing at all!"

There was dead quiet after this address, which came totally unexpectedly from such lips. No one laughed. The Colonel looked away from Abreojos. One corner of his mouth turned upward in an expression of self-indulgent arrogance and uncertainty.

"Very well, Sanrubio," he turned to the Captain, ringing with precious metal, "but kindly take notice that you will be made fully responsible for every new crime of this admirable scion of an honored family . . ."

No sooner had the warning been uttered when Esteban Abreojos approached the officers with a free stride, clicked his heels and lifted two fingers of his right paw in oath:

"Fear not, Señores! . . . You will have no reason for complaint . . . I swear it on the blood of the Saviour . . ."

VI

It must be admitted in all honesty that the former convict kept his oath. Captain Sanrubio had not the slightest trouble on his account. True, his deeds of valor were not celebrated in song, and many of his comrades insisted that he was a cowardly and vicious dog; but there was little to set him apart from other prize specimens among the Spanish rabble.

After the death of Mehmed the Scipetar, Abreojos advanced to the rank of sergeant, provost, and indispensable executioner. This rise to such a position of a man who had himself been executed at least twice remains a miraculous career. It was, nevertheless, an entirely appropriate and natural career. His advancement caused the shedders of blood no hardship; quite on the contrary. He was so cruelly overworked that he had to be withdrawn from the front. The arbitrary desperado had developed into a splendidly disciplined desperado. In this same wise, Nature has snakes and other reptiles devour creatures whom man declares harmful. The bloody deeds which filled the heart of the murderer with rich satisfaction now stood in the service of the so-called "racial community." They were good works.

A documented legend like the present must be far freer of exaggeration than a purely fictitious story. The number of victims executed by this victim of execution (by means of rifle, machine gun, revolver, or even club and bayonet) was very large. But it is sheer, irresponsible, biased nonsense to speak of ten thousand. Sergeant Esteban Ahimundo y Abreojos thrived in his hard profession. Every day saw an increase in his self-confidence and sinister grandeur. His mouse-grey eyes had ceased their shifting altogether. Tiny and rigid, they remained fixed upon their victims. Ever more gravely the hidalgo heritage asserted itself in the man. His face and body lost their apelike characteristics. His superiors were of one mind in recognizing in him one of the strongest personalities in the entire troop. Thus Abreojos could not escape fame. Death had done well to refuse him. Death further smiled upon him. Once, during an advance, an entire farm house crashed down over his head. Among nine dead and wounded, Abreojos was the only one to escape without a scratch. He was born to die in bed—to reach that happy end reserved, in the words of the Bible, for the elect, for those sated with life.

Translated by RUTH *and* HEINZ NORDEN

Hugo von Hofmannsthal

CAVALRY TALE

BEFORE 6:00 A.M. OF JULY 22, 1848, a raiding force made up of Squadron II, Wallmoden Cuirassiers, Captain Baron Rofrano, with 107 men, left Casino San Alessandro and headed for Milan. An indescribable calm lay over the free, glistening landscape; morning clouds rose like quiet clouds of smoke from the peaks of the distant mountains to the shining sky; the corn stood motionless, and between clusters of trees, which looked as if scrubbed, farmhouses and churches glistened. The raiders were hardly a mile beyond the foremost picket line of their own army, when weapons gleamed up in the cornfields and the vanguard reported enemy infantry. The Squadron formed itself to the charge, by the roadside, heard oddly loud, almost meeouwing bullets whir overhead, attacked across open fields and drove a band of unevenly armed people before it like quail. They were men of Manara's Legion, with strange headgear. The prisoners were handed to a corporal and eight privates and sent to the rear. Outside a fine villa, its driveway flanked by ancient cypress trees, the vanguard reported suspicious figures. Sergeant Anton Lerch dismounted, took twelve men armed with carbines, covered the windows and captured eighteen students of the Pisan Legion, well-bred, good-looking young men, with white hands and flowing hair. Half an hour later the Squadron picked up a man walking past in the garb of a Bergamo peasant, whose all too harmless and unobtrusive manner aroused suspicion.

Sewed into the lining of his coat, the man carried very important and detailed plans concerning the establishment of partisan bands in the Giudicaria and their cooperation with the army of Piedmont. Toward 10:00 A.M. a herd of cattle fell into the hands of the raiders. Immediately afterward, the raiders ran into a strong enemy detachment firing on the vanguard from behind a churchyard wall. The first platoon under Lieutenant Count Trautsohn hurdled the low wall and, right among the graves, laid into the bewildered enemy, part of whom escaped into the church and thence by the vestry door into a thicket. The twenty-seven new prisoners reported as Neapolitan guerrillas under Papal officers. The Squadron had one man killed. Scouting round the thicket, Corporal Wotrubek and Cuirassiers Holl and Haindl took a light howitzer behind two farmhorses by cutting the crew down, grabbing the horses' reins and turning them about. Corporal Wotrubek, slightly wounded, was sent back to headquarters with a report on the several actions and other fortuitous incidents; the prisoners were likewise transported to the rear; but the howitzer was taken along by the Squadron, which, after detaching an escort, still numbered eighty-seven horse.

According to coincident statements from the various prisoners, the city of Milan was quite deserted by the enemy, both regulars and irregulars, as well as stripped of all artillery and stores, and so the Captain could not deprive himself and the Squadron of the pleasure of entering this great, fair, helplessly sprawling city. To the toll of the noon-day bells, to the general march, blared into the steely glitter of the sky by the four trumpets, clanging past a thousand windows and thrown back on eighty-seven cuirasses and eighty-seven drawn, presented arms—streets right and left like aroused ant-heaps, filling with stunned faces—pale, cursing figures vanishing into doorways, sleepy windows opened by the bare arms of unknown beauties—past Santa Babila, past San Fedele, past San Carlo, past the world-famous marble Cathedral, past San Satiro, San Giorgio, San Lorenzo, San Eustorgio—with all their age-old iron gates opening for silver saints and brocade-clad, starry-eyed women to beckon out of candlelight and clouds of incense—expecting fire from a thousand attics, dark archways, low dives, and never seeing anything but half-grown girls and boys showing white teeth and dark curls—seeing all this with flashing eyes, from trotting horses, through a mask of blood-spattered dust—in by the Venetian Gate, out again by the Porta Ticinese: this was how the fair Squadron rode through Milan.

Not far from the last-named city gate, where pretty plane trees grew on a spreading glacis, Sergeant Anton Lerch thought he saw a familiar feminine face in the ground-floor window of a new, bright yellow house. Curious, he turned in the saddle; and since at the same time some stiff paces by his horse led him to suspect that it had caught a stone in a front shoe, and since riding at the tail end of the Squadron he could break ranks without disturbance, he was induced to dismount, having virtually steered the head of his horse into the hallway of the house in question. There, he had hardly lifted the bay's second white-stockinged front foot, to examine the hoof, when indeed a door opened into the hall from the interior of the house and a corpulent, still rather young woman in a somewhat ruined morning-gown emerged from a bright room, whose garden windows held some little pots of basil and red geraniums. Also, a mahogany cupboard and a mythological group made of candy appeared to the Sergeant, while in a pilaster mirror his sharp eyes took in the opposite wall of the room, filled by a large, soft bed and a tapestry door, through which a fat, clean-shaven man was just retreating.

As the Sergeant recalled the woman's name, and many other things —that she was widowed or divorced from a Croat paymaster sergeant, and that he had spent a few evenings and half-nights with her in Vienna nine or ten years ago, in the company of another, her real lover at the time—his eyes were seeking to draw the old, lusciously slender figure out again from beneath her present fullness. The woman stood there, smiling at him in a half flattering Slavic way which drove the blood into his strong neck and under his eyes. He felt shy, because of a certain affected manner in which she addressed him, as well as because of the morning gown and the furniture. His somewhat awkward glance followed a big fly across the comb in the woman's hair, and all he seemed interested in was how to chase this fly by quickly putting his hand on the white, cool neck. Still, the consciousness of the actions and other fortuitous incidents of the day filled him from top to toe, so that he pushed her head forward with a heavy hand and said: "Vuic"—this was her name, which he certainly had not uttered in ten years and, in fact, had completely forgotten—"in a week we'll be marching in, and then this here," pointing to the half open door of the room, "will be my quarters." Meanwhile, on hearing several doors slam in the house and feeling himself urged to leave by his horse, which first silently tugged at the reins and then loudly whinnied after the others, he mounted and trotted off to catch up with the Squadron, without taking with him any reply from Vuic but an embarrassed laugh, with her head bent down against her neck. But the spoken word showed its power. Riding along the file column at a walk that was no longer fresh under the heavily, metallically glowing sky, his glance caught in the accompanying dust cloud, the Sergeant saw himself living more and more in the room with the mahogany furniture and the basil pots and altogether in a civilian atmosphere, yet with something warlike shining through—an atmosphere of comfort and pleasant violence outside the service, an existence in slippers, with the saber guard sticking out of the left dressing-gown pocket. The clean-shaven, fat man who had vanished through the tapestry door, something in between a cleric and a retired valet, played an important part in this existence, almost more so than the fine wide bed and Vuic's fine white skin. Now, the clean-shaven one took the place of a familiarly treated, somewhat obsequious friend, who related court gossip and brought tobacco and capons; now, he was pushed around, had to pay hush money, was connected with all sorts of doings, was a Piedmontese confidant, Papal cook, procurer, owner of suspicious houses with dark garden rooms for political meetings, and grew into a gigantic, spongelike figure into whose body you could strike bung-holes in twenty places and draw gold rather than blood.

The raiders encountered nothing more in the afternoon hours, and the Sergeant's reveries were not disturbed. But a thirst for unexpected income had stirred in him, for gratuities, for ducats suddenly dropping into his pocket. The thought of his imminent first entrance into the room with the mahogany furniture was like a splinter in his flesh, about which wishes and desires festered.

Toward evening, having fed and somewhat rested their horses, the raiders sought to advance in an arc in the direction of Lodi and the Adda bridge. There, after all, contact with the enemy was highly probable; and a village lying off the road in a darkening hollow with a half crumbling bell tower seemed so alluringly suspicious to the Sergeant that, beckoning Privates Holl and Scarmolin to him, he turned off with the two from the Squadron's course and all but hoped in the village to surprise an enemy general with scant escort, or otherwise to earn an extraordinary reward—so excited was his imagination. Coming to the pile of wretched, seemingly deserted hovels, he ordered Holl to circle them on the right, and Scarmolin on the left, while he himself, pistol in hand, prepared to gallop down the street. Soon, however, feeling hard flagstones under him on which some slippery grease had besides been poured, he had to pull his horse up to a walk. The village remained deathly still; no child, no bird, no breath of air. On either side stood dirty little houses with the mortar fallen off the walls. On the naked bricks, here and there, ugly sketches had been drawn with charcoal; peering inside between stripped doorjambs, the Sergeant saw an occasional lazy, half naked figure slouching on a bedstead or dragging itself about a room as with wrenched hips. His horse walked heavily and pushed its hindlegs up under its body with an effort, as if they were of lead. While he turned and bowed down, for a look at the rear shoes, steps shuffled out of a house, and when he straightened up there was a female walking right before his horse. He could not see her face. She was half dressed; her dirty, ragged skirt of flowered satin dragged in the gutter, her bare feet were stuck in dirty slippers; she walked so closely in front of the horse that the breath from its nostrils moved the greasy, shining curls that hung down on her bare neck below an old straw hat. Yet she walked no faster and did not get out of the horseman's way. From a doorsill to the right two bleeding rats, teeth dug into each other, rolled into the middle of the street; the loser squealed so piteously that the Sergeant's horse stopped and stared at the ground with slanting head and audible breath. A squeeze of his thighs sent it forward again, and now the woman had vanished in a hallway, without the Sergeant's having seen her face. Out of the next house a dog came running hastily with its head up, dropped a bone in the middle of the street and tried to dig it into a crack in the pavement. It was a white mongrel bitch with hanging teats; she dug with devilish zeal, then picked the bone up in her teeth and carried it a bit further. Starting to dig again, she was joined by three more dogs. Two were quite young, with soft bones and flabby skin; without barking and unable to bite, they pulled at each other's jaws with dull teeth. The dog that had come with them was a light-yellow whippet with a body so swollen that it could only carry itself very slowly on its four thin legs. Its head seemed much too small on the fat, drum-tight body; in the small, restless eyes lay a dreadful expression of pain and anxiety. Then two more dogs leaped in: a skinny, white one of an utterly greedy ugliness, black creases running down from its inflamed eyes, and a bad dachshund with long legs, who raised his head to the Sergeant and looked at him. He was very old. His eyes were infinitely tired and sad. The bitch, however, ran round before the horseman, in stupid haste; the two pups were snapping soundlessly at the horse's shanks with their soft mouths and the whippet dragged its ghastly body right in front of the hoofs. The bay could not move a step. The Sergeant wanted to fire his pistol at one of the beasts, but the pistol missed fire. He drove both spurs into the horse and thundered over the cobblestones; but after a few strides he had to pull up sharply, for here the road was blocked by a cow which a lad was dragging to slaughter on a tight rope. The cow, shuddering back from the smell of blood and from a fresh, black calf-skin that was nailed to the gate-post, dug her legs into the ground and sucked the reddish, sunny evening haze into distended nostrils. With wretched eyes, before the lad got her across with stick and rope, she grabbed herself a mouthful of the hay that the Sergeant had fastened to his saddlebow. He had passed the last houses of the village by then and, riding between two low, crumbling walls, could see his way ahead, beyond an old, single-arched stone bridge over what seemed a dry ditch; but in the steps of his horse he felt such an indescribable heaviness, such an inability to move on, that every inch of the walls to his right and left, indeed each of the centipedes and roaches seated there, seemed to be moving laboriously past his eyes, and it appeared to him as though he had spent ages riding through the repulsive village. A heavy, roaring breath came from the horse's chest and Anton Lerch, failing at once to interpret this unaccustomed sound correctly, looked first above and sideways for its cause, and finally in the distance. There, beyond the stone bridge and approximately as far from it as he was, he noticed a man from his own regiment approaching—and a sergeant at that, and mounted on a bay with white-stockinged front legs. Knowing well that there was no such horse in the whole Squadron except the one on which he sat at that moment, but still unable to make out the other's face, he impatiently spurred his horse to a lively trot, at which the other increased his pace in just the same way until no more than a stone's throw parted them and —as the two horses, each from its side, at one instant, each with the same, white-stockinged front foot trod on the bridge and the Sergeant, dumb-foundedly recognizing himself in the vision, tore his horse back like mad and held his right hand with fingers outstretched against the specter—the figure, similarly pulling up and raising its hand, suddenly ceased to be there, Privates Holl and Scarmolin emerged right and left from the ditch with untroubled faces, and simultaneously across the meadow, strongly and not very far off at all, the trumpets of the Squadron blew to the charge.

Racing up a mound at top speed, the Sergeant saw the Squadron already at a gallop toward a copse from which hostile cavalry with pikes were hastily debouching, saw, as he gathered his four loose reins in his left and wrapped the check-rein about his right, how the fourth platoon swerved from the Squadron and slowed down; was now on thundering ground, now in the strong smell of dust, now amidst the enemy; lashed out at a blue arm wielding a pike; saw next to him the Captain's face with eyes wide open and teeth grimly bared; was suddenly wedged in a mass of hostile faces and strange colors, went down in a mass of swung blades, thrust the nearest one into the throat and off his horse; saw Private Scarmolin by his side laughingly lop off the fingers of a man's bridle hand, cutting deeply into the horse's neck; felt the melee loosen up and all at once was alone on the bank of small brook, behind an enemy officer on an iron-grey horse.

The officer wanted to get across the brook; the grey refused. The officer wheeled him about, showing the Sergeant a young, very pale face and the mouth of a pistol—when a saber with the full weight of a galloping horse behind it drove into his mouth. The Sergeant pulled the saber back, and at the very spot where the falling man's fingers left it he caught the curb-rein of the iron-grey horse, which lightly and daintily as a deer lifted its feet above its dying master.

As the Sergeant rode back with his beautiful prey, the sun, setting in a dense mist, cast a huge red glow over the meadow. Pools of blood seemed to spread even in spots where there were no hoof-marks whatever. Red was reflected on the white uniforms and laughing faces; armor gleamed and glowed, and blankets, and most of all, three small fig trees on whose soft leaves the laughing horsemen had wiped the blood-rills of their sabers. The Captain was halting to one side of the red-mottled trees, and by his side the staff trumpeter raised his trumpet, which looked as if dipped in red juice, to his mouth and blew Assembly. The Sergeant, riding from platoon to platoon, saw that the Squadron had not lost a man but had gained nine led horses. He rode to the Captain, to report—always with the grey beside him, who pranced with his head held high and sniffed the air like the young, beautiful and vain horse that he was. The Captain listened absently to the report. He waved Lieutenant Count Trautsohn to him, who promptly dismounted and with six men unhitched the captured howitzer behind the front of the Squadron, had the piece dragged aside and sunk by the six in a small backwater formed by the brook, mounted again and, after driving the two now superfluous draught horses off with the flat blade, returned in silence to his post before the first platoon.

While this went on, the Squadron, lined up in double file, was not actually restless; nevertheless, a not quite usual mood prevailed, traceable to the excitement of four successful engagements fought in one day and expressing itself in quick outbursts of half restrained laughter as well as in half loud shouts exchanged among the men. The horses were not standing quietly either, least of all those that had strange captured horses put between them. After such opportunities, the formation seemed narrow to all; inwardly, horsemen and victors of this kind were now demanding to ride in open swarm against a new foe, to hit out freely and capture other horses. At this moment Captain Baron Rofrano rode close to the front of his Squadron and, lifting great lids from somewhat sleepy blue eyes, commanded audibly but without raising his voice: "Release led horses!" The Squadron stood deathly still. Only the iron grey beside the Sergeant stretched his head until his nostrils all but touched the forehead of the Captain's horse. The Captain secured his saber, drew one of his pistols from the holster and, flicking a speck of dust off the gleaming barrel with the back of the bridlehand, repeated his command in a somewhat louder voice, following up at once with a count of "One" and "Two." Having counted "Two," he fixed his veiled gaze on the Sergeant, who sat motionless in the saddle before him, and looked rigidly into his face. Anton Lerch's stiffly controlled eyes, in which only now and then something dejected, doglike, flared up and vanished again, might have expressed a sort of humble trust sprung from a service relationship of many years, yet his consciousness was hardly touched by the tremendous tension of that moment and entirely swamped by the divers images of an odd comfort, and from depths in him that were quite unknown to himself a bestial anger rose against this man there, who would take the horse away from him—so awful a wrath at this man's face, voice, presence and whole existence as it can only spring mysteriously from living close together for many years. Whether in the Captain something similar went on, or whether to him the whole soundlessly spreading peril of critical situations seemed concentrated in this instant of mute insubordination, remains in doubt: he raised his arm with a relaxed, almost affected gesture, and while, contemptuously drawing in his upper lip, he counted, "Three," the shot cracked and the Sergeant, hit in the forehead, struck the neck of his horse with his chest and then fell to the ground, between the bay and the iron grey. He had not hit the ground before all subalterns and privates got rid of their captured horses by a wrench at the reins or a kick, and the Captain, calmly securing his pistol, could lead the Squadron, which still quivered from a lightning-like stroke, anew against the enemy that seemed to rally in an indistinctly dusky distance. The enemy, however, did not accept the new attack, and not much later the raiding force, undisturbed, reached the southern outposts of its own army.

Translated by E. B. ASHTON

Richard Beer-Hofmann

MEMORIAL ORATION
ON WOLFGANG AMADEUS MOZART

FROM LOFTY MOUNTAINS the water gushes down to deep valleys below. It breaks forth from a glacial lake; wildly storming waters from contiguous valleys rush to join it; and, plunging and falling from level to level, gaining amplitude and richness, it seeks its way. From treasure hoards that slumber secretly, deep in the stark mountains roundabout, confluent brooks bring revealing evidences of their origin to it, and if one grasps in the hollow of one's hand the sand from its banks, there sifts with the sand itself, through the fingers, dark iron ore, red copper, gray cobalt and the gold and silver from the Rauris. And should one dip a hand in the rushing stream—even where it has descended to the plain—one will still feel: from the heights comes this turbulent flood which must to the sea. Fed by glaciers which border the primordial ice, the surging stream leaps bright-eyed. Deep below, is the mist of the valleys.

From the Venetian coast a highway rises to the snow-covered passes of the Tauern and seeks the slopes where once the now forgotten Ambisontians and Alauni guarded the sacred salt deposits. Laden with oil and dark wine, mules first trod the trail; the marching feet of Roman legions stamped it wider, and, before the ancient gods retire to their final rest, their sacred nakedness still glistens in the mountains.

Where these two meet—the stream from the Nordic Alps and the highway from the sea coming up from the south—a city has spread. There Mozart will be born!

Music is around this child when it wakes: The ponderous bells of many churches, bright and somber, vibrating like human voices, and with them, smaller chimes, braided together in the graceful songs of the "Residenz" glockenspiel; and over all this—greeting the hours of the day from the mountains—the organ of "High Salzburg Castle."

No alien sounds swing down to the child from above. What now echoes over the precincts of the city from the organ tones on the mountain had been in his father before him; music for him only, inaudible to others. But now there sounds, so that all may hear, Leopold Mozart's shepherd minuet in May, a hunting song in September and in February a carnival piece. And morning and evening they have captured the wind up there in mighty bellows; and the wild morning wind which rends the mountain mists and the gentle evening winds—they are all servants of music!

And when the bells of the city fall silent, its streams murmur to the lad. Not only those of the marble fountain where, over the dolphins, enticed of old by music, the triton flourishes his horn. A road leads to the castle of Marcus Sitticus, where brightly gushing fountains are harnessed to furnish power for ingenious displays. There he will first see the radiant god flay the bungler Marsyas; in a stone grotto, Orpheus will stand, his hand lifted, ready to play the song which will open for him the way to the land of the dead; a door will spring open and on a stage of many colors crowded about a house in course of building, laborers, knocking and hammering, perform their work, citizens go about their business and noble gentlemen bow to each other out of their windows. And in the midst of this noise and the comical haste of the animated figures is heard a choral; the water which drives this mechanism also gives power to the organ which now sounds. The boy may first here, by an outward sign, perceive the task of creative genius which God had conferred upon him— as on all whom He has summoned to creative work: to observe the continual hustle and bustle, the daily toil, the evanescent desire and ultimate pain of little people, smile gently, enjoy its colorfulness—and at the same time to listen to the chorus of thanksgiving which solemnly and enduringly ascends from the noisy restlessness of their activity, and to know that one source gives life to both.

But before he is able to understand all this, he outgrows this city. Other children may listen to fairy tales where kings and emperors, distant and magical, pass by like fabulous beasts and good fairies. But to this child's wonderful fingers was early given the power to turn the pages of the world like a book of fairy tales. Far behind him now are the city and the "Untersberg" where the ancient emperor of legend sleeps. His imperial majesty, the ruler of the Holy Roman Empire, sends him gold-bordered apparel and invites him to his court; the emperor's daughters lead him by the hand through its mirrored halls; the empress kisses him on the mouth; the emperor himself stands near him and grows speechless when he begins to play.—And this now is the City of Paris; and when the descendant of Saint Louis sits down at table, this child stands near the queen who offers him fruit from golden plates— And now again is he on the island of Britain, and when the king rides with his queen in the park, he bows from the royal carriage to this boy and smilingly winks at him.

Is this a fairy tale?

That they affix to the organ on which he once played a tablet, as an enduring memorial; that the Pope in Rome hangs about this thin childish throat the Order of the Golden Spurs; that a famous old musician, upon hearing this child, sees the labor and the fame of a lifetime crumble to dust: "This child will cause all of us to be forgotten!"—Is this a fairy tale?

If it is not—then what more can he experience who has experienced this? Indignities? They glide down from one about whose slender hips the proud memory of such a childhood rests like golden armor. Poverty? He will bear it smilingly like the costume of a carnival evening. And death? Orpheus knows this: when he dies, his lyre will flame up in the starry heavens as an eternal constellation!

And so this youth may fearlessly reach for the reins of his empire—and what is not within his empire? The elements swarm about him; from the waters loud murmurs rise; all the fires of the deep yearn upwards to him; from the untamed air above come voices, clamorous and insistent. They will be changed to music. And all the vanishing passion and grief of created things lift themselves, demanding that they be given immortality in music! And he touches them—and behold, the reflection of his countenance illumines all! Bright, uncorrupted child's eyes look upon this world; these lips have not tasted bitterness or disgust.

From richly nourished, old and blood-soaked soil grows all that moves us. May it not be—who knows?—that the unstilled yearning of many generations past demands upon these and no other lips to be assuaged? May not, perhaps, our hate be the unexpiated torture of the dead? And what touches us with icy fingers mysteriously in the dark—is it a resurgence of the scarce forgotten terrors of primeval night?

But this master's tones are redolent of meadows bathed in quiet, gentle sunlight in mountain-locked valleys. From virgin soil spring certain elemental forces and, as in the innocence of nature, their various aspects may thrive by the side of one another: hate and laughter, sweet voluptuousness, brutal greed and noble grief, grow upward on slender stalks, their roots laved by clear paradisean streams, and the merry breeze of blissful gardens blows about their chalices!

The master beckons!

And on the coast of Crete the sea furiously foams and threatens— Has Idomeneo broken his oath! Withdraw, sea, behind your shore! Make place for the March! Masks, did you think? No masks! For where could be more truth than he gave each face? Ghosts? But feel how their hearts beat! Listen to Leporello, how he still shivers with the cold of a sleepless night; how he flogs his courage to tell his master off—yet, bragging, cowardly, voracious and thrashed, he will remain with him to the end. He

may take Osmin with him—reeling Osmin—and Monostatos, the lustful
ape—(careful there! Have him on a chain!). And Papageno mincingly
will bring up the rear!

But here are others! You two, clinging to each other, Belmont and Con-
stance you are the faithful lovers; things that trouble you vanish quickly,
like a shower on an early summer night.—And the voices which now
weave through each other, I recognize too! Make room, you peasants,
that I may see your masters— Have you changed your costumes? Are you
hiding behind bushes? Are you using the darkness as a mask before your
faces to conceal your lovemaking? Is this really but a boisterous day of
jolly confusion, a rollicking day for light hearted love! Do you see Don
Juan's white plumes glisten? She who glides behind him like his shadow
—behold! She loves! She may warn, threaten, curse him to his face. But
beneath all her veils her cheeks flame crimson red with memory! Greet
Donna Anna! Black crepe flutters about this pure brow; but if you think
she is bowed low with suffering—have a care! She will snap back to her
revenge like a noble steel blade! Are there more, crowding forward? Is
the procession without end? Strange costumes and priests and incandescent fire and steam— Are they gathering into a cloud? You, who burst
forth from the clouds like shafts of light—you blessed youths—are you the
last? Is no one else behind you? Silence! I need no answer! For even he
who has never seen him recognizes the eyes of him who paces behind
you. Even to you, Somber One, who stand beckoning at the end of every
road, the master has given a voice— It resounds from dark choirs when
he sings himself to eternal peace!

So here the master stands—placed by destiny—on the common border
of two epochs. To him, as to no other, was it given to make known to
those who were to come after him the face of his own time before it
changed and at the same time to be the blessed harbinger of that which
remains eternally sheltered behind the changing faces of all times.

Behind golden garden gates his prisoners may still taste the free air,
and the name of him who guards them is Osmin; the time will come
when their flesh will rot away in the dark in a damp stone prison, and
their master's name then will be "Pizarro." At Don Juan's feasts there is
still heard the jubilant choir of masks in an All Hail to liberty; the time
will come when choirs of prisoners in dismal dungeons will groan to
heaven for liberty. The master's "Masonic Threnody" may still mourn in
pious song for the death of noble men— Blood and more blood must flow
before a highway will be free for "The Funeral March of a Hero."   .

Our soul does not always wish to tarry with you, Wolfgang Amadeus

Mozart! Too long have we been taught to search the most secret recesses of our soul. We know much too much of suffering. We turn our gaze away from the white and carefree forehead of Jove to seek the compassionate eyes which dwell under the painfully knitted brow of Prometheus.

But in spring and in the days of happiness when we step into our gardens of an early morning and with limbs still relaxed from sleep, enjoy like a boon the moist air of early spring and the fragrance of the earth:— and high above us a bird, its earthly bonds eased by flight, thrusts itself against the sky, pouring out the happiness of its life in song—then we greet you, Wolfgang Amadeus Mozart! And to the spring and to our happiness and to you, flows our soul—irresistibly—as the water gushes from the high mountains above down to the deep valleys below!

Translated by SAMUEL R. WACHTELL

Arthur Schnitzler

PIERRETTE

"I SAY," said Nachtigall after some hesitation, "if there is *one* man to whom I should not grudge it . . . yet, how is it to be arranged?" Then, suddenly, "Are you courageous?"

"Funny question," said Fridolin, giving himself the air of an offended student, ready to fight a duel.

"I do not mean it—*that* way."

"Then what do you really mean? Why is a special courage necessary for just that opportunity? What could happen to anyone?" He laughed sharply and contemptuously.

"Nothing could happen to *me*, except that today for the last time . . . well, that, too, is perhaps. . . ." He stopped short and again peeped behind the curtain.

"Well, what next?"

"What do you mean?" Nachtigall asked it as if out of a dream.

"Go on—since you have begun . . . Secret meeting? Restricted set? Invited guests only?"

"I don't know. The other day they were thirty, the first time only sixteen."

"A ball? Dancing?"

"Of course a ball." Now he seemed to resent having spoken at all.

"And you are playing music for it?"

"What do you mean by 'for it'? I don't know for *what;* really I don't know. I play and I go on playing and playing . . . blindfolded. . . ."

"Nachtigall, Nachtigall, what song are you singing here?"

Nachtigall sighed gently. "Yet not thoroughly blindfolded; not so that I could see absolutely nothing. You must know, I can see in the mirror over the black bandage on my eyes. . . ." Again he was silent.

"In one word," said Fridolin impatiently and with contempt, yet in some strange excitement, "naked wenches."

"Don't say *wenches,* Fridolin," Nachtigall was rather offended. "You never have seen such women."

Fridolin cleared his throat slightly.

"And how much is the admission?" He asked it casually.

"Tickets you mean, and so on . . . What an idea! . . ."

"Well, how do you get in?" asked Fridolin with his lips tight, drumming the table with his fingers.

"Password, password, my dear, you must know the password; and there is a different one each time."

"And the one for today?"

"Don't yet know, not yet; shall get it from the coachman."

"Take me with you, Nachtigall."

"Impossible, too dangerous."

"But a minute ago you said you would not 'grudge' me. . . . You *will* make it possible for me?"

Nachtigall looked him down discriminatingly.

"You could not go anyway as you are now, in this suit of yours. Because everyone is masked. Have you got a mask or something? Ladies and gentlemen masked. Impossible. Perhaps next time. Shall try to invent something, find something."

He listened to some noise outside and peeped again behind the curtain and, obviously eased, he said, "There is the cab. Goodbye."

"You cannot escape like that. You must take me with you." Fridolin had seized his arm.

"But, my friend . . ."

"Leave everything to me. I know already that it is 'dangerous'—perhaps that is just what makes me want it so badly."

"But I told you, without a mask and without a fancy-dress. . . ."

"There are costume shops."

"At one o'clock in the morning? . . ."

"Listen, Nachtigall, at the corner of Wickenburg street there is such a shop. Every day I pass the sign several times." And hastily, with increasing excitement, "You will remain here another quarter of an hour, Nachtigall, whilst I am going to make a bid for luck. The owner of the shop is likely to live in the same house. If not—I have to resign hope. Fate shall decide. There is a coffee-house too, Vindobona I think is the name. You will tell the coachman that you have forgotten something there. You will get out of the cab and enter the coffee-house. I shall be waiting behind the door, you will tell me the password in a jiffy and return to the cab. I, in case I should have succeeded in getting a fancy-dress, shall take another cab and follow yours; what will happen after that we must leave to luck. Your risk, Nachtigall, on my word of honor, is just as much my risk."

Several times Nachtigall had attempted to interrupt Fridolin, but in vain. Fridolin now paid his check by throwing the money on the table together with too large a tip—for this seemed to Fridolin to match the style of that night—and then he went away. Outside there was a cab waiting. In the driver's seat the coachman sat motionless, dressed in black, a high hat on his head; like a mourning-coach, thought Fridolin. After some minutes, almost running, he reached the house that he had been looking for. He rang the bell and, when the janitor came, he asked him whether the costumer Gibiser was living in the house; at the bottom of his heart he hoped that this would not be the case. . . . As a matter of fact, Gibiser did live there, on the floor beneath the shop. The janitor didn't seem surprised at the late visitor. Made affable by a good tip from Fridolin, he even told him that it was not unusual, at carnival-time, to see people coming in the dead of night to borrow fancy-dress costumes. He kept the lighted candle high above his head, so that Fridolin might see the steps, till he heard him ring the bell. Mr. Gibiser, as if he had waited behind the door, opened it himself. He was a haggard man, bald, without a beard; he wore an outmoded, flowered dressing-gown and a Turkish cap with a tassel, so that he looked like a funny old man on the stage. Fridolin told him what he had come for, and that he didn't care about the price. To that Mr. Gibiser remarked, almost with disdain, "I charge what is due me, and not more."

By a winding staircase he led Fridolin into his store-room. There was a smell of silk, velvet, perfume, dust and dry flowers; from the flimsy darkness there came flashes of silver and red; and at once there were many little bulbs glimmering between the open closets in a long, narrow corridor, the end of which was invisible in the darkness. At the right and at the left there hung fancy-dresses of all kinds: at one side, pages, knights, peasants, hunters, scholars, orientals, fools; on the other side, ladies-in-waiting, bourgeois girls, peasant women, chambermaids, queens-of-the-night. Above were placed the head-gear that belonged to the costumes. Fridolin had a sensation as of walking between rows of hanged men and women who were about to engage in dancing. Mr. Gibiser walked behind him.

"Has the gentleman any special wish? Louis-Quatorze? Directoire? Old-German?"

"I need a black monk's habit and a black mask, nothing else."

At that moment there came from the end of the corridor a clashing as of breaking glass; frightened, Fridolin looked into the costumer's face as if he were bound to give an explanation at once. Gibiser himself, however, stood transfixed. He groped to find a light-switch—a dazzling brightness fell immediately, down to the end of the corridor. There stood a small table laid out with dishes, glasses and bottles. From the two chairs at the left and the right two men rose, masked as hangmen in red robes, whilst at the same moment a fragile little girl disappeared under the table. With long strides Gibiser precipitated himself towards the table, reached over and grasped in his hand a white wig; just then the little girl, very young, almost a child, crept from under the table. She was clad in a Pierrette's costume with white silk stockings. She ran down the corridor so fast towards Fridolin that he inevitably caught her in his arms. Gibiser had dropped the white wig upon the table and, to the right and to the left, he held fast to the pleats of the maskers' costumes. At once he called out to Fridolin, "Sir, please hold on to the little girl." The girl pressed her body close to Fridolin, as if he should protect her. Her small, narrow face was powdered white, some beauty-spots upon it; from her tender bosom came a fragrance of roses and powder; her eyes smiled whimsically, with a show of lust.

"Gentlemen," Gibiser shouted, "you will have to stay here till I can turn you over to the police."

"What do you mean!" the two men shouted back, as if from one mouth. "We followed the girl's invitation."

Gibiser let go, and Fridolin heard him say, "You'll have to explain that in detail. Didn't you see at once that you had to deal with a lunatic?" To Fridolin he said, "Will you kindly excuse this incident?"

"Oh, never mind," said Fridolin. He would have liked best to stay or to take the girl with him—wherever and whatever the consequences. She looked up at him childishly and alluringly, as if spell-bound. The two maskers spoke excitedly to each other.

Mr. Gibiser said in a matter-of-fact manner to Fridolin, "You wish a monk's habit, sir, and a pilgrim's hat and a mask?"

"No," said Pierrette, with her eyes shining, "you must give the gentleman an ermine cloak and a red silk jacket."

"You're not to budge from my side," Gibiser told her. He pointed to a dark gown that hung between the costumes of a lansquenet and a Venetian senator, "This is your size; there is the hat to match; take it, quick, and go."

Now the two others spoke up again. "You must let us go without further delay, Mr. Chibisier."

To Fridolin's great astonishment they pronounced the name Gibiser the French way.

"Nothing of the sort," said the costumer sneeringly. "For the time being you will be kind enough to wait here till I return."

Meanwhile Fridolin donned the habit, bound the ends of the dangling white rope into a knot; Gibiser, on a narrow ladder, passed him the black, broad-brimmed pilgrim's hat, and Fridolin put it on. Yet he did all these things as if under some spell, for stronger and stronger he felt a kind of obligation to stay and protect Pierrette from some threatening danger. The mask that Gibiser now pressed into his hand, and that he tried on at once, smelled of some strange and repulsive perfume.

"Go along in front of me," said Gibiser to the girl, and he pointed imperiously towards the staircase. Pierrette looked over her shoulder to the end of the corridor and waved her hand in a tragi-comic farewell. Fridolin followed her eyes; no hangmen stood there any longer, but two slim, elegant, young gentlemen in tail-coats and white neckties, yet both with red masks on their faces. Pierrette flitted down the winding stairs, Gibiser walked behind her, Fridolin followed. Below, at the landing, Gibiser opened a door that led to the inner rooms and said to Pierrette, "Go to bed at once, you vile creature; after I shall have settled with the two men, I shall have a word with you."

She stood in the door, white and fragile, and shook her head sadly with her eyes on Fridolin. He looked in the mirror on the wall and saw a haggard pilgrim who was none other but himself; he was astonished— although everything had come about in the most natural way.

Pierrette had disappeared; the old costumer locked the door behind her. Then he opened the outer door and forced Fridolin towards the staircase.

"I beg your pardon," said Fridolin, "wh . . ."

"Let that alone. You will pay when you return the things. I trust you."
Yet Fridolin did not move on.

"Will you swear that you won't hurt the little one?"

"That's none of your business, sir."

"I heard you call her a lunatic some time ago. Now you call her a vile creature. A very striking contradiction, you won't deny?"

"Well, is not a lunatic vile in the presence of God?"

Fridolin shivered with disgust. "Anyhow," he said, "we shall have to find ways and means. I am a physician, you see; we shall have to discuss this matter tomorrow."

Glibly and silently Gibiser laughed. In the staircase some light flared up suddenly. At once the door between Gibiser and Fridolin was closed, and the bolt shot. Fridolin, going down the stairs, took off the hat, the gown and the mask and tucked everything under his arm. The janitor opened the door—the mourning-coach was standing opposite with the motionless coachman in the driver's seat.

Translated by MARY P. BITTNER

Hermann Broch

INTRODUCTION TO A PEASANT NOVEL

THE SNOW LIES on the branches of the fir woods outside, it lies in my garden, it clings to the rocky clefts and fissures of the Kuppronwand, the bulk of which rises high and steep behind my house, hidden, it is true, behind the treetops of the surrounding forest, not to be seen from any of my windows, nevertheless constantly felt through the might of its turreting stones: one is aware of the mountain without seeing it, just as one senses even the snow that covers it. A man living on the seashore is unable in the surf of his thinking to think a single thought out of unison with the sea. The same is true for one who has settled on the shores of the high mountains: everything that reaches his senses, every tone, every color, every bird-call, every sunbeam, all of this is but an echo of that great silent mass, echo of the quiescent mountains, their furrows kindled by the light, painted by the colors, submerged into unearthliness by the night, surfed round by sounds—then must not man, he who in his soul is ever again a bird-call, a color, a sunbeam and night, must not he also become a lasting echo of this overpowering silence, a vibrating and responsive instrument on which the silence plays?

Here I sit, an aging man, an old country doctor, trying to write down for myself something of that which lies in amorphousness behind me and which, nevertheless, I once realized. I try to write it and yet I can scarcely lay hold on it. Alas, it all lies in getting possession of the knowing and forgetting through which our life-course runs, now emerging, now sinking down again and sometimes vanishing completely, as frightening as though a person standing in an open field under the full rays of the sun were to be conjured away suddenly, sucked up by space, sucked up by time, overwhelmed by both.

Year after year I have gone on in this formlessness although mine was the congenial and uncommon lot of working on the lofty edifice of science, not, to be sure, as one of its master-builders, but only as a modest member in a line of workers, limited to the almost anonymous work of the hospital and laboratory, one of many bringing stone after stone to this immense structure, often merely seeking and recognizing the next partial achievement, but always with an inkling of the whole plan, illumined by the invisible goal of humanity, the goal never to be reached, which is set up for just such work as this. That was my life, its welfare and its drudgery, and for all that it had passed in amorphousness, it may be, because of the smallness of my soul which could not bear that the knowledge of the whole has to remain incomprehensible, reserved for the whole of the never-ending humanhood, whereas I could only be enlarged by particles of knowledge, but it may be, also, that this smallness of soul simply was no longer able to endure the weight of silence pertaining to the scientific world. Yet neither could I bear any longer the muteness of a daily round that makes the word superfluous in work and in life, nor that dumb punctuality with which the patients were delivered to the hospitals and nursed back to health—a silent mechanization that could hardly be called nursing—nor that punctual taciturnity in which the city noises play themselves out, the traffic of the trolley-cars, the opening and closing of shops, and when I think it over today I almost conclude that the retching disgust that had come over me had a universal significance and not one limited to myself alone.

Yes, it seems to me as if the formlessness of existence in which one day after another is dissolved to a has-not-been, were an outcome of that same noisy taciturnity, as if the formlessness of existence and its language had already become so overpowering that, in a certain sense, it forced people to want it even against their wills, to want it with a kind of loathing, and as though along with this, something terrible were in the offing, something driving uncontrollably toward chaos, something inescapable by which the world would be devoured. And just because this common threat came into such general consciousness, perhaps there awoke in me also the fear of having to lose the diversity of my own life in the mute order of things and city life unless I could rescue myself in time. For many-sided though man may be, there comes a moment in which the path once chosen becomes unchangeable and nothing, not even his manifold gifts, can liberate him from its ruts.

And this is how it came about that with a sudden decision I gave up my scientific life, a deserter, as it were, from science, whose edifice, all at once, though no doubt unjustly so, appeared to me like a tower of Babel, and was driven to come here into the tranquillity of a modest country practice, tired of knowledge, yearning for wisdom, tired of an infinity that did not belong to me but to mankind, tired of a muteness that extinguished yesterday and conferred a value only on tomorrow, tired of the impersonal, and yearning for the infinity of one's own soul, feeling with the force of my every fibre, that only this inner infinity, born into every human being, has the capacity to overcome chaos, muteness and forgetfulness, this infinity that gives rise to a wisdom replete with the super-timelessness of the soul, with yesterday as well as tomorrow, replete with sense of the past as well of the future, that is strong enough to sustain us in joyful expectation over the short span of this life, to lend joy and firmness to our steps as we wander through the time allotted to us, our eyes serene as they sweep here and there in this our world. Such was my yearning and my hope. And yet, on this account, was it necessary to leave the town? Was it not just to escape the systematic aspects of knowledge? Did I desire, perhaps, the disorder of the immediate, or was it only my love of nature? After all, the town also lies embedded in nature as well as the village to which I have fled, and the town's order is also merely a part of the entire human activity. Was my wish only for solitude? Certainly I walk alone through the forest and go over the mountain alone, but in spite of this I am always bound to human existence and human labor; and the tranquillity is there for me in the stables and farms, in the markings of the fields, in the knowledge of the mine-shafts sunk into the body of the rocky hills under my feet, in all this human production and living amidst plants and animals, and whenever I encounter it it seems to be a beautiful reassurance, hardly less than that of nature, even at times greater. Indeed it often happens that a single gun-shot in the woods gives me more than all the wonder of the forest-rustling itself, because it lets me feel myself once again a part of the great human family. Why then had I to escape one human order only to enter another? Why this preference? Perhaps some day I shall find a more exact answer, today I can only conjecture: this rural order has a different relationship to infinity than that of the city or of science, which had become unbearable to me and which I left behind me with so few regrets. There the infinite remained forever and ever an unattainable goal, here it is endemic, sunk into every single element, sunk into every useful act that is carried out in the service of the life-order; and although back there it was my mental efforts for science that guaranteed me an entrance into the order, here it is doing and living, here I am given the opportunity of dwelling in communion with and giving help to others, for it is an order that reflects the wisdom of the soul and its infinite qualities. And because I have succeeded in participating in it more and more, it may also be assumed that here my life may again assemble itself more and more, waiting quietly for that yesterday to manifest again, not, it is true as memory, rather as an unlosable constituent of existence, attesting to the significance of a tomorrow for the sake of which we must live through and wait through this time, short though it may be. Therefore I believe it has not become too late for me and that what I did was right.

For at my age it would be unseemly to cling too much to life, still more unseemly to find life not worth the living and to let it fade away uncomprehended and empty, devoid of that meaning by which we give it the stamp of an infinite order and in which even the seeming forgetfulness does not get lost, comprehensible and apparent today as it once was before it became forgetfulness—, how can, how could it be otherwise! For our ship becomes heavier and heavier, and for all that lighter, as it nears the harbor, hardly any longer a ship, almost wholly cargo, scarcely moving thither, on the contrary, drifting in motionlessness on the placid mirror of evening, weightless though almost overladen, and no one could say whether it sinks down or escapes into the clouds. No one knows anything of the cargo, no one knows the harbor, unfathomable the waters over which we have traveled and are still traveling, unfathomable the heaven that arches above them, unfathomable our own knowledge, disappearing even as it grows—oh, what a deep base of forgetfulness is that on which life rests, how far back must we send memory that can scarcely be considered memory!

Yet, in spite of all, life is a unit, and birth and death are so close that the dying one comprehends his entire life in one last gasp of farewell! Year after year has lapsed since I fled here in order to bring formlessness into form again, and often it seems to me that this came to pass because of impatience, impatience for the last hour in which the unity should reveal itself and take shape, and again it seems as if that hour is growing out to meet me from a future forgetting, past and future merged together, incomprehensible, like a portent, simultaneously gain and loss in a joint shape. And now as I wish to transcribe the unforgettable within the forgotten, to indicate the invisible that lies within the visible, finding my way back to language and form, it is with all the hope of a young person and all the hopelessness of one grown old, trying to seize the meaning of what has been and what is still to be, as far as it may be granted to me. Oh, how deeply must a man plumb his own life in order to be able to comprehend it!

And I write this down because the snow is falling outside and because it is growing dark although it is still early afternoon. And actually I only want to note—since otherwise I might forget it—that the snow has not always lain here, instead that all sorts of things have preceded it in this year, bud and fruit and the resinous odor of the forest, water that dripped and drizzled over the stones of the Kuppronwand, wind that came from afar and blew off again, light that burned and then died down, and the sky showing the day and then again the night. For all this happened while my heart was beating, there was wind, sun and clouds, and they flowed through my heart and through my hands as well.

Translated by JEAN STARR UNTERMEYER

Stefan Zweig

THE INVISIBLE COLLECTION

An Episode of the Inflation Period in Germany

AT THE FIRST JUNCTION beyond Dresden, an elderly gentleman entered our compartment, smiled genially to the company, and gave me a special nod, as if to an old acquaintance. Seeing that I was at a loss, he mentioned his name. Of course I knew him! He was one of the most famous connoisseurs and art-dealers in Berlin. Before the war, I had often purchased autographs and rare books at his place. He took the vacant seat opposite me, and for a while we talked of matters not worth relating. Then, changing the conversation, he explained the object of the journey from which he was returning. It had, he said, been one of the strangest of his experiences in the thirty-seven years he had devoted to the occupation of art-pedlar. Enough introduction. I will let him tell the story in his own words, without using quote-marks—to avoid the complication of wheels within wheels.

You know (he said) what has been going on in my trade since the value of money began to diffuse into the void like gas. War-profiteers have developed a taste for old masters (Madonnas and so on), for incunabula, for ancient tapestries. It is difficult to satisfy their craving; and a man like myself, who prefers to keep the best for his own use and enjoyment, is hard put to it not to have his house stripped bare. If I let them, they would buy the cuff-links from my shirts and the lamp from my writing-table. Harder and harder to find wares to sell. I'm afraid the term "wares" may grate upon you in this connexion, but you must excuse me. I have picked it up from customers of the new sort. Evil communications . . . Through use and wont I have come to look upon an invaluable book from one of the early Venetian presses much as the philistine looks upon an overcoat that cost so or so many hundred dollars, and upon a sketch by Guercino as animated by nothing more worthy of reverence than the transmigrated soul of a banknote for a few thousand francs.

Impossible to resist the greed of these fellows with money to burn. As I looked round my place the other night, it seemed to me that there was so little left of any real value that I might as well put up the shutters. Here was a fine business which had come down to me from my father and my grandfather; but the shop was stocked with rubbish which, before 1914, a street-trader would have been ashamed to hawk upon a handcart.

In this dilemma, it occurred to me to flutter the pages of our old ledgers. Perhaps I should be put on the track of former customers who might be willing to resell what they had bought in prosperous days. True, such a list of sometime purchasers has considerable resemblance to a battlefield laden with the corpses of the slain; and in fact I soon realized that most of those who had purchased from the firm when the sun was shining were dead or would be in such low water that it was probable they must have sold anything of value among their possessions. However, I came across a bundle of letters from a man who was presumably the oldest yet alive—if he was alive. But he was so old that I had forgotten him, since he had bought nothing after the great explosion in the summer of 1914. Yes, very, very old. The earliest letters were dated more than half a century back, when my grandfather was head of the business. Yet I could not recall having had any personal relationships with him during the thirty-seven years in which I had been an active worker in the establishment.

All indications showed that he must have been one of those antediluvian eccentrics, a few of whom survive in German provincial towns. His writing was copperplate, and every item in his orders was underlined in red ink. Each price was given in words as well as figures, so that there could be no mistake. These peculiarities, and his use of torn-out flyleaves as writing paper, enclosed in a scratch assortment of envelopes, hinted at the penuriousness of a confirmed backwoodsman. His signature was always followed by his style and title in full: "Forest Ranger and Economic Councillor, Retired; Lieutenant, Retired; Holder of the Iron Cross First Class." Since he was obviously a veteran of the war of 1870–1871, he must by now be close on eighty.

For all his cheese-paring and for all his eccentricities, he had manifested exceptional shrewdness, knowledge, and taste as collector of prints and engravings. A careful study of his orders, which had at first totalled very small sums indeed, disclosed that in the days when a taler could still pay for a pile of lovely German woodcuts, this country bumpkin had got together a collection of etchings and the like outrivalling the widely trumpeted acquisitions of war profiteers. Merely those which, in the course of decades, he had bought from us for trifling sums would be worth a large amount of money today; and I had no reason to suppose that he had failed to pick up similar bargains elsewhere. Was his collection dispersed? I was too familiar with what had been going on in the art trade since the date of his last purchase not to feel confident that such a collection could scarcely have changed hands entire without my getting wind of the event. If he was dead, his treasures had probably remained intact in the hands of his heirs.

The affair seemed so interesting that I set forth next day (yesterday evening) on a journey to one of the most out-of-the-way towns in Saxony. When I left the tiny railway station and strolled along the main street, it seemed to me impossible that anyone inhabiting one of these gimcrack houses, furnished in a way with which you are doubtless familiar, could possibly own a full set of magnificent Rembrandt etchings together with an unprecedented number of Dürer woodcuts and a complete collection of Mantegnas. However, I went to the post-office to inquire, and was astonished to learn that a sometime Forest Ranger and Economic Councillor of the name I mentioned was still living. They told me how to find his house, and I will admit that my heart beat faster than usual as I made my way thither. It was well before noon.

The connoisseur of whom I was in search lived on the second floor of one of those jerry-built houses which were run up in such numbers by speculators during the sixties of the last century. The first floor was occupied by a master tailor. On the second landing to the left was the name-plate of the manager of the local post-office, while the porcelain shield on the right-hand door bore the name of my quarry. I had run him to earth! My ring was promptly answered by a very old, white-haired woman wearing a black lace cap. I handed her my card and asked whether the master was at home. With an air of suspicion she glanced at me, at the card, and then back at my face once more. In this God-forsaken little town a visit from an inhabitant of the metropolis was a disturbing event. However, in as friendly a tone as she could muster, she asked me to be good enough to wait a minute or two in the hall, and vanished through a doorway. I heard whispering, and then a loud, hearty, masculine voice: "Herr Rackner from Berlin, you say, the famous dealer in antiquities? Of course I shall be delighted to see him." Thereupon the old woman reappeared and invited me to enter.

I took off my overcoat, and followed her. In the middle of the cheaply furnished room was a man standing up to receive me. Old but hale, he had a bushy moustache and was wearing a semi-military, frogged smoking-jacket. In the most cordial way, he held out both hands towards me. But though this gesture was spontaneous and nowise forced, it was in strange contrast with the stiffness of his attitude. He did not advance to meet me, so that I was compelled (I must confess I was a trifle piqued) to walk right up to him before I could shake. Then I noticed that his hand, too, did not seek mine, but was waiting for mine to clasp it. At length I guessed what was amiss. He was blind.

Ever since I was a child I have been uncomfortable in the presence of the blind. It embarrasses me, produces in me a sense of bewilderment and shame to encounter anyone, who is thoroughly alive, and yet has not the full use of his senses. I feel as if I were taking an unfair advantage, and I was keenly conscious of this sensation as I glanced into the fixed and sightless orbs beneath the bristling white eyebrows. The blind man, however, did not leave me time to dwell upon this discomfort. He exclaimed, laughing with boisterous delight:

"A red-letter day, indeed! Seems almost a miracle that one of the big men of Berlin should drop in as you have done. There's need for us provincials to be careful, you know, when a noted dealer such as yourself is on the war-path. We've a saying in this part of the world: 'Shut your doors and button up your pockets if there are gipsies about!' I can guess why you've taken the trouble to call. Business doesn't thrive, I've gathered. No buyers or very few, so people are looking up their old customers. I'm afraid you'll draw a blank. We pensioners are glad enough to find there's still some dry bread for dinner. I've been a collector in my time, but now I'm out of the game. My buying days are over."

I hastened to tell him he was under a misapprehension, that I had not called with any thought of effecting sales. Happening to be in the neighbourhood I felt loath to miss the chance of paying my respects to a longstanding customer who was at the same time one of the most famous among German collectors. Hardly had the phrase passed my lips when a remarkable change took place in the old man's expression. He stood stiffly in the middle of the room, but his face lighted up and his whole aspect was suffused with pride. He turned in the direction where he fancied his wife to be, and nodded as if to say, "D'you hear that?" Then, turning back to me, he resumed—having dropped the brusque, drillsergeant tone he had previously used, and speaking in a gentle, nay, almost tender voice:

"How charming of you. . . . I should be sorry, however, if your visit were to result in nothing more than your making the personal acquaintanceship of an old buffer like myself. At any rate I've something worth while for you to see—more worth while than you could find in Berlin, in the Albertina at Vienna, or even in the Louvre (God's curse on Paris!). A man who has been a diligent collector for fifty years, with taste to guide him, gets hold of treasures that are not to be picked up at every street-corner. Lisbeth, give me the key of the cupboard, please."

Now a strange thing happened. His wife, who had been listening with a pleasant smile, was startled. She raised her hands towards me, clasped them imploringly, and shook her head. What these gestures signified was a puzzle to me. Next she went up to her husband and touched his shoulder, saying:

"Franz, dear, you have forgotten to ask our visitor whether he may not have another appointment; and, anyhow, it is almost dinner-time.—I am sorry," she went on, looking to me, "that we have not enough in the house for an unexpected guest. No doubt you will dine at the inn. If you will take a cup of coffee with us afterwards, my daughter Anna Maria will be here, and she is much better acquainted than I am with the contents of the portfolios."

Once more she glanced piteously at me. It was plain that she wanted me to refuse the proposal to examine the collection there and then. Taking my cue, I said that in fact I had a dinner engagement at the Golden

Stag, but should be only too delighted to return at three, when there would be plenty of time to examine anything Herr Kronfeld wanted to show me. I was not leaving before six o'clock.

The veteran was as pettish as a child deprived of a favourite toy.

"Of course," he growled, "I know you mandarins from Berlin have extensive claims on your time. Still, I really think you will do well to spare me a few hours. It is not merely two or three prints I want to show you, but the contents of twenty-seven portfolios, one for each master, and all of them full to bursting. However, if you come at three sharp, I dare say we can get through by six."

The wife saw me out. In the entrance hall, before she opened the front door, she whispered:

"Do you mind if Anna Maria comes to see you at the hotel before you return? It will be better for various reasons which I cannot explain just now."

"Of course, of course, a great pleasure. Really, I am dining alone, and your daughter can come along directly you have finished your own meal."

An hour later, when I had removed from the dining-room to the parlour of the Golden Stag, Anna Maria Kronfeld arrived. An old maid, wizened and diffident, plainly dressed, she contemplated me with embarrassment. I did my best to put her at her ease, and expressed my readiness to go back with her at once, if her father was impatient, though it was short of the appointed hour. At this she reddened, grew even more confused, and then stammered a request for a little talk before we set out.

"Please sit down," I answered. "I am entirely at your service."

She found it difficult to begin. Her hands and her lips trembled. At length:

"My mother sent me. We have to ask a favour of you. Directly you get back, Father will want to show you his collection; and the collection . . . the collection. Well, there's very little of it left."

She panted, almost sobbed, and went on breathlessly:

"I must be frank . . . You know what troublous times we are passing through, and I am sure you will understand. Soon after the war broke out, my father became completely blind. His sight had already been failing. Agitation, perhaps, contributed. Though he was over seventy, he wanted to go to the front, remembering the fight in which he had taken part so long ago. Naturally there was no use for his services. Then, when the advance of our armies was checked, he took the matter very much to heart, and the doctor thought that may have precipitated the oncoming of blindness. In other respects, as you will have noticed, he is vigorous.

Down to 1914 he could take long walks, and go out shooting. Since the failure of his eyes, his only pleasure is in his collection. He looks at it every day. 'Looks at it,' I say, though he sees nothing. Each afternoon he has the portfolios on the table, and fingers the prints one by one, in the order which many years have rendered so familiar. Nothing else interests him. He makes me read reports of auctions; and the higher the prices, the more enthusiastic does he become.

"There's the dreadful feature of the situation. Father knows nothing about the inflation; that we are ruined; that his monthly pension would not provide us with a day's food. Then we have others to support. My sister's husband was killed at Verdun, and there are four children. These money troubles have been kept from him. We cut down expenses as much as we can, but it is impossible to make ends meet. We began to sell things, trinkets and so on, without interfering with his beloved collection. There was very little to sell, since Father had always spent whatever he could scrape together upon woodcuts, copper-plate engravings, and the like. The collector's mania! Well, at length it was a question whether we were to touch the collection or let him starve. We didn't ask permission. What would have been the use? He hasn't the ghost of a notion how hard food is to come by, at any price; has never heard that Germany was defeated and surrendered Alsace-Lorraine. We don't read him items of that sort from the newspapers!

"The first piece we sold was a very valuable one, a Rembrandt etching, and the dealer paid us a long price, a good many thousand marks. We thought it would last us for years. But you know how money was melting away in 1922 and 1923. After we had provided for our immediate needs, we put the rest in a bank. In two months it was gone! We had to sell another engraving, and then another. That was during the worst days of inflation, and each time the dealer delayed settlement until the price was not worth a tenth or a hundredth of what he had promised to pay. We tried auction-rooms, and were cheated there too, though the bids were raised by millions. The million- or milliard-mark notes were waste-paper by the time we got them. The collection was scattered to provide daily bread, and little of that.

"That was why Mother was so much alarmed when you turned up today. Directly the portfolios are opened, our pious fraud will be disclosed. He knows each item by touch. You see, every print we disposed of was immediately replaced by a sheet of blank cartridge-paper of the same size and thickness, so that he would notice no difference when he handled it. Feeling them one by one, and counting them, he derives almost as much pleasure as if he could actually see them. He never tries to show them to anyone here, where there is no connoisseur, no one worthy to look at them; but he loves each of them so ardently that I think his heart would break if he knew they had been dispersed. The last time he asked someone to look at them, it was the curator of the copper-plate engravings in Dresden, who died years ago.

"I beseech you"—her voice broke—"not to shatter his illusion, not to undermine his faith, that the treasures he will describe to you are there for the seeing. He would not survive the knowledge of their loss. Perhaps we have wronged him; yet what could we do? One must live. Orphaned children are more valuable than old prints. Besides, it has been life and happiness to him to spend three hours every afternoon going through his imaginary collection, and talking to each specimen as if it were a friend. Today may be the most enthralling experience since his sight failed. How he has longed for the chance of exhibiting his treasures to an expert! If you will lend yourself to the deception . . ."

In my cold recital, I cannot convey to you how poignant was this appeal. I have seen many a sordid transaction in my business career; have had to look on supinely while persons ruined by inflation have been diddled out of cherished heirlooms which they were compelled to sacrifice for a crust. But my heart has not been utterly calloused, and this tale touched me to the quick. I need hardly tell you that I promised to play up.

We went to her house together. On the way I was grieved (though not surprised) to learn for what preposterously small amounts these ignorant though kind-hearted women had parted with prints many of which were extremely valuable and some of them unique. This confirmed my resolve to give all the help in my power. As we mounted the stairs we heard a jovial shout: "Come in! Come in!" With the keen hearing of the blind, he had recognized the footsteps for which he had been eagerly waiting.

"Franz usually takes a siesta after dinner, but excitement kept him awake today," said the old woman with a smile as she let us in. A glance at her daughter showed her that all was well. The stack of portfolios was on the table. The blind collector seized me by the arm and thrust me into a chair which was placed ready for me.

"Let's begin at once. There's a lot to see, and time presses. The first portfolio contains Dürers. Nearly a full set, and you'll think each cut finer than the others. Magnificent specimens. Judge for yourself."

He opened the portfolio as he spoke, saying:

"We start with the Apocalypse series, of course."

Then, tenderly, delicately (as one handles fragile and precious objects), he picked up the first of the blank sheets of cartridge-paper and held it admiringly before my sighted eyes and his blind ones. So enthusiastic was his gaze that it was difficult to believe he could not see. Though I knew it to be fancy, I found it difficult to doubt that there was a glow of recognition in the wrinkled visage.

"Have you ever come across a finer print? How sharp the impression. Every detail crystal-clear. I compared mine with the one at Dresden; a good one, no doubt, but 'fuzzy' in contrast with the specimen you are looking at. Then I have the whole pedigree."

He turned the sheet over and pointed at the back so convincingly that involuntarily I leaned forward to read the non-existent inscriptions.

"The stamp of the Nagler collection, followed by those of Remy and Esdaille. My famous predecessors never thought that their treasure would come to roost in this little room."

I shuddered as the unsuspecting enthusiast extolled the blank sheet of paper; my flesh crept when he placed a fingernail on the exact spot where the alleged imprints had been made by long-dead collectors. It was as ghostly as if the disembodied spirits of the men he named had risen from the tomb. My tongue clave to the roof of my mouth—until once more I caught sight of the distraught countenance of Kronfeld's wife and daughter. Then I pulled myself together and resumed my role. With forced heartiness, I exclaimed:

"Certainly you are right. This specimen is peerless."

He swelled with triumph.

"But that's nothing," he went on. "Look at these two, the *Melancholia,* and the illuminated print of the *Passion.* The latter, beyond question, has no equal. The freshness of the tints! Your colleagues in Berlin and the custodians of the public galleries would turn green with envy at the sight."

I will not bore you with details. Thus it went on, a paean, for more than two hours, as he ransacked portfolio after portfolio. An eerie business to watch the handling of these two or three hundred blanks, to chime in at appropriate moments with praise of merits which for the blind collector were so eminently real that again and again (this was my salvation) his faith kindled my own.

Once only did disaster loom. He was "showing" me a first proof of Rembrandt's *Antiope,* which must have been of inestimable value and which had doubtless been sold for a song. Again he dilated on the sharpness of the print, but as he passed his fingers lightly over it the sensitive tips missed some familiar indentation. His face clouded, his mouth trembled, and he said:

"Surely, surely it's the *Antiope?* No one touches the woodcuts and etchings but myself. How can it have got misplaced?"

"Of course it's the *Antiope,* Herr Kronfeld," I said, hastening to take the "print" from his hand and to expatiate upon various details which my own remembrance enabled me to conjure up upon the blank surface.

His bewilderment faded. The more I praised, the more gratified he became, until at last he said exultantly to the two women:

"Here's a man who knows what's what! You have been inclined to grumble at my 'squandering' money upon the collection. It's true that for half a century and more I denied myself beer, wine, tobacco, travelling, visits to the theatre, books, devoting all I could spare to these purchases you have despised. Well, Herr Rackner confirms my judgment. When I am dead and gone, you'll be richer than anyone in the town, as wealthy as the wealthiest folk in Dresden, and you'll have good reason for congratulating yourself on my 'craze.' But so long as I'm alive, the collection must be kept together. After I've been boxed and buried, this expert or another will help you to sell. You'll have to, since my pension dies with me."

As he spoke, his fingers caressed the despoiled portfolios. It was horrible and touching. Not for years, not since 1914, had I witnessed an expression of such unmitigated happiness on the face of a German. His wife and daughter watched him with tear-dimmed eyes, yet ecstatically, like those women of old who—affrighted and rapturous—found the stone rolled away and the sepulchre empty in the garden outside the wall of Jerusalem. But the man could not have enough of my appreciation. He went on from portfolio to portfolio, from "print" to "print," drinking in my words, until, outwearied, I was glad when the lying blanks were replaced in their cases and room was made to serve coffee on the table.

My host, far from being tired, looked rejuvenated. He had story after story to tell concerning the way he had chanced upon his multifarious treasures, wanting, in this connexion, to take out each relevant piece once more. He grew peevish when I insisted, when his wife and daughter insisted, that I should miss my train if he delayed me any longer. . . .

In the end he was reconciled to my going, and we said good-bye. His voice mellowed; he took both my hands in his and fondled them with the tactile appreciation of the blind.

"Your visit has given me immense pleasure," he said with a quaver in his voice. "What a joy to have been able at long last to show my collection to one competent to appreciate it. I can do something to prove my gratitude, to make your visit to a blind old man worth while. A codicil to my will shall stipulate that your firm, whose probity everyone knows, will be entrusted with the auctioning of my collection."

He laid a hand lovingly upon the pile of worthless portfolios.

"Promise me they shall have a handsome catalogue. I could ask no better monument."

I glanced at the two women, who were exercising the utmost control, fearful lest the sound of their trembling should reach his keen ears. I promised the impossible, and he pressed my hand in response.

Wife and daughter accompanied me to the door. They did not venture to speak, but tears were flowing down their cheeks. I myself was in little better case. An art-dealer, I had come in search of bargains. Instead, as events turned out, I had been a sort of angel of good-luck, lying like a trooper in order to assist in a fraud which kept an old man happy. Ashamed of lying, I was glad that I had lied. At any rate I had aroused an ecstasy which seems foreign to this period of sorrow and gloom.

As I stepped forth into the street, I heard a window open, and my name called. Though the old fellow could not see me, he knew in which direction I should walk, and his sightless eyes were turned thither. He leaned out so far that his anxious relatives put their arms round him lest he should fall. Waving a handkerchief, he shouted:

"A pleasant journey to you, Herr Rackner."

His voice rang like a boy's. Never shall I forget that cheerful face, which contrasted so grimly with the careworn aspect of the passers-by in the street. The illusion I had helped to sustain made life good for him. Was it not Goethe who said:

"Collectors are happy creatures"?

Translated by EDEN *and* CEDAR PAUL

Joseph Roth

THE LEGEND OF THE HOLY DRINKER

ON AN EVENING in spring, in the year 1934, a gentleman of advanced age descended the stone steps leading from one of the bridges over the Seine down to its banks. There (a fact known virtually throughout the world and yet worth calling to mind on this occasion) the vagrants of Paris are wont to sleep—or to camp, rather.

One of these vagrants happened to meet the gentleman of advanced age—who was well-dressed, by the way, and gave the impression of a tourist planning to view the sights of foreign cities—and while the homeless man looked just as battered and pitiable as all the rest whose life he shared, he struck the well-dressed gentleman of advanced age as meriting special attention; why, we do not know. It was evening, as stated, and on the banks of the river, under the bridge, darkness gathered faster than on the quay above. The visibly battered vagrant was swaying a little. He did not appear to notice the elderly, well-dressed gentleman. The latter, however, who was not swaying at all but walking straight and securely, had evidently seen the swaying one from far away. The gentleman of advanced age actually barred the derelict's way, and they both came to a halt, facing each other.

"Where are you going, brother?" the elderly, well-dressed gentleman inquired.

The other looked at him for a moment, and then said, "I do not know that I have a brother, and I do not know where my way will take me."

"I shall try to show you the way," said the gentleman. "You must not mind, though, if I ask you to do me an unusual favor."

"I am ready for anything," replied the derelict.

"I can see that you have a few faults, but God has sent you my way. You certainly need money, if you do not mind my saying so. I have too much. Will you tell me frankly how much you need? For the moment, at least?"

The other thought a few seconds, and then said, "Twenty francs."

"That is unquestionably insufficient," replied the gentleman. "I am sure you need two hundred."

The derelict took a step backward and seemed about to drop; however, he remained upright, though swaying. Then he said, "I certainly prefer two hundred francs to twenty, but I am a man of honor. You misjudge me, apparently. I cannot take the money you offer me, for these reasons: first, because I do not have the pleasure of knowing you; secondly, because I do not know how and when I could return it; thirdly, because you have no way of dunning me. I have no address. I live under another bridge of this river almost every day. But as I said, I am a man of honor, albeit without address."

"I have no address, either," replied the gentleman of advanced age. "I too live under another bridge every day, and yet I ask you kindly to accept the two hundred francs—a ridiculous sum, by the way, for a man like you. As for repayment, I must digress somewhat to explain why I cannot tell you a bank, for instance, where you could return the money. I became a Christian after reading the story of little Saint Theresa of Lisieux. And now I worship especially the little statue of the Saint in the chapel of Ste. Marie-des-Batignolles, which you will find easily. So whenever you have the paltry two hundred francs and your conscience prevents you from further owing this trifle, please go to Ste. Marie-des-Batignolles and deposit the money with the priest who has just read Mass. If you owe it to any one, it is little Saint Theresa. Do not forget, though: Ste. Marie-des-Batignolles."

"I see," said the derelict, "that you understand both me and my integrity perfectly. You have my word that I shall keep my word. But I can only go to Mass on Sunday."

"Sunday, please," said the elderly gentleman. He took two hundred francs from his wallet, handed them to the swaying one and said, "I thank you."

"It was a pleasure," replied the other and presently disappeared in the dusk. For down below it had grown dark in the meantime, while above, on the bridges and quays, the silver lamps lit up to hail the merry night of Paris.

The well-dressed gentleman also disappeared in the dusk. He had indeed met with the miracle of conversion and made up his mind to live the life of the poorest. That was why he lived under the bridge. As for the other, however, he was a drinker—in fact, a drunkard. His name was Andreas, and he lived by chance, like many drinkers. It was a long time since he had had two hundred francs in his possession; and it may have been because it was so long a time that in the spare gleam of one of the infrequent lanterns under the bridges he produced a scrap of paper and a pencil stub, and made a note of little Saint Theresa's address and the sum of two hundred francs which he owed her from this hour. Then he climbed the steps from the bank of the Seine to the quay. There, he knew, was a restaurant. He went there, and ate and drank amply and spent plenty of money; and he took a full bottle along, too, for the night, which he meant to spend under the bridge as usual. He even picked up a newspaper from a waste basket—not to read it, though, but as a covering. Newspapers keep one warm, as any vagrant knows.

Next morning Andreas rose earlier than was his habit, having slept unusually well. He remembered after long contemplation that yesterday he had experienced a miracle. A miracle. He also thought that in this last warm night under the newspaper he had slept better than ever in recent times, and so he decided to wash. It was something he had not done either for many months—that is to say, in the cold season. Before taking his clothes off, however, he reached again into his left inner coat pocket. There, bearing out his memory, was the miracle's tangible remainder. Then only did he seek a lonely spot on the embankment, to wash his face and neck, at least. But as it seemed as though everywhere people, wretched people of his own kind (shiftless, he suddenly called them to himself in silence) might watch his ablution, he finally dropped the idea and was content to dip his hands into the water. Then he put his coat back on again, reached once more for the bank note in the inner pocket and felt completely clean and actually transformed.

He went on into the day, into one of the days which he was in the habit of wasting since time immemorial. He was determined, as on other days, to go to his usual rue des Quatre-Vents, the site of the Tari-Bari Russo-Armenian restaurant, where he invested in low-priced liquor the few coins daily sent him by chance. However, he stopped at the first newsstand on his way, attracted by the covers of certain weeklies but also suddenly seized by curiosity—to know what day this was, what date and name it bore. He bought a newspaper and saw that it was Thursday, and suddenly he remembered that he was born on a Thursday; and without looking for the date he decided to consider this very Thursday as his birthday. And, already in a childlike holiday mood, he yielded without further hesitation to good, in fact noble, intentions; to pass up the Tari-Bari but, newspaper in hand, to go to a better tavern and there have coffee (with a touch of rum, of course) and eat a sandwich.

Thus, confidently despite his ragged attire, he entered a bourgeois bistro and sat at a table; he, who so long had used to stand only at bars —that is, to lean on them. He sat down. Facing his seat was a mirror, so that he could not help observing his face. It was like renewing his acquaintance with himself, and it rather startled him. He also knew now why he had been so afraid of mirrors in recent years. For it was not good to see your decay with your own eyes; as long as you did not have to look at it, it was almost like having either no face at all or still the old one, of times before the decay.

But now he was startled, especially by a comparison of his features with those of the respectable men around him. He had been shaved a week ago, for better or worse, by one of his fellow-vagrants who at times was willing to shave a brother for a small gratuity. Now, however, with a new life decided on, he would have to get a real, a definite shave. He decided to go to a regular barber shop, even before ordering.

No sooner said than done. He went to the barber shop.

On his return to the tavern the seat which he had previously occupied was taken, so that he could look at himself in the mirror only from afar. But he saw enough to realize that he was changed, rejuvenated and beautified. It was as though a radiance issued from his face and made his ragged clothes insignificant, his visibly frayed shirt and the red-and-white-striped tie wound about a collar with torn edges. He sat down, our Andreas. Conscious of his renovation, and with the assured voice that had been his once and now appeared to return like a dear old friend, he ordered one *café, arrosé rhum*. This he got, and with all due respect, as he believed to notice—with the kind of respect waiters usually show to venerable guests. It flattered our Andreas peculiarly; it elated him; and it confirmed his assumption that this was his birthday.

A gentleman sitting alone near the vagrant looked at him for a while, turned and said: "Do you want to make money? You can work for me. I am moving tomorrow; you can help my wife and the movers. You seem to be strong enough. You can, can't you? You will, won't you?"

"Certainly I will," said Andreas.

"And how much do you want," asked the gentleman, "for two days of work? Tomorrow and Saturday? Because you should know I have a pretty large apartment, and am moving into an even larger one. And I have a lot of furniture. And I myself am busy at the office."

"Right with you," said the vagrant.

"Do you drink?" asked the gentleman. He ordered two pernods, and they raised their glasses, the gentleman and Andreas, and they agreed on the price, too; it was two hundred francs. "Shall we have another?" asked the gentleman, having emptied the first pernod.

"This is on me, though," said the vagrant Andreas. "Because you don't know me; I am a man of honor. An honest workingman. Look at my hands." And he displayed them. "They're dirty, calloused but honest working hands."

"I like that," said the gentleman. He had glistening eyes, a pink baby face and in its very center a black little mustache. All in all, he was a rather friendly man, and Andreas liked him. They drank together, with Andreas paying for the second round. And when the baby-faced gentleman rose, Andreas saw that he was very fat. He took a visiting card from his wallet and wrote his address on it. Then he took a hundred-franc note from the same wallet, handed both to Andreas and said: "So you'll be sure to come tomorrow! Tomorrow morning at eight! Don't forget! And you'll get the rest! And after work we'll have another apéritif together. Goodbye, my friend!"

With that, the fat, baby-faced gentleman left, and nothing amazed Andreas more than the fact that the fat man had drawn his address and money from the same pocket.

Now that he had money and the prospect of earning more, he decided to purchase a wallet. To this end, he started on a search for a leather-goods shop. Standing in the first that lay on his way was a young sales-girl. She seemed very pretty to him, standing there behind the counter in a strict black dress with a white bib over her breast, little curls on her head and a heavy gold bracelet on her right wrist. He took his hat off to her and said, gaily, "I am looking for a wallet."

The girl cast a fleeting glance at his poor clothes, but there was no evil in the glance; she just wanted to appraise her customer. For the shop carried high-priced, medium-priced and very cheap wallets. To save unnecessary questions, she climbed a ladder at once and got a box from the top drawer; there, wallets were kept which customers had returned and exchanged. On this occasion Andreas saw that the girl's legs were very beautiful and her pumps very slim, and he remembered half-for-gotten times when he himself had stroked such calves and kissed such feet; but he no longer remembered the faces, the women's faces, except for one, the one on whose account he had been jailed.

Meanwhile, the girl came down from the ladder, opened the box, and he selected one of the wallets that lay on top, without looking closer. He paid and put his hat back on and smiled at the girl, and the girl smiled back. Absently he pocketed the new wallet, but the money he left on the counter. Suddenly, the wallet seemed to make no sense to him. His mind was occupied with the ladder, instead, with the legs, the feet of the girl. This was why he turned in the direction of Montmartre, to look for the spots where he had found pleasure in the past; and there, in a steep, narrow alley, was still the tavern with the girls. He sat at a table with some of them, paid for a round and selected one of the girls—the one who sat next to him. Then he went to her. And though it was merely after-noon he slept till dawn broke; and because the proprietor was good-hearted she let him sleep.

Next morning, Friday, he went to work for the fat gentleman. He had to help the lady pack, and though the packers were already on the job there were plenty of more or less difficult assignments left for Andreas.

But during the day he felt the strength returning to his muscles and he was glad at his work. For he had grown up at work, a miner like his father and still something of a peasant like his grandfather. If only the lady of the house had not upset him so with senseless directions, ordering him here and there in one breath so that he was quite bewildered. But she was upset herself, he realized that. It could not be an easy thing to change your residence from one day to the other, and perhaps she was afraid, too, of the new house. She was all dressed to go out, with her coat, hat and gloves on, carrying her pocketbook and umbrella, though after all she should have known that she had to stay in the house another day and a night and tomorrow too. From time to time she had to paint her lips; Andreas understood perfectly. For she was a lady.

Andreas worked the whole day. When he was finished, the lady of the house told him, "Be on time tomorrow, at seven o'clock in the morning." She took a little purse from her pocket-book, with silver coins in it. She rummaged at length, seized a ten-franc piece but dropped it again; then she decided to extract five francs. "Here," she said, "your tip. But," she added, "don't spend it all on drinks, and be here on time tomorrow!"

Andreas thanked her, went and spent the tip on drinks, but not more. That night, he slept in a little hotel. He was called at six in the morning and briskly went to work.

So on this morning he arrived even before the movers. And, as the day before, the lady of the house was standing there dressed, hatted and gloved as if she had not gone to bed at all, and amiably told him: "I see you took my advice yesterday and really didn't spend all the money on drinks." And Andreas went to work and he accompanied the lady to the new house into which she was moving and waited till the friendly fat man came, who paid him the promised wage.

"I'll buy you another drink," said the fat gentleman. "Come along."

But the lady of the house stopped that, by stepping between them and actually barring her husband's way, and saying, "We must go out to dinner now." So Andreas left alone, drank alone and ate alone that evening and visited two more taverns to drink at the bars. He drank much but he did not get drunk, and he took care not to spend too much money. For tomorrow, true to his promise, he wanted to go to the chapel Ste. Marie-des-Batignolles, to repay at least part of his debt to little Saint Theresa. Still, he drank just so much that he could no longer find the cheapest hotel in the neighborhood with the sure eye and instinct which only poverty bestows.

So he found a hotel that was somewhat more expensive, and he paid in advance because his clothes were frayed and he had no baggage. But he did not mind that in the least and quietly slept far into the day. He woke from the tolling of bells from a nearby church and knew at once what an important day this was—a Sunday—and that he must go to little Saint Theresa to repay his debt. He dressed hurriedly and with quick steps walked to the square with the chapel. Even so, he did not get there in time for ten o'clock Mass; the people just came streaming toward him from the church. He asked when Mass would be read again, and heard that it would begin at noon. He felt a little helpless, standing before the chapel gate; he had another hour left, and certainly did not wish to spend it in the street. So he looked round where he best might wait; and when he saw a bistro to the right, diagonally opposite the chapel, he went there and decided to wait out the hour that remained to him.

With the assurance of one who knows money in his pocket, he ordered a pernod; and he drank it with the assurance of one who has drunk many such before. He drank a second and a third, pouring less and less water into the glass, and when the fourth came, he did not know any more if he had drunk two, five, or six. Nor could he recall how he had happened into this café or to this place. He merely remembered that he had a duty here, a duty of honor. So he paid, rose, went out the door, still master of his legs, and as soon as he saw the chapel across the street to the left he knew again where, why and for what he was here. He was about to turn toward the chapel when he suddenly heard his name. "Andreas!" a voice called, a feminine voice risen out of buried times. He halted and looked to the right, whence the voice had come. And at once he recognized the face on whose account he had been jailed. It was Caroline.

Caroline. True, she wore a hat and clothes he never had known on her, but it was her face just the same; and so he did not hesitate to fall into the arms which she spread instantly. "What a meeting!" she said. And it really was her voice, Caroline's voice. "Are you alone?" she asked.

"Yes," he said. "I'm alone."

"Come, we'll have a talk," she said.

"But—but," he replied, "I have an appointment."

"With a woman?" she asked.

"Yes," he said apprehensively.

"Who is she?"

"Little Theresa," he replied.

"She doesn't mean a thing," said Caroline.

At this moment a taxi drove up, and Caroline stopped it with her umbrella. And she was telling an address to the driver, and before Andreas knew what was going on he sat in the car next to Caroline and they were rolling, they were racing along, it appeared to Andreas—through streets partly known, partly unknown, to God only knew what regions!

Now they came into a suburb outside the city; light green, early spring green, that was the landscape in which they stopped—or rather, the garden behind whose scant trees a discreet restaurant was hidden. Caroline got out first, with the stormy stride which he remembered about her she got out first, across his knees. She paid, and he went after her. They went into the restaurant and sat side by side on the window-seat of green plush, as in young days, in days before the Law. She ordered for them as always and she looked at him and he did not dare look at her.

"Where have you been all the time?" she asked.

"Everywhere, nowhere," he said. "I have been working only for the last two days. I've been drinking all the time since we saw each other last, and I slept under the bridges like all our kind, and probably you've had a better life.—With men," he added, somewhat later.

"And you?" she asked. "Between being drunk and out of work and sleeping under the bridges you still have time and a chance to meet a Theresa. And if I hadn't happened to come along, you really would have gone to her."

He did not answer; he was silent until they had eaten the roast, and the cheese came, and the fruits. And after gulping the last of the wine in his glass, he was seized anew by that sudden terror he had so often felt long years ago, during the times he lived with Caroline. And once again he wanted to escape from it and called out: "Waiter—check!" She, however, cut him off: "I'll take care of it, waiter."

The waiter, a mellowed man with knowing eyes, said, "The gentleman called first." So it was Andreas who paid. On this occasion he got all the money out of his left inner coat pocket and, after paying he saw, with a dismay slightly softened by the consumed wine, that he no longer possessed the whole sum due the little Saint. But, he told himself silently, so many miracles running occurred to him nowadays that next week, surely, he would raise and repay the balance.

"So you're rich," Caroline said in the street. "I suppose you let this little Theresa keep you."

He did not answer, and so she was convinced that she was right. She demanded to be taken to a movie; and he went to one with her. After a long time he was seeing a picture again. But it was so long since he had seen one that he hardly understood it any more and fell asleep on Caroline's shoulder. Later they went to a night club with accordion music, and it was so long since he had danced that he no longer knew how to dance properly when he tried it with Caroline. So other dancers took her away from him; she was still fresh and desirable. He sat alone at their table and drank more pernod, and it seemed to him like old times, when Caroline had danced with others, too, and he had drunk alone at their table. Therefore, he took her suddenly and forcefully away from one partner and said, "We're going home." Took her by the neck and did not let go again, paid, and went home with her. She lived nearby.

And so all was like old times, the times before the Law.

Very early in the morning he awoke. Caroline was still sleeping. A single bird twittered before the open window. He lay a while with his eyes open, not longer than a few minutes. In these few minutes he reflected. It seemed to him that not for a long time had so many strange things happened to him as in this one week. Suddenly turning his face he saw Caroline to the right of him. He noticed now what he had not noticed yesterday, at their meeting: she had aged: pale, puffed up and breathing heavily, she slept the morning sleep of aging women. He perceived the change of time which had passed him by. And he perceived the change in himself, too, and he decided to get up at once without waking Caroline and to leave just as casually, or rather, fatefully, as both of them, Caroline and he, had met the day before. He stealthily dressed and went away, into a new day, into one of his usual new days.

That is to say, really into one of his unusual ones. For when he reached into the left breast pocket where he used to keep the money he had lately earned or found, he discovered that all that remained to him was one fifty-franc note and a few small coins. And he—for years ignorant of what money means and no longer in the least heedful of its meaning—was shocked now, as a man will be who is accustomed to having money in his pocket at all times and suddenly, to his embarrassment, finds very little in it. Suddenly, in the dawn-grey, deserted street, it seemed to him that he, penniless for countless months, was abruptly impoverished because he no longer felt so many banknotes in his pocket as he had possessed in these last days. And it seemed that the time of his indigence lay far, very far behind, and that he had really spent the amount which should maintain his proper standard of living in an impulsive as well as reckless way, on Caroline. So he was angry with Caroline. And all at once he, who had never valued the possession of money, began to esteem the value of money. All at once he found that the possession of a fifty-franc note was ridiculous in a man of such worth and that altogether, if only to realize clearly the worth of his own personality, it was quite essential for him to think quietly about himself with a glass of pernod.

From among the nearest inns he chose one which appeared to him most likeable, sat down there and ordered a pernod. While he drank, he recalled that actually he was living in Paris without a residence permit, and he looked up his papers. Whereupon he found that he had really been expelled, having come to France as a coal miner, and was a native of Olschowice in Polish Silesia.

Now, spreading his half torn papers on the table before him, he recalled having come here one day, many years ago, because of a newspaper announcement that miners were sought in France. And he, all his life, had longed for a far country. So he had worked in the pits of Quebecque and boarded with his compatriots, M. and Mme. Schebiec. He had loved the woman and as one day her husband wanted to kill her, he, Andreas, had killed the husband. Then he sat in jail for two years.

This woman was Caroline.

All this Andreas thought while he regarded his long expired papers. Then he ordered another pernod; for he was quite unhappy.

When he finally rose he felt a kind of hunger, but only that which can seize drinkers. It is a special kind of desire (not for food) lasting only a few moments and instantly quenched if he who feels it imagines a certain drink, which at that moment seems to agree with him.

Andreas had long forgotten his family name. But now, having just seen his expired papers again, he remembered that his name was Kartak: Andreas Kartak. He seemed to rediscover himself after long years.

Still, he resented it somewhat that fate had not, like the last time, sent a fat, mustached, baby-faced man to this café, who would enable him to earn fresh money. For men get used to nothing as soon as to miracles after they have happened to them one, two, three times. Yes, human nature is such that they actually get angry if all is not incessantly granted them which an accidental, passing fate seems to have promised; men are like that. . . . And what else could we expect of Andreas? He accordingly spent the rest of the day in divers other taverns and gradually resigned himself to the fact that his time of his miracles was past, was finally past, and his old time had begun again. And, bent upon that slow perdition for which drinkers are always ready—the sober never will experience it!— Andreas went back to the banks of the Seine, under the bridges.

There he slept, half by day and half by night as for a year had been his habit, borrowing bottles of liquor here and there from one or the other companion of his fate—until the night from Thursday to Friday.

That night, though, he dreamed that little Theresa came to him in a blond, curly-haired girl's form, and asked him: "Why weren't you with me last Sunday?" And the little Saint looked exactly as years ago he had imagined his own daughter. But he had no daughter. Still, in the dream he said to little Theresa: "How do you speak to me? Have you forgotten that I am your father?" The little one replied, "Forgive me, father, but do me the favor and come to me tomorrow, Sunday, at Ste. Marie-des-Batignolles."

After the night of this dream he rose refreshed, like a week ago when the miracles had still been happening to him, as if taking the dream for a true miracle. Once again he wanted to wash in the river. But before doffing his coat for that purpose he reached into the left breast jacket, in the vague hope that there might still be some money, perhaps, of which he had not known at all. He reached into the left inner breast pocket of his coat, and there his hand met, not a banknote, but the leather wallet he had bought some days ago. This he extracted. It was an extremely cheap, slightly used, exchanged one, as was to be expected. Slit leather. Calf's leather. He looked at it because he could not recall that, where and when, he had bought it. How did that come to me? he asked himself. At last he opened the thing, and saw that it had two compartments. Curious, he looked into both, and in one was a banknote. He drew it out; it was a thousand-franc note.

Whereupon he put the thousand francs into his trouser pocket and went down the embankment, and without bothering with his fellow-sufferers he washed his face and even his neck and did it almost gaily. Then he put his coat back on and went into his day, and he began it by entering a tobacconist's shop to buy cigarettes.

Now, though he had change enough for the cigarettes, he did not know when he might change the thousand-franc note he had found so miraculously in the wallet. For he did have enough worldly wisdom to sense that in the world's eyes—that is, in the eyes of the world that mattered—an important discrepancy existed between his attire, his appearance and a thousand-franc note. Still, emboldened by the renewed miracle, he decided to show the banknote; although, with the rest of prudence still remaining to him, he told the gentleman at the tobacco counter: "Please, if you cannot change a thousand francs I'll give you coins. I'd like to have them changed, though."

To Andreas' surprise, the tobacconist said, "On the contrary! You've come in at a very convenient moment; I just need a thousand-franc note." And he changed the thousand-franc note, and Andreas remained standing at the counter a while and drank three glasses of white wine—out of gratitude to fate, so to speak.

As he stood at the counter, Andreas' attention was drawn to a framed etching on the wall behind the proprietor's broad back. The etching reminded him of an old schoolmate, in Olschowice, and he asked the proprietor, "Who is that? I think I know him."

Which caused the proprietor, as well as all the guests who stood at the counter, to burst into terrific laughter. And they all exclaimed: "Why, he doesn't know him!"

For it was indeed the great football player Kanjak, of Silesian descent and well-known to all normal people. But how should alcoholics know him who slept under the bridges of the Seine, such as our Andreas for instance? Feeling ashamed, however—especially since he had just changed a thousand-franc note—Andreas said, "Oh, of course I know him. In fact, he is a friend of mine. But the picture looked bad to me." Then, lest he be asked other questions, he quickly paid and left.

He felt hungry now; so he looked for the nearest restaurant and ate, and drank some red wine and some coffee after the cheese and decided to spend the afternoon in a movie. However, he did not yet know in which movie. So, conscious of possessing as much money just now as any person of wealth he might pass in the street, he went to the Grands Boulevards. Between the Opéra and boulevard des Capucines he looked for a picture he might like and finally he found one. For the subject of the poster announcing this picture was a man who evidently meant to perish in some far adventure. On the poster he was crawling through a merciless, sunburnt desert. Andreas entered the theatre and saw the picture of the man walking through the sunburnt desert. And he was just about to find the movie hero sympathetic and akin to himself, when suddenly the picture took an unexpected, happy turn and the man in the desert was saved, by a passing scientific caravan, and returned to the bosom of European civilization. At this point Andreas lost all sympathy for the movie hero. He just wanted to get up, when the screen displayed the picture of that schoolmate whose etching he had lately seen behind the innkeeper's back, while standing at the counter. It was the great football player Kanjak. Now Andreas remembered that twenty years ago he and Kanjak had sat on one bench in a classroom, and he decided to find out, first thing tomorrow, if his old boyhood friend were staying in Paris.

For our Andreas had no less than nine hundred and eighty francs in his pocket.

And that is plenty.

Before leaving the movie, however, it struck him that there was no earthly need to wait for the address of his friend and schoolmate till tomorrow morning; least of all in view of the fairly high sum he carried in his pocket.

By now this remaining money had made him so bold that he decided to ask the cashier for the address of his friend Kanjak, the famous football player. For this purpose, he had thought, one would have to ask the theatre manager himself. But no! Who else in Paris was so well-known as the football player Kanjak? Even the doorman knew his address. He lived in a hotel in the Champs-Elysées. The doorman also gave the hotel's name to Andreas, who immediately set out for it.

It was a small, distinguished and quiet hotel—the very kind in which football players and prize fighters, the elite of our time, usually reside. Andreas felt a little strange in the lobby, and he also appeared somewhat strange to the hotel employees. Still, they said that the famous football player Kanjak was at home and would come down into the lobby at any moment.

After a few minutes he did come down, and the two of them recognized each other right away. Even while standing there, they exchanged old school reminiscences, and then they went to have dinner together and there was great joy between them. They had dinner together, and on this occasion it happened that the famous football player asked his derelict friend the following question: "Why do you look so shabby, and anyway, what sort of rags have you got on there?"

"It would be terrible," replied Andreas, "if I tried to tell you how that happened. And it would greatly disturb the pleasure of our happy reunion. Better let us say nothing about it. We'll talk of something cheerful."

"I have many suits," said the famous football player Kanjak, "and I'll be glad to let you have one or the other. You used to sit next to me in class and let me crib. What is a suit to me? Where shall I send it?"

"You can't," replied Andreas, "for the simple reason that I have no address. For some time I have been living under the bridges of the Seine."

"Well," said the football player Kanjak, "then I'll take a room for you —just so that I'll be able to send you a suit. Come along."

Having dined, they left; and the football player Kanjak engaged a room which cost twenty-five francs a day and was located near the magnificent church in Paris which is known by the name of Madeleine.

The room was on the fifth floor, and Andreas and the football player had to use the elevator. Of course Andreas had no luggage. But neither the desk clerk nor the elevator boy nor anyone else among the personnel of the hotel was surprised at this. For it was a miracle, and within a miracle nothing is surprising. As they both stood up in the room, the football player Kanjak told his classmate Andreas, "You'll need soap."

"My kind," Andreas replied, "can live without soap. I mean to live for a week here without soap, and yet I'll wash. But I should like us to order something to drink now, in honor of this room."

The football player ordered a bottle of brandy, which they emptied. Then they left the room and took a taxi and drove to Montmartre, to the café with the girls, where Andreas had been just a few days past. After sitting there for two hours and trading reminiscences of their school days, the football player took Andreas home—that is to say, to the hotel room he had rented for him—and said, "It's late. I'll leave you alone. Tomorrow I'll send you two suits. And—do you need money?"

"No," said Andreas, "I have nine hundred and eighty francs, and that is plenty. Go home."

"I'll be back in two or three days," said his friend, the football player.

The hotel room in which Andreas was living now had number 89. As soon as he was alone in it, he sat in the comfortable arm-chair covered with pink grosgrain and began to look around. First, he saw the red silk wall covering scattered with soft-golden parrot's heads; on the wall, three ivory buttons to the right of the door-jamb; near the bed, the bed-side table and over it the lamp with a dark-green shade, and then a door with a white knob which seemed to hide something mysterious, at least to Andreas. Then there was a black telephone in the vicinity of the bed, placed so that a man lying in bed could grasp the mouthpiece easily with his right hand. Andreas, having looked at the room a long time with the idea of getting really familiar with it, suddenly grew curious. For the door with the white knob vexed him, and despite his fear and inexperience with hotel rooms he got up and decided to see where the door was leading. Of course he expected to find it locked. How great was his surprise, though, when it opened voluntarily, almost invitingly! He saw now that the mystery was a bathroom, with shining tiles and a glistening, white tub, and with a toilet; in brief, that which in his circles might have been termed a public convenience.

At this same moment he felt it convenient to wash, and let hot and cold water run into the tub from the two faucets. And in undressing, to enter it, he also regretted that he had no shirts; for in taking his shirt off he saw that it was very dirty and was afraid in advance of the moment when he would get out of the tub and need to get into this shirt again.

He got into the tub, knowing well that it was a long time since he had washed. He bathed with actual pleasure, rose, dressed again and then did not know any longer what to do with himself.

More from helplessness than from curiosity he opened the door of the room, went out into the corridor and saw there a young woman just emerging from her room, like himself. She was young and beautiful, or so it seemed to him. She even reminded him of the salesgirl in the shop where he had bought the wallet and a little of Caroline, so that he bowed lightly to her in greeting and, since she replied with a nod, he gathered his courage and told her straight out: "You're pretty."

"I like you too," she replied; "just a moment! Perhaps we'll see each other tomorrow."

And she passed in the dark corridor. But he, love-starved as he had suddenly become, looked at the number on the door behind which she lived. The number was 87; and he remembered it in his heart.

He returned to his room, waited, listened and was already determined not to wait for the morning to meet the beautiful girl. For although he was convinced by the almost unbroken series of miracles in these few days that grace had descended on him, he felt entitled to a kind of boldness just for that reason—and he assumed that manners, so to speak, required him to forestall the grace, without insulting it in any way. When he thought he heard the light steps of the girl of room 87, he cautiously opened his own door a mere slit, and saw that it was really she who returned to her room. What he failed to see, however, owing to his many years of inexperience, was the not inconsiderable circumstance that the pretty girl had noticed his spying, too. Therefore, as professional habit had taught her, she hastily restored her room to a semblance of order and switched off the lights at the ceiling and lay down on the bed, and by the gleam of the bed-lamp she took up a book and read in it; but it was a book she had finished reading long ago.

After a while, in accord with her expectations, someone timidly knocked at her door and Andreas came in. He remained standing on the threshold, though by then he was certain of being invited to approach more closely in a moment. For the pretty girl did not change her position; she did not even put the book down; she merely asked, "And what do you want?"

Andreas, reassured by bath, soap, arm-chair, wallpaper, parrot's heads and suit, replied: "I can't wait till tomorrow, Madam."

The girl was silent.

Andreas moved closer to her, asked what she was reading and honestly said, "I'm not interested in books."

"I'm just here temporarily," said the girl on the bed. "I'm only staying till Sunday. Monday I have to appear in Cannes again."

"As what?" asked Andreas.

"I dance at the Casino. My name is Gaby. Haven't you ever heard it?"

"Certainly, I know it from the newspapers," Andreas lied—and he wanted to add, "with which I cover myself." But he thought better of it.

He sat on the edge of the bed, and the pretty girl did not object. She even put the book down, and Andreas stayed in room 87 until morning.

On Saturday morning he awoke firmly determined not to leave the pretty girl till her departure. In fact there blossomed in him the tender thought of a trip to Cannes with the young woman; for as all the poor (and especially the poor who drink) he tended to regard small sums in his pocket as large ones. So, in the morning, he counted his nine hundred and eighty francs again. And since they lay in a wallet, and this wallet stuck in a new suit, he considered the amount ten times magnified. He was accordingly by no means upset when an hour after he had left her the pretty girl entered his room, without knocking, and when she asked him how the two of them should spend the day before her departure for Cannes, he simply said: "Fontainebleau." Somewhere, half-dreaming, he may have heard this place name. In any case, he no longer knew why and how it had come to his lips.

They took a taxi and they drove to Fontainebleau, and there it turned out that the pretty girl knew a good restaurant where you could eat good food and drink good liquor. She also knew the waiter, whom she called by his first name. If our Andreas had been jealous by nature he might have got angry. But he was not jealous and so he did not get angry either. They spent some time eating and drinking and then, again in a taxi, drove back to Paris, and suddenly the radiant evening of Paris lay before them and they did not know what to do with it—just as people don't who don't belong to each other and have only met by accident. The night spread before them like too bright a desert. And they no longer knew what to do with each other, having frivolously wasted the essential experience given to men and women. So they decided to do what remains to people of our time when they don't know what to do: go to a movie. And there they sat, and there was no darkness, not even a semi-darkness—one could barely call it twilight. And they held hands, the girl and our friend Andreas. But the pressure of his hand was indifferent and he suffered from it, himself. Then, when the intermission came, he decided to go into the lobby with the pretty girl and drink, and they both went and drank. And the movie no longer interested him at all. They returned to the hotel in considerable embarrassment.

On the following morning—it was Sunday—Andreas awoke in the consciousness of his obligation to repay the money. He got up more quickly than the day before, so quickly that the pretty girl was startled out of her sleep and asked him: "Why so fast, Andreas?"

"I must pay a debt," said Andreas.

"What—on Sunday?" asked the pretty girl.

"Yes, on Sunday," replied Andreas.

"Is it a man or a woman you owe money to?"

"A woman," said Andreas hesitantly.

"What's her name?"

"Theresa."

Then the pretty girl jumped out of bed, clenched her fists and struck Andreas in the face with both of them.

And he fled from the room and left the hotel. Without looking further around he walked in the direction of Ste. Marie-des-Batignolles, in the certainty that now at last he could pay back little Theresa's two hundred francs.

Now as Providence would have it—or chance, as less pious people would say—Andreas came once again just after ten o'clock Mass. And it was natural that near the church he should see the bistro where he had drunk the last time, and there he went again.

And he ordered a drink. However, cautious as he was and as all the poor of this world are even after experiencing one miracle after another, he first looked whether he had really money enough, and pulled out his wallet. And then he saw that hardly anything was left of his nine hundred and eighty francs.

All that remained was two hundred and fifty. He thought back and realized that the pretty girl in the hotel had taken the money. But our Andreas did not mind that. He told himself that one must pay for every pleasure; he had had his pleasure and therefore he had to pay.

He wanted to wait here for the bells to ring, the nearby chapel's bells, and then go to Mass and there at last repay his debt to the little Saint. Meanwhile he wanted to drink. He ordered a drink. He drank. The bells began to toll, calling to Mass, and he called, "Waiter, the check!" and paid and rose and went out, and right in front of the door he ran into a very big, broad-shouldered man. He promptly called him "Wojtech." And the other simultaneously exclaimed, "Andreas!" They sank into each other's arms, for they both had dug coal together in Quebecque, in the same shaft.

"If you'll wait here for me," Andreas said: "just twenty minutes while they read Mass. Not a moment longer."

"Just for that, I won't," said Wojtech. "Since when do you go to Mass, anyway? I can't stand the priests, much less people who go to them."

"But I'm going to little Theresa," said Andreas. "I owe her money."

"You mean little Saint Theresa?" Wojtech asked.

"That's the one," Andreas replied.

"How much do you owe her?" Wojtech asked.

"Two hundred francs," Andreas replied.

"I'm coming with you," said Wojtech.

The bells were still tolling. They went into the church, and when they stood inside and Mass had started Wojtech said in a whisper: "Give me a hundred francs right away. I just remember there's a man waiting for me over there—I'll go to jail otherwise."

Andreas promptly gave him both the hundred-franc notes he still possessed and said, "I'll be right with you."

And seeing that now he no longer had the money with which to pay Theresa back, he deemed it pointless further to attend Mass. He waited five minutes more, just to be polite, and then he crossed over to the bistro where Wojtech was waiting for him.

Henceforth they remained pals, for they mutually pledged each other that.

Naturally Wojtech had no friend to whom he owed money. He carefully hid one of the hundred-franc notes Andreas had loaned him in his handkerchief, tying a knot on it. For the other hundred francs he invited Andreas to have a drink, another drink and one more drink, and at night they went to the house with the accommodating girls; and there they both remained three days and when they emerged it was Tuesday, and Wojtech parted from Andreas with the words: "See you again Sunday—same time, same spot, same place."

"Hi," said Andreas

"Hi," said Wojtech and vanished.

It was a rainy Tuesday afternoon, and it was raining so thickly that in a moment Wojtech actually had disappeared. So it seemed to Andreas, at least. It seemed to him that his friend had been lost in the rain, just as he had accidentally met him. And having no more money in his pocket but thirty-five francs, believing himself spoiled by fate and certain of the miracles which surely would continue to happen to him, he decided, as do all men who are poor and accustomed to drink, to entrust himself to God again—the only God he believed in. He went to the Seine, and down the well-known steps to the home of the vagrants.

Here he met a man just about to ascend the steps, who seemed very familiar to him. For this reason Andreas greeted him politely. It was a somewhat elderly, fastidious-looking gentleman who stopped, looked Andreas over closely and finally asked, "Do you need money, dear sir?"

Andreas recognized the voice of the gentleman he had met three weeks ago. So he said, "I remember that I still owe you money; I was to give it back to Saint Theresa. But you know, all sorts of things have come up. Three times now, I've been kept from returning the money."

"You are mistaken," said the elderly, well-dressed gentleman. "I do not have the honor of your acquaintance. You evidently are taking me for someone else, but you appear to be in some embarrassment. And as for Saint Theresa whom you just mentioned—my human obligation toward her is such that I am of course ready to advance you the money you owe her. How much is it?"

"Two hundred francs," replied Andreas, "but—pardon me, you do not even know me! I am a man of honor, and you can scarcely dun me. For although I have my honor, I have no address. I sleep under one of these bridges."

"Oh, that doesn't matter," said the gentleman. "I usually sleep there myself. And by taking the money from me you will actually do me a favor I can't appreciate enough. For I, too, owe so much to little Theresa."

"In that case," Andreas said, "I am of course at your disposal."

He took the money, waited a while until the gentleman had walked up the steps, and then went up the same steps and straight into the rue des Quatre-Vents to his old restaurant, the Russo-Armenian Tari-Bari, and there he stayed till Saturday night. Then it came back to him that tomorrow was Sunday and he must go to the chapel Ste. Marie-des-Batignolles.

There were many people in the Tari-Bari, for many who had no homes slept there for days and nights, behind the bar in the daytime, and at night on the upholstered seats. Andreas got up very early on Sunday—not so much because he feared to be late for Mass as because of the proprietor, who would ask him to pay for drinks and food and lodging for so many days.

He was wrong, however, for the proprietor had risen much earlier than he. The proprietor, whose acquaintance with our Andreas was of long standing, knew that he was inclined to seize every opportunity to evade payment. In consequence, our Andreas had to pay—from Tuesday to Sunday, for ample food and drink, much more even than he had really consumed. For the proprietor of the Tari-Bari knew how to distinguish those of his customers who could count from those who couldn't. And our Andreas, like many drinkers, was one of those who couldn't. So he paid out a large part of the money he had on him, and went nevertheless in the direction of the chapel Ste. Marie-des-Batignolles. But he may have known that he no longer had enough money to pay Saint Theresa in full. And he thought just as much of his friend Wojtech, with whom he had an appointment, as of his little creditor.

When he arrived in the neighborhood of the chapel it was unfortunately again after ten o'clock Mass, and again people streamed at him. And he turned toward the bistro, as usual—when suddenly he heard shouts behind him and felt a rough hand on his shoulder, and when he turned it was a policeman. Our Andreas (who, as we know, lacked papers as do so many of his kind) was frightened and reached into his pocket—simply to give himself the appearance of one who possesses papers which are in order. But the policeman said, "I know what you're looking for. You won't find it in your pocket. You just lost your wallet. Here it is—and," he added in jest, "that's what comes of drinking so many apéritifs, early on Sunday morning!"

Andreas quickly took the wallet, had barely enough composure to lift his hat, and went straight into the bistro.

There he found Wojtech already waiting. He did not recognize him at first sight but only after some time; then, however, our Andreas hailed him the more cordially. They could not stop mutually inviting each other; and Wojtech, polite as most men are, rose from the window-seat to let

Andreas have the place of honor, walked round the table, no matter how unsteadily, sat down on the opposite chair and made polite conversation. They drank nothing but pernod.

"Something odd happened to me again," Andreas said. "I'm on my way here, to meet you, when a policeman takes me by the shoulder and says, 'You lost your wallet.' And gives me one that isn't mine at all and I put it in my pocket, and now I'm going to look what it really is."

With these words he took the wallet out and looked, and there were all sorts of papers in it which in no way concerned him, and he also saw money in it and when he counted the notes they totaled just two hundred francs. And Andreas said, "You see? That's a sign from Heaven. Now I'll go over and pay my debt at last."

"For that," Wojtech replied, "you have time till Mass is over. What do you need Mass for, anyway? At Mass you can't pay a thing. After Mass you go to the vestry, and in the meantime we'll drink."

"Of course—as you like," replied Andreas.

At this moment the door opened and Andreas, feeling an odd pain in his heart and a great weakness in his head, saw a young girl enter and sit down on the window-seat exactly opposite him. She was very young, so young as he never thought to have seen a girl before, and dressed entirely in sky blue. She was as blue as only the sky can be on some days, and that only on blessed ones.

So Andreas swayed toward her, took a bow and said to the child, "What are you doing here?"

"I'm waiting for my parents to come back from Mass; they will call for me here. Every fourth Sunday," she said and was quite shy with the elderly man who had so suddenly addressed her. She was a little afraid of him.

Then Andreas asked, "What is your name?"

"Theresa," she said.

"Oh," cried Andreas now, "that is wonderful! I didn't think such a great, such a little Saint, such a great little creditor would honor me by coming to me—after I didn't come to her for such a long time."

"I don't understand what you're saying," said the little damsel, rather bewildered.

"That's just your delicacy," Andreas answered that. "That's just your delicacy, but I appreciate it. For a long time I've owed you two hundred francs and I never got around to giving them back to you, Miss Saint!"

"You don't owe me any money; but I have some in my pocketbook—here, take it and go. My parents will be here soon."

And she gave him a hundred-franc note from her pocketbook.

All this Wojtech saw in the mirror, and he swayed on his chair and ordered two pernods and was just about to drag out Andreas to the bar so they might drink together. But as Andreas gets ready to step up to the bar he drops like a sack, and all the people in the bistro get frightened, including Wojtech. And most of all the girl called Theresa. And because there is no doctor near and no pharmacist, they drag him into the vestry of the chapel—because even the godless waiters believe that priests know about dying and death; and the girl called Theresa cannot help going along.

So our poor Andreas is taken to the vestry, and unfortunately he can no longer say anything; he just makes a move as though wanting to reach into his left inner coat pocket where the money lies that he owes to the little creditor, and he says, "Miss Theresa," and heaves his last sigh and dies.

May God give all us drinkers so easy and sweet a death!

Translated by E. B. ASHTON

GERMANY

INTRODUCTION

By Franz Schoenberner

WITH REGARD TO German literature in general, my point of view necessarily diverges somewhat from that represented by the arrangement of the different sections of this anthology. Klaus Mann's preface sufficiently explains the purely tactical and even technical reasons why many another belonging in a larger sense to German literature are here listed under other nationalities. But in principle there is no disagreement between us that the world of literature knows no other frontiers than those of culture and language. Perhaps no other literature is, and always has been, so far from political provincialism as German literature, which existed as a spiritual entity long before Germany became a politically united Reich. To be world-minded, cosmopolitan, supra-national and international is the very characteristic, the best tradition, of German literature. Our greatest poets and writers, beginning with Luther, continuing through Goethe, Schiller, Herder, Schlegel, Tieck, up to Rainer Maria Rilke, Stefan George, Heinrich Mann, have been at the same time translators, aiming at, and often succeeding in, enriching German literature by the adaptation and adoption of foreign poets and writers who sometimes, like Shakespeare, became an inherent part of German literature. The idea of "Weltliteratur"—world literature—disregarding even the frontiers of language, is a typically German idea, paradoxically illustrated by the fact that, according to their passports, nearly all the authors listed in the German section belong to other nationalities. Heinrich Mann became a naturalized Czech, René Schickele, Annette Kolb, Alfred Doeblin became French citizens, and should any other German exile succeed in becoming an American writer, he would not abandon his role as a representative of German literature, which is German precisely in so far as it is European.

The great decisive influences of Scandinavian and Russian literature came to Europe, to the world, most through the medium of German translations. The world fame of Ibsen and Strindberg, of Hamsun and Sigrid Undset, of Tolstoi, Dostoevsky, Chekhov, Gorki and so on, was originally "made in Germany," having left its imprint first of all upon German literature. Especially after the first World War, this cosmopolitan tendency became so marked that many German publishers more or less specialized in translations from Russian, Scandinavian, English, American and French and, to a lesser extent, from Spanish and Italian literatures. An increasingly large proportion of the nearly

6000 books published annually in Germany were translations, and it is characteristic that this tendency was even accentuated under the Nazi regime, despite all impediments, because the German public, by reading translations of foreign literature, adopted a passive resistance to what Goebbels tried to impose as truly German, that is, Nazi literature.

I cannot resist the temptation to suggest at least some of the decisive foreign influences upon the most outstanding figures of German literature. There is Stefan George, inspired by Dante and French Symbolism; Rilke, unthinkable without the Danish novelist, Jens Peter Jacobsen, and Russian mysticism; Heinrich Mann, related to d'Annunzio, Stendhal, Flaubert, Maupassant and Zola; Thomas Mann, indebted to Tolstoi as well as to Dickens and the Danish poet and novelist, Hermann Bang. This faculty to absorb and to amalgamate many different and even contradictory elements into a new organic creation is a sign of distinction. Without such ingredients, German literature would be in danger of becoming provincial, regional, and particularistic up to the point of "Heimatkunst," rooted locally in a narrowly circumscribed geographical section and finally ending up in the terrible Nazi morass of "Blood and Soil." The great German writers are and always have been "good Europeans," to quote Friedrich Nietzsche, who, in spite of Goebbels, was not a Nazi philosopher, but the most pitiless critic of what seems now a relatively harmless prefiguration of the Third Reich.

The shameless effrontery and cowardice of the despicable Wilhelm Petersen (Dean of Berlin University) was needed to declare in 1933 that Goethe and Schiller had been the first National Socialists. In fact their books ought to have been burnt, like those of Lessing and Heine, in the famous auto-da-fé of May 8, 1933. Had not Goethe's anti-nationalism and pan-humanism exasperated all good German patriots of his time? And Schiller—was not his motto, "In tyrannos," given to his first drama *Die Räuber,* also valid for the *Tell,* for *Don Carlos* and for *The Liberation of the Netherlands?* Was not his whole work impregnated with the subversive ideas of the French Revolution and thus more dangerous than Lessing's *Nathan the Wise,* more radical even than Heine's witty polemicism in verse and prose? And the dramatic genius Georg Buechner, the author of *Woyzek,* of *Danton's Death* and many flaming manifestos, who died at twenty-three, in exile, after a stormy revolutionary life—it was only from a lack of literary education that the Nazis overlooked burning his books. To repudiate the great majority of contemporary German writers under the ridiculous pretext of their being Jewish or subversive, or both, implied the impious and impossible attempt to destroy the continuity, the most legitimate tradition, of German literature, in the name of a fictitious and farcical, deeply un-German Germanism. The occasionally slightly hysterical outbursts of exasperated nationalism in the works of Heinrich von Kleist, that genius full of conflicts, or of Ernst Moritz Arndt, or of Johann Gottlieb Fichte, are merely the voices of a German underground movement fighting desperately against the French world conqueror, Napoleon I. And even during the first World War the nationalistic psychosis became no more outspoken in German literature than in French or English. In the midst of the war, courageous magazines like René

Schickele's *Weisse Blaetter* or Wilhelm Herzog's *Forum* tried to save and to preserve the European idea.

The revolution of 1918 naturally gave a new impulse to the revolutionary tendencies of a literature which traditionally had been anti-nationalistic, anti-bourgeois and highly critical of the social order as well as of society in a more exact sense, but at the same time almost a-political in terms of active participation in civic life. It is true that the romantic irony directed against philistines by Friedrich Schlegel and the old romantic school had no more real political meaning than had the pathos of social accusation that characterized the Naturalism of 1890 under the influence of Zola. It was rather an aesthetic, artistic attitude, without a real feeling of social responsibility. Social drama, like Gerhart Hauptmann's *The Weavers,* discovered a new theme in the life of the lower classes, but ignored the real political issue of its time, the struggle of the social-democratic movement against Bismarck. Naturalism was dead even before 1914. Hauptmann had plunged into the pale blue romanticism of his *Sunken Bell,* he had returned to the noncommittal sphere of "pure art," assuming the pseudo-Olympian attitude and even the hollow mask of a minor, already somewhat senile Goethe. Johannes Schlaf, Arno Holz, Hermann Sudermann had fallen into oblivion. The only dramatist who at least in the limited field of sexual morality and bourgeois hypocrisy had preserved the aggressive attitude of a liberator and emancipator was Frank Wedekind, a sort of grotesque and romantic moralist, in the same sense as D. H. Lawrence was a puritan in reverse. But Wedekind never overcame the ultimately sterile attitude of the artist who with fantastic jokes seeks to "épater les bourgeois." It was more or less a pure coincidence that he became a sort of political martyr through one of his contributions to the radical and satirical *Simplizissimus* and that he was sentenced for the crime of lése-majesté to serve some months in a "fortress." Even his political satire was the expression rather of a more general feeling of revolt than of a clear political conception, and his revolutionary influence was limited to the sphere of literature. He became one of the ancestors of German Expressionism (together with Rimbaud and Lautréamont). In Carl Sternheim, Georg Kaiser, Fritz von Unruh, who began to dominate the stage after the War, the political element became much more vocal. Ernst Toller, who as a student had participated in the tragi-comic leftist putsch in Munich in 1919, had become politically mature by the terrible experience of five years' imprisonment. His dramatic work—similar to Johannes R. Becher's verse—became the expression of, and the vehicle for, a consciously revolutionary tendency. He followed the great example of Georg Buechner—up to the tragically premature end of his life.

But German Expressionism on the whole was a rather romantic and anarchistic revolt of "vitality"—heavily overrated and often hysterically exaggerated—against every kind of "form." Freud's startling disclosures of subconscious and repressed forces within the human soul were enthusiastically misinterpreted and exploited by youth iconoclasts, some of whom had not yet outgrown the rebelliousness of puberty. As usual, this rebellion was directed against all "conventions," but especially against family and school, as in Hasenclever's drama *The Sun* and in the first novels of Leonhard Frank and

Franz Werfel. The reaction to war experience, on the other hand, made these young poets indulge in panegyrical, purely emotional praise of an all-embracing human brotherhood. But Expressionism was at the same time a revolt against traditional artistic forms, against the laws of language, of grammar and syntax, yes, against reason and rationality itself. This fact may explain why some obstinate expressionists, like Gottfried Benn, Arnolt Bronnen, Hans Johst and others, succumbed so easily to the temptation of the Nazi "myth" of the upsurge of elemental, anti-rational forces of nature against the sterile intellectualism and moralism of modern civilization. Knut Hamsun, long before he became an actual Nazi, had very effectively prompted this sort of poetic nihilism, exerting a fatal influence upon a whole section of young writers that eventually ended up in the synthetic barbarism of Nazi letters. But a certain cosmic mysticism is one of the characteristic elements of Expressionism, a quality which is discernible in Alfred Doeblin's early novels as well as in Franz Kafka's somewhat transcendental writing.

The brilliant pamphleteering aggressiveness of Heinrich Mann's novel *The Subject* (the publication of which in a literary review had to be interrupted in August 1914) remained an exceptional phenomenon, and his attempt to mobilize the progressive forces of the German intelligentsia in a "Political Council of Intellectual Workers" found an inglorious end when, in the spring of 1919, the forces of reaction began to reorganize in Munich. After some excellent speeches and manifestos, most of the German writers returned in disappointment from their short political excursion to their ivory towers. It was a rare exception that an author of rank like the Alsatian René Schickele dared to explore in a series of novels the actual problem of his homeland—and of Europe—the question of Franco-German understanding, without shying away from the danger of compromising his poetic vision by clear political insight. Thomas Mann, in an article published in exile, has rightly deplored the fatal fallacy of the dogma that "art has nothing to do with politics." It was this attitude of artistic isolationism which prevented Mann himself and other outstanding representatives of German literature from realizing the full danger of Nazism, not only as a simple political movement, but also as a total revolt against the very foundations of Western culture. The mortal enemy was not opposed, but simply ignored, as long as the battle was still in the balance. The rabid individualist, Karl Krauss, wasted his brilliant polemic gift in the "one man crusade" of his *Fackel* against the stupidity of the Viennese press. The actual fighting was left to some small political weeklies like *Tagebuch* and *Weltbuehne* or to the political satire of *Simplizissimus*. But a courageous political journalist like Carl von Ossietzky—who certainly deserved the Nobel Peace Prize that reached him, a dying man, in a Nazi concentration camp—did not belong in the strict realm of literature. Rainer Maria Rilke wrestled with the terrible angels of his *Duino Elegies* in the voluntary confinement of the little Château de Muzot in Switzerland. Hugo von Hofmannsthal escaped into an atmosphere of aesthetic hedonism, enjoying and wisely administering the eternal treasures of Austro-German literature. And Stefan George, living in Switzerland, assumed in his poetic messages, *The War* and *The New Reich,* an attitude of esoteric, aristocratic mysticism, celebrating the strong anti-democratic myth of the great leader and the selected élite as against the despicable vulgar masses. The understandable misinterpretation of George's work, confusing his "New Reich" with Hitler's Third Reich, was eagerly exploited by those disciples who, like the pale, professorial poet, Ernst Bertram, had the advantage of being "pure aryans" in contrast to many other devoted followers. The Jewish scholar Friedrich Gundolf, for example, teaching history of literature at Heidelberg and interpreting Shakespeare, Goethe and George in masterly books, could not prevent one of his less gifted students, Joseph Goebbels, from destroying by fire, in truly Herostratic spirit, the temple of German literature.

This historical novel represented by the work of Alfred Neumann, Robert Neumann, Lion Feuchtwanger and others, even if its topic was the immediate past, as in Joseph Roth's *Radetzky Marsch,* carefully avoided any sort of real political implication. The "Neue Sachlichkeit" proclaimed the impartiality of the photographic lens. The same was true in part for the war novel, the great vogue for which was started by Arnold Zweig's outspoken anti-militaristic and pacifist *Sergeant Grischa.* But Remarque, whom an international success inflated out of any proportion to his literary significance, tried to preserve the neutral superiority of "pure art." Up to this moment Remarque had never felt an inner compulsion to take a clear and direct stand aganst the Nazis. He answered their vicious attacks by retiring silently into a voluntary and comfortable exile long before the final battle was lost in 1933, whereas Ludwig Renn, the author of *Krieg,* became one of the most active political fighters, risking his life in Germany and in the Spanish Civil War. Hans Carossa, deeply rooted in the tradition of Goethe, Stifter, Moericke and Jean Paul, tried to transpose war experience, exactly like that of his individual life, to the transcendent and symbolic sphere of poetry. Logically enough, this last refuge, an illusory realm of spiritual liberty, was conquered and gradually destroyed by a really total dictatorship that did not tolerate any sort of neutrality or escape. Carossa and many other conservative writers who stayed in Germany, hoping perhaps to weather the storm, succumbed to the systematic pressure of alternating threats and promises. From one concession to the other, they were forced into the shame of declarations of loyalty, accepting even the disgrace of Nazi honors. Serving false new gods, they have forfeited their spiritual birthright; betraying their mission, their holy office, they have lost face, lost caste and—by a kind of inner nemesis—lost even their art. Most of them have become silent or have been silenced; the others are gradually absorbed, asphyxiated, sterilized, by the deadly atmosphere of self-contempt, corruption and terror.

The more aggressive forces of opposition came from the ranks of a younger generation, mostly of the "Class of 1902," though Glaeser, the author of a novel with this title, later became a renegade, returning to Germany after having tasted the bitter—though for him not even so very bitter—bread of exile. But others like Bert Brecht, Gustav Regler, Anna Seghers, Walter Mehring, Kurt Tucholsky, Oscar Maria Graf, became more and more outspoken in their political attitude, sometimes even to the point of dogmatism. Some of the younger writers whom I introduced to the public through the magazines, *Jugend* and *Simplizissimus,* have become Nazi writers, as Waggerl. Some others got lost in No-Man's-Land, like Erich Kaestner who, after some books of brilliantly aggressive verse lost his impetus in the hour of decision, preferring to stay in Germany and to write innocuous books for children. But others—most of them represented in this book—survived all tests, as writers and as men. They steadily improved their stature amidst the tribulations of ten years of exile, proving the vitality and validity of what is left of German literature: the German literature in exile.

The history of literature, especially of German literature, knows many exiles, many refugees. But probably it has never before happened that a whole literature emigrated at the same time, following for the most part approximately the same itinerary, through French internment camps to the final freedom of the Americas, leaving scattered groups in England, Russia, Switzerland, Palestine or, at worst, in Nazi-occupied countries. The small army, preferring exile to shameful capitulation, has suffered terrible losses in ten years of never ceasing and often losing battle. It is too early to count the casualties, we do not know how many were wounded—mortally perhaps. And we have to bury many dead, those who died prematurely, like Jakob Wassermann, René Schickele, Odon von Horvath, Werner Hegemann, Joseph Roth, or voluntarily when no other opening to freedom in dignity seemed left, like Kurt Tucholsky, Ernst Weiss, Ernst Toller, Walter Hasenclever, Stefan Zweig, and finally those who were murdered, like Theodor Lessing, Erich Muehsam, Carl von Ossietzky and many others. Some, not all of our dead, are helping here to represent German literature; they are yet more alive than Goebbels' literary lackeys.

The general principles determining the editors' choice for this German section of the anthology are certainly sound, though, of course, open to discussion. The attempt to represent twenty years of German literature in 125 pages involves the necessary injustice of incompleteness. But even this small collection is sufficient proof that German literature, today as in the past, is a part of world literature, that it speaks the universal language of art and is engaged—to use the classical expression—upon the great objects of mankind, *den grossen Gegenständen der Menschheit.*

Thomas Mann

GOETHE'S CAREER AS A MAN OF LETTERS

THE 22ND OF MARCH 1832 had come. In his armchair, a coverlet upon his knees, a green shade over his eyes, Goethe died. The fear and anxiety which often precede death by some time were over and done. And when he asked what day of the month it was, and was told the 22nd, he replied that since spring had now come, it would be all the easier to get well. After that he raised his arm and traced signs in the air. His hand kept moving outward, then downward to the left; he was actually writing, line beneath line, and his arm sank lower, not only because there might be no more room above for the shadow-writing, but also because he was weak. At last the hand rested on the coverlet, but still he continued writing. The dying man seemed to be repeatedly writing the same thing in these invisible lines. He was seen to punctuate with precision; here and there letters could be descried. Then his fingers turned livid, they ceased to move, and when the green shade was lifted, his eyes were already sightless.

Goethe died writing. In the last blurred dreams of his conscious life he did what he had always done, either in his own clear, neat hand or by dictation—he wrote, noted, practised that activity which resolves hard fact into spirit, or which preserves as hard fact the manifestations of the spirit. The moment of death found him fixing in symbols of script his ultimate experiences in the life of the mind, which may have seemed to him a final perception most worthy of expression, though it may have been no more than a fantasy born of his great weakness. Thus to the very end he sought to uplift what was in his heart and mould it into a spiritual sphere. To the very end he was a man of letters, just as he had been in the beginning, when in an early epistle his joy at the strong creative impulse in his inmost soul made him break out in the cry: "Truly I was born to be a man of letters. When I have put my thoughts on paper well, I feel a stronger happiness than at any other time." Just so he had been in the evening of his days, when, after the brief sleep of old age, he struggled at dawn with the sacred weakness of his brain, and wrested from the tonal spheres the last notes of *Faust*—one short paragraph daily, or even less—so linking the close of his life to its beginning with the lines:

> "Neige, neige
> Du Ohnegleiche."

> "Incline, incline
> To us, Thou Incomparable One."

A man of letters, then. It is a fruitless and futile mania of the critics to insist on a distinction between the poet and the man of letters—it is an impossible distinction; for the boundary between the two does not lie in the product of either, but rather within the personality of the artist himself; and even here it is so fluid as to be indistinguishable. Poetical invasions into the field of pure letters, "literary" invasions into the field of poetry, are so frequent that to affirm a distinction between them is mere stubbornness, born of the wish to disparage the fruits of reason in favour of the unconscious, prereasonable—in short of what is commonly regarded as the product of sheer genius. Goethe's prodigious mind, to which Emerson paid homage in his comment on the Helena episode in the Second Part of *Faust,* is really sufficient to put such quibbling to shame. "The wonder of the book," he says, "is its superior intelligence. In the menstruum of this man's wit, the past and the present ages, and their religions, politics, and modes of thinking, are dissolved into archetypes and ideas."

A completely unintelligent poet is the dream of a certain romantic idolatry of Nature. It does not exist. The very conception of poetry, uniting, as it does, Nature and spiritual mind, contradicts it. No unintelligent creative power could ever succeed in surviving into a time of life where Nature no longer—or at least not to the degree it does in all-daring youth —comes to the help of production; or, to speak with Goethe: a time of life where principle and character have to take the place of Nature. When it comes to naïveness or directness—that is a different matter; this is an indispensable condition of all creation. But it is hardly necessary to state—and Goethe himself is a wonderful example of this—that the purest naïveness and the most mighty intelligence can go hand in hand.

Nothing, then, could be further from my intention than to separate the young Goethe, out of the rhythm of whose blood immortal love-songs sprang, from him who in his old age spoke basic truths in orphic words; or to separate either of these from the masterly analyst and psychologist: the novelist who wrote the *Lehr-* and *Wanderjahre,* as well as the most daring and trenchant novel of adultery which the moral culture of the Occident ever produced: the *Wahlverwandtschaften.* When I speak of Goethe the man of letters, I use the term simply as the common designation for the life on earth of the poet; preferring the everyday, moderate, and objective terminology to the more elevated, with its earnest fanaticism. Goethe lived in the flesh, he was a human being, a citizen—and he was a man of letters. This was his destiny, and he not only accepted his lot, but loved and confirmed it and admitted it with all its difficulties.

A strange destiny, a perplexing lot; there is no denying it. A lot which must often have seemed to him who bore it an abnormality and a curse. "To be a man of letters is an incurable disease," wrote Goethe in 1820, already an old man, "and so the best one can do is to come to terms with it." And he reminded himself and others that a human being is really only called upon to exercise influence from man to man, directly. "Writing," he declares, in an anti-literary moment, "is an abuse of language, and reading to oneself a sorry substitute for speech. A man can have no effect on mankind save through his actual personality alone." But is this not also true in the mental sphere? Goethe knew, and said, that it was only through the character and personality of the author that a work actually had influence and became a monument of culture. "One must *be* something in order to *do* anything." That was his incisive formula for the organic mystery of creative production, so that, after all, the use of written language is no sorry substitute, but this very same effect of personality on a higher plane. As for reading, he expressly refers Schiller's astonishingly rapid development to his urgent receptivity, to his passion for reading. Moreover, there exists a fat volume consisting exclusively of the titles of books which Goethe himself took out of the Weimar Library to read and study. His productivity is closely bound up with his capacity to admire—his positive genius for admiration, as we see from his conversation with Eckermann concerning the great Italian, Manzoni. This admiration is one of the main supports to his power of artistic creation. It was this quality that, when he studied the *Elegies* of Propertius, aroused in him the desire to produce something similar. He admits that he could not read without feeling such compulsion; and he brings home to all artists the fact that it is necessary for them to keep in constant contact with masterpieces, so that the creative spirit may be maintained at its height and prevented from relapsing ("Zurückschwanken").

There are few authors who have paid tribute in warmer terms than Goethe to the very joy of the profession they practise. At thirty-three he cried: "How priceless it is when a glorious human brain can reproduce what is mirrored in it!"

But this business of reproducing the outer world through the inner, which it re-creates after its own form and in its own way, never does, however much charm and fascination may emanate from it, quite satisfy the outer world. The reason is that the author's real attitude always has something of opposition in it, which is quite inseparable from his character. It is the attitude of the man of mind towards the ponderous, stubborn, evil-minded human race, which always places the poet and writer in this particular position because of his character and temperament, so conditioning his destiny. "Viewed from the heights of reason," Goethe wrote, "all life looks like some malignant disease and the world like a madhouse." This is a characteristic utterance of the kind of man who writes: the expression of his painful impatience with mankind. More of the same thing than one would suppose is to be found in Goethe's works: phrases about the "human mob" in general and his "dear Germans" in particular, typical of the specific irritability I mean. For what are the factors which condition the life of the writer? They are twofold: perception and a feeling for form; and both of these simultaneously. The strange thing is that for the poet they are one organic unity, in which the one implies, challenges, and draws out the other. This unity is, for him, mind, beauty, freedom—everything. Where it is not, there is vulgar, human stupidity, expressing itself in lack of perception and imperviousness to beauty of form—nor can he tell you which of these two he finds the more irritating.

> "Übers Niederträchtige
> Niemand sich beklage;
> Denn es ist das Mächtige,
> Was man Dir auch sage."

> "Over the base
> Grieve not your heart away;
> For baseness is mighty,
> Whatever men may say."

I repeat: There is in his work more evidence than we should wish or expect of the torments which the base and the stupid could inflict upon Goethe. More, indeed, than we are ready to admit or than should, in fairness, be quoted. For we are aware, especially in Goethe's case, of the powerful correctives, the compromise and assuagements produced upon him by sheer courtesy and kindliness. In place of kindliness, let me use a stronger and a warmer word—I mean love. Goethe knew that mind and art are not much without love, indeed that they are nothing without it; that mind cannot live with the world, nor the world with it, where love is not. It manifests itself as consideration, as delicacy, as kindness, as truly Goethean reluctance to give pain. We have at hand the conversation with Eckermann where he says: "If only mind and real education could become common property, the poet would be well off; he could always be entirely truthful and never shrink from uttering the best he has. But things being as they are, he must always remain upon a certain level: he is forced to remember that his works fall into the hands of diverse readers and that he has every reason to be careful not to speak too openly and so give offense to the majority of decent men." Thus speaks the compliant spirit of love, which is ready to make allowance for the lowly if not for the evil. It is this kind-heartedness that we observe in the closing words of *Wahlverwandtschaften:* the words of comfort at the death of the united lovers: "What a happy moment it will be when, at some future day, they awake together!" This is strangely compliant, truly courteous, and spoken with an arabesque which engages to nothing. For the disciple of Aristotle, with his faith in the continuation of the strictest entelechy, could hardly have believed in the resurrection of the body. The whole is a sort of poetical license, a polite turn of speech, conciliatory, simple, but by no means fundamentally dishonest; for as an old man Goethe finds it in him to say, with moist eyes, in all sincerity: "We shall all meet again above."

I should like here to enlarge upon a thought, a trend, an idea which is the main expression of that love which the intellect feels for life. I mean, of course, the idea of education. Goethe was a born educator. His two great life-works, *Faust* and *Wilhelm Meister*, are conclusive evidence of the fact. *Wilhelm Meister* in particular shows how the tendency to autobiography, to confession and self-portrayal, becomes impersonal, turns outward and becomes socialized, even statesmanly, and finds pedagogic expression. But a trend or vocation towards educating others does not spring from inner harmony, but rather from inner uncertainties, disharmony, difficulty—from the difficulty of knowing one's own self. The urge to educate in the poet-man of letters can be defined as a proclamation of insecurity, an admission that he deviates from the norm, while he none the less feels his responsibility towards all mankind and himself as a representative of it. "True symbolism," says Goethe, "lies where the particular represents the general." This is precisely the symbolism of the poetic ego, which needs only complete self-expression to loosen the tongue of the multitude—not that he does this with intention, or with any sort of claim, or as if expecting to be universally accepted, but simply as a person, with all the charm and qualities of a personality as such, who happens to have the quality of especial importance. The boon which finds expression in a work of art is essentially important in this sense of being representative, of unwillingly and unwittingly standing for the many—and this without changing one's own personal destiny, the inner life to that of the average, normal man. Perhaps all this is redolent with suffering and abnormality. But let us think of the strangeness of Rousseau's life, for instance, how perfect an example of his epoch he was; how his artistic production gave voice to its deepest yearnings, and how he moved his entire world simply by making his own confessions. He, who surely was no favoured darling of the gods, had a definitive influence on that godlike youth Goethe. Goethe derives his entire idea of education from Rousseau. Ottilie's speech in the *Wahlverwandtschaften* is at once Goethe- and Rousseau-like: "I do not deny it: I think it a happy destiny to educate others in the ordinary way, if only we ourselves have been most strangely educated." One may define a man of letters as an educator who has himself been strangely educated; and in his own case education always goes hand in hand with his own inner battle; here we have a welding of the inner and the outer self, a simultaneous wrestling with the ego and with the outer world. Merely educating others, on the assumption of the perfectness of one's own ego, is sheer schoolmastership. But in this other form it is a wrestling with an extended ego—I mean the nation—an insistence upon self-discipline and self-control, a pedagogic identification with the outside world, which may, of course, look like aloofness and the coldly critical attitude observable in all great Germans, especially in Goethe and Nietzsche. And yet how responsible such an attitude is, compared with the yelpings of the patriotic boosters!

Goethe's inclination towards educating others and moralizing is shown particularly in his tendency towards sententiousness: the moral and psychological *aperçu;* this appears in his prose and even in the classical dramas (in antique stylization). The moral and social remark, however, is in itself one of those excursions into the realm of the poetical which make all didactic differentiation between the poet and the man of letters impossible. For here we have a human task accomplished which really belongs to the poet in his quality of man of letters. This particular type of remark seldom gives utterance to something new. "New discoveries," says Goethe, "can and will be made, but nothing new can be thought out which has reference to man as a moral being. Everything has already been thought and said which we might reproduce, at best, in another form." The task, then, consists in the definitive formation of human knowledge. Perhaps nowhere does beauty as a sheerly human phenomenon become so easy to recognize and worthy of respect as in a poetical *aperçu.* "We must," writes Goethe, "make the indomitable attempt, each day anew, to seize, with fundamental seriousness, a word and unite this with all that is felt, seen, thought, experienced, imagined, and reasoned!" We have perhaps no utterance in which the passion that makes the man of letters, the instinct to a beautiful exactitude of expression, is so well expressed; and here, too, we have the distinction between critical and plastic exactitude. The latter was Goethe's, as it is always that of the poetic man of letters. For him, even abstraction is plastic. There is another sort of exactitude which has to do with incisiveness and sharpness; but this is not of his sort. His has rather to do with the precise essence of things—it is plastic.

It is not beauty's task to serve abstract perception; that which is purely mental is not bound up with form, nor does it strive to be. The artist as poet and man of letters is connected *through the senses* with the idea of human dignity; he represents the necessity of clothing experience in its worthiest, purest, most enchanting form. His very being is based upon a union—which is not without its perils—between dignity and sensuality. The human office he performs gives him some stamp of the priest which does not always sit well with the libertinage of the sensual man in him. Two forces are above the average strong in him: his sex life and his intellectual life; the two together inevitably make him a revolutionary, a disturbing, upsetting, even an undermining force, urging futurewards. "In every artist," says Goethe, "there is a touch of audacity without which no talent is conceivable." This audacity springs from his peculiar relation to the two forces I have mentioned, which, for the species we call artist, are the greatest incentives towards life. They were that for Goethe. "For life is love, and spirit the very life of life itself." Moral boldness in matters of sex, a revolutionary attitude in the realm of the senses never ceased to express themselves in Goethe's works, up to the last and highest. But this finds expression most naturally and powerfully in his youth —most simply perhaps in his *Stella*. At the close of this play, the words spoken by both women: "We are thine!" have been interpreted as being addressed to the man who loves them both. This has often been described as grotesque when applied to reality, where a triangle is regarded as a painful if not impossible situation—and that point of view is reasonable. Yet we must permit this human audacity and liberty for its own sake. If, however, one admits a thing here because we are speaking of Goethe, then we must take the consequences and admit this sort of audacity in the case of any poet, even if this might seem to be dangerous or morally subversive. It is, as a matter of fact, right and necessary. Poetical license must be not only understood but worthily accepted, if we admit it at all.

A rebellious, pitiful lament for Gretchen's fate rings through the centuries; but this lament is not aimed at human institutions. "It was never my way," Goethe declared in his old age, "to rail at institutions. It always seemed like presumption, and it may be that I learned courtesy too early."

But he was a liberator as is every poet and man of letters: he liberates by arousing the emotions and extending by analysis our knowledge of man. This he did even against his own conservative intent. The effect of the *Wahlverwandtschaften* made and still makes an impression quite contrary to its real social and ethical tendency. Goethe often had to defend himself against the reproach that his books had an immoral influence.

"I let Gretchen be condemned and Ottilie starve to death," he cried; "what more do they want?" But it is of no use. The poet's austerity is not to be taken too literally. After all, he does arouse sympathy for the human, he is akin to the power of love, which does not refuse its presence even to the greatest of sinners, and so has a disintegrating effect upon Philistia, even where in his conscious mind he is conservative—as was Goethe when he tried, in the *Wahlverwandtschaften,* to preserve the institution of marriage. Byron's ironical pronouncement is well known, where he speaks of the "old fox" who "would not leave his lair, but who from there uttered most proper sermons." The *Wahlverwandtschaften* and *Werthers Leiden* Byron in his irony calls the mockery of marriage, such as Mephisto himself could not have written better. He maintains that the endings of both of these novels are the peak of irony. But this is the rather too far-reaching utterance of a spirit who, in a far greater degree than Goethe, found pleasure in shocking the world. This was not what Goethe cared for. But he expressly objected to being called a conservative, as though that might mean that he desired to uphold everything as it existed—even social evils. But he was far from belonging to that type of renegade of which Sainte-Beuve wrote that "they had nothing of a writer but the talent." He was remote from the hysterical self-satisfaction of the anti-intellectuals, from any morbid self-surrender to unspirituality. "Let us cling to life and the future!" "The main thing, after all, is to go forward!" Such are his words. They are simple and straightforward; they are his.

Goethe's career as a man of letters—and now I mean his outward career as a writer—displays characteristics so singular that its like is scarcely to be found in the history of an intellectual life. It began with two great, even sensational successes, one in drama and one in fiction; one comfortingly national and the other morbid and cosmopolitan: *Goetz* and *Werther.* The word "comforting" in this sense is not mine, but Goethe's, who himself, in *Dichtung und Wahrheit,* explains the nature of the success *Goetz* scored. "There is a peculiarly comforting feeling," he says, "felt by a whole nation when somebody succeeds in calling up its history in a telling and sympathetic manner. It rejoices in the ancestral virtues and smiles at the ancestral failings, as though it had long since overcome them. A work of this kind is bound to reap sympathetic applause, and so I was able to rejoice in a considerable success." No more modest and at the same time apt description can be imagined. As for *Werther,* the whole wealth of the young man's nature was apparent in the deviation from the norm portrayed in this early work. The extreme, nerve-shattering sensitivity of this little book, which made it the horror and detestation of the moralists, evoked a storm of applause which went beyond all bounds and fairly intoxicated the world with an ecstasy for death. It ran like a fever and a frenzy over the populated earth, acting like a spark in a powder magazine, setting free a dangerous amount of pent-up force. We must be aware that an audience already existed for the book before its appearance. It seemed to fill the world with a very rapture of death; it was as though the public in every country had been secretly and unconsciously waiting for this very work, produced by an unknown citizen of a German city, to release for them, as though by a revolution, the suppressed yearning of their entire world. It was as though a bullet had hit the bull's-eye; it was the word of salvation. There is a story told of a young Englishman who in later years came to Weimar, saw Goethe walk past, and fainted in the street, overpowered by the sight of the author of *Werther* in the flesh. This tempestuous success must have been bewildering and burdensome to the young hero of it. It is dangerous to have the world take you to its bosom at so early an age. But Goethe proved equal to his exposed situation: he meditated upon the experience, observed it, and drew his conclusions from it. He cites a French writer: "When a good mind, by producing a meritorious work, has drawn upon itself the attention of the public, the public does all it can to prevent it from repeating the performance." "It is so true," he adds, "something good, full of talent and vigour, is produced in the peace and quiet of a man's youth; it gets him applause, but loses him his independence. People fret away his concentration, they worry and distract him, thinking they can pinch off a bit of his personality and adapt it to their own use." He makes the acquaintance of the inconsiderate and importunate world, with its criticism. His remarks on the subject are of an exhilarating pithiness unsurpassed by any other pen. "I early noticed a characteristic of readers," he says in *Dichtung und Wahrheit,* "especially comic in those among them who express themselves in print. They seem to harbour the illusion that if a man accomplishes something he is in their debt; that is, that he is always a little in arrears with delivering what they really wanted and needed—even though they had no idea, before they saw his work, that such a thing existed or was even possible." No more apt or witty words have ever been found for the relation between the artist, aware of the freshness and originality of his offering, and the critic limping behind him. And who was more justified in this taunt than a man whose every work, as it appeared, had a sensational effect on receptive minds, affecting them like a marvellous surprise, like something unimaginable, of which, until its sudden and vitalizing appearance, nobody could have dreamed? "Every morning," sighs Emile Zola, "each of us has to swallow his toad." Goethe, too, had his toads to swallow—not only when he was young, but on into his old age. The contemptible things which people permitted themselves to say about this venerable old man whose intellect commanded the world, are hardly to be believed, were it not that they can be quoted. He took it without flinching, but he heard it all. Composed and convinced of the inevitable necessity of what he was and what he did, he says in a letter written when he was forty-four: "We can do nothing but what we do. Applause is a gift of the gods." Such is the fatalism of a man who knows he must live his life and does not care what the world makes of it. At bottom it is modesty which determines his attitude towards his work—I mean now each single work, each stage and creative phase of his life. "For who produces nothing but masterpieces?" he asks; and such an improvisation as *Clavigo* he abandons to its fate with the fling: "Everything cannot be just beyond words!"

Just the same, he has his tender spots. He is sufficiently an artist to need praise and to drink in applause like a thirsty man. He was only twenty-five when critical observers found him "not manly enough against praise or blame." And there were people who were close to him later, like Karoline von Wolzogen, who commented on his susceptibility to praise and said that this weakness was actually increasing at an age when he should have overcome it. Goethe is a very great man; but he is like us all. In spite of his great gift of admiration, jealousy is not unknown to him. There is a characteristic question in his *West-Oestlicher Diwan:* "Does a man live when others also live?" And Boisserée, speaking of Goethe at sixty-six, says: "And then, regrettably, a weak side appeared, consisting of mingled envy and the fearsome pride of old age." In a talk about the Romanticists, Novalis and Schlegel, he shows this weak side; he takes offence and is greatly irritated at Novalis's criticism of his prose, at Schlegel's ignoring the *Natürliche Tochter*, and so forth.

The striking feature, then, in Goethe's career, the unique feature, is that after the two extraordinary successes—*Goetz* and *Werther*—the figure of the young artist fades, retreats, and disappears. We now come to the decade following his entry into the service of the Duchy of Weimar— those ten years of his life which he "sacrificed to serious business." This fading from sight and memory of an author only lately so belauded is strange indeed. It afforded much gratification to the enemies of *Werther*. The phenomenon called Goethe seemed a thing of the past. People had seen a meteor flash, had said "Ah!" and that was all. Moreover Goethe never entirely regained the lost ground; possibly something like it was in the hearty popular success of *Goetz* and, briefly, in *Hermann und Dorothea*. At heart he was not bent on popular success—"*popularisch*" he calls it—or on catering to the public. This is not to his taste. I have especially noted one little anecdote: in the year 1828 Tyrolese folk-singers came to his house in Weimar and filled the rooms with their songs and yodelling. The young people present were much pleased. Ulrike and Eckermann especially were charmed by "*Du, Du, liegst mir im Herzen.*" But the same source notes that Goethe himself was by no means so enchanted. He shrugged his shoulders and said: "One must ask children and sparrows whether or no cherries and berries are a healthful diet." That was not the result of chance bad humour, but is a definite aristocratic-humanistic rejection. We also recall how pained the good Eckermann was when Goethe told him his writings would never become popular. He could say that despite the first part of *Faust*, whose popularity is of a lofty, ideal, implicit kind, not so actual as that of more than one of Schiller's plays. The paradoxical truth is that Goethe's Germanness, his strong, substantial, and—if I may say so—his Lutheran Germanness, was not nearly so calculated to catch the public as the half-Gallic art of his friend. Goethe, indeed, declares that Schiller was far more of an aristocrat than himself. That may be true; but even so, the aristocracy of Goethe, based as it was most intimately and inwardly upon the personal aims and problems of his artistic temperament, had a far more decisive influence on his personal fate. He could realize the value of popular success in a way quite foreign to Schiller, who was cut out to be a demagogue. Goethe knew how gullible the public was. "The cruder minds," he says, "are taken in by variety and exaggeration, the more educated by a sort of ceremoniousness." And there is some of this, perhaps, in *Hermann und Dorothea*, that inspired poem of the German bourgeoisie, with which he once more seized the public ear and awoke that feeling of national satisfaction he had awakened in *Goetz*, although, strange to say, he himself makes merry over it. In a boisterous letter to Schiller he writes that he feels like a successful conjurer who has mixed his cards well. And in this ironic mood he suggests that it might be possible to write a play that would be acted on every stage and that every spectator must regard as excellent, without the need for the author to share his opinion—a fantasy which was surely understood by the very speculative Schiller. But, seriously speaking, the human German, the bourgeois, which in *Hermann und Dorothea* he elevates and refines, is his one avenue to popular success, his claim to being essential German. This is offensive to him in its pure form, as an ethical and cultural tendency; I mean that he is against it consciously, deliberately, pedagogically. But his own mighty nature embraces both: the German and the Mediterranean, the European and the national. And this combination is, of its nature, the same as that other in him: of genius and intellectualism; of mystery and clarity; of the deep chord and the polished word; of the lyrical and the psychological. He is the greatest of them all because he so happily unites the daemonic and the urbane, in a way that is probably unique; and it is precisely this combination which has made him the darling of mankind.

But let me repeat: his conscious desire to teach the people is directed against the purely folkish. Like Nietzsche, who here follows him entirely, he looks upon the barbaric and ethnic as an exotic phenomenon which can arouse curiosity but can never be satisfying. A good illustration is his dislike of the whole atmosphere of the Edda. He tells Eckermann: "There is as little for us in the sombre old-German epoch as we could get out of Serbian folk-songs or other barbaric folk-poetry. One reads it, of course, and for a while is interested, but only to cast it aside. Mankind is already too much shadowed by its own passions and dooms to need still more darkening by contemplating the gloom of primitive and barbaric times. Mankind needs clarity and serenity, it needs to turn to those epochs of art and literature in which superior human beings achieved a finished culture and then, serene within themselves, were able to pour out the blessings of that culture upon others." He seeks to disclaim the familiar characteristics which are supposed to belong to the archaic stage of German art, and to it alone. "The uninspired naïveté," he says, "the stiffness of honest worth, the righteousness, and whatever other phrases one may see fit to use in a characterization of our older German art, surely all of them are equally characteristic of any other archaic art. The old Venetians, Florentines, and so on, all possess them. And we Germans are supposed to be original only if we do not rise above our beginnings!"

It is worth while to look at this statement from another point of view as well, not merely as a political, cultural, or stylistic expression. The school through which Nietzsche went is clearly to be recognized in his characteristically psychological terminology, and his prose derives directly from that of Goethe—especially the young Goethe—who, similarly, derives from Luther. Goethe's interest, as a man of letters, in Luther's Bible, which persisted into his old age, is a matter of common knowledge. He compared his own prose with that book and declared that he had perhaps only succeeded in making delicate passages more tender. The delicate music which speech undergoes in Goethe's hand as compared to the folkish quality of Luther is a great creative factor in our spiritual history; none the less the sturdiness of Luther is conserved by Goethe. This genealogy is then continued through the completely unsturdy and unbourgeois Nietzsche, who is repelled by the all too robust Luther, but who, none the less, in his *Zarathustra* parodies the style of that Bible with great virtuosity. The position of pupil to teacher is as clear between Goethe and Nietzsche as it is between Luther and Goethe.

But to resume it: it was a long time before Goethe again stood out as a figure in the intellectual life of the period: very long before he became a commanding one. The hope he voiced in his youth that "these dry sticks may yet give fruit and shade" took a long time before it was realized. His natural slowness, the inherent hesitation of his being, has, curiously enough, been recognized only in our own epoch. His life was constructed at long sight. It was ruled by an instinct to leave himself plenty of time and even shows traces of indolence. Goethe needed a great deal of time for everything. His prodigious achievement, growing like a tree, the mighty record of his life, was never again, as at first, to be greeted by the applause of the crowd. The response to his classical period, in *Tasso* and *Iphigenie*, was cool. There was no general perception of the delightful, almost piquant contrast between the classical form and the poetic intimacy and boldness of the subject-matter. In no other poet in the world, perhaps, can we so well and rewardingly study the personal mystery of conception, the inward spur compelling production. There is a beautiful, disturbing saying of Degas, the French painter: "A picture must be painted with the same feeling as that with which a criminal commits his crime." This is the precious and guilty secret I mean. "It went against my grain," Goethe confesses, "to talk of any of my projects. I carried them about with me in silence; as a rule nobody knew anything about them until they were finished."

Amid hostilities from high and low, cultured and crude, covert and overt, accompanied too by the steadfast veneration of lofty minds, his authority grows with his years, solely by virtue of his age and the ever-increasing weight of his personality. The hatred he had to endure was essentially political, it had to do with his coldly obstinate and repellent attitude towards the two main tendencies of his century, the nationalistic and the democratic. All the reproaches, all the embittered complaints that were levelled against his egoism, his lack of sympathy with the people, his "enormous power of obstruction," as Boerne puts it, were chargeable to this account.

In any case it redounds to the honour of the German intellectual fibre that, at a time when Germany was stirred to its depth by national feeling, patriotic men were found ready to defend this phenomenon, born out of its time, against the charge of anti-Germanism. It was Father Jahn, the great patriot, who in 1810 declared of his own motion that Goethe was the most German of writers, careless of the fact that the poet had so violently turned aside from "German brotherhoods." And when, in 1813, he had all but succeeded in achieving a reputation for expatriation, Varnhagen von Ense exclaimed: "Goethe not a German patriot? All the freedom of Germania was early collected in his breast and there it became the root of our education, our example, although insufficiently recognized by us all."

Freiherr vom Stein und Ernst Moritz Arndt thought and said the same. Despite certain short-comings in the matter of national feeling, Goethe was a national writer and spoke to the nation as a whole; in his own later years the consciousness of this stood unshakably as the very foundation of his self-knowledge—a knowledge which is never natural to any human soul, but into which a creator must find his predestined way in the course of time. We have his touching words that he had "painfully to learn greatness"—greatness to search in wide national spheres or epochs for adequate material. And upon this principle he had to order the economy of his life, which in many ways was more suited to privacy than to greatness, and to temper his human kindliness with regard for higher claims. "The harshness," to speak with Kleist, with which he encountered young poets who approached him "on the very knees of their hearts," bringing him their verses, is tragicomic. I mention only one of them, the unfortunate Pfizer, not the worst of them, who in the year 1830 sent Goethe his poems with a fervent letter. Goethe replied: "I have glanced through your little book. Since, however, one must protect oneself at the start against an epidemic of cholera, I have laid it aside." One cannot escape wondering whether Goethe was aware of the catastrophic effect of such an answer upon the recipient. But he had much to ward off, and one must understand his anger when people who declared themselves his disciples sent him foolish stuff.

Goethe knew very well that this matter of being a genius is to a great extent a question of luck: that it is important to be at the right place in the right moment. "When I was eighteen," he says, "Germany was just eighteen too—a man could do something. I am glad I began then and not today, when the demands on one are so much greater." But he is right when he tries to make the young understand that the world is served only by what is out of the ordinary; also that it is no service to reap in a field where others have sowed. "The whole trouble lies in the fact," he says, "that poetical culture is so widespread in Germany that no one ever writes bad verse any more. The youthful poets who send me their work are no worse than their forerunners; and since these are praised so highly they cannot understand why they should not also be praised. And yet one must do nothing to encourage them, simply because there are today hundreds of such talents, and no one should promote the superfluous."

No doubt Goethe found it more congenial to be inexorable with the young Germany of his time on the ground of his wholesale disapproval of its attitude to life. Indeed, he had never lost his deeply fundamental kindness and the sweetness of his nature; and we have his own word for it that he loved the young, and himself when young better than he loved himself now. But the words occur among others which make no secret of his impatience with the new stock, his deep-seated lack of confidence in it. "When one sees," he writes in 1812, "not only how the world altogether, and especially the youthful world, gives in to its lusts and passions, but how that which is higher and better in it is shoved aside and turned into a grimace by the earnest foolhardiness of the epoch, so that all that might lead to blessedness becomes damnation—then no one wonders at misdeeds through which man works havoc against himself and others." "The incredible arrogance," he writes, "in which the young are growing up will show its results in a few years in the greatest follies."

The growing loneliness and congelation of his old age are none the less affecting because they happen in obedience to natural law.

> "Ich bin euch sämtlichen zur Last,
> Einigen auch sogar verhasst,"

> "On all of you I am a weight,
> To some the object of your hate,"

as he well knows, even repeating it in his *Diwan:*

> "Sie lassen mich alle grüssen
> Und hassen mich bis in Tod."

> "They all bow low,
> And each a deadly foe."

It seems that he reckoned with the possibility of being assassinated. Was that but the expression of his Tasso-like hypochondria, consonant with the confessed traits of that character? Or was it so inconceivable that some overwrought student, seeing in Goethe's stiff-necked authoritarianism an obstacle to the political rebirth of Germany, should take this frightful idea into his head?—Goethe gives the mildest possible expression to his remoteness from his age and his world when he says: "Why should I not confess to myself that I belong more and more to the people *in* whom one may glady live, but *with* whom it is not so pleasant to live?" Not that he led his life undisturbed: he was encompassed by curiosity from all quarters of the globe. But genuine loyalty he gets only from the few devoted friends who surround him every day; otherwise he lives afar in the wide world and draws his satisfactions chiefly from foreign lands. Carlyle sings his praise, and the Paris *Globe*. He is pleased and proud that his *Helena* is celebrated at one time in the chief reviews of Edinburgh, Moscow, and Paris. "No nation," he declares, "is a good judge of what goes on within its own frontiers. This is true of all periods." A modern Frenchman has pithily said the same: "L'étranger, cette postérité contemporaine."

And in truth in his own country he is rather like a famous fossil: an honour, yet something of a burden to have within its walls. Survivors who had known him earlier very likely told their young people that he was a "wicked old man." Wicked because old and powerful at the same time—a great old man must always be a depressing sight. There was a great relief at the death of Frederick the Great. And one is reminded of Napoleon's question to one of his marshals as to what the world would say of him after his death. The man launched into a solemn lament which he said humanity would raise, but Napoleon cut him short with the words: "Nonsense! They'll say 'Ouf!'"

Goethe knew that, loud or low, people would be saying "Ouf!" too when he died. He felt himself a manifestation of that greatness which oppresses as much as it blesses the earth. He embodied this greatness, though in the mildest, most peaceable form which greatness can assume: that of a great poet. But even in such guise it is none too comfortable for contemporaries. Bewilderment and revulsion as well as love and amazement are its portion.

But I had not meant to speak here of his greatness, nor of his immortal growth above and beyond the mass of average mortals, so that school boys learn his love-affairs by heart, like Jove's. We were interested in something more sober and solid. My theme was the life of the man of letters, in which we moderns, who are but heat-conductors between that greatness and our own times, may recognize the essential part of ourselves in a manner that will tolerate the scrutiny of friendly and enlightened eyes. And I need have recourse only once more to the great world of his own works to find the conciliatory note—in a letter full of consolation to everyone who is fighting the fight of a life called to expression in the face of the world: "It is worth the trouble to live long and suffer the diverse pains which an inscrutable ruling providence mingles into our days, if only, at the last, through others, we see ourselves clearly and the problem of our striving and erring resolves itself in the clear light of the effects we have produced."

Translated by RITA MATTHIAS-REIL,
based on a draft by MARIE HOTTINGER MACKIE

Thomas Mann

LOTTE IN WEIMAR

IN OCTOBER of the year 1816, and early in the month, when the weather was still almost summery, a singular experience befell the head waiter at the inn Zum Elefanten in Weimar. His name was Mager—a man not without some pretension to education and culture. Thrilling, even bewildering the experience had been; though there was nothing supernatural about it, Mager could scarce persuade himself that he was not in a dream.

On that morning, shortly after eight o'clock by the regular diligence from Gotha, three women were set down at the famous hostelry on the market square. At first glance—or even at the second—there was nothing remarkable about them. They were mother, daughter, and maid; so much was easy to see. Mager bowing in the entry, looked on as the steps were let down and the ostler helped the first two to alight upon the pavement. Klärchen, meanwhile, the abigail, took leave of the jehu; she had sat beside him on the drive, and quite evidently enjoyed herself. Now, holding up her skirts, with coquettish, unnecessary twists and turns she got herself down from the lofty seat, the man watching her with a sidewise, retrospective grin, probably at thought of the outlandish dialect the travellers had spoken. Then he pulled at the cord of the horn slung on his back and began to blow with great unction, to the joy of some watching urchins and a few early passers-by.

The ladies still paused, with their backs to the house, while their modest luggage was fetched down from the top of the coach; and Mager stood awaiting the moment when, their concern for their property being satisfied, they would turn their faces in his direction. Then, quite the diplomat, he advanced upon the pavement to meet them, with a smile at once cordial and deprecating on his rather sallow face, framed in side-whiskers of a reddish auburn. He wore a buttoned-up tail-coat, an expansive collar, and a much washed neck-cloth; his trousers tapered down to a pair of enormous feet.

"Good day, my friend," said the more maternal of the two ladies then. A matron she was, at least; no longer young, certainly at the end of her fifties, and plump. She wore a white frock, a black shawl, and worsted mitts. Beneath a tall capote her hair peeped out; it had once been blond but was now an ashen grey. "We require accommodation for three; a double room for myself and my child"—said "child" being nearer thirty than twenty, with brown corkscrew curls and a little frill round her neck; the mother's small, finely arched nose had in the daughter's face turned out rather sharp and severe—"and an attic, not too far away, for my woman. Could you give us that?"

The lady's fine if tired blue eyes were directed past the waiter's head upon the facade of the inn. Her mouth was small and the movement of the lips as she spoke uncommonly pleasant, embedded though these were in the plumpness of her aged cheeks. She must in her youth have been prettier than her daughter was now. The most striking thing about her was a trembling and nodding of the head; it looked, however, only in part like weakness, suggesting as it did a lively and decided temperament and a challenge to the agreement of the person addressed.

"Quite easily," responded the waiter, as he attended mother and daughter inside the entry, followed by the abigail dangling a bandbox. "Our hotel is, as usual, well occupied, and we might at any moment have to decline the advances of even persons of station; but we will spare no pains to satisfy the ladies' needs."

"That is most gratifying," replied the stranger, exchanging a glance of amusement with her daughter, for the waiter's words, though well turned, had a strongly local, Saxon-Thuringian flavour.

"May I beg you to be kind enough to step this way?" said Mager, ushering them into the lobby. "The reception-room is on the right. Frau Elmenreich, the proprietress, will be pleased to see you—pray come in."

Frau Elmenreich had an arrow stuck in her hair, and her high-corseted bust was enveloped in a knitted jacket against the draught from the outer door. She sat among her pens and sand-shaker, enthroned at a calculating-machine behind a sort of counter shutting off from the rest of the lobby the recess which formed her bureau. There was likewise an assistant, who had left his standing desk and stood on one side talking in English with a man in a coachman's cape, the owner, presumably, of the boxes piled by the door. The proprietress viewed the new clients with phlegmatic eye, acknowledging the elder's greeting and the younger's slight curtsy by a dignified bow, though her gaze went past instead of resting upon them. She lent an ear to the request for rooms, communicated by the head waiter; and taking up the houseplan, a fanlike arrangement on a strick, she moved her pencil-point to and fro upon it.

"Twenty-seven," said she at length, turning towards the green-aproned boots who stood waiting with the ladies' effects. "But I cannot oblige with a single room. The mamsell will have to share with the maid of the Countess of Larisch from Erfurt. We have at the moment many guests attended by their own domestics."

The abigail pulled a face behind her mistress's back; but the latter raised no obstacle. The two would soon get on quite well together, she declared, and, turning away, requested to have the room shown her and the luggage sent up at once.

"At once, madame," said the waiter. "There is but one formality, a small one. In heaven's name pray write us a few lines. Not on our account, we are not so pedantic; it is the 'holy Hermandad.' It can never forget anything. It seems as though laws and rules kept on propagating themselves like a disease. Would the lady be so gracious?"

The lady laughed, casting another side-glance at her daughter, while her shaking head seemed to express her amused surprise.

"Yes, of course," said she. "I forgot. I will do whatever is proper. And I am pleased to note, my man, that you are well read and know your literary allusions." She used the third-person form of address; probably it had been the custom when she was young. "Here, give it to me!" And turning back to the desk, she took in the slender fingers of her bemitted hand the crayon the proprietress handed her; it hung there on a string beside the register, whereon were already a few names.

As she bent and slowly wrote, her laughter died away, subsiding into faint little gasps like an expiring echo of her mirth. The nodding and shaking of her head showed plainer than before, probably because of her awkward posture.

They watched her as she wrote. The daughter looked over one shoulder; the pretty, evenly arching brows which she had from her mother were lifted high, and a wry, almost mocking expression sat on the firmly closed lips. Over the other shoulder peeped head waiter Mager, partly to see if the lady was correctly filling in the rubrics, partly from small-town curiosity and the malicious satisfaction one gets when somebody has to abandon the grateful role of incognito and admit his name and status. For some reason or other the clerk and the British traveller had also left off speaking to observe the lady where she stood bobbing her head and forming her letters with well-nigh childish pains.

Mager blinked as he read: "Frau Councillor Charlotte Kestner, widow, née Buff. From Hannover. Last address Goslar. Born Wetzlar January 11, 1753. Accompanied by daughter and maid."

"Will that do?" queried Frau Councillor. As nobody answered, she was fain to do so herself, and said: "It must." She laid aside the crayon, forgetful that it was fastened, with such energy that she pulled down the metal stand whereon it hung.

"Stupid!" she admonished herself, flushing, with another swift glance in her daughter's direction, who, however, kept her eyes cast down and her mouth disdainfully shut. "No matter, it is soon mended—and now do let us get up to our room!" She turned abruptly.

Daughter, maid, and waiter followed her across the yard to the stairs, behind them the bald-headed boots with handboxes and bags. Mager had not ceased to blink. He blinked as he went; first winking two or three times in quick succession and then staring straight ahead with his inflamed eyes. His mouth gaped open—but it was not a stupid, rather a delicate, well-regulated gape. On the first landing he brought the party to a stand.

"I beg pardon," said he. "I most humbly beg pardon, if my question—it is not actuated by unseemly curiosity—but—have we the honour to be entertaining Frau Councillor Kestner, Madame Charlotte Kestner, formerly Buff, of Wetzlar—?"

"The same," the lady confirmed, with a smile.

"But I mean—of course it cannot—I mean—it cannot be the same Charlotte—or Lotte for short—Kestner, whose maiden name was Buff, from the house of the Teutonic Order at Wetzlar, the former—"

"The very same, my good man. But I am not 'former' at all, I am present in the flesh, and would wish to be shown at once to the room—"

"This very instant!" cried Mager, and took a running start, with his head down. But then he stuck again, as though rooted to the spot, and wreathed his hands together.

"Good gracious me!" said he, with great feeling. "Goodness—gracious—me, Frau Councillor! Frau Councillor will pardon me if my ideas—if I cannot all at once, adjust my thoughts—the revelation of your identity, and the prospect—it has come upon me, as they say, out of a blue sky. Then our house has the inestimable honour and distinction of entertaining beneath its roof the actual original—if I may so express myself—in short, it is vouchsafed me to behold Werther's Lotte in the—"

"That is indeed the case, my friend," replied the Frau Councillor with quiet dignity, reproving the tittering maid with a glance. "And I should be glad if that were a reason the more for showing us tired travellers to our room without further delay."

"This instant!" the flunky cried again, setting himself in motion afresh. "But the room—number twenty-seven is up two pairs of stairs. Ours are easy stairs, as the Frau Councillor sees. But if we had dreamed—! We could probably, despite our crowded—however, the room is a good one, on the square. Madame cannot fail to be pleased. Only a little time since it was occupied by Herr and Frau Major von Egloffstein, from Halle, when they were visiting their aunt, the First Lady of the Bedchamber, of the same name. And last October the adjutant general of His Imperial Highness the Grand Duke Constantine—a historic date, one might say. But, my God, why do I talk of history when, for a man of sentiment, it cannot compare with . . . Just a few steps farther, Frau Councillor! Down this corridor, no distance at all from the stairs. We have had to renovate very thoroughly, since the visit of the Don Cossacks, at the end of 1813: stairs, chambers, passages, salons, and all. Maybe the renovation was long overdue; anyhow, it was forced upon us by the violent, world-shaking course of events. They taught us, perhaps, that it is precisely violence that is needed to produce all memorable and historic moments. Yet I should not give the Cossacks all the credit for our improvements. We had Prussian and Hungarian hussars in the house as well—to say nothing of the French who came before them! Ah, here we are—may I invite the Frau Councillor to walk in?"

He bowed and opened the door wide with a flourish as he ushered her within. The ladies with swift appraising glance took in the starched mull curtains at the two windows, the gilt-framed console mirror, rather dull and tarnished, between them; the two white-covered beds, sharing a little canopy, and the remaining conveniences of the bedchamber. The wall was adorned with a copper-plate engraving, a landscape with an antique temple. The well-waxed floor shone with cleanliness.

"Very nice," the Frau Councillor said.

"We shall be overjoyed if the ladies think they can do with it. Whatever they need—here is the bell-pull, close at hand. I will see after hot water myself, of course. We shall rejoice if we can serve the Frau Councillor to her satisfaction—"

"But surely, my good man. We are unspoilt people, with simple tastes.

I thank you," said she to the boots, as he deposited his burdens on the floor and the luggage trestle and took his leave. "And thanks to you, too," with a nod of dismissal to the waiter. "We are well provided, all we need now is a little rest—"

But Mager stood fixed, his fingers interlaced, his red-eyed gaze devouring the old lady's features.

"Ah, my God, Frau Councillor, what an event! An event to be set down in memory's tables! Perhaps the Frau Councillor cannot quite enter into the emotions of a man of feeling at a happening so unhoped for, so unexpected, so pregnant with thrilling possibilities! Frau Councillor is used to her situation, and her identity with a being so sacred to us all— it is an everyday matter to her, she takes it lightly. She cannot guess at the emotions that must animate the soul of a man, literary from youth up, to whom, now, all undreamt of—to whom is vouchsafed acquaintance with—if I may say so, I humbly beg pardon—is vouchsafed the sight of a being so surrounded with the effulgence of poesy and, as it were, borne up on fiery arms to the heaven of immortal fame."

"My dear, good friend!" said the lady with a deprecating smile. One might at the same time have interpreted as agreement the nodding of her head; at the waiter's words it came on more than ever. Behind her the abigail peered, greatly tickled, into the man's face—actually, it was moved almost to tears. In the background the daughter with ostentatious indifference busied herself about the luggage.

"My friend, I am just a simple old lady, with no pretensions, a human being like everybody else. You have so unusual and high-flown a way of expressing yourself—"

"My name is Mager," said the waiter, as though in explanation. He pronounced it Macher, with a soft, middle-German enunciation which made it sound propitiatory, even touching. "I hope I shall not seem to boast if I say that I am the factotum here, the proprietress's right hand, she having been widowed these ten years. Herr Elmenreich died anno six; falling victim to the violence of historical events under tragical circumstances which are at the moment neither here nor there. In my position, Frau Councillor, and even more in such times as our city has lived through, a man comes in touch with all sorts of people. Many a personage striking for birth or achievement passes before his eyes. So much so that he can grow callous to the claims of even the most resounding names and the most prominent actors on the stage of world history. So it goes. But whither now, Frau Councillor, has fled the indifference by rights belonging to my calling? Never in my life, I confess it, has it been my privilege to perform a service so near to my heart as today's, so worthy to be set down and enshrined in the tables of my memory. I knew, indeed, without knowing, as a man will, that the admired female, the original of the immortally lovely creature, still dwelt amongst us, in the city of Hannover, to be precise. Ah, I knew, but only now I am aware that I knew. For my knowledge had no reality heretofore; never would it had entered my head that I might one day stand in her sacred presence, face to face. Never could I have dreamt of such a thing. When this morning—but a few short hours since—I awoke, it was in the conviction that today was like a hundred others, to be filled with the wonted activities of my calling; waiting at table, keeping my eye over the house. My wife—for I am married, Frau Councillor, my life-partner occupies a superior post in the kitchens of the establishment—my wife would tell you that I had no presentiment of anything out of the ordinary. I thought nothing else than to lie down tonight the same man as when I arose. And now! The unexpected always happens—how true the popular saying is! I trust Frau Councillor will pardon my confusion and the perhaps quite unwarranted way my tongue runs on. 'Of what the heart is full, the mouth runs over,' as the saying goes, and how true that is, however uncouth the form! If Frau Councillor but knew the love and veneration which from my birth up, so to speak, I have felt for our prince of poets, the great Goethe; my pride as a citizen of Weimar that we may call this eminent man our own; if she realized what fervent echoes this very work, The Sorrows of Werther, awoke in my heart. . . . But I say no more. It is not for me to speak —though well I know that a masterpiece of feeling like the work in question belongs to high and low in humanity as a whole, animating it with the most fervid emotions; whereas probably only the upper classes can aspire to such productions as Iphigenie or The Natural Daughter. When I recall how oft Madame Mager and I have sat beside our evening taper and our souls have melted as we bent together over those celestial pages . . . and now their famous and immortal heroine stands before me at this very moment in the flesh, a human being like myself—good gracious heavens!" he cried, and struck his brow with his fist: "I run on and on, Frau Councillor, and all of a sudden it comes over me in a burning flash that I have not even asked Frau Councillor if she has had coffee!"

"Thank you, my friend," responded the old lady, who had been listening to the good man's outpourings with a reserved air if a slightly twitching mouth. "We took it betimes. But my dear Herr Mager, you go too far, you greatly exaggerate, when you simply identify me, or even the young thing I once was, with the heroine of that much lauded book. You are not the first whom I have had to warn; I have been holding forth about it, indeed, for four-and-forty years! That character in the novel did become so real, so living, and so widely celebrated that actually a person could come to me and say that between us two she was the real and more substantial one—the which I was, of course, most seriously concerned to disclaim. But the character in the novel is quite different and distinct from my former self, to say nothing at all of my present one. For instance, anyone can see that my eyes are blue, whereas Werther's Lotte is well known to have black ones."

"Poetic licence!" Mager cried. "As though we did not know what that is! But no amount of it, Frau Councillor, could suffice to diminish by one jot the verity of the identification. What if the author did avail himself to some small extent of—what if he did play hide-and-seek a little to mystify us—"

"No," protested the Frau Councillor, with a shake of her head, "the black eyes are from another source."

"And even so!" retorted Mager, with some heat. "What if the likeness be a little blurred by such small variations—"

"There are much greater ones," interpolated the lady, weightily.

"—yet there remains unshakable, there remains wholly untouched, that other identification so interwoven with and inseparable from it: the identification, so to say, with itself—with that other personage of legend, of whom the great man has lately drawn for us so glowing a picture in his recollections. If Frau Councillor is not, down to the very last hair, the Lotte of Werther, she is, even so, in every particular the Lotte of Goe—"

"My worthy fellow," interrupted the lady, stemming the waiter's eloquence in full tide, "it was some little time before you had the kindness to show us our room. It obviously escaped you that till now you prevent us from occupying it."

"Frau Councillor!" implored the waiter of the Elephant, folding his hands in prayer. "Forgive me! Extend your pardon to a man who—my conduct, I know, is unpardonable; yet none the less I beg for indulgence. By taking my leave at once I will . . . and indeed," he said, "quite aside from considerations of propriety and manners, I am, urgently summoned, I am called away and should have been off long since. There is so much to do—and when I think that up to this very instant Frau Elmenreich has not the faintest idea, that in all likelihood she has not cast a glance at the register, and even so her simple mind . . . and Madame Mager, Frau Councillor! How I itch to be with her in the kitchen, to tell her of the great local and literary sensation of the hour! And yet I venture to im-

plore leave and pardon for one single question more, to fill the cup of
novelty to the brim: in these four-and-forty years—ah, four and forty
years!—has the Frau Councillor never, even once, beheld the Herr Privy
Councillor again?"

"So is it, my friend," answered she. "I know Dr. Goethe, the young
lawyer of the Gewandsgasse in Wetzlar. The Minister of State for the
Duchy of Weimar, the famous poet, I have never beheld with my mortal
eyes."

"It is too much!" breathed Mager. "It is too much for a human being
to support! And so the Frau Councillor has come to Weimar to—to—"

"I am come," the old lady interrupted him with slight hauteur, "to visit
my sister, the wife of Councillor Ridel, of the Board of Domains, whom
I have not seen for many years; and to bring here my daughter Charlotte,
who has come to me from Alsace, where she lives, and accompanies me
on this journey. Counting my woman, there are three of us; we should
overburden my sister if we lodged with her, she having a family herself.
Will that content you?"

"To my heart's depths, Frau Councillor! And even though we thus lose
the pleasure of the ladies' company at our table-d'hôte. Herr and Frau
Councillor Ridel, Esplanade 6—as well I know. So Frau Councillor Ridel
was before her marriage a—of course, of course! I knew the circumstance,
it but escaped me for the moment only. So then—ah, merciful God!—the
Frau Councillor Ridel made one of the troop of children who thronged
round Frau Councillor in the entry of the hunting-lodge when Werther
for the first time entered it, stretching out their little hands for the bread
and butter Frau Councillor—"

"My dear, good man," Charlotte broke in once more, "there was no
Frau Councillor at that hunting-lodge. And our Klärchen is waiting to be
shown to her room. But before you go, pray tell me, is it far from here to
the Esplanade?"

"No distance at all, Frau Councillor. The merest step. In Weimar there
are no distances. Our greatness is of the spirit alone. Most joyfully would
I myself be at your service to show the ladies the way, unless they prefer
a hired coach or post-chaise—the capital abounds in them. But one more,
only one more little question, Frau Councillor, I implore: Frau Councillor is here, of course, to visit her sister. But surely she will take occasion to go to the Frauenplan—"

"We shall see, we shall see! But now, only make haste and bestow my
maid in her quarters for I shall soon have need of her."

"Yes, and on the way," the young thing twittered, "you can tell me where the author lives that wrote Rinaldo. Oh, what a ravishing book! I have read it five times without stopping. Do you think we might chance to see him in street?"

"Yes, yes," replied Mager distractedly, turning towards the door. But on the threshold he braked again, one leg in the air.

"Only one single word, Frau Councillor," he begged; "one single question, quickly answered; Frau Councillor must perceive, when one stands, all unexpected, before the original, when it is vouchsafed one to inquire at the very source, one cannot refrain: Frau Councillor, that very last scene before Werther takes his leave; that heartrending scene between the three of you, where you speak of the dear, departed mother and the final parting and Werther grasps Lotte's hand and cries: 'We shall meet again, in all the world we shall know each other's forms again!'—that was real, was it not, it actually happened, the Herr Privy Councillor did not make it up?"

"Yes and no, my friend, yes and no," she good-naturedly answered his importunities, her head shaking more than ever. "But go now, go!"

And the waiter hastened off, his head in a whirl, with the mamsell beside him.

Charlotte heaved a sigh and took off her hat. During all the foregoing her daughter had been busy hanging up her own and her mother's clothes in the wardrobe and laying out the contents of their nécessaires on toilet-table and wash-stand. She now looked up, with mocking eye.

"So now your crown of glory stands revealed," said she. "The effect was not so bad."

"Ah, child," the mother replied, "what you call my crown is in truth more like a cross! But cross or crown it remains a decoration visible whether I will or no. I cannot obscure, I cannot hide it."

"Yet hidden it might have been a little longer, dear Mama, if not for the whole duration of this rather fantastic journey, if we had chosen to stop with Aunt Amalie instead of at a public inn."

"Lottchen, you know yourself it was not possible. Your aunt, your uncle, and cousins have no rooms to spare, despite the excellent quarter they live in—or perhaps on that very account. The three of us could not burst in upon them and discommode them, even for a few days. Your uncle Ridel has his living as an official, but he is not a rich man, he has had his troubles, and in 1806 he lost every penny. To live as his charges would not be right. Yet who could take it ill of me that I wished, after all these years, to embrace once more my youngest sister, our Malie, and rejoice in the fortune which is hers at the side of her honest and energetic helpmeet? Recollect that I may be useful to her: your uncle has pretensions to the post of director of the finances of the Duchy, and I may perhaps help her by being on the spot, with my old friends and connections. And the moment seems to me well chosen—when you, my child, are beside me, after ten years' separation. Shall I then hesitate to follow the dictates of my heart, simply because of that strange episode which once fell to my lot?"

"Certainly not, of course not, Mama."

"And how could we expect," the Frau Councillor went on, "that we should run into such a fanatic as this Ganymede in side-whiskers? Goethe in his memoirs complains that people pester him to find out who was the real Lotte, where she lived, and the like. He says that no incognito could protect him from their importunity—speaks of it, I believe, as a perfect penance, and declares that if he sinned in the writing of his little book, he has paid for it over and over again. But see how men—and poets too —think only of themselves! He never once reflects that we, too, have to endure the inquisition, on top of all the harm he did to us, your dear, departed father and me, with his wicked mixture of truth and make-believe."

"And blue and black eyes."

"The injured party may be sure he will be laughed at too—and certainly by Lottchen. But I had to prevent the crazy creature from calmly identifying me with Werther's Lotte."

"It was impertinent enough that he consoled you for the uncertainty by saying that you were Goethe's Lotte."

"But I stood out against that too, I did not mince matters. I know you too well, my child, not to be aware that your sterner nature would have kept the man in check from the beginning. But tell me how. By denying my identity? By showing him that I wished nothing to be known of myself or my connections? Have I the right to do as I like with these, which, after all, are public property? Our natures are so different—which, I hasten to add, does not in the slightest detract from my love for you. But you are not what one could call affable; and by the word I mean something very different from the spirit of willing self-sacrifice. Indeed, it has often seemed to me that a life of sacrifice and service develops a sort of routine, a—I might, in no spirit of censure, but rather the contrary, call it a hardness, which is little conducive to affability. My child, you can doubt of my respect as little as of my love. For ten years you have played in Alsace the part of good angel to your poor, dear brother Karl, when he suffered the double misfortune of losing his young wife and his leg as well. Misfortunes seldom come singly. My poor, afflicted lad—where would he be without you? You are his nurse, his aide, his housekeeper, a mother to his orphaned children. Your whole life has been a selfless labour of love; how then could you have failed to evince those serious traits which are opposed to idle sensibility whether in yourself or in others? You set greater store by sterling worth than by what is merely interesting, and how right you are! Relations with the great world, the world of beauty, intellect, and passion, such as have fallen to our share—"

"Our? I have no such relations!"

"My child, whether we like it or not, they will remain ours and attach themselves to our name, until the third and fourth generation. And when on their account people of sentiment importune us—out of enthusiasm or even out of mere curiosity, for it is hard to distinguish between the two —have we the right to be chary of ourselves and contemptuously repulse the interest we evoke? Herein lies the difference between us. Life was serious for me too, it did not lack in resignation. I was, I trust, a good wife to your dear father of loving memory. I bore him eleven children, and brought up nine of them to man's estate, two being taken from me. But I have still been affable—or good-natured, if you like to call it so. The harshness of life has not made me harsh, and simply to turn my back on Mager and tell him: 'Leave me alone, you fool!'—no, I could not bring myself to that."

"Dear Mama," replied Lotte the younger, "you speak as though I had reproached you, or unfilially presumed to set myself above you. I had not even opened my mouth. It does vex me when people try your patience and kindness to such lengths as happened just now, exhausting you with their importunity—and would you be vexed with my vexation?—This frock," she said, holding up one taken from her mother's box, white, garnished with pink ribbon bows, "should it not be pressed out a little before you put it on? It is badly crumpled."

The Frau Councillor blushed. It was an appealing, a becoming blush, it strangely brought back the charming girl of long ago, one could see what she had been like at twenty. For a few seconds that rosy glow evoked the tender gaze of the blue eyes beneath the evenly vaulted brows, the finely arched little nose, the small, charming mouth; one could see the warden's stout-hearted little daughter and mother to his brood of children. Even the fairy heroine of the Volperthshausen ball came surprisingly to view in the radiance of that elderly blush.

Madame Kestner had laid aside her black shawl. She stood there in a white frock much like the one her daughter was holding up, though simpler in style. She affected white frocks for summer wear, and the weather, as we have said, was still warm. But the one in her daughter's hand was trimmed with pink ribbons.

Both mother and daughter had averted their gaze, as it seemed involuntarily; the one from the frock, the other from her mother's blush, which affected her painfully with its sweet suggestion of reawakened youth.

"No," responded the mother to Charlotte's suggestion. "We need not trouble. That sort of crêpe shakes out quickly with hanging—besides, who knows whether I shall put the thing on my back?"

"Why should you not?" the daughter said. "Why ever else should you have brought it with you? Surely you will put it on, for this or that occasion. And that brings me back, dear Mama, to the question I ventured to ask you before: might you not replace the breast- and sleeve-knots, which are rather too light, with a darker colour, perhaps a rich violet?"

"Oh, be quiet, Lottchen," said her mother, almost pettishly. "You have no mind for a joke. Why would you deprive me of my pretty and suggestive little allusion? Really, I know very few people with so small a sense of humour as you!"

"One should not," responded the daughter, "take a sense of humour for granted, with people one does not know, or no longer knows."

The elder Charlotte would have retorted; but the colloquy was interrupted by the return of Klärchen, bearing hot water. The puss reported blithely that the Countess Marisch's maid was not half bad, they would get on well together. And that droll Herr Mager had solemnly promised she should see the librarian Vulpius, author of that glorious work, Rinaldo, and brother-in-law to Herr Goethe to boot. Mager would point him out as he passed to his office, and his little son too, named Rinaldo after the hero of the famous work, going by on his way to school.

"Very nice," said the Frau Councillor. "But now it is high time for you both to be off. You must go to the Esplanade, Lottchen, to announce our arrival, and Klärchen shall attend you. Aunt Amalie does not dream that we are here, she expects us at earliest by afternoon or evening, thinking that we broke our journey with the Liebenaus in Gotha instead of coming straight on. Go, my child. Have Klärchen inquire the way; kiss your dear aunt for me, and make friends with the cousins. Being an old lady, I must lie down and rest for an hour or so, when I will follow you."

She kissed her daughter, to make up for the late little difference; acknowledged the abigail's curtsy, and was presently alone. On the console table were pen and ink. She sat down, took a sheet of paper, dipped the pen and wrote, her hand hurrying over the paper and her head nodding above it, the words already composed in her mind:

> My honoured friend:
> With my daughter Charlotte, I am paying a visit to my sister and shall spend a few days in Weimar. It is my wish to present my daughter to you; and I myself should rejoice if I might look once more upon a face which, while each of us has been pursuing his appointed lot in life, has become so well known to all the world.
>
> Weimar, Hotel Elephant, October 6, '16.
>   Charlotte Kestner, née Buff.

She strewed sand upon the writing, let it run off, folded the sheet of paper, dexterously slipping one end inside the other, and wrote the address. Then she pulled the bell.

Translated by H. T. LOWE-PORTER

Stefan George

TO A YOUNG LEADER OF THE FIRST WORLD WAR

NOT AS you had dreamed was the battle's issue . . .
When the broken army yielded up its weapons
You stood with me, sad, as when, after feasting
The sober work begins, stripped of its honors . . .
Tears welled from your eyes, for the wasted treasure
Of crucial years.

Do not, however, ape the unthinking masses
Who acclaim today and discard tomorrow,
Who smash the landmark over which they stumbled . . .
Sudden rise, right up to the gate of victory,
Plunge, in oppression—both contain a meaning
That lies in you.

All to which you grew through the glorious struggle
Stays with you untouched, steels for future dins . . .
See, as you looked up, walking with me slowly,
The shine of the sunset around your flaming
Hair became a ring first of rays around you
And then a crown.

      Translated by E. B. ASHTON

Else Lasker-Schüler

MY PEOPLE

THAT ROCK is crumbling
Whence I spring,
That rock whereto my hymns I sing . . .
Abruptly I sheer from the path,
And privily
I purl, far, far, across the mourning stones,
Toward the sea.

I have streamed off
From the fermenting must
Of my own blood.
And still, and still, ever the echo thrills
In me,
When shudderingly against the east
That crumbling rockrib,
My people,
Cries to God.

     Translated by BABETTE DEUTSCH

René Schickele

ANGELICA

I THOUGHT TO MYSELF, as she stepped out of the ice-covered train: some
people have exactly the right name. To her I said, "Good morning,
Angelica."

She was fifteen years old. Her parents had sent her on ahead, and I was to keep an eye on her until they had finished their sulphur baths in Egypt and could resume the government of Angelica. After my first glimpse of her I realized that that expression was merely a thoughtless remark on the part of over-confident parental authority. Grown-ups with some degree of modesty might hold this child: they could never govern her. Can the forester govern the morning in the woods? It slips away from him as he presses deeper and deeper into the forest after it, and in the end he is left with nothing but a handful of excuses. The same is true in dealing with a high-spirited child. Of course it is, I kept repeating to myself, for I always take the part of the children. . . . There are great factories which pour their waste into the stream that flows by them. They prosper and the stream is not entirely ruined. That is how childhood flows along beside the activities of grown-ups. Yet a municipal officer, who really cared about the purity of the stream, would do better to prohibit the factories from dumping their waste into it and oblige them to find some other way to dispose of their refuse. Let children alone! Think quickly: what do you lack, what does any child lack, in order to be natural and true? . . . She lacked nothing. Her name was Angelica.

It was a pleasure to say, "Angelica." It was the only possible name they could have given her when she came into the world.

Already, as we rode from the village of St. Moritz down to our resort, my eyes traveled happily from her blond young face to the birch woods where the sun lay on downy pillows behind transparent white curtains and was weaving threads of gold into a pattern of human smiles. . . . I had to restrain myself from addressing the young lady by my side in terms of some fairy tale romance, perhaps of some highland Snow White toward whom a bold young Snow Prince might be coming across those gleaming snow fields (it was impossible to tell from here whether they were part of earth or heaven). Or should it be the story of the Ice Fairy of the Morteratsch Glacier, whose body, when the evening light falls on it, begins to chant, and whose rhythm the skiers coming down from the Diavolezza are obliged to follow, becoming hopelessly lost? Or should it be some other version of one of our fairy stories reshaped to suit the white purity of the winter landscape of the Engadine? As we slipped through the Maloja Valley and I looked first at the immaculate world around me and then back to Angelica, and as the sleigh bells rang with the clear, joyous tones of a child's voice, I felt that I was no longer dealing with an abstract conception of "Innocence" somewhere off on the edge of the world, that I was sitting beside her incarnate daughter and I held her cool little hand under the fur lap-robe. And this made me feel as young as a boy and, at the same time, immeasurably old.

That night it snowed. From my bed I could see the snowflakes whirling around the street light, thicker and thicker, faster and faster. I fell asleep on a freshly created, round, white, turning world. Then I seemed to see the great ball roll suddenly away and a gentle cloud hanging in my room. It was as though through all the whirling and glittering I had expected this; I murmured happily, "Angelica."

I waited in vain for her at breakfast. At last I was told that the young lady had been in the hotel hall where she had become interested in a ski professional who was arranging a class for beginners. Whereupon she had borrowed some skis of a strange lady, promising to come back by lunch-time with some of her own. Actually, she appeared toward dusk and told a story, which was corroborated by some newly arrived guests, about how she had hitched herself with a rope to the back of a sleigh and skied all the way from St. Moritz to Sils Maria.

"Do you mean to say that you already know how to ski?" I asked.

"As you see," she replied and pointed to her feet, which she was swinging back and forth over the Persian rug in the hall and which to me did not appear to offer much evidence in the matter. But strangely enough all the other bystanders who looked at her tiny, swinging feet seemed completely convinced.

"How did that happen?"

"It was very simple." After the morning class was over, she had engaged the ski teacher and practised with him until five o'clock. "And then?" Then she had taken the mail sleigh down to St. Moritz to buy some skis, on credit incidentally, since by this time her supply of cash had been spent on food, for herself, for the teacher and for her lesson. "After all, the poor man had worked all of the time from nine to five!"

"Yes, and then?" Good Lord, it appeared that she had stood in front of the sporting-goods shop and hailed people who went by in sleighs, asking them if they were going to Sils Maria!

Again the guests at the hotel nodded their heads in confirmation as though that was the most natural thing in the world for her to have done.

Apparently there had been a number of sleighs full of hungry travelers in search of nearby hotels. To the last one, in which an elderly couple were seated, she simply called out, "Stop!" And, half crying, half laughing, she went over to it with a long rope in her hand. She began with a description of the incomparable beauties of Sils Maria and of the laud-

able qualities of the hotel there, but the gentleman in the sleigh interrupted her: "You know, my child, I have come here every winter for
many years and I really do know my way around. Nevertheless, your
hotel in Sils will not have been so charmingly advertised in vain. We shall
spend the night there tonight." Meantime Angelica, still laughing and
chatting, had tied her rope to the back of the sleigh and then she gave
the order in a loud voice, "Ready, let her go!" Then, in a rather frightened
tone, she added: "They call this skijöring." At one point the sleigh went
over a sudden declivity and she was thrown bodily against the back of
it. Otherwise she did not utter a single word. And she did not fall down,
no indeed, not even once, the elderly couple assured all the bystanders
who were now grouped in interested fashion around Angelica and me.
As for the elderly couple, they spent not only the one night, as originally
intended, but four full weeks at the hotel. They stayed until poor
Angelica quietly, oh so quietly, left us.

It was the joking remark of a Swiss army officer, who had nicknamed
her "The Daughter of the Regiment," that suddenly made us realize one
evening how this youngster had, with a wave of her magic wand, turned
us all into one family whose focal point, motive power and source of
imagination was called Angelica. Those who had never learned to ski
made up for lost time now, so that they could be on hand while
Angelica, without ever saying a word, encouraged both teacher and
pupils to outdo themselves during the strenuous hours of the morning
lessons. . . . These were times that they looked back upon afterwards as
they might have upon the most entertaining dancing lessons. Then, after
lunch, they all went off in a rioting, jolly band on expeditions in the
neighborhood. In the evening it was again Angelica that drew old and
young on to the dance-floor, and it seemed as though all ages naturally
took to her. More than that, it seemed as though she had only to associate for a short time with a person of any age, and immediately whatever was best and deepest in his nature would come out.

She danced with a Swiss captain who ordinarily abhorred jazz, and
also with his stout wife. She was the partner of an Italian prohibitionist
and of an Irish drunkard. And she danced just as seriously with the
youngsters of her own age. No one would have dared to show her so
much as a fraction of an improper expression. Once she sat down by
the rather impudent young son of the Irish "Consul" and asked him to
put his arm around her because she was tired and wanted a little brother
on whose shoulder she could lean her head. The otherwise bold youth
sat with her for quite a while. His face was pale, his eyes were fixed, he

never budged; his manner was sweetly respectful and he made one think
of a young gorilla tenderly holding a human being in its arms. The hotel
guests instinctively realized that they would be delighted to empty their
pockets to make up a present for Angelica should she suddenly decide
to marry, and they also felt sure that they would come from the ends
of the earth, bound by the same purpose, to kill any man who would
make her unhappy.

When she sprained her ankle, out skijöring on the lake, her frightened
friends nearly came to blows deciding who should carry her home. In
the end she was passed from hand to hand and relayed back to the
hotel.

"It is nothing at all," said the doctor who was called in. He was a short
man and his curt sentences were pushed out reluctantly through a bristling, overhanging mustache, below which his chin shone with a pale
bluish tinge although the rest of his unusually broad face had a healthy
tan on it. He had dark eyes that gazed rather sadly over his spectacles
when he was speaking to anyone. As long as he was in the sick-room he
walked softly, but the minute he came out of it he stamped off in a martial manner. In other words, he was a kindly old soul and obviously the
opposite of a charlatan. Nevertheless I felt a dagger of fear go through
me as he came in. He made me think of some figure I had met with in
some terrifying place I could not quite recall. "It is nothing at all," he
repeated, with his thick Swiss accent, as he came out into the hall and,
through the glasses which veiled his sad eyes, looked sharply at the
frightened faces of the guests.

The hotel was in upheaval for several days. Angelica's room was full
of visitors at all hours, for no one dreamed of going out into the snow
without her. Her band of friends sat around in corners or tramped up
and down the stairs. It also milled around in the corridor near the room
of its incapacitated leader. Boxes of fresh flowers poured into the hotel,
and each person pretended not to have any idea where they came from.
The Swiss captain's stout wife never left Angelica's side, although there
was nothing for her to do except to rub her swollen ankle with alcohol
and arrange the incoming flood of flowers.

I had not notified her parents. They should have been on their way
home now, after postponing their departure several times because of the
aversion of Angelica's mother to sea crossings. At last they were due to
embark on a boat returning from India via Port Said, for in Alexandria
the only available ships were the French Mediterranean packets, of
which the best ones were booked up for weeks in advance and the others

unsuitable. By that time, however, they should have started, although another week had gone by without any word from them. At the end of the week we took Angelica on the Diavolezza tour.

We climbed above the houses of Bernina and crossed the Morteratsch Glacier. It is a beautiful and easy trip and even poor performers on skis get an enormous amount of pleasure from it. While we were up on the glacier I suddenly thought again of the Ice Fairy, about whom I had refrained from telling Angelica the day of her arrival. Now I told the story of how she stands on the ice, her arms above her head, looking like a human column, and how the light of the setting sun as it falls on her makes her body sing. . . . We stopped in the middle of the glacier. It seemed to float in the rosy evening light. Both old and young were enveloped and made beautiful by the magic atmosphere around us. No one moved. We stood still and listened for the music to be released by the setting planet in this high and remote corner of the earth. We were enthralled by our own thoughts and by the glowing beauty of the solitary white world around us. We heard the rippling, crackling music of the Fairy. We felt, with a kind of intoxication, the ground beneath our feet resound through its taut, surging surface. The peaks echoed all around us. We heard the high, tender, throbbing song, and Angelica stood among us with her face upraised and her sturdy, slim little body trembling.

That evening, for the first time, there was no dancing. Our group sat together and told stories, which was a most unusual thing to happen in a modern hotel in our world.

"We have been consecrated," was Angelica's firm opinion. "The Ice Fairy consecrated us up on the Morteratsch Glacier." She looked each person in the eye, and even the Swiss captain, who certainly was a hard-headed individual and did not believe in any supernatural powers, nodded in a friendly, serious way. For the further edification of the gathering, I invented the legend of the Snow dwarfs, who are the enemies of human beings and who, when they become really angry, toboggan down into the valleys on avalanches, in order to do mischief around the hotels. That is why, I asserted, it would be very possible that the Irish "Consul," on such a night, might awake to find his nose frost-bitten and that the Italian prohibitionist might feel his beard filled with frozen claret. "And what about me?" called out Angelica, vigorously raising her hand as she used to do in school. "And you," I answered, "you will find yourself missing from your bed in the morning. You will have to take a train at once and search for yourself in the larch woods near Pontresina. If you are lucky you will find yourself out there playing with the white snow kittens. These snow cats have golden heads, amber eyes and long tails the color of the sunset glow on the Morteratsch Glacier. As they jump around from tree to tree in the woods, shaking snow from the branches, or they dash from one tree trunk to another, you can readily see that they make you think it is sunset-time all day long. But you may find yourself sound asleep in the little birch grove near St. Moritz. Who can tell where the naughty snow sprites may have carried you?"

"In that case," spoke up the Irish boy, "we shall undertake the search. That is what we are here for."

"I quite agree," put in someone else, "I have been coming here for thirty years and I know all this country."

We spent the whole evening as though we were out in the open in the sun. We could almost feel the snow spraying our faces as it does when you follow each other on skis through the little windless groves or out on the open fields through which we now raced in our thoughts. Gone was the artificially heated atmosphere in which the jazz band usually swayed the mixed crowd, pounding its sensibilities until they were reduced to a pulp. Everything was pure and bright as the driven snow we felt around us, and if anyone had the Ice Fairy in mind he would have been sure that she was sitting there with us and that her name was Angelica.

It was the next day that the tragedy happened.

No one saw Angelica leave the hotel. Without arousing her bands of friends who were mostly still at breakfast, I found out that she had dressed herself and that her skis were missing. I searched every path leading away from the hotel in the hope of finding fresh tracks but the ground was frozen so hard that no trace remained. I telephoned in all directions. An inn in the Fextal answered, yes, at the crack of dawn, a young lady had come in to drink a glass of warm milk but she had firmly declined breakfast on the ground that she wanted to reach the lake at once and looked forward to having a tremendous appetite when she returned home.

To save time I took my skis along. When I reached the inn I put them on and began the descent to the lake. The snow was full of frozen ruts. My skis rasped and clattered and when I came to the open field near the woods and was going at full speed I tried to make a cautious turn to slow down, but I slipped and slid with a crashing noise into the first trees. And there, five yards farther, right on my path, lay Angelica. Her face was drawn with pain, but she was throwing kisses to me.

Her skis, with her boots attached to them, lay beside her.

"I have broken at least one leg," she stammered. "Moreover, I think my feet may be frozen. I took my shoes off and I couldn't get them back on. Oh, dear!"

She wrung her hands and rocked back and forth. Her voice trembled, her face twitched with pain and her eyes were wild with anguish, yet she tried to laugh. She made me think of a spinning top being lashed as she forced herself to laugh.

Out on the lake the others caught up with us. The captain practically took her away from me by force. He bent over as he carried her and he took long strides. We followed silently and anxiously and held our breaths when the tortured girl swallowed hard and tried to laugh.

It was late in the evening when the doctor came down from her room, and he was immediately surrounded by the guests in the hall. He laid a finger on his lips and said: "Quiet. Absolute quiet. I ask you most emphatically to keep quiet. One lady and one gentleman have undertaken her care, and that is sufficient. Do you understand? That is sufficient. There is a fracture of the right leg and—pneumonia."

I sent off telegrams to Heluan, and also to the steamship offices in Cairo and Marseilles.

The first night and the following day passed without incident. Her delirium began during the second night. The third night I had to stop my ears because I could not bear to hear how she was raving.

Her candid young girl's face was clouded over by another, a darker mask. The child we had laid into bed with such tender, shy hands now became a ruthless, abandoned, determined creature, gritting her teeth, clenching her fists, threatening, begging, despising, and fighting with her nails and teeth—for a lover. Once she made me think this lover had betrayed her, then again that she was the one that had done the wrong. She tore her hair and complained endlessly of herself.

Her mouth was twisted into one long scream, to which something inside of her struggled to attach itself. Even her hands lost their quality of selfless charm. They clawed the bedspread, they seemed to have caught some wild animal and were strangling it. Then she would moan with satisfaction. "You never have any time in Berlin. You! But now I have hold of you. Yes. Now will you stay still while I ask you something. That's right. Ah!" Then she would fall back on the pillows and whimper. "Don't leave me alone all of the time. I am so frightened. Think of Angelica a little, my darling, just a little bit of Angelica. . . ."

I called to her desperately, "Angelica! Angelica!"—but she did not even hear me.

I was thankful that she fell asleep before the captain's wife relieved my watch at her bedside.

"Telegraph to George!" was Angelica's first order as dawn broke. The captain's wife did not know who George was and was not able to find out. Instead of making any reply to the question, Angelica began to carry on a conversation with George in a low and thrilled tone of voice. Then she went to sleep again.

"We must telegraph to George," said the captain's wife, her face covered with tears. Then she was embarrassed, blushed and looked away.

I spoke to the doctor after he made his morning call, and he arranged to have the captain's wife replaced by a trained nurse from Maloja, who could understand no German. She made no objection. But her eyes flooded with tears again. The captain was furious and offered to take her place himself. When this was refused, he shrugged his shoulders and mumbled that he did not understand what kind of a comedy was being played.

"Telegraph to Papa!" was Angelica's next demand. "And if he does not come at once I shall run away with George. . . . He is waiting for me with a car down at the corner," she added slyly. She giggled and gently smoothed the counterpane. I knew. She had come to an understanding with George. They were agreed.

Suddenly she raised herself up in her bed. "If you do not wire at once," she said slowly, with her eyes on the ceiling—then she fell back on the pillows. "You murderer!" she murmured and made a wry face. . . . After a while she smiled gently and said, "You ass. . . ."

When she wakened again she lay on her back for a long time, sighing, and staring at me. Gradually she seemed to recognize me.

"Uncle, indeed!" she said ironically. "What good is it to have an uncle if he isn't there when you are dying?"

"Tell me quickly what his name is," I demanded, jumping to my feet. It had just occurred to me that she did have an uncle in Berlin, who had put her on the train four weeks ago and who had sent me a message at the time although I did not know him.

She made a jubilant exclamation and, pointing one finger at me, gave a telephone number. She repeated it and then, turning her face slowly to the wall, she said: "Good night, dear, dear, George."

I rang and sent for the captain, who came and sat stiffly in my chair, while his eyes searched the corners of the room as though he expected to discover some enemy lurking in them.

I had hardly reached the telephone booth and taken off the receiver when I heard a long distance call: "Hello, is that Sils Maria?" At first I tried to counter with an effort to get St. Moritz and put in a call for Berlin.

"This is Berlin! Is that Sils Maria?" was the reply.

I yelled into the telephone: "Steglitz 5498!"

"Yes, this is Steglitz 5498."

"My God!" I exclaimed. "Are you Uncle George?"

"Ha!" came over the wire and then: "Yes, of course, it is Uncle George. They have cabled me from Cairo that the child—hello, can you hear me? I am taking the 2:16 train. Look up the time of arrival."

"Fly!" I screamed. "You must fly!"

The apparatus rumbled, then the wires hummed. A faraway voice was speaking in fluent English.

"Damn! . . . Hello, are you still there? . . . I am taking a plane."

I went back and sat down close to Angelica. I took her hands in mine and said: "Angelica, I have telephoned him. He is taking a plane and will be here this evening."

She smiled and shook her head. "Oh, I don't believe it. You just say that. Perhaps tomorrow morning. . . . But then Papa will be there and he will throw us both out."

She died shortly after midnight.

The doctor scratched his pale blue chin, leaned over and gently closed the child's eyes. Then he stamped vigorously out into the corridor, vigorously as life itself that goes on with a firm step.

At two o'clock Uncle George arrived by motor from Zurich. His bald head glistened as he walked rapidly through the brightly lighted hall. Angelica's friends were scattered in various corners, each one an eternity apart from the others. Near the staircase the captain straddled a chair and sobbed into his folded arms. Otherwise there was absolute silence. The old captain wept for us all.

Suddenly Uncle George appeared again and demanded food. The night porter laid a table in the small parlor and brought some wine and cold meat.

I sat down by the man she had loved.

He talked endlessly about the dangers of modern sports to young people, and once he spoke of Angelica as a self-willed child, for whose death destiny had set this particular stage—and perhaps it was a good thing after all. I asked him, incidentally, whether he had been fond of the child.

"Who wasn't fond of her?" he exclaimed with relish.

"Yes," I went on, "but I think you were nearest of all to her."

He brushed that aside. "What nonsense! It was her mother. I used to take her to the Zoo sometimes, and chatted with her now and then. No, indeed, she and her mother were like two youngsters. My poor sister could never get ahead of the child."

"And her father?" He had no idea what my question meant. "Oh," he said, and then he added: "In Berlin, men have work to do! And they can't skimp it either!"

There was no doubt about it, Uncle George was aware of nothing. He had no conception of it all. He was as free from all sense of guilt as were her father and mother. They had all been fond of her.

And her name was Angelica.

Translated by ELIZABETH REYNOLDS HAPGOOD

Annette Kolb

CONVENT LIFE

ONE DAY I too was there—the seventh child of my parents—and could look at this planet. For better and for worse. My first recollection has never faded. I was five, and standing under a tree whose leaves rustled in the wind and let the blue sky shine through. Life is beautiful, I thought. Then a leaf flew down into my hand, and while I slowly plucked its rough veins and fibers apart I grew unspeakably depressed. My share, I dimly felt, was not the high, gladly moving treetop but the lone, dull thing in my hands. It was a hot evening. The air hung in quiet weariness. Unwillingly, I let myself be dragged through the garden gate across the dusty street to the other gate, which led into our yard. So, for the first time, the dominant chord of our being rings at our consciousness; for in man there is nothing new. The *fin mot* of any self is a leitmotif, and all things added to it are amplifications.

Only a year later, in the convent, I got to know the boredom to which I inclined as others do to gouty pains or rheumatism, and which could strike me as suddenly as a gust of wind round a corner.

In my convent, about thirty miles from Innsbruck, it blew through the whole house, around all walls and through the giant garden—except the part that was laid out by my father, where a pretty bridge arched over the brook, dragon-flies whirred unconventually and the trees stood in park-like clusters. But otherwise all was ugly. In the north two tall, clumsy mountains locked the world out, and peonies stood, mostly withered, about a huge cross in front of the house. Whatever I saw I had to feel at the same time. How painful here the light seemed in spring, when the alpine ridges stood out so roughly in the snow and the blooming trees shivered. Oh, how desolate the smell of the fields in winter (for there were fields in this garden, too), the stubble and molehills in them and the heavy, fat flight of the ravens over them!

For entertainment I resorted to a strange thinking game. I would sit down by myself, put my arms up, close my eyes and ever faster, with bated breath, think: "I am I." For on this thought I could slide down as on a rope into ever darker depths, till I got dizzy, and my self, unconscious. How I managed it became a mystery to me, later. Has our mind a juggler's speed when we are seven—is it both more transparent then and acute, more soluble from ourselves, as it were? I do not know. But I found it exceedingly thrilling to hunt for myself, down to a root that no longer was I. "Oh, I'm caught!" I would think then. "Not even for an hour can I ever get away from myself; and no matter how much I shall like others, I never can be them."

Once, however, having just made an outstandingly successful mental slide of this sort, I was seized by a horror as though I had lost myself, as though the rope of my identity were hanging in the air, no longer retrievable—and like one drowning I gasped and fought back to the surface, that is, to consciousness. Some instinct told me to give up the eerie game. Thus I rapidly lost the ability, and only the memory of it has stayed with me. Other problems, which I was no more capable of solving, began to plague me instead. If one of the nuns died, the pupils were allowed to see her once again on the bier. Then I, two feet tall, would march in ahead of all the others, and searchingly gaze at the pale face which lay before me, expressionless, senseless. And to me nothing seemed to cast so heart-rending a light on convent life as Death. For I was too small, and it was a mistake to let me confront it.

More and more things came to displease me.

One Sunday I found in a book the picture of a group of palms, a tiger about to pounce and a beautiful girl, who with mortally fearful mien wanted to flee—but in vain! The beast had seen her and could not fail to tear her to pieces.

Outraged, beside myself, I ran about the room. I looked up at the illustrated inscriptions on the walls: "Behold, thus much hath God loved the world . . . He, however, loveth His own unto death . . . No eye hath seen it, no ear hath heard it . . ." Over my drawer a pelican spread its wings with a similar feeling proverb. But how did this fit together? And again my mind clung to the horrible picture. How could God permit this if we were His images and His children?

Another time, the fire bell had rung for about an hour because of a farm burning nearby. Finally a nun—I can still see her—came hurrying up the corridor with flying steps and said, "Thank God, children, no human life was destroyed. Only sixteen cows were burned." In the night I could see the howling animals race through the flames. What a world was this, in which children buried their parents and the lord of creation was debased into a tiger's prey? Charming people whom I knew or had seen, and who were unlikely to collide with wild beasts, came before my eyes. Certain possibilities were enough to raise my Weltschmerz to a fortissimo. There was no escape from such a world, no death, no more unconsciousness for our immortal souls. I slept near the window and the mountain brook murmured black plaints up to me. "Oh!" I thought, "how is that— I cannot love God."

On the next morning presents had come for me, and I showed myself so avid to receive them at once that the Mother Superior reprimanded me. "You pleasure-seeking child," she said severely. This word was new to me and I heard it with interest. Indeed, I hated nothing so much as pain. Why was I so immensely excited over every joy and why were even my blackest moods as light as clouds which a gust of wind drives away?

But these meditations merely wearied me, and I was glad to get rid of them. I no longer thought of anything but Rosa Flatz, Paula Baselli, Irene Angermeier and Livia Gelmini.

Rosa Flatz was tall, with golden curls and the head of a siren. She was almost grown up and so it was only in winter, when the pupils had to walk in silence, that I dared to take her hand and happily, sideways, look up at her. Where she went there was no winter; no frost impaired the lovely red of her cheeks; violent rose bushes blossomed on all roads she walked on, and even her sure and absent glance recalled the spring.

Paula Baselli had too dark a complexion and unwieldy hair. But the cut of her face was pure as an Aegina gem's, and I liked to be near her for a close view of her noble eye-sockets and the delightful pattern of her lips.

But Irene Angermeier was the most beautiful—calm and tired like a nymph in the moonlight.

Livia Gelmini was from Salurn and as melodious as chimes. I could never see enough of her stretching her arm out toward the banisters, and of her walk. And when she said: *"il gallo, il gatto, la primavera, la catena"* —then my heart soared like a butterfly in the sun. With Livia, who was only nine, I might have kept company, but I liked her too much. I could not admire without worshipping. Actually, I was interested neither in friends nor in familiarities, but in higher beings who raised me above myself; and before those four charming figures I yielded to a condition rather than to feelings. I never talked to them and never sought to draw their attention. They only had to be near, in the same room. When I lifted my head and could see all four of them, my convent was a fair and chosen place. But Rosa Flatz and Paula Baselli soon left it, Irene Angermeier was too beautiful to live, and Livia Gelmini also fell ill and was taken away. With them all poetry vanished from my convent existence; I was bitterly bored and longed to get away. Besides, my books were confiscated one after the other because I read them at the wrong times, and before I knew it I stood apart from the pupils as insubordination personified. Each year we celebrated the so-called "King's Festival," when the boarding school became a court and every pupil got a part according to her merits, from the Queen down to the cooks and chimney-sweeps. For the first years, as a page in cork-screw curls and gold bandeau, I was all day in the service of the Queen—who was either Rosa Flatz or Paula Baselli, and once Irene Angermeier in silver gauze and diamond crown. Later, though, the lovely festival was made to vex me. In a slanting shepherdess' hat and a tarlatan dress, which was too tight —as a former evening gown it had a waistline and I had not—I would stalk behind the landgravines, alone and mortally embarrassed, as royal reader with a giant book, and in the parade, when my turn came, the court jester in his red belled cap would dance ahead of me and publicly announce my pranks. Now, although secretly I had all sorts of private views about the world order, I lacked all personal judgment on the measure of my own misdeeds and was unduly ashamed. But was not the wide, gorgeous world the theatre of all liberties? There I planned to recompense myself. Oh, you just wait!

On some days, however, I despaired of ever getting back to it. Hadn't my father recently asked me if I did not want to remain in the convent forever?

"Oh no, oh no!"

"Et si je le veux?"

He had not been serious—he liked to joke—but some irritableness still was to be felt in it. Two more children had arrived in our family. Three had died, so we were six now; and I was the odd one. But I'd soon lie on a bier on the bottom floor, with a small crown of white peonies on my head, surrounded by nuns until the end. And I, the sole mourner, wept bitter tears at my untimely death, for at home I had been forgotten. My mother was good—I adored her when I was a child—but she came much less often than my father; and his visits merely frightened me. I did not resent it in the least that he preferred my sisters to me; I liked them better myself. But he was in far too great a hurry to respond to children. He had hardly greeted me when he turned to the Mother Superior and took an interest in her garden, making sketches for her on a piece of paper. On her, everything depended.

For one year everything was all right—when the Mistress of the Novices, Soeur Caroline, was promoted to Mother Superior. Exceedingly slim, so quick that she never seemed to walk but to glide; the narrow brunette head, carried lively and high as an asp's; nervous features full of *esprit* even in their irregularities—alas! suddenly she was gone, ill, transferred to another convent? We never found out. But the one who succeeded her was a fearful personage, pushed about in a wheel-chair, with Lampo, her snappish little dog at her feet. She liked to make speeches, untiringly mentioning God. No occasion was too commonplace for her to name Him. She laid the mystical on thick, with a materiality as if it were rice or coffee. How great is the wisdom of Goethe's counsel in *Wilhelm Meister*, to let boys view the most mysterious events of the Christian cult behind a veil until adolescence, so as not to confuse their impressions. For what a donor of the esoteric, alas, was this Mother Superior? There is something dreadful about the contempt of children. It can indeed hang like a millstone round their teachers' necks. For children thirst for good influences and know themselves susceptible to bad ones.

Among the youngest pupils was the rather homely daughter of a widow who kept a humble confectioner's shop in the small Tyrolean town nearest to our convent. When the Mother Superior addressed this girl, she could hardly ever refrain from inserting a word about *Linzertorte*, in a voice clearly hinting that her background was not good enough for our fine school. It was unforgettably embarrassing, how the child's ears would redden. The climax was a speech on the eve of vacations, before the assembled student body, in which some were praised and others reproved, with antecedents playing no mean part there, either. The flaws in the performance of the confectioner's daughter were especially sharply condemned by this Mother Superior with the shattering words: "And your mother hasn't even paid your board bill!" Presumably the victim soon got over this brutality, for at the start of the new term the child did not return; and it may be hoped that her mother deemed herself square for an unpaid board bill presented in such manner.

Vacations, however, were so beautiful that they extinguished all, that I saw my sufferings only in shortened perspective, as not worth mentioning until the dread day when I must go back. Thus six years passed. Then my mother visited me at Easter and took me on a two-day trip to nearby Innsbruck. Maria Theresa Street, in its way one of the world's most beautiful streets with delicately painted old houses, festive and cozy at the same time and lined up as for a dance with colored shutters beating in the vernal wind, and, as their immediate background, the snow mountains rising to the sky in incomparable grandeur, the charming, then as yet unrenovated inn "Zur Sonne," which I entered freely at her side —all this together so transported me with joy that my mother had to laugh a good deal before she finally said, *"Mais enfin, calme-toi donc!"*

The contrast was too great, however. I tore my hat from my head, tore the ugly pelerine from my neck and declared that I should never go back to my hated convent, in which I'd been buried for six years now. *"Six ans, c'est cruel!"* I screamed.

My mother, frightened and amazed by my outburst, sought to calm me, questioned me and promised that I'd come home for good in the summer vacation. That she would keep her word I knew; for children know much. So I contented myself, and a new, mad joy rose within me.

About this time Mère Angelini lived in Innsbruck—I do not know whether this was her real name or an assumed one. My mother, put in touch with her by a very distinguished priest, felt more attracted to her than to any other woman. She was the founder of the Order of the Eternal Adoration—related to that of the Sacré Coeur, but purely, contemplative in character and far more strict. Authorized by the Pope to establish a number of convents in France, Italy and Austria, she had devoted her enormous fortune to that purpose. Traveled, well-born, a woman of the world, she finally retired as the Mother Superior of a nunnery located in a quiet square in the heart of Innsbruck, with an inspirational little church as annex.

This was where I was taken on the day before we left the town. The reception room was not equipped for numerous visitors: two chairs and a table by the window filled it, and the grille was even tighter and more darkening than ours. But an Easter egg ringed by silver threads lay waiting for me—how do I happen suddenly to see it so plainly again?—and in it was a gold medal, for me, too! Likewise, a box of candy. *"Car,"* said Mère Angelini, *"pour bien aimer le bon Dieu il faut bien manger!"* I was convulsed with laughter at that. Not that I misunderstood her. By then, after all, I was familiar with the terminology prevailing behind convent walls. But here it sounded oddly gay and unliteral, as if all was easy. And this, although here all was so hard, and this order so strict! And how Mère Angelini laughed in turn, when I complained of seeing so little of her. As if she could not show me enough kindness, she told me to come quite alone to the gate when we left. But it was that of the clausure: it opened before me, and at the threshold a veritable image of light appeared in white habit and scarlet scapular, and a lovable head, no longer behind the tight wooden grille, so nobly raised that I had to think of the snow walls at the end of Maria Theresa Street. Bowing down to me, she thrust me back very gently, and the gate fell shut.

I drew courage from this rare encounter, but it also confirmed my distate for my own convent. Soon after my departure it was investigated by the government, another Mother Superior was installed, and future pupils were spared many an unnecessary hardship. Too many had complained of them to their parents. Frequently, physical defects that we acquired during that time remained with us for life. The winters were very cold. If we suffered from frostbite, we had to force our unhealed feet into boots that by morning had become too tight; slippers were not allowed. If we hobbled around, or complained, we were told once again about God, for love of whom we should be glad to bear the burning and the itching. Pretty children's feet went to the devil, of course; our toes were crippled like those of little Chinese girls.

In summer we got up at 5:15 A.M., in winter at 5:45—and that quickly, for only half an hour later we got fairly good coffee with a fresh roll, to which I always looked forward. At 9:30, part of the children marched back into the dining room for a glass of milk or the like. I was eager to belong to them—my mother had favored it—but I was excluded for the reason that then I would eat so much less at noon. As things stood, however, I was starved by then, my head ached and I bore myself quite crooked from ten o'clock on. There are large, normal and small stomachs; but this idea did not occur to anyone there. Today, with so many millions in Europe suffering the agonies of hunger, I feel satisfied that, for six years, for a few hours daily at least, such torment was not unknown to me.

But it was no wonder that I was counting the days now. The one nun I was very fond of had long been taken to the sick ward. And was never seen again.

My heart beat high when the heavy convent bolts locked behind me, forever. Perhaps no one had yet rushed from these walls so expectantly, and with so many illusions about the world.

Translated by E. B. ASHTON

Alfred Doeblin

THE CHIEF

IT JUST WENT ON and on like that with the Chief. The reddened area on the left leg spread beyond the knee; they applied compresses daily and once tried a salve, but they did not find the right remedy. They painted a line about the edges with iodine and ringed it with a thin strip of adhesive; that was to check the gangrene and, in fact, even appeared to, till suddenly it streaked away underneath and pushed forward. "Never mind," the Surgeon-Major said soothingly, "never mind; we'll catch the runaway," and recommenced the magical iodine painting and, with the aid of the Chief's wife, framed the whole in the pink adhesive. The temperature rose and sank. If it rose, the scientific view was, "That's part of the picture"; if it sank, there was delight—"There you are!"—and the good Oberstabsarzt, whose body they thus administered, beamed in contentment at the ups as well as the downs.

He was always cheerful. He said his heart had never been so good. He loved to lie on his back and get thoroughly rested; you could do that only when you were ill. Just as lovely (but he never told that to anyone) were the dreams in the afternoon. He soon found out that they had to do with the fever. He fought hard against the Major who wished to give him a febrifuge. "That weakens the body and saps the power of resistance," he explained to his physician. "After all, I know my body. You surgeons never think of that. Let me alone with your poisons." They finally agreed to one argument of the patient's—"Besides, a febrifuge would blur the curve." That satisfied the doctor, and the Chief could go on resting and dreaming superbly.

On Sunday a splendid blutwurst was served on the train; the kitchen gave its best; even the small keg of wine received in the little town was finished on that Sunday. It was November 17.

More than a week had passed since the outbreak of the revolution. On that same day something odd happened in the Chief's compartment. When the luncheon dishes were collected at another whistle-stop, and all who could walk were strolling beside the train, asking for the news of the day and besieging the station-master for information about where the trip was going and how much longer it would last—at this small depot the Frau Oberstabsarzt too had left her compartment and gone back to chat with Lieutenant Maus who looked out of his window. She was still standing there when several people came running, calling for her. She ran, frightened; Maus got out too. There had been a slight disturbance up front. The sick Chief, in his night shirt, had sought to climb down the steps of his compartment. He had been seen immediately and was now arguing kindly but confusedly with the soldiers who held him tight and pushed him back without trouble. By the time his wife came, he smiled at her from his bed again; his bandages lay on the ground. The Major came soon. The patient was chilled and shivering. In the afternoon he looked a grayish white; he was plainly changed; his eyes gazed peaceably as ever but they were sunken and the skin around them was yellow.

The Chief lay in the corridor-car now, with the special cases. The Major drew the woman out into the passage; they looked at each other, under the lamp; the doctor rubbed the leather lining of his cap: "We'll be in Würzburg in an hour. I can no longer accept the responsibility. There'd have to be a blood test, a serum injection; we have nothing here."

"You want to put him off in Würzburg?" She made outraged eyes. "I don't know a soul there."

"This is Germany, Madam. Doctors are the same. Würzburg is a big town."

She nearly flew into a rage: "Why didn't you take serum along? You said you had everything."

He calmly slapped the cap on his head, with his hands on the door handle. "I don't know which serum. Only the blood test will show."

She, anxiously pleading: "So it is—blood poisoning?"

He, shrugging shoulders: "We can't exclude it."

"From corns—from a corn?"

She pouted, wept, protested bitterly like a child, clutching at the window frame with both hands. The train was running exceptionally fast and swaying.

There was immense activity on the Würzburg freight station. The red flag in the town was visible from the train. All doors were opened; it was late afternoon, and the train-master announced that they'd stay here overnight and perhaps tomorrow morning; but they'd be switched to another track in fifteen minutes, so nobody was to get off. They looked out of the windows. Ambulance men went down the train with a stretcher, searching; at some windows shouts greeted them: "Wrong number—we're for Momma's." But then they were seen to halt in the rear —another croak, let's get out and see who it is. Then a lady got out, that was the Frau Oberstabsarzt—yes, the old man; probably lives hereabouts —then the ambulance men lifted their stretcher out of the car, carefully —they've covered him all up; is he dead yet? The Major slowly followed the stretcher which was carried down the length of the platform, back on the tracks. The old Chief! He lives here? No, they're taking him to a hospital. Sure—but because he lives here. No, they say he's in bad shape; his heart's bad. Everybody was sorry for him. Then the switching kept you busy, and then you got ready for a stroll in town as best you could and decked yourself out in red ribbons.

In the hospital they did not let the woman in to her husband for two hours. When she came in—he had a bald, single room, with a solitary electric bulb burning overhead—he held his hand out to her in his old cordial way as soon as she closed the door, rubbed her cold hand between both of his and thanked her for bringing herself to take him off the train and put him here: "I thought about it a few times, Antonie, because it shook so—but I didn't want to impose on you."

He was visibly improved. Soon, however, he became more quiet, more serious and strangely mysterious in his high pillows.

"Do you want something, Otto?"

"No."

"You were nodding."

"Was I? I—was just thinking of the Eastern front. They have a much longer trip than ours. Hm." He had a blood test behind him, he said, and a serum injection.

"Thank God! That's why I had to take you off; the Major couldn't make them on the train."

"No, we aren't equipped for serum." Strangely, he did not ask by one word why he got the serum. He was pleased with it, though. "Tomorrow you can bring me my seed catalogue. The one in my suitcase," he said, half asleep.

But at 6:00 A.M. when she spryly showed up in the hospital—happy, for the first time in many days, to have had a full night's sleep in a hotel

—the night nurse was just emerging from his room with a champagne bottle and a bottle of brandy. "How is he, nurse?"

The nurse did not recognize her right away. "The night was good at first. Then the fever went up; I gave him champagne, the pulse was uneven."

The woman wanted to go in, but the nurse blocked the door: "We have to wait for the doctor, I've had him called."

They stayed outside the door in silence, the nurse with both arms full. "Why won't you let me go in?" the woman asked. She heard an odd, regular sound from the room and she was worried. "Is he asleep? Then why can't I just sit with him?"

Then the doctor came—unkempt, without a collar under the white surgical coat—a long-legged, pale gentleman with a cold expression. He opened the door without greeting. The nurse followed. They closed the door and did not come out until long minutes later. The doctor viewed the woman from above, put the narrow collar of his coat up and after clearing his throat remarked: "You wish to see the Oberstabsarzt?"

He saw her fearful glance, hesitated, asked: "Didn't the nurse tell you? Well. Yes. It doesn't look good. We gave another injection. How did it start, anyway? How many days is it now?"

"Since Tuesday, Doctor."

"Short time, really. Yes. Well. The heart."

He looked at her a while—obviously without thinking, seeming fast asleep—nodded and left. In the room she immediately saw everything. It smelled of alcohol and camphor. The nurse was cleaning hypodermic syringes in bowls on the small white table. He lay with his head raised, both arms on the blanket. His eyes were closed. In his red, sunken face it jerked and flickered constantly. Seized by cold shudders, she cautiously touched one hand. There was no reaction.

It was plain that he was enormously busy. He was snoring mightily, sawing terribly deeply, loudly, regularly, as if he were doing an important job. Frequently he blew his cheeks up and the breath fled from his mouth, so that the lips popped from within and formed bubbles of saliva. The drops ran down to the chin over his white stubble.

She saw, observed, with feelings she did not dare admit to herself—pain, fear, disgust, shame in the nurse's presence. This regular snoring and sawing and blowing up of the cheeks. She turned to the nurse who was still rubbing a large syringe and facing away from her, she asked: "Is he—has he been doing this long?"

"Oh. He got restless after four. Then it started. I gave caffeine right away."

Uncertainly the woman stood, looked to and fro, between the nurse and the bed: "Why—is he doing that? Is it the lungs? Can't he breathe?"

The nurse looked at her in surprise: "You're a doctor's wife, aren't you? Haven't you seen any patients?"

"My husband is an officer in the Medical Corps."

"I see. The snoring, that's always like this. They do it when—well, you see."

Then the woman took a chair and quietly sat by the bed—an hour, two hours. The patient simply kept working. "You see"—that plainly meant when you were dying. She wiped the sweat off him with her handkerchief, then with a towel. In wiping she thought of the expression, "last sweat," stopped, paralyzed with dread, and dropped the towel. She was trembling. She opened the door, happy when the day nurse came in, whose conversation with the head nurse of the ward had just ended with the day nurse lauding her superior's judgment—for if the Oberstabsarzt had gone into the double room, with the cardiac colonel, there'd have been trouble and now they'd have to roll the new one over into the single, anyway. The day nurse, an elderly, strong person, with nickel glasses, regarded the patient attentively. His wife covered her eyes: "How long is this going to last, nurse?"

"A couple of hours—or it might take all day. We've had them lying like this for two days."

"Is he in much pain?"

"He? He doesn't feel anything." She bent over him, touched his shoulder, addressed him: "Herr Oberstabsarzt! Herr Oberstabsarzt! See —he doesn't hear anything." She quickly wiped his face, straightened the pillows and the head which fell to one side and said, "Well, you just sit tight now. If anything happens, come out into the corridor."

Frau Antonie sat down obediently, facing the window. This is Monday; we started out on Thursday; this is Würzburg—I never thought I'd get as far as Würzburg with him. The snoring is dreadful, dreadful. If only I could stuff something in my ears. Why am I sitting here? The nurse goes off and I sit here. That's the way they are in a field hospital. If he knew that.

She looked at his face; it was pale, almost blue; small pearls of sweat were forming again on his forehead. He feels nothing. This is death. Actually it is all over. I'm a widow. I don't know what time the train leaves; maybe they'll stay till tonight, and if this is over soon enough I can still make it; the things are going on to Naumburg anyway. Otherwise I'd have to get them unloaded; they may have unloaded them already, without asking me. She did not think of the burial. She became restless. The men may just have put the things on the platform and nobody'll know whose they are; they'll be dragged off and stolen, now in the revolution. I really can't sit here. She looked at her wrist-watch. All right —another half-hour.

She sat as if on coals for the half-hour, tortured more and more by the snoring, with fear added, and impatience. I haven't any business here. This is the nurse's business. They're simply leaving him to me— it's unheard-of.

At eight she rose jerkily, and softly, touching his hand, said, "I have to look after the things, Otto." Tears came into her eyes. "Your trunks are there—all the books. If you just were well again—that's what you're doing, leaving me here."

Outside she dabbed at her eyes, stood by the door till the nurse came; then she sobbed aloud: "Nurse—I must get some air. You must let me go."

"Yes, you just go, child, go ahead. Come back after lunch. We'll be here. Yes, it's a bad time."

And the woman had no sooner left the pavilion than she started running. She ran as if chased by a nightmare, in fear and confusion, through the terribly intricate gardens of the hospital. At last she reached the main gate. At last she was outside and calmed down. And now a cab. I'll go to the station. It seemed as if she were driving to her husband. Here this wasn't he.

And then, behold! there was the train, her train. She walked past it; these were her men, nodding to her; over there were the ambulance men, back there was her car. Nobody had yet bothered about the luggage. The officers were chatting and smoking in front of their compartments. The cook ran up to ask about the Chief and whether he was to put something aside for her. She entered her old, disorderly compartment; right away the cook brought her coffee and bread; she ate and drank, dried her tears and then started crying all over, violently, because here she sat all alone and Otto was over there and who could think what he was doing now. She writhed in fear when she recalled the snoring. Now she had had to take him to the hospital, and only yesterday or the day before he'd had coffee with her, and his catalogues still lay about. She could think no further. What was to become of everything, now that he was really dying. It doesn't have to be true, either. They can be wrong too. And we have the house together, and he works in the garden. . . .

She wept softly to herself. And when she had finished the coffee and bread she searched the compartment for his briefcase and began a letter to her brother: that she was stuck in Würzburg with Otto; he was sick, in the hospital. And then she felt so horribly alone again and found it so inconceivable that Otto was lying in the hospital over there and due to die, really die—that she could write no further.

The mess sergeant broke up her mourning. He came for the dishes, and because there was a revolution now, this fellow, whom she didn't even know, dared to nod to her: "Well, Frau Oberstabsarzt, it's all just half so bad. You see how I'm hobbling. I've had half my leg torn off by the Russians. But I'm hobbling, and I get along." Insulted, she looked away. She went back to the hospital; nothing had changed. It was still her husband lying there, but an uncertainty had come between them.

The train left at 7:10 P.M. He lived for an hour after its departure. She lay on his neck, to say goodbye. But they lifted her off, and tied a napkin under his chin with a knot on top of his head, because his jaw kept dropping. It looked horrible and silly, with the two ends on tops. The nurse said, "It's just for a few hours—later we'll take it off."

She stood beside him, thought of him, of the war, of the long years before and how good he was with all his quirks and how she'd got used to him. She heard trains rattle in the distance. That was his field hospital gliding away into the dark, without him. It is all over, the war is over, we're being left here.

She rose, wearily. They were asking a question. The funeral—yes, how do you do that?

For him, as for many others, there were no solemn officer's rites. One had to act with discretion. They dumped his body en route, in a Würzburg graveyard.

Translated by E. B. Ashton

Leonhard Frank

BREATHE!

At home Annette had felt no worse than usual. Riding to the doctor, she felt every jog of the street-car tenfold. Life became crass. Nothing but blows! Hard, powerful blows, to which she was helplessly exposed.

The grey bulk of the church and the tall, pointed tower bent down on the car's roof. The car was moving forward and backward at the same time.

Blows. Blows. The car was turned rapidly round itself. She grew pale with vertigo and fear. Was this fear of death? She had never felt fear of death. She had to get off. She staggered toward the door. She soared.

The car stopped. Where was her head? It circled and flew over to the far side of the street. Her body slid automatically down the steps. For another second she stood in the thronged street. Then all strength left. She crumpled in a heap. Nobody caught her.

Two men, one of them thickset, with pursed lips and a pince-nez which sat like a weapon in his bull-dog face, carried her to the first aid station. A black dog ran alongside, barking. The thickset one kicked it. She opened her eyes and gave her name and address. The dog barked furiously.

"What's the matter with her?" The doctor in the first aid station washed his bloody hands in the sink. In the next room yelled a woman who had been run over.

"Put her there." Drying his hands: "What's your name?" He went over to her. The towel fluttering before her eyes increased the dizzy feeling; she thought she was racing soundlessly through a dirty snowy landscape in a swaying railroad car.

Her head dropped on her shoulder. "Call 1745. My own doctor."

"What's your name!"

She closed her eyes and laid the trembling fingertips on the big artery in her throat. "Annette Vierkant." She lacked the strength to lift her head again. Her full, beautiful face was white. The brown under the eyes had darkened. Unasked, she repeated her address. "Have them take me home."

"Then it is my duty to inform you that you'll have to pay for the ambulance. . . . Are you married?"

"And your maiden name?" The telephone rang. "Your maiden name?" He threw the notebook on the table. "First aid station?"

Behind the closed door of the next room the woman who had been run over screamed without pause. Leaning against the doorjamb was a four-year-old girl weeping snot and water.

"What? What does she look like? . . . Tall? What does that mean, tall? . . . That those people can't tell what relatives they spend their lives with look like," he told his assistant, a girl whose mouth was a straight, thin line with the calmest, clearest blue eyes above it.

"Hello! Did your mother have a little girl with her? . . . Then it isn't her." He hung up.

"When were you born and where? . . . Sorry, I have to know first when and where you were born," he calmly told Annette, taking notes.

The room swayed. A new fainting spell was near. "My own doctor . . . 1745."

"What was your maiden name?" He repeated it and asked, "With an *i* or *y*?"

The thickset one tore off his pince-nez. "Do you have to dot every *i* in the file before you help the woman?" He threw the weapon back into his face and pushed his mouth forward.

Annette battled the new fainting spell with a tremendous effort. She was afraid of dying and felt that this man with the notebook was killing her.

"If for any reason, and if it were sympathy, we fail to do that at once, sir, we may not be able to identify an accident victim for days. Meanwhile uncertainty drives the relatives crazy. That's the other side of it. . . . Call that doctor, miss."

The woman who had been run over suddenly changed her tune: now she was screaming like a strange animal. The child cried out. Annette wanted to lift her head; it fell back again.

"All right, what's wrong?"

"Heart!"

"The doctor asks that you give her digitalis at once and have her taken home."

The door was pushed open. Two policemen, carrying a well-dressed old gentleman. His face was green; the dirtied derby lay on his stomach.

The thick, warm odor of carbolic acid promptly swallowed the fresh air.

"Have you got his personal data?"

"He hasn't waked up yet. When they called us he was already unconscious."

The doctor dropped the old man's hand. "He's dead. Heart failure. Call the morgue."

He turned to the thickset one. "He may have children, a wife—don't you see? There are fifty-six first aid stations here. Fifty-six! And every single day every station gets several accident cases. We live in a city of millions. Now just think what an inextricable mess would result if . . ."

"Yes, but . . ."

"There's no but about it!"

"Yes, but won't you finally give her the medicine!" Together, he and the doctor leaped over to Annette who fell off the chair, fainting.

"Madam's got sick. The doctor called. He'll come right away." And the small, dainty maid from Pomerania smiled even at that, as at all she saw and heard in Berlin. She was seventeen, blond as an apple, healthy as an apple, and in the two weeks had already learned to wear high heels and silk stockings.

Michael's hand reached automatically for the receiver. Even while the doctor told him what he knew, Michael heard the heavy steps in the staircase. Two ambulance men in grey uniforms were bringing her up on a stretcher, feet first.

Strands of hair had dropped into the waxen face. The transparently thin hands lay on the body, one above the other, folded as if for the coffin. She looked like a woman after an operation, still unconscious as she is carried away from the knife.

His terror was so great that it could not last over a second. "Get the bed ready." He rushed toward her.

She opened her eyes and closed them again: one short glance, in which lay not even the strength of a glance, a mere opening of the eyes, in full accord with her condition, deeply earnest, fatalistic and composed at the same time: a person seeming touched by the finger of death.

In bed she could not speak, either; she just looked at him once more. Again he was shattered throughout, as by a cleavage. He had to read her wishes from the pale-blue lips.

She felt his tenderness when he stroked the hair out of her forehead, and tried to smile. It was more than if a well woman had taken up the load of the whole world for her lover.

The doctor, a friend of the couple, took off his overcoat on the stairs, put the stethoscope together while crossing the hall, waited before the bedroom door a fraction of a second and quietly went in.

Some time before, he had had to promise her definitely to hold nothing back from her about her condition, even in the extreme case, and he himself had believed that here he might make an exception and keep his promise. She was an intelligent woman, very hard to deceive, and her soul had long been as near to death as to life.

Then, as he sat on the edge of the bed, hiding his surprise at her appearance, with the far too slow and hardly tangible pulse between his fingers, she opened her eyes again. Her glance knew of death. She remained composed. But behind this knowledge, in the depths, rose the fearful question.

The doctor answered it by saying with quite inconspicuous calm: "A heart weakness. An attack of heart weakness. That will come, and go again. Only, in the near future you can't afford any excitement."

Not until then did she ask, in words: "Am I going to die, doctor?" And was already displaying a lovely smile made up of hope and faith.

"No!" He laughed convincingly. "You're much too young to die. If you were fifteen years older. But this way—!"

"Please, give me the comb, Michael. . . . And the mirror!"

She got an injection. The pulse grew stronger. She arranged her hair herself. Then, comforted and breathing quietly, she fell asleep.

"I'm surprised. I hadn't expected such a bad attack. But there's no danger," he told Michael. And that was his opinion. He wrote some prescriptions.

"You're telling me the truth, aren't you?"

"The whole truth. . . . I'm at a dinner this evening. If necessary, you can call me there."

Michael sat at the desk in his study. Over there lay a woman who was ill. It was not unpleasant, this feeling. One region of his nature and of his love for Annette asked to be allowed to nurse her and watch over her. Nothing would be neglected; her slightest wish would be fulfilled.

He was no longer afraid for her now. Annette had been ill for years. Both of them had grown accustomed to that, as man gradually becomes accustomed to distress and to luxury.

For a long time, Michael had fitted the much faster pace of his healthy, tough nature to the sick woman's possibilities, had done without pleasures and enjoyments, lived quietly with Annette and pressed his vigor, when it wanted to burst out, into the work at his desk. His was forty.

The forehead over his brows was built far forward. These knobs had grown increasingly larger in years of the heaviest desk work. The forehead dominated the narrow face, and its fanaticism returned in the thin, firm mouth. The eyes alone betrayed his sensitivity. The hair was greying. His slender body, trained in sports, allowed him to leap up four flights of stairs in ten seconds and breathe as easily before the door as down below.

It was completely still in the apartment. Michael was writing. The maid, sitting watch before the half closed bedroom door, drew her skirt up over her knees and looked delightedly at her flawlessly straight legs, thrusting them out again and again, pressed tight against each other.

She had shortened her skirt seven inches, three days after her arrival in Berlin, and only now had got to know her legs.

Smiling, she pulled a small mirror from her apron, showed her teeth which were white and beautiful, and for the third time in her life powdered the apple-fresh cheeks with a tiny puff.

At ten o'clock she went to bed. Michael lay down on the davenport in Annette's dressing-room and listened and thought, listened and thought: of Annette, of his work, of Annette. And fell asleep.

A moan wakened him. In her distress she had twisted the upper part of her body into the chair, leaving only the legs in the bed, and was slowly moving her head from one side to the other. The heart was not working. The face was sallow.

"What is it? What are you doing?" Fright shook him down to his feet. He carefully lifted her back into the bed. All strength had left her.

Suddenly he sobbed out and started to cry. From one second to the other he had felt that her life was in danger. This feeling came like an earthquake from far away and disappeared immediately. "I'll call the doctor!" he gave her the medicine and leaped for the telephone.

No, he was not worried at all. Michael was to put a cold compress on the heart. Michael believed again, because he wanted to believe.

She recovered a little. She seemed to fall asleep. Her breath fluttered weakly. Michael watched by the bed, for difficult hours. Deep fear and anger at the doctor alternated with hope that the doctor might be right.

At eight in the morning he heard the hurried steps. Annette's full face was greenish and bloodless. The eyes alone were alive and full of repressed fear.

"I'm blaming myself now. I should have stayed here overnight."

"Tell me the truth!"

"Pretty serious! We have to get a nurse. Your maid doesn't know enough."

From then on Michael could no longer eat. He no longer shaved, no longer washed, no longer dressed. He walked about in his dressing gown for days. And when he stepped to the bed, he smiled peacefully and with anxious tenderness. He played well. For a week, he carried hope about in his study.

A specialist was called. For the rigid fear in Michael's heart, he looked too young. Only after the examination, when he came into the study, Michael could see from the beardless, wrinkled face that this man had seen much in his life.

The specialist spoke a few words, calm as his face, words that let Michael's fear and hope live on.

Toward evening, twenty-four hours before her death, Annette told the nurse in Michael's presence: "It's nice to be sick when you're so well taken care of."

That was Annette. Thus she had kept faith with life, always and in every situation, always felt the beautiful even in the grave, and made others happy with a word coming directly from her kind heart.

Michael had to flee quickly into the study. His rigidity had dissolved. Sobbing, shaken by sobs, his hand pressed to his mouth lest she hear him, he fell into the chair by the desk, his head on his arms.

Early in the morning the nurse came into Michael's bedroom. She remained standing in the door. He shot up into terror. The nurse looked excited. "It's going badly."

"What happened?" He jumped out.

"The night was so good. She slept quietly. Suddenly, just now. . . . You'll have to call the doctor right away."

Already, he heard the hurried steps on the stairs.

The nurse held Annette's head and tried to quiet her. She kept saying, "Yes, yes," although she did not understand Annette's words.

Annette was stammering excitedly, and talking violently with the thin hands. She had lost the power of speech.

"Stroke," said the doctor. She got an injection.

Michael stood by the bed like one shot in the heart, who can still stand. Every sensation had suddenly vanished. There was a cut.

Minutes later she fell asleep. When she woke up she was calmer. The face was calmer. She tried to form words and while doing so looked at Michael as a good pupil, trying hard, looks at the teacher. Tears hung in her eyelashes.

Toward noon she could speak again. She was beautiful. The clear face. Excitedly, and smilingly, she complained of the doctor in the first aid station. "That hour did me so much harm. I'd be much better now."

Once again joy and hope stormily entered Michael's soul. The doctor stayed around. The maid sat idly, timidly in the kitchen, reviving only when Michael asked her for coffee for the doctor.

Out there, the coffee grinder. That was life. "Oh, doctor, she won't die, will she?"

"It was just a very light stroke." He started talking of something else, to divert Michael who could no longer be diverted.

It grew quiet in the apartment. The doctor was with Annette. Michael cut a little frame of grey cardboard, glued a movable cardboard strip at the back so it could be stood up, and put the smiling picture of Annette inside. Even in this small picture you could see how the brown of her eyes became gorgeous against the soft-tinted ivory complexion, and how that again won its rare purity from the eyes' deep golden brown.

For hours Michael had cut and glued the little frame with inconceivable joy. A few times he had crept to the bedroom door and back. Everything was quiet. The picture stood before him. Already there was the pain of life softly drawn into the enchanting smile.

She'll be glad when I show her the frame, he thought and crept again to the bedroom door.

She was not to see the frame.

Suddenly Michael heard excited voices and a horrible rattle.

Annette had had a new stroke. She was sitting upright, held by the nurse. Her breath failed, far too long. The eyes were rigid when she succeeded in drawing breath again, from far away.

With arm and forefinger stretched straight out, she pointed at Michael and severely, with a voice that was suddenly quite clear, demanded: "Come here!"

Then she pressed and held his hand with unexpected strength. "Stay. Stay here."

The great second had come. And she knew it.

The intervals between the breaths grew longer with every time.

The doctor, in the greatest hurry, made three injections into her thigh, one after the other. He pushed in ruthlessly, shouting: "Breathe! Breathe!"

Michael shouted, "Breathe! Breathe!"

She did not breathe.

"The respiration center was hit," said the doctor.

Once more and once again she inhaled, in the very last moment and with heavy rattling. Then came a long pause. She did not inhale, she did not exhale. She stared. She looked at death. Living was breathing. She could not do it. In this last struggle she let Michael's hand go. At the very last, man is alone.

Both of them were shouting: "Breathe! Breathe!"

After a dreadfully long half-minute she managed for one single time to draw air, already from beyond to breathe life once again. That was enough for another half-minute. For final seconds. She fell back.

"Dead," said the doctor.

"Dead? No!"

"She's dead." The doctor immediately went into the adjoining bathroom—the door remained open—bowed over the wash basin to wash his hands and looked back into the death room.

Suddenly Michael shouted: "Doctor! Doctor! She's breathing. She just breathed. She's alive."

The doctor ran over, his hands still full of soap lather.

One last sigh, a remnant of air, had issued from the lungs mechanically, when Annette was already dead.

"She's dead."

Michael, stricken, collapsed by the bed, crying aloud, with his stricken life.

The nurse stood there; her work was done. As so often before. She wanted to think what she had to do now. Hands folded under her chin, she looked shaken and helplessly at the group of death.

How a man straightens up! How he straightens up! Up from the floor! Michael rose, slowly, in the slow, heavy, heavy course of life, and said, eyes on Annette's death-strong face, with a changed voice, with a tender voice high in his throat: "Are you dead, Annette, are you dead? Now you're dead. Oh, my Annette is dead."

The nurse wanted to close the lids.

"Let me alone. I'll do that." With a trembling finger he closed the eye, closed the other one. It opened again.

He closed it once more. It opened again. The eye remained half open. A brilliant eye. A brilliant slit, brilliant as life.

"The lid is paralyzed," said the doctor. "Come over here, Michael, come."

He let the doctor lead him into the study. The country girl from Pomerania, the seventeen-year-old one, met them in the corridor. Tears ran down her cheeks.

Translated by E. B. ASHTON

Bruno Frank

THE SUITCASE

HE WATCHED HER disappearing down the platform, watched her energetic tread which was still young and elastic but no longer elegant— rather homely she looked. She turned round once more to wave to him, with a smile, then he saw her held up for a moment at the barrier before she was lost amongst the crowd on the other side.

He took his seat and before the train drew out of the station spread out his papers on the table before him.

He had the carriage to himself. When he looked up from time to time from his work, his eye rested on a dreary Prussian landscape in the grey light of a November afternoon. A pale red glow fast fading behind a low line of hills told of approaching darkness. The train slowed down at a level crossing, and he noticed a shabby little car waiting at the gates, as fantastic a bit of scrap iron as ever adorned an American comedy. This set him thinking of his own car at home. It really was time he sold it and treated himself to an up-to-date one. In any case, he told himself, he might have looked round the showrooms before now and tried out some of the latest models. But he remembered that his practical, perhaps rather too practical, wife did not consider that they were justified in buying a new car yet. He turned back to his papers.

When he reached his destination it was dark, and there were not enough porters to go round. He kept his brief-case under his arm whilst he watched his trunk and his small suitcase being piled on to an already overloaded trolley and pushed towards the barrier.

The hotel was a good distance from the station. It was theatre time, and all Berlin's millions of people seemed bent on pleasure. The traffic moved at a crawl, and it looked as though every available car had been pressed into service. Of all the women in furs and jewels whom he glimpsed through the windows of the dimly lighted saloon cars, there was not one but appeared beautiful and glamorous.

Once every two months he drove through these evening streets from the station to the hotel. Every detail of the drive was imprinted on his memory, and he knew in advance each time just what his reaction would be. He always had to ask himself, and to-day was no exception, whether it was right that he should spend his remaining years all those dark miles away in a provincial town, whilst life glowed here in such rich colours. A successful business man, at peace with the world, living in a sort of mental torpor, obediently following the path which was marked out for him—thus he saw himself, and he could not help feeling that at forty-five he should not have been content to settle down in a rut like that.

And so he reached the hotel. They knew him there and had his usual room ready for him—a large, quiet, double room. A heavy curtain could be drawn in front of the two beds, transforming it into a sitting-room, where he could work or receive his business friends if he so wished.

He signed the register, his luggage was brought up, and then he was

alone. He would have to make an early start the next morning, so he
decided to go to bed early.

He opened the suitcase and drew back in amazement, for on the top
lay a dark green silk garment which did not belong to him. He realized
with annoyance that he had been given the wrong suitcase—one misses
little articles of personal use when one is no longer so very young. Summing up the position quickly in his mind, he decided that it was not
really serious. He had had some money in the lid of his case, but not
more than he could afford to lose. All his papers were in his brief-case,
though as a matter of fact he admitted to himself that he would almost
rather have lost his papers than his nail-brush and his slippers and his
shaving tackle—and in any case it did not please him to think of all these
personal possessions under the gaze of a stranger at this very moment,
and of a woman at that, for this case belonged to a woman. A delicate,
fastidious perfume emanated from the dark green silk.

He closed the case again, just for curiosity. It really was exactly like
his own—the same shiny brown leather, the same size, even the same
silver-plated locks. The porter couldn't be blamed. Anyway, he supposed
they would be able to rectify the mistake at the station. He would send
the case back there immediately, the lady would surely do the same, and
all would be well. He had already put out his hand to ring for a porter,
but he let it fall to his side again. There was another way. Perhaps he
could find her name and address somewhere in the case—her card, or an
envelope addressed to her. A faint trace of her perfume still hung in the
air. He opened the case again, and at once the perfume was all around
him.

He lifted out the dark green silk dressing gown which lay on top, taking care not to disturb its folds. He stood there with the flimsy thing
resting across his outstretched arms, and the daintiest of travelling out-
fits lay exposed to his gaze.

Truly, he thought, women were of a more delicate breed than men
and lived more delicately. He was ashamed to think of the contents of
his own suitcase, which was probably being opened at this moment in
another hotel room. She would be shocked, even perhaps a little disgusted. He could imagine her drawing back. There was nothing wrong
with his things, of course, they were quite good, but mostly old and used
and very ordinary and practical. On top, he hated the thought, lay his
old black leather slippers, worn and shapeless and rubbed shiny inside,
and next to them the shaving brush which he could not bring himself to
throw away, in spite of its advanced state of baldness. And that wooden

nail-brush which a moment ago had seemed more important than many a paper in his brief-case, that was on top too, and it too had seen better days. But the worst of all was his nightshirt, newly laundered, faultlessly ironed, but nevertheless a nightshirt, that inelegant but, alas! so comfortable symbol of a comfortable middle-class, about which he had for years been waging a friendly war with his launderer. "You know, sir," he could hear the man saying, "you're the last of my elegant customers to hold out against the pyjama!" Of course, the man was only flattering him —he wasn't really such an elegant customer, and as he stood there looking at her things, he was pained to think what her impression would be when she saw his nightshirt.

Her perfume filled the room. It was an expensive one, fresh, almost bitter—somehow it reminded him of the fragrance of her quick-breathing young mouth, and suggested a slim, athletic figure, strong, slender hands, a rounded, self-willed chin, light-coloured rather scornful eyes, and pale gold unruly hair falling over a courageous brow. Very well imagined— but supposing the case belonged to some fat old lady, or to a shrivelled old maid with a hooked nose? Ah no! he was sure it didn't!

He seemed bewitched. His emotions were strangely excited, and a slight dizziness came over him. What he was about to do was not quite correct, indeed he felt rather like a criminal. He went over to the door and locked it, very much as he might have locked himself in with the strange lady. He wanted to examine all her possessions, one by one, without interruption.

Dark green seemed to be her favourite colour, which met with his immediate approval. It went very well with the dark tortoiseshell of her brushes and combs and powder-box and her oval hand-mirror. All these shimmering things and also all her crystal bottles were marked with a little golden monogram, an "M." Madge, Margaret, Mona—only English names seemed to describe her fresh, energetic youth. He found a novel bound in white, which she had probably read on the train. But there was no name, not a word to indicate who she might be.

Her little manicure case was in dark green. Her dainty slippers were of soft green leather, with swansdown round the edge. Taking them out, he was comforted to find that they were not quite new. They were a little worn on the inside where they had rubbed together as she walked, and the lining shone a little from contact with her bare feet.

Her nightdress, in a lighter shade of green silk, lay folded before him in the left-hand corner of the case. His launderer could have found no fault with that exquisite garment. The little creases in it told him that it had been worn. Then he came across a small box in dark green leather, which looked like a jewel case. The discovery impressed upon him the irregularity of what he was doing; his temples throbbed, but he enjoyed the guilty sensation.

He opened the little box, half fearing yet half hoping to disclose a collection of sparkling jewels. Was his honesty not being put to the test? He had no right to keep valuables for more than an hour without reporting them, yet he would hate the idea of giving up this precious find. He could picture it reposing forlornly on a shelf in the lost property office in unworthy company.

Great was his relief when he saw the contents of the box—modern necklaces and brooches made of metal and big, bold imitation stones such as are so much worn nowadays—a return to West African customs, he could hear himself saying—but that had been ridiculous of him, the fashion was an attractive one, gay and daring as it was, given the right type of woman; the charm and self-assurance of youth alone could justify this exotic masquerade. Whatever else he thought about these childish baubles, he was at least thankful that a man of his position need not feel like a thief for failing to report them.

It was very late before he could get to sleep, and then he slept badly.

The next morning he sent the hotel porter out to buy a few essential toilet articles, and at nine o'clock he left his room, locking the door carefully behind him. His business friends could not help noticing how absent-minded he was at their conferences, and once when he took out his handkerchief his neighbour was surprised by a waft of perfume. It was a tiny lawn handkerchief which had been taken out of a little collapsible leather handkerchief case.

Going up in the hotel lift that evening, his heart thumped as though in anticipation of a mistress awaiting him upstairs. He unlocked the door, switched on the light, and stood amazed. The maid had already prepared the room for the night, but not for him alone. Anxious to please, she had unpacked the little suitcase, which now stood empty on a chair. The tortoiseshell brushes and the crystal bottles were arrayed on the dressing-table, the dressing gown was draped across an armchair, the dividing curtain in front of the beds had been drawn back, and both beds were turned down ready for sleeping in. Beside the bed which had not been slept in, nearest the door, stood the dainty slippers, and on the pillow lay the sea-green gossamer nightdress. All these things seemed to be awaiting their mistress, and their mistress them.

The moment in which he had failed to return the suitcase to the station had been his first act of unfaithfulness. He often heard his business friends, cigar in mouth, recounting with innocent cynicism the easy adventures which they always had during their stay in Berlin, and they spoke of them as though they were something to which every man became entitled after several years of marriage. He had never had the least desire to do as they did. He would have been repelled by the idea of going straight home from one of those little adventures, getting out of the train in his own provincial town, and kissing his wife gaily on the mouth as though nothing had happened. Nothing did happen to his business friends which they needed to forget. Something would have happened to him. His reserve was well known, it was indeed enough to have made a less respected and less important man look ridiculous.

No man could have had a happier marriage than he. His wife had been beautiful, and indeed she still was, in her dignified, charming way, although she had given him three sons of whom he was very proud. She was a perfect housewife, but she never talked about her work in the house—indeed she always knew how to be quiet at the right moment, though taking an intelligent and helpful interest in his business affairs. She was broadminded. She had a delightful sense of humour and she never behaved foolishly; she was sympathetic, but much too healthy to be sentimental; she was frank and open; susceptible to beauty, but never afraid to look the realities of life in the face. She was very popular and everybody who knew her thought her a fine woman; and so she was.

But the finest woman in the world is powerless to overcome the distaste which a man at the turn of life often feels for the existence he has led till then. And so it was that he could scarcely bear to look ahead along the gradual uphill road on which his feet were set and which stretched out before him without side-track or cross-road until it lost itself somewhere in the darkness beyond.

There had been some critical moments in his life during the past few years of which nobody knew but himself. One of them had been on his fortieth birthday, just as he had risen, glass in hand, to thank them all for their good wishes. He had nearly made a most unexpected speech. For the space of a second he had been on the point of severing all the threads which bound him to the life he had loved till then—but when he had spoken, he had said just those things which they had expected him to say, and nothing more. Another moment was still very fresh in his memory. It was less than a year ago. They were on a winter holiday in Cairo, going through the gaudy, dirty crowd of the native quarter, when they

698

HEART OF EUROPE: *Germany*

came to a crooked alleyway leading off from the main street, and in its deep shadow he saw draped figures moving like phantoms. Quite suddenly and unexpectedly he had become possessed of an urgent desire to snatch himself away from the arm of his travel-dressed wife, to leave her without a word of farewell and rush headlong into that alleyway which was no different from dozens of others, to find his way along it until he emerged at the other end, to let himself be carried away on the great anonymous flood of the East, which had its beginnings there, let himself drift into the heart of Africa, mingle with the swarming millions of Asia, be swept on still farther, anywhere, as long as he were taken right away for ever from his respectable existence and his successful marriage. . . .

How many of us know that relentless urge! It buds in all souls with imagination and a consciousness of death, and perhaps most vigorously of all in men at the turn of life. It is rather a dissatisfaction with one's self than with one's surroundings, a longing to escape from the prison of one's own personality, a rebellion against being only one man from the cradle to the grave, when there are so many million ways of living! And since breed and blood are there and cannot be altered, the only escape lies in adventure, in the urge over strange lands and many-coloured seas, in the longing of the artist who finds his way in an ecstasy of suffering into the intimacies of another's face, in the flight of the world-weary into the dumb-cloistered stillness of La Trappe. This discontent, this sense of insufficiency it is which acts will-o'-the-wisp to every unfaithful deed, along all the cross-ways and side-paths of love.

The stranger, present only in her dainty and fragrant belongings, was a greater temptation to him than all the thousand women who offered themselves in the streets of the metropolis. He could not have spoken of this temptation to anybody. He realized how fantastic its sensual enchantment was in a man of his type—man of action, father of a family, keen and respected business man. He was ashamed, as he had not been ashamed since his boyhood, and the unusual emotion excited his senses and helped to ensnare him still more completely.

It occurred to him that the maid on his floor must be curious about the woman whose bed she prepared every night but whom she never saw. Meeting her on the corridor, he slipped a banknote into her hand, probably the biggest tip she had ever received. As she answered the pressure of his hand a sly, saucy smile spread over her face, the smile of an accomplice. He felt the blood rush to his face at this silent evidence of conspiracy, and even this last humiliation was sweet. He was always careful to keep his door locked and he carried the key about with him.

That evening he washed himself with the stranger's soap. It was his first physical approach to her, and it left him emotionally exhausted. The soap was a piece she had already used, but the name of an English firm could still be distinguished on it. The lather seemed to him whiter and frothier than any he had ever known, and the fresh, almost bitter fragrance of that same youthful perfume filled his bathroom. Now it rose to his nostrils from his own body, it clung all about him; and as he lay in bed it was almost as though her own sweet body lay in a light embrace upon his own.

This was the most intimate contact he ever had with her. He awoke the next morning knowing that he had to make an important decision. A crisis had arisen overnight. Lying on his back in bed, his arms resting beneath his head, his thoughts were with his wife, who was waiting for him all those miles away. He felt sorry for her, but he did not see how he could alter anything now. He had already stayed away longer than usual, and now, quite suddenly and definitely, he knew that he would stay away for ever. Nothing short of a miracle would be able to make him go back. Perhaps he almost hoped for that miracle to happen, but he did not see how it possibly could.

He dressed absentmindedly and then sat at the dressing-table and considered the practical side of the situation. He wanted to do the right thing. He despised those people who grew mean and selfish on the eve of a separation. He would be able to leave his family independent and reasonably well off. It would be just as though he had died. Didn't men of forty-five die every day, hundreds of them? He had loyal colleagues who could run his business for him for many years to come. And before so very long his eldest boy, who showed promise, would be able to go into the business. But what about himself? Could he give up the work of a lifetime just like that? Didn't he care? Hadn't he been spending his time here in Berlin, bargaining and scheming and planning, all in the hope of securing some new advantage for his firm? He touched the long-familiar chord within him, but it no longer gave forth any sound.

All this time, without knowing it, he had been turning the little tortoiseshell mirror round and round in his hand—once he had caught sight of his own face in it, a lean, manly face with a generous mouth. Now, breaking off his train of thought, he noticed what he held in his hand, and at the same moment he realized to his astonishment that the pretty thing had lost its power. The same applied to all the other delightful feminine possessions in green and shimmering brown—they had ceased to exist for him, they had been no more than an excuse, an occasion. He had imagined that he wanted this unknown woman, and all the time it had been the great unknown for which he longed. He wanted his freedom back, wanted to be at liberty to make new decisions and to start all over again from the beginning.

He very rarely thought of his boyhood, but now there appeared before him one particular page of one of his school books, even to the blue pencil mark with which as a boy he had marked two particular lines of a particular poem, forgotten through thirty long years from that day to this, and now once more before his eyes:

> And understand that Freedom means
> To choose the way you go. . . .

He had dealt with all his business, but he still did not leave. He chose to see nobody, preferring to live alone with his thoughts. With the exception of two hastily scribbled postcards, he sent no word home.

One entire afternoon he had spent walking at a brisk pace up and down the snow-covered Tiergarten, and he did not return to his hotel until the light was fading. He found the key in his door—he had not been locking it for the past few days. Pushing it open, he felt at once that someone was in the room, and he held his breath in suspense until he heard a woman weeping, not loudly, but there was no mistaking the sound. Switching on the lights, he saw his wife at the dressing-table, her forehead pressed against its glass top, amongst the array of tortoiseshell brushes and crystal bottles, her shoulders shaking as she sobbed. His first glance had taken in the whole room. It was prepared for the night. The green silk dressing-gown lay over the armchair, the gossamer nightdress was on the open bed, and the slippers seemed to be awaiting the stranger's bare feet.

Neither of them moved or spoke. So she had come to fetch him home, as she had done once or twice before—without the slightest suspicion, of course, just to give him a pleasant surprise. She had simply asked for his room and let herself in. The shock must have been terrible for her. How long had she been cowering there? What had she endured? But the worst was that he could not explain, could not put it right. The truth was even worse than she believed. Her tears flowed for a phantom of her imagining; nothing had happened, and yet much more than she suspected. How was he to dismiss this terrible and grotesque scene from her mind without lying! And he must not lie. Facts had overtaken him, he must not hesitate, now was his opportunity, now at this very moment he must confirm her worst fears without trying to spare her feelings. Like a boy he would have to speak of the dark inner workings of his mind, of his unrest, of his lonely mental tortures and his longing to escape. To dismiss these realities of tortoiseshell and silk, he would have to confess that a great fear, a fear of life and of death, was forcing him at this age to take up his stick again and go forth. Yet was such a thing possible—to go forth and leave one's work, one's sons of whom one had hoped so much, the loyal, blameless wife of so many years? Possible or not, ridiculous or not, for him it had become a necessity, and only a miracle could hold him back.

And then she lifted her head, and he saw her face. A woman is not beautiful when she has been crying for hours, when horror and dismay have played havoc with her features. Her dark hair was untidy, a loose strand of it fell over her inflamed eyes. She pushed it back and looked at him. Her lips moved silently, and then at last her voice came, low and hoarse.

"Here in your hotel . . . she lives with you altogether. It's too awful. . . ."

Now, now would have been the moment to tell her everything, to finish it all in two final sentences; but he sought in vain, he could not find them. An unbearable pity had started to burn within him, and he said what any man would have said in his place:

"There has been no woman here."

She stood up and faced him across that room which spoke so eloquently of a love-night, and it seemed to him as though he could already hear her sarcastic laughter—but instead he saw the trouble ebbing from her face, saw something like the reflection of a smile shining through her tears.

"There hasn't?" he heard her ask. "Really?"

And he, incapable of answering otherwise:

"No. I swear it."

"Then I've been crying all for nothing!" he heard her glad voice. "Oh, thank God, thank God!" and she ran to him and took his hands in hers. He swayed a little. Something seemed to tear in his heart, painfully and unbearably sweet. It was the miracle.

She believed. All those tangible proofs under the glare of the electric light weighed as nothing against his word. The contents of the little suitcase, the possessions of the strange woman, she no longer saw them, for his words, which she believed, had robbed them of all meaning. She needed neither explanation nor proof.

The miracle of trust, the miracle of absolute unity—there it was, and the world had nothing greater to offer. And should he take up his stick and go forth again and wander over the face of the earth and experience all its wonders, should strength be granted to him to enjoy them until his last far day, Life, after this, would have nothing more to offer him, for its greatest experience had already been his.

Translated by BARBARA HALLEWELL

Ernst Toller

PRISON

. . . IN THE SPRING a pair of swallows nested in my cell; they lived with me all the summer. The nest was built, and the female brooded on her eggs while the male sang his little twittering song to her. The eggs were hatched and the parents fed their young and taught them to fly, until one day they flew away and did not come back. The parents had a second brood, but a premature frost killed the young, and they huddled close together silently mourning their dead children. With the coming of autumn they flew away to the southern sun.

That summer was very kind to me. The shy little birds became so used to me that they would come and sit on the lamp when I was working at my table and twitter playfully together. I was very quiet in my happiness and thankfulness.

All that I saw and heard and felt and thought, I wrote down in a little book which I called *The Swallow Book*. Nothing could have been more innocuous, but the Governor confiscated the manuscript. The bald official explanation for this was that the poems were simply cover for subversive propaganda.

I sent a letter of complaint to the Reichstag:

"I have never asked for special consideration, and even now it is not consideration I am asking for but merely the confirmation of my rights as a special political prisoner. Even under the barbaric tyranny of the knout in Tsarist Russia it was possible for imprisoned writers to keep the freedom of their minds. In the Bavarian Free State in this year of grace, 1923, freedom of the spirit is punished as a crime.

"I said nothing when the fortress authorities forbade me a few months ago, in direct contravention of the law, to discuss my health with a visiting relative who was also a doctor.

"I have scorned to complain in the past about various other incidents which were in direct contravention of the terms of my sentence.

"I have scorned to complain when the Bavarian authorities in the Diet and through the press have thrown mud at me in my completely defenseless state.

"I have scorned to complain when the fortress authorities have prevented me from getting an exact idea of the nature of these attacks by confiscating newspapers.

"I have refrained from signing the innumerable petitions presented by the prisoners here to various authorities outside.

"One thing certainly I could not be silent about: that was when I accused the prison doctor of criminal neglect after the shocking death of August Hagemeister. On that occasion I learned that Socialist prisoners in Bavaria have not even the rights of common criminals: I was never allowed to give evidence.

"But now I appeal to the German Reichstag.

"Are you prepared to tolerate the suppression of works of German literature by prison officials whenever the spirit so moves them? Are you prepared to tolerate the virtual outlawing from the German Republic of a prisoner just because he is a Socialist?"

The Reichstag did not favor me with a reply, so I had to help myself. A friend wrote down *The Swallow Book* in minute writing on a single sheet of paper, and a prisoner who was being released managed to smuggle it out of prison with him and sent it to be published.

The Governor revenged himself in his own inimitable way. Birds will never build in a covered space except when the window opens to the east, therefore I was transferred to a cell facing north.

In the spring the swallows returned from who knows what primitive forests and blazing sunshine. They picked out our prison from a hundred other prisons and my old cell from a hundred other cells and began to build their nest. Then, at the Governor's command, warders clattered into the cell and callously tore down the almost completed nest.

I thought of the bewildered misery of the swallows when they found their little house gone, how they must eagerly have explored with their little beaks the wall where their nest had been, fluttering anxiously round, searching in every corner of the cell. But next day they had already begun to build again, and again the warders destroyed their work.

The new occupant of my cell, a builder from a Bavarian village, wrote to the Governor,

"Honored Sir,

"I beg you leave the swallows in my cell to nest in peace, they have worked so patiently and been sore tried, also they are industrious and useful. I should like to say that the above do not disturb me in the least nor do they dirty the cell. Also that I have known other prisons where swallows nest and anybody who disturbs them is punished.

                                     Yours faithfully,
                                     Rupert Enzinger of Kolbermoor."

The Governor in answer merely observed that stables were the proper place for swallows to build in, and they would find plenty of room elsewhere.

The nest which the birds had in the meantime been building again was accordingly destroyed, and the prisoner, like myself, transferred to a cell facing north. The swallow cell was locked.

Then the swallows, bewildered and passionately eager, began to build three nests simultaneously in three different cells. But they were only half finished when the warders discovered them and repeated the outrage.

With the energy of despair they started six nests simultaneously. Perhaps they hoped that one nest might be spared them as a gesture of generosity.

But the six nests were all torn down.

I don't know how many times the process of building and destruction was repeated. The struggle lasted for seven weeks; a glorious and heroic struggle between the united forces of Bavarian law and order and two tiny birds. After the nests were torn down for the last time some days went by without a new nest being discovered; evidently the swallows had given up.

But soon whispers were going round among the prisoners that the swallows had found a new place in the wash-house behind the overflow pipes where nobody would find them—neither the spying warders without, nor the spying warders within. Rarely had we experienced a purer happiness. The swallows had won after all in their fight against human beastliness. Their victory was ours too.

But even this nest was doomed to discovery.

After that the swallows built no more. In the evening they would fly into a cell and spend the night huddled close together. In the morning they would fly away. One evening the male swallow came alone; the female was dead.

It was the last year of my sentence. Until now my will to freedom had been unconquerable, unbroken by punishment or illness; but now that I could count the days to my release, something strange happened to me: my eagerness for life ebbed away. I lay all day apathetic in my cell; I did not rejoice in my impending freedom. I dreaded it.

I dreaded the duties and responsibilities which would call me. In the prison I was protected from reality; prison was like a mother to me, a cruel mother who yet ordered my days, fed me, released me from all outer cares. And now I would have to leave the sheltering walls and go out into the world where new struggles awaited me. Would I be equal to it? I had received thousands of letters during my imprisonment; so many people were looking to me, imagining me greater than I really was; they expected great things of me and I should only disappoint them. I felt myself weakening from day to day. The nights were darkened by thoughts of death; my pulse grew fainter, and I longed for death, and when death did not come I was lost in a confusion of horrible temptations. There was a night when I almost took my life. But in the morning my foolishness had vanished. My strength increased; I could only be what I was. I wanted to stand up to life; and stand up to it I would. If defeat came I would learn to endure it.

The day before my release I was called before the Governor, who smiled at me in quite a friendly way.

"I have two messages for you, Herr Toller," he said, "one pleasant, the other not so pleasant. Let us get the unpleasant one over first. You are a Prussian, and the authorities are convinced that you have not changed your outlook during the last five years, which means that you are just as dangerous to the safety of the country as ever you were before, and we can only render you innocuous by keeping you away. So to make sure that you leave Bavaria you will be personally conducted over the border. You yourself will be called upon to meet the cost of your transportation. And now for the pleasant message. You were to be released at eighteen minutes past one tomorrow, but we are letting you go a day earlier. You can return to your friends today. These two gentlemen"—he indicated the two detective sergeants who bowed and touched their caps—"will accompany you across the borders of Saxony."

"What time is the next train?" I asked.

"You needn't worry about that, Herr Toller. We ourselves have chosen the route especially to avoid big towns and industrial centers where the workers might conceivably want to demonstrate. Obviously all you want now is peace and quiet; and in spite of going by a somewhat roundabout way you will reach the border safe and sound on the morning of July 16th. In short, we make you a present of several unexpected hours of freedom."

I was not allowed to go back to my friends. I had to strip and submit to body and clothing being thoroughly searched. I packed up my things, and, with a detective sergeant on either side of me, walked out through the prison gates. I was free. I breathed in the air of the unbarred sky. The road to the station was patrolled by a cyclist detachment of the *Landjaeger* who rode like trick cyclists, curved and graceful, and at the station itself was a special company of heavily armed police.

"What have I done to deserve such honor?" I asked.

"There was to be an attempt on your life," one of the detectives answered. "And as the Bavarian Republic is responsible for you until you're over the border, it's doing the handsome thing by you so that you'll always have friendly memories of us."

At the border they left me in the train.

I was alone.

I was free.

I stood at the carriage window and looked out into a night of friendly stars.

I thought of some lines in my *Swallow Book:*

> "Through the barred window I gaze into the night
> The swallows twitter in their dreams
> I am not alone.
> The moon and the stars are my companions too
> And the gleaming, silent fields."

No, I had never been alone all those five years, never alone in my comfortless abandonment. The sun and the moon had consoled me, the wind that flurried the puddles in the yard, the grass that sprang up in spring in the cracks of the stones.

All these were my friends, telling of greetings from the world outside, of comradeship among the prisoners, of belief in a world of justice, of freedom, of humanity, in a world without fear and without hunger.

I was thirty.

My hair had turned gray.

I was not tired.

Translated by EDWARD CRANKSHAW

Joachim Maass

FAREWELL FROM THE UNKNOWN

AND SO ONCE AGAIN they all sat together in Jaquemar's wretched hotel room in the rue de la Glacière: Goron, the chief of the Sureté; Jaquemar's fiancée, who as usual sat knitting at the window, his friend, charming Germaine Chottin, and Jaquemar himself. Two weeks had passed since Jaquemar's brother-in-law, Gouffé, had disappeared from Paris without leaving a trace. That morning Goron had finally decided to open the little strongbox he had found in the missing man's safe. All sorts of papers were in it, papers of a purely private nature, also a certified copy of his last will, making Jaquemar the only legatee of his fairly considerable fortune. There was also a letter to his brother-in-law.

"I would like you to open this letter in my presence and to read it to me," said Goron. He stopped for a moment and added in a tone of irritation. "These documents have been confiscated by the police!"

"Very well," murmured Jaquemar in his lazy manner, "after all there were no great secrets between us."

For a second Goron stared at him through his obliquely hanging pince-nez; then he drew a small envelope out of the bigger one that had also contained the copy of the will and handed it to the young man. The address on this envelope was obviously written in the same hand as the other document, but it was even more trembling; the letters went in all sorts of directions, in two places they were crossed out and replaced by others written on top of them, and the whole made an impression of disorder, especially as the last line had been crossed out and apparently blotted with a worn-out blotter, its letters were dreadfully smeared. The address ran: "Mr. Edmond Jaquemar. To you, brother-in-law Edmond, friend, for—when all is over."

Jaquemar gazed at it for a long moment and muttered something incomprehensible. He now sat on the edge of his bed, his bare feet on the thin carpet; his face was motionless, but the toes of his feet contracted convulsively, relaxed and contracted again, and this made a harrowing impression. A strange picture: beside him, the only ornament in the shabby room, stood a kitchen pail with a few very large sunflowers whose faces shone brighter and brighter in the growing twilight. Jaquemar's toes were now still. Absorbed, and seemingly calm, he opened the envelope and drew out four or five sheets of thin paper covered with writing (it was the kind of scrap paper used for notes); from the thin paper something heavy rolled down into his lap. He picked it up and held it pensively in his right hand. It was a fairly long, very delicate gold chain with a heart-shaped charm about the size of a small finger-nail; it was of smooth, bright gold, almost as thin as a sheet, and in its center a strange inscription was engraved.

"An amulet!" cried little Germaine Chottin. "And what a curious inscription!"

Everyone looked at the chain with the little heart. Without putting it away, Jaquemar unfolded the crackling pages. He smoothed them out carefully on his knees, but his face had a strikingly clouded, even dark expression. He seemed to be unable to make up his mind to read them. But finally he turned his body somewhat, so that the light from the windows fell on the letter, and began to read. He read very slowly, almost scanning the phrases, as though he were reading in a foreign language and had to make an effort to grasp the meaning of the words. At first he paused broodingly for a short while after each sentence, but gradually he was carried away by what he read, and at the end even read very rapidly, as though he were anxious to get it over as soon as possible.

This is what he read:

"Edmond, my dear boy:—How strange after all is the human heart, its ways are as sinuous as the ways of destiny. Is it not so? Do you know, my hat is still beside me on the desk—the hat I put on a moment ago intending to see my notary and disinherit you? You, the only person I really love! And yet I wanted to disinherit you—yes, I suddenly hated you, can you understand that? A little while ago when you were here and refused to take money from me, as you have often done before, this hatred again pierced my heart, I thought it was low of you . . ."

Jaquemar interrupted himself, for a few moments he looked straight ahead of him and murmured: "How right you were." Then he again turned his eyes to the letter, thought for a while, and went on reading:

"Forgive me for this piece of stupidity, dearest boy, but that's the way it was. Tomorrow I'm going to see Germaine, your 'little' friend, Germaine. I had been happy all day looking forward to seeing her, but when you came my happiness departed. I told myself: after all I'll never have her —all on account of him! He doesn't want her in the least, but he holds her! If he doesn't want her why doesn't he give her to me! And I hated you even more—you see, I wasn't thinking: man is not an animal, no one can give a human being to another person, each human being must give himself or herself (and perhaps he can't even do that, at least that is what you once said); but all I could think of at the moment was that obviously you get everything you want and even what you don't want, while I get nothing at all. And do you know that it was perhaps an even baser thought that held me back, so that I put my hat down and said to myself: stop, think it over carefully! For it suddenly occurred to me that perhaps I wouldn't punish you at all that way, I have no idea whether you really care for money. Maybe, on the contrary, it would be a punishment for you to inherit my fortune? Then I took a bottle of cognac and a little glass from the cupboard and sat on my chair near the window (I am in the office); from time to time I took a sip while I thought about all this.

"Do you know that once you really frightened me very badly? Shortly before Génie died (oh, how I loved her, my friend, that beautiful sister of yours) you had a conversation with her, she had asked you whether life was good; you said: 'Yes, life is marvelous!' I was then not quite in my right mind out of fear for Génie's life, but this remark of yours struck me profoundly, and I thought with irritation: what immature rubbish he is talking, and at such a moment, too. Later I couldn't help thinking of it again and again and each time I recalled it I was frightened! How, I thought, can he, who seems to everyone so silent, impenetrable and melancholy, how can he find life 'marvelous'—not just beautiful, but even marvelous—while I, whom everyone considers balanced and calm and even cheerful, am tormented and do not find life beautiful at all? Could it be true that he loves life and that I do not love it?

"Maybe I was foolish to be so tormented by this question? Or don't you think so? I felt as though I were being cheated out of my life, and each time I reached this conclusion a certain event of my youth came to my mind.

"When I was twenty years old I had a Jewish girl as a friend, who was pretty and very intelligent but also very warm-hearted. Despite her so-called 'braininess' she was extraordinarily naive. We were as good as engaged. She lived with her older married sister and her brother-in-law, and had come from a small town where her parents were still living—yes, she wanted to learn about 'life' here. One night she had a party, all of us drank a little and danced quite a lot, we were all young people. Aside from her, I danced a great deal with a young woman whom I found very attractive, she was blonde, supple, childlike, a friend of Marcelle's (that was the name of my fiancée) who had come without her husband. By midnight the party broke up. Now, this house had a long corridor leading from the entrance. With Marcelle on one arm and her friend on the other I preceded the rest of the company down the hall—we were all very unrestrained, and as my relations with Marcelle were no secret to anyone, I kissed her as I said goodbye. 'Children!' cried the other young woman laughingly, 'I can't look at that! It's enough to make one jealous!' As she said this she tore open the house door to run out; unfortunately Marcelle stood in such a way that the heavy door struck her temple with all its weight, so that she was hurled toward the wall and was thus hit in the back of the head also. Naturally, we all crowded around her at once, particularly her guilty friend. Marcelle was very pale, tears rolled down her cheeks, but she soon smiled again and seemed perfectly all right.

"On the way home the company gradually dispersed, in the end only the young woman and I were together. I was still a little drunk, I was also young and happy. I pressed the young woman's arm close to me and cried: 'Ah, to love, to love—I want to love!' 'Why don't we?' she replied in a low voice. We looked at each other—well, you can guess the rest. So it happened, in a dark spot in the park. It was very pleasant, too. Then I took her home and we knew that we would never say a word of what had happened, to anybody.

"But when I approached my own house I was terribly scared because, even from where I was, I could see the servant from Marcelle's house standing at my gate and talking excitedly to my landlady. Then, without thinking, I did something of which I was later very often ashamed (curiously enough I was not ashamed of my faithlessness): I ran softly and as fast as I could around the nearest street corner, came to the garden behind our house, climbed over the fence, ran across the garden and slipped in silently through the back door; I hastily slunk upstairs to my room, unlocked it, tore off my collar, necktie, coat and vest and went downstairs again. 'What's going on here?' I cried, emerging from the darkness toward the door. 'Here you are, Monsieur!' my landlady exclaimed. 'But I've been knocking at your door . . .' Well, to make it short, Marcelle had fallen ill, she had vomited, and her sister had sent the maid to get me; I was supposed to calm her, she was in an extremely nervous state. We went at once, I, as I was, without my coat or collar, and hastened to Marcelle's home.

"I was taken in to her at once. She was sitting up in bed. Her cheeks were red, and her eyes shone feverishly. 'O, my beloved!' she called out to me, stretching out her arms. 'How good that you've come. I have been yearning for you! Come, give me a kiss! Oh, my Alphonse—my own!' And she kissed me several times on the mouth. We were left alone. The doctor had already seen her, she was to be given cold compresses, and I was to soothe her excited nerves. I put the wet cloth on her forehead and she lay back docile and happy. I held her hand which was hot. It was obvious that she had not the slightest suspicion of me, but my bad conscience made me ask her: 'Didn't I come very fast, Marcelle?' 'Oh, yes, yes,' she said and at once sat up again so that the compress fell onto the blanket. 'Oh yes, my beloved, thank you, I'm so grateful to you, I'm happy with you, Alphonse, when shall we get married? Ah, I'm so happy!' Suddenly she opened her nightdress and with both hands unlocked a little chain around her neck with a little golden heart attached to it. 'This is my *Shadai* locket!' she cried in blissful excitement. 'I've worn it since I was in my cradle, on my breast, the letters mean "Shadai," the Hebrew for "The Eternal." It's an amulet, I've never been separated from it, but now you shall wear it because I love you more than my own life!'

"The next morning she was dead, having died suddenly of a cerebral hemorrhage. I wore this amulet until my marriage with Génie, your beautiful sister Génie, and then I put it away; but after Génie died I wore it again. In fact it didn't bring me much luck and now I want to put it away again. But I shall will it to you, Edmond, so that you will have it after I die, and remember sometimes those who are cheated out of their lives.

"I didn't really mean to write you all this, but something quite different which I don't even remember any more—after all I must have drunk too much cognac (even while I wrote this I took two glasses), and now I don't feel like writing any more. Edmond, forgive me for having hated you for a moment, forgive me for having hated you more than once, ah, my God, I must really be drunk, what kind of 'eternal' words are these I am calling out to you as though from my grave! After all, I'm still alive —you even said once that I lived a double life! Didn't you also say: You, you'd be another Gilgamesh, that curious king Gilgamesh of Uruk who went to the demons to find a magic herb against death? Ah, you Gilgamesh-Edmond, may you have better luck on your way to the demons! And I with my double life—I wish I could be happy some day! I'd squander all your inheritance for that, dearest boy! Would you then make a long face and complain about me—to your demons? Forgive me, my friend, I don't want to hurt your feelings, only I'm suddenly, quite suddenly, very drunk; this happened in the fraction of a second, everything is turning before my eyes. Phew, it's disgusting!

As ever, your brother-in-law, Alphonse

Paris, June 24, 1889.

P.S. What if Germaine, your 'little' friend Germaine said 'yes' after all?"

No sooner had Jaquemar completed the reading of this mysterious drunken letter of farewell, than he held out the pages, almost hastily, to Goron, without even folding them again. In a gloomy voice he said ironically: "These documents have been confiscated by the police!"

But Goron did not take them. He gazed at Jaquemar, as he had done during the reading of the letter, very carefully through his tilted pince-nez—surprised and somewhat puzzled. Jaquemar handed the letter that Goron did not take to Germaine, little Germaine Chottin, without explaining why he did so. He rose rapidly and went to his fiancée who sat at the window. She had dropped her knitting needles on her lap and was gazing straight in front of her with a stern forbidding expression on her thin face. Jaquemar bent over her slightly, so that she looked at him with wide questioning eyes. He said:

"Now, my dear, put this dubious sign of blessing on me—only our love can make it a blessing or a curse!"

Translated by NORBERT GUTERMAN

Gustav Regler

CLAIR DE LUNE

(Fragment from the novel *Thou Day in Night* dealing with the Spanish Civil War in which the author took part as an officer in the Loyalist Army.)

> . . . doff thy name;
> And for that name which is no part of thee
> Take all myself.
>
> *Romeo and Juliet*

"WHERE ELSE?" she asked, looking over the radiator into the night of Madrid. In all the city there was not one friend. The youth by her side had no friend, either; he shot down Red patrols wherever he found them, and they in turn hunted him. They were bound to catch him sometime. It was mere chance that so far he hadn't piled up on a barricade. The one place where for once they could be safe again was the Duquesa's castle, the confiscated mansion which the Reds did not use—why were they not using it? Was it a trap?

"We have nothing else left," said Juanita.

"Good," he said and sent the car bounding forward. It was a house for this hour. Between life and death, midnight and dawn. For this love of which neither was certain.

"Perhaps the ghosts are already there," Juanita said.

"I have five bullets left," said Francisco.

"We'll have to be very quiet."

"Because of the ghosts?"

"Because of the others. They mustn't know that I'm back. They never drew any lines between the housekeeper and the señora."

"Why should they," he said and hurled the car into a side street.

"This is the wrong road," said Juanita.

"There were Guards back there."

"Sorry. Your eyes are better."

"Shall we set fire to your old palace, afterwards?"

"I'm not thinking of afterwards. I want to sleep."

"So do I."

She was silent.

"Of course we aren't married," he said.

"No," she said. "We aren't married."

He was silent a while; then the road rose steeply and he shifted gears: "Well, why don't we get married?" He bent over the steering wheel.

"Yes, why don't we just get married," she said softly.

He laughed. "Got your house chaplain on ice?"

"Don't laugh. The house is back there."

He slammed the brakes on, got out fast and swiftly changed the license plate of the car; now, it displayed a number of the Diplomatic Corps. "How do we enter the haunted castle?" he asked, linking arms with her.

"The back door to the park isn't locked. And at the kitchen door you can reach in, through the window."

They stood in the sepulchrally cool staircase, waiting for their eyes to get accustomed to the twilight.

"I can see now," Juanita said. "Give me your hand."

They slowly climbed the stairs; he held on to the railing which felt cold and moist; their steps echoed as though behind them two others were treading the same path.

"This is the dining room," said Juanita.

He tried to joke: "I don't see anything to dine on."

"You're hungry," she said, as though relieved, and ran away. He stood by the door, a bit helplessly. Good thing that what little he saw resembled his own house—that of his mother, whom the peasants had killed. Beaten to death, in her own patio. He breathed deeply and closed his eyes. Far off he heard glasses tinkle. Then a knife fell on stone and rattled. A cork popped. Now the girl's steps came back. He opened his eyes and saw Juanita. She was walking toward the broad table, with a platter; a candle illumined the oval of her face, kindling small yellow lights in her eyes. He came slowly closer. He was hungry.

"I'm sorry I was not informed of your visit till now, Don Francisco," Juanita said. Her voice was trembling. She put plates and glasses on the table. "But unusual times make for unusual dinners. This is the Bordeaux Father Pedrillo bought when he was in Lourdes." She poured two glasses. "I should have liked to offer you cold turkey, but I found it in an impossible condition. Here is paté-de-foie and smoked ham. Let's start with a drink, though. It is the first we'll have together. Make a wish, first."

He gulped the wine down, put the glass on the table and moved toward her. She raised her glass like a shield. "Saint George won't eat anything?"

Abashed, he sat down and laid some ham on his plate, smeared mustard on it, reached for the hard bread. Then he threw the fork down. "In a night like this one can only drink," he said and handed her the empty glass. "It's really getting lighter," he said, astonished to see furniture emerge from the depths of the hall, tapestries, a suit of mail.

"It's the moon," she said, breathing over the wine.

"We won't need a lamp then, to undress."

"We shouldn't have lighted one, anyway."

"I might have wanted to see you."

"You talk like a man eloping, in a novel."

"Seems to me that's what I'm doing."

She gave a start. He was right to remind her. He had eloped with her, from the death-house of the Red police, back into life. For that his arms, tonight, should hold a live woman. She looked out into the park. *The lamp is lighted—look! A round silver duro.*

"Come with me," she said and her eyes filled with tears. She led him over the shimmering floor, into the hallway, and opened a door to their right. Strangely, it was a chapel into which she invited him. He entered, hesitating.

The scent of faded flowers and sweet incense hung in the air. Moonlight streamed in through the altar windows. It drenched the veil of the Mother of God who stood in the center.

Juanita bent her knees and went to light the altar candles. Then she returned with a Bible and asked him to stab into the book.

Francisco had let her carry on so far; now the game seemed to him to become undignified. He had saved her two hours before, at immense risk, from the hands of the Reds who doubtless would have shot her as a spy fifteen minutes later. They had had sufficient evidence. What was left now? He drew his pistol; he felt like shooting into the room, smashing the candles, tearing down the chandelier, when Juanita pointed at the gun: "Yes, stab with it—"

Maybe she needs that, he thought. *Women are rarely straightforward.*

He raised the gun and parted the pages of the book. She quickly pressed her finger on the chosen page and moved close to the light of the candles, to read.

"Herein is our love made perfect," she read, "that we may have boldness in the day of judgement; because as he is, so are we in this world." Happily, her eyes rested on the book. "It fits," she said. He merely nodded.

She is much crazier than I supposed, he thought. *It's still the shock of the afternoon.*

Juanita spoke again. It was more like singing. "You, Francisco, who stand here before me—do you take Juanita for your wife, to guard and protect, cherish and be true to her until the end?"

He was surprised. *Do they really need that? Outside there is civil war. They may catch me tomorrow. Where does she want to go with me?*

But then her idea flattered him. She was switching off the world. There was no one else for her. Why shouldn't he say Yes? The word was like a pistol shot. It flew away with the smoke. *They need it,* he thought and tried to smile ironically. *Don't seem to sleep well without it.*

He stared at the altar and suddenly saw Juanita without clothes. "Yes, I do," he said, and unsolemnly, almost hastily added, "And you?"

She was still looking over at the Madonna as if she had spoken to her. A smile raised her lips; then, in the singing voice, she said, "I do take Francisco for my husband, to obey and follow him wherever he goes, and to love him with all my strength of body and soul."

Her head was held high, as if listening and waiting for an "Amen." She felt the light of the moon on her fiery cheeks like a soft hand. Moon in the church window. *It will shine in my room too. We'll draw the curtains back and let it in all the way.*

She turned to Francisco. He drew her to him with both hands. "Not here," she said.

He awoke in the middle of the night and sat up abruptly. "I dreamed that you tricked me. You cut off my hair." He laughed. He looked boyish with his disheveled hair. It did not surprise him at all that Juanita lay still awake. "What nonsense you can dream! All the doors suddenly jumped open like so many black holes. I counted them; they were eight. As many as I've killed, since the beginning. There were eight men standing in the doors, and I only had five bullets left. And then the gun was gone, too." He snatched his weapon off the bedside table. "It was exactly as if you'd been gone."

"Thanks," she said. He did not feel the irony.

"You don't know how much I think about you."

"Go back to sleep," she said. "You were fast asleep."

"Is the moon still there?" he asked.

"Shall I hold it back?"

"When it is gone, we'll drive on."

"I'll hold it back."

"We have to use the hours between day and night to get home."

"All hours," she said.

He was not listening. "I love my hatred," he said. "I know it now. It's my disease. It's there whenever I'm awake. It is there now; I feel it more strongly since you came. Can you understand that?"

She drew him to her. "You ought to sleep," she said and gazed at the trees outside, moving in a soft breeze. *I thought he was much farther away from the old things. He still is right in the heart of this town. Why am I so far away?*

"I remember," he said slowly, haltingly. "Peasants on my threshold which they were forbidden to cross; they were crossing it ten times now. I remember. Beggars spitting into a nobleman's face. Day laborers lying in beds such as this. The alcalde, reaching for shoulders like yours." He broke off and wrapped himself in the blanket, shivering. She held him tighter and stroked his forehead.

She had lain there dreaming, carried away by her happiness to quite another inlet of the world; she had been a raft drifting on deserted seas, quite free, far from any city, far from this incomprehensible city in particular. Now he wanted to bring her back. She hadn't been strong enough. He had not forgotten.

She heard that he was asleep again. *I'll never let him go back,* she thought, *to his consulate, to his companions, to his revenge.* Soon she fell asleep too.

She was wakened by the sound of a shot fired in the street, near the palace. The cedar trees were silhouetted in the open window. The moon had vanished. In an hour, the wretched sea of grey dawn would swamp the night's dark velvet and drown every star. The city would wake up to the last shots of the patrols. Posters would be glued to the walls and start screaming into the grey. Long lines of women would form at the barricaded markets. Why did the hour not stay? For a night there had been no civil war here, no consigna had been called, no carnet shown. Neither Reds nor Whites had approached the bed. There had been love. Why should love no longer be?

She saw the pistol on the bedside table. Why not kill yourself before the city started to scream again, before all were wrong—he, the sleeper, as well as those he secretly shot down? Everywhere, in this hour, rifles pointed at men; here as well as on the other side. It was the hour of execution, wasn't it?

"One should go away altogether," she said, aloud, looking at Francisco. She wanted him to hear it. "Go away before it is too late." But Francisco only turned bluntly over in his sleep.

Cautiously she slid out of the bed and went to the chests, to pick some linen and clothes. She filled a little trunk with her best things, and on top of it she put the papers from the gypsy woman who had been right. "The soldier" had come. The "dogs" were no longer barking, the "telephones" no longer ringing. These "enemies" were dead. But the soldier lived and lay in bed back there, and now she would run away with him, away from his "friends," from his hate, from all that could trouble their love.

"What are you doing?" his voice said.

She leaped up, startled, and ran to the bed to hold her clothes to her. She was still naked. "We're going away," she said. "This is my trousseau."

"Still the same idea?" he yawned.

She threw her slip over. "Yes," she said. "The same idea."

He started dressing too. *Every word matters now*, she thought. *I've got the whole city against me. The city and his friends, hiding in the consulates. The city and his enemies from whom he saved me. I'll kiss him once more. He won't deny me anything. He'll drive wherever I want. Just for this one day, I'll tell him. We know how to drive through barricades. There must be some place for us without a war. A wood, a mountain shack, a valley where the echo does not return shots but bird calls and the sound of the brook. A bed where he can forget his blood-stained village. I'll put on another dress each morning. Have I packed enough?*

Francisco stomped his boots straight and tightened his belt. "Come," he said, stretching.

No, she could not talk now. She would lean against him in the car and tell him where to drive. She could not speak here. She was afraid of being left alone then, in this room. For the Madonna's sake—not be alone! He would learn to love her.

In the car she looked at him. "Put the window down," he said. "One doesn't shoot so well through glass." His face was changed entirely; he was older; he no longer seemed to know that he was at her side. She looked away. Her lips started praying softly. Ave Maria, gratia plena . . . *what kind of man is he?* . . . benedicta tu in mulieribus . . . *have I really kissed this mouth? I might have a child from him* . . . et benedictus fructus tui, Jesus . . .

"Damn it, here they are again!" Francisco shouted. "But this time I'll get them." He pushed the accelerator down. Through the windshield, Juanita saw militiamen stand at the end of the street, waving their rifles.

The dark figures grew. Now, one of the men stood in front of them, a giant; Francisco swerved slightly; screaming, the militiaman had jumped to the wrong side and hit the fender. Juanita heard him hit the ground; then the car careened round a small square and sped intᴜ a side street with a walled courtyard opening on the left. Francisco drove into the yard on two wheels.

"I know my town," he said to himself, proudly, and switched the motor off. A siren screamed in the distance, grew stronger, trembled very close past, grew fainter, and lost itself in the night.

"It was a sign from Heaven," Juanita said. She thought she might speak now.

"We don't have much farther to go," he said and pushed the starter.

She realized that he wanted to go back to the hideout, back to his hate. She made one last attempt: "I wish you would drive on. I mean, make a detour. I mean—drive much farther."

"Wrong," he said, "wrong. The shortest way is the best."

She no longer dared reply.

Translated by E. B. Ashton

Bert Brecht

YES, I LIVE IN A DARK AGE

I

To THE CITIES I came in troubled times
When hunger ruled.
I grew among men in times of rebellion
And I rebelled with men
So went the time
Assigned to me on earth.

I ate my food between battles
I lay me down to sleep with murderers
I used to make love offhand
And nature I watched without patience
So went the time
Assigned to me on earth.

Highways led to swamps in my time
Speech betrayed us to the killer,
What could I do? I hoped
At least the mighty felt safer without me
So went the time
Assigned to me on earth.

Strength was lacking.
Achievement was far away
In sight
But out of reach
So went the time
Assigned to me on earth.

II

All of you—survivors of the flood
In which we went under
Think—
When you speak of our insufficiency—
Of the dark age
Which you have never known.

Remember how we walked through the clash of classes
Wearing out our passports quicker than our shoes,
Desperate
When there was evil without upheaval.

Still we know
Even hating the hateful
Scars the face
And talking against injustice
Roughens the voice
Oh we who wanted to make our soil ready for kindness
Could not ourselves be kind

But you
Who begin to live
When men help men
Think of us kindly.

Translated by RUTH LANDSHOFF *and*
JOHN T. LATOUCHIE

Carl Zuckmayer

MY DEATH

A Pious Wish

SOME DAY, all unawares, alone in the deep forest
I'll fall flat on my face. Felled by a stroke.
My legs still jerking in a short-lived struggle
Even as darkness veils the wandering eye.
The little gash will shortly cease to trickle;
The final gasp swallow a taste of pitch;
The final fist be clenching moss and earth.
The final pain is like a deer's, shot through the heart.
Then it roars in the treetops.
Then it purls from the branches.
Then
Stillness.

Perhaps there'll be a dog
To guard me. I'll no longer know. May be
That I'll be found and carried to my grave
Before the rigor yields. And with the forest's peace still in my face.
Perhaps I'll be snowed in! Then they will find
My bones in spring, and a few tufts of hair:
Hawthorn-blossom-white.

For this
Is how I like my death. This, how I seek it:
On my life's unvacated field of battle.
Amid the children all, my dreams.
Within my father's house. Within my mother's arms.
High in years—!

Translated by E. B. ASHTON

Hermann Kesten

COLONEL KOCK

WHEN I LAID aside my paper at Jamaica station yesterday, I discovered that the man next to me, who had just got off, had forgotten his valise under the seat. I promptly jumped out of the train with the suitcase, caught up with the man outside the station and held his valise under his nose.

"Your valise," I said. "You left it in the train. Don't mention it."

He surveyed me from head to foot.

"I dashed off the train," I said, "to bring you your property. . . ."

"The suitcase doesn't belong to me. You know it. Or don't you? I've had enough of this, do you hear?"

"I beg your pardon," I said. I went back into the station and turned in the suitcase, my address and a brief statement.

My unknown one accosted me at the corner. "In better years I had a better knowledge of people. Now I can see that you aren't a detective. But I could tell you of some strange experiences."

"My fault," I replied. "I was overzealous . . ."

"And yet," he said, scrutinizing me, "I may have made the decisive mistake now. That wretched valise—you haven't got it?"

"I turned it in."

"Mentioning me?" he asked and turned pale.

"Casually. I don't even know your name."

We had been walking slowly down Sutphin Boulevard.

"Either the valise is yours," I said; "then why don't you take it? Or it isn't yours—then I was wrong. But what's it to you?"

"And my ruined life?" the man asked, halting. "Three months ago a valise popped up exactly this way, and hell on earth began for me with a mistake precisely like yours. Fundamentally I didn't do anything different three months ago from what you've just done. For that I was in jail almost three months. I'd be sorry for you, if . . ."

"Just because I found a suitcase? But suppose we share the reward this time?"

"You're an honest man," he replied with deadly earnestness, "and you're laughing. A human being may be lost. His neighbor sees only the humor of the situation. I, too, spent a lifetime laughing and could see the joke of everything. . . ." He fell silent.

I looked at the odd stranger more closely. His bearing betrayed the man of mark, his smile, an ironical view of himself. I liked his smile. Oddly enough most people have nothing to tell. They are the extras of history, who toast their slice of bread over the hot ashes of burning Rome. This stranger roused my curiosity.

"Let's have a drink in the bar over there," I suggested.

Although there was just the bartender in the half dark place, my stranger sat down at the hindmost table.

"I'm a fugitive," he said, "one of millions. My name is Marian Kock. Colonel Kock. I've fought the Tsar, the Bolsheviks and the Germans. In 1939, during the siege of Warsaw, I was in a hospital and finally fled in women's clothes under the noses of the Nazis from the ruins of Warsaw.

"But perhaps I ought to start with my birth—my real mistake. I was an ardent Polish patriot. But Poland isn't my fatherland at all. This preposterous situation sharpened my sense of comedy—the cause of my ruin.

"In December, 1940, I came from Europe—that temporary German hell with the emergency exit at Lisbon. I walked about New York and felt at home from the first. . . . You often pay more dearly for being wrong than for being guilty.

"One morning, on the platform at Rockville Center, I saw a man having his shoes shined. Five steps away, abandoned like an orphan, stood a valise. It was red and faded, as if standing there for a long time in rain and sun—a pitiful valise. It obviously belonged to the man who was having his shoes shined.

"Suddenly I thought I recognized the man as Dr. MacKerry, a pediatrician I had once met. From the very first moment this Dr. MacKerry had made fun of me. He cracked brilliant jokes at my expense. He always felt superior—the result of his profession. Now I wanted to get my revenge and have some fun with him. Those perpetually surprised blue eyes, the tiny, cheerful, red nose, that mouth as round as a spittoon, those thin, eloquent legs: a born joker. What a funny face he would make when his valise was gone! The blank astonishment of people who shrug off revolutions and then howl bloody murder when they lose so much as a collar-button. . . .

"The idea was beginning to please me irresistibly. It was my lucky day anyway. I had a date for lunch with my friend Kochaner. We were going into business together; all we had left to do was sign the contract. Later I would see Anna, a Swedish girl I had been in love with for five months.

"I picked up the valise with a smile. It was surprisingly light. I had reached for it experimentally; now I asked myself uncomfortably, 'What next?'

"Then the riot started. A dozen strangers jumped at me, my nose was bleeding, somebody yelled 'Police!' and before I could say, 'Here's your valise—it was a joke,' I found myself at the police station.

" 'Let me explain,' I asked the detective.

" 'Later,' he said, and took down my personal description.

" 'It was only a joke, you know.'

" 'We'll see how much of a record you've got,' the officer said.

" 'You see I thought it was Dr. MacKerry,' I explained.

" 'I know him,' said the officer. 'He operated on my little girl. The operation was a success. Three days afterward he died.'

" 'Dead?' I cried. 'Dr. MacKerry dead? The one who was always kidding?'

" 'You're in luck,' said the officer. 'It's still early in the day. The judge can see you this afternoon.'

" 'But . . .' I said, 'for a joke?'

"The judge fixed bail at a thousand dollars. The valise contained drawings for an invention. Electric baths. 'The bath of the future,' the owner of the red valise declared. 'I'm submitting the patent next week. The plans are worth their weight in gold.' The inventor's name was Jack

Fadden. 'The thief is a foreigner,' he said enthusiastically. 'Maybe the Gestapo is behind him. To the German General Staff those baths, used in an army of . . .'

" 'Bail is a thousand dollars,' said the judge. And added, 'Cheap enough.'

" 'Tomorrow you'll be free,' I told myself. I wrote to Anna. A week later I got a letter. She had loved me because I had taught her to see the seriousness of life. A fiancé shouldn't play tricks with other people's property. And she would never forget me.

"I wired my friend Kochaner. He's a citizen now, a splendid fellow. The idea of going into business together was out, he wrote. According to the papers I'd stolen patents worth half a million dollars.

"Soon I realized: while I was behind bars I couldn't raise bail; without bail I couldn't get out. So I wrote to Mr. Jack Fadden, the owner of the valise: Must a man die for an unsuccessful joke?

"He answered by return mail. He had given up the electric baths. Good idea; but the manufacturing cost was too high. Now he was working on his new invention, a depilatory; at the same time he had produced an infallible remedy for falling hair. He had withdrawn the charge and was hoping that this would remove all obstacles to my release.

"My discharge dragged on. The questioning piled up.

"I had supposed I had behind me the ordinary life of a modern man.

"The police, without half-trying, proved the opposite.

"In the course of the investigation I lost my name, my nationality, my character, my honor, my self-respect, my courage and my identity. Accomplishments I was proud of began to look like derelictions. Wherever I sought support I evoked distrust. I was required to prove the obvious. That's how suspicious any ordinary life begins to look, once you check up on it.

"Oddly enough I had thought that precisely my life would stand any amount of checking. And yet the detectives had the very best of intentions; my life was at fault. I was bound to strike them as suspicious; I began to strike myself as suspicious. After three months I had the heart of a thief. Today, I have the mind of a criminal. All I need in order to be a thief is the delicious habit of stealing. No man should leave his country. There they know him; there they understand him. But what if you've never had a country, like me?"

"Aren't you a Pole?" I asked.

"The only answer to that would be the history of the Polish Republic. The police asked me: 'Were you born in Poland?'

" 'I'm older than the Polish Republic.'

" 'Where were you born?'

" 'In Odessa.'

" 'Then you're a Russian?'

" 'My mother was Swiss.'

" 'And your father?'

" 'Unknown.'

" 'You're Swiss, then?'

" 'My mother married an Austrian university professor, who adopted me."

" 'Then you're an Austrian?'

" 'Hitler has seized Austria.'

" 'Well, are you a German?'

" 'And a colonel in the Polish army?'

" 'Well, then aren't you a Pole after all?'

" 'I protested against the personnel of the Polish government in exile, and now my consul won't receive me. I wasn't born in Poland; how am I to prove, in exile and with no papers, that my Polish father adopted me?'

" 'On what papers did you enter this country?'

" 'On a French identification card.'

" 'Are you a French citizen?'

" 'Not at all.'

" 'Stateless, then.'

" 'I'm a citizen of the world,' I confessed.

" 'No cracks!' they yelled. 'You're making things look bad for yourself. Have you any relatives in Europe?'

" 'I don't know.'

" 'A proper person knows his family. Is your mother still living?'

" 'I don't know.'

" 'Your mother's last residence?'

" 'She hadn't any.'

" 'Was she a vagrant?'

" 'On the contrary. She was locked up in a concentration camp near Warsaw.'

" 'What for?'

" 'They claimed she said in a street-car that the Germans were human too.'

" 'Aha. A pro-German.'

" 'On the contrary. The Nazis were punishing her for slander.'

" 'What?'

" 'That's right.'

" 'Oh. Meaning? . . . Did your mother never write to you?'

" 'No. But the Swiss consul at Ankara sent me news of her.'

" 'Ankara?'

" 'In Turkey. He's a cousin of my mother's. His brother-in-law is a major in a Saxon regiment garrisoned in Biarritz, the French resort on the Spanish border. The major has a niece in Berlin. The niece has a girl friend. The girl friend has an affair with a Gestapo official stationed in Warsaw. So I got word from my mother by the fastest imaginable route, in a bare four months—by telegraph, of course.' "

The police, in complete geographical confusion, understood nothing. Why did a telegram take four months?

" 'Perfectly simple,' I explained. 'In Europe any child would understand. My mother had remained a Swiss citizen. She wrote from the camp to the Red Cross. The Red Cross turned to the Swiss consul in Berlin. The consul made representations to Himmler. So Robert Locke, the Gestapo official, went to the concentration camp near Warsaw in order to intimidate my mother by questioning. She told him she was worried that I might be anxious about her. At the start of the war, she said, we had arranged that in case of a partial occupation of Poland (a complete one we thought out of the question!) we'd send each other news by way of this cousin of my mother's, the Swiss consul at Ankara.

" 'Locke of the Gestapo, who of course couldn't write abroad to a Swiss consul, wrote to his fiancée. After that, everything was straight routine. The fiancée went to her girl friend, and she to her aunt. The aunt met her husband, the major, in Paris; he was on leave, she was shopping. The major, on an excursion across the Spanish frontier to San Sebastian, wrote from the writing-room of the casino to the Swiss consul at Ankara. The consul immediately sent me a cable; I had long since cabled him my address in America.'

" 'So you admit you're connected with the Gestapo?' they asked me. 'Locke was hardly willing to send such a dangerous message abroad for nothing, was he?'

" 'But,' I said, 'a Gestapo man is a murderer in government employ, with a monthly salary and a right to a pension, in the service of the well-known German world-conqueror's clubs. In private he may be fond of children, or hen-pecked.'

" 'And why did Locke send such a dangerous message?'

" 'Probably he was thinking of his mother. The Germans are sentimental. Incidentally, all the message said was that my mother was getting along as might be expected.'

"'As a Swiss citizen, why didn't your mother go back to Switzerland?'

"'On account of the high mountains,' I said.

"'What? Repeat that!'

"Just you try," said Colonel Kock to me, "to explain my mother's life to the police!"

"She was a wonderful woman, God bless her! She made so many happy. She was the daughter of a Geneva watchmaker. All the watches in her father's house made her melancholy. At fifteen, she was running after every hour. She went to the station every day, to see the Paris train leave. She dreamed that tomorrow a count would elope with her to Paris, into the great world.

"One day a man actually did accost her at the Geneva railway station. Next day she went off with the stranger, but to the Crimea, to the estate of a Ukrainian petty nobleman, who had hired the stranger as tutor. The stranger did not come out of a dream; he was bald, pot-bellied and hoarse of voice, a southern Frenchman from Toulouse; he was enthusiastic about Rabelais and Swift, liked his wine and had black, fiery eyes. His name was Arouet. Of course, he boasted of being descended from Voltaire's family.

"At the start of the journey he introduced my mother as his daughter; at the end, as his wife. On the estate, daughter again, she instructed the bearded squire's daughters, befriended his two sixteen-year-old twin sons, and became his own darling. Obliging toward every man, she went into the shady woods all summer long, by turns with the squire, with one twin, with the other twin, with the tutor, and at times even with her charges, the little girls—to pick berries. Nine months later I came into the world.

"The following morning the squire sent my mother a check for three thousand roubles and a note saying, 'Call my son Pyotr!'

"At noon one of the twins flung himself at his father's feet. It was while berrying, he confessed tearfully. The twins were so much alike that the embittered father first enquired, 'Which one are you?' 'Your son Ivan,' replied the guilty one and was thrown out the door. That afternoon the squire sat by the beehive, brooding mutely, when the other twin slunk up with downcast eyes and fell abruptly at his father's feet. Weeping, he cried out, 'It's I, father! I'm guilty. Punish me.'

"'What?' cried his father.

"'You can't guess,' cried the twin. 'I bear a mortal load of guilt. . . .'

" 'Have you got any more children?' yelled his father.

" 'How did you know?' asked the astounded twin. 'Out berrying. . . .'

" 'Which one are you?' asked the irate father.

" 'Your son Alexander,' replied the twin. At the very moment when the squire had put his son Alexander to flight with a well-aimed kick, the embarrassed tutor came and confessed (out in the woods, berrying) and he was ready to marry the fallen one—for in fact he was not my mother's father at all, but my father.

" 'You're the fourth father today,' replied the angry squire, 'and the day isn't over yet.'

"The tutor slunk off as if stunned. Later he must have talked to his pupils. With the boys you can understand the silly upshot; but the tutor was a man of forty-nine, from Toulouse, the city of gourmands, a reader of satirists, a mocker, an Arouet!

"That very evening he went for a swim in the Black Sea with the twins. It was a marvelous starry night, and the tutor and the twins drowned. The squire and his hands searched all night, with torches and dogs. The torches shone so far through the woods; the dogs barked so loud by the sea. . . .

"The squire bought my mother a railroad ticket to Geneva. In Vienna, she got off the train with the infant in her arms, to drink a quick soda-pop. She stayed in Vienna three years. My first memory is of Grinzing near Vienna. I was standing on a chair, in a blue sailor suit with a white collar, next to the orchestra in one of the garden inns of Grinzing, where the innkeepers serve the new wine, the *Heuriger*, along with the oldest popular songs. There I stood, deadly serious, watching my mother, a girl of twenty in a white gingham dress, waltz past with young gentlemen, and then with elderly gentlemen.

"I had often asked her, 'Who's my father?' She used to answer, 'I'm looking for him'—I can still hear the *tumta tumta* of the drums. I can smell the aroma of wine, and of great stars in the dark, all but precipitant, nocturnal sky. I can see my mother, waltzing past, hot and lovely; she is calling: 'Have fun, darling!'

"I anxiously studied every gentleman—was he my father? I found one on a Saturday night, when I was three—not too soon. He was pot-bellied, bald, and had a hoarse voice. He wore a black pince-nez on his red, alcoholic nose. Thick bunches of reddish hair sprouted everywhere, like wildflowers in an abandoned garden, from his half-naked skull, his high collar, his ears and nostrils. He was a learned man, as I found later, and a good man. His smile enchanted me then, little boy that I was—it was so gentle and drunken.

"He couldn't dance. He sat over a glass of wine, watching the young girls. He was learned and short-sighted. Unsure of myself, I studied him for a long time. Finally I scrambled down from my chair—a daring exploit for a little shaver like me—and went over to the stranger. I put my hand confidentially on his knee, looked searchingly at his face and asked him, man to man: 'Aren't you my daddy, maybe?'

"If he'd laughed, I'd have cried. But he shook his head and said, 'My name is Thaddeus Kock and I'm a professor of Polish at Cracow University. Is your father from Cracow?'

" 'I don't know,' I answered worriedly. 'I'll ask my mother.'

"She came over after the waltz, with hot cheeks, looking like fifteen in her coy little white frock, and apologized for her little boy. She sat down just for half a minute and drank a glass of wine so as not to be rude, a second glass of wine because it tasted so good and a third glass to the professor's health. The wedding took place two months later. Professor Kock became my father, my best friend on earth—and my seducer.

"He was a gentle man who would not hurt a fly; when I was a little older he used to go walking in the fields with me, and he would look around carefully under the laughing sky to make sure there was no gendarme around, with an Austrian double eagle on the visor of his cap. Then he would cry out in his hoarse voice: 'Woe to you, my son, should you ever lose your thirst for freedom! A man without freedom is a butterfly without wings, an ugly worm!'

"Then he would sigh deeply: Unhappy Poland! So noble in misfortune, blood-stained from the blows of insolent oppressors—Austrians, Russians, even Prussians!

"For my father was a fanatical patriot of his country which had not existed for a hundred years.

" 'Swear!' he cried, pointing heavenward. 'Swear that you will fight for Poland's freedom to your last drop of blood!'

"I swore—in German, incidentally, my Polish being still too shaky.

"He, however, began cautiously to sing the Polish anthen: *Poland shall not perish yet*.

"In 1914 I entered Pilsudski's Polish Legion. My father entered jail.

"He had said from the lecture platform that Austria-Hungary would die and Poland would live!

"After the fall of Austria-Hungary, I got a captain's commission in the

Polish army, and my father a professorship at the University of Warsaw.

"When I came home from the war against the Bolsheviks, a colonel, my father was back in jail. He had said from the lecture platform that the uniformed tyrants would die and democracy would live!

"After considerable wire-pulling, I managed to see my father in his cell without witnesses. The old man received me with tears. I asked, 'Is this where our ideals lead to? To prison for you? To the battlefield for me?'

"As there was neither chair nor bed in the cell, we sat down on the floor. The old man held his bushy beard in both hands and looked at me for a long time. Finally he replied: 'My son, it was a dream. I've gone a step further. The freedom of Poland—democracy—all well and good. But today I know that something new will come. The United States of Europe! Swear, my son. . . .'

"I didn't swear again, of course. I went in desperation to my mother. She comforted me. Your father is an idealist, she said. Always admire him; never imitate him. He runs even faster than Europe's nations who are changing their ideas on the double. It'll cost him his neck in the end. But he's a philosopher. He has learned to count his life as nothing. You, my son, are a soldier. You must back up your nation, sword in hand. Be loyal! Always think like your superiors.

"So I did.—Just you try to explain the fine points of a political career in Europe to the American police!

" 'Did you advocate the overthrow of the government?' the police asked. 'Are you in favor of the war with Germany? Were you ever in favor of the Communists? National Socialists? Answer each question yes or no.'

" 'I want to confess the truth,' I said.

" 'Aha!' they cried.

" 'I can answer each question yes *and* no. For example, did I fight for democracy? Yes *and* no.'

" 'How are we to understand that?'

"I said: 'I was always loyal. I always obeyed my government. My leaders, like most leaders, went from left to right and then crosswise. Pilsudski, the generalissimo of the Polish Republic, participated in the Russian revolution of 1904, blowing up trains. In 1914 he was a socialist. In 1926, as dictator of Poland, he despised socialism and the revolution. So with Pilsudski I was a socialist and with him I was an anti-socialist. When the democratic pianist Paderewski became prime minister of Poland, I was a democrat. When our foreign minister Colonel Beck worked for collaboration with Hitler, I was for Beck. And with Beck, later, I was against Hitler but for Chamberlain. Today I'm ready to advocate the overthrow of many governments in Europe, for the good of Poland.'

" 'Well,' they asked me, 'aren't you a museum of all European political trends for the last twenty-five years?'

" 'I'm a man of honor. For that I made every sacrifice. Otherwise I could have sat in the cabinet, or made millions. I never followed my own inclination or personal convictions. Like most of the respected people in the world I thought, with inflexible consistency, as my government of the moment did, and I was proud of my impeccable fidelity to Poland. But could I have acted otherwise without going to jail, like my father, or into exile, like other fanatics?'

" 'You went into exile later anyhow.'

" 'Was I to plow German fields for Hitler, or dig iron as his slave in German mines? I'm a nationalist emigrant, not a political one. Political emigrants flee from their own country, where not everything goes to suit them, to a foreign country, where nothing goes to suit them.'

"The police were baffled. There they were with my complete confession. Why, I admitted everything. I was suspicious in every way—and claimed to be a typical European. The police shuddered at me—and at Europe.

"When I think of Poland, I see the graves in the streets of Warsaw and the raped girls, the trampled fields, the old peasants hanging from the nut trees before their shacks, the millions of Jews jammed into ghettoes to die in haste and in heaps—and I see the armed murderers, clean-shaven, with well shined shoes, and among them the rats in uniform, the Gestapo, and they march through the country and occupy the four village exits and say, 'Reprisal!' and shoot the innocent, the old man and the child and the child's mother; I can hear every shot. I hear the death-cry of Poland across the plains, across the mountains and the sea. Particularly at night the wind carries the groan of Poland to my ears; I hear the somber, piercing sound—and I shudder too.

"Aren't the police always right?

"I've stopped believing in mankind since my father died. My father came out of his prisons a shriveled greybeard. No longer allowed to teach, he wrote inflammatory little articles for malcontent little magazines. My father's friends no longer dared go to visit him. In the midst of his native land he was living in exile. I shall never forget the last evening in our country house outside Warsaw, at the end of July, 1939. We were sitting before the front door. The sun had set. Myriads of crickets began their shrill, triumphant song in the corn fields. The sky gleamed like an ocean. The stars winked like the lights of distant ships.

"'My son,' said my father, 'I've progressed to another stage.'

"My mother smiled darkly.

"I waited in vain for a statement of his new and better principles. I was too respectful to ask my father what he didn't tell me of his own accord.

"My father murmured, as if dreaming, 'My son . . . swear!'

"One rainy morning in August I was sitting beside his bed, two days before he died.

"He said, 'My son. I'm on the threshold. During my sleepless nights I've pondered, with sighs and, when I couldn't stand it, with screams. I went on from stage to stage: now, I thought, you have truth in your hand . . . now. . . . I confess that even then I sometimes mistrusted mankind. Now suddenly I can see clearly: mankind has no future. What would you think of a zoologist who spent his life studying hedgehogs—and swore by the moral future of the hedgehog race? Hedgehogs? After a hundred or a thousand years their young will still be mere hedgehogs. My son, forget my teachings! Break your chains! Rend your garments! Let your nails and hair grow! Live like a hedgehog. Swear, my son, that you'll live like a hedgehog! Swear!'

"I swore, of course. The old man died.

"'Come on,' I said to my mother. That was the first time I noticed that she was getting grey. 'Let's go to Switzerland. Wasn't your father a watchmaker in Geneva? Let's live at the foot of Mont Blanc. I'll learn to make watches and watch the rest of time pass by.'

"'Never!' cried my mother. 'I love Poland!'

"'What do you love about Poland? It's an impoverished country, and . . .'

"'Quiet!' said my mother. She smiled like a young girl. 'I love its yellow fields in July. And the singing of the peasant girls around the village well. I'm a Pole! And my son isn't going to run away just an hour before Satan rides into the country.'

"'Satan doesn't ride any more,' I said. 'He flies—in a bomber!'

"My dear mother . . . When Warsaw was bombed, she ran among the crashing houses of the besieged city every day to get milk for the strange children in her air-raid shelter. And when the German soldiers marched in. . . ."

Colonel Kock broke off in the middle of a sentence. With an almost hysterical gesture he squeezed my hand. He stared at the table beyond us, where two men had sat down. "We're being spied on."

"What's the danger?" I asked, smiling.

"You're right. But didn't I tell you that I'd acquired the keenness of a criminal? I can recognize any policeman in plain clothes now. When I'd been under arrest at Rockville Center for three months and was on the point of breaking down and confessing anything they wanted after all the questioning, the police suddenly let me go.

"So here I am. And I suspect that the police only let me go so they could watch me the better. I'm a suspicious character, like millions of refugees. Now I'm beginning to ask myself, What does innocence look like? What must a man do, to seem an ordinary person? Trying to avoid anything conspicuous like the plague, I behave sensationally and get involved in the most extravagant adventures. Why did you run just after me with that valise? And did anyone really forget it? Or was it left on purpose? Were they trying to test my honesty? What's in the bag? They'll open it. And find—what?

"So what do I do? Instead of obeying my first instinct and running away, I talk to you, go into a bar with you, put my name, my story, myself in your hands. If you'd been from the police after all, I'd have gone right ahead and told everything. Detectives are poor listeners; they have a monotonous mania of waiting for the same thing all the time: a confession of guilt.

"You had patience. Who are you? Don't answer. I'd be ashamed of myself if I shouldn't believe you. You won't bring me any luck. It was splendid of you to come after me with the valise. But you'd have done better not to, better for me and perhaps for you too. You got off the train with someone else's bag. Are you a thief?"

"I reported finding it."

"You're too sure of yourself. Three months ago I was like you. I envy your blindness."

"We all die."

"Die?" asked Kock. "I'm a soldier. But the humiliations. And the fear. And the fear of fear. Come on. I can't stand this bar any longer. Please, let's go!"

I called to the waiter. When we got up, the two men at the next table barred our way.

"I knew it," said Colonel Kock calmly.

The detectives civilly asked us to go with them. Why? Where to?

"A formality. Did this gentleman lose a valise?"

"Found it," I said.

"You were the finder. But your friend there—wasn't he the loser?"

"I brought Colonel Kock the valise, but he told me right away that it didn't belong to him."

"No?" asked the detectives. "I suppose you gents have been working together quite a while?"

I stared at the detectives and Colonel Kock by turns. What was I to believe? Had I blundered into some preposterous business? Good God! And this Colonel Kock? Was he a colonel? Was he a Pole?

"Allow me," I said, "gentlemen . . ." I broke out in a sweat.

At the police station they took us into an almost bare room. On a table by the wall stood the famous valise. We stopped at the door.

"But damn it!" I yelled. "I turned in the valise of my own accord. I'm no thief!"

My nerves were cracking. Did I really stress that *I* was no thief? Kock, who was calmer than I, turned to the detectives and said, "This gentleman is really quite innocent. I've never seen him before. He thought he was doing me a favor by coming after me with the valise. I'm the only one to arrest. I'll assume all responsibility. My name is Kock. Colonel Kock. I'm entirely at your disposal."

"Shut up!" said the detectives.

"But," I cried, "the suitcase was turned in."

"Shut up!" cried the detectives.

The room was so quiet now that you could hear the faint tick of a clock. The detectives glanced sharply at us. We thought we kept hearing the tick louder and louder. Suddenly Kock and I looked at each other. We saw why the detectives had stopped at the door with us. The tick was coming from the valise.

"What's that?" I asked with trembling lips. But I knew already: there was a bomb in the valise, of course with a clockwork timer; I had found a bomb. I looked at Kock. His face was white. So that was why he had repudiated the valise? Started to run away? A bomb-thrower! An assassin! And I was involved, suspected. I was an honest man. People knew me. I was innocent. My whole life went to prove . . .

My life? Hadn't he told me the story of an innocent man? Was innocence any protection? How does a man prove he's harmless? Good God, I was sunk.

Kock (if he was Kock!) asked the detectives: "Are you waiting for the explosion?"

"Then you admit . . . ?" the detectives asked.

I said, "For God's sake! Confess, if the valise is yours, before a disaster blows us to bits!"

Kock smiled, not unamiably, but simply with melancholy, as if to say: Do you see what you've done to me? That's the way you men of good will are—impatient, suspicious, undependable.

I was ashamed. I was furious. I was very much scared.

"Do you know how to handle those things?" Kock asked the officials.

"For the last time, does that valise belong to you?" a detective asked.

The other commanded: "Don't provoke a disaster. That will make your position worse!"

"If I'm torn to bits?" asked Kock.

At that moment the explosives experts from the police arrived. We were led off. After several hours' questioning, during which I looked shudderingly into the abysses of my life, whereas Kock tried most generously to exonerate me, even at his own expense, there was a phone call.

The detectives laughed. They told us the valise had just been opened, with all the usual precautions, and not had only a clockwork been found, but four dozen watches, of which, however, only one had been going. Which of us was a watchmaker?

Neither one was a watchmaker. To me the detectives explained that if the watches were not claimed, after a year I would have watches enough for a lifetime. I told the detectives I wouldn't forget them in a lifetime and if the watches came to me a year hence I would make each man a present of one.

"Time to eat," I said to Kock. "The day is gone anyway. Will you do me the honor to have dinner with me?"

"I'm sorry," said one of the detectives, "but I shall have to interfere with your plans for this evening."

"How so?" I cried indignantly. "Aren't we free?"

"You may go. Mr. Kock we shall unfortunately have to keep here tonight. It's because of his previous arrest. We've got to look up the files and see if Mr. Kock was properly discharged. A mere formality."

"How about doing it now?" I asked.

"Sorry. But the offices are closed."

"You're out of luck," said I to Kock, blushing. "We must eat together in any case. I'll be in the bar across the street about 5:30 tomorrow. We'll have a drink and then eat together somewhere. Right?"

Colonel Kock held out his hand. He was bearing up well. Only his eyelids twitched.

The next day I ran to make up for the day before. At 5:30 I was sitting in the bar. Colonel Kock was not there yet. At six I began to get nervous. But I told myself, The man forgot—or the man has had enough of you.

At 6:30 I went to the police station. Had they detained him again? How long this time? I wanted to send him my lawyer.

The detective came in hurriedly, looked at the table, and said, "Stupid business."

"What? What did you say?"

"Didn't you see it in the papers?"

"What?"

"Mr. Kock hung himself in jail. With his underpants. This morning between five and six. He'd have been released by noon. It was a formality."

"A formality," I repeated softly.

"Stupid business," said the policeman. "The Polish consulate has taken it up. It seems the man amounted to something and had a good reputation in his own country."

"In his own country . . ." I repeated. "And . . . did he leave any note—did he explain . . . ?"

"What *would* he leave us? Nothing but trouble, anyhow."

I went up Sutphin Boulevard to the Long Island station. I wanted to get to Rockville Center, to New York. Anywhere, so long as it was away.

When I got into the train I stumbled over a red valise in the car. I broke out in a sweat. I walked through the whole train to the rear car, and looked out into the night. Mirrored in the window I suddenly seemed to see the shadow of Colonel Kock running after the train. My hair stood on end.

"Get away!" I said. "I'm not your murderer!"

The shadow pursued the train.

Get away! I said. And I only wanted to do you a favor when I took the valise after you. I shouldn't have done it. You might still be alive then. I'm pretty sure you'd still be alive. But couldn't you wait until noon? A man has to have patience.

With patience, I said, you can even endure life.

Translated by BARROWS MUSSEY

Heinrich Mann

THE SUPERNATIONAL MANIFESTO

(Published in *Die Neue Rundschau* in January 1933, shortly before the Nazi seizure of power.)

I. PASSAGE OF AN ERA

RACINE FELT, lived and wrote in full unison with the kingdom of Louis the Fourteenth, his actions, his spiritual foundations. He was dependent on the king's favor but he accepted it with the best possible conscience, and it was not until he had lost it that he lost himself. He died of this break in an inner accord, rather than of frustrated ambition.

Goethe asked, "What makes Germany great, if not an admirable popular culture evenly permeating every part of the Reich? And does it not flow from the several princely seats, do they not bear it and care for it?" He favored nationhood for all the thirty-six countries. He felt no conflict between the status quo of power and his own task. His creative strength knew motives of all kinds, but the urge to contradict the ruling world was the least among them—or at least he let it affect his genius as little as possible. Of course he was not a pure classic as was Racine.

The classic peace between reality and idea was increasingly more difficult to achieve. The Reich that began in 1871 has never known it—not for an instant, neither as empire nor as republic. This was the main reason why it finally fell to dictatorship. Dictatorship is the natural state of social organisms in which idea and reality no longer know each other. We have come to a point where only two alternatives remain. Who will own the future, who will shape it: force, invoking obsolete ideas as a pretext but content with being force—or the better knowledge of the living? So far, knowledge was irresolute. Force, afraid of it, carries itself to extremes now which will eventually compel the better knowledge to buckle down. Events have seldom followed any other course.

The reality of the 1871 Reich never looked like anything but war preparation. It consisted of armament, and after the defeat it became an ever noisier cry for rearmament. It was the artificial maintenance of a permanently unproductive system of large landholdings. It was the state's conspiracy with the corporations, with the money-making class; the distaste of the governing personnel for direct contact with the people; its unwillingness to admit any one into the closed circle of the economically and politically guilty—after 1918 as well as before. Public business, in the main strictly secret before and after, had to be kept free from spiritual control.

In the face of unchanged reality, the idea also remained, fundamentally, in 1930 what it had been in 1890. The idea constantly insisted on security—not of frontiers and dominions which could not concern it, but of life. Life was to become less painful. Life at last was to be measured on the idea of justice; masses of men should not pay with their irretrievable lives for the mistakes and interests of a very few.

The year 1890 strove to solve all questions from the social side. Toward 1930 efforts were proceeding to reach a temporary goal by the international route. The goal was never within reach, despite certain hopes, and today it seems very distant. One reason is that strength and honesty of thinking are at their lowest ebb and soon will pass it. Another reason is that honest efforts are increasingly unpopular and involve risks—far greater ones than before and still growing with the decay of reality and its forces.

For it is not true that a forceful reality is the worst enemy of the idea. Rather, reality becomes embittered and intolerant when it begins to lose ground. A freshly victorious Reich in its abundance will grant some leeway to the lonely thinker. But a Reich fleeing from chaos into dictatorship extends its purgative actions to the idea—especially to the idea.

In Bismarck's Reich, there was a Socialism Act but nothing remotely resembling the notion of "cultural bolshevism." The Reich did not feel menaced by the thinkers. In 1894, Darwin's work was brought out by Reclam in a cheap edition and began to permeate all public consciousness. Its spirit found its way into the schools and was not held inadmissible. One could read the Bible story of the Creation in one class and expound the natural origin of species in the next; one let it remain to be seen which view would prove the stronger.

Actually, the spiritual basis of so warlike a realm could only be the belief in authority and power. God warrants your rulers; God gives them power over you; you have your very life just so they can dispose of it. That would have been perfect. However, William II's personal attempt to take the doctrine in full earnest proved a failure. He seemed belated. The freedom of the spirit had been part of the Reich from the day it was founded. Freedom of the spirit and spiritually unchecked force—both maintained their place in it. In fact, one might think that each stood up for the other.

This does not mean the thinkers and the poets. The most important of them viewed the martial Reich with thorough suspicion, particularly at its height. Adjusted to it, though, gladly adjusted to it were those politicians and parties whose whole right rested on the idea; even then, democracy made a habit of shelving truths for the sake of immediate advantages. The quarrel of social democracy with the ruling powers ended when it got its social legislation, and by way of compromise it changed into a nationalist military party like any other. It changed within, while outwardly continuing in opposition. It became accustomed to secretly rating the national above any social demand. Unbelief and a bad conscience presided over its international demonstrations. Had this not been true in the days of the Kaiser, the Republic, afterwards, would have had a different story.

There remains the memory of opportunities offered in the nineties to pure spirituality. One did not go to the dishonest trouble of justifying the spiritually untenable. It was known that doers were immoral, and the political doers on view were loved so much the less. Sufferers found their cause espoused, both intellectually and emotionally. The poet who rose at the time, Hauptmann, owed his best to the gift of compassion.

About 1900 human sympathy diminished among the thinkers. (They like to call themselves non-political at such times.) What took its place was beauty of soul—which has its values too; it has made great works possible and would not bar strength of character. What became dangerous was a combination, consisting of estheticism and doubts about reason. Almost throughout the nineteenth century, reason had loomed too large; it simply was not to be borne any longer. The godlessness of educated citizens and working masses had become too much a matter of course. When in the end natural science took up almost the entire space of religion, including philosophy, its position seemed usurped. The great Helmholtz had been cautious; he had begun every lecture with a qualifying phrase, to the effect: if nature could be understood at all . . .

This did not prevent the mediocre intellects from presupposing it as utterly comprehensible—for they no longer were philosophers, as Helmholtz had been. Rather, at the end of the century, they had for all metaphysics only contempt and laughter. One really must have seen that: before Nietzsche's triumph, every living philosopher was to the mediocre intellects an outdated or devious type, and what later had to be rediscovered as thought with the same rights as natural science—as in Wilhelm Dilthey's case—was taken for twaddle. The counterblow to this impoverishment of thought fell about 1900; but unfortunately it did not mean enrichment of thought. The purpose was to devalue it altogether. For what other reason was all weight placed on the irrational?

We have nothing but reason. Not even what we bring to light from subconscious depths is otherwise accessible than by reason. Above all, there is no art without rational thinking. Observation does not come to life till it has been thought through. Representation is a form of thought peculiarly connected with the senses—not that its other forms were unconnected with them. But the counterblow to intellectualism used even art merely as the most striking, though false, instance of the irrational among the great forces of life. The inferiority of reason was no less emphasized for the instinctive, deep realms, that were to be called nation, dream, love and war.

The new turn of mind, dating from 1900, deserved respect as long as it was searching and opened new sources of knowledge. It lost all claim to leniency when it opposed thought with other means of spiritual experience. These may be called sentiment, or presentiment; their essence always remains a failure to think. There is no antithesis to thinking except not thinking. This was perfectly well understood by the whole mediocrity—as all inventions of great minds get their final meaning only when they reach the little ones. They could smell that they were well off now. The rational has to be worked for, but the irrational is anybody's, anyhow; it always tends to spread and sweep away the precarious edifices of reason. The reintroduction of the irrational was a great chance for human weakness to let itself go, to give itself over to instincts which are not examined because they are deep and which must not be examined because depth makes them sacred.

Only thus could this half-century's decisive movement—nationalism—drive on to its extreme, and beyond. The Four Years' War truly looked like the last possible effort of nationalism; but in running amuck its muscles have not suffered since, and its impetus has grown. It cannot come to a halt until the irrational age has ended, for this was what made it ripe for its deeds; and it lasts and lasts—!

The mental attitudes of the body politic change terribly slowly. If their intolerability were universally established, they still would keep their traditional rights for a long time. In fact, it is not until a certain mental attitude is fundamentally obsolete that the body politic will put it to its most atrocious uses. At present, this is the case of irrationalism. We know that it is a thing of the past; all facts of life are against it. We know, but we do not want to know. The body politic and its barbaric inertia crush the individual awareness.

The nineteenth century, a great era of thought, had to descend and flatten out till every littlest monist had personally conquered the eternal enigmas. Then the mental attitude of the old century was finally ended, and contempt struck not only ratiocination but reason. Unreason, ascendant since, has risen to the most magnificent catastrophes. First there is a mental reversal, then an event; the irrational comes—and, not until its victory, the war. In 1890 it surely would have been prevented—by the reigning intellectualism, if by nothing else. By 1914 unreason had climbed high enough.

By 1932 irrationalism on its part has become small and ugly. It still occupies the entire reality; it would also favor a repetition of the catastrophe—but there, reality is already resisting. Though unreason just now might well suffice for a war, the world has become too weak for it. Instead, it maintains itself in disorder, distress and hatred, as we all know. We feel, too, that amidst this chaos the irrational era will come to its end sooner than if war were still a possibility. The last segment of any spiritual era is the noisiest. Seized by secret despair, men will have a last fling. Then somebody shouts into a microphone, in 1932: "We refuse to think intellectually!" No doubt. "We" should be embarrassed otherwise. Intellectual thinking has not been practised for some time and will have to be resumed by others.

The irrational era will expire toward 1940. Reason may prepare for its re-entry.

II. ACCIDENT TO A REPUBLIC

The German Republic of 1918 was placed into the dense core of an irrational era. From the beginning, it found it hard to breathe and live. A task of the highest reason, but an atmosphere of panting passions tired but not quenched by war—that was the situation of the nascent republic and that is its excuse for succumbing. No one, then or later, asked anything of it but that it substitute for the collapsed empire and replace it with its own lesser strength. The previous enemies made only one condition: that it be harmless. The Germans were content if only the Reich remained.

But a new republic is inwardly justified only when it expresses a thoroughly new state of mind. That it is new to the people happening to try it is not enough; and no belated aping of the "Western democracies" could justify the German Republic. It had to receive, even to anticipate, the content of its time. The least it might have done was to realize the social gains which entire parties in the country had spent decades demanding and preparing. But when the time came, nothing happened—or worse than nothing. The feudally bound large estates, those remnants of an outdated economic age, got hundreds of millions from governments of the Republic who betrayed their mission.

Not even in the social field did this republic do its self-evident duty; in foreign policy its acts were proportionately less progressive—and yet it had had bestowed on it, as its very own mission, the reconciliation of nations. The altogether most important, because newest, words in the Weimar Constitution invoked the spirit of international reconciliation. The German Republic would have been the first to work on it, and its work never would have vanished from the earth. It would have eased the lot of men; and although history so far lists only those who made things especially hard for them, a place was waiting for the names of the leaders to peace. They will come in any case, sooner or later; and by rising in time they would have spared the world, this continent, this country, the bulk of their present suffering. The German Republic was to furnish the leaders to peace; its share in immortality was to work on uniting Europe. This conception of itself, on the part of a state, would have been its present greatness and historic fame. Of course, these are dreams and idle big words.

In reality, we can only wonder how the few letters about reconciliation of nations got into the Weimar Constitution at all. It must have been the brief self-contemplation of the vanquished. Many a man feels called to an inner change after some disaster in his life; but nobody lets him make it, others regard him as what he always was, and he does not seriously believe in his new Adam, either. So it went with the Republic of Weimar. Its good intentions flowed from disconnected impulses; not joined to each other by the spirit of the time, they remained isolated, ineffectual, and were forgotten before the ink was dry on them.

Besides, the Peace of Versailles had just been concluded, and this, by necessity, was a product of the same nationalism which had made the nations ripe for the great war. Obviously, if the statesmen of Versailles had been capable of dictating a different peace, there would have been no war in the first place. The Germans, in turn, never did forgive their enemies for having remained the men of the war in the moment of peace. It finally shattered their own weak resolution not to remain the same. Ever since, the German majority has refused to notice the others' sundry departures from their nationalism; it gradually pushed its own to the level of the war and higher—and that in a republic whose import it failed to grasp though it had it in writing: reconciliation of nations.

The nationalist surge took place not against the Republic but in it. This is the truth, no matter what may be said to the contrary. For only a few days in its life did the Republic act otherwise than the old, war-like Reich would have acted after an involuntary abridgment of its power—and the attempt to act differently was made by an individual: Stresemann. The final accord with France was brought tangibly near by this one man. But nothing followed. The nation as a whole did not back him; the parties only just suffered him; beyond immediate utility, his goal was never seriously considered. It even made his own sincerity waver. After he died—more of his isolation than of his illness—no further step was taken toward understanding, only away from it. There was not a word or a thought of thanks for the good will that had waived contractual rights; instead, new claims were raised. All of them were more or less obtainable, too, but not without the other party's good will; and to that no appeal was made, only to the own, constantly tightened national excitement—which is already war, in so far as a state of mind can substitute for it.

In the minds of today's civilized people, war does not maintain itself as a definite fact to which they feel equal. It is a coercive notion, and weariness alone does not let them get rid of it. Horror, not self-confidence, would drive them to war. But the less they think of themselves, fundamentally, the more violently they will hate another. We cannot fight, so we will hate at least! We cannot even earn a living except by reaching an agreement with you; so all is your fault and we hate you! This is the hatred of many Germans for France, and of them, more live in distant parts of the country than near the border. National hatred must not meet its object in person; that would deprive it of some of its required ignorance. If the reverse were not certain, national hatred would look like a relic from days of slow transport and insufficient information—but it was moderate then, compared to the one now embedded in the artfully benighted heads. A poor individual in the mass hates, first, his competitor on the street corner and second, a foreign people—which is to say millions of men, their ancestors, life, work and fate for a thousand years. A truly suitable target for the corner store's enemy! He has his second foe now, and luckily knows him a little less than the corner store, of which at least he has heard gossip. There is no other way of hating freely.

But national hatred, this emptiest, least understood, least lived of all emotions, makes history at times, besides daily making the weather. The rulers, even in the Republic, did not only tolerate it; they used and spurred national hatred whenever reasons of domestic power distribution made it expedient. The most national of them cared in all things for power at home—more so than the republicans, in any case. The latter, the state proprietors, were only feebly convinced of their own right and, because they had no republican ideology, they feared that of the others: nationalism. Mustn't be lacking in that! The republicans were so anxiously respectful of nationalism that they governed almost always together with reactionaries or alternating with them and full of consideration for them. This is why, now that the reactionaries finally have grabbed all power and are permitting only their own in the state, nothing has really changed. Republican speeches have ceased, that is the outstanding difference; ministers are no longer put up on top of the administration to voice the word "republic" from time to time without ever having been full of its meaning. Nothing has changed; for never, not for a day, was there a thoroughly republican administration below the cabinets. One must have heard the stories of high officials who happened to be republicans—of their continuous battle, their isolated, undermined lives, ever in valiant contrast to the hostile intrigues of their own assistants. And in the country, at the same hour, a word came into use which, if true, would have honored the Republic: "the system." There never was a system.

Worse, rather: the prevailing system was the used, used-up one which the Republic first had found—the same preparation for always the same war, the same injustice in favor of monied groups that would yield nothing, and class interests with irreconcilable claims. The judiciary was never republican, everyone could see that; neither was the army, or the university. No part of the administration was pervaded by the republican spirit, least of all the Foreign Office. Open counter-revolutionaries of 1919 remained at their desks there; uncensured, this office kept working against the Republic. The plain conclusion never seems to have been drawn: that governments winking at that cannot have been deeply convinced themselves, either of the Republic or of their own right. At best, the governments of the Republic behaved like actors on rehearsal, not as if it were evening and the real thing. They only went through the motions of defending and maintaining a state. Logically, they were not around for the play's decisive performance.

Being unserious and unconvinced, they had to dissemble. Every minister would block disclosures about state enemies within the state. Every cabinet of the Republic would resign when it was faced with any frank republican decision; each would yield readily to the declared enemies of the Republic even when they lacked a majority. Let them show what they can do! If they get through with the Republic, the blame will not fall on us ministers, or us parties, but on democracy. There is our saving phrase! Democracy grants equal rights to all, including those who would abolish it. If we cannot help passing a republican law, we are the more willing to take some reactionaries into the government for our protection. In with our dear reactionaries! They must be around whenever possible —if not in the cabinet, then in our salons, at our parties! No official dinner was complete without them. The Chancellor who had styled himself non-partisan, because he opposed not only the essence but the form of the state, sat next to his republican colleagues. The inflation Chancellor, the Chancellor who promptly passed the 700 millions of the first American loan on to heavy industry—all highly placed, all still around. Always the same society; excluded was, and remained, anyone who had not governed in the Republic but only thought and fought for it. A writer, who did his bit for the Republic's fulfillment with its own meaning, enjoyed not even the advantages of the Law for the Protection of the Republic. He was no "public person" such as the minister of the smallest German state. There was no system, but there was a clique.

The republicans never felt safe in their own state. And the governing personnel constantly took the position of merely having to administer—not to safeguard, not to lead. The best reputation was that of a good administrator, of labor unions or of state police. However, when these two ought to have saved the Republic, they were not called upon. This quite untried state showed the symptoms of a very old democracy, getting careless as if nothing could happen to it at all because the ballot will make the final decision. This, as we know, was made by other means.

Where all think in like manner, noise will win in the end. There is no doubt that the Leftist ministers were nationalists; it never occurred to them that they might be something else. But they neglected to shout their depleted ration out loud; only thus was its preservation possible beyond its time. The Rightist governments, as usual, were not so scrupulous. They drew all attention to the national, so as to put through social reaction under its cover. At last, when reaction and nation had become one in the public mind, National Socialism could break out— the great, new movement, the movement of standstill, the novelty of an old-age phenomenon, the claim of the crippled and empty to a great rise and upheaval. Still, no people's movement is long a mere tool of ambition; in time it really turns into the people's cause—and thus into an equal danger to all, to its own leaders, financiers and false friends, particularly to the ruling clique without distinction of Right and Left. And so, in the end, it was a dictatorial Rightist government which came to the aid of its Leftist friends when they no longer knew where to turn. The Republic, already more than halfway in civil war, was saved from foundering altogether by a traffic accident—honorably described by the names of the new ministers.

They are not names of traitors but of rescuers. A republic without a spirit and faith of its own needed monarchist life-savers. This can hardly add to its disgrace; but the National Socialists may congratulate themselves, on whose account one side resorted to flight and the other to a coup d'état. At this stage of events the National Socialists represent the people. To bar and disenfranchise them, all play hand in glove, no matter what they call themselves; and even an otherwise repulsive movement of lies and brutality seems justified.

But—the republicans are here and they will remain. The majority can be nothing else, despite all drives against "the system." Basically, open reaction meets a united people. It is no longer the same people; it was transformed by slackened class and moral lines, by new communal habits, a more human attitude and more accessible mind—all unaccustomed to pre-republican Germany. It has changed since the end of the martial empire—which for that reason will not return—as no other people in so short a time. For some of the Republic's years, after the revolution and before the civil war, these people knew themselves free, for once, and they will not forget the experience. The people were on the right way; they were halted only by economic distress which made them listen to the furious rhapsodists of a "Third Reich," while in the Republic they held the practical promise of an ever more popular state right in their hands. The Republic needed only to be taken at its word and it had to find men who took it seriously. The election laws had to be bettered, and the parliament made truly responsible to the people. The people were always ready. They were filled with the Republic, more than they knew. In the last weeks before the reactionary upheaval the word "freedom" was heard in the streets—shouted by Communists as well as bourgeois. The word "freedom," and all that it contains in values, dignity, self-chosen duty, right and hope, had scarcely been explained to them by their parties. The rulers had employed it hardly at all. The streets had never heard it. But when the Republic came under the most perilous pressure, that word rose on its own.

If freedom is no chimera, it means the intense claim to obey no one but reason. Where the word freedom regains its meaning, there is always a foreboding of the approach—not much longer to be delayed by force, stupidity and lies—of a new age of reason.

III. UNPLEASANT FACTS

The dawn of an age of reason depends on men, on their readiness and their intentions. Irrationalism prevailed effortlessly, but reason never conquers by itself; no automatic causes inject it into the course of events. It has to be fought for.

The defeat of irrationalism is no warrant yet, no matter how forcefully and completely it occurs. The irrationally determined century has borne nothing but destruction, destitution, hatred and a great void in culture. This would not keep it from sinking still lower, ever lower, into endless depths. A part of mankind can sink endlessly as well as rise; why not the few countries extending from the border of the Russian realm to the Atlantic coast. We cannot count on the axiom that recovery must follow upon exhaustion, that suddenly we shall be on top again without knowing how. Without the tensest determination to start afresh such things do not happen—least of all when the powers of ruin and decay are so active and filled with hatred.

Political irrationalism is already calling for another war. Already it needs another. And though for lack of inner preparedness war does not break out, the odor of it is present. Its atmosphere reigns; people feel at war—especially here, with many of the young generation no longer consciously unreasonable but simply mentally non-existent. Militarism is being warmed up in Germany; it is known from hearsay and said to have constituted the ideal of a people's community. Declining finance capitalism prepares for a last, desperate act; the hopes of nationalism rest on the final round, after it has lost all those before. If the old system really were still in power, war would break out and be waged, logically, against Russia. Nothing else is left to men who refuse to learn and insist on sticking to the old, national, monopoly-economic system. Though national German politics is still aimed against France, the only end of this aim is "equal rights"—and the two interested arms industries interpret these somewhat differently than do prestige politicians and enraged nationalists. Rearmed Germany would be sent forth against Soviet Russia—that

alone would conform to the old system. As far as can be foreseen, the
system would lose. No revolution of which the idea is based on reality,
and which has like-minded men on the other side, will be beaten. Nor,
by the way, does the old system figure on winning; the arms industries
make money in either case, and the revolution's spread would be halted
by its very military victories—as in the past another one was stopped by
Napoleon's triumph. Triumphs bring their own revenge; and the system
would have gained time, as it did then. At least it thinks so. Actually,
nothing remains for the system of Europe's old national states but irresistible, unlimited decline—through war or without it.

They need not end in great disasters; they can bog down. German
nationalism in its temporarily last phase is an example. Forbidden, so far,
to let off steam without, it still finds ways and means to work out at home.
Torturing one's own people also is something, as long as the enemy stays
inaccessible. In fact, the nationalist of the last phase prefers it. The most
despised foes of this nationalist are not foreigners but compatriots. whom
he wants to expel and calls "un-German." To him, it seems a commandment of the nation's greatness to reduce it by a good half—not to mention
economic blockade and political isolation; these he imposes upon the
nation out of pride, because it could not conquer and rule the others.
He is incessantly screaming about its peril, from wars which no one in
the world wants to wage against it; he turns superfluous armament into
a question of to be or not to be, instead of simply heeding the command
of life and cooperating with the other nations. Anything that excites,
exhausts, anything that feeds desolate hatred is national and satisfies
nationalism.

The other nations need not look so askance at Germany's movements.
At best, it is due to trifles that they do not furnish the same sight. Victory
or defeat are superficialities. They were victorious; this country was defeated and does not bear its defeat well; that is not what matters. Nationalism prevails abroad as it does here and in the same historic circumstances would lead to the same excesses. In the victorious and powerful
countries more heads are clear enough to grasp supernational facts. But
the ruling policies cling to the same system of national states jealously
guarding their distances from each other, distrusting, outwitting, checking each other, not one wanting to know the other save by espionage and
war. A restriction and reduction of the chance to live, to see and enjoy
the world—that is nationalism in its last phase; but, furthermore, it coin-
cides with the known climax of technical progress and communication.
Just at the time when everything, especially food supplies, could more

easily than ever be secured for any nation, unbeaten or conquered, and for the poorest individual—just now an unremoved obstacle has to lie there; and it lies in men themselves. Wheat is poured into the ocean, and beyond it men starve. Cotton that might have clad millions is purposely destroyed. At first sight, all that seems chargeable to monopoly capital: it has not even learned how to distribute, it does not control the world it wants to control. Still, monopoly capital can only afford inefficiency because nationalism covers it. Nationalism, in men, is the co-conspirator of every outward abuse.

It is invoked by all who cause and exploit human misery. It serves as the ideal justification when men, crammed into frontiers, go hungry, fail to work and run to seed. It excuses the planless disorder of an economy, just as, in war, it glorifies the finished chaos. It outranks finance capitalism and militarism. They are its moral dependents; they would not have come into the world but for it; and it was here first. A feeling and a state of mind always precede the actual facts; the national idea and passion came before the armed people and before the subject of industrial capital. If only this were quite understood, this priority of the idea!

At first, nationalism was life-giving like other ideas. In its course, it became for every waking consciousness the terror we see. It was a French invention (a fact which has yet disturbed no German nationalist) and originally won the nation's status in combat—from the king. The French Revolution was directed against a kingdom, and later too exclusively against kings; though nationalist, it did not hate any people. Rather, it loved them all; intellectually, both it and nationalism were descended from the philosophical humanitarianism of the eighteenth century. The dawn and sunrise of one of mankind's days look different from its nocturnal end. In Germany too, nationalism started with democratic fraternization, as the people's cause against their rulers. "Unite, unite, unite!" wrote Schiller, the sympathizer with the French Revolution; and the word sounded so powerfully on the stage because the powers that be kept it from being reality. The highest, the purest things which German nationalism had to say, were said while no German national state existed. The latter, long awaited in vain, finally came into being—but unfortunately not because an inner command, "Unite!" had freely brought it forth; a foreign war had to be brought about and brought to a victorious end; that finally produced it. Besides, by then this was nationalism's general procedure; from the libertarian wars of the Revolution, nationalism had progressed to national wars. It had ceased fighting kings. It served all rulers to goad their peoples against each other. In this late phase it was adopted by the German national state—a late arrival, as the Republic was afterwards; both were newcomers showing symptoms of senility.

Rooted in an age of optimistic reason, overflowing with good will and self-confidence—this was the nationalism which we, the living, did not know. The one we have had to bear is composed of negations, and nothing, in nations, parties or individuals, is so sure to cause its infuriated eruption as a sense of inferiority. "They are maltreating us." This is where an adult people, the Germans, look for guidance—as a bewildered child will decide for or against playing, depending on how "they treat" it. A man acts himself, following only his own knowledge and his own will. "Equal rights"—meaning the outdated, irksome right to arm for war! Whoever has it would be glad to surrender it. Not mere "equal rights," precedence was what the Germans could have had—and missed; of course, it concerned the rights and duties of nations of today and tomorrow—not those of generations passing with their nationalism, which with much noise are already half underground.

The psychological phenomenon of maniacal extinction is clothed, in the case of nationalism of the last phase, in an ideology of madness. No real fact conforms to it; it misunderstands and denies all. Fittingly, the nationalist ideology opposes personal thinking. The gentleman who lately was allowed to rule and teach all of us here, spoke of "alien intellects." It seemed advisable to him, for his purpose, to separate the people carefully from those who think for them. A nation, then, is assumed to bring its ideas along with it into the world, once and for all, without their having fathers. In reality it is the lonely thinker who spawns the ideas—with his nation, with all nations, with the spiritual world. Even the least nationally contested intellectual property is owned by thinkers who in their day were called aliens by all orators without vision. But in every fertile brain live germs from all other fertile brains; the spirit is not alone the highest but the most varied form of cooperation, between nations which have long appeared united in the persons of their thinkers. The spirit must be supernatural because there is only one spirit—and it is neither French nor German. The law of the spirit is truth, which carries neither a passport nor a tax receipt. To think nationally, one definitely must "refuse to think intellectually"—and even this formula is owed to some "alien intellect."

He who cannot bear the spirit invokes the blood. Strong and fertile generations never found that necessary. They needed no "Nordic race"— a free invention, resorted to when the remaining strength will barely suffice for gestation but not for proper thinking. That is when blood mysticism gets its inning. The nation is supposed to be a "blood community" —as if it had not obviously become a community of interests, with the participants interested in varying degrees, with cheats and cheated, as customary. History has arbitrarily thrown most nations together, and everywhere the "blood community" consists mainly in the fact that one part bloodily compelled the other to go along. Besides, every part of the nation would find its closest relatives beyond the borders; after a hundred mixtures of all European tribes, let a new migration of races try to mix them more thoroughly! All that is known; the facts are based on experience; no child would deny them. But entire sciences are dug up to spirit or talk them away.

Cancelled conceptions are continued in the lists, like dead voters in an election register—for example, the sovereignty of states, or, if you please, of nations. For a long time, no state—Germany least of all!—has made any domestic or foreign decisions, unless allowed or urged to by the total will of Europe. For us that evolution began with the founding of the Republic; and it will not be ended when we wage or refrain from our next war according to the decision of a greater source of power than we are. The sovereign right to wage war has long been yielded; the decision rests with the League of Nations; and in order to regard the League as non-existent, as German nationalists would like to do, a state still must take the trouble of locating itself in East Asia. Here it would have seriously unpleasant consequences, as nobody knows better than this state. But it is sovereign! And facts are spirited and talked away.

In its domestic policies, of course, a nation can go still farther. So far, nobody stops it from ruining itself, just so that this, at least, will resemble a voluntary act. It is still permitted to transform itself into an autarchy as a medium puts himself into a trance. At a stroke, all connections, all dependencies of world economics, vanish. By a simple spiritual act, an industrial nation of today has moved back into the stage of a small business man who believes in his independence until he is bought up or shut down. Among nations, too, each may still frivolously cause its own collapse and thus speed that of the others. An ideology of madness will block the path of facts which stride on without even noticing it. But it is sovereign—though all the facts of life should trample over it!

Life itself opposes nationalism. All living facts and demands mean plainly the supernational; neither doubt nor escape remain. Nationalism has finally run aground, politically as well as economically; it can no longer safeguard any state and it destroys the people. What part of the

world we own, its spiritual and physical existence, the very structure of
its states, can only be maintained and set in forward motion by supernational proceedings. Practical reason compels it, if not the plain truth
of thinking and feeling. No man who has examined himself retains an
honest feeling for the closed national state; by now it has brought too
much misfortune and cost too many senseless sacrifices; its measure is
full. The emotions—supposing one has any—no longer speak in favor of
a state of interests, no matter how often it may call itself a people's state,
nor in favor of a military, tariff, force and hunger state. Free thought is
through with a closed national state which beyond any reasonable vindication grew into an end in itself and which will rob the nation of the
freedom of spirit and conscience, along with all other freedoms, rather
than relieve it at last of its nightmare.

The Germans accomplished their most lasting deeds without a national
state, and some of their most deeply felt ones while they were longing
for it. Whoever sees *Tell* must realize, first, that emotions and ideas
brought a whole reality to life—but then, that not just the reality that
rose at that time called for spiritual preparedness. Of us, too, such preparedness is required; and unless we move beyond the previous achievement we shall lose it, and every other. Great works, as those of the German classics, do not come into being except to proclaim the next reality,
and that in turn does not come unless we have thought it first. But in this
country life goes on in the past, as obstinately as nowhere else any longer.
More than that: here, force is used just so as to stagnate; entire upheavals
are staged and suffered just so as not to move from the spot; and whoever thinks beyond the old power and national state shall be intimidated
by epithets like "un-German." He is exactly as German as was Schiller,
who called for nationalism when it was still dangerous. Every next stage
is German, just as it is French, and the previous one is no longer distinguished by any mark other than that it wobbles and threatens to break
down. But when that happens, it will drag everything with it, without
national distinctions.

IV. THE MANIFESTO

. . . Events tend to extreme; we are no longer free to suppress the truth
even when faced with a roaring sea of untruthfulness. What is required
is an accounting of a politico-intellectual system. This is no job for political experts who have become one with it. Nor is it a job for the bankrupt business leaders who for so long were one of our national supersti-

tions; now, at last, the anxious faith in business is shattered by the desperate straits of the country. What remains? So deep a renewal can only start where men think. True, the new notions should be accepted by now; they are so evident in the facts themselves. But heretofore so-called leaders could live more comfortably against the facts, and now each is afraid of the other. For too long they have vied with each other in nationalism; if suddenly one admitted that it is nonsense, the other who persists in it might succeed for one more little while—the last while, before the game is up! That would be asking too much of the doers. At least some confessors must precede them—men who are accustomed to succeeding only in the long run and who do not fear the people.

Nothing has been stated here but hidden matters-of-course. The obstinacy of their concealment is unusual. The confessor, too, may run other than everyday risks. Many could do the intellectual work. In addition, courage alone is needed—first, the courage to wage a big battle for so much overripe truth, waiving all claims to originality, and then just plain courage. I wish it to the individual intellectuals, for this is their hour. A spiritual system is to be replaced. The old, which ruled the expired part of our century, was irrationalism; it coincided with the last phases of the national idea. The supernational idea, which alone has any vitality, presupposes a restoration and rejuvenation of reason, a whole new way of living in reason and truth. The very confession of the supernational idea opens the new era. To confess is to act, and among the actions of the moment this is the only one not quite in vain.

Besides, the isolated confessors will be amazed how little alone they are. Probably, a majority in this country are really tired of obeying unreasoning passions instead of better knowledge. Sometimes the better knowledge and conscience have but to appear to be answered promptly by hitherto unheard inner voices. Belief in blind force, in not thinking, in senseless battle and evil hate—perhaps all that has reached the point of being mere consensus, without inner consent. Men are waiting for the word of deliverance, though they still bellow when it is voiced. The very party that appeared last, that of utter anti-reason, might be the first to feel uncertainty and weariness. No one carries on like that for long. These National Socialists are just a mass of the people, without firm principles other than the will to live. With socialism unfulfilled, they turned to nationalism of the final phase. Nothing is so easy as vigorously to convince a suffering and helpless mass of people that a known object is the latest achievement. But just as quickly they will be disillusioned. They cannot help seeing that their worst social enemies are by no means less

national—that they themselves, on grounds of this same nationalism, are
shelved and finally enslaved. The first result will be that they find other
masses of the people less contemptible; the next, that they will form an
emergency coalition with the socialists of their country. The emergency
is urgent; the coalition will not be long delayed. It can lead far. For the
first time, the entire harassed majority of a people would have united
against the few whose declared position of power is the national state.

Individuals must confess that they have left the national state; for they
are but the beginning of the mass and anticipate a people. They must
speak simply, as if in fact they were the mass—though until now it would
rather beat them up than listen. At this stage alone, however, is it necessary to speak—not later. They must confess:

I desire the supernatural state—because nothing else can promise the
facts their natural results and the people their freedom. A single country
can no longer live in Europe—neither economically nor politically, and
morally least of all. Several, supernationally bound, can hope to make
their peoples better and happier. A man can no longer serve a single
country; whoever says so, is lying. There are only interrelated interests
to serve.

They must confess:

I have left the old power and national state because its moral content
has been expelled from it. It still maintains itself only by hatred and bru-
talization, and to the immoral force it must apply are due all the crimes
abounding in it—including those seemingly private. Men are sacrificed to
the nationalist lie. Humanity is sacrificed to the nationalist lie. I am thoroughly tired of hearing the impudent lie that the highest calling is not
the fight for humanity but the fight against it. The most decent way for
the worshipers of the martial existence to reach their goal in life would
be suicide—without millions dying with them involuntarily.

The individual must confess:

The fatherland, in the shape of the present power and national state,
has lost all sense and value. It does not love us, it tortures and destroys
us; and therefor nobody loves it. Millions hate it as they never hated an
enemy. (Ask the victims of the "voluntary" labor service!) All the slaves
of an inhuman fatherland throw it mutually at each other's heads, so as
better to hate and exploit one another; this, while it retains the form of
the old national state, is its sole purpose. Restore the security and dignity of life, and you will remember your moral nature, self-respect, good
will toward the world—your need to join it, in place of this wrathful aversion forced upon you by an inhuman state.

The individual must confess:

I believe and know that in their deepest, traditional core the Germans —they especially—stand high above their state. They, having listened more closely to themselves, will find it easiest to leave it. The next step is always German—and the next step is the supernational.

The creed needs only to be spoken; the truth, once voiced, is always well on its way. It is the mark of the living truth that it stands ready and is still dangerous. It was a German, as Germans used to be and shall be again, who wrote:

> "Down here, it is not worth our while to falter;
> But to speak true and freely suits us all,
> For in sepulchres soon we all shall rest."

And that remains true though no ornate tomb awaits us, but only a small mound, quickly forgotten.

Translated by E. B. ASHTON

BELGIUM

INTRODUCTION

By Marnix Gijsen (J. A. Goris)

BELGIUM ENJOYS some of the advantages of being a country with a bilingual culture, but she suffers also some of the inconveniences of this particular situation. In the estimation of the world her literary achievements are very often absorbed by her neighbors, either by Holland or by France, and at times it may seem that she has no literary production of her own. This is due to the fact that those authors who reach an international audience are claimed by the French or are classified—for simplicity's sake—among the Dutch. On the other hand, a number of Belgian writers—French-language authors, as well as Flemish ones—devote themselves to ardent provincialism, and the charm of their books depends greatly on the reader's knowledge of the country and the people depicted. All too often universal human qualities emerge from their work only with difficulty and late in their career.

Among writers of both language groups, the spiritual upheaval created by the first World War resulted in a strong urge to avoid and even combat provincialism and to attain a way of expressing themselves that would allow their works to reach beyond the narrow borders of Belgium. Morally uprooted and puzzled as they were, through the anguish which all young Europe felt when it became apparent that the peace was being lost, they wanted to destroy the last vestige of the provincial complacency some of their elders had revered. Having suffered from the war more severely than many other peoples in Europe, they wanted to speak their mind in the chaotic post-war world. They did so with vigor and eloquence.

Except for authors like Maurice Maeterlinck on the French side, and Karel van de Woestijne on the Flemish, who had, long before the first World War, attained their full and impressive stature, most of the Belgian writers of significance who published between the two wars broke with pre-war canons and isms. They looked for inspiration and guidance not to their immediate elders—ensconced in what they considered unworthy sensualism or petty individualism—but considered as their masters writers like Romains, Duhamel, Vildrac, Appollinaire, while the Flemish underwent the influence, to a certain extent at least, of the German expressionists, of Werfel, or Rilke and very much that of Claudel and Léon Bloy.

In the name of liberty and with the excuse of Dionysian inspiration, much

756

damage was inflicted upon the traditional poetical technique. Verse became free to the point of anarchy, grammar and syntax were forced to acrobatics often as painful to the eye as to the mind of the reader. Most of these experiences coincide with the history of the literary tendencies in the rest of Western Europe. In the end, the benefit reaped by literary expression from these vagrancies was far greater than the irritation they inflicted upon the bourgeois reader and even upon those who naturally felt sympathetic to new movements and "frissons nouveaux" in art.

After a short period of aggressive modernism, during which the technical and social flies-by-night of the jazz age (a short age at that) were considered the true proofs of the new poetical spirit, things quieted down, and poets as well as prose writers reverted to a new classicism: they sought simplicity, limpidity and honesty. They were still convinced that aesthetic writing was enemy No. 1 of real writing, but they understood also that modernistic accessories in a poem had nothing to do with its intrinsic value. The pilgrimage among the forms was to an end, the real thing could start.

FLEMISH AUTHORS

The influence of humanitarian ideas, which so generously flowered at the outcome of the first World War, made itself felt with dramatic intensity among the young Flemish writers. The conflict between the older generation and the younger centered around the work of *Karel van de Woestijne,* the greatest poet Flanders has known since the Middle Ages. His verse developed from a rich and sonorous sensuality to a pathetic and profound mysticism. It was timeless and extremely individualistic, the exact opposite of what the younger authors valued and went so far as to consider indispensable. His unconcern with the social and political problems of the day, his aristocratic attitude scandalized them. But as years passed by, it became apparent that he had pursued with unfailing genius the permanent and deeper values of life. When he died, in 1929, recognition of his tragic talent was universal.

Those devoted to peasant lore and cosy provincialism suffered most heavily in the bagarre. The modernists, as well as a group of younger poets that remained faithful to traditional prosody and kept a strictly individualistic outlook on life, rejected their popular writings. Only one of them victoriously withstood all attacks: *Felix Timmermans,* an excellent story-teller, a moderately sensuous optimist, who developed a colorful although incorrect language of his own. After a great deal of decorative writing, he was to outgrow his comfortable limitations in an excellent peasant novel of universal appeal.

Completely allergic to the influence of literary tendencies, *Stijn Streuvels,* the grand old man of Flemish letters, continued his forceful naturalism and, with easy grace,, reached the heights of the Russian and Scandinavian story-tellers who had always inspired him.

On the antipodes of the "écriture artiste" and of the commonplace rural novel stood *Willem Elsschot,* a novelist of merciless humor and grim moral courage. Humor to him is only a shield against life's vulgarity and pettiness. He writes about middle-class people with such deep sarcastic anger and such chastely hidden feeling for man's misery that his position is quite unique in Belgian letters and perhaps even in the European literary field.

An impressive group of young novelists, who began to publish after the war, found out that the one and only subject of the novel is *man,* not the climate or the fauna and flora that surround him. This discovery was responsible for an increase in tempo and a better psychological insight. Among these writers, the most classical-minded is *Maurice Roelants.* His novels go back to the great tradition of Benjamin Constant's *Adolphe* and to the works of other keen analysts of the human soul. With less technical perfection, but with extreme generosity, *Lode Zielens* devotes his attention to the Flemish proletariat. He flows over with the milk of human kindness. But the most powerful and productive of them all is *Gerard Walschap.* Using all the resources of rhetoric, his story rushes down like a mountain stream. His search is essentially along psycho-pathological lines. Although his personages often border on the abnormal, the moral of his work is always a belief in the profound goodness and greatness of life and of man. Aside from his torrential tempo, which comes close to the tornado pace James Cain used in *The Postman Always Rings Twice,* the European author he may best be compared with is François Mauriac.

Two definite trends characterize Flemish poetry between 1918 and 1940. *Paul van Ostayen* took the lead of the modernistic group, but as a guide he acted more as a Pied Piper than as a Moses in search of a poetical Canaan. He switched from a prophetic, social kind of poetry to complete dadaism, and ended in the air-tight regions of "poésie pure." His experiments, and his wild renunciations of successive allegiances, were a very interesting spectacle. A born acrobat, he never broke his neck. To Flemish poetry he brought a freshness and an alertness unknown since Guido Gezelle. Parallel to Van Ostayen's action, although very different in technique and in sensibility, we may name the contributions of *Wies Moens, Paul Verbruggen, Victor Brunclair, Marnix Gijsen, Pieter Buckincx, Bert Decorte, Karel Jonckheere, Albe* and *R. Verbeeck.*

Most outstanding among the classicists—those who refused to believe in free verse or in a strictly personal rhythm—was *Jan van Nijlen,* a wise poet and a warm-hearted moralist (as a moralist should be). Among the human poets, who refused to be "humanitarian" or cosmic, *Raymond Herreman* is the most outstanding.

The Flemish theater cannot boast anything very remarkable for many decades. *Herman Teirlinck,* a talented novelist of the naturalist school, introduced into Flanders the revolutionary technique of such European playwrights as Capek, Gordon Craig and others. Although a good deal of his work was purely experimental, his influence should not be underestimated.

The influence of Flemish letters on Dutch writing has augmented tremendously since 1918. Most of the young Flemish writers, by increasing the distance between their work and the folk-lore novelistics of their elders, come close enough to Dutch literature to make their works indistinguishable from Dutch publications. But, although their works may be idiomatically identical, they keep a special flavor for which these authors' closeness to, and their easy contacts with, the Gallic spirit is to be held responsible.

FRENCH WRITERS

The authors who began to express themselves after 1918 were preceded by an impressive lineage of writers. The work of some of them had had a profound influence on European literature; Maeterlinck who actively survived, Verhaeren (1916) who sang his mechanical age with Whitman-like gusto and some of his model's verbal barbarism, Van Lerberghe (1907) a lyricist of pure and noble perfection and Max Elskamp (1918) whose inarticulate archaism had an irresistible charm. To equal them or to surpass them would have called for a revolt that did not materialize. Therefore prose-writing in the period to which this volume is dedicated was strictly individual and never inspired by the precepts of a school. Among these writers the most noteworthy are *Franz Hellens, Jean Tousseul, André Baillon, Charles Plisnier* and *Henri Michaux, Marie Gevers* and *Madeleine Ley.*

Franz Hellens moves on the border of reality and fantasy with a kind of perverse grace. He has been described as "an explorer of uncharted realms of mystery." It is indeed evident that his sympathy goes to the hidden side of our psychic life and that he, personally, has no difficulty whatsoever in moving around in an atmosphere that has a strange quality of hallucination and solemn earnest. *Jean Tousseul* is the patient chronicler of life in a small, Meuse valley village, whose inhabitants he depicts with patient care and deep comprehension. The utter simplicity of his style is in accord with his deep love of the humble. His major work, *Jean Clarambaux,* was published in translation in 1939 in this country. His books have the aroma of the Walloon countryside. His characters are often tragic, but life to him has a charming sadness which reminds one of Glück's ballet of the Elysian Fields: a land where even suffering has become harmonious, an inevitable, decisive and indispensable part of the game Destiny plays with us.

As for *Charles Plisnier,* an abundant and solid writer, he divides his attention between the psychology of modern—i.e. unhappy—marriage and the atmosphere of latent revolution that prevailed in Europe for many years. There was little in his work that would make him recognizable as a Belgian: from the very beginning, he was a truly international author, a European observer who had completely discarded the home atmosphere and the "wisdom" of the village or small-town philosophers. Although his style may not be exceptional, the construction of his books proves him to be a novelist of rare power and intuition. In 1938 his outstanding merits were recognized by the award of the Prix Goncourt.

Among these authors, *Henri Michaux* is certainly the most penetrating and the most original. He is a professed phantasist obsessed by an urge for indirect moralization. He seems to have adopted a shrewd nonsensical attitude toward life. At times he is charmingly impudent, at other moments his keen observation spirals down into little known mental and emotional regions. Like Paul van Ostayen, he belongs to the acrobatic intellectual type. His flip-flops are graceful and done with the greatest of ease but the reader still has the feeling that the performer might break his neck and after all that's what the audience is waiting for. The popular and simple novels of *Marie Gevers* have a quaint provincial charm, while the only novel published by *Madeleine Ley* (*Olivia*) proves her keen sense of psychological observation and her merciless gift for analysis. The pathetic "true confessions" of *André Baillon,* who died young after a tempestuous existence, should also be mentioned.

When the era of experiment was over, it was evident that *Odilon Jean Périer* and *Eric de Haulleville* had been the most talented among the poets. As the gods will it, both died young. Périer was a poet of exquisite grace and sensibility. His verse is fresh and wise with a Mozartian combination of fluidity and underlying strength. *Eric de Haulleville* was a charming fantasist, whose prose was as close to poetry as possible, without the annoying pretensions of poetical prose. His playfulness, the highly lyrical and at the same time ironical quality of his abrupt poems, made him the Puck and the Ariel of the Belgian Parnassus.

Among the living who have outgrown victoriously the experimental age, *Marcel Thiry, René Verboom, Maurice Careme, Paul Vanderborght, José Gers, Léon Kochnitzky* and *René Guiette,* should be mentioned.

Foremost among the playwrights—facile princeps with H. Soumagne and H. Closson—is *Fernand Crommelynck,* a tormented genius, eruptive and abundant. His dramas give his audiences a feeling of definite uneasiness. He is never their equal, their comrade. He is their superior, their terror. Gifted with psychological second sight, he steps in when the situation is tensest, and his powerful lyricism lifts the event and the dramatis personae to the height of Shakespearean drama. Undoubtedly, there is a baroque flavor about this art, but a baroque so grandiose and so rich that even Giraudoux' devilishly clever plays may look bleak compared to the forceful humanity of Crommelynck.

I am well aware that this survey of two very rich literatures which I have crammed into a few pages is extremely unjust through faults of omission, but wishing to avoid dry and useless enumerations of authors and works, I preferred to put the spotlight on the most outstanding of our Belgian writers, even giving preference to those whose works have already come to an end.

(In the selection of the Flemish contributions for this anthology I was, unfortunately, very much limited by circumstances.)

Maurice Maeterlinck

NOTES

WHY SHOULD WE not one day know all that nature knows? It is even surprising that we have not learned it yet.

✿   ✿   ✿

Great physicians and surgeons think that they can cheat death, but they cannot cheat death any more than they can destiny, which is but one of its names. They merely succeed in cheating their patients.

✿   ✿   ✿

It might be said that certain children have no guardian angel. Other children seem to feel it and avoid them. . . .

＊ ＊ ＊

We should love all that surpasses us, all that is beyond us and, above all, all that is higher than us.

＊ ＊ ＊

Before Christ's time, one might have said, by way of excuse, that God did not know what suffering was. But since the martyrdom of His son, He must know what it means.

＊ ＊ ＊

As the past is always sad, why should the future not also be sad?

＊ ＊ ＊

Do you sometimes ask yourself: How and in what light do I appear to God?

＊ ＊ ＊

Why should the world know where it is going? What does it mean to know where one is going?
Where should it go, being everywhere?
Do you know where you are going? Yes, towards death. But what is death? Death is neither an aim nor an end.

＊ ＊ ＊

I never saw anything miraculous in any one life, because everything in life is miraculous.

＊ ＊ ＊

What would have happened to me had I not been born?

＊ ＊ ＊

The folly of men is only equalled by the folly of the gods they created.

＊ ＊ ＊

Astronomers are able to calculate, in terms of our time, the movements of all visible worlds.
What meaning can it have, this measuring of an eternity that ignores our time?

＊ ＊ ＊

When time and space have been annihilated what will remain for us? For both time and space will be annihilated when we no longer have a body.

✿   ✿   ✿

What man thinks he is admiring in the God he has created or is looking for, is always himself; everything ends in idolatry.

✿   ✿   ✿

I am never alone. I can see and hear all my dead friends who surround me and follow me everywhere.

What happens to those dead which we resuscitate in our conversations and memories and who then sink back into their tombs?

✿   ✿   ✿

I saw my mother dead. It was she, and it was no longer she. There was something inexplicable between us called eternity. Even the soul of a mother is unable to transcend it.

✿   ✿   ✿

If God wished to die, if God could die, what would become of us? We should be nothing, like Him; but nothing would become God, and nothing would be changed in the universe. Everything is, was and will be as before; and death would become life again.

✿   ✿   ✿

"God does not know what He is doing!" cried the hero of some play, I have forgotten which. This is the cry that should never be uttered. It is we who no longer know what God is doing.

✿   ✿   ✿

Everybody is looking for happiness, and only succeeds in finding death. Is it in death then, or beyond death, that happiness is to be found?

✿   ✿   ✿

The more I revolve round my God, the larger the circles become with which I surround Him. The further I get away from what He represented in my mind, the nearer I get to what He will be in my life beyond the tomb.

✿   ✿   ✿

God has not said His last word. Probably He has not yet spoken His first one.

✦   ✦   ✦

What is the language of death? We do not know yet, as no one understands it.

And what about the dead?

They do not speak, they say everything with silence.

Translated from the French by SYBILLE BEDFORD

Henri Michaux

A DOG'S LIFE

I ALWAYS go to bed early and exhausted; at the same time it would be hard to point out any kind of tiring work during my day.

Perhaps it would be hard to point out anything.

As far as I'm concerned, however, what surprises me is that I manage to keep going until evening, and that I haven't got to go bed at four in the afternoon.

What tires me like this are my perpetual interferences.

As I said already, I fight with everybody in the street; I box people's ears, I seize women's bosoms, using my foot as a tentacle I spread panic in the coaches of the subway.

Above all I am harassed by books. I can't let a word keep its sense, not even its form.

I catch it, and with some effort I root it up and take it away for good from the author's herd.

There are easily some thousands of sentences in a single chapter, and I have to sabotage them all. It is a necessity to me.

Sometimes certain words remain like towers. I have to attack them several times and, suddenly, at the turning of an idea, when I'm already well advanced in my work of destruction, I come across that tower once more. So I hadn't really knocked it down and have to go back and find its proper poison, and thus spend an interminable time.

And then, when I've finished reading the book, I feel sorry for myself because I haven't understood a word . . . naturally. I wasn't able to fatten on it. I stay thin and dry.

It must be that I thought that when I had destroyed everything I should find balance. Possibly. But it does seem to take a long time, a good long time.

❀   ❀   ❀

SIMPLICITY

What used to be lacking in my life up till now was above all simplicity. I am beginning to change this.

Now, for instance, I am always going out with my bed, and when I see a woman I like, I take her and sleep with her at once.

If her ears are large and ugly, or her nose, I take them off along with her clothes and put them under the bed, so that she can find them again when she leaves; I only keep what I like.

If her underclothes look as though they might gain by being changed, I change them. That would be my present. If, however, I see another and more charming woman pass, I make my excuses to the first one and immediately make her disappear.

People who know me contend that I'm incapable of this, I haven't got the temperament, they say. That's what I used to think too, but it all came from the fact that I didn't do everything *the way I wanted to*.

Now, I always have good afternoons. (I work in the morning.)

❀   ❀   ❀

PERSECUTION

Once my enemies still had some density, but now they've become fluid. My elbow is being touched (I'm jostled all day long). It is they. But they vanish at once.

For three months, I have undergone continual defeat: by enemies without a face; by the root, by the very root of enemies.

After all, they already dominated my childhood. But then . . . I had imagined that I would have more peace now.

❀   ❀   ❀

ON GOING TO SLEEP

Going to sleep is awfully difficult. To begin with, the blankets always weigh a ton, and as to the sheets, they feel like corrugated iron.

If one uncovers oneself altogether, all the world can tell what's going on. After some minutes of—unquestionable—rest, one is projected into space. And in getting down again, one is subjected to a series of abrupt descents that stop one's respiration. Or, lying on one's back for instance, one might feel like raising one's knees. Which isn't at all a good idea because it makes the water in one's stomach churn and churn more and more quickly; and who could think of sleeping with such a top spinning away inside one.

This is why some people resolutely decide to lie on their stomachs, but as soon as they do so they begin falling—they knew they would, but what the hell, they said—they fall and they fall into some unfathomable depth and however low they get, there's always someone to give them an extra kick to make them sink lower . . . and lower.

This is why to some people bedtime is an hour of unparalleled anguish.

◦   ◦   ◦

HAPPINESS

Sometimes, suddenly, and without any visible cause, a great shiver of happiness comes over me.

Coming from a center of myself—a center so far inward that I am unaware of its very existence—the shiver, though traveling outward at extreme speed, takes considerable time in spreading to my extremities.

The shiver is entirely pure. However long a time it is traveling within me, it never meets with any low organ, in fact with no organ at all; nor does it meet with any ideas or sensations, its intimacy is absolute.

And it and I are entirely alone.

Sometimes, perhaps, in going through all my parts, it may ask one or the other of them in passing, "Well, and how are you getting on? Can I do anything for you?" It is quite possible that it does meet them in this way. But I am not told.

I should also like to cry out my happiness, but what am I to say? It is all so strictly personal.

Soon this enjoyment becomes too much. Without my realizing it, it has turned, in a few seconds, into atrocious suffering, it has turned into murder.

This is paralysis! I tell myself.

Quickly, I begin to move about and sprinkle water over me, or, more simply, I lie down on my stomach, and it passes.

◦   ◦   ◦

CASTING A SPELL

The friend I lost is still living in Paris. She is walking about, and laughing. I expect her mother to come to me one of these days and say, "*Monsieur,* I don't know what's the matter with her. They cannot find anything wrong, and yet she's lost another eight pounds this month."

The day her weight's down to a hundred and ten, her mother, who never bothered about me and treated me like the negligible man of a moment, will come to see me and say, "She only weighs a hundred and ten pounds now. Perhaps you could do something for her." And next month, "Now she only weighs forty-eight pounds. This is extremely serious."

But I shall say, "Forty-eight pounds, come back at twenty-eight."

She'll come back at twenty-eight, it's thirty-four really, but she says twenty-eight because of her great fear that exactly twenty-eight pounds will mean death. She'll come back and say to me, "*Monsieur,* she is dying. Wasn't she anything to you?"

"*Madame,* don't worry, she won't disappear entirely. I can't kill her. Even at four and a half pounds, she will continue to live."

But this mother, whom I always detested, will throw herself upon me. It wasn't possible that this could be her daughter. Her daughter must be dead. Surely this was another one made by some trick and kept alive out of cruelty.

And she would go away trying to disentangle her ideas.

❊   ❊   ❊

From "THE NIGHT'S ASTIR"

All the time we are three in this galley. Two for the talking and I for the rowing.

It is hard, one's daily bread, hard to earn and hard to get oneself paid!

These two chatterboxes are all I've got by way of distraction, all the same it's hard watching them eat my bread.

They keep on talking away all the time. If they didn't, they say, the immensity of the ocean and the noise of the storm would get the better of my strength and courage.

It isn't easy to keep a boat going all by oneself, with a single pair of oars. It's all very well to say that the water doesn't offer much resistance

. . . It does offer resistance, believe you me. It does, particularly on certain days . . .

Oh, how I should like to give up my oars.

But they keep their eye on me, having nothing else to do but gossip and eat my bread, my small share of bread already ten times pared down.

❖   ❖   ❖

DUMB HAPPINESS

When then, shall I be able to talk about my happiness?

There is no straw in my happiness, no trace, no sand.

It is not comparable to my unhappiness (did it ever appear in my past, and when?).

It has no limit, it hasn't any. . . , hasn't any. It goes nowhere. It isn't an anchor, it is so sure of itself that it fills me with despair. It takes all the bounce out of me, it affects my sight, my hearing, and the more it . . . the less I . . .

It has no limits, it hasn't any . . . hasn't any.

And at the same time it is only a small thing. My unhappiness was more considerable, it had properties, it had memories, excrescences, ballast.

It was myself.

But this happiness! In time, or yes, in time it'll manage to create a personality for itself, but it won't have time. Unhappiness will come back. It's huge axle cannot be far off. It's coming nearer.

❖   ❖   ❖

WEDDING NIGHT

If, on coming home, on the day of your wedding, you put your wife to soak all night in a well, she'd be dumbfounded. It's all very well for her that she always had vague forebodings . . .

"Well, well," she'll say to herself, "so this is marriage. No wonder they make such a secret of the practice. And I allowed myself to get caught in this bad business."

Being upset, she won't say a word. This is why you can put her to soak for a long time and as often as you like without causing any scandal in the neighborhood.

If she didn't understand the first time, there is little chance that she will later, and you'll have every chance of going on indefinitely without the slightest risk (except bronchitis), that is if you happen to be interested.

As far as I'm concerned, being even more easily hurt in other people's bodies than in my own, I had to give it up pretty soon.

✿   ✿   ✿

EVERYONE'S SMALL WORRIES

An ant does not bother about an eagle. The fury and ferocity of tigers evokes nothing in its mind, the eagle's ferocious eye doesn't fascinate it, doesn't fascinate it in the least.

No one ever talks about eagles in an ant hill.

A dog is not worried by minute leaps of light. But a microbe who can see the advance of light, the innumerable hard elements of a ray only a tiny bit smaller than itself, feels with despair the countless beatings that will dislodge it and shake it to death. Even the cursed gonococcus, who does so much toward complicating the relations between men and women, is seized by despair and, against his will, abandons his hard life.

✿   ✿   ✿

TOWARD SERENITY

a) The Kingdom of Ashes

Above all pleasure, above all terror and desire and transports, there lies an immense stretch of ashes.

From this country of ashes, you can see the long train of lovers looking for their loves, and the long train of women looking for their lovers, you can see such desire, such prescience of unique joys in them, that you realize that they are right, and it becomes obvious that you should live among them.

But whosoever finds himself in the kingdom of ashes will no longer find a way. He can see, he can hear. But no longer will he find a way but the way of eternal regret.

b) The Plateau of Subtle Smiles

Above this elevated but wretched kingdom lies the kingdom elect, the kingdom of the soft coat.

Whenever there appears some height, or some promontory, they cannot last; hardly emerged, they disappear again, shuddering, among small folds and wrinkles, and all becomes smooth once more.

When the waves that carry away meet the waves that bring back, they produce between them a great rustling, a rustling at first, and then, gradually, there will come silence and one shall not meet them any more.

> Oh! Country of warm flag-stones!
> Oh! Plateau of subtle smiles!

Translated from the French by SYBILLE BEDFORD

Franz Hellens

THE DUCK HUNT

THE PUNT WASN'T put into the coach-house, that winter. It was caught in the ice and held fast, unable to move. Without the oars, the pit of it was hard to see. The spring freed it, but it was leaking; it had to be refitted and repainted. Then we found out that the garden bench had suffered too, and needed a new coat of paint.

Although it looked so elegant among its chairs, at the head of the table, nobody ever gave it a glance before June—and yet the pond in front of it was never so beautifully decked out in rushes, swans and ducks, and the refitted boat never cut prettier capers when a gay ripple touched it. It took the chance arrival of visitors on a sunny afternoon; a few turns on the paths and my mother suggested resting, and we all sat down quite naturally under the elm as if we had been doing that every day. I remember that the bench creaked.

I knew the visitors well but they always made me afraid. The banker and his wife—he fat, she thin and stiff—came out of another world where all people seemed alike to me, despite differences in size. To look at their measured gestures, in which you felt no accord whatever with the garden's movement—the only one I knew well—it was as if they had never left the stone walls of their houses. The artificial ring of their voices silenced me. I was as if nailed to the spot.

They never looked at anything. I asked myself if they could see—if the banker, who smoked big cigars and wearily blew out the smoke, would be able to get up again once he was seated, and if his wife would find her way back all alone. Their son seemed even more foreign. Where did he come from? "From his tailor," my father said, disdainfully. He was about twenty and a student of engineering—a great mystery, which impressed me, though I failed to see how such a dandy, whose main fear was of disturbing a crease of his coat, could build ships and bridges.

It was he who talked most of the time. I stood back of the bench, trying hard to make something out of his words that to me seemed ciphers rather than nice patterns. When he laughed, I shuddered. But no one else laughed with him, either. "He's such a pedant," my mother said one day. I didn't know what the word meant, but I made it my private term of reference to him—who was otherwise called Jules—in the firm belief that it applied to his hard voice and cold manner, and to the irritating color of his tie.

We had coffee in the same place. The sun shone fully on the pond. Not one of the three guests had yet turned an eye in its direction.

I had come closer, to get some cake, but the pedant was looking at me; I could swallow nothing. Then, for the first time, his voice inclined toward me almost as if it were human, and this softness quickly touched me. I could suddenly talk to him myself, and I remember that finally it was I who began to ask questions. With the picture of the dancing punt before my eyes I asked him how you built a ship. He took a piece of white paper from his wallet, and a pencil which he sharpened with his penknife, and told me to draw a ship and show it to him. It took me just a few seconds. I proudly surrendered the sketch, and then found that the vessel, which I had drawn in profile, was much too long. Shame burned my cheeks. But the pedant returned the paper and pencil and said, "Now, full-faced."

Instantly I felt his stature increasing. The grave problem became as weighty as the name of engineer, which I could not yet give him. I looked at the paper. The pencil died in my fingers. Full-faced? I could see him, the pedant, Jules, the engineer—but the ship bulged hugely in my head, as if to swell my shame. The engineer fixed his blue, ironic eyes on me; his round little mouth seemed to whistle. I might have run away, if I could have learned the secret of this vessel with the diabolic, elusive face without admitting my incompetence. He grabbed the pencil, nearly wrenching my hand off, and without taking the point off the paper for even a moment he let the front view of a steamer rise before me—a majestic silhouette, which promptly swept me out to a stormy sea.

I fled, with the paper and pencil. At each step I heard the engineer's voice: "That's how you build a ship!"

When I was out of sight I started copying the sketch. It was so simple!

My heart was pounding fit to burst; the great face of the ship approached as if to devour me. I drew it several times with elating ease.

When I came back to the bench the pedant had resumed his lecture. I gazed in awe at his tanned face, blue eyes, round little mouth. His tie was transfigured. He no longer was the same; Jules had definitely vanished; the pedant had been replaced by an engineer, and the engineer by a magician. I dreamed of the number of ships I would build from now on.

My father asked the guests to dinner. I saw my mother blush and then pale, in an embarrassed, apologetic silence. She had nothing to offer them. It was Sunday; the grocer lived far away; she had not expected them. The banker's wife apologized in turn and talked of leaving, without getting up.

"We'll kill a duck," said my father.

My mother replied, "You know very well that it's Bernard's day off."

We had to catch our duck first. All eyes turned to the pond. It was pure gold in the sun; its surface glistened, full of live fruit. The gentle swans were thrashing like white balls among green and white ducks. I ran down to the bank. I felt like drinking the whole pond. Suddenly I heard a sharp voice, like a whistle—just one word:

"The carbine."

I went back up the hill.

"That's impossible," my father said. "We'd need a rifle. But I'm all out of cartridges."

I knew who had called for the carbine. The blue of his tie cast a cruel reflection. He had resumed his true name, that of Jules.

"No, no. The carbine will do."

My father went to get the carbine from the house and came back, loading it. He looked at the pond, aimed the weapon, then lowered it again. Under the elm a circle of silence seemed to spread from the table over the pond. The whole garden fell silent—all but the ducks, whose joyous cries played with small waves rippling with laughter. They dove, and their tails quivered in the air as they strained to reach the bottom with their beaks.

"I can't," said my father.

Jules leaped to the front and grabbed the carbine. My mother begged, "Don't kill the swans!"

I saw him take aim, and closed my eyes. The shot went past me; it shattered my fear and a kind of triumphant intoxication made me look at the water. In the sunny cove a struggling blue and green ball spun round itself; a flock of loose feathers rose and descended. The ducks were in headlong flight. The swans, side by side, necks high, were swiftly gliding toward open water.

My mother hid her face and cried, "Finish him!"

Jules turned to my father who stood behind him. He reloaded and fired, but the water remained a whirl of feathers and sun. Horror froze my limbs and my head; my widened eyes took in all the pond and that live ball that died spinning in its feathers.

The pedant's voice echoed behind me: "He's got enough."

I shuddered, as from the shock of a new discharge. The water grew calm. The blue and green ball stayed motionless on the surface. I wondered why it did not sink.

A ray of sunlight, from the meadow where the hay was drying, fell across the width of the pond in a straight line over to us. Jules was in the punt, manipulating the oars. When he came back, with his prey, disgust rose in my throat. This is how I've seen him since: shirtsleeves rolled back on hairy arms, hands covered with blood. I recall that when he stretched his shoulders a moment I saw his coat-flaps open up.

Once, my father had shot a rabbit—from so close that nothing remained but the skin. At another time Bernard killed a half-frozen wood-pigeon before my eyes, which had dropped on the snow. But love and the snow erase everything.

Jules had put the carbine on the table and gone to wash his hands.

Translated from the French by E. B. ASHTON

Charles Plisnier

DITKA

I MET Multi in Amsterdam. A Party comrade had told me his name, adding two or three words which had a strange resonance in that café full of music: A Bulgarian, an exile. I observed that his lips were drawn almost too fine, but that evening he didn't open them except in smoking. I gave him no further thought.

Only once, as I was watching a tropical bird in a shop window, it seemed to me that he was standing beside me, saying: "Look . . . look . . ."

When we finally spoke, it was perfectly natural, and as though I had always known him and loved him. It was near the station, under the bridge, where the little waves of the Zuiderzee break and die against the worn piles. I saw him from the back; he was leaning forward, with his arms thrust back, like a man preparing to drown himself.

I said to him: "You like the water?"

He straightened slowly and turned toward me his swarthy face, waxen where the light struck it. He replied:

"In my country there are stone mountains, so beautiful you would think they were silver."

Then we left the place together.

⁂

In the days that followed we saw each other often. Both of us loved the desolation of empty mornings. The autumn was drawing to an end. We were living in the center or the city, where the streets are canals. Rain fell on the cabbage-laden bark of the market gardener; on the melancholy song of the rag-picker. We were afraid that the rain would wash away the red, black, blue façades, the rosy cheeks of the girls and even the piercing green of the canal water. We lived in a cinema landscape, and we ourselves were photographs.

We spoke little. Sometimes Multi threw away his cigarette after it had been out a long time, and seemed to dream in the language of his country. I heard beautiful words: Vitasha, Nedelya. I had the impression of warm flowers glistening far behind all the rain.

Often we went as far as Rembrandt Square. Abruptly we entered a beer-hall bursting with warmth. We asked, as though some calamity were imminent, for coffee, tea, something that tasted of life.

And so one morning, as though suddenly relaxing, Multi told me his story. The rain dripped slowly down the window panes, changing the image of the passers-by to phantoms. In the café, still empty, the waiters were setting up the tables. The tea was steaming. Multi turned his long bloodless face toward me, seldom raising his black pale eyes.

"How shall I tell you, comrade? Multi is not my name. My name is sonorous and cumbersome. It recalls a country that is not at peace with itself, a country that raises images of heads shot through, of cavalry charges, of hangings.

"Well, anyway, call me Multi . . .

"My father is something down there, in the army, the police, let us say. He thinks I am dead, and that's the only thing that leaves him a little peace.

"I used to have a taste for adventure. And it pleased me to drag my bones around the world. In 1915 I worked for a time in a Singapore bank.

"My country was about to enter the war. To escape the English police, I left for Batavia. While working in a shipyard there, I learned Dutch. As you see, it was to come in handy one day.

"In '19 I returned to my country. The soldiers were going home, not fully disarmed. Trials for high treason were being organized. It was the invasion of disorder. The idea of country, the idea of victory had to be revised. My father who had bet on the wrong card thought only of saving his head. I doubt if he noticed my return.

"I became school-teacher in a village near Lom Palanka.

"It takes a kind of courage for me to approach that period of my life. For it was almost heroic. And what am I now beside these moments from the past?

"You do not know me well. No doubt you take me for one of those painters without colors, those poets without breath, that one is sure to find in every place that is a little photogenic, a little cruel. Very well, if you must. But have you noticed that, in addition, I am very, very cowardly.

"I could not describe to you that kind of madness which, for a long moment, raised me out of myself. It was like a miracle. Even today I cannot account for it.

"I had so long been deprived of my country. I found it torn. On one hand the University, big business, the petty finance of Sofia. On the other the peasants, avid and exhausted, and that vast demagogue Stambouliiski. I took the hard course, fighting both parties, by the side of a few firebrand workers who published leaflets in a cellar.

"There came the day of June 9, 1923. A new dictatorship. Civil war closed in on us.

"It was then that I met Ditka."

Suddenly Multi fell silent. It was as though this word Ditka had exhausted him merely by passing his lips. I had the feeling that he was fighting his weariness. Then he began to talk rapidly, like a man conjuring up a dream that is still bathed in sleep:

"It was one night in Sofia, in a little office at the end of a corridor. We were talking through the acrid smoke of our cigarettes, the heavy vapor of Turkish coffee. No one had heard her come in. As I was speaking, I suddenly saw her facing me across the table—erect and very tall. I understood the meaning of the words: a naked face."

Now Multi spoke as in a trance.

"Nothing lied in this face, it was a face reduced to the essential lines of the human type. And her short hair, so black that it was almost blue.

And those open eyes with their straight look. And that warm, white flesh. And those hands without end, that body hard as a figurehead."

Multi took a long breath.

"I spoke like a man who is drunk and knows it. I assembled the fragments of my reason scattered through a vague, mounting dream.

"Then I had finished. And she said: 'Yes, that's right.'

"Next day, I went back to Lom Palanka with our slogans. But life was no longer the same.

"I began to be gloomy, as in the days when I embraced yellow women on mats even hotter than the night; when at the bend of the grey-green channel I watched ships departing.

"That this woman should exist deprived me of hope. That she had given her body to this formless thing, the cause of humanity, made me hate a struggle which until then I had tried to love.

"One day Ditka returned. It was a Sunday. The whole village was in church. And more alone in the world than anyone had ever been, I sat sadly smoking at my bare table. She closed the door behind her.

"The oven gave forth a dense heat. The light shone through the closed blinds and trembled in the room. Do I remember it clearly enough? A false summer. Ambiguous light. With horror I saw her perfect body through her dress. Yes, I saw it as the anatomist sees the skeleton through the garment of flesh. Yes. Exactly that. Cruel ransom for this life . . .

"Did I listen to her? She told me that on the 16th it would be double or nothing, that we must be prepared for anything, that she was leaving for near Kustendil and had come to say good-bye. I understood that she too was attracted by my dismal body, bathed in strange climates. She too.

"I begged her not to die. I confessed my cowardice, my threadbare heroism, the lucidity of my reason, and that sometimes my hand was so heavy I dared not raise it to touch a page, to touch my forehead.

"'Ah!' she said, tearing off her dress, 'so that is what I love with my body.'

"She was so beautiful that I didn't feel her contempt.

"A horrible day. I heard the Sunday bells. It was a sin, a real sin. I touched her body, it was mine, I imprisoned it in my arms. When the lights went out in windows, peasants passed by. They were singing. They were not holding half, just half of love in their arms, the remains of an absent woman.

"Then Ditka stood up, told me the time of the train, and left me.

"On the 17th news came from Sofia that the Cathedral of Holy Week had been blown up at two o'clock the day before. Already, cavalry detachments were arriving in the villages, followed by trucks full of bleeding workers. I swear to you that I didn't much care whether I died. But some of my harder comrades came by, who didn't know my secret wound. They took to the mountains and I followed them.

"One morning, near Berkovitsa, my comrades who had gone down to the village for bread and milk, failed to return. I heard several shots near the tobacco factory. I hid. At night there was a storm. Sitting in the rain, I thought of Ditka.

"On May 12th I crossed the border near the railroad at Tsaribrod."

Multi fell silent and stared for a long while at his too-beautiful hands. "And so," he said finally, "here I am. Here I am."

❂   ❂   ❂

One day Multi appeared before me with shining eyes. His fine lips trembled. He said to me: "She is alive."

Beneath the rain, which had begun again, he opened a newspaper of his country. The strange characters meant nothing to me. He explained to me that Ditka Gersheva had appeared suddenly in workers' meetings at Plovdiv, at Shaskovo; that the leaders of the Military League had set a price on her head; that she had just been taken . . .

The rain fell on the paper, on his trembling hands.

❂   ❂   ❂

I brought him to my room, gave him tea. He raised the cup to his lips and set it down without drinking, like a man who has forgotten the meaning of ritual gestures. Then he poured himself some liquor.

I had known that Ditka was in danger. But Multi had never said that he thought her dead. I looked at this ravaged face, his discolored lips trembling over the golden fluid. At this moment, when it seemed to me that every fibre in him was stretched to the breaking point, I didn't dare to ask him any questions.

But now he spoke. He spoke too much. And I wasn't sure that I could bear to listen.

"Multi," I said. "Calm yourself."

"Ah! If she were dead. Did I want to believe that she was dead? You understand? Did I think so because I wanted to? Or was it the way she said good-bye to me, opened the door and vanished like an escaping prisoner? No. No. I wanted her not to be alive. I put her in the midst of all the shooting. She was among the unknown victims whom the police bury in heaps, at night, in the Macedonian plains. She was on all the lists of the murdered that the revolutionary agencies published. Dead. For the convenience of my heart."

"Multi," I said. "Pull yourself together. You will speak tomorrow."

"Now the whole question is alive again. She has come back to life with her saint's body and her two radiant breasts. She is alive. Again I have become the great coward man who at the first shot ran away from the task he had begun; a very poor man, feeding beneath his clothes the parasite jealousy and every nightmarish specter. Ah! Ditka, what will my nights be like?"

"Multi," I said, "you are mad."

"Ah! If I were mad! No, reason has been given back to me."

He pointed to the paper.

"You see. The truth has come to find me here. Where shall I go? I shall have to reconstruct my life, piece by piece, to cheat my dreams by night, my desires in the morning, to tell myself every day, face to face: 'Georgi, you have no courage!'"

He had pronounced his name. Suddenly he heard it and began to tremble.

* * *

Multi did not come back.

I became anxious. But this scene—I never knew how much drunkenness, how much folly, how much real love was contained in it—kept taking form in my mind. And I was afraid to visit him, for fear it would be repeated.

I think that I loved this young man. I listened with an irritating distaste to his confessions without greatness. But I brought forth no word of blame or exhortation. Privately I thought: "Go back. Take foot again. Impose yourself on the thoughts of the woman who saw you so wretched, who took you as one takes a coat to clothe oneself; show the mask of courage!" But I restrained myself from speaking. I felt that this man's bright flame had burned all at once, that it was long extinguished. Never again would a beam of light issue from those vast, tired eyes. And to see him move along the rectangular canals, beneath the rain, beside the soundless waters . . .

It was then that I learned by chance from a friend who Ditka was: a kind of saint without hope.

She had risen out of the people, suddenly, in the year '19. The workers called her the teacher; the students called her the Amazon. She was one of those who, through the twelve months of '20, brought the revolutionary flame into the last mountain parishes, into the last traktirs of the suburbs. Twice arrested by Stambouliiski's men, she had twice escaped from the Central Prison of Sofia. After the 9th of June, when the unions were dissolved, the Party outlawed, she continued to rise up like an image, at Varna, at Kustendil, at Pleven, before the assembled workers. She had just been captured after a chase in the woods near Nevrokop, like a wolf. In the cart, guarded by white police, which carried her away, she cried out to those who are always on hand when the Calvary passes: "Farewell, brothers!" She loved life. She laughed. She was all the more beautiful.

I also learned that they were awaiting the news of her death or torture.

I went to see Multi. His room was empty. On a table, the Bulgarian newspapers of the last twenty days were piled up. Their wrappers had not been broken.

          ✿   ✿   ✿

One evening I received a strange letter:

"My friend. Have you too abandoned me? If you are afraid of cowardice, do not fear. It is not contagious. Or love either.

"I can no longer escape. Alcohol is expensive.

"To be left face to face with myself, ah! How shall I escape from this interview? I don't dare go to you. But beg you to come, yes. I want to lay bare my heart.

Multi."

I set out.

As usual his door was ajar. He did not hear me.

When I stood behind him, I saw that his table was covered with sheets of paper full of calculations.

He was still tracing figures and signs. A strange malaise invaded me. I laid my hand on his shoulder.

Then he turned toward me that face which I had never seen laughing. A kind of joy distended his lips, stretched the wounded corners of his eyes. And he said to me:

"You see. I am not wasting the night."

          ✿   ✿   ✿

A mission called me to Saloniki.

Hearing this name, Multi seemed to recover the clarity of his gaze. When I departed several days later, he took me to the station. On the

high glass dome I could hear the dripping of the rain. Multi gave me a
letter and said:

"You will see her. I have written this for her. You will see her. Give it
to her."

What could I answer? I took the letter, put it in my wallet, managed
to smile.

And as the train was pulling out, he ran along beside the car, shouting:

"And if she is dead, don't forget! A simple note. A simple note . . ."

❀   ❀   ❀

I was busy with all sorts of duties. I forgot Multi a little. And—I must
admit—removed from his equivocal charm, I came at times almost to hate
him. His name remained for me associated with enervating rainy mornings, interminable avowals of cowardice, an acrid taste of journeys over-
seas, of adventures without issue, of wasted life.

I felt closer to Ditka, and not in space alone. If I still pitied Multi
for his inability to rise to this exalted love, this courage, how I pitied her
too! It seemed to me that a phantom, passing across her life, had left behind it a wake of restlessness and mischance.

One night at Vienna, as I was having tea with some friends, I heard
her name spoken near me. So abruptly did I turn to inquire after her, to
find out if at least she were alive, that my neighbor considered me with
alarm—almost with suspicion. He was obviously wondering whether it
was safe to answer me, whether he had not already said too much, for
these revolutionary circles are not always hermetically sealed against
police informers. But doubtless the very vivacity of my question, the impatience which thrust my face forward, did not suggest the policeman.

"You know her?"

"I have never seen her. But I know a woman who admired—who loved
her very much."

I lied. In this circle of militants I didn't dare to mention Multi who,
importunately, had just appeared to me as he was in reality,—as a kind
of deserter.

I added: "Is she alive?"

"She is alive."

"Free?"

"Free."

The replies were terse. I felt that I could not insist. Why, after all?

Would I not know the whole story soon? But when I went home that night I found word that I should have to leave two days later.

I paid a farewell visit to my friends. In view of the circumstances under which we had met, they could not doubt me. They had spoken of Ditka. They seemed to know her well. Masha was alone.

"Masha," I said. "I must know where Ditka Gersheva is."

Masha made a scarcely perceptible move of surprise. Her face remained closed, silent.

"You must?"

But without waiting for my answer, she spoke of Ditka. Once again she had escaped from prison. At what price, it was not known. What could have happened this time in the cellars of the prefecture, from which so many hardened girls and young men of steel had gone out livid, their eyes emptied of reason? It seemed that she herself had given a kind of report in a form not without irony: "Let us not speak of these incidents. Those are my own little troubles. They interest no one." The comrades had made her cross the border. Ditka, who for six years had bathed in the heart of hell, was resting.

I felt as though tight chains were being lifted from me. I breathed easier. But suddenly I perceived that the one question I had asked, remained unanswered.

Would I tell them the story? Would I? I felt that I had to dissimulate, to lie. I said nothing of Ditka's visit to the house in the village, transformed Multi's carnal passion into a romantic admiration, put the accent on the weakness of a man exhausted by travels, and on his variety of madness. And the more I cut, the more I dressed up his story, the angrier I became at Multi. I thought of his indiscretion, his lack of shame. I felt how much there was in his passion that should never have been confessed. But why, then, should I persist in inquiring, in knowing? Why ask Masha:

"Tell me, Masha, I beg of you, where she is. I must speak to her, bring her a message from my friend."

Masha shrugged her shoulders. She said—and at once I felt all the indulgence and irony, all the displeasure and disdain in her voice:

"Ditka is in Belgrade. Go and see her. When you see her, you will decide whether you can trouble a woman like her with such threadbare things."

✿   ✤   ✿

I was very ill at ease as I approached Belgrade. I was to spend one night there.

I watched the cornfields pass by, and the whole plain. Some Hungarian baroness was relating the misfortunes of her country which had lost this rich province. Her hate-filled words lulled me in melancholy.

But it was Masha's words that I heard.

Should I trouble this woman with such threadbare things? Who knows? The hardest courage cannot resist certain memories. There are statues which begin to weep. Should I speak of the rain, the canals without face and those eyes slowly laid bare by madness? Where was Multi? Exactly what place did he have now in my mind, in my heart? Or was it a secret curiosity, some other sentiment . . .

The Danube. Lights on the dark waters, the first of this Orient I was entering. Have the passions a different sound in this country?

Ditka: I was vaguely afraid of standing before a saint.

          ❂   ❂   ❂

On my way out of the station, I felt myself seized by an immense despair.

Around me travelers, those who thought they knew where they were going, poured out, lost themselves on that great black square, and were swallowed up at once by the dense night. One by one, the cabs drove up with their red lamps, stopped, took in a shadow or two and departed.

I had the feeling that for Ditka this sad village of night was a refuge that I must not violate. What could I add to this climate, except some shadow even more confused? What could I leave her in passing, except the foul vapors of cowardice? I would go back to the train and continue southward.

Driven by a mysterious force, I found myself at the edge of the waiting room. On the spittle-covered tiles lay bodies in rags, bodies of men, women, children, sleeping in piles amid sacks and packages. They, too, were waiting for a time to come. But it was marked in the time-tables. And the guard would appear in the doorway to tell them: it is time.

The very excess of my despair flung me back on the square. And I left, groping my way through ascending streets, black and deserted. Here and there, in a cellar, behind a broken pane, a woman offered stale candy for sale, an invalid was tapping shoes.

I was no longer conscious of any thought when I found myself on a dark landing before Ditka's door.

          ❂   ❂   ❂

I had barely knocked when the door opened wide.

A woman stood before me. It was as though she wished rather to bar my access to the room than to welcome me. With her back to the dim light, she seemed tall and extremely thin.

Quickly I said a few names which were to serve as pass-word. For a second she seemed to hesitate, holding her arms straight at her sides; her face remained hermetic and cold. Then, abruptly, she stood aside with a gesture almost of command. I went in.

When the door was closed, she leaned against the frame and held out her hand.

"Comrade . . ."

How much proud questioning, how much bitter doubt was there in this welcome?

The light of the table lamp illumined her vaguely from below. Only then did I see her. A dozen feelings shared my heart.

Was this the Amazon who had electrified a people, the woman who held a man at the other end of Europe under her charm?

This tall, bony, emaciated woman. These yellow, unending, sunken hands. This grey skin, these dull eyes. And beneath her close-cropped hair, this smooth forehead without madness. Her flat body was covered by a black dress of an old style, with a vertical row of buttons, recalling a uniform.

I pronounced her name.

Then her eyes had a brief flash, her lips a movement without sound. Ashamed, I saw that she had understood me to the bottom of her soul.

She felt that people had spoken to me of her, that I was confronting her image with the image of a dream. She did not doubt that I had been sent by one of her people.

"A friend?" she said with a naked voice. And she showed me an ancient arm-chair. With a single look, I took in the accidental room, the worn papers, the faded looking-glass, the loveless bed, the table beneath the lamp, cruelly exhibiting its tattered books, a few folders, a flower in a glass.

She sat down beside me and said as though in answer to a question: "Yes, I have aged."

That was all. Then we spoke as though we had always known one another and loved one another a little.

But a strange malaise persisted in me.

We spoke of our friends in Vienna, of the misfortune of Bulgaria; we uttered names of the dead; confided in one another our reasons for hope.

I dared to say nothing of herself, of her courage, of her last imprisonment, of this mysterious thing because of which my meeting with her had been presentiment more than recognition. I didn't dare speak to her of Multi.

And yet, I would soon have to leave.

Then, without any will of mine, this happened:

She had stood up to fill the tea-cups at the samovar. I saw her back, a little bent over. I felt that if I did not speak to her now, I should leave Belgrade with my message, my secret. And suddenly I heard my voice saying:

"A friend in Amsterdam gave me a letter for you: Georgi Jordaev."

She made no answer, she did not turn around. She went on filling the cups. She put sugar in the tea and returned toward me. Had she heard me? Her face was dreadfully white.

She took the letter but did not open it. She said in a voice that was almost natural:

"What is he doing in Amsterdam?"

And before I could answer:

"There are places even farther from here, Bergen, Dublin . . ."

In this contempt I recognized the Amazon. I had expected contempt, at once wishing and fearing it. But it was so calm that it made me afraid.

Quickly I told her how I had met Multi. I told her of his loneliness and our walks. I told her how he had confided in me. And of the thing which, unable to find another name, I called his madness.

To hide my embarrassment, I had stood up and taken a few steps. And now, leaning against a low cupboard, I spoke without looking at Ditka.

Suddenly I fell silent. Under my eyes I had the photograph of a group of girls. All of them, excepting one, wore the costume of Bulgarian peasant women, covered with embroidery and braid. And all of them seemed beautiful. But who was the one in the dress of solid white, this radiant goddess' mask, with the bottomless eyes and the form of a statue?

"Yes," said a voice behind me that I feared to recognize, "that is how Georgi Jordaev sees me."

But I dared not turn round, find myself face to face with this phantom that was speaking.

"How was he to understand me? He was a kind of sleepwalker who had strayed into the fighting lines in a state of trance. How should I have understood him? But at that time I was possessed. Come and sit down, comrade, and let us speak of something else . . ."

She gave me tea. We spoke of the summer, of life on the international express trains, of the civil war, of insomnia.

The moment came for me to arise and take my leave. I wanted to ask a question—the last—but I didn't dare. We were near the door and Ditka was going to open it.

Suddenly she strode to the table and took Multi's letter.

"What for?" she said.

And she handed me this message that had not been opened.

"You haven't seen Ditka Gersheva," she said. "You have found in a little room a woman who has escaped four times from the Central Prison in Sofia, who has made the acquaintance of the most refined third-degree methods. These things are bound to take a little blood, a little flesh. You haven't seen Ditka Gersheva . . ."

Had I understood? Suddenly I was afraid of Multi's eyes, which even now had lost all limit. I held out the letter.

"I think," I said, "that this means madness."

I watched Ditka. Almost touching mine, her face which for a long while had seemed almost paralyzed, began to live, with a wild disordered life. Her lips trembled. Her lids covered her eyes which had lost all radiance. Then a kind of wave passed over that flesh, transformed it into a frozen mask of bitterness.

Ditka recoiled.

"Don't worry. Tell him what you have seen . . ."

Her hands groped their way over her bosom. Suddenly, as though torn, her dress was open. In place of breasts I saw two immense, blood-red scars.

Ditka turned to me with a tremulous smile.

"Go," she said. "Leave me."

She regained her calm, closed her dress and accompanied me to the bottom of the stairs. She opened the street-door, remarked that the night was cool, advised me to watch out for gaps in the pavement, held out her hand, smiled again, wished me a pleasant journey.

❖   ❖   ❖

At Saloniki where I spent a month, I learned that Ditka, despite the entreaties of her friends, had again crossed the Bulgarian frontier, that she had spoken in a village near Kirli, that the police were tracking her along the Greek border.

On my way back through Vienna, I found these lines in a newspaper:

"Ditka Gersheva, the Communist militant, having been condemned by the Special Tribunal for the fifth time, was hanged yesterday at Sofia."

❖   ❖   ❖

I saw Multi running beside my car in the Amsterdam station. I heard his voice: "And if she is dead, don't forget. If she is dead, a simple note. A simple note."

Translated from the French by RALPH MANHEIM

Karel van de Woestijne

FLANDERS, O HOUSE OF PLENTY

FLANDERS, O HOUSE of plenty, where we sit as friends
at tables heaped with food!—now waving fields
of summer grain stretch out their breathing yields
far towards the crimson east where dawn ascends
while morning wakes in Flanders and the sky:
Oh, who can know you and not feel his heart leap high?—
not speak his thanks for days so gloriously spread,
the thanks a beggar gives for warm wheat bread? . . .

O Flanders, gay with present-bearing hands
and as you go in gold and purple dress
bestowing fruit, all heavy with your fruitfulness;

—Flanders, who knows you and the dawn's caress
and feels no love flare through him where he stands,
like this warm morning through the fertile Flanders lands?

OH SICK, UNCERTAIN . . .

OH SICK, uncertain and defiled,
our only care for our own life,
we've no quick shudder, no taut smile,
but for the foredoomed strife.

Ever on the sullen sea, the silent
sunken sails, the sun's dull shine—
ever the same unchanging island
on every new horizon line.

AGAIN THE LATE LAST LIGHT . . .

AGAIN THE late last light of asters blooms,
Again a fall draws near. And this sore heart
When summer's smoking torch sinks into gloom
Once more is torn apart.

I in whose hand the ripe fruit seemed to be
A bliss denied, no taste of it my own,
Who, knowing you, O autumn sympathy,
Feel all the more alone—

Eternal mower, I, who cut the grain
But never bound the sheaves nor owned a part,
Unending sailor on this furrowed main
Who never came to port—

Again a fall draws near, again denying
This heart that, hopeless, still feels longing's sting,
That, always hankering for this autumn dying,
Past winter knows a spring—

Again my blood burns in its autumn mood,
Again my heart grieves in its battered rooms—
How bronze the gold grows in the chestnut wood!
The silver aster blooms. . . .

        Translated from the Flemish by E. C. *and* F. STILLMAN

Paul van Ostayen

UNDER THE MOON

UNDER THE MOON glides the long river
Over the long river glides the weary moon
Under the moon on the long river glides the
     canoe toward sea
Along the high rushes
along the low bushes

the canoe glides toward sea

the canoe glides with the gliding **moon**
toward sea

thus companions toward sea the **canoe**
and the moon and the man

Why do the moon and the man those **two and**
so passive glide toward the sea?
Translated from the Flemish by E. C. *and* F. STILLMAN

Gerard Walschap

CURE THROUGH ASPIRIN

FROM MY YOUTH on I suffered from pain in the throat, two or three times a year for a period of two or three weeks. During the intervals I felt either a remainder of the last pain lingering on, or the next one coming. If by chance I didn't feel anything at all, one had only to call my name from behind, to make me turn my head by surprise. Then, the collar of my coat would hit under my chin against a tumor that hurt me, a tonsil. But how little did I know about tonsils at that time!

I sat near the stove by the window, sick, wrapped in a heavy shawl, very thin, very bleak—and the eyes I had then! If I was given a penny, I opened them wide and let them lighten with rage. Every uncle, aunt, cousin or niece I had was willing to spend that cent to see them, for such eyes, they said, they had never seen. I myself often looked at them in the mirror when I was alone. I held out till I had to give in, for they made me uneasy. Restlessly I sought something that would absorb me so completely as to forget them. Now I see in the mirror that they are quenched and veiled. Their glance is soft. I ask them: what ails you, what hurts you? Everything. At that time I didn't dare to swallow or to gargle, and yet I had to eat. Eating was like rubbing raw flesh with emery-paper. Add to that a headache, a raging fever and that feeling of a sick animal that steals away and curls up. However, I suffered all that gladly, even bravely, because I could remain silent for two weeks, could read, dream and be alone with myself. Also for the sake of the greater amount of affection that was only then shown to me, to a degree to which I thought myself entitled when I was well.

Later on I got rid of that pain in the throat. I had to drink cod-liver oil,

I felt like a skunk. I breathed cod-liver oil. Every time one of my chums came too close and backed up in disgust, I laughed, but with pain. In school I belched from cod-liver oil, disgusting and sour. I could not smell anything else; everything I ate tasted like it. I thought that people smelt me coming from afar and I made presents of everything I had to my pals around me in class, because they endured my stink. Thus I hoped to prevent them from crying out (a danger I feared every minute): "He stinks!"

And now the throat-ache has come back. Has my body already passed its peak—does it go back to the feeble state of its childhood, to demolition, to decay? Do I already have to pay for a life that consisted in burning the candle at both ends? Am I aged before my time? Mon Mulder died in his thirty-second year; according to the doctor, he was as worn out as a man of ninety. Or do I still call throat-ache, out of pure habit, something very different, the soft and dreadful tumor of cancer. Who cares?

I have no more time to be sick. I can scarcely keep Mary and the three children alive by working constantly to the point of becoming neurasthenic. I never get neurasthenia, but it nearly gets me: I keep it at arm's length, by racing up and down in my room every five minutes, by splashing in lots of cold water and by eating "rationally." I and reason! I damned myself to this kind of petty life by the Lord's decision, the Lord who gives and takes. The greatest hero breaks down under it; I don't.

As soon as that well known feeling arises, I am ready with the unsurpassable aspirin tablets. I take two of them, and Mary's fear that I will be unable to do anything at all for two weeks subsides. A hundred times I have given her the assurance that no throat-ache in the world will prevent me from working. She knows for certain that my will-power is something inhumanly cruel, but anxiety about daily bread is never still: the typical fear of the poor, a sentiment of merciless constraint.

Some time ago I came too late. A faint dizziness when I awoke didn't seem enough to justify two aspirins. I had asked for an audience with So and So, whose help I needed. For three days I had been angry with myself for ordering myself: You'll go. At noon I shivered with fever like a dog, but I didn't think about aspirin any more. I had to face my own resolution, to leave, so I only made fun of myself. Mary wanted to rest and talk for a while after lunch. I still had fifteen minutes left. I couldn't sit down. Turning my back to her I stood up and tramped up and down and couldn't remain silent. "I will go and look up that scholarly and

mighty man, Mary"—I said—"and say to him: 'Sir, help me. He will pat
me on the shoulder, offer me a cigar and an armchair. It is really a joy
to be able to treat a poor man well for once. He will sit down in the seat
of his might and splendor and he will encourage me to formulate my
wishes openly and frankly. Mary, I will master my passions. I will drive
out my pride. I will think of you and the children and I will make a
modest and sympathetic impression. I will not think: you damned dumb-
bell, you climber, you snail, you pretentious, filthy intriguer, I would
rather dissolve into snuff than to ask you for anything. No, Mary, I
will bear in mind that all power derives from God, who knows how
to make use of the most modest tools. Truly beloved, only one danger menaces me. There are no thoughts in that powerful head but I could
imagine myself that he thinks: 'There he sits, that haughty man, who
stubbornly follows his own desperate way. How small he is, in reality,
when worrying about earthly goods. There sits the hero, and he trembles
for a loaf of bread.' Mary, what is going to happen then, to me or to him?
Let us put aside these somber premonitions and let us together, rising
reverently, humble ourselves in the spirit and repeat the prayer that this
very day I will say to him. Stand behind me, Mary, and repeat slowly
with me: 'Sir, I have only brains. Sir, I have only brains, and modesty
compels me to say that they aren't worth very much. You, Sir, you have
only power, and modesty compels me to say that it comes from God and
is great. If all that were true, I could starve as I deserve, for I am fed up
with it all, for I suffer from the throat since birth. Eating and drinking
are painful, and now breathing is almost unbearable.' I choke! Mary, I
choke! 'But I have a wife and children, Tremolo: but I have a wife and
children. Tremolissimo: and for them, Sir' . . ."

I did not suspect that Mary had been weeping in silence. From experience she knows that these monologues relieve and calm me, and
therefore she listens patiently to the most terrible things. She considers
them, it seems, as an outlet for my nervousness and does not attribute to
them any more importance than to the babble of a dead drunk. But this
time she literally threw herself upon me, sobbing. She didn't want me
to go any longer. She had always felt that way, but she had concealed her
feelings, because I seemed to feel otherwise, for I had been so quiet and
calm. Now she understood how I suffered. My pride made her love me
more. Her husband ought to be like that, and so on, and so forth. I could
scarcely get away. But even after I had succeeded in closing the door, I
opened it again and said: " 'Sir,' I will say, 'give me bread for five peo-

ple, and for four of them some Bologna sausage too.'" Through her tears,
Mary laughed, but a little too high-pitched and too shrill. Of course,
nothing more had been said about the aspirin.

At six o'clock I was back home. Mary asked me casually how things
had gone. Fine. No other question, so as not to force me to ruminate. I
was her hero, and so on, and so forth. All those hours she had been
thinking about me. Something noble had made her stand up proudly and
full of courage. And, indeed, she looked heroic. But when I did not want
her to kiss me, when I felt it again—the pain—she all of a sudden went
to pieces: there again was that fear typical of the poor. She began
to run around nervously. First she brought me aspirins, then "bleu de
Mytilene." The third time she stormed into the room to tell me to go to
bed immediately: water was already boiling for a warm grog. Her fears
increased constantly. The fourth time she rushed in with a bottle—a gift
from friends—a special medicine which was sure to cure within the hour.
The fifth time she had not been able to find or to invent anything more.
Very agitated she stood before me, asking helplessly with great, anxious
eyes: "What are we going to do now?" Calm and decided I rose. She had
only to wait till supper. I would take a couple of aspirins and sit down
in the bedroom in an armchair. After an hour and a half I would be fit.
I would eat with them, take our usual stroll and go back to work, with
the bottle of gin. Tomorrow everything would be forgotten.

This manly language revived her. I was her tough and brave darling.
While I was going upstairs with the aspirin, she kept the three children
away from me. They know that I play with them when I am not working.

I took four aspirins, sat down, stood up again and savagely took two
more. Very soon I felt pleasant. The street and the house were quiet. I
floated between consciousness and sleep, nice memories came to me.
I was showing the whole series of drawings which I had made when a
young man, before I was condemned to publicity drawing. Many people
stood around me full of admiration. I talked to them about my art. All
of a sudden I was able to tell in clear, plain words how much I enjoyed
it, how the drawing lived inside me and how I felt myself blessed. I struck
a distinguished attitude. I explained how every line was in my hand and
such gracefulness in my wrist that once I had kissed it. Later on I was at
home and everybody was there, even those who had passed away. My
children played quietly with a footstool. My mother smiled, saying that
once more we were all together.

I smoked my pipe and saw clearly before me the work I had still to do.
I was happy and quiet. But I thought, father who sits there is dead, and

I am sitting in my bedroom just to get a little rest. But this seemed unimportant.

I got my father to tell a story of his youth which I had always heard with great pleasure when I was young. The seven of us sat with our feet on the stove. Now I started to arrange my work for the future, while father's story went on cosily.

Later on I was at the house of my youngest child, the three-year-old Elsie. She was a splendid woman, had two beautiful children. She was tall and wore a white knitted woolen dress. Suddenly she turned to me and said: I am happy. Tears welled in my eyes. I wanted to tell her that this was everything I had expected, all I had always lived for. But happiness paralyzed me. I couldn't utter a word and I felt a pain right through my heart.

I was awake, but could not cry or move. My eyes darkened. Twice more, at short intervals, I felt that pain in the heart. I knew that this was the end. In our family we all die that way. We get a little feverish, we feel tired, we smile and our heart gives in. We die in a friendly way, allergic to display. My aunt asked for a drink, tried to sit upright, said "thank you" before she drank, leaned back, smiled and died. My uncle sat with a little fever behind the stove. In mid-winter, a neighbor brought him a handful of splendid apples. One of them rolled down from the table. My uncle picked it up, put his hand to his heart, whispered, smiled and died. My father's big, good hands were at his sides on the edge of the bed. He turned them up with the palms open, so that mother and I each took one of them, as if he had offered them. Twice he acted as if he felt a nice taste on his lips, and died.

Downstairs I heard Mary and the children. A horrible fear seized me. A couple of seconds later I wanted to stand up and couldn't. I thought: knock on the floor—but I didn't do it. I remained lying down. I saw the anxious eyes of Mary when she got the bills for my funeral. She could not pay them and didn't dare to tell anybody.

All this can only have lasted one moment, probably not longer than the crisis itself. Later on I was waiting calmly till the last cramp would come and kill me.

Death cannot come closer than that. In a train, for instance, or in a car, when an accident happens, instincts work in a very different way. In one lightning stroke the human animal is conscious of its health and understands its chances in that short, brutal game of unleashed violence. To suffocate by gas is banal. One faints immediately, one scarcely realizes the beginning of the fainting and one does not feel that one is dying.

Other more intriguing touches of death are even softer than what I describe here. For instance, late at night in the park one is held up by a heavily built scoundrel. With a revolver in his hand he demands your money or your life. Everything turns over in you, you are tempted to take a chance, you give him the money and you say: "But now kill me, here where I point." He looks around, incited by a demonic lust, trying to find out if he can get away safely. At that moment death is fairly close. He tells you to do it yourself "Give me your gun," you say. "You damned fool," he replies, "then I lose my gun." Or another instance: when you go to bed you find a newspaper at the bottom of the stairs, you take it up ten steps and casually you read that a scholar expects the earth to be struck any minute by such a tremendous meteor that its mere approach will burn us to the bone, will make the seas boil and reduce the continents to a liquid state. You grin. You throw the newspaper over the stair-rail. You fall asleep without more ado and later you awake, trembling and perspiring with a panic, animal fear. Even then death is not so close.

But now death was in me. The point of its stiletto was on my heart. It accomplished its task by the same necessity as my organs do theirs. It was impossible for me to prevent its striking, as it would be impossible to prevent my liver from purifying my blood. I need only wait one more moment. Now I began to become conscious of my condition. Downstairs: Mary and the children, and up here I was dying. Later on Mary would have the oldest child call me for supper. The lad would not succeed in awakening me, he would go downstairs to say that I was sound asleep and Mary would answer: Then let father rest. After an hour she would put the smallest of our children to bed. She would turn on the lights and find me dead. Could I do such a thing to her? Should I not knock on the floor, so that she would tear up the stairs. But then what? What could I tell her, even if I should be able to speak: "Mary, I let you down and I do not see any solution for you." In fact, I felt only one urge, to say "Mary, I thank you," and close my eyes for ever. But now from everywhere I heard loud laughter and I saw in rapid succession three or four heads bursting out laughing and screaming, as films sometimes interpret the reactions of the public to one of Chaplin's gags. "I thank you, Mary, for table and bed and the children. Everything tasted fine and now I am leaving you. Without insurance, without pension, without fortune. But it's your problem. Goodbye." I was confused by this travesty of a deep and solemn gratitude, but I had not enough strength of mind to refute it. Weak and sick I confessed that I wanted to call Mary only in order not to have to die like a dog. It would only lengthen her sufferings, and I gave up the idea. Thinking of what she would have to suffer from this night on did not trouble me any more. For the first time I saw myself as I was in reality. Maybe myself alone, maybe everybody. Well, I said to myself, could you die without saying adieu, don't you feel the need to see your three children once more? My indignation confused me and I didn't dare to come out with the truth at once. But soon a cruel sincerity prevailed. Hypocrisy fled as death came closer. I realized that I always had been solitary, in a solitude so absolute that no words or images could pierce it. I had never liked anybody, I had never believed in anything. With astonishment I looked into myself. As a child I had been "educated," but a hidden voice told me that all that was nonsense. Yet I noticed that other children believed in it, loved their parents, suffered anguish when they died, prayed faithfully, valued courage, self-sacrifice, respect and good breeding, and tried to attain them. I knew I couldn't do anything against that and I said to myself: Well, it has to be that way, it is probably all right, only I alone am bad. I put this harness on but I never carried it with conviction. My teachers gave me also other ideas, "higher ideas." The first time I heard them I didn't even take them in earnest. I remember that they looked to me like texts to be learned for the examination, and to be forgotten ever after. I considered them as conventions like those required by etiquette, which tell one to put up a front and appear to be something different from one's own nature. Often I had the feeling that all this didn't concern me.

I wondered if I alone was intelligent. Sometimes, burning with passion, I threw a nasty word into the conversation and looked everybody in the whites of their eyes. But the only thing I noticed was annoyance and I withdrew with the bitter suspicion of my evilness. All the time I saw clearly that everybody around me took these things in painful earnest, and I put on that yoke too. Even those things which are supposed to be innate, the natural feelings, I did not have and I had to simulate them. I have expressed sorrow, joy and love, as I saw others do, or as I heard or read that they did. Always, always. Once my wife's life was in danger. The doctor sent me with a prescription to the pharmacist. Halfway, on the sidewalk, all of a sudden my blood curdled at the idea that I could lose her. I screamed with happiness and I groaned aloud: "I love, I love." Two years later my son Eric broke his arm. He was wearing a blue and white sweater. When we took it off with the utmost care, we didn't yet know that splinters of the bone had gone through the skin. One splinter caught in the blue wool and my child cried out as a wolf must cry when his paw cracks in the wolf-trap. That cry went through my marrow. I felt all the pain the child felt. Sobbing, I kissed him. I was unspeakably happy. My loneliness was over. Twice in a life-time.

How I snickered when poets called themselves lonely because their neighbors did not like the sunset as much as they. Or intellectuals be-cause they could not talk to everybody about their hobbies. Or colonials, because they had to live among colored people. I have lived among humans and am not human, at least if humans are what they pretend to be.

From time to time I was overcome by the deadly fear that, although people didn't know it, I was insane. For months I wore myself out in a desperate inquiry about the state of my mind. I mistrusted my introspec-tion and I submitted my intellect to logics which, according to normal persons, are the criterion of sound thinking. I examined ideas and theo-ries with exacting system. I analyzed the writings of "great minds" and I found out that my intuition had guided me very accurately from my youth on. Thus I became haughty, inhumanly hard, ironical, cynical, sarcastic. Since childhood, I was timid and hopelessly bashful because of my feeling of moral inferiority, and now I became stranger and still more inexplicable to those who discovered underneath this modesty an immense pretension. When I am drunk I rave about my brains. My ideas, I claim, begin only where yours end. After two more drinks I stand up, white with anger. I bang my fist on the table and pretend that I will not admit any longer that I alone am not a man. All of you are hypocrites in what you do, and idiots in what you think. I alone, I all alone, against all of you, I am a man. Then I move freely and with a manly air. I address myself in a friendly way to the women I used to fear, imagining that they will be at my beck and call. But when the fit is over, I see fearful eyes looking at me inquiringly and I am more lonely than ever before. Then I get drunk alone and weep. I have to play with little chil-dren, then reality does not exist any more. . . .

This loneliness could have been the end for me. On one of these many days, when I had had enough of lying and pretending, I could have shot myself like a dog. Without faith in what is written in books, in what believers teach, in what people recognize as valuable or use in the valua-tion of all things, I should have fallen a victim to my own cowardice. I should have believed myself a monster and consequently I should have destroyed myself, but something else has prevented me from achieving that fate, from going down every day a little deeper into my loneliness and into the uselessness of everything: a fanatic desire for justice. The injustice in this world has kept me awake, has made me jump through sheer rage out of my bed, the bed in which I should otherwise have preferred to die.

Injustice, done to me or to others, man or beast, has tortured me, has embittered me. It made me rage and fight desperately, mercilessly. I "owe" my continued existence to the dirt, for it kept altruism burning in me although it increased my contempt for that dirty pack, which with all its noble motives I never believed in, which was more cowardly and vulgar than I, a monster, dared to imagine. I fought them all like a Don Quixote. Now all that has come to an end.

I smiled. At the ultimate moment I had wanted to simulate, for I had read and I was told that one has to die decently, expressing the desire to see one's wife and children one last time and say adieu. Now I realized that it left me indifferent. They would grieve and be in need. It didn't touch me. I was going to the dogs. So what?

The two older children had silently sneaked up the stairs. At the door of the bedroom they forgot about being quiet, so that mother would not hear them. They had a dispute over who was going to open the door. They fell down fighting on the carpet and all of a sudden they tumbled into the room, pulling each other's hair and still pushing each other around. They saw me lying on the couch and, timidly, they came closer. I had the impression that they felt the presence of death but suddenly they shouted loudly in both my ears to frighten me out of my sleep. I let them have their fun. It proved exactly how lonely I was, dying, just as I had lived. When they noticed that I did not move they began to quarrel over me in whispers. They reproached each other for not having left me in peace. They told each other they should leave me alone, but neither one wanted to go first and they left me, menacing each other: "Just wait, boy, till we are on the staircase." Scarcely was the door closed than I heard them again rolling on the floor. The one that was down probably was hitting the door with his heels, then Mary must have noticed their absence and told them to come downstairs.

My head becomes hollow and clear. Everything echoes in it, like steps in the night. Every image is surrounded by the hard light of an icy moonlight. The postman carries around my death notice. The mail-boxes make a little noise. One by one I see my enemies open the obituary letter. They are numerous. I am proud of it. I did everything to have it that way. Some among them have never seen me, but they constantly had the feeling that I saw through them and despised them. I am very proud about them. The first one is upset and suddenly he is very much pleased. He hated me in secret and feared me. Out of pure joy he rings the bell in the afternoon, in order to be, if possible, the first one to call and be chivalrous. I see Mary standing in front of him, I hear his voice tremble: "Differences of opinion, temper, you know . . . But he always esteemed me very highly. Yes, Madam, you would not believe it, but he was even close to my heart."

My head became so clear that I attained a kind of ubiquity. I see them all at once in their homes and apartments, opening the letter and becoming pale. One of them imagines that he has a share in my death, on account of an incident between us once, that made me sick. He combats this thought and piously recognizes the Lord's ways: Although we never can scrutinize God's intentions, it is clear to him that my sudden death is the only solution. He knows that my dead lips have sealed some secrets, and he thanks the Lord who arranged everything for the best. He prays for my soul.

Another one grieves immediately. He gets in touch with his friends and he deplores my death in a sad voice and with sighs. He throws some earth on my coffin. He turns around, a feeling of safety comes over him, and he is no longer ashamed.

I see them coming out of their houses for the funeral: the choir of those rejoicing. A heavy, mellow and unctuous voice speaks at my open grave. It's the voice of the sacristan of a village in the Kempen. I used to go there once a year, always on the same date. I had a glass of beer in his café, opposite the church and he used to offer me a pinch of snuff. I see how the rejoicing listen, and wrath overcomes me. I cannot leave my enemies, I want to destroy them.

I am panting. To die decently, one has to forgive. I have been decent long enough. Dying, I want to be myself. I want to get this riff-raff away from my coffin. I want to spoil the fun of their simulating, but what happens to me is exactly what happened to Mary when she brought the bottles and the pills: when I have thought everything over, I feel powerless. Then in cold blood, I resolve to put their names on a piece of paper and to write underneath that they have killed me. Why, do you think, I didn't do it? You who praised "the noble sides of my character," you who would have accused my volcanic temper for having played this last joke on you? I didn't do it for this reason only, that nobody would have believed it. Nobody would have believed me capable of doing such a thing in my sound mind. For they are noble throughout, they have scrutinized human character and they know that to overstep certain boundaries is abnormal. Those rejoicing would have come to my grave with

even lighter gait and they would have stood around all the more noble
and forgiving.

I understood what I have always refused to understand: my powerless-
ness. I did not live, I underwent life. I didn't act, others, men and things
made me act. I carried around my duplicity like a damned cowardice
and I didn't know that it was impossible for me to be myself. If I had
broken my chains when a child, I should have been locked up with the
abnormals from birth. Had I done it later, the consensus would have
been that all of a sudden I had become schizophrenic. Now I write it
down in black and white. They will call it literature. My enemies who
take this seriously will declare that I am a poor lunatic. The others will
defend me and stick to the theory that it is just literature. So that is literature then! It has been impossible for me to be taken seriously. The
creature I was had no right to exist. Therefore it does not exist for you.

All right, I said between my teeth, all right. It was not a poetical desire
for death on the part of a very healthy poet, but a passion lewd and turbulent as for a woman. I pushed my breast against the point of a dagger
poised against my heart. Push on, you damned poseur!

I sat upright and looked around the room in amazement. How long
had I been waiting now? Did I have to die? I asked myself if such a
violent desire for death would not be an increased desire to live and,
behold, I began really to think about my work. And again that childish
illusion of old: to be able to get through my work for a living so fast
that I could find time for my art. Again it seemed to me that I had spent
more time on dreams than on work. And that on publicity drawing! I
firmly believed again in a rational working plan, which would allow me
to devote half of my time to my art.

I said aloud: "My art." It was as if I kissed somebody in ecstasy. Even
Mary does not believe that I will ever be able to produce a work of art
again. I will grow old and die, slaving for a living, if I don't die now.
Slowly I am overcome by an anxiety, a feeling of cold in the stomach.
It creeps up to the lungs, I breathe with difficulty. Death comes slowly,
then, and will strangle me. I see "Bad Eye" before me, a teacher at our
college: I never met a meaner, more brainless person in my life. He looks
at me out of the corner of his swollen eye and he uses a red match to
fidget at a great black tooth. He does not speak but he looks at me so
nastily and so provokingly that I understand him. "Your art!" he says.
"Learn your Greek lessons, do your mathematics homework. You've been
in my class for years now and I've got your number. Your works of art
will be nothing but lies. Paint pictures the way we people like and in

which we recognize ourselves as we are. This cannot be your art. You have confessed it yourself, you aren't like the rest of us, you are of another breed."

I feel he is right. He grins as he did the time he made fun of me in front of the whole class till I went green in the face. He puts a finger in his nose, he digs up his great red handkerchief full of snuff that always nauseated me so, he sniffs, expectorates and goes on teaching: "We humans . . ."

He is right. I dreamed cowardly and hypocritically of a conventional art, the art that would express my own self would not be an art. Maybe the arts also have art, but what is that to us!

At that moment I jumped up. I was quite certain that such a violent gesture would kill me. I would be dizzy, I would fall down and have a broad smile so that everybody could see how glad I had been that everything was over.

But I was not dizzy and on the contrary I began to walk up and down the room with energy. It was the challenge of one who has nothing to lose any more. My gait was juvenile, gay and forceful. I counted on my fingers to make out where I stood now. The index: devotion to my wife, children and friends. The index down. The middle finger up: devotion to my enemies. The middle down. The ring finger up: devotion to my work. The little finger: something for the little finger, perhaps? Down, the little finger. I talked loud and like a speaker addressing a mass meeting: Now we will proceed with the physical exercises. I started violent gymnastic movements. My gestures were supple and forceful. It gave me a singular pleasure.

The kids hadn't closed the door very well. The smallest one opened it, pushed her head inside and said peek-a-boo. With me all she did was play peek-a-boo. I did the same. Come here, little one. I grabbed her and went on with my exercises, burdened with her weight, but well determined to hold her above my body if I fainted so that she may fall on me and not get hurt.

When Mary came up to call us for supper, I had my pants and shirt on and I was as red-faced and excited as the child. She laughed about my long nap. I ate as usual, hurriedly, a great deal and gluttonously, without a word. Mary's fear was gone, her love was great. Then I locked myself up with a bottle of gin and I worked with ease and gusto.

But the next day I awoke. I felt with terror that I had to live on. Without love, without faith, without enemies, without art. And look at me. I live on and I tell you: that isn't all. No, I am young and strong and every day I laugh! A belly laugh, careless, jovial and indestructible. Laughter attracts me. When I hear laughing I join in. Laughing, I look the laughers straight in the eye and then we become serious for a moment and then there is something we understand about each other. Of course, I am human.

Translated from the Flemish by MARNIX GIJSEN

THE NETHERLANDS

INTRODUCTION

By J. Greshoff

THE WAR OF 1914–1918 effected no essential changes in the intellectual constitution of the countries which were not directly involved in it. The Netherlands unquestionably followed passionately the dramatic events of those days. An antithesis arose between the masses and the intellectuals, on one hand, sympathetic to the cause of the Allies and, on the other hand, a group consisting largely of Rotterdam merchants, reinforced by some professional officers, who were dependent on Germany in an economic and intellectual respect. This sympathetic interest and this antithesis, however, did not touch the deepest essence of Netherlands national existence, and individuals were not affected by them in the inmost recesses of their being, so that they find expression in the literature of those days only sporadically and superficially. The new Dutch poetry is in general deficient in reflections of contemporary issues.

Before the first World War the intellectual development of our country had proceeded not entirely apart from the events, yet after all alongside them, and the trend was not violently interrupted in 1914. We can call this development normal if in so doing we affirm that influence from beyond the frontiers must be regarded as normal in the development of any nation. What really matters is only to what extent and how these foreign influences are assimilated.

And if we thus follow the gently undulating trend along which our literature has moved from about 1875 on, we discover in it during the period from 1914 to 1918 no violent zigzags nor a more rapid pace.

From 1875 to 1940 numberless movements, theories, and groups made themselves felt. Periodicals were born and died and became superannuated. Slogans were greatly in demand for a shorter or longer time. Fashion showed itself no less capricious in its tyranny in literature than it did in clothing. Yet, if we scrutinize all these antitheses and strongly, all too strongly, pronounced differences, we reach the conviction that the complete period of a half-century will later come to be regarded as a connected whole. And it is not out of the question that future historians of literature will give that period the name of "transitional baroque." In any event we ascertain among the so-called writers of the Eighties, as well as among the generation of 1910, and equally so among the young and youngest authors, one and the same undeniable, predominating, romantic trait. That must not surprise us, for under the circumstances only a romantic attitude toward life is imaginable. The Dutch national character and the transition from the nineteenth to the twentieth century, that is, the people and the time, render any other escape impossible. For individualism has always a romantic side, while every classical mode of life and imagination presupposes a hierarchy and therefore a closed community. The Netherlanders have been romantic from the most remote times, and they will long remain so.

Every literature constitutes a flowing continuity. It does indeed happen now and then, however, that this flow is temporarily damned up by unforeseen circumstances and is led into a different channel. The first World War was was not such a circumstance for the Netherlands. The young Socialist movement between 1870 and 1900 eventually exerted a deeper and broader influence on Dutch literature than all the horrors of 1914 to 1918.

I go further and ask myself whether any war can ever exert an essential influence on intellectual life. By this I naturally do not mean the phenomenon that a number of writers turn their attention to war topics in order to meet a temporary demand on the part of the public, which is eager for the things of the moment. I am speaking of a genuine influence, and I wish to indicate thereby a lasting change in the nature and the appearance of intellectual life. Did the first World War furnish a "masterpiece"—not a tragic and deeply felt, but formless book like *Le Feu*—but a masterpiece in the highest and fullest sense of the word?

War, misery, horror lead us away from the founts of life. They leave no time for reflection and deliberation. They make demands on us which are so urgent and compelling that no energy remains for anything else. Two forces stimulate poetic creativeness, fear and hope: Fear prior to war, and hope afterward.

The curious thing is that fear, which is such a strong poetic impulse, practically failed to assert itself in 1914, because the war came unexpectedly.

But after 1918, it was predicted, hope would blaze up as an awe-inspiring force. Joy at regained freedom, the desire for a new, better future, would exert a far stronger influence on man and his creative urge than the recollection of suffering that had been experienced.

The past furnishes material and examples for moralists and historians. The future, that which is not yet in being, is the domain of the poets. It is too often forgotten that reality and poetry, events and poems, belong to two worlds which have only slight points of contact with each other and therefore get little opportunity to affect each other. And if there can be a question of influence, it is rather poetry which influences the world than the world which influences poetry.

The reality was quite different from the expectation. Before 1914 there existed, at least in the Netherlands, no fear and after 1918 no hope. The writers completed, in the midst of the roar of war, their life-work which they had begun prior to the war. Of a war literature there is no question in our country, and equally little is there any of a total reversal or renewal. Some war poems were written, of little importance and without mutual connection, and there originated, practically unnoticed, as a rarity, the mobilization novel by J. K. van Eerbeek. The only war poetry of any importance was written by a mysterious person, A. H. Feijs (man or woman?), of whose existence nothing is known and whose work is accessible only in so far as it is quoted in an article by Albert Verweij. After one little volume, which never got on the market, we never heard anything more about this strange phenomenon in our literature.

During the war, H. Marsman printed his first poems, and shortly thereafter a group of young authors came into being, first in connection with the monthly *Het Getij* and later around *De Vrije Bladen*.

From this turbulent group three great poets ultimately worked themselves to the top: H. Marsman (1899–1943), J. Slauerhoff (1898–1936), and Hendrik de Vries (1896–   ). If one attaches any importance to literary connections, one can point out in the youthful Marsman the influence of German expressionism, and in the youthful Slauerhoff the influence of Tristan Corbière; but both very soon assimilated those influences completely in their strong individual lives.

In view of the fact that few obstacles exist in the literary life of the Netherlands, youthful talents can unfold rapidly and completely. This has a detrimental effect on those who are but little gifted. The latter must be forced by necessity to concentrate, in order to be able to give the best of which they are capable. But strong natures are not harmed by freedom.

This triad of young authors, welcomed by the others with enthusiasm, very soon gained rightful recognition and this dominated literary life in the Netherlands from 1920 to 1930.

A reaction and reversal never fails to appear where there is life. As a protest against the satellites and imitators of the *De Vrije Bladen* the monthly *Forum* was established.

After the ecstatic emotional strain of Marsman, the pent-up romanticism of Slauerhoff and the hallucinated baroque of Hendrik de Vries (a bizarre combination of the Gothic and Manuel styles), *Forum* sought relaxation in a simple warm humanity. After "the word which sings itself loose from its meaning" (to borrow from the poet M. Nijhoff a definition which is as correct as it is beautiful), the new group defended the direct utterance from man to man. Menno ter Braak called himself "a fighter for the common word." And people glorified the poetry of the unpoetical. For this reaction I am in part responsible, and my intention and that of my supporters was not always understood.

The opposition of *Forum* was not directed against a Marsman, a Slauerhoff, and a de Vries, who for that matter all belonged to the collaborators of the periodical, but against the degeneration of what they represented and stood for. We further defended, by the side of "great" poetry—the poetry of revelation—the rights of "minor" poetry, the poetry of confession. This antithesis of heavenly and earthly was ingeniously motivated by A. Vestdijk, born in 1898, poet, novelist, essayist, the most important author of the younger generation who is now, so far as we know, still alive. In addition to him, Menno ter Braak (1902–1940) and E. du Perron (1900–1940) are the leading personages of this group.

After *Forum*, which existed for four years, had disappeared, I realized that we had waged a fight on chimeras. Poetry is neither great nor minor, neither earthly nor heavenly, but a completely separate world in which both our physics and our metaphysics have lost their validity.

Out of *Forum's* battle for sobriety, critical genius and a studied pedestrianism as an antidote against a false sublimity, there arose a poetry of decadent successors (which was denominated "cocktail poetry" by Anthonie Donker), repugnant in its vulgarity and joviality.

And once more we observed a complete reversal.

The very youngest authors, who came to the fore after *Forum,* denied all rational laws with the delightful absoluteness of youth, and exalted inspiration as the inducement and aim of every art expression. The words cryptic, mediumistic, somnambulistic and anti-rationalistic came into fashion and were applied excessively in every theoretical consideration. Here, consciously or unconsciously, a threefold influence makes itself felt: Bergson, Freud and Surrealism.

Two poets of importance, G. Achterberg (born in 1905) and Ed. Hoornik (born in 1910) wrote a kind of poetry in which the unexpressed and inexpressible is the most important element. The significance no longer lies in the word, but *behind* the word. It is a poetry of fanatical conjurations and magical indications.

Finally there arises the question: Is there a relationship or at least a connection between these three generations, between a Marsman, a du Perron, and an Achterberg? I think that I discover this in the atmosphere in which these successive generations of authors lived and in which their works originated.

Now this was an atmosphere charged with fear. The war of 1939 did *not* come unexpectedly. The entire period between 1918 and 1938, twenty long years, is dominated and characterized by fear of the inevitable. And all literary expressions group themselves around this main theme. So emphatic an affirmation of life as "vitalism" can have its cause only in the desire to conquer death. The equally emphatic enthusiasm for the earthly and the amenities of daily life is only a means of escaping from the obsession of death. Surrealism endeavors to derive from the denial of reality the right to deny death.

Inseparably connected with fear is flight. Slauerhoff's mania for roaming, du Perron's aggressiveness, Achterberg's sleepwalking—these are all forms of flight. And I know of no period of literature whose inner impelling force manifests itself so clearly. We have here the literature of "basic anxiety," an element which is defined by Dr. Karen Horney, one of the neo-Freudians, as follows: "Basic anxiety: a feeling of being alone and helpless in a hostile world." Alone and helpless in a hostile world the authors felt between 1918 and 1938, and truly not without reason.

This period was thus one of intense life and of exceptional richness, for fear is and remains the most powerful impelling force. It brought the young authors to the edge of the abyss and of destruction, but stimulated their creative urge to the utmost.

Of the poetry and prose that has appeared during the occupation, i.e. after May 1940, I have been able to gain only inadequate knowledge. But all that I have been able to collect of it does not give me the impression of an essential change in spirit and in form. The Curaçao periodical, *De Stoep,* has gathered a collection of Dutch poems from the years 1940, 1941 and 1942, and this indicates clearly that there has been no abrupt break. Life goes on.

A renewal is possible only when in the future fear is dispelled by hope, when, after the flight into night, we may experience the flight into day.

Johan Huizinga

FUNDAMENTALS OF CULTURE

WHAT DO WE MEAN by Culture? The word has emanated from Germany. It has long since been accepted by the Dutch, the Scandinavian and the Slavonic languages, while in Spain, Italy, and America it has also achieved full standing. Only in French and English does it still meet with a certain resistance in spite of its currency in some well-defined and traditional meanings. At least it is not unconditionally interchangeable with civilization in these two languages. This is no accident. Because of the old and abundant development of their scientific vocabulary, French and English had far less need to rely on the German example for their modern scientific nomenclature than most other European languages, which throughout the nineteenth century fed in increasing degree on the rich table of German phraseology.

Oswald Spengler posited the terms culture and civilization as the poles of his sharply pointed but all too dogmatic decline-theory. The world has read him and heard his warning words, but it has not been able to accept either his terminology or his judgment.

In general usage the word culture is not apt to create misunderstanding. One knows more or less what is meant by it. To give an accurate description of its meaning, however, is a different thing altogether. What is culture, what does it consist of? An exhaustive definition is practically impossible. All we can do is to enumerate a few essential conditions and requirements without which there can be no such thing as culture.

Culture requires in the first place a certain balance of material and spiritual values. This permits the emergence of a social condition which is appreciated by those living in it as affording more and higher values than the mere gratification of want and the desire for power. These values lie in the domain of the spiritual, the intellectual, the moral, and the æsthetic. These several domains themselves must again be in balance and harmony to render the concept of culture applicable. By stressing equilibrium and not absolute level one is enabled to include early or low or crude forms of society in a cultural evaluation, and to avoid the danger of over-estimating the highly refined civilizations and of one-sided appreciation of one of the several factors of culture, be it religion, art, law, political organisation or any other. This equilibrium may be viewed as a harmonious and energetic functioning of the several cultural activities within the whole. The result of such co-ordination of the cultural activities manifests itself in order, structural strength, and rhythm of the particular society. It is clear that the historical evaluation of different cultures, no more than the appreciation of present environment, can free itself from the preconceived standards of the judging subject. In this connection it must be noted that the general qualification of a culture as a "high" or "low" culture appears ultimately to be determined by its spiritual and ethical rather than its intellectual and æsthetic value content. A culture which does not boast technical achievements or great sculptural art may still be a high culture, but not if it lacks charity.

The second fundamental feature of culture is that all culture has an element of striving. It is directed towards an aim and this aim is always an ideal, not the ideal of an individual, but an ideal for society. The nature of this ideal varies greatly. It may be purely spiritual: celestial bliss, nearness to God, liberation from earthly ties; or: knowledge, rational or mystical, knowledge of nature, knowledge of self and the mind, knowledge of the divine. It may be a social ideal: honour, respect, power, greatness, but always honour, respect, power and greatness for the community. Again, it may be economic or hygienic: prosperity or health. For the bearers of culture the ideal always means betterment or weal, weal here or elsewhere, now or later.

Whether the aim is in heaven or on earth, wisdom or wealth, the essential condition of its pursuit and attainment is always security and order. Culture could not be a striving if it did not first of all fulfil the imperative task of maintaining security and order. From the requirement of order springs all that is authority, from that of security all that is law. At the bottom of scores of different systems of law and government there are always the social groupings whose striving for betterment gives rise to culture.

More concrete and more positive than the first-mentioned fundamentals of culture, balance and striving, is the third, chronologically its first and most typical feature. Culture means control over nature. Culture exists the moment man discovers that the hand armed with the flint is capable of things which without it would have been beyond his reach. He has bent a part of nature to his will. He controls nature, his enemy and his benefactor. He has acquired instruments, means; he has become *homo faber*. He uses these means to gratify a want, to construct an implement, to protect himself and his kin, to destroy animal or foe. Henceforward he changes the course of nature, for the results of his handling the tool would not have occurred without it.

If this control over nature were the only prerequisite of culture there would be little reason to deny ants, bees, birds or beavers the claim to its possession. They all turn parts of nature to their use by altering them. Whether or not these activities include a striving for betterment is a question for animal psychology to answer. But even if they did, the attribution of culture to the animal world would still meet with the spontaneous reaction that this is abusing the term. The spirit cannot be eliminated quite as easily as some would think.

In fact, to say that culture is control over nature in the sense of building, shooting and roasting is to tell only half the story. The rich word "nature" includes human nature as well and that also must be controlled. Already in the earliest and simplest phases of society man becomes conscious that he owes something. The animal's care and defence of his young are not sufficient to warrant the conclusion that there too this consciousness exists. It is only in the human consciousness that the function of caring and providing takes on the aspect of Duty. The recognition of this duty is only in a relatively small degree attributable to natural circumstances such as motherhood and protection of the family unit. At an early stage of social organisation the obligation expands into conventions, rules of conduct and cults, in the form of *taboos*. In wide circles the popularisation of the word *taboo* has led to an undervaluation of the ethical element of the so-called primitive cultures, not to say anything of that body of sociological thought which with truly modern simplicity disposes of everything called morality, law, or piety, as just so many *taboos*.

The consciousness of owing something contains an ethical element as soon as there is no absolute material necessity to honour what is felt as an obligation to a fellow-man, an institution or a spiritual power. Ethnologists like Malinowski have shown that the view that in primitive civilizations obedience to the social code is mechanically determined and inescapable, is untenable. Whenever in a community the rules of social conduct are generally observed, therefore, it is through the operation of a genuine ethical impulse. The requirement of control over nature in the form of domination of human nature itself is then fulfilled.

The more the specific feelings of being under obligation range themselves under a supreme principle of human dependence the clearer and the more fertile will be the realisation of the concept, indispensable to all true culture, of service; from the service of God down to the simple social relationship as between employer and employee. The uprooting and discrediting of the service-concept has been the most destructive function of the shallow rationalism of the eighteenth century.

Were we now to sum up what we have set out above as the essential features and general requirements of culture, the contents of this concept might perhaps be formulated in the following statement, which cannot lay any claim to the quality of exact definition, however. Culture, as a condition of society, is present when the control over nature in the material, the moral, and spiritual field maintains a state which is *higher* and *better* than would follow from the given natural conditions, and whose characteristics are a harmonious balance of material and spiritual values and a more or less homogeneous ideal in whose pursuit the community's various activities converge.

If the foregoing description—from which the valuation higher and better with its subjective tinge cannot be eliminated—contains a certain amount of truth, the question now arises whether in our time the essential conditions of culture are present.

Culture presupposes control over nature. This condition does, indeed, seem to have found a greater degree of fulfilment than in any known civilization of the past. Forces whose existence was hardly guessed at a century ago and whose character and possibilities were completely unknown, have been harnessed in a thousand ways with effects in the heights and the depths undreamt of a generation earlier. Nor is the end of this march of conquest yet in sight. Hardly a year passes without the discovery of new forces of nature and the means to turn them to advantage.

Physical nature lies at our feet shackled with a hundred chains. What of the control of human nature? Do not point to the triumphs of psychiatry, social services, or the war against crime. Domination of human nature can only mean the domination of every man by himself. Has he achieved this? Or, perfection being beyond his reach, does his domination of himself bear any proportion to his vastly increased control over physical nature? There is hardly reason to think so. Only too often it seems as if man, abusing the freedom obtained through his control over physical nature, refuses to dominate himself and is ready to abdicate all the values which the spirit had gained him. The rights and claims of human nature are everywhere called upon to question the authority of absolute ethical laws. The condition, control over nature, is only halfway fulfilled.

For the fulfilment of the second condition of culture, the pursuit of a largely homogeneous ideal, everything is lacking. The desire for betterment driving every community and every individual looks through a hundred different eyes. Every group pursues its own particular conception of weal without integrating it in one all-embracing ideal superimposed on the various particular desires. It is only the expression of such a common ideal, whether attainable or illusory, which could afford full justification for the term "*our* culture." In older times we do find such common ideals: the glory of God, however understood, justice, virtue, wisdom. Obsolete metaphysical conceptions, the spirit of to-day will object. But with the abandonment of such conceptions the homogeneity of culture is in jeopardy. For what replaces these high principles of action is then nothing but a conglomeration of conflicting desires. The factors linking the cultural aims of our time together can only be found in the series prosperity, power and security (security, because it includes peace and order as well), all ideals which are more apt to divide than to unite and all springing directly from natural instincts, untouched by the spirit. Even the cave-dweller knew them thousands of years ago.

Now one hears a great deal to-day of "national cultures" and "class cultures," that is to say, the concept culture is made subservient to the power, prosperity, or security ideal of a particular group. Those doing so, however, deprive the concept of all its real meaning; for they forget the paradoxical but, in view of the foregoing, inescapable conclusion that one can only speak of culture when the ideal dominating it transgresses the interests of the community claiming the possession of culture. Culture must have its ultimate aim in the metaphysical or it will cease to be culture.

✻   ✻   ✻

Can the world of to-day claim that balance of spiritual and material values which we took to be a prerequisite of culture? Again, the answer must be largely negative. There is intensive production in both fields, certainly, but—balance? Harmony and equipollence of material and spiritual power?

The manifestations of our time all around us seem to exclude every thought of a true equilibrium. A highly refined economic system daily puts forth a mass of products and sets forces in motion which nobody wants and which bring advantage to none, which everyone fears, which many scorn as unworthy, absurd and mischievous. Coffee is burnt to maintain its market, war material finds eager buyers but no one desires that it be used. The disproportion between the perfection and capacity of the productive apparatus and the power to turn it to advantage, poverty in the midst of plenty: they all leave little room for the idea of equilibrium. There is intellectual over-production as well, a permanent surfeit of the written and the "wireless" word and a well-nigh hopeless divergence of thought. Art has been caught in the vicious circle which chains the artist to publicity and through it to fashion, both of which are again dependent on commercial interests. Throughout the whole range, from the life of the State to the life of the family, a dislocation seems to be in process such as the world has never known before. Of true equilibrium, of balance, there can be no question.

Translated by J. H. HUIZINGA

Arthur van Schendel

THE STREET SINGER

HE HAD been an ordinary man who lived unnoticed, without anyone having anything to praise or blame in him. He was seen going out in the mornings, punctually to time, neatly dressed; he was seen coming home late. No one asked his name or what he did all day. Not until he began to go out and come home irregularly did he attract attention, and then it was noticed that he was ugly, thin and shabbily dressed. Previously, it was thought, he might have been a clerk, but now he was in low water and the pallor of his face, where want and grief were clearly visible, his staring eyes, his unkempt hair must have come from a disorderly life. It was now observed that he was a street singer, although he had never been seen with a guitar before. People said he had changed very much.

He noticed a change himself, but it did not concern his outward appearance or the manner in which he earned a livelihood. For him the world had become empty, and the spot where he walked, black. He saw more clearly than other people how ugly it was here, for his eyes had changed. The town was an incomprehensible maze of streets, so large that he was always afraid of losing his way; the houses were all alike, all low, all inhabited by beings with glassy eyes, grey clothes and voices without a ring. There were still uglier houses with empty windows, all built about the same time. Vehicles went through the town, grey cages, and every time he had counted them, another passed. He remembered that he used to sit in one when he was not afraid of them. He used also to look at the people, but now he preferred to look at the stones of the street, for he had lost something there.

Yet sometimes he had to look at them when he held up his hand. Generally it was women who gave, and to look at women and to accept from them was the worst he had to bear, for they were the ugliest of all that existed. Sometimes he had to stand still before a certain face, it was not real, but so beautiful that he did not want to think of it. Anyone who had not seen it could not realize how ugly the others were.

It was this face which had caused the chant in his heart that constantly forced him to utter words with the same sound, words that ended on a heavy note. They had a meaning, he knew well, but too far away from him to comprehend. It seemed that people understood them when he sang, for they stood round him in rows, next to each other, staring into the center with mournful faces as if someone had met with an accident. And then they threw pennies into the circle, like flowers dropped into a grave, and he sang till his throat hurt him:

> The day I was born was a Sunday
> And all paradise was my own,
> But that very day I lost it
> And started my journey alone.
> And endless now were the years
> Of seeking and staring and tears.
> When I thought to hear the angels—
> For it seemed I had striven well—
> The devil came to torment me
> And I stumbled dismayed into hell.

But the chant in his heart became monotonous. One day it was as if he had forgotten all his songs except this one; he heard himself always singing the same words, and all others remained away. Particularly the last word often came out of his mouth—long, sorrowing, deep. He also noticed that it frightened people; they stepped back, and the women laughed, shuddering, with open mouths. And no more pennies were dropped; there was shouting and cries that he should sing something else. He is always thinking of murder, they said, he sings of nothing but misery; the man has lost his senses. Then they hooted at him, and the police came to chase him away. He was taken before the judge who said he might not sing about hell because it did not exist, nor about blood because it was really not so bad as all that. But how could he sing other than what wrung his heart, even if it was always the same song? It wore out his strings, but his throat brought forth the same words, and he now wandered at night, when there was nobody left to run away from him or hoot at him, singing in front of closed windows:

> I looked in her eyes on Sunday,
> On Monday I wooed her long,
> But she lied of love on Tuesday
> And her words were false and wrong.
> Two days then together I bore
> Of giving and asking still more;
> But on Friday, alas, she deceived me;
> On Saturday I took it well—
> Till I could not bear it longer
> And on Sunday, bright blood fell.

Windows were pushed up, abusive language and threats were heard and sometimes a heavy object fell at his feet. Then he walked on, singing, hearing nothing but his own voice.

But one night men came out of the houses and attacked him furiously, dragged him out of the town and beat him and threw stones at him, until he disappeared in the darkness. His song was heard in the distance, through the night.

The watch-dogs barked themselves hoarse when he approached and passed by, seeing nothing, understanding nothing, feeling only his heavy heart full of lamenting sound. The country people, in the fields at dawn, stood still when they heard his lament approach and then grow silent again. The peasant women came to their doors when they heard his voice and wiped their eyes when he had disappeared, wondering what this grief might be that was being carried by. For they well understood that he was a man of misfortune. In the woods the birds grew silent, only the cuckoo, who could sing almost as monotonously, answered and accompanied his song.

And he came to a wilderness of sand and thorn bushes where it was so still that he noticed it and grew silent. Here he did not dare to sing. Yet, with his mouth closed, his heart became so bursting full of sound, that he had to sit down on the ground, wringing his hands to heaven.

That was how the solitary one found him at sunset. The street singer was made aware of him by the long shadow that moved over the sand. And he knew that the pain would be taken out of his heart; he opened his mouth, and his lament resounded through the stillness as if it would never end. The silent one took him by the hand and led him to his sleeping place under the thorn-bushes. There he poured him water from a jug, but when the man did not want to partake of it, and went on singing, he sat down at his feet and listened. The evening fell, the stars came out, and the little song rang on in the darkness.

But as the stars moved on, the voice grew smaller, the singer fell back and his eyes closed. The solitary one knelt before him and, with hands uplifted, prayed throughout the stillness of the night.

And he prayed so loudly that the singer dreamed that he sang with a voice from heaven. When he opened his eyes at sunrise, he still heard it, far more beautiful than any song he had ever sung, and the words were different. He lay quietly, as if he had been washed clean with the scent of flowers. The quiet man all in white appeared in the light and, kneeling, said: We are poor creatures that we cannot sing. The chant of your song has always filled my heart, too, but I know so few words, and the only thing I know is something which I have to think of all the time. It is the same way with me, always the same song. And he sang his song:

> He came a-riding Palm Sunday,
> He rode to the temple gate,
> And after a day of sadness
> On Wednesday his woe was great.
> On Thursday he gave without strife
> His body, His blood and His life.
> On Friday he suffered all
> Was laid in the grave without stain—
> Ah, deep be the prayer of our hearts!—
> And on Sunday he rose again.

They came out into the sunlight, they folded their hands and this was the song they sang over the wilderness. Drops from all the thorn-bushes fell at their feet.

Translated by JO MAYO

Henriette Roland Holst

FROM TIME TO ETERNITY

I WILL ENTHOUGHT you ever deeplier, Death,
So that you grow within me like a child.
Are you not our child when the day withereth
And the evening glow is into twilight chilled?

I will enthought you until you are known,
As far as to know you possible be,
Till your face becomes familiar to me,
Till I feel I have become your own.

When you come, the long-awaited guest
Of our waking thought and our dreaming toil,
I shall not be surprised nor be aghast,
But greet you with a welcoming smile,

And follow you to the gate your hand
Shall unbolt, the dark gate to the garden
Beyond the vast, infinite land,
Mist-shrouded, of which you are warden.

Translated by A. J. BARNOUW

Simon Vestdijk

RUBBER FINGERS

HARDLY HALF AN HOUR had elapsed since Rudi had carried out his resolve to run away, when he suddenly came across his parents. He hid behind a tree and let them pass by. His feet sank into thick summer grass, and as he slowly crept round the trunk so that he could watch his parents unobserved, thistles, and once even a stinging nettle, repeatedly pricked him through his stockings. It did not hurt very much but for the first time it gave him a taste of the adventure, of the romantic yet hard adventure, that had thus far been lacking. If one wants to run away, one must suffer pain, he mused dully, going down to the edge of the ditch, now that the danger was over, and rubbing his legs. How his parents had looked!

Rudi looked over the meadows to where the outskirts of the great town began. Rust-colored houses there reflected a blood-red sunset which was, however, already half shrouded by mist and little clouds so that, in the West too, something rust-colored seemed to be approaching; a town in the air, but no celestial town. Red is not always a gay color, especially not with that green, turned mauve by contrast, in front of it, and that avenue in the distance not belonging to the town and yet leading to it, and the covered cattle besieged by a thin mist round their feet, and a solitary cricket with its metallic little voice, and a boy, bent over forward, rubbing his ankles with both his hands as if the trouble sat there. But that was not where it sat. It was in his head, and over there in the town that he had wanted to escape. He had intended walking on all night along lanes like that one in the distance but without the little lights that were now beginning to twinkle between the trees. After all, it was not yet time to rest by the edge of the ditch! But what he had just gone through would suffer no delay. He would have to think about it until the impression passed into something that he could understand.

His parents had walked in the direction of the town, thus toward him, the fugitive, and not after him as anyone would have expected, and only half an hour after he had left the parental house! When he became aware of them, they were close by. They were walking, each on one side of the road by way of precaution against the traffic, but there was never any traffic here, particularly not at this evening hour. They had walked as children do at the end of a tiring summer day, with bunches of withered flowers in their hands, some distance apart, a little sulkily as if they were blaming each other for their thirst and weariness. This walking, this sauntering—one could tell immediately: these two people have come a long way, they have a fatiguing day behind them, and only Rudi knew, and even he not exactly to the minute, that they had walked only half an hour, possibly even less, for they could not have discovered his departure the very moment he left. All the more astonishing was the rapidity with which they had got ahead of him. Perhaps along another road, along that avenue yonder in the distance where the street-lamps were twinkling against the purple mist. He would have to think it over well; they must have walked along streets and roads in less than no time, stumbling, stepping aside for cars and carriages, bicycles and pedestrians, looking for him meanwhile, and then they must have hurried back again, this other way, until, quite near the town, they had come toward him.

Yes, they had walked, as quick as lightning, presumably floating hand in hand while birds uttered shrill cries; his father always taller than his mother, stumbling forward in his impatience, dragging her along; and when he fell forward, she shot up with a jerk, her hat on one side and her skirts fluttering so that his father held his head to one side. One could tell by their appearance that they had gone through something like that.

His mother's face, he remembered, was tired and vacuously swollen, like that of a drunken woman, with a few dirty smudges across it. Her crushed hat sat askew, and too high, as if her hair stood on end. She ran with her hands stretched in front of her, a little straddle-legged, making one think of a flock of little animals that she was driving along and might escape her on this wide road. What had her eyes been like? He believed they had been half closed; that was in keeping with this sort of despair, and with the precautionary measures for the little animals for which the hands sufficed. If one kept one's eyes open too, it would be a hopeless case, for one could not drive animals along, and simultaneously chase back the stragglers that had run off; one had to trust to one's hands, and to the straddle-legged gait in those skirts; any that still managed to escape then did not count when compared with those that were brought into safety. She brought them all home safely but she herself would probably be insane on account of all the misery she had endured.

His father, on the other side of the road, had looked as if he were angry. He had pushed his bowler hat over his eyes so that his red ears stood out. His father had not even glanced at his mother, but let her drive her animals. Between his lips stuck a stalk of grass with a spike at the end of it, on which he chewed, pushing it in a little further with his right hand when a juicier part came along. His other hand he had held clenched. Perhaps this expressed less anger than one would have supposed. This clenching of the fist was due to the activity of the muscles grown tense—the soul held itself aloof. For, to begin with, this was an utterly exhausted man—and naturally, an afflicted, a sorely afflicted man who had just had to suffer great grief. But taking all in all, his weariness surpassed his affliction and, for instance, his rage against his wife, whom he could have blamed, most unreasonably—but after all, he was no longer the man he had been half an hour earlier—for Rudi's running away. Incidentally, if one had put him to bed, he would have slept like a log, with his bowler hat and his clothes on, and the stalk of grass hanging from the corner of his mouth.

That is how Rudi saw the procession of his parents pass by, their retreat, their irreparable defeat. These were not people of whom he need be afraid. But then, when evening fell while he was sitting like that at the edge of the ditch, the water all liquidity with stars reflected in it, and a rust-colored sky, already growing paler, over everything, he began to feel so unbearably lonely,—although it was just solitude that he had longed for—that he could do nothing but rub his ankles, stare into the water, and think continuously of his parents and how they had come toward him, not after, but toward! This was the terrible part of it: that he was now as it were looking at their backs, although he could no longer see them; that they, completely engrossed in their weariness, their grass stalks and the little animals of their madness, had written him off long ago. Shivering in the mist that crept up the bank, he yielded to a state of indecision in which he could go neither forward nor backward. It was entirely indifferent to him if he walked on all night as he had intended, or in the opposite direction after his parents who were no longer expecting him. It was pure chance that, instead of sticking to his guns, he changed his plan and abandoned his flight; it was no decision, it was chance. When he stood up, his joints creaked and cracked like an old man's, but that passed; he had really sat very uncomfortably at the damp edge of the ditch, and although his heart thumped like that of a pursued criminal, he ran quite ordinarily, quick and lithe, along the dusky road, back to the town.

Half an hour later—it was already dark—he rang at the door of his parents' house. It was opened without delay; in the passage he heard the voice of one of his sisters, afterwards that of his mother, commanding and clear, a command that apparently referred to chairs; and then of a whole crowd of children, his little brothers and sisters of all ages. Someone came stamping loudly down the top stairs, landing with a jump. Everybody in the house seemed very gay; everywhere he heard laughter and shouts mixed; a clutter.

Halfway up the stairs he chanced to look up, and looked right into the eyes of his father. His father seemed to be in a good mood. His eyes shone, his cheeks were red as if he had drunk something, or had laughed a long time at a stretch, and between his friendly, laughing lips he held a grass stalk from a big bunch of exotic grasses in a vase in the hall that tickled the man as he came and went. Absent-mindedly, or in boyish recklessness, he must have pulled it out in passing. He had done that before, Rudi had often seen him do it. Lisping a little, he addressed the boy whose face had grown so pale that he looked as if he would faint if nobody supported him. But the father apparently did not see much of that.

"A visitor has come unexpectedly, Rudi," he rattled. "Here are a couple of quarters; fetch a few cigars; it is not yet eight; you are late, but we have kept something for you; do it quickly, will you?"

Rudi had two quarters pressed into his trembling hand and went off to fetch cigars. Outdoors it was white with a rising mist, the same mist that had made him shiver at the edge of the ditch. He began to run hard to get warm, panting and with his heart still thumping, past dark houses and already closed shops—it was on the stroke of eight—and side streets that all led to the same square, a dimly lighted space in the distance, which, invariably looming up behind each street opening, seemed to be floating along with the running boy. He scarcely thought of the things he had just experienced; at best he was curious as to who the visitor could be, the man for whom he had to fetch the cigars. For some reason or other he knew for certain that it was a man. Then, close to the shop, he dropped one of the two quarters; five minutes were lost finding it and he came too late, not even receiving an answer to his repeated ringing. All the shops were closed; for that matter, he did not know another tobacconist in the neighborhood.

While he was running back, he had repeatedly to dismiss the thought that he should flee again, in possession of the two quarters. He realized how stupid he had been to undertake a thing like that without any money. But cold and hunger, and curiosity regarding the visitor, made him resist the temptation, even when his ring at home was not immediately answered. From this fact one could gather that the festive uproar had redoubled during his absence. Oh well, he would get something to eat, anyhow. Instead of a stair ruffle from higher parts of the house, the noise of footsteps right on the lowest flight startled him. He stared into the flushed faces of three boys spread all over the stairs, without understanding what they wanted from him. From the sitting room came the sound of singing, accompanied by bangs on the table.

"The cigars, Rudi!" shrieked the boys, sliding down, climbing up, pushing each other and giggling. "Come on! He is dying for a cigar!" It was two younger brothers, and a slightly older school friend, a dark, ruddy boy with spectacles through which leered grimly searching, greenish-brown eyes. Now the riddle of the tumult was at least solved! Children had been invited too; his own family would never have been able to raise such a din!

"Everything was closed!" he called up, but they did not even listen, and as the three boys barred his way, he remained standing where he was, with one foot on the bottom step. Suspiciously he looked up, expecting to see his father.

"Give them to me," shouted the school friend and made a plunging motion with both arms outstretched as if to fall round Rudi's neck, "and us the cigarettes."

Again footsteps in the hall—there was his mother, leaning with her left hand, in which she held a teacloth, on the little gate that shut off the stairs from the youngest child when necessary. She too looked flushed, but calm and decided as always, a woman with clear, blue eyes and a firm chin; when she stuck out her chin and kept it motionless, she made the impression of a kind of pious invincibility.

"Let Rudi get by, boys!" Obediently the boys leant back against the wall, looking round comically. "Where are the cigars, Rudi?"

"I haven't got them," he answered guiltily, "the shop was closed; I was too late; a quarter fell on the ground."

"And lost a quarter as well!" said his mother, not unkindly but obviously not intending to overlook a thing like that. "What a nuisance! Your father doesn't find the money in the street! Where did you lose it?"

"I haven't lost it," Rudi stammered, and mechanically dived his hand into his pocket for the two quarters, still with one foot on the bottom step. The boys again stood between him and his mother, the little brothers sniggering, the older boy looking up with something like awe as if to see how one behaves, as a parent, in such a case. Rudi's mother came down a few steps with hand outstretched. It looked as if she thought he would not dare to come higher, like an errand boy.

At that moment a loud bang rang from the sitting room, followed by laughter such as Rudi could not remember ever having heard in his life. A barbarous thunder led by male voices, rent by girls' shrieks, flooded by a children's choir, resounded through the house. Dogs seemed to participate, donkeys, cats, owls, parakeets, and cockatoos. It was impossible! It was of such dismal, furious gaiety, so revoltingly vulgar and rude, so bestially stinking of ruttish carouse—and chocolate—smells, with a dash of gin mixed with it, that Rudi closed his eyes and resignedly leaned against the wall.

Meanwhile his hand fumbled for the quarters in all his pockets. Strangely enough, he found only one . . .

Scarcely had the laughter begun when his mother hurried back with her hands over her ears. The boys encircled Rudi who was still looking for the missing quarter, which he knew for certain he had picked up in the street. This he tried to explain to the boys but, while they believed him regarding the main point, they did not believe that he had the quarter on him and could bring it to light any moment, if he only looked for it long enough. He had lost it, of course, lost it again; it was still lying in the street; they would all have to go and look for it; a quarter was a quarter. They agreed not to stay away for more than a quarter of an hour, and to take the blame, if there was then still a question of blame, upon themselves together, he and the school friend; the little brothers had torn upstairs again in the middle of the deliberation.

The two boys ran through a thick fog. They could not see further than halfway along the side streets, and the square was probably not much more than a ghostly monument of a naval hero wrapped in cotton wool. Tired and dazed, though less hungry now, Rudi asked his friend—and he was not even a friend; he did not like him—who had come to visit them, and what had been going on at home before he rang the first time.

"You didn't come," the boy explained, shifting his lizard eyes in Rudi's direction till they looked over his spectacles, and walking on at such a pace that Rudi, who had to tolerate this boy as a guide to the place where he had lost his own quarter, began to pant, "Why didn't you come? It was so jolly!"

"How did you know that there was something going on?" asked Rudi, whereupon the boy stood still and began to laugh at him. "It is your birthday today! Well, I never!"

"It isn't my birthday," said Rudi, although he was suddenly by no means so sure of it any more, "I never have a birthday, now . . ."

"It is your birthday and it remains your birthday," the friend said decidedly, "and next year, again, and every year.—Where is the quarter?" They had started walking again, but then the friend stopped, without troubling in the least about Rudi, at a spot where the quarter could not have rolled, even with a stiff breeze behind it. The mist wafted past them gently; the mist tasted of smoke from distant steamships and of blue mixed with the smell of oranges from a fruiterer's or warehouse in the neighborhood. In these uncertain smelling surroundings the friend crept like a toad over the paving-stones, went down to the gutter, searched with his hands in places where he could not see well. Rudi kept repeating that it wasn't his birthday; when the other ceased to go into the matter, he realized that if this boy from school was so sure of his ground, his parents would almost be capable of making it his birthday even if he had had his birthday just two weeks before. Hereupon followed a long silence.

"Who is at home?" he asked at last.

"A friend of your father's."

"Who?"

"Then you should have come home," muttered the boy, entirely absorbed in his efforts to find the quarter. Rudi touched him with the toe of his boot and repeated his question.

"That man with the rubber fingers."

"Oh, he . . ."

It was a friend of his father's, a traveler in rubber articles, rubber tubes and such things, who turned up about once in three months and threw the house into a state of confusion. Not a nice man perhaps, but mercilessly gay and exacting in this gaiety. Not only had everybody, great and small, constantly to listen to him and laugh at him, he also had special wishes and commands; that of the cigars, for example, could very well be based on a caprice of this buffoon who had found that his father's cigars were not strong enough or too strong, or not good enough. Sometimes after another three or four months, during which one did not hear from him, for he did not even send a picture postcard, he shuffled into the house and stuck his rubber fingers round the sitting-room door when they were all at dinner; it looked like a skeleton hand sanitarily equipped; everyone was startled but the man himself who came into the room behind the hand was so gay and gracious and sprightly that nobody could remain cross, least of all his father who really revived when he caught sight of this, in many respects so eccentric, friend. He had to stay the night, was pampered, and got everything for the asking. In return, he gave them rubber fingers of which he always had many on him; in reality they were nothing but samples of gas pipes that happened to fit onto the finger. Soon all the children wore brown lengthening-pieces on their fingers, even the older girls and Rudi's brother who worked at an office; if one could believe the man, his own boys also ran around like that all the time, which used then to be contradicted by Rudi's father, because, according to him, his friend had no children.

Already dreaming about his father's friend, Rudi thought he saw the seeker pick up something and put it into his pocket. Immediately afterwards he jumped up saying that he had had enough of it and that he was going home. Although Rudi thought it too much trouble to ask for the quarter, which would doubtless have started them off on a long dispute, he did not agree to this because he did not wish to have to run back alone. The boy, however, was inexorable; he did not even say goodbye properly, and Rudi saw him disappear in the mist. When he moved his cold hands in his pocket—at first absent-minded, then more purposeful —he noticed that the second quarter had also gone.

When he stood before the house, now for the third time, he wanted first to make sure that there was still a light burning. Perhaps they had all gone to bed at the guest's command who, in his jolly way, had had enough of the jolliness and wanted to dream of cigars. But no, the light was still burning behind the windows, three big, yellow windows with black crosses and thinly covered with slanting net-curtains, and then he also saw what was going on behind them, behind the bars and behind the drapes. There were ghosts, shadows, walking in a procession one behind the other, an endless row of adults and children, all, without exception, with both hands up, the monstrously long fingers ending hazily blunt or squarely when the merry-makers came nearer to the windows, stretched up as if for a double oath, a brotherhood of gaiety. And meanwhile they sang and stamped and shouted. It seemed almost impertinent to disturb such a feast by means of a door-bell, but as he had again become hungry, he decided to try and penetrate to the sitting-room at last, or at least to the kitchen. Without considering the ghosts up there worthy of another glance, he rang; he rang five minutes on end; when his arm became lame and his fingers almost stuck to the brass with the cold, he stopped, walked back a few paces and fetched out his handkerchief to wrap round his hand.

Before he had finished, he noticed that the door was moving. The door was opening slowly, very slowly and very gradually. Undeniably Rudi knew that this could not be one of his little brothers and sisters, apart from the fact that he would certainly have heard them, messengers from all that boisterousness, come down the stairs. The door moved in a pronounced grown-up manner. When the opening was wide enough for a child to pass through, something slid round the doorpost: five brown tubes next to each other, their size, shape and arrangement reminding one of a German flute. So it was the rubber man who had come down! And a moment later he really turned up; five pieces of rubber tubing of unequal lengths on each hand, which he emphasized by spreading them demonstratively.

"Have you the cigars, you lazy bones?" cried the man, the night air making him cough. Rudi shook his head and hastily stuck his handkerchief in his pocket. Hereupon the man turned up his collar, or rather tried to do so, while one of the rubber finger stalls fell to the ground, where the man simply let it lie; for that matter, Rudi knew that his pockets were full of the things. Finally both the coughing and the movement of the arms turned into a most unseemly fit of yawning. With a half turned-up collar, in a black overcoat, with two spindle-legs below it, the arms up, the head thrust between the shoulders, the man, who was rather heavily built, looked exactly like a shark's egg standing on end, such as one finds on the beach. This yawning figure, posing so impudently symmetrically, was perhaps new to Rudi, but the man's face he knew well. As a child he had often gone ride-a-cock-horse on his knee and often he had had to accept gifts from him, not counting the rubber fingers. During later years, with the constant increase in the family, Rudi had not received so much from him any more. He had a clumsily cut face in which the badly outlined wishy-washy eyes had an enigmatical expression as of someone who sees a fantastic world grow before his eyes in which he must act, taxing his sense of duty as well as his power of imagination—further, a rather snobbish, tuberous nose, and whiskers; below them, however, a haughty, angular, fragile chin that one could imagine behind the finest jabot. The strange thing was that the gaiety for which the man was famous, was nowhere to be seen in his face, which was more like that of a spy who must earn money for his old mother, or of a not too inhuman superintendent of the police.

"Do you want some fingers, Frits," asked the man, "my boys at home run round with the things on, all the time."

"I'm not Frits, sir," said Rudi, holding out his hand for the rubber fingers although he loathed them.

"Then who are you?"

After Rudi had said who he was, he was forced to push rubber tubes onto all his fingers, even long ones. Meanwhile the man kept talking in a deep, soft but convincing voice.

"I remember they talked about you. They saved a croquette for you, and a tartlet. If I had brought them down with me, we could have gone across together. Oh no, it is true, you haven't got the cigars. How did that happen with the cigars, Rudi?"

"The shop was already closed, sir."

The man laughed, playing meanwhile with Rudi's fingers. "Then we'll go out for them together. See, you are ready. We'll drum the tobacconists out of their beds. You are a resolute boy, aren't you?"

"Yes, sir."

"You must wave your hands, Rudi, not conceal them, see?"

"No, sir."

"Long fingers are always a nuisance, but this is rubber, thus Ersatz, so they are not real fingers, eh?"

"No, sir, not real long fingers."

That was the kind of joke his father's friend made. Meanwhile they walked on steadily, side by side, waving the rubber lengthening pieces on their fingers like defiant merry-andrews who would have worn paper caps to better advantage than the felt hat and the cap they had on. It struck Rudi that the man who knew his way about in this district had taken another street, not the one to the cigar shop where he had lost his first quarter. Having skirted the big square on the left, they first came to busier streets, then to a quiet, narrow one that Rudi hardly knew. Sometimes he looked round at shops which were obviously tobacconists but the man at his side apparently had something else in mind and hurried on. At last he stopped in front of a very small shop where mainly tobacco was apparently sold, which was in keeping with the poverty of the district. The man not only rang the bell, he beat a ruffle with some rubber fingers on the shop window. Soon a stoutish man appeared behind the glass, and opened the jingling door.

"Good folks," said Rudi's companion promptly, "we know each other from last year." And when the shopman bluntly shook his head: "Then two years ago, oh well, three years ago, or as long as you like. Tell me, friend, have you three or four incredibly good cigars for me in exchange for the two quarters this young man will hand over to you?"

"That may well be," said the man, with a glance at Rudi who was pushing forward to say that he no longer had the quarters. But it was already too late; the shopman, who was not allowed to sell in the shop after eight o'clock, came out with opened boxes, and let the customer smell, feel and compare and finally make his choice: cigars a quarter a piece, only to hear that nothing could come of the whole purchase. He himself happened to have no money on him and as the shopman could not be induced to sell on credit, they walked on some moments later into a new street, all the time waving their hands on which the rubber fingers still sat.

"One should really be able to change them into cigars," reflected the man, "rubber stinks so terribly when one lights it. Did you know that, Rudi?"

Rudi nodded to show he knew. He held his hands a little away from his body. When the man spoke about "stink" he suddenly smelled the rubber, not the burnt smell in question, however, but as they really smelt, a bold, matter-of-fact smell, a real manly smell. The thought that he would not get home again that night, that the man at his side, whom he did not dare resist, would drag him through the whole town to possess himself of cigars at any cost, could no longer be dismissed. The strange thing was that his companion did not visit the center of the town where he would perhaps still have got cigars in a café where he was known as a traveler, but more and more the outskirts.

"We could first go and look for the quarters," he said, "who knows where they are lying now. One just mustn't think where quarters may lie! Wave your hands, Rudi. It looks as if you were afraid of the fingers.— The whole idea of a quarter has something improbable. Between a dime and a dollar; between a napkin and a tablecloth. Who can define the place of a quarter? That is why they roll away so confoundedly easily, too, because they don't know where they belong. And once they are away from home, they don't come back, never! Do you think we could still get some cigars on tick somewhere, Rudi?"

"I think so, sir."

"All right, my boy, all right. In any case we shall walk the whole night for the cigars if necessary, walk the whole night." These words he repeated with a sideway glance at the boy. "You don't mind, do you?"

"No, sir."

"I have heard something about you," the man began a little later, when they were walking by a group of little pleasure gardens, little fenced-off flower-beds in a bold bend of the road traversed by irised, glistening tram-rails. The little pleasure gardens sank away in the mist, making way for a public building,—a school. "They said—people say so much—they said that it is your birthday today and that all those children were invited in your honor, and not because I came unexpectedly. You think so yourself, don't you?"

"No, sir, I just said to . . ."

"I didn't think that held water, either. By the way, do you like it at school?" Here he made a gesture in the direction of the building they were just passing.

"What do you mean, sir?"

"I wouldn't go to school *too* much," said the man without further explanation. Several times he tried, by means of irrelevant remarks, to keep up the conversation, but it was obvious that he had something on his mind, a long story or a more important piece of advice with which he did not dare to come out. He had put his left hand on Rudi's shoulder so that a piece of the rubber, on account of the bend in his arm, pressed against his jaw. They walked on like this, very confidentially side by side, but the man apparently had not found the right words yet.

Almost like lost vagabonds in the mist, they crossed a wide high road of concrete with long crumbly cracks and a stripe down the middle, grandiosely prehistoric in structure. It gleamed, it was smooth and firm, and yet ripped-up; it was abominable. Then they entered a ridiculous little rustic path leading down to something boggy, with willows. On a willow branch hung an old bicycle tire that swung gently to and fro. But they climbed again and passed a heap of rubbish—papers, dented kettles—then a fence behind which there must have been some allotment gardens, then a house either being built or pulled down, a barren field which may have been a deserted football field—a sample-card of landscapes half blurred in the mist, but in which the man seemed to know his way.

The rubber hand still pressed on Rudi's shoulder as if to prevent the boy from jumping into the air with fright, he finally broke the silence with a question: whether Rudi knew anything of his parents' home life. They led a very bad life together, perhaps Rudi didn't know, he said, though people were crying shame upon it. This was indeed new to the boy who had wanted to run away chiefly on account of the constant din and quarrels with one particular sneaky little brother in connection with which he had sometimes been treated unjustly. But his parents were really outside all that, and he had never blamed them except vaguely, for the fact that had struck others, too, that they had so many children. Besides, he saw his parents as one power, without internal discord and he believed the man, who now came out with quite different data, more because of his convincing voice and the possibility that the hand on his shoulder would be removed when he had finished speaking, than because of the probability of his assertions.

"Look," said the man, reducing his pace a little, "the last few years I have been coming to see you as much as possible in order to create peace. In some respects it is easy, for as soon as I am there, all is well. Particularly your father is quite a different man then. But of course, I have my work, and I dare not think of what happens in my absence. How often have I contemplated giving up the rubber agencies and moving to live with you people. They are your parents, Rudi, I know, but you are old enough to understand what I am telling you. Your father and mother are people who must constantly be cheered up, from early in the morning till late at night, and, if they had no neighbors and children sleeping almost all over the house, in the middle of the night, too. But then, it is not much fun playing clown all the time with rubber fingers, and thinking up round games for the children. Sometimes I think to myself I'll chuck the whole thing. Then I go and stand in the middle of the room, the rubber in the air to command silence,—there your father, here your mother,—and I say to them: "Why don't you simply knock each other's brains out, folks?" And then again, to see it from the funny side: "Here you are, a finger for each of you, use them as truncheons, and hit hard.—Oh well, then we are not above taking a stiff glass—stop!"

Rudi heard that "stop!" like a metallic crack just by his ear. Until then the man had spoken good-naturedly and lengthily, with a certain humorousness as if to kill time. Now, however, he took to action. He let go of Rudi, ran forward pushing up the sleeves of his overcoat, while most of the rubber fingers fell to the ground, and some moments later, he was sitting astride on a mouldered fence that stuck out above the dense mist that hung particularly low here. Then he looked round at Rudi. The latter approached slowly; one by one his rubber lengthening pieces fell from his fingers, too, as if these had grown thinner. He allowed himself to be helped up without opposition and then he too sat on the fence; a musty smell was rising from the ditch, and now he had to pay attention for the man was pointing to the road that they had approached, a road with high trees, lonely in the mist, a road with only a few dim street-lamps.

"Do you recognize the road?" asked the man.

He slid from the fence; a chain rattled. Will-less, he followed the man, who apparently expected no answer and ran with quick steps over the muddy dam. This dam merged into a bank with high grass and stinging nettles behind the trees.

Of course he recognized the road—he would have recognized it with his eyes closed, just inferring it from the circumstantial manner in which he had been brought there. His companion's intention to buy cigars had apparently fallen from him with the rubber fingers; he had eyes only for what was happening on that lonely country road. And before they stood side by side, motionless, in the middle of the road with their faces turned away from the town, staring into the distance that reached no further than eight or nine trees—Rudi saw his parents approach, as he had seen them approach some hours before, in exactly the same way. Each on one side, close to the dark tree trunks, his mother with her hat on one side, her arms stretched forward as if she were driving something; his father with one clenched fist, and chewing something. They were coming nearer steadily, with a weary, shambling gait, out of the weakly lighted mist that floated past in long trails. There where they came out of the mist, they were quite black; their feet and legs were more ghostly. They apparently neither saw nor heard anything of the wild whispering of the man, who, a prey to violent excitement, had caught hold of Rudi's arm; they stumbled on, passively. They were now close by; trembling, the man turned with them, and Rudi turned with the man, his teeth chattering and his forehead wet with sweat. He heard the man muttering: "You left, Frits, and I, right; in the name of thunder don't let them get by," in a tearful voice full of self-pity, as if he were being thwarted by all kinds of unwilling elements while fulfilling a superhuman mission. Then everything began to sway; he was dragged along forcibly, after his parents with whom they easily caught up, the man calling out all the time: "But now we're letting them get by, now we're letting them get by!" He thought he could see, askance from behind, that his parents had sunken, half wasted faces, with pieces and' corners missing as if even the skeletons were no good any more. Perhaps skulls in the muddy hollows of which stalks and blades of grass grew—yes, he saw them, these stalks and blades. He stood still, overcome by horror. Like surf, the two rows of trees dashed against each other, while the man shrieked and whistled to hurry him along. Then there was a storm, a storm that overthrew everything, and to which his weak boyish body could no longer offer resistance.

He awakened, pain in all his joints and with tired eyes. But he saw quite clearly that it was early in the morning, with birds and gossamer, and the wet grass in which he lay was the grass at the edge of the ditch of the preceding evening to which he had returned later under such totally different circumstances. How deep blue was the water! For a time he divided his attention between this blue that was so blue in places that there should have been stars in it, and the tingling feeling in his fingers that felt as if they had been tightly tied for a long time and now, on the rebound, reached further than at first.

The avenue in the distance still ran to the outskirts of the great town. In front of this avenue, more to the right, he had a general view of the things that had been concealed from him the night before because all the light had fallen on the distant houses, although he remembered them from before. He had often played on that barren football field. Beyond that, were the allotment gardens, a group of willows—everything looked very small there—and then the greyish-white strip of the concrete road, the partial continuation of the avenue which forked just behind an isolated house. All this was clear and surveyable; there was no possible doubt as to how the roads and paths ran, how one went here and came from there, and in which direction one had to escape something that was after one and that could once take the trouble to get ahead of one.

Rudi saw with his child's mind that one must never flee in the evening because then one is caught up and seized by one's memories. One must flee in the morning! Then rubber fingers do one no harm; they don't even lie in the grass where they have dropped from one's hands; they are just fun. He still thought with a smile of those funny rubber fingers before he rose and began to walk down the road in the direction that was now prescribed.

Translated by Jo MAYO

Menno ter Braak

MARGINAL NOTES

Good Bad Novels

There are people—I know them by the dozen—who are able to explain to me offhand and with precision why this or that book has its valuable points, but cannot for that very reason be called a good novel; apparently they dispose of a recipe enabling them to make out what should be understood by the term "novel" in all countries and for all times; their disposition is such, that the pleasure of reading an important book is spoiled for them through the knowledge that they ought not to enjoy it, because it is not a good novel. These people always remind me of the American who wanted to cross the Sahara on a camel, realized his desire, had a beautiful and fascinating journey and felt fully satisfied—until, at the end of his expedition, he heard by chance that his camel had been a dromedary; then his pleasure was entirely spoiled, because he considered himself duped, swindled and disillusioned. The same thing happens to those who, while reading a book, continually keep the camel "novel" in view; they are fettered to a construction, a procedure, they have accepted a dogma; seated on a dromedary they can no longer accept the experience they gathered on the illusory camel.

Authors who have something more to say than the average publicist will as a rule not take too much to heart the criteria which the historical experts have bethought themselves of as the characteristics of the various pigeon-holes of literature; they will write good books, and if these good books also happen to be good novels in the sense attributed to the word by the literary historians, that is merely accidental. Dostoyewski's novels are nearly all *bad* novels according to Western European criteria; but I should not like Dostoyewski to have written good novels on the irreproachable example of *Madame Bovary*! All these criteria of form are quite unessential from the moment a creative personality handles the form; it may safely be asserted that the rigid criteria of form are a serious impediment on the path of the great author (provided he lives in an individualistic period and consequently ignores the unquestioned subjection to the rites of the court, the church or the aristocracy). He does not wish to produce good novels, i.e. formal constructions; he wishes to express himself in such a way that the matter finds optimal adaptation to his intentions, and he is indifferent to the result being good, bad, or no novel at all. At best he has a fatherly affection for the child he created, which, if it happens to be born as a novel, is also loved by him as a novel.

When there is too much talk of the "good novel," there is every reason to be on one's guard against the proximity of a bad one that is in need of protection.

Individual and Law

The artists of the word not infrequently overlook the binding character of language, and the well-known formula of the Dutch literary school of the eighties declaring, that art is "the most individual expression of the most individual emotion" bears witness to this way of thinking. The whole impressionistic movement in literature is a protest against the binding social character of language. And this attitude towards language is of course a consequence of an attitude towards life. The impressionistic artist does not want to bind himself in respect to the "others," he refuses to recognize the law, because he identifies it with lifeless tradition. He considers writing so much a strictly personal matter that it does not even occur to him to realize the nature of the instrument with which he works. Until, through some event in his life, a moment comes when the existence of the law forces itself upon him, and then, suddenly unprepared for this discovery, he faces the existence of the law as something entirely alien to himself and therefore impressing him as a contrast; the law takes him by surprise, makes him—the artist, individualist and player—realize, that he is a being dependent on others (and the Other, who surpasses all others). One can find this process mirrored in numerous conversions of wild individualists to one or the other form of mystic assuredness.

Roman Catholicism especially opens a tempting perspective to artists who discover the law without being prepared for this discovery. Their entire past suddenly appears to them as an error which has to be atoned for, or as a prelude that should be closely analyzed; life without "knowledge of the law" seems to them a form of presumption. And so the neglect of the law avenges itself by a hypertrophia of the law in a "second life" after the "conversion", the miracle.

For all that, individualism and law need not be mutually exclusive; of which opinion the work of Kafka furnishes a good example. Responsibility for individual life found with Kafka the form of the most binding, formalistic and legalistic thing imaginable: the law-suit. For me Kafka is the most sublime example of an author in whom the mystical (i.e. the most personal in human experience) never sets the law (i.e. the most compelling tie) at defiance. With him no "leap in the dark," but a darkness which is light at the same time. In Kafka's style no shade of the individual is suppressed, although there is not anywhere the smallest opening promising the prospect of a domain where law has lost its validity. In his work responsibility before the law exists without the panic tumult of the previous picturesque conversion.

Consolation through the Formula

It seems that our advantage above our mediaeval colleagues is a possibility to contemplate matter in a scientific order, whilst that matter appeared to the man of the Middle Ages to be subjected only very occasionally to laws open to verification: the strife between God and the Devil. This systematization allows us a certain superficial gratification as we realize that everything can be expressed in formulae. What gives formulae their reassuring power is that they are of human provenance; whilst the mediaeval man felt himself passively subjected to a transcendental game, of which at best he could try to interpret the signs, the contemporary man boasts of his astronomy. Because we have been taught at school that the comet of Halley puts in an appearance at regular intervals, or, if ill luck will have it that it does not do so, that very likely it has fallen to pieces and will at least provide a representative in a meteoric shower, part of our fear of the appearance of comets has been done away with; in every case where the formula suggests a subjection to law we get more and more immune to panic. An illness is less frightening when one knows that it is caused by a bacillus. History loses much of its bloodthirsty and very unedifying confusior, when the philosophical historians have made it clear to us that an evolutionary principle (or something else) underlies all the tumult and murder. And so we live peacefully by grace of the formula—but only so long as the formula appears adequate. Whoever is of the opinion that the irrational element could be fully overcome by abundant application of the formula does not know the Germans or any other human beings. Only the stupidly fostered faith in the formula has considerably weakened the faculty of resistance against surprise, the faculty that helped the mediaeval person to assign catastrophes to a "higher power", so that now-a-days also the irrational has to be served in the quasi-rational form of a quasi-scientific formula; the racial doctrine.

Translated by CAROLINE WIJSENBEEK

Adriaan van der Veen

THE SHADOW OF THE MILL SAILS

ON SATURDAY, when the sun shone into the room smelling of tea, our cotton suits were ironed. My mother did it, pressing her lips together and holding the iron in her hand convulsively. On Sunday, when the church bells had long ceased ringing, we put them on; they were tight at the waist and the white shirts felt cool against our necks. The footsteps of the walkers rang in the streets that lay arched in the quiet Sunday sun. We knew that we were being watched from the upstairs window as we walked away but we pretended not to notice it. The crease in our pants stood sharply above our bare knees. Our shoes shone but the holes in the soles felt cold on the paving stones.

Two rows of trees with young leaves stood bolt upright along the lane that led to the woods. First there was the park with the mounds and fountains laid out in a rough circle, with a board at the entrance as warning: "No admission after sunset", and a monument of the Queen Mother with a face that had turned out too severe. If one went along a smooth path and ducked under some gnarled trees that felt left out by the spring, one came to the path with the bumpy cobblestones, and a bridle-path that led to the tennis courts. With as much indifference as our tight little suits would permit, we put our hands in our pockets and, unruffled and whistling, we approached the Bench, the quarters of the tennis caddies. They stood in a bunch, shouting, cutting sticks or sitting nonchalantly at one end of the Bench. As we went by, they became silent, watching our movements with suspicion, and one of the biggest of them walked toward us slowly, swaying his hips, so that Rik nearly bumped his nose into his shoulder. But we kept our eyes glued to the pointed cobblestones hurting our feet and disappeared into the woods.

There was a winding path with hawthorn in the distance, and the twittering of birds and other buzzing, odorous sounds, as if it were already summer.

We looked through the trees intently toward the beginning of the tennis caddies' path, which one could see best from here. Cor jumped up and pointed to the cyclists coming round the corner. With our heads bent forward we ran along the bridle-path, like a flash past the Bench, so there was mostly dust to be seen at the quarters by the time we reached the cyclists, players on the Red Court. We followed them running close to the bicycles. At the Bench they were all standing in a heap ready to drag us away, but the leader in a turtle-neck sweater just shook his fist and sent three tennis caddies after the bicycles. They trotted along too, at the same time trying to tread on our heels. We got closer to the bicycles, moving our arms and legs rhythmically. At the path where the cyclists had to get off, the boys whined, but the tennis players decided to take the cotton suits. A stone hit Rik through the trellis work, a beginning of what was awaiting us.

But the sun was already low on the horizon when the players on the Red Court stopped, and we sauntered along the road holding forty cents in our moist hands. Our knees were trembling and the crease had disappeared out of our pants. Everybody had gone home, only one early couple was already walking into the woods, where the birds were chirruping their loudest just before the sun entirely disappeared. The little tent where the caddies sacrificed their money was still open. Klaas and Leentje were waiting for the evening strollers and they revived when we arrived. When we were licking our ice-cream wafers Klaas asked, "Are you new?" and Leentje said, with two big wrinkles in her freckled face, "Tomorrow they will waylay you and they'll bring knives." And, muffling her voice, she told us about the ways of the tennis caddies from Vriendschaps Street; how they had followed her one evening and thrown her to the ground. Klaas listened disdainfully, raising his shoulders higher and higher till they left no room for his neck. He knew everything and therefore gave Leentje a sign to go away for a minute while he called us behind the curtains of the tent and told us what we had to do. When we ran home after that, I was already seeing Rik lying in the dust at the side of the bridle-path bleeding from the stomach. They would not have to punch me in the stomach. Not below the belt, that's what we had been taught.

The windows were open when we came home and we smelt fresh fried potatoes and salad. In exchange we were able to give ninety cents.

With the tea after supper we had cookies, and sitting on the closed veranda, I heard every movement in the cane chair in which my father sat. From the garden came the sound of cats nearing each other and miaowing. The wind played with some neglected rose garlands over our neighbor's gate. My mother stroked my hair, staring vacantly into the distance. Rik and Cor were in the street with Wout and Lange Jaap.

It was our duty to go to the tennis courts the following evening, but first we walked along the dike and the ditches, gazing at the weeping willows through which the white crosses of the churchyard gleamed. Rik listened attentively to the frogs that were croaking at the side of the ditch, but Cor gave him a push, and without further roundabout ways we came to the bumpy road and approached the Bench. We had white sweaters on, with the sleeves pushed up. There was a hubbub and hissing as we came near. Pebbles clattered on the cobblestones quite near us. One of the boys whose name was Tinus came toward us. He danced out in front of us, distorting his wrinkled face and cursing uninterruptedly without perceptibly opening his mouth. I looked at his feet that hardly touched the ground, like a marionette held too high. Rik held his head high, Cor swung his arms and I felt my knees tremble. At the Bench they then performed a screeching Indian war dance and one, two and then three figures broke away and rushed towards us with heads bent, howling like factory sirens. We stood still, our bodies tense, when suddenly the signal of the leader sounded: "The bicycles!" The group drew up in order of march and swarmed round the cyclists from Court A, sending shrieks into the air. We remained behind and then ran along too, pushing and kicking as the others were doing to us. All found something to do on courts A and B and the Red Court. Cor and Rik were busy too, and for a moment I looked bewildered at the caddies deftly unrolling the nets and putting the balls in their places. Cor and Rik waved to me, and the others used abusive language whenever they got a chance. I stood leaning against the trellis-work when I felt something wet from behind. I looked round and saw Tinus; the water was coming in a wide arch watering the flowers. "Beat him up," I heard, and slowly, my legs still trembling, I approached Tinus. He pressed himself against a tree and for a moment his face was still. I saw the warts on his hands and his thin legs through the holes in his pants. His throat contracted nervously. "Beat him up," I repeated to myself, but he was already giving me vicious punches. I felt them land on my shoulders and coming lower to my stomach, and I turned red. My hands grabbed at his body, at his neck, but couldn't find them until I had raised my arms in front of my face; going toward him in this way I seized him and twined my left arm round his hot neck. He yelled but I pressed against him and pulled my other arm around his neck like a vice, bending his head down. His long legs trampled to and fro, kicking my ankles, but his neck glowed against my arms till I threw him to the ground with a jerk. It seemed an unnatural position, to find myself so empty, without his neck. But he was already jumping up and, while the caddies forgot their duty and pressed their faces against the trellis, he hit me on the lip with a trembling paw. He immediately recoiled when I approached, and bounced back. His arms were beating and churning as if a giant were after him and I felt myself breathing more deeply and my chest expanding. Then I seized him, this time easily, and while he yelled and his parchment face glowed as if I were lighting mysterious little lights, I bent his body almost coaxingly and pushed his head between my knees. I pressed his seat against the fence and beat him, the more vigorously the harder he tried to wriggle. When I stopped I looked at my hands; they were glowing. Rik and Cor were dancing on the court, the others were hissing at Tinus who opened his mouth wide, showing decayed teeth, and yelled.

With my hands in my pockets I was sauntering to the Bench when Vles, the well-known Jewish dealer in old iron, stepped out of his car and said, "I need you." The day before, although I had not been working on his court, I had handed him a ball, and he had not forgotten me. His trousers had a sharp crease and covered a fat, squat body. His pale face with horn-rimmed spectacles was serious. His forelock through which a cream colored skin could be seen was stuck to his skull. I followed him as he opened the door to his court. I fetched the balls out of a dark shed smelling of shower and perfume. Vles did not move while I stretched the net. The copper-colored light of the sun twinkled on his spectacles while he indicated to me to stand on the other side and throw the balls to him. First one, and he caught it and threw it aside; then a second, and a third, and the third he hit back. "Catch," he said, and while my sweater stretched round my body, I leaped and missed the ball, once, a second time, a third time, up to ten times. After that I caught all the balls. We went on till the light had gone. All the tennis courts were empty. The noise had died away. Vles looked at me seriously when he gave me my pay, and nodded. Cor and Rik were waiting for me at the exit, and we celebrated the victory over Tinus and the Bench with ice-cream.

The Christian schools had a day off and Cor and Rik went fishing as soon as the sun was visible on the horizon. I got up later and first did some gymnastics. My body was smooth, with very fair little hairs and a three-cornered birth mark. My arms were thin, but yesterday I had tried them on Klaas when he enquired after Tinus, and he had not been able to throw me off.

I sauntered along to the Bench where, to my disappointment, I found only one boy with fat white legs, short pants, a receding forehead, large watery blue eyes and a small mouth that stood open. It was as if I had seen his head before. I sat down next to him on the dewdrops that were still on the Bench. We both remained silent, and I drew little figures on the sandy path. In the distance I heard hammering at the dockyard, steam whistles on the Maas and sometimes the bicycle bell of somebody still on his way to the office.

"Tinus would have beaten you up if you hadn't cracked him," said the boy. "But I did crack him," I answered, suddenly restless and thinking over how I had done it. "Why are you caddies?" I said nothing. "Tinus and Govert call you poor lice, and Heinz knows from the grocer that you have debts everywhere." I stood up and bending over the hedge cut off a stick with soft green bark which I cautiously peeled off, sniffing up the smell of the pale wet wood. "Have you finished school?" asked the boy. "No." Then, remembering in a flash how strong I was, "Say, do you want a beating? Poor lice!" But I had no desire to get up, and he said, "I could stab you in the shoulders with my knife, and then your arms would hang limp." Slowly I swished the stick through the air, but the boy paid no attention. "I wanted to stab my father with my knife," he resumed, "but he threw me down the stairs." "Where do you live?" "In Vriendschaps Street; all tennis caddies live there." "My father never hits us. He just grins and threatens with a stick."—"My father is a lunatic. He shouts so loudly that my mother wakes up. She is ill." "What's your name?" "Lambert."

In the distance some cyclists were approaching, fat De Hoed, his wife, son and daughter, of the Red Court. We got up and without arranging anything trotted along too. We stretched the net and ran after the balls for hours while the sun stood above us setting Lambert's head afire.

When we were free we bought apples and wandered off to the grass field with the pit; it was one o'clock. I looked at Lambert who could only eat his apple in small pieces. "How did you get such a big head and small mouth?" "I am like my mother. You should see her." "How long has she been sick?" "Twelve years; she is paralyzed and lies in the cupboard-bed in the dark so that sometimes I only see her forehead and eyes. It smells of old apples in the cupboard-bed, when the sewer doesn't stink." "What's your father?" "He is a machine fitter but he has been on the dole for the last five years." "Have you any brothers?" "No, a sister who has been living with an aunt in Gelderland for a long time. She doesn't want to come home any more."

We ate the apples and he asked: "Do you give that money to your mother?" "No." "We all do, except Tinus who lives with an uncle who works at the Hazekamp gin distillery." Before we went home Lambert warned: "They'll take your brothers grazing tonight." I walked alone through our street musing on that egg-shaped head that would bend over a white forehead and large eyes in a cupboard-bed with old apples. Rotten apples perhaps.

It rained the next day and the day after, and both evenings I was alone by the Maas where a green light winked. There wasn't a single couple in the Prive. Only the rain from the branches dripped cool on my eyes as I lay stretched out on a seat with my raincoat over my legs.

But on Saturday evening, after a hot day, there was fighting at the Bench. Cor stood panting by a tree and his victim crawled onto his feet for the last time. Rik was still fighting, and I admired his body that advanced and recoiled while his arms and fists moved steadily warding off, pushing forward, high and low, punching the bulldog boy's nose to right and left, a movement that made blood flow. Rik's forehead was grazed, blood ran from his lips, but then he shot forward and pummeled the bulldog, who closed his eyes and moved his mouth foolishly.

Rik stopped, and we stood side by side waiting to see if anything else would happen. We had seen no knives. Opposite us stood the group: Tinus leering over the heads of the others; Lambert a little off-side. Machte, the chief, had let the others fight so far, but then he ran forward, hitching up his pants, waddling as he ran as if we were three ninepins desirous of being overthrown.

Something else did happen. Just in front of us a cat shot past, black, with a tail that stuck into the air like a quivering arrow. After it came a big dog, his head to the ground. For a moment everybody watched the chase; then, without signal, we ran after the animals, Tinus in front and Rik next to him, Lambert and I behind them, through the lanes, along the tennis courts, over the grass fields. We heard the cat spit before she disappeared into the woods. Breaking branches, bumping into each other, we followed in the dark until we lost both animals. Panting we stood facing each other not knowing whether to thrash each other. But finally we walked, somewhat self-conscious with our hands in our pockets, back to the tennis caddies' path.

After the chase we were welcome on the Bench where Machte explained the rules to us and where Lambert and I considered ourselves partners. Being official caddies meant that we would not merely follow the bicycles on Sundays, proud when we were chosen. We now sat on the seat and waited for the sign that it w.· our turn. When Vles sent Tinus back and I could come, there was fighting again and Machte said that we didn't belong there. But we had captured our places for good by the time Machte went to the factory.

Everybody knew us. On hot afternoons we fetched ginger ale for the red-haired Volets, and the girl whose black hair fell over her pale face gave us a drink even when I accidentally kicked her glass over. Rik was greeted smilingly by a worthy lady whose clothes rustled and who lived in a big house with chestnut trees. Vles had, when helping a lady into a car, turned round and nodded to me. We were asked who we were and what we generally did. We felt we were the center of interest and sometimes we talked about how we had come into power.

II

The son of the baker in our neighborhood formed a tennis club with some friends and they occasionally succeeded in hiring one of the courts. The caddies did not come, and the sons of the notables joked about these poor devils. We stood near them and glowed with enthusiasm at giving information. "The one is a baker in our neighborhood," I remarked, and one of the tennis players said, "Say, that is the fellow who brought tartlets to the party on Saturday." They laughed about the chaps who dared to play tennis too, and we joined in before we began our task. Not until I was on my way home did I try to find an explanation why I, a little slave, laughed with the masters at the baker and his companions. Did I hate him because he had a bad racket and his pants were too short and because his laugh was too loud? After all, everyone could play tennis, everyone, we too and the tramp who picked up cigar ends too. Mrs. Stoffles who forbade us to sit too near the resting tennis players was crazy. We belonged everywhere. I belonged everywhere, even pummeling her head and stomach, she didn't understand a thing. Picking up balls was an adventure, to run after the bicycles and the balls, to fight for power with Tinus and Machte. I could have fought with the notables too and exterminated them, preferably together with the bakers who laughed too loudly. All the tennis courts should be for the tramps with cigar ends in their pockets and for girls with fair hair and pink dresses with flared skirts.

Lambert and I were late the following evening and we watched the swallows circling against the turbid sky. Near the forester's house a leaking tap was dripping. All the courts were occupied by tennis players and caddies and we ran into the woods. Lambert's white knees sometimes gave way as if he were just on the point of abandoning walking as useless. We skimmed past couples, outgrowths of the trees along the lane.

"Would you like to play tennis?" I asked Lambert. He did not look at me when he answered: "No, I wish my father would die. Yesterday he came home and tried to lift the blankets from my mother's bed. She was afraid of him; I listened."

Three birch trees stood on the grass field at the side of the lane. We dropped into the grass and looked at the sky now empty of swallows but full of rumbling.

"I have tried to stab him. I followed him to Noordmolen Street near the gin distilleries where he used to work. I jumped into the cellar just by the grain shoots and I saw him go by. I ran after him as far as the gin shop and I waited there for hours. He recognized me when he swayed out of the door and I supported him and led him close by the water not knowing what to do. I had no knife, but near the pipes I had picked up a file, rusty but with sharp edges. A policeman walked by and I quickly stuck the file into my father's pocket. After that he leaned heavily on me, his hands on my neck. At home I left him lying in the hall and went upstairs, stepping over his body. My mother lay in bed with open eyes, but I know then that she is asleep, and I played with her hair. The next morning he kicked me out of bed and asked how he had come by the file."

Then big drops fell, but we lay motionless in the grass with our heads down. I closed my eyes and comforted Lambert. "Can't you flee with your mother? Can't you take her on your back instead of leaving her in the cupboard-bed with rotten apples? You are strong. Take one of those boats in the Maas, row to the other side. Go to Vlaardingen and hide her in one of the barges, that smell of fish that is salt and not rotten. Sail far away from Vriendschaps Street. Stay alone with your mother somewhere in the sun where you can stroke her hair as long as you like without having to fear kicks from your father and to think of files to which dust from the gin distilleries is sticking."

Lambert turned round, his face wet from the rain that was now splashing on us. He came close to me and whispered, "You are a stinking fool, a blithering idiot. Go to hell and back to where you belong." Long after he had gone I still lay in the grass feeling the water on my body.

Rik and I looked in the woods for cigar ends that came flying, sometimes right across the path and fantastic, till we heard the voices, and figures came out of the dark. But always when the noise had all died away, only the cigar ends remained behind.

I told Rik that I didn't want to pick up balls any more and he said I was crazy. "Mother needs the money." "Then I must do something else, one can do everything." Rik remained silent and in the dark I didn't see his face. We walked on, past the cigar ends, sometimes brushing along the bushes. I said, "In a little while Lambert won't be picking up balls any more either, he will stab his father to death." Rik laughed. "Nobody stabs his father to death." "But Lambert is no liar. He told me how he would do it. One night when his father is drunk and beats his mother and gets him out of bed. Then he will jump on him—and you know how strong he can be—and take a rusty file out of his father's pocket where he stuck it long ago. He knows exactly where a throat is most tender. He will first cover his mother and then he will take his father on his back and carry him to the canal. You know near the little bridge there is a boat with a hole in it. He'll stuff his father into that hole and let it sink half under water. Then he will go back to his mother and flee with her."

"And where to?"

"You can go anywhere. Everything is open to everyone. And in Vriendschaps Street she is lying in a dark cupboard-bed with rotten apples. You will see, Lambert is capable of anything. He hasn't got a big head for nothing. He won't be a minute longer in the streets. He will row to one of the big ships where everyone speaks English, French or Italian and where they throw oranges overboard, they have so many. And we'll never see Lambert again, unless perhaps we pass one of the islands where palms grow."

"Lambert should go to the rope factory," said Rik, "he's pale enough for it." "And his mother?" "She should keep lying and waiting for Lambert and Lambert's father." "Do you think they will stay together and set the place on fire on New York's Eve to begin another New Year?" Rik did not answer but when we came out of the woods he said: "I shouldn't read so many Sagas and Legends. What you talked about never happens."

When I walked to the tennis courts, Vles was just stepping out of his car and he asked why I didn't come any more. When I explained, he told me to come and see him the following evening. Why, I asked myself when I saw him walking slowly to the court, and in bed I imagined that he wanted to take me along to his house on the cliffs in Germany or that he wanted to undertake a cruise to an island in the South Sea. Perhaps he had heard of Lambert and his file. It was also possible that he wanted to teach me to play tennis in the garden with the fountain and the tortoises behind his house.

Nobody could enter the house with the austere double windows until he had banged the knocker that awakened a brassy sound which echoed all over the house and over the canal so that a policeman whose helmet I could see in the distance stood still and looked round. A maid with a stiffly starched cap showed me into a room with dark paintings and red velvet, where it smelled of dust until Vles' perfume came wafting in. He took my hand and held it while he asked me to take a seat. Sitting opposite me and looking at the palms of his hands he said that the house would be pulled down stone by stone and that no painting would remain in its place and that the tortoises would be placed in Blazers Zoological Gardens to everybody's pleasure. He was starting for France the following month and so he would not come to the tennis courts any more. He had been pleased with the way I had always thrown the balls to him and therefore he would like to do something for me. The word "do" got all the emphasis of the careless sentences and for the first time his eyes, behind the glistening spectacles, looked at me. What I wanted to be. What I would like to be? Everything, nothing, only not tennis caddie. Then his voice became modulated. "Then begin in an office, don't go in for old iron, that presses too hard, but keep buying and selling. My broker needs a junior clerk. Report to him on Wednesday morning." Then he stood up and I stood up and he put a hand on my shoulder and nodded. With the other hand he rang the bell and a butler came to lead me to the hall from where I saw a glimpse of Vles' head, round and serious, when I turned round. On the steps in front of the house I stood still. I felt empty. How much I wanted to ask him! Why did he throw balls with me and not with the notables. Did he mean by pulling down stone by stone that he would make a bonfire of his house? But finally I sauntered along the water lost in thought. Would a broker's office be like Vles? As if every word and every action had gigantic and quite different meanings and were introductions to things unheard-of, of which one could not even dream.

Over the Kippeburg, high up in the mill, cries had been heard in the afternoon. Lambert's mother had died unexpectedly and quietly at noon. Lambert had come home, had scarcely looked and only stretched out a hand as if he wanted to touch her. After that he had been seen running to the mill where his father was working for a few days. One of the neighbors ran after him and asked him what had happened, why he was running. And he had answered: "My mother is stiff, she is dead." Perhaps he ran to stab his father to death at last, perhaps to seek consolation. But when Lambert hastily climbed the ladder high up in the mill, his father, who had seen him stand by his bed one evening, took a certainty for an uncertainty; he kicked with his boot against his chest and then watched him fall with his mouth wide open. The boss and his men heard Lambert yelling and came running up. When they had attended to him and at last rushed upstairs, the father was still tugging at the bars of the window, perhaps in order to be able to jump into the water, perhaps just to be doing something too. In the cell at the police station, he stared straight in front of him as if the dirty walls could solve all riddles and make everything undone. Lambert had broken ribs and there was something not in order with his brain. He didn't recognize me when I came to visit him. But the Sisters said that he had roared when he was brought in until his mouth could no longer pronounce the word "mother" and he groaned softly with pain. There was not much left for him without the woman who had the same mouth as he, for whom he picked up balls and who lay in the cupboard-bed so that he could bend over her. He even had no longer a father to stab to death.

On Tuesday evening I walked on the Westvest by the mill that creaked and threw long shadows over the crooked houses that leaned over to the Oranje market. I thought of the mother who had been buried that day at the expense of Vriendschaps Street. Lambert would probably go to a rush-and-mat asylum and later to a Poorhouse where he would gradually turn yellow.

And my cotton suit lay ready ironed for me to present myself in at the broker's office the next day. My life would have to be like the shadow of the mill sails that flashed by ever more quickly until one could no longer follow them with the eye. Everything could happen, everything would happen.

Translated by JO MAYO

J. Slauerhoff

COLUMBUS

LIKE A TRINITY floated his little shoal
Of ships across the wide, uncharted waste,
On towards the land he expectantly faced,
As sure as he knew death his life journey's goal.

He knew, without information or test,
That a new continent lay on the brim
Of his ken, and that it would rise on him
From the ocean's deep if he went on west.

With patience proof against petulance
He reckoned each day the remaining gap
And marked it on the yet empty map,
But was ever refuted by the sea's expanse.

At times there was anger in his face
When the little Pinta lagged behind,
And he wrote in his log at night: "The wind
Steady, crew grumbling, of land not a trace.'

Rebellious shouts that sometimes grated
On his ears, in his solitude, he didn't heed.
He feared neither death nor void, but the need
Of turning back to the Spain he hated.

But at last—on a grey and tenuous line—
Strange, tall, plumage-waving trees!
The jubilant crew threw their fears to the breeze.
But he stood bowed by a deep-hidden pain,

Wounded by the knowledge that they weren't bent
On a quest for gorgeous discovery,
On sailing for ever and ever. He
Knew his life now aimless, to be endlessly spent.

Exile would be his lot, he fore-understood.
After disgrace: in dungeon cell detained,
His rapier broken, his glory stained,
His old head doomed into a monk's dark hood.

At once in that first moment he found
Escape: to flee on shipboard with a few
And save into the ever receding blue
An illusion of space: the world isn't round.

Translated by A. J. BARNOUW

INTRODUCTION

By Karin Michaëlis

IT WILL ALWAYS be a difficult task to transplant a literary masterpiece from one language into another, although in many cases it has been done with astonishing results. But even the most skilful and *spiritual* translation lacks something that can only be told in the author's tongue and emphasized by the music of the individual words and the way they are strung together.

For instance there are in all languages comparatively good translations of our *Hans Christian Andersen;* if it were not so, his fairy-tales would not belong to children's favorite reading throughout the entire world. And yet, I—a Dane— tell you that Hans Christian Andersen can never convey in any foreign tongue what he conveys to us, his countrymen. We have the precious privilege of being given *his way* of saying everyday things so that even the words for us seem to acquire a new and deeper meaning, new music and new magical beauty.

Hans Christian Andersen went to his rest long ago, but he lives through his fairy-tales and stories, as if he were still walking round among us—tall, thin and ugly, a little bit vain and longing for kind and appreciative words with which to feed his always love-hungry soul. There are several immortal writers who spread light in the darkest times of humanity, but there is only *one* Hans Christian Andersen, who wrote the sad story about "The Little Jewish Girl." There not a single Danish child that has not wept while listening to this tale. If Herr Hitler had been taken care of in his childhood and had read "The Little Jewish Girl"—perhaps the world of today would not have had to cry blood. And if Denmark should sink into oblivion, I wonder if Hans Christian Andersen's fairy-tales would not be the last things to survive.

There is another Danish writer, who, although he did not earn such world-wide fame, to me seems closest to Hans Christian Andersen. He was cut off from all that, because his works would turn into ashes in being translated. Not even the most sensitive poet would be able to transplant Herman Bang. And as with his work, so with himself. He was not to be transplanted into foreign soil. He came to the United States in order to visit the places where Danes had settled and to speak to them here. His heart gave out while he was on the road.

The doctor said: "The altitude was too much for his heart." Maybe the doctor was right. But Bang's heart had broken.

All his life Bang was an unhappy soul. Fate had played an ugly trick upon him, and, because of this, he had to suffer torture during his entire existence. He belonged to those who in the eyes of "normal people" seem vicious lepers. His was the same case as that of Oscar Wilde. Wilde I never met; Herman Bang I knew well, Herman Bang I loved, Herman Bang I saw at a time when the cross he carried felled him to earth and he was nearly killed by its weight.

One of our most gifted and esteemed writers had—quite openly—made a public attack on Bang, not because of his work but on account of his private life. After that Herman Bang locked himself in, would see no one, not even his closest friends, and among ourselves we feared that he would commit suicide. One evening in my home two of those who were closest to him sat for hours discussing what could be done. They were the writer, Peter Nansen, his friend since their student days, and Nansen's wife, Betty, our famous actress. She owed to Bang her unique way of using the Danish language on the stage. Herman Bang was a dramatist to the core of his soul; he often functioned as a stage-manager and could, it was said, make a good actor even out of a doll filled with sawdust. Betty was not filled with sawdust, and he had added his own burning fire to hers. Grateful, of course, she was prepared to do anything in order to save him, but what was to be done? Till long past midnight we discussed how to lift the burden of sorrow and guilt from Bang's shoulders. We did not find any solution. But once during this sad evening we had to laugh till we were nearly choked: All of a sudden we remembered a party in honor of Bjornstjerne Bjornson, where the two best speakers in Denmark, Georg Brandes and Herman Bang were present. They were so very different, and it would be hard to tell who was the more witty, the more dramatic, the more entertaining, and, sometimes, the more malicious speaker of the two. When they happened to meet, both of them felt uneasy and did their best to keep at a distance. On this particular evening, after some restless walking about, each of them began to cast his spell over the guests nearest to him, and, after having secured an audience, each retired to another room, together with his followers. In no time the entire, very large, party was divided into two camps, and it was more than evident that here was a competition as to who would succeed in drawing more guests over to his side. Both of them really surpassed themselves at this and the two audiences screamed with delight and, for months and years, never forgot it.

Herman Bang talked unlike anyone I have ever heard, just as he wrote unlike anyone I have ever read. When writing, just as when talking, he used half-sentences, ejaculations, pauses, repetitions. As a child at school, it would have been a sheer impossibility to define his language according to the laws of grammar. For him no laws seem to exist. He made his language and he made it living. He twisted his sentences as he twisted his face when talking. And the result was that every word, every pause even, opened up for the reader or listener new secret paths into his own soul; he saw and heard things never said or shown before; he became witness to confessions never made before, to sorrows never previously admitted. And Herman Bang understood women better than women understood themselves. He took us to abysses of sufferings, where hitherto we had only visualized the most uninteresting everyday life.

When my guests left, I could not go to sleep. So I sat down and wrote a letter to Herman Bang. I do not remember what was in the letter. But I received an answer from him: he had been on the verge of making an end; my letter had made him cry and those tears saved him from despair.

A month later, at a festival given in honor of a mutual friend, Bang and I sat next to each other. He took my hand and squeezed it till I nearly screamed with pain and he whispered: "Do you know, I lived only with help of stimulants, morphia and alcohol. I could not face life any more. Your letter gave me the same feeling, as when I was a little boy and my mother, my adored mother, told me stories, and I tried to swallow my tears, so that she should not suffer. . . . My mother . . . how beautiful she was . . . how lovely." After a pause he added: "One thing I have decided, you and you alone will be the one for whom I shall open up the tomb containing what once was and what became of Herman Bang. You shall know everything. Then at least one human being will understand and . . . forgive."

Herman Bang was to speak for the wife of the man for whom the celebration was given. She and I had known each other since we entered our first school at the same day. As Bang spoke, it seemed to me that—a very rare thing for him—his words fell flat and sounded commonplace. When he had finished and sat down, I told him flatly how disappointed I felt and I added under my breath: "From you I had expected a different sort of toast—after the long friendship between Agnes and you—even I could have done it better." He looked at me: "Do you really mean what you say?" "Of course I do."

He jumped up, knocked over his glass and began again: "Karin Michaëlis tells me that it was a bad speech. Will you permit me to try and make a better one?" And he now delivered one of the most fascinating speeches ever heard. When he stopped this time, there followed a dead silence, then a roar of applause. He looked at me, smiled and nodded: "Now you are satisfied, aren't you?"

When we sometimes met after this evening, he would mention his promise that I was to get his papers after his death and among them his "confessions," the key to his "sins and sorrows." That never happened. As I have said, he died in the United States, alone, far away from relatives and friends. Still, we may hope that the reception he was accorded in New York gave him real satisfaction. He had written to people over here that he intended to come on a lecture tour. Danes who were informed agreed that it would be impossible to find an audience willing to listen to Bang. Therefore they decided to send him a cable: "Stay where you are." Just then a cable arrived from him, saying that he was already on his way. Nothing could be done to stop him, so the Danes looked out for a hall—small enough to be comparatively easily filled. No, not even to be filled, but where the few who were interested could sit without feeling too badly about the empty benches. Such a room was found, and the evening came. Not only was the hall crowded to capacity, but it was necessary to open two connecting rooms, where the audience, packed like herrings, had to stand the whole time. Outside the building, hundreds and hundreds waited while the lecture went on, in order at least to catch a glimpse of the writer afterwards. But among the listeners one man drew attention to himself for a few moments: he got up demonstratively, dragged his wife out and thus showed his loathing of the "depraved" Herman Bang.

Henrik Pontoppidan, with the centuries-old, latinized name—originally meaning "bridge"—stood for us all like an old, dignified massive tower, pointing upwards, proud, without vanity, simply aware of its own value. He is an unusually handsome man. Small of stature, with delicate aristocratic narrow hands and feet. He walks a little pompously and even at a distance it is evident that here comes a man who is somebody and knows it himself. Pontoppidan is one of the Danish Nobel prize-winners. For this and for many reasons he deserves to become better known outside Denmark and the Germany of pre-Hitler days.

His father was a pastor in my native town in Denmark, but Henrik had already left for the University shortly after my birth. Old Mr. Pontoppidan died when I was about seven years old. I liked him very much. He used to cross the street when he saw me, and, putting his hand on my hair—always wildly flying about—would ask me questions or take me to the old parsonage and see to it that I was stuffed with cookies and preserves. Once I happened to tell Henrik—then already the king of living Danish writers—that I had liked his father very much. Pontoppidan shook his head: "No, you did not like my father!" I replied: "I liked him, and he was exceedingly kind to me!" His reply was: "You could not have liked my father; he was not *kind* at all." I gave him my word of honor, but he remained unconvinceable.

As time went on Pontoppidan and I became good friends. The town itself bound our pasts together. We had wandered round in the same narrow, crooked streets, we remembered the same smell of decaying fish from the fjord, stagnant water, peat smoke, not to speak of the odor from the many pigsties in the upper part of the town where the poorest people lived. He had long ago written his version of Randers—our native town—then I wrote mine. This first volume was very well received by the press and by the public. Pontoppidan invited me to dinner, and for what to me seemed hours fought with me—about a dog in the book: "You want us to believe," he said, "that you were strongly attached to this dog from your earliest days, until you were ten years of age. I tell you, that is impossible. You did not even trouble to tell what sort of a dog it was, the very first thing a real dog-lover wants to know." I tried to defend myself, admitting that until that day I had no idea what kind of a dog it was, I only knew that my father used to go hunting with him, (we always said "him" though it was a "her"). Pontoppidan settled the question: "I am certain that during your childhood you never gave a thought to your dog or to any other dog. But later on, when you got interested in dogs, you tried to remember something from your early days, and so you simply went astray." I had to give in he was the stronger. And if he had told me that I had murdered the dog, I would have confessed to this too.

In his youth he had fought great religious battles within himself. Although he came of a prominent, highly cultured family, suddenly he married the daughter of a peasant, a sweet, subtle and sensitive girl. His family was shocked,—just as the family of Tycho Brahe, three hundred years before, when the nobleman and astronomer committed the sane crime. (Tycho Brahe and Henrik Pontoppidan must have had something in common, at least the same stubbornness, the same conviction of being right. Somebody might be wrong—but not they!) Pontoppidan's first marriage was happy for a time, but gradually the difference in education made itself felt. Perhaps there were other incidents; anyhow, several years later it ended with a divorce. When he married for a second time, he had two children, whom he adored as he adored their mother. After she passed away he became, voluntarily, a solitary man. He was never very communicative; there remained a halo of reserve surrounding him, but when he stepped out of this natural reserve, it was impossible not to love him.

One summer we spent lots of time together. His wife was ill in a sanatorium, so, in order to finish a book in undisturbed quiet, Pontoppidan settled down for a few months in the provincial town of Svendborg, close to my little island, Thurø. He lived in a respectable and modest hotel where he had secured two small rooms high up, with a good view over water, islands and shipyards. All day long ships came and left, fishermen brought their catch, the harbor was busy as a beehive in summertime.

One morning I heard on the radio that something wonderful had happened to Pontoppidan, so I immediately prepared to sail to town in order to congratulate him. Just then a telegram arrived: "Do come and have lunch with me, please, I need you badly!" The telegram made me fear that he had had bad news about his wife. I arrived and knocked at his door, which was opened in such a hurry that I fancy he had stood inside waiting for me. Indeed he seemed to have expected me most eagerly and was quite boyish in his happiness when he saw me: "Thank you, thank you so much," he cried, "I feared you would be prevented from coming, and you know . . . today . . . just today . . . I would have felt so miserable staying quite alone. I really am happy that you came."

I asked when and how he had received the good news, and he told me that for a few days he had not had any letters about his wife, so when, late in the evening, a bellboy came to his door with a telegram, he went cold with fear. He hardly dared open the telegram, and when he finally did so and found out that he had become Nobel prize-winner, he felt completely lost. In those dazzling moments he thought of hurrying over to me, but his inborn sense of decorum prevented this: One could not visit a lady shortly before midnight. His next impulse had been to treat the bellboy to a glass of wine, but this impulse also was smothered, and he remained alone, not even daring to call up the sanatorium and tell his wife.

We then had a pleasant dinner with a bottle of claret. After dinner we strolled about for hours, in the town and out in the lovely beech forests. We walked arm in arm like good old friends, and I sensed his deep joy, less because of the money than because of the honor it bestowed. It was Saturday, and I had my marketing to do for the coming week. I suggested that Pontoppidan help me with my shopping in the big, picturesque fruit-flower-vegetable-and-meat-market, situated at the foot of an old red church among low, old-fashioned gabled houses. But each time we neared the market, he drew me away, asking for still half an hour of my company. I said: "Let us buy the necessary provisions now, then take the boat over to Thurø, where we can celebrate the whole evening." He asked what I needed, and I promptly told him: "Meat, cabbage and cauliflower, cheese, eggs and onions and . . ." He stopped, shook his head: "Dear friend, please don't ask me to buy . . . cheese and . . ." (he made a grimace) "onions! I couldn't do it." I laughed and bade him goodby. He still followed me to the market, through lines of pails and baskets filled to the brim with flowers. Here again he took my arm and with his free hand he pointed to an enormous jar with long-stemmed roses: "Those," he said to the woman. She gazed at him: "How many?" He repeated: "Those!" She looked again, unbelievingly: "All those?" He nodded. I tried to explain how ridiculous it would be, with my garden a fairy-tale of roses, and that I could not even manage to carry these down to the boat. But then I thought of what it meant to become a Nobel prize-winner. I skipped my other purchases, and we spent the evening on my little island where all the stars came out in honor of Pontoppidan, and many mosquitoes too, and where we had a bottle of my favorite wine, Chateau Yquem, and that was that.

Pontoppidan was never very talkative, and so once, when returning from abroad and visiting him in his home, I was more than astounded to find him talking and talking without stop. I myself am a chatterbox, but I could hardly get in a word. All of a sudden he began to laugh, and then came the explanation: "You certainly must have believed me stark mad with all this chattering, but you see I have had such terrible sinus trouble, which not even morphia could suppress. It was so bad that for months I was unable to speak a word. In reality I have lived like a man with a paralyzed tongue. Now it is over, and since returning from the hospital I have to make up for this long silence by unceasing babbling."

The last time I visited him, he had aged greatly; his wife had died, his children lived in distant places and he had moved to a smaller apartment outside Copenhagen. We were a few guests for dinner, and the meal was served on lovely old cream-colored Wedgwood. I exclaimed joyfully that I was lucky enough to have a dinner-set matching this perfectly. Pontoppidan smiled: "Not quite matching. This is the only set of real old Wedgwood in Denmark." I wanted to say more, but he stopped me with a gesture: "I tell you, it is as I say. This Wedgwood has been in our family for generations and generations, I just inherited it when a cousin of mine died."

For once I wasn't willing to let him have the last word, and so I said that I could prove my words, telling him exactly how the different plates, and even the ladles, looked, how the whole set was nearly as light as paper, and how it was marked underneath. He only said: "I know, of course, that you are not boasting intentionally, you only happen to have forgotten exactly how your set looks compared with this."

I asked him to come to Thurø once more, where in his honor I would use my own precious set, which I hardly dared touch for fear of breaking. I won-

der what would have happened if he had come and seen that I was right.
I still fancy he would have believed that I had secretly borrowed his set in order
to fool him.—And now Mr. Hitler has prevented my proving anything. Denmark
is handcuffed and gagged.

I have told these little incidents, since, though they have nothing to do with
the work of the writer Pontoppidan, they throw some light on certain aspects
of the human being. He has had an enormous influence on Danish youth during
the last fifty years. His *Hans in Luck* is generally regarded as his greatest work;
in this he painted the doubting-Hamlet nature of the Danes. But *Hans in Luck*
appeals more to men than to women and more to philosophical thinkers than
to emotional natures. I feel closer to his short stories about life in the cottages
out in the country. It is a wonder that a man not born in such surroundings was
able to reproduce, not only what can be taken in through the senses, but
also the very soul of the soil, of the air, of the landscape, of the heavy quietness
covering the low-ceilinged, peat-dust-filled, always smoky houses out in the
heather.

And now this old warrior is supposed to submit to a Hitler. Pontoppidan submit? Never. Not he. He cannot submit. But he can keep silent as the grave, and
I think this is what he is doing. He closes his door, shuts his mouth, stuffs his
ears and pulls the lids down over his sky-blue eyes. And so, as if blind and deaf
and dumb, he sits there, hour after hour, waiting for the freedom of his old
country.

Martin Andersen-Nexø

LIFE SENTENCE

Mattis Lau was the sole child of early-spent parents. His mother was in
her forties when he was born, his father ten years older; he did not
come as God's gift to a young, hot-blooded couple, but as a somewhat
tardy hand-out to two people already in fear of age. Every child more
or less carries the weight of the grown-ups' years; it is not exactly
lessened if the child is born as late as in this case. When Mattis came, his
parents had used up the rest of their surplus vitality. He had enough
for all three of them, but it was hard to keep a fire blazing under the
wails of his mother and his father's bleary eyes.

They never understood the urge in his play, but let it wither. He was
allowed to do neither this nor that—neither to write with charcoal on the
loam walls of the tumble-down fisherman's hut, nor under any circumstances to pound the rough spruce-wood table with one of the things
that only had to fall into his busy little hands to turn into tools. Like

most parents, they rated dead things above the living child; and little Mattis soon saw clearly that he was the most worthless thing on earth. It certainly was owing only to the parents' infinite goodness that a small boy got permission to stay alive after breaking a tooth off the rake, or tearing a few knots in the old fishing net. By rights he should have been beaten to pulp long ago.

Actually Mattis' parents weren't such bad child-beaters. They just let him know on sufficient occasions that justice was again being tempered with mercy. The stick hung over his childhood like a constant threat.

At an early age he had to do his share of work—which did not bother him at all. He merely wished to be alone with it; then, as it went on, his work turned quite of its own accord into the most fascinating play. But if his father and mother were present it soon became galling toil, as it long was for the parents.

Despite all, he grew up to be a real boy, who preferred the harbor and the beach to the schoolhouse and learned much that might come in handy once he got out into the world. And he would get out into the world! He was afraid of no boy in the fishing village, and the parents whimpered when they heard of his recklessness and his foolhardy pranks. They liked best to see him sit by the window in his free time, with a copybook in his hand; then they knew where he was, and he neither ruined nor ate so much. When somebody called, he had to show how good he was at reading and writing. Perhaps they were trying to make up somehow, through him, for their own failure to obtain an education; at any rate, he never made them so happy as on the day when he came home and reported that he was to stand first on the church platform.

After confirmation, most of the boys in his class were scattered to the four winds. Poor people's children take to the air early; down there by the beach, it was customary for the young to leave the nest as soon as they had the pastor's blessing to cease being children. The ones who had something in them went to sea; the others took jobs in the capital or on the far side of the island—but fly they must! Only stick-in-the-muds remained at home to care for the soil and the womenfolk. From long ago there were two kinds of men on the beach: those who had been to sea in their young days and now were plying the fishermans trade, and then the stove-warmers who were working the land.

Throughout his childhood, Mattis had known that he wanted to go to sea when the time came—far out, where none knew its depth and where Father and Mother could not watch him from shore, clucking like troubled hens. And yet he resigned himself to staying at home and doing

more and more of the two oldsters' work. Between times, if he ever harbored plans to break out, they clung to him with trembling hands. His
father led him round about the tiny patch of land, talked of it as though
it were a patrimony and begged him not to desert all this. And his
mother would confide with a chuckle that someone or other wasn't sleeping nights, on his account. One could always find him a nice girl with
money way back in the closet, if only he continued to stay at home.

Mattis didn't give a damn for the promises and fine words. The shack
wasn't a mite too good to put a match to it, and the girls he'd never seen
were more alluring than the ones he knew. He was longing to get out—
out where the rolling waves tossed the great tarred, oaken cradles from
port to port.

And getting out was not even so very difficult. Often enough, when
he came in with a catch of sea bass and lay alongside the windjammers
to sell a fish, the captains offered him hire—all he had to do was climb
aboard and let the dory drift ashore with the tide. But when the crucial
moment came he stayed. Duty, toward the two old grumblers in the
shack, held him fast—he could not escape.

"I have to wait till they're dead," he thought, pulling the heavy oars.

It always was easier for Mattis to row out to sea than back home; and
he knew the reason quite well. The way home was the sour way of duty;
that made it so arduous. He didn't feel a trace of filial love; it did not
warm his heart to care for the two old people, who under cover of the
parental name had always cramped his life. He would not mind if death
were to deliver them. But it could never occur to him to desert them.

So he stayed at home and took the load off his gouty old father's back,
looked after the nets and tilled the bit of soil—joylessly, yet so that there
was enough to eat. He milked the two shaggy cows for his mother, cut
nettles for the pigs and twice annually made a pilgrimage to town to pay
the taxes. Inwardly he did not get richer, fooling around like this. He became close-mouthed and sluggish.

On one thing his mind was firmly made up: not to be caught by some
wench. Once his parents died, he wanted to be his own master and free
to go wherever in the world it drew him.

The Laus hailed from the interior of the island—from the Lauenhof, a
farm situated a mile inland. It belonged to Hans Lau, an uncle of Mattis.
Since he was the only one with a farm, he was regarded as the head of
the family.

He was arrogant and ruthless by nature and took various liberties,
while the Laus otherwise strictly observed the proprieties, as befits little

people. He was reputed to be reckless at cards and a rake; the poor relations could not help admiring this, as big-farmer manners.

The farm was neither big nor good, by the way; most of its soil was rock. But it was still a farm, and all the Laus took pride in being farm-owner's children. It even flickered in the corners of the eyes of Mattis' used-up, shriveled father.

Hans Lau was well advanced in years, and as he had no children—at least in a manner of speaking—the question was to which of his nephews and nieces he would choose to leave his farm. Each family entertained a well-founded belief that it was the preferred one, and secretly acted on it. Thus the Laus came to draw apart from the rest of the poor in the district; there was something in their bearing as though they were merely disguised, and might take it into their heads one fine day to doff the poor man's garb. It was said of them that they were riding the high horse.

One day the Lauenhof owner turned up quite unexpectedly under his brother's low roof. Mattis was out behind the woodshed, tarring an old boat. He saw Hans Lau coming but he went on with his work; it angered him to see everything stood on its head if the uncle so much as showed himself.

Shortly after, his mother came round the corner of the house, on the run; he had not seen her so quick on her feet in a long time. "It's you he's come to see," she panted and pulled his sleeve; "now you'll probably be picked to own the farm. Be a little nice now!"

Mattis looked after his work and let his mother prattle; he did not seem to know that she was there. She had to watch out for his motions with the tar-brush. But she kept nagging and pestering, and followed him round about the boat, undaunted: "You should put your time to use and drop your grouchiness just this once," she persisted. "Uncle Hans wants to talk it over with you personally. Can't you show a little manners for once!" When he still didn't answer, she ran inside again, to catch as much of what went on there as possible; her skirts flopped about her heels. It was the greatest day in her life.

Mattis did not look up, but he heard his mother bustling and he got mad. What did he care for Uncle Hans and his farm and the whole business? He only saw his relatives when he needed them, Uncle Hans did. When his mother promptly came back, Mattis threw some tool on his shoulder and withdrew toward the beach.

However, she had stated the case quite correctly. Hans Lau wanted to make the farm over to Mattis. It was to be transferred after his death, and until then he would pay Mattis and his parents 100 thalers a year—

on the one condition that Mattis marry at once. For his wife, Uncle Hans had chosen Bodil, the Lauenhof housekeeper, a good, faithful girl who had sacrificed the best part of her youth to him and the farm. To reward her loyalty, Hans Lau wished to see her well married and to know that she'd be on the farm, as its mistress, when he was called away—in a little while.

Mattis had set his heart on being his own master, once he were rid of his duty to support the parents. It was hard to budge him. But the old people did not let him rest. They nagged him from dawn to dusk, tempted him with the prospect of one day being a big farmer and the head of the family. When this did not help, they whined that he would not lift a finger to lighten his old, toil-worn parents' old age. They sighed whenever he approached, and at meal-times their talk inevitably turned to parents who had worn themselves out for their children and reaped the blackest ingratitude in return.

Soon all this became too much for Mattis; it was something he couldn't get around. Duty had left deep tracks in him, in which it was always easy to tread again. He was used to having to make sacrifices, and one day he yielded. It was merely as if the one porthole into the light and the world were being slammed shut.

His uncle strangely revived after the wedding, to the great indignation of the two oldsters. They had a long way to go yet, before being farm-owners! As for Mattis, he didn't care. He kept to himself, and it did not make him more sociable that Bodil hastened to present him with a little boy. It just meant somebody else to stay clear of.

Mattis was not kind to the boy, nor did anyone expect him to be. To see him was to get a splinter into his eye. It angered him to witness the child's careless joy and it angered him when, cautioned by experience, it shunned him—it only had to come before his eyes for wrath to flare up in him. He did not exactly account to himself for the causes of his feeling toward the child. There had to be an explanation for everything—to one-self, too; and he explained his conduct to himself as being about that of a strict but just pedagogue. If the others winked at the youngster's first boyish pranks, he took firm, heavy-handed action. His youth had been hard; he was passing the legacy on now.

Bodil dared not oppose him; she had no very clear idea anyway of whether and how he might be handled. He never reproached her, but she was nonetheless afraid of him; there was something in his eyes that told her to watch her step.

It would have served no purpose either, to dispute with Mattis about his treatment of the child—he suffered enough under it. His inability to find a way out turned the very pangs of his conscience against little Hans. One day Mattis caught him. The boy was standing out in the shed, letting the grindstone whir, so that a bright waterspout stood between the stone and the floor; he was so absorbed in the game that he sensed nothing until his father had him by the neck. He cried out insanely with fear when he saw the father above him, and this cry paralyzed something in Mattis and stayed his heavy hand. Bewildered, he flung the boy into a pile of hay and staggered to work, dazed by the youngster's horrible dread of him.

The boy's desperate, plaintive wails rang over to him as he worked, drowned out the blows of his axe and incessantly trickled at him, like an indictment. He struck more forcefully, to deaden the sound, but he could not get rid of it. Finally he could not stand it any longer; he threw the axe away and rose, irately—what the hell, wasn't there a stick around so the damned brat could be shut up once and for all! He was blind with rage.

And suddenly it was as if the whole had burst—his rage and everything else—and collapsed within him. He led his hand over his eyes and fearfully stared over at the wall of the shed. The tortured small boy lying there, huddled and trembling and trying to swallow his tears so he wouldn't get a worse licking—that was he, Mattis! And the grindstone— why, he had just sneaked in and let it whir, because the spurting water was such fun when the stone really moved. Speed, speed! Nothing delighted his childish heart more, at the time, than to set something in rapid motion, that the sparks flew roundabout. But you weren't allowed to do that and so you did it in secret, as everything else that was worth while. It wetted the floor, and some day retribution fearfully caught up with you—as it now did with him. The floor was loam and couldn't be damaged; young as he was then, he had realized and understood that there was something called a curdled disposition. And now? His whole life had consisted of surrenders, piece by piece, until he too had become an embittered, shriveled sourpuss like his own father. Now he himself stalked the innocent joys of the child, catchpoll that he was.

The choked, broken sobs hurled accusation after accusation at him; they shattered him, until his heart ached and he could not breathe any more —he *had* to silence that sound! He looked round, helpless, bewildered, as if searching for the stick again, and then he suddenly rushed over to the boy and lifted him up. Mattis wasn't accustomed to embracing anyone; the little body surprised his palms and filled them with a tender warmth. How strangely dear it was to embrace someone! He took the boy on his knees and tried to get the small, dirty hands out of his face; he had never noticed them before; they were like a pair of little shovels, bearing every trace of their surroundings and hard inside, exactly like his own. He was a real boy who didn't spare his fists.

Silently the youngster let his hands be removed from his face—in fear, perhaps. But he would not look at Mattis' eyes; he turned his face away and kicked, to get down.

Mattis did not know what to do; it occurred to him to take the boy inside the shed, to the grindstone, and whirl it round till the water splashed over the floor. The boy was suspicious and kept close to the door, but his eyes could not resist; they stole out secretly, eager to catch something. And when a spray flew all the way across to his feet, it made him laugh.

"Well, how about splashing Father?" Mattis said and stood by the door—it was the first time that he gave this name to himself. The boy, still somewhat diffident, thrust himself over to the grindstone; soon the game was in full swing. It amused even Mattis, this play with the opaline water that stood in the air like a cock's tail and then suddenly burst into sprays. Here by the grindstone—a little late—he recaptured a piece of his childhood and vied with the boy in laughter.

At first Hans was still timid, and it was up to Mattis to come to him. The boy's distrust hurt and, at times, even angered him, but he had no choice. He humbled himself and went to look for the little chap and inveigle him. When nothing else worked, he could always win him over by tempting him with the grindstone.

Soon, however, the tot came quite by himself and put his little hand into the big one, and Mattis marveled how quickly a child's soul can forgive and forget—and was ashamed of himself. There was not much to be done about it now; his own soul had long congealed and no longer could be transformed. But it seemed to him as though in being with the boy he lived the other side of his childhood, as it were—the one that might have been. And this was why he could not be without him.

Everything, both play and earnest, started with the grindstone. When Hans got bigger, the stone was overshadowed by other and more fascinating things. Hans learned to fish and run a sailboat, and he helped his father till the soil. The boy was right behind Mattis all the time; they could not stand being apart, and in time grew strangely close to each other. Toward everyone else Mattis was and remained the surly grouch, and added to it was the fact now that he had the boy to defend.

"He's not going to live my life," Mattis told himself and saw to it that the boy was restrained as little as possible. When the others laid plans as to what he should become, Mattis cut off the debate with the curt statement that he was to have the right to make his own choice when the time came.

Mattis knew what the boy would choose—long before Hans knew it himself—and the knowledge made him anything but glad. But he sealed his feelings within himself, and after Hans's confirmation he himself took him to town and saw to it that he hired on with the right crew. When he got home he went out into the shed; there he sat almost the whole day, sunk in rumination, while his hard thumbnail chiseled and chiseled at the soft grindstone. He did not see the sense of everything.

It was not until the boy, too, came home after some weeks, explaining that he had been laid off because the sloop had sprung a leak and was to be laid up, that his existence began to have a meaning again. Mattis knew well that an explanation also was required for the fact that the boy came home instead of looking for another seagoing job—but he did not love him any less for it.

Working together, they frequently talked about having to listen round for a new hire for Hans, and on Mattis' part the talk was meant sincerely. He would have been the last to stand in the way of the boy's future.

However, the winter passed without anything turning up, and in the spring Hans declared that he would learn carpentry and then sail as a carpenter; this promised higher wages. Mattis had some objections but there was no real weight in them, and the boy's wish prevailed.

In the following summer the Lauenhof owner died at last. Mattis' parents were still living but they were very old and decrepit; the prospect of a Lauenhof residence had kept life in them far beyond a reasonable time. Mattis himself would have liked to sell the farm, but the old couple and Bodil objected. So he let them move up; he himself remained in the shack. He had nothing to do with the farm, and very little with the three of them, aside from their having imprisoned him. Now—at last —he was rid of all pressing bonds. He was not free and never became free; he felt that he had been imprisoned for too long a time to be able to become free again. But the bonds that held him now did not cut into his flesh. Here in the shack he had all that tied him to life: the sea which had sung its song in him since he was born, and the boy.

The boy remained living with him during his apprenticeship, and Mattis sunned himself in his young mind. He could not bear to think of it that he and Hans would have to part sooner or later; the boy was his link to the world, through which he lived and breathed. He no longer had any wish for his own future; quite imperceptibly, everything had turned into blind devotion and admiration for the lad. He no longer yearned for distant spaces, either. What he could still expect of life now had to be fufilled through the boy.

Hans was to experience life for him. All that he himself had missed in his youth should be bestowed on the lad—gladly. But then, he could not even let him go.

Gradually this feeling grew into a gnawing hidden pain, into self-reproach for accepting the sacrifice of the boy and holding him back at home. One day the full, hard thought dawned on Mattis: he stood in Hans' way precisely as others had once stood in his. It cut him to the quick, but it terrified him to think of the only way out—for that led back into loneliness. He himself was to turn away the one being that had warmed his heart and gladdened him. Mattis, long accustomed to re-nunciation, fought a hard fight this time before he won.

One Sunday morning he took Hans out to sea. For several hours they dragged for bass, over the "grounds," where the "grass bass" keep themselves; then they rowed about and offered them for sale on various ships that lay at anchor, brought here by the land breeze. Mattis went aboard and bargained with the skippers while Hans remained in the boat to weigh the fish.

From one of the vessels, a large bark, Mattis climbed back into the boat with such strange movements that for a moment Hans thought, "They surely poured him some, there on board." But he suppressed the idea at once; his father never drank liquor. Mattis seated himself on the bench and stared in front of him; his expression was terribly serious, almost petrified.

"You'd better go aboard right away," he said in a hoarse voice. "They need a carpenter, and they offer good wages."

A sudden joy lit up the face of the son—until he caught the old man's lightless glance.

"But you—Father?" he asked slowly.

"I?—I'll row back and pack your stuff. I'll be back before nightfall—and the wind won't turn till then." Mattis stared up at the clouds.

"Yes, but I mean you, yourself. What'll you do then?"

"What I'll do? Well—I—" Mattis spoke tonelessly and fell abruptly silent.

"Come along, Father! You've got nothing to keep you here. We'll hire on together, here or on another ship. Let's go to sea together, you!"

Mattis sat there, withdrawn as if hearing nothing or listening to far-off music. Suddenly he straightened up. "Yes, we'll hire on together, you and I," he said and gripped Hans's hand. "Now go aboard."

"And you come with two bedrolls," Hans called down from the rail. Mattis nodded. Two bedrolls! Did the boy really mean it?

Could his youth not demand an end to having to drag a weight on his leg? He had been a good and loving son, he who had turned up in the nest as unexpectedly as a young cuckoo. Mattis had received his due from him and more; and now it had to be done with. There wasn't room for him on board.

He packed his son's sea chest and bedding, and let someone else row it out; he himself couldn't. He followed the boat with his eyes till it was alongside the ship; then he went into the tool-shed and set out to mend a net. He felt the wind beginning to turn, knew that the bark and the other sailboats out there were now weighing anchor. But he did not look up.

He had returned to his prison—what was the use of looking back!

Anonymous translation

Marcus Lauesen

WANJA

THIS IS a tale about the friendship between two people who did not have an earthly thing in common, but who happened to be thrown together by fate. Nothing great or important came to pass during the short time of their friendship, but in a child's mind there was planted a seed which perhaps later was neglected or perhaps grew secretly—I do not know. I feel that seed somewhere in my soul, but I cannot name it. If I had to explain its nature, I should use words like these: willingness to obey, willingness to be humble, willingness to be silent when surrounded by indifference or scorn. . . .

My friend was called Wanja. His real name was Iwan, but he was the best beloved of all the Russian prisoners whom the war had brought to our village; not only his comrades, but also the villagers loved and revered him, and so they always gave him the soft Russian pet name Wanja.

On the day of their arrival there was no great difference between him and the other Russian prisoners. What difference there was, was to the advantage of the others, for Wanja's face had the swarthy hue that is often found in the face of a poor Jew.

His features were young and girlish, but the dark stubble of beard that covered his cheeks, the shiny, black, uncombed hair that clung to his forehead and temples, and his somber, roaming eyes gave his face a tinge of something boorish and repellant. His grayish-brown Russian uniform was wetter and more clotted with clay than that of any of the others, and added to all the rest, his clothes were too large for his small, frail figure. His coat almost reached his ankles, and the bottom of it was stiff with clay. The sleeves were turned up twice and covered his wrists like thick muffs. A piece of string tied around his waist held the coat together, and he shuffled along in a pair of muddy boots much too large for him.

I suppose it was pity as well as fear that made us look more at him than at the others. And yet Wanja was not pitiable.

The brutality which was prevalent among the youngest crop of Prussian sergeants did not affect him. He seemed to submit to rules and regulations with a peculiar matter-of-fact willingness. When the overseer thundered a command at him, Wanja would already be in his place and therefore invulnerable. Of course this would arouse the anger of the irascible officer and make him vent his rage by kicking Wanja's neighbor who perhaps chanced to be an inch or two out of line.

There was nothing cringing in Wanja's obedience. It was simply characteristic of him not to take blows that he could avoid. The inevitable ones were numerous and hard enough.

But the very first time I saw him I discovered still another of his peculiarities. The prisoners had come to the playground of the village school an hour before they were expected. The farmers who were to put them to work had not yet arrived; only we village children gathered around the little group. Three or four young, gray-uniformed Prussian officers marched in sullen silence up and down, shouldering their rifles. The prisoners were commanded to stand at ease while they waited, and were allowed to eat their crusts of bread.

This was to become one of the decisive events of my life, one of those experiences that are bound to come to every child, crushing the beautiful faith in the old doctrines, arousing the poisonous doubt of the truth of what the elders say. Didn't we remember the thanksgiving service, the holiday that had been given us when Hindenburg had sent an army of Russians into the Masurian swamps? Didn't they tell us that the Russians were worse than wild animals, and did not deserve any pity? That they were impious beasts? That God in His heaven was glad to get rid of them? We thought of all these careless words such as grown-up people toss to children, filling their minds with ideas fit for devils or hyenas. And then we saw that Wanja and his comrades were human beings. For days afterwards one or another of us would ask the grown-ups every time they told us anything: "Is that really true, now? *Is* it really true?" For if they could lie to us about the Russians, they might lie about other things, too, we thought.

That day one or two of us children lost our hearts to a group of tall, thin men in ragged, grayish-brown coats, and for many nights we remembered the dreamy, sorrowful eyes of these prisoners. Some of the Russians made the sign of the cross upon their breasts and foreheads before eating their miserable crusts.

I was standing near Wanja when the prisoners were allowed to eat. It appeared that Wanja's piece of bread was larger than that of his neighbor, and when the overseer had passed, Wanja gave his comrade a slight nudge, to offer him a share. Taken by surprise, the man stumbled and grasped the prisoner next to him, and three or four of the men tottered. At once an officer rushed over to them, struck one in the side with his fist, and kicked another. There was a strange contrast between the young, well groomed officer and the shabby Russians who calmly let his blows pass over them. I have never been able to forget Pjotr, whom the officer struck with his fist. No sound came from him; his face did not twitch; he was a picture of tenacious composure, and yet he was no thrall. His eyes looked past the officer, moved calmly from spot to spot in the landscape, with a royal dignity, like a captured eagle that is not affected by the crowing of a rooster, that does not lose its pride because a hen scratches dirt over its body.

And now Wanja. He straightened himself and saluted. It was only his garb that was comical. The little man within it grew in my eyes when at that moment he said some words of which I guessed the meaning: that he was the cause of the disturbance. The young officer went at him with clenched fists, showering him with abuse. The little Russian stood at attention looking at me, letting the words pass him without flinching. A stony calm, a masterfully controlled anger illumined his face. I can imagine that such a calm might freeze a man to death. But it only egged the officer on to still more violent words and blows, and at last he lifted his foot. At that moment Wanja looked at the young German's brutal face and said:

"Kamerad, Offizier."

I do not remember the rest, except that the farmers came, the roll was called, and the prisoners disappeared. The farmer to whom Wanja was assigned was told to keep him hard at work, since he was refractory and could not stand kind treatment.

Some impulse made me follow them. Wanja walked behind his new master, gazing calmly around him. Once he turned and looked at me. "Did you want to go with me, boy?"

I suppose I was a bit frightened. At any rate I turned and ran home quickly.

※   ※   ※

I do not remember how our friendship began; I only remember how it developed. Every day I followed Wanja to the fields. Every Sunday I told him about the children's service. I learned one or two things that I would rather not have learned. I was worried when Wanja said that our large, red church would be shot down some day. I prayed for Wanja's unbelieving soul, and I loved him.

Wanja was not treated harshly. He was allowed to do his work as he wished, and he worked well. He asked many questions, learned many things, and followed each answer with a pondering "So-o."

Sooner than any of his fellow prisoners Wanja began to look like other men. After a couple of weeks he had new clothes which fitted him, and his master said with pride that Wanja had never had lice.

Besides, Wanja could read and write.

Every Sunday morning, when the prisoners were free, a score of them would assemble in the cow barn. Wanja would sit on a milking stool with a pile of letters in his lap, and the other Russians would sit or stand around him. They would always assemble in the same warm barn, and I can still see it clearly. It was small and dark and dirty, low under the rafters and narrow. There were six or seven cows in single stalls, some empty pig pens, covered with ancient dirt, some fodder boxes, a watering trough, a dung-barrow; everything available was used by the prisoners to sit on. A faint light came in through two dim windows. Wanja sat under one window. The others sat on trough and barrow and fodder boxes, or leaned against the pig pens.

I remember that each man was always in the same place. Quietly and naturally they would sit or stand as usual. There was a singing softness in their greetings. All their boisterous gaiety disappeared when they entered this stuffy, dark catacomb.

For what was it but a catacomb, where a score of persecuted exiles in silent ecstasy sustained their holy faith, recalled their common, distant sanctuaries? There was a strange, earthy warmth, a happy, humming animal stillness in the place. Some of the cows would chew the cud; the sound of their chewing gave a quiet, rhythmical accompaniment to the human voices. During the silences the cows were always there with their satisfied, sedate munching. And that was good.

Wanja would read letter after letter. I did not understand the words, yet I became the partaker in a sum of remote happiness and remote sorrow that came from distant steppes and revealed itself under the low roof of a little barn in North Slesvig.

The words themselves resounded with human confidences and made me cry and laugh, not because I saw the others do it, but because Wanja spoke like a child practising difficult words. Sentence after sentence would come out slowly and heavily, with long pauses in between, allowing for time to get used to new feelings, time to put warmth into every word.

Now I know why Wanja had such a big heart.

It did not matter whether I looked at him or at the prisoner whose letter he was reading. I know now that it was a long and laborious transmission of love between people whom the war had put thousands of miles apart. For the wives of Pjotr and Wassili and Alexi could not write, either. The priest had received the word from the wives and had written them down. And Pjotr and Wassili and Alexi had to ask Wanja to read their letters. But that didn't matter. The words were there, only it took time. The words had to warm so many hearts on the way before they reached the one for whom they were meant.

Wanja did not have to tell me that Wassili's wife wrote that their child had died. I saw from Wassili's and Wanja's faces that the letter told about a great sorrow. I had learned two words, Batjuska and Tutja. Every letter began with Batjuska, Little Father, and almost always Tutja, Child, was mentioned several times in all the letters.

The next letter was taken up. Alexi looked happy, and his joy was reflected in Wanja's face. Perhaps in the following letter there would be something that would make Pjotr or Marek look angry or worried.

This quiet performance would last some hours, leaving one man sorrowful, another happy. Only Wanja would remain behind with a large and heavy heart, neither happy nor sorrowful. Since that time only the high mountains have been able to give me the sense of peace that Wanja's companionship gave me when I was a child. Now I also know that our friendship was like the friendship between a mountain and a little hill. I would walk around Wanja with the feeling of security that a young animal feels towards its mother. In my heart there was an unswerving devotion to this foreign heart that held the infinite and had borne such manifold experiences, and to Wanja it meant happiness to feel himself the protector of a little boy like me. It is this feeling of being useful, being indispensable, which alone can keep a man alive when he is in exile.

Of course I don't know this for sure. I only know that there existed that great delicacy between us which is the first condition of friendship. Our questions to each other were kind and gentle and we agreed in all things.

There was nothing sentimental in Wanja's voice when one Sunday he said to me: "You are my tutja and I am your batjuska."

I suppose he had to find a being to whom he could take the wealth of his thoughts.

Then came the end, unexpected and hard.

One day I went out to the cow barn to find Wanja. He was there. And I saw that he who bore in his heart the sorrow of so many others, was now struck by a greater and more piercing agony of his own. He was sitting on his milking stool with a letter in his lap, his face buried in his hands, and his frail body shaken by convulsive sobs.

"Wanja—Wanja!" I cried.

But he was lost in his despair. I had to go over to him and lay my cheek against his.

"Wanja dear, what is it?"

"Tutja, Wanja's mother is dead."

His words made me feel my helplessness. My little hands pushed themselves in under his and were moistened by his tears.

"Don't cry, Wanja."

"Go away, Tutja."

But how could I go away when my best friend was in misery? I stayed and said all the words to Wanja that a child considers consoling. I tried to tell him that he still had me. But all that I could say was in vain.

At last Wanja stopped crying. He rose and thrust the letter into his blouse.

"Wanja is going to escape."

For the next hour his will fought a desperate battle against reality. He planned to flee across the frontier to Denmark that very night. In Denmark he would steal a boat and row to Russia. That would take him four days. His mother's grave would still be new when he reached it, and he would lay a fresh wreath on it.

Even I knew that all this was impossible. With my meager knowledge of geography I tried to convince Wanja that he was mistaken. Months would pass before he could reach Ukraine. But I spoke in vain; Wanja could not believe it.

So he made preparations for his flight. He did not know the simplest things. He asked me what way to go; were there large waves on the sea? Did I think that he could get food on the way? He possessed twenty pieces of Russian hardtack; if he could get food on the way, he would give them all to me; otherwise he would have to take ten of them with him. He spoke so convincingly that at last I myself believed that he would succeed. Wanja was so good; how could he fail?

In the evening he knocked at my window.

"Remember the hardtack, it is in the fodder box."

I did not sleep for several hours, and when I went to sleep I dreamed that Wanja was standing on the other side of a large river where I could not reach him. . . .

The next morning two sergeants with loaded guns came walking through the village and between them trudged a little Russian prisoner. His face had changed during the two years that had passed since he had said "Kamerad, Offizier" on the day of his arrival. I was told that his mouth was drawn with bitterness and there was wild anger in his eyes. When he passed our house, he looked up to the windows, but I was not there. When I did not come, he called, "Tutja, I'll kill these fellows!" Then he sprang at the first of them and knocked him down with one blow. The other knocked Wanja unconscious with the butt of his gun and the two sergeants dragged him away as one drags a dead animal.

All this I was told by people who saw it. I was not ashamed of Wanja. He was right, of course, even though things went against him; that did not alter the matter.

In the fodder box I found twenty large pieces of hardtack of the kind that the Russian women sent to their countrymen who had been made prisoners in Germany. Wanja had left them all for me. I kept them in my window where they grew soft after a while.

Later I was told that for a month after Wanja's death I would sometimes cry out in my sleep:

"Kill them, Wanja! Kill them!"

Translated by LIDA SIBONI HANSON

NORWAY

INTRODUCTION

By Lise Lindbaek

THE MAIN THING to be observed about Norwegian literature between the two world wars is that it is remarkably untouched by the experiences of the first or by any foreshadowing of the second. Since 1900, the country had gone through two major crises without being forced into war; in 1905, it was separated from Sweden without any bloodshed, and in 1914–18, in spite of the precarious situation, it was able to remain neutral. These facts gave an illusion of security to Norwegian minds. Instead of observing, with anxiety and foreboding of evil, what was happening in Europe and the world, Norwegian poets and writers went on studying human nature and human psychology, their proper material. There was a strong trend in the direction of deeper psychological interest, into the subconscious of the human mind, and at the same time into social questions. These two groups, the "psychological" and the "social" group, are by no means clearly distinguished from each other; many of the most important writers of the period have both psychological and social interests (Arnulf Överland, Sigurd Hoel, etc.).

It is a period in the history of our literature which is definitely closed, because the destiny and the mental structure of every Norwegian was fundamentally changed on April 9, 1940, when the Germans invaded the country. The whole background of our existence, a feeling for the stability of life and human values, crumbled and is being replaced by something which it is still too early to define. It may not be less valuable; and it may well be affirmed, even at this early date, that its literary output—with which we are here concerned—will prove to be high-ranking. From Norway we learn that the Germans have tried to force the writers to write—without success. Norwegian writers *in* Norway do not write today; only those who managed to escape abroad can express themselves now. In Stockholm a volume of Norwegian war poetry has been published and has been generally hailed by Swedish critics and the Swedish public as outstanding poetry, quite apart from its sentimental and national background of actuality. But it is different from anything written in Norway before 1940. Quite other things are now at the surface—and certainly deep and profound emotions are in the subconscious—of Norwegian minds.

During a period of four hundred years, from 1392 to 1814, when Norway was united with and dominated by Denmark, very little of lasting value was written by Norwegians, Ludvig Holberg being the most prominent exception. Immediately after 1814, when Norway had its free constitution, Norwegian literature began flourishing. Whereas Wergeland and Welhaven, in the earlier part of the nineteenth century, did not attain more than national or rather Scandinavian reputation, our two great writers of the closing part of the century, Henrik Ibsen and Bjoernstjerne Bjoernson, both belong to the literary masters of the world. And in this century, our literature begins with two great names: Knut Hamsun and Sigrid Undset, both of whom have written some of their best work between 1920 and 1940. It is hardly necessary to repeat the reasons for omitting Hamsun from this anthology. Many Norwegians have removed his books from their home libraries, but it is said that they often leave the space open in their book-shelves, so as not to forget. This is symbolic of the reaction of the Norwegian people to Knut Hamsun and his work.

Sigrid Undset received the Nobel Prize for Literature in 1920, for the first volume of her powerful trilogy *Kristin Lavransdatter*. Her deeply moral attitude towards life, given special emphasis since her conversion to Roman Catholicism, her profound knowledge of history and her rich sense of beauty, have produced masterpieces which belong to world literature, as well as the earlier works that impart, better than those of any other writer, the atmosphere of Oslo in its age of development.

Some of the Norwegian writers have had religion or religious sentiments as their chief source of inspiration for creative work during these twenty years. The greatest of them is Olav Duun. We may also mention Sigurd Christiansen, Ronald Fangen, and Bishop Eyvind Berggrav under whose eminent leadership the entire Norwegian Church has taken up and maintained its unbroken stand against Nazidom. Bishop Berggrav has published many books, and one of them, *The Land of Tension* (1937), gives a vivid description of life and conditions in Northern Norway where Berggrav for many years was a bishop. Ronald Fangen's adherence to Christian ideals and his courageous attitude against the Nazis have been punished by confinement in concentration camps and hospitals; his health has been crushed, but not his spirit.

Among the most well-known of the older writers of the period is Johan Bojer, whose numerous novels found a still wider and more appreciative public outside of Norway than in his own country. Amongst his best books are *The Last of the Vikings*, telling the story of life and death of the fishermen in Lofoten (published in New York in 1923) and *Emigrants* (published in 1925), a plastic and interesting picture of life and conditions among Norwegian pioneers in this country in the final decades of the last century.

A younger group of writers, whose interests are predominantly of psychological character, was profoundly influenced by Freudian theories and, at the same time, by recent American novelists, particularly Hemingway and Dos Passos. The spiritual leader of this group was Sigurd Hoel, a witty and discerning critic, with vast knowledge and culture, and also the author of some highly successful and very amusing novels. Helge Krog, who has written several plays and many short stories, shows himself to his greatest advantage as an essayist and student of literature. But the most important creative writer in this group is Aksel Sandemose. His book, *A Fugitive Crosses His Tracks*, was published in this country in 1936. Sandemose uses modern psychological techniques and succeeds in tracing back to "the petrified humanity and iron laws" of the world of his childhood, Jante, the influences which frustrate his life and prevent a normal fulfillment of gifts and desires.

Although the main interest of this group is in psychology and the inner events of human lives, several of the authors show deep interest in social conditions and their influence upon human psychology. It is significant that Norwegian literature since the days of Bjoernson and Garborg has been rich in novels about peasants and fishermen. New writers have treated similar subjects in a more realistic way, influenced by modern psychology.

This leads us, finally, to the two names which, more than any others, are going to be considered the representatives of Norwegian literature from 1920 to 1940—and later: Nordahl Grieg and Arnulf Överland. Although differing greatly in style and development, they have this in common, that far more than their contemporaries they were aware of what happened outside of the Norwegian horizon; in their production we find the pulsation of the entire outer world.

Nordahl Grieg belongs to no group. He is just past forty, and his personal history is unique in the literary history of Norway. He has an insatiable appetite for life; he has been everywhere, seen everything. A great-nephew of Edvard Grieg's, of a very influential family in Bergen, at the age of nineteen he went to sea as an ordinary seaman on a freighter. Grieg's first novel, *The Ship Sails On*, aroused a storm of indignation at its outspokenness, but also immediate admiration for its unquestionable talent and healthy gift of indignation. His dramas, especially *Our Honor and Our Power*—a play of Norwegian sailors during the first World War—(1933), and *Defeat*, a historic play about the Paris Commune, have been acted not only in Norway, but in Sweden and Denmark as well, more often than any dramas since the days of Henrik Ibsen. Nordahl Grieg's last book before the German invasion, *The World Must Still Be Young*, is a broadly conceived book that takes its subject from Russia in the thirties and from the Spanish Civil War. Nordahl Grieg, who is now in England, is perhaps the foremost Norwegian writer between the two wars and during the present war; there is every reason to believe that his chief work is still to come.

The last name to be mentioned is that of Arnulf Överland, who belongs to the advance guard of the psychological and the social group of Norwegian writers between wars. For many years he was considered Norway's finest lyric poet. He uses the language as his instrument, more deliberately and more finely chiseled than any other contemporary poet. The exquisite form in which he excelled even as a very young poet (he published his first book in 1911, at twenty-two) grew to full maturity after the first World War, when Arnulf Överland saw with pain and despair what was happening in Europe and in the world. Injustice, social or international, deeply aroused his feelings. He has been called "the conscience of the Norwegian people," and he was "a leader in the remarkable advance of the Norwegian people towards the cause of social justice in the years before the present war." The injustice done to the Spanish people by the powers of the world made a deep impression on his

soul, and his poem, "Guernica," ought to be as well-known as Picasso's picture.
Överland's prophetic poem, "You Must Not Sleep," was not to remain the high
point of his production. When the Nazis invaded Norway, he, who had more
reason than anyone else to fear revenge, chose to stay on and to write. His
poems appeared anonymously, but his genius was stamped on every line and
could not fail to be recognized. "We Shall Survive" has been chosen as *the*
poem of the home front, of Norwegian resistance against German violence.
Arnulf Överland is today in a concentration camp in Germany; he did not
escape.

Sigrid Undset

HAPPY TIMES IN NORWAY

"Winter-spring" is the name people in Norway give to that odd season
that begins in February. When day after day the sun beams down from
a high and cloudless deep-blue sky and every morning the whole world
is encrusted with glistening frost crystals—but later in the day all the
eaves are dripping. The sun licks the snow from the trees, and one sees
the tops of the birches beginning to turn a shiny brown and the bark of
the aspens taking on the greenish tinge that betokens spring.

Snowdrifts still lie high along the roads and fences and on the fields
the snowcrust shines like silver in the sun, the ski tracks drawing bright
lines in crisscross. Crows and magpies fly about with twigs in their bills.
They have more or less begun to repair last year's nests, and once in a
while they pierce the stillness of the winter day with their squawks and
chatter.

As soon as the sun goes down there is biting cold. But a reflection of
the daylight remains, a fringe of flame, along the black-forested ridge
to the southwest. For many hours afterward a light, the color of old
green glass, lingers on the horizon. In the morning long icicles hang
from all the eaves, but in the course of the forenoon shining drops begin
to fall. And every day is a little longer and a little lighter than the day
before.

It is a glorious time of year for the children and the young people.

The boys came home from school and bolted their food—they were
going over on the hill for ski training. And they did not come home until
the first stars began to twinkle in the sky. After the evening meal there
was coasting on the long roadways that wind with many a hairpin curve
down from the mountain and straight across the town. These roads were
far from safe for coasting. There was a great deal of traffic on them—

cars and buses and trucks—and moreover they cut across Main Street, which also is the main road leading into the valley. Mothers could do nothing but warn: "Now do be careful!" And the sons pointed out that they certainly did not need to be told that! No one would go coasting and get killed for the fun of it.

When and how those same boys ever studied their lessons and wrote their exercises was hard to conceive. But they must have done so, somehow or other, for their grades at school were no lower than for the fall semester. Perhaps the teachers were more lenient at ski time. Every school had a ski tournament during the winter, and in place of physical training courses the boys were allowed to go with the physical training teacher on skiing trips up through the forest. And it was possible to "glance" at the lessons in the morning, before one had to start, for on skis or Swedish "kick-sled" it took only five minutes to get to school. So the boys did not leave home until after they really should have been at their desks.

"Kick-sledding" is a Swedish invention, but it had become tremendously popular in Norway in the course of a few years. It sounded disrespectful when Anders offered to kick Mother downtown, if she had some errands to do, and strange when Thea kicked Tulla a long way out in the sun every morning. Thea sought vainly to get her to keep her sunglasses on—Tulla took them off every time she saw her chance and slung them in the snow at the roadside.

There was always some accident or other. Little by little the ski courses and skiing roads became worn down to bare ice. It hurt to fall now. In homes all about the countryside were boys lying abed who had fallen and had water on the knee or a slight concussion of the brain. It was only strange that no one got seriously hurt more frequently. On those hills owned by the various ski clubs, where the real training took place, fresh snow was, of course, hauled in, and the snow on the slope below the jump was kept from getting packed and hard. But the slopes in the forests were frightful; many of them were being used for logging. Yet just when they were about to become impossible, a few days' snowfall usually came and saved the situation—and all the courses were velvet again.

It was an enjoyable time for the grownups as well. The sun grew stronger day by day, and the potted plants in the windows had their own springtime. The Norwegians console themselves for the length of their winter with splendid window gardens. The rooms were fragrant with the odor of sprouting bulbs and tulips. The day it was possible to

eat dinner without turning on the lights was always a red-letter day—
even though one did have to turn them on the day following, if there was
fish for dinner.

March is always colder than February, with frequent dark and foggy
days, and occasionally a howling snowstorm that lasts from three to four
days. But "March is not so bad, for she makes half the road bare," the
old saying goes and it always holds true. A strip of black earth grins up
from the southerly edge of the road without fail before the month of
March has ended.

Every day Hans came home at least an hour late for dinner, soaking
wet from his leather boots to his hair and streaked with horse manure.
He and his playmates could never resist the temptation to make canals
of the ruts that were overflowing with water everywhere in the middle
of the day. They built dams in them and measured the depth of the
water by stepping into it!

"Now you must not go out on the Holme pond, Hans," said Mother
sternly. Hans stood, music case in hand, ready to leave for his music
lesson. "Do you hear?"

"Oh, no, I won't ever do that again," Hans peered sorrowfully up at
his mother. "Not after seeing that poor girl who tried to slide on the ice
there. She plunked in, poor thing . . ." Hans heaved a sigh that seemed
to come from the depths of his soul.

"What? What happened to her?"

"Oh, she's lying there on the bottom yet, I suppose," said Hans in a
sepulchral voice. "She never came up again. Oh, she yelled so, mother. I'll
never forget it as long as I live. It was the last time I went to Mrs. Anker's.
That was when I saw it."

"But to think you didn't try—" began Mother, completely horrified.
Then she continued rather more calmly. "How did it happen that you
did not go out and save her? The Holme pond is no deeper than your
waist anywhere. Hans, Hans, you simply must not run around and tell
such stories! That's lying, Hans!"

"Is it?" asked Hans, surprised. "I thought lying was when I lied when
you asked if I've done something I've done that is naughty to do."

"Yes, of course—that is the worst kind of lie. But it is also lying when
you go around telling something you have made up, so that people
think it is true."

"Is it?" asked Hans again. "But, mother, then you lie too, when you tell
us about the time you and Aunt Ragnhild and Aunt Signe were young?"

"I most certainly do not, Hans. I do not tell anything but what was really so."

"Is it *true* that you went by steamboat to Denmark and went to a theater in Copenhagen when you were little girls?" asked Hans in deep wonder.

"Of course it is true. You know Grandmother's father was living then and we went to visit him on our vacation. And Grandmother's brother in Copenhagen took us to the Royal Theater."

"I have never been on a steamboat." Hans looked most disgruntled. "And I have been to the theater only once—the time we saw *King Ragnar and Aslaug*. And Anders said that was an awfully dumb play."

"If we go to Oslo for Easter you may go to the theater—if there is anything playing that is suitable for children."

"Don't worry, there won't be." Hans spoke as a man who had no illusions left. "But, mother, when you write books, you make up what goes in them? Then you lie, don't you?"

"At least the books I write are what we live on," said Mother curtly—but then she had to laugh. "People know that what is in books is not true in the sense that everything has happened just that way."

"Then I think I could learn to write good books, too," said Hans brightly. "Because I can think up an awful lot of stuff, can't I, mother?"

"Time will tell. But get along now—it's already five of five. And you won't go down and wade in the Holme pond, do you hear?"

"But, mother, you said yourself just now that it was not deep enough to drown in anywhere," Hans laughed, then dashed out the door before Mother had a chance to say anything further on the matter.

In April the snow begins to melt in earnest down in the valley. On the slope above the kitchen garden the withered lawn peeped through, a bare spot that grew larger and larger every day. The ski jumps left from the Christmas holidays were only two patches of dirty snow out in the middle of the lawn. Here and there and everywhere as the snow melted Mother found mittens and caps and scarves—picking up a little of everything whenever she went for a walk in the garden to see whether the snowdrops and the daffodils had begun to sprout.

Anders went with her on these walks. He liked flowers and liked their garden, as long as he did not have to be bothered with it. But it was always Anders who brought Mother the first coltsfoot to turn up its bright eye from the edge of some ditch and the first white anemones from the birch groves on the other side of the creek.

The air over the valley was full of the sound of running water. Every creek and every ditch was flooding its banks. It was still freezing cold at night—the creek that flowed through Mother's garden lowered its voice toward dawn, and there was a silvery tinkle in it when the thin crusts of ice forming along the edges broke as fast as they froze. The dogs dashed down to the creek the moment they were let out in the morning and lapped the muddy water, rolled in the wet, dead grass, and raced down to the big birch at the farthest end of the garden to tell off the magpies that lived in it—whereupon the magpie family replied point for point. But up in the mountains there was a fine ski course still, and the Easter holidays brought a new invasion of tourists to all the hotels. And every Sunday Anders disappeared early in the morning—he had to go up to the mountain and make use of the skiing roads while there was still something left of them.

About three o'clock one morning all the apple trees in the orchard were full of red-winged thrush that whistled and sang. It was light as day, and the sky the pale gold of dawn. The red-winged thrushes were only passing through—as soon as there was food to be found up in the forest they would leave. The chickadees that had kept themselves around the house all winter, living a life of ease in the Christmas sheaves, now went off in twos to play and sing their ti-ti-ty, ti-ti-ty and bustle in and out of all the birdhouses looking for housekeeping quarters. One day there were hundreds of chaffinches on the bare spots in the garden. They would wait here for their wives—the female of the species always arrived from the south a week later than the male. Mother and Thea scattered birdseed for them, and tried to keep the cats indoors. But that was easier said than done—to keep cats indoors in the spring.

Chestnut cats are the best mousers but the worst cats for killing birds, the peasants say, and this held true for Sissi. But Sissyfos pretended there was nothing in the world that interested him less than bird hunting. Then one day he disappeared and did not return. The boys maintained that he was out courting. Finally there came a message that the hired man at the Rand farm had shot Sissyfos. He had caught him in the act of killing all Mrs. Rand's baby chicks out back of the barn. Now, it appeared that Sissyfos had been a great hunter. Only he had been clever enough never to hunt in his own neighborhood but went on his predatory expeditions in other parts of the community.

"At least he died a death worthy of a tomcat," declared Anders.

But Hans wept a little over Sissyfos. And Mother felt bad because she feared Tulla would miss her very own cat.

Every day the roar of the cataract could be heard more clearly all over the little town. The mist-smoke lay like a white band along the river's course, but underneath the bridge in Main Street it came down like a shower upon the passers-by.

One Sunday noon Anders came home from the skiing hill with his cap full of blue anemones and violets.

"There are thousands of them up there, mother. . . . Yes, we have been hauling snow for skiing until today, but today is very likely the last time we use the hill this year." He sighed. Then, "Mother, one month from today is the Seventeenth of May," he announced radiantly.

"But aren't you going to study now?" Mother reminded him as he prepared to go out again as soon as he had finished his dinner.

"Haven't time. I've got to run. There's a committee meeting today."

"Committee meeting?"

"Entertainment committee, of course—that's what I'm on. But I'll try to look over my lessons tonight a little."

A pig is big when it can put a curl in its tail, and a boy is big when he can serve on a committee. Hans and his friends, Ole Henrik and Magne, were also on a committee, they said, though they seemed to represent no one but themselves and their work consisted chiefly of counting their savings—which grew less week by week. But they had great plans on how to improve their finances by the Seventeenth.

"You know you'll get a half crown in Seventeenth of May spending money, Hans," Mother reminded him. "That is enough for you to go to Maehlum on."

"Ole Henrik gets a crown . . . from his grandmother," whispered Hans, a pained look on his face.

"That's nice for Ole Henrik."

"Don't you think Grandmother will come up for the Seventeenth?"

"I haven't heard anything about it."

Hans appeared to be deeply grieved over Grandmother's faithlessness.

Finally one night came the rain. For three successive days it streamed down, mild and still.

"Mother," said Hans triumphantly, "I thought it was just something people said. But now I can hear it—the grass grow."

Yes, the soft, sweet sound of falling rain that awakens the smell of earth and the first green blades of grass that are breaking through the earth. . . .

"Yes, it is true. Now we can hear the grass grow."

The fourth day the sun came out and before evening all the birches were golden with tiny buds shaped like mouse ears. By next morning these buds had turned into tiny leaves and the trees stood there—green. Hans went with Mother when she went out to pick some of the first young birch leaves and white anemones for the Sunday dinner table.

"Mother, tell me the story you told me last year. About the pants-coat."

"Dear me, have I told you that one? That was in a reader Aunt Signe had when she was little."

It was a story about a father who was explaining to his two little daughters, Kirsten and Else, the meaning of the Seventeenth of May. To illustrate, he reminded Else of the coat she had that was made out of an old pair of his pants. Else did not like this coat at all. It did not fit her, although Mother had done the best she could with material that had been cut originally for an entirely different purpose. All the children in the street shouted "the pants-coat, the pants-coat" whenever she wore it. And the day that Else got a new spring coat which had been made just for her was the happiest day of her life.

The union with Denmark had become a kind of pants-coat for Norway. It was so many hundreds of years ago that the two countries had united that people had almost forgotten how it happened in the first place. Queen Margrethe, mother of Olav Haakonsson, the last descendant of Norway's old royal family, was also the daughter of the King of Denmark. When her father died, Margrethe got the Danes to select her son Olav to be Denmark's king. Olav inherited the crown of Norway from his father. But Olav died quite young. And so Queen Margrethe got both the Danes and the Norwegians to choose a little German prince, who was the son of her niece, to be king of Norway and also king of Denmark. And after him came other German princes who had nothing more to do with Scandinavia than be descendants of Danish princesses who had married in Germany. And in a measure these foreign kings united Norway and Denmark into one kingdom. But Norway soon became the stepchild in the union. It was a poorer land than Denmark, and so far-flung and difficult to rule—Norwegians were known to be headstrong and obstinate—that public officials and clergymen considered it almost like being banished to be sent to Norway. Finally, when the last king that ruled over the "twin kingdoms" lost a war with Sweden, he was forced to cede Norway to Sweden.

But the Norwegians did not want to be ceded to anyone. They remembered their ancient right. Norway was not a part of Denmark, but an independent kingdom. It was the Danes who had chosen to unite themselves with Norway when they chose Norway's King Olav to be their king also. And they knew every man in Norway had always had greater freedom than people had had in Denmark and Sweden. There the peasants were subjects of powerful proprietors and noblemen, but in Norway the peasants had never been serfs. Even when they were renters and cotters, they had only to pay certain sums to the owner—they did not have to give him their services. He could not command them to become soldiers. The Norwegian army was a people's army, and in the Danish-Norwegian fleet it was the Norwegians who had always made the best sailors and marines. The Norwegians did not want any Swedish pants-coat. They knew it would never fit them.

Representatives from all over Norway gathered at Eidsvold to discuss how they could rescue our independence. While the Swedish army and the European powers, by means of blockade and threats, sought to force Norway to accede, the fathers sat at Eidsvold and worked out a statement that expressed our ideas about the rights and justice, the dignity and honor of the Norwegian people. On May 17, 1814, Norway's constitution was adopted and the men at Eidsvold swore to protect our right to live under laws "sewn" to meet our own requirements. That was our new spring coat. . . .

Translated by JORAN BIRKELARD

Nordahl Grieg

THE SHIP SAILS ON

A SHIP COMES into port and halts for a while on her way from sea to sea.

Fires are raked out, engines slow down to a dead stop with their glistening cranks and piston-rods, and the propeller churns up the foam in a last spasmodic stroke like the tail of a dying fish. One more turn of the wheels, and the ship swings slowly in to the quay. Steel and hemp hawsers make her fast to the shore, and she is delivered over to the dry land and its human forces.

The roar of motor lorries reverberates in the ship's iron sides, and the street casts its shadows and its mud where the ocean solitude has murmured day and night, where the blue seas crooned their songs of longing and the dawn quivered on plates still wet from the storm. To-day the surf of town surges about the ship.

Winches rattle, cranes thrust their claws into the open holds and sling their booty ashore. The dockers, bow-legged and bent from their loads, are now masters of the ship. But in the evening all is quiet and only the ship's own people are left on board. They go ashore in a body, answering the call of the port, the call of destruction with its husky laugh. In the course of night they stagger on board. But some of them leave the ship, bending under a grey seaman's bag, and they never come back.

Next day, however, there are no gaps in the crowd as they go ashore for their spree. New men quickly step into the vacant places, crawl up into the empty bunks and find the leavings of those who went ashore and are forgotten. That is the way of it; life has no time to waste.

But one night a young face appears on the quay in the darkness; a new hand who knows nothing. He stares up at the mighty world of iron that rises up before him, and he wonders within himself: What is there inside the ship, what does she conceal?

And this is what he guesses:

She is a warehouse that moves about from port to port and sometimes visits lands of beauty. A community of human lives, with darksome clefts and ravines, but also with mountains rosy in the dawn. A Moloch that crushes the lives of men between its iron jaws, and then calmly turns its face to the solitudes as though nothing had happened. All this the ship is, and a thousand things besides. And he feels drawn to her and afraid of her.

Behind him the town blinks its myriad eyes, and one of them is dear to him. But the ship rises up before him, dark and still as death. The town and the ship: to-night it seems that he must choose between life's happiness and life's adventure.

Benjamin Hall goes on board the ship.

        ❈   ❈   ❈

Benjamin found his sea-chest in a corner among a pile of oilskins and sea-boots, in a pungent smell of grease and turpentine. He pulled out his bed-clothes and flung the old ones out of his bunk.

There was nothing but a foul and ragged mattress, shredding its hay in all directions.

How strange to think that once its owner came aboard with a new mattress to live his life in the ship. Up there another man had lain and thought and dreamt for months, it was his little world on board. An old

worn-out mattress is all that is left of it. Another man spread his blankets
and lives up there until the hour strikes for him too. And then a new
man comes and kicks aside his relics. Lives and destinies come and go in
the forecastle, but the ship does not change.

                              *   *   *

Santos was the ship's dog, a lively little Argentine terrier that Sivert
stole down in Rosario last trip. He ran all over the ship from morning
till night and was hugely beloved by all hands.

He bounded up to Aalesund and jumped on to his knees. Aalesund
pushed him off, but he jumped up again and licked his hand. Then
Aalesund began to stroke his head, and his face seemed to soften a
little.

All at once the door was flung wide open with a bang. It was Risør.
"Is Santos here? Hide him, hide him! The second mate's going to kill
him, I just heard it amidships."

And he vanished again into the dark.

Quick as lightning Aalesund seized Santos and lifted him into his
bunk. "Lie still," he said and spread the blankets over him.

The second mate was in the doorway, with a marlinspike in his hand.
He was met by a dull, brooding silence.

"Is Santos here?" he asked.

"No," answered Aalesund.

"No," answered Narvik.

"That's strange, I was certain—Santos has got to be killed."

"Killed?" asked Narvik.

"Yes. There's a six months' quarantine for dogs in England, and
we're calling at South Shields for bunkers. That's why Santos has got to
be killed."

"Then you'll have to find him yourself," said Sivert, looking at him
defiantly. "And he won't be so easy to find. But didn't I hear that the
skipper had a fine Angora cat amidships?"

"Well, what about it?"

"Only that I've been told cats are liable to go overboard when she
rolls a bit," said Sivert calmly, looking him in the eyes.

"I've heard that too, Sivert," said Narvik with a smile.

"So have I."

"So have I."

The second mate looked round at the cold, determined faces.

"Don't be absurd, boys, Santos has got to be killed."

"It may be a difficult job, that," said Aalesund.

"Do you think I am going to kill him for my own amusement? The skipper has given orders and it's got to be done. Where is Santos?"

"Santos," said Sivert. "Who's that? Oh yes, I believe there was once a dog for'ard called Santos, but we didn't care about him. We let the skipper kill him."

"Not so much of your lip, Sivert!" growled the second mate. "You, Narvik, you're the oldest here and you are generally a sensible man—where is the dog?"

"I don't care to say anything about it," replied Narvik.

"Look here, boys," said the second mate in a familiar tone, sitting down on the bench among them. "Santos has got to be killed. That's as clear as daylight. The man who finds him will get a nice reward and thanks into the bargain."

Oscar put up his face, began to light up and he sent a longing glance in the direction of Aalesund's bunk. If the dog was going to be killed anyhow, somebody might as well have the reward, and why not he? Besides, he never liked Santos or any other dog.

"A nice reward," repeated Aalesund. "Thirty pieces of silver is the rate, isn't it? I don't believe there's anybody here who wants to betray Santos for that."

But the officer was not listening to him; he followed the direction of Oscar's glance. Now he knew where the dog was.

He got up: "So you force me to search for myself. All right. I'll have a try."

He crouched down and looked along the deck. The stillness was enough to hurt. All hands sat like statues, following his movements. Benjamin thought he could hear their hearts beating around him.

The second mate was finished down below, where will he look now?

O God, he's starting to search the bunks. He shakes out the blankets and goes from bunk to bunk. Nearer and nearer—now there is only Aalesund's.

He knew that Santos was there. He could even distinguish the soft outlines of the little body under the blanket. Then he seemed suddenly paralyzed by the thrill of the silence around him.

He turned and looked at the men.

Oscar was all ready to greet the finding of the dog with a snigger, but the others gave the officer a queer feeling.

Some of the faces were pale and drawn with anxiety, but others were hard and threatening, full of hate.

The nerves of all were taut as backstays.

Was he touched at this fidelity to a dog, or did he feel there might be danger in tempting the men too far?

He calmly passed his hands over Aalesund's bunk and said: "No, I can't find the dog. I give it up. It's a bore. Good-night, men."

"Good-night," they gasped.

The door closed behind him.

Shouts of joy filled the forecastle. They all jumped up, howling, laughing, dancing. Benjamin suddenly found Aalesund embracing him. Oh, they were wild with delight!

Sivert dashed to set Santos free. The dog jumped down on the deck and was pitched about like a nutshell in a sea of caresses.

"Little Santos, yes, you're a beauty, our own little Santos. Did you see how quiet he lay? He knew what was up. Yes, Santos is a tiptopper, he is. Good little Santos!"

The men stammered their meaningless little outbursts of affection, in the language only used to dogs and little children.

"I'd like to know if the second mate saw him," said Narvik.

"What are you thinking of," said Sivert; "he'd have cracked him on the head with the spike."

"I'm not so sure," Narvik wondered. "But my word, it was a good thing Aalesund was so smart at hiding him when the mate came in."

"Yes, that was neatly done! But for Aalesund it would have looked pretty bad for Santos." And Sivert hugged the dog in his arms and pressed its head against his.

"Oh, it was nothing much I did," said Aalesund modestly. "But you were good, Sivert, the way you gave him that about the Angora cat. You'd heard cats got lost overboard when she rolls, you said."

"By gum, that cat would have gone overboard too, if they'd killed Santos," Leif swore.

"Yes, the skipper could bet his boots on that," said Benjamin.

He felt so happy that he could have cried. His soul went out to the others; he could have fallen on his knees and thanked God that Santos was saved and that he had a share in the happiness.

Translated by A. G. CHATER

Helge Krog

HENRIK IBSEN

HENRIK IBSEN is with us this very day: we play his plays, we study the same problems that occupied him. Fragments of his world of thoughts have so thoroughly penetrated our consciousness, many of his words have been merged so perfectly into our daily speech, that without realizing it we quote him constantly. We honor his memory; but when we think of his work, it is not only with the reverence due to great men of the past, but also with gratitude because this son of man came to us, fulfilled his mission among us—and left us!

For if some day our Lord should come and announce that, in appreciation of our gratitude, he would send us a new Ibsen, all good citizens who understood the meaning of this message would unite in requesting the Almighty to withhold the gift. Most of us would even cross ourselves in terror if we learned that a new poet was to be born who would become so deeply revolutionary against our time as Ibsen was against his.

Such is the relation between the past and the present, between the idea that is still fighting for its life and the idea that has won out.

Now we have canonized this rebellious poet, who in his time was hissed, hated and reviled. But although Ibsen was born more than one hundred years ago, he has not yet become quite harmless. If Peter and Paul were to look closely at a work like *Ghosts*, they might be a little frightened and think that we should have waited another hundred years before canonizing its author. Ibsen has not yet become a prey for the dry-as-dust critics and philologists. They will have to wait for him a few more years. And I really believe that they will never possess him altogether. It has long been clear to modern Bible critics that our Lord was thinking of such as these when in sublime frenzy he said to the serpent, "Upon thy belly shalt thou go, and dust shalt thou eat all the days of thy life."

When we speak of Ibsen, there comes a mental picture of a small man, faultlessly dressed, looking very formal and reserved; a cold expression and a manner a bit gruff and grouchy making him seem quite unapproachable. That is the picture the world has preserved of the famous elderly playwright. But his contemporaries remembered a very different picture—a vivid picture of a gay Bohemian youth, carelessly dressed, fond of drinking, talkative and full of anecdotes, defiant, exuberantly mocking —from a bourgeois point of view a rather dangerous and offensive fellow.

The change in Ibsen took place after he had won his first decisive victories with *Brand* and *Peer Gynt*, and it was so complete that it affected even his hand-writing, which had been negligently sprawling and now became precise and neat and as fine as that which we see in the writings from the old monasteries.

During the first twenty years of his literary life his existence was a constant and bitter fight for daily bread and for the appreciation which was necessary for his activity as a poet. He was half starved both physically and mentally. By the end of the sixties, however, his fame was established, and beginning with the seventies, he was financially secure.

With this change in his life came a change in his writing. In form and kind, if not in deeper content, the period that ends so brilliantly with *Peer Gynt* is widely different from the one that is introduced by *The Pillars of Society*. But the main difference is of a most unexpected nature. The unique fact is that the drama of his mature years was more rebellious than that of his youth. This fact cannot be too strongly emphasized. The work of the poor, defiant, notorious, small-town Bohemian was challenging. The drama of the wealthy, correct, already famous cosmopolitan was revolutionary. It was not until this century that English censorship lifted the injunction against *Ghosts*.

Ibsen is often mentioned as a visionary and a dreamer. This really means only that he is an idealist. But even this beautiful word has a tinge of something unrealistic, and, when applied to Ibsen, it seems to suggest that his demands on human beings are so great that flesh and blood cannot possibly meet them.

This view can be challenged by a question: Were Copernicus and Galileo devoid of a sense of reality when they declared that the earth moved around the sun? Their contemporaries answered this question by a unanimous "Yes." Everyone could see with his own eyes that the sun was moving round the earth, and he who insisted on the opposite view must be mad or possessed by the devil. This logic is described in Holberg's classic comedy, in which Erasmus Montanus is beaten because he insists that the earth is round. In Denmark of all places, it was easy to see that it was as flat as a pancake!

But there are two kinds of realities. One is narrow, fragmentary and deceiving; the other is perfect, uniting, revealing. We can all see the small nearby reality. But who is able to see the greater and more distant one? Who else but the seers, the elected and visionary, the pathfinders of their generation? In science the great theorists; in art the great dreamers; in politics the great revolutionaries—these are the ones who grasp and recognize reality, the ones who change the course of history.

In this sense it is quite right to say that Isben was a visionary. By rising to the height of his ideals he obtained the wide view. This wide view alone enabled him to unite all scattered impressions and experiences into one mighty whole. Against the perfect harmony of his world of dreams he saw plainly the discord of the actual reality, saw it with exaggerated clarity and vividness.

There is in this a beautiful inner symmetry. In the richly endowed man his first meeting with reality creates an indefinite longing; this longing creates and nourishes the dream of perfection. And this dream finally leads to the greater comprehension of reality. Such a comprehension alone makes it possible for us to see the great divides of our time, and to draw the line between old and new, past and future, between that which is decadent and that which has possibilities of growth. Ibsen had that comprehension. And in that statement lies a short summary of his work and his deed.

His development describes just such a curve as I have here suggested. The more prominent of his older dramas are each determined by its own idea. The idea is the starting-point and the source of inspiration, giving birth to the play. The characters are grouped symmetrically around the idea, are born and shaped in the imagination of the poet as living fragments of the central thought, as its bearers; or else they oppose and ridicule that central thought. Undeniably the poet often violated his characters in order to force them to serve his central purpose. It is evident also that Ibsen's earliest polemic dramas, *Love's Comedy* and *Brand,* are decidedly speculative and abstract. One has a certain right to call them negative, since they merely express a preconceived and universal contempt for the wretchedness of the time, without any attempt on the part of the poet to explain the causes of this wretchedness or to point out any remedy. Not until he begins to write his realistic dramas does Ibsen test ideas and ideals, experiment with them, humanize them, measure the lives of his contemporaries by their standards, with innumerable variations and according to an almost scientific method.

The League of Youth is filled with sarcasm, but *The Pillars of Society* is Ibsen's first realistic indignation drama. It is a severe, forceful, moral sermon, going straight to the point. In *A Doll's House* there is rebellion without any false reconciliation; but the attack is still only relatively specific. In *Ghosts,* his first perfect work, he attacks a universal human problem and does it on such a broad front that this drama even in our days has full validity as a revolutionary play and will retain this validity for centuries.

As Ibsen becomes more and more absorbed in presenting dramas of real life, we see that his interest in human beings gets stronger and stronger, until it becomes his primary poetic impulse, his primary creative urge. More and more his mind occupies itself with purely psychological problems and crises. The individual replaces the social problem, and the "idea" of his dramas, which used to be an abstract concept, is now transformed into the logical development of human destiny.

In *The Lady from the Sea* one notices, as Brandes says, with a certain sadness that the warlike epoch of Ibsen's writings is over. All the plays that follow are deep psychological dramas and analyses, without any tendency or direction and of varying poetic value. Most Ibsen scholars agree that he reached his zenith in *Ghosts, The Wild Duck* and *Rosmersholm*. In these masterpieces the high qualities of his youth and of his maturity are united. Idea and purpose are completely merged in a portrayal of human nature which reveals an almost omniscient understanding. In these plays the poet does not use any compulsion upon his characters, nor does he seem to judge them. He does not argue; he has reached the understanding that reality is far more convincing than all arguments; he shows us men and women moving among the powerful forces of contemporary life that have explosive quality. The purpose is so completely and naturally released by the various situations and the psychology of the drama that it would simply be weakened if the poet added anything to emphasize it. This accounts for the enormous effect of these dramas. In *Ghosts, The Wild Duck* and *Rosmersholm*, the prophet, the contemplator, the accuser and the humanist unite; the impetuosity of youth is blended with the wisdom of age. This last expression contains no whit of irony when applied to Ibsen, for in his age he possessed an even greater mobility and a more all-embracing liberality than in his youth. In Ibsen's dramatic epilogue, *When We Dead Awaken*, a freer spirit prevails than in any of his earlier works. This is nothing less than miraculous.

In a literal sense none of Ibsen's plays is realistic; at least none is naturalistic. Ibsen did not share the interest of shortsighted authors in giving exact photographic details. When we come right down to it, I suppose there does not exist any poetic work of first rank which is absolutely naturalistic. Many profound essays have been written about Ibsen's symbolism. It is true that he used symbols, and sometimes misused them. But the discussion of "symbolism versus realism" is on the whole superficial talk. In poetry which is as full of ideas as Ibsen's, everything is symbolic. No image has any value for him unless at the same time it is a symbol. It would take too long to develop this point here. But all who want to study the forms in which Ibsen sought to express himself, would do well to remember the following remark of the poet himself: "Spiritually man is a far-sighted creature, seeing most clearly at a distance. Details blur the vision. We have to get away from that which we wish to judge. For instance, we can best describe summer on a winter day."

The typical traits of the phenomena, their quintessence and inner meaning, their energy and possibilities, the reaction of the soul of man to these phenomena—these are the things that occupy the poet far more than the phenomena themselves.

Ibsen is usually considered a pessimist. To be sure, he was a pessimist at some periods of his life—for instance when he wrote *Brand* and when he wrote *The Wild Duck*. But this term when applied to Ibsen must be used with some reservation. He himself must, I suppose, be the best authority on that point. In 1887 he said in a speech in Stockholm: "On several occasions it has been said that I am a pessimist. That is true inasmuch as I do not believe in the immortality of human ideals. But I am also an optimist, since I fully believe in the ability of the ideals to procreate and develop."

For a time optimism got into bad repute in Norway. Björnson and especially his imitators brought this about by their childish and naive belief in the possibility of swift improvement of the human race from without. By contrast some younger poets attracted attention by darkly fussing with their souls. In Norway, "pessimism" almost came to mean profoundness of character. It was considered modern and fashionable to be a pessimist—and who wanted to appear out-dated?

Of course Ibsen is not an optimist in the usual sense of the word, but in a deeper sense. He believes in "the ability of ideals to procreate and develop." He believes in the "revolt of the human spirit," and the "law of transformation." The free man is his hero, and his definition of freedom is far more spiritual and radical than that of any earlier poet. He writes to Georg Brandes: "What they call 'liberty,' I call 'liberties'; what I call the struggle for liberty, is nothing but the constant reaching for the idea of liberty. He who possesses liberty without having sought it, possesses it in a dead and shallow way; for the idea of liberty has this characteristic, that it grows even while one struggles for it; so that when anyone stops during the search and says, 'Now I have it,' those words show that he has lost it."

What to Ibsen was essential was not outer circumstance or palpable results, but in his early dramas the will toward perfection, and in his later ones the growth toward perfection.

When the "spirit of compromise" reveals itself to Brand in his delirium in the shape of lovely Agnes, and tempts him to give up his fight, pointing out that his struggle is hopeless because the Almighty drove man out of paradise and closed its doors, Brand answers, "Open he left the path of yearning!" These words, almost terrifying with their depth of meaning, can be regarded as the keynote of Ibsen's work. In this marvelously condensed sentence is to be found the full significance of Ibsen's poetry.

Ibsen was not a reformer, but a revolutionary. And the revolutionary is in the very nature of things an optimist—how else could he hope for anything through a revolution? If one wishes a summary of the revolutionary, anarchistic Ibsen, it will be found in the same letter to Brandes: "The State must go! That revolution I agree to. Undermine the idea of a state, set up free will and spiritual kinship as the one condition for union—that is the beginning of a freedom worth something.—The point is, not to let oneself be frightened by time-honored cults. The state has its root in a certain period of time; it will end in that period of time. Greater things than the state will fall; all religion will fall. Neither moral ideas nor conceptions of art are eternal. How much must we, after all, hold on to? Who can vouch that two and two are not five on Jupiter?"

The ratio between Ibsen's doubt and his faith, his pessimism and his optimism, his contempt for his time and his almost religious faith in the future, can be traced back to the above mentioned relation in his works between the concrete and the abstract, the relative and the absolute. His doubt refers to the small, the passing and casual; his faith is in the greater, the permanent, that which is based on universal law.

It is often said that Ibsen is bound by his time in this or that respect, and that this fact will shorten the life of his writings.

But the expression "bound by his time" may mean different things. *The Pillars of Society* and *Rosmersholm* are both greatly bound by their time. We have already outgrown *The Pillars of Society;* but *Rosmersholm* has still a long future before it. In what does the difference consist? On what does it depend?

Naturally it does not depend on the outer forms within which a human problem is treated. But it depends on this: Is the problem itself a vital one, and has the treatment of it such universal value that in all essentials it can be transferred to the new forms under which the same problem arises again and again?

Of course Ibsen is bound by his time even in his greatest dramas, as were Dante, Shakespeare, Goethe, in fact all poets. Why not? If Ibsen had not belonged to his time, he would not have belonged to any time at all. It is only the most minor poets who are quite independent of all times, their own as well as those to come. He who does not think the thoughts of his time, does not think at all. He who is not modern during his life, how outmoded will he be after death! He who does not live the life of his own time has no possibility of living in the future. A grave error, widely believed, is that there is an indefinite, abstract time in which the great poets live. The close association with the narrow life of a small Norwegian town in no way restricted the scope of Ibsen's dramas; nor did the outer circumstances connecting them with the time of their birth limit them to that time.

Poets of an earlier day always occupy a privileged position in public opinion. If during some discussion one points out that even Shakespeare was greatly bound by his time, the reply comes, "Why yes! But he is a classic!" The common man feels vaguely that even the clothes worn by the characters in classical dramas, be it the dramas of Shakespeare, Molière, or antique tragedy, are the clothes of poetry itself, abstract or astral clothes, clothes of eternity. But a hundred years from now the clothes of Ibsen's characters will be admitted into this magnificent sartorial community.

It is quite true that *Ghosts,* for instance, made a special plea in a great struggle of that day, a fact which gives it much of its immortal strength. But it did more than that: It started another struggle—a struggle which is still raging, no matter how many outer circumstances have changed. The milieu of *Ghosts* is not that of our days; but the contest that Ibsen described was seen by him under such great perspective that it became symbolic of the eternal struggle between old and new, habit and idea, past and future, with the present always the battlefield.

The masterpieces of world literature continue to live because they apply to generation after generation without losing any of their force. To Shakespeare's contemporaries the Jew Shylock was a mixture of a villain and a clown. But the poet's psychological imagination and more or less conscious sense of justice gave Shylock such large proportions and such rich, although at that time hidden, human reserves that we now see him as the tragic hero of the play. As the *Merchant of Venice,* originally a comedy, has now become almost a tragedy, so similar changes take place constantly in plays like *Ghosts, The Wild Duck,* and *Rosmersholm.* What to us is the quintessence of these dramas is not exactly identical with that which seemed the substance in Ibsen's time. This change of viewpoint will continue. New generations will look at these works from other angles, and extract from them that wisdom which is the most essential for their own time. There will always be new perception to be gained from them.

We know that the light from distant stars does not reach us until many decades after it has started on its journey. So with the light from the great poetic works. The source is the same, and the light shines constantly; but it is always new light that reaches us. Fifty years, a hundred years after the creation of Ibsen's great dramas, new sources of light will develop in them, illuminating our lives and inspiring us as much as these dramas did the first time we saw them acted. And new light from them will continue to shine on many generations yet unborn.

Translated by LIDA SIBONI HANSON *and* ADDA GENTRY GEORGE

Aksel Sandemose

THE LAW OF JANTE

A FACTORY was located in Jante, and the town had a large population of laboring men. It was, on the whole, an impoverished town and, according to statistics, always had been. Located as it was, it had little to offer, but economically Jante was secure at least on its natural level. Neither good times nor bad affected its fundamental structure. Conditions were reflected merely in the rise of some certain obscure individual and his subsequent collapse. Jante is a town of frugal toilers. It is pleasantly situated, but low, and certain sections of it are subject to inundation during the autumn rainy season. Its environs are, in their way, extremely beautiful; a smiling, varied landscape.

So much I know to be true. But this is objective description, such as might be concocted for a guide-book and which, though free from the ballyhoo of the touring-club press-agent, likewise waives the emotional reactions of the individual. But for me it is the most dismal place in the world. For me Jante represents something wholly different—my personal relationship to a group of persons. Had I grown up in Arendal or Jonkoping in contact with these same individuals, my attitude toward either one of these places would, I am sure, be much the same.

✿   ✿   ✿

I shall not, lest I be accused of later contradicting myself, pretend that I felt impoverished when I was small. Such was by no means the case. One reason for this may have been that nearly everyone we knew as neighbors was existing under the same if not worse conditions. The fundamental reason, however, was that we all looked up to Father and never for a moment dreamed that he could possibly be poor. On the contrary, there was frequent mention of certain poor unfortunates, and this implied that we ourselves were not poor. It was when I was about twelve that certain things began dawning upon me; I had begun to go out more and thereby acquired more material for comparison. And, with that, my course of reasoning became more divided, for it was impossible for me to give up the notion that my father was a great and important man. That we were proletarians I discovered first after we had ceased, according to the fullest meaning of the word, to be precisely that, though we still bore the stigmata which all proletarians must bear—those marks which have been the determining factors in my life. The marks of the slave are so indelibly imprinted on a man's soul that it would certainly make but very little difference were he actually to be black of skin, like the slaves of the past in America—it was not his color alone that betrayed the fugitive slave. No matter what his color, he was bound to give himself away as soon as he found himself in the presence of his betters. It is said that in the early days of Australia the authorities could determine whether a man were a fugitive from some penal colony by rattling a chain in his presence. The former prisoner would receive such a shock at the sound that he would betray himself at once. Kipling has a tale of an Englishman who had been in exile in Siberia; many years later he heard a command uttered in Russian and fell sobbing to his knees.

I tremble to this day whenever I hear the clanking of the chains of Jante, and turn my head like a snarling cur. It is thus that men behave who have spent their lives in chains, though they believe this to be the normal way for human beings to behave and are, in truth, unconscious of the chains which bind them.

✿   ✿   ✿

You have grown up in other environments and will never be able to grasp the inexorable effect of the Law of Jante. You will probably laugh at it and fail utterly to sense the deadly influence it had upon that working boy in Jante. By means of the Jante Law's ten commandments, Jante holds Jante down. And now you must hear them all:

1. Thou shalt not believe thou *art* something.
2. Thou shalt not believe thou art as good as *we.*
3. Thou shalt not believe thou art more wise than *we.*
4. Thou shalt not fancy thyself better than *we.*
5. Thou shalt not believe thou knowest more than *we.*
6. Thou shalt not believe thou art greater than *we.*
7. Thou shalt not believe *thou* amountest to anything.
8. Thou shalt not laugh at *us.*
9. Thou shalt not believe that anyone is concerned with *thee.*
10. Thou shalt not believe thou canst teach *us* anything.

Some of these commandments may perhaps be quite all right as they sound. But he who has lived under the Law of Jante during the fifteen years it took him to develop, who has come to realize its bloody emphasis and its hysterical thirst for power, regards these commandments very differently. By means of the Law of Jante people stamp out each other's chances in life. All struggle against it and writhe beneath it, but all heartlessly exercise it against all others. Because of it the people of Jante are godless, without first having become human. Each is nailed to a cross of his own and requires no Christian symbolism. There they all hang, screaming, their brows wet with bloody sweat, turning and twisting in pain, and hissing to their brothers in crucifixion: "Do you think for a moment that anyone bothers his head about *you?*"

The Law of Jante was not merely a set of laws, it was the very core of the speech of the people; all they ever said could be traced straight back to the Law of Jante. This is Jante: each little soul's struggle for coequality and recognition, never without consciousness that all the others are greater than he. With a decree gleaned from the Law of Jante every conversation was at length concluded, without fail! I remember the coffee parties! Words perhaps embodied merely in a glance, but none the less suffocating to us all, deadening the very air we breathed and creating an atmosphere which could nourish only dreams of revenge. Its effect was that of poison gas, slower perhaps, but more heartless. It would poison the soul without killing it utterly. It had no winding-sheet to spread over its victims.

In the ancient laws of the land and in the Law of Moses you will forever detect the spirit of the Law of Jante; from the Law of Moses, in particular, flow numberless decrees designed to hold the pack in check. Obedience, modesty, respect—these are the virtues attributed to us when we have lived up to such commandments. The eighth commandment in the Law of Jante—Thou shalt not laugh at us—has already been sung by David: Let them be sore oppressed for their infamy, those who give me the haha!

But few topics could be discussed there in Jante, and these only if brought up by the eldest in the family, who would speak slowly over a sounding-board of incertitude, while all his younger brothers would sit about with downcast eyes taking inventory of their hatred. Were they to ask a question, it would have to be to the accompaniment of much reassurance: Of course, we know nothing, but you who are so wise . . . Then the reply would come from Olympus. For within that mighty reservoir information was always on tap. The opposite was unthinkable. But even if younger brother said nothing in return, often enough he would sit there laughing to himself at the information he had received. How may an individual ever hope to develop a soul in such an environment? How shall Jante ever be able to foster other men than slaves—with an occasional scorpion or murderer? What will our heavenly Father do with this appalling gang who will sit through all eternity with sour expressions on their faces on the point of exploding simply because they happen to catch sight of someone else sitting off yonder on another cloud and believing he *is* something.

In union there is strength. This united attitude rendered Jante successful in holding Jante down. How we suffered, how we squirmed! All are equally big, but each must believe all the rest are bigger. This is the foundation upon which the town is built. It has become impossible for the individual to rise there—long years elapse before he discovers that he has been held down, if he ever discovers the bitter truth. The majority never do. They are the tireless toilers in the factory, men who have gone forth and returned regularly each day for three generations, until they can come and go no longer. The ant and the bee have consolidated themselves better than the human being, and with less hardness of heart. They create their distinct and vital types by means of systematic undernourishment, but we destroy souls with poison gas, accidentally, without rhyme or reason—no one goes unscathed, all must suffer and all do their bit in the general gas attack. The Jante man cannot arise from his condition. Instead he bluffs. He *bluffs* the others into believing him as great as in reality he *is*, the whole time doubting this himself.

How may one describe the riots when kinsmen clashed in Jante? Not precisely by stating that we spoke the plain truth to each other. Never did we venture that far; we knew each other too well—and the hatred each bore for the rest. We uttered no truths, but held instead to the Law

of Jante, the good old well-proven catechism with all its poison. That is
to say, the younger element kept still, of course, but would release the
poison whenever they dared and wherever it proved most effective.

And yet the truth was uttered at last—it was Petrus who dared the
attempt after many years of wearing strife. He had thought, no doubt,
of delivering one decisive blow—or, rather, I prefer to believe that he
dropped the bomb by mistake! Either way, I can bear witness to the fact
that there was a mighty detonation. Whereupon, we all got out our hand-
grenades and flame-projectors as though by military command. In twenty
seconds all the miracles of the Bible came to pass; truths fell from our
lips with such force that the roof caved in, the table danced on four legs,
and Elias streaked to heaven in a chariot of fire. The wasps' nest had
been broken into and the devil was to pay.

But often I had seen it otherwise, too: all the heroes in the drama aiming for each other's hearts and simultaneously finding their mark. Afterwards the scene would be littered with dead as in some tragic farce. By
this token may the older brother realize that he has uttered a truth: the
knife-thrust he receives in his own heart. The affair is so wild and confused that no one observes the knife in little brother's hand until after he
has struck.

No, never may I lay claim to having been a paragon of virtue. Mine
was no case of persecuted innocence, far from it. I am to such a degree
conscious of this that I may occasionally blacken myself *slightly* more
than necessary. I was not innocent. But innocence is something which is
taken from one, and who took mine from me? Gradually the whole thing
developed into such a state of seething frenzy, a tragedy played through
again and again, that at length I, for my own part, fled from the whole
business.

Yes, we have been extremely cruel to one another. But at home, where
misfortunes occurred, the time is past for forgiveness and atonement and
I do not suppose that they would do anyone any good. All that is a finished and closed saga, though some blood may still seep out from between the pages.

It is incredible that people have time for such things. Time? Time is
the barbaric crucible wherein we are tested to see whether we are human
beings or pack-horses. The many are but pack-horses and it is their will
that we shall all be beasts of burden: Maybe you think you are better
than *we?*

Translated by EUGENE GAY-TIFFT

Eyvind Berggrav

MAKKAUR

IT IS NOT so easy to find Makkaur on the map, but if you look exactly midway on the coast of Varanger peninsula I think you may see the name. It is an old fishing-ground, but is now best known for its light-house. I am not sure that the light is the most powerful in the North, but they say so at Makkaur. I readily believe, however, that it has saved many boats, for where Makkaur thrusts its nose out into the Arctic Ocean is a wicked spot.

One hundred and two people live there. They live by the sea alone and the sea is frequently difficult. There is neither beach nor harbor, nothing but crags and huge rocks. Weeks may pass when it is impossible either to land or to depart. The first time I was to have been in Makkaur, we were obliged to omit the call.

When you do land, you climb an iron ladder that is firmly attached to the perpendicular rock. It takes experience to manage it when there is a heavy sea, and it is impossible even for the most agile when the ocean is in an uproar. No ship can lie at anchor outside Makkaur.

Naturally, under such conditions, life may be difficult for almost any-one. I knew how poor the people were. But then all of a sudden I re-ceived a letter from the minister to whose parish Makkaur belonged: they wanted a church in Makkaur.

It was mean of me that I did not immediately become enthusiastic. But there were something like fifty-nine other places on the waiting list, at several of which the people had been collecting money for a long, long time. In fact some of them had been working at it for a generation. De-cidedly it was their turn to receive the small allowance which the Nord-land Church and School Fund could occasionally contribute. And here comes Makkaur with one hundred and two souls—people of small re-sources to put it mildly. But the minister supports the request. He writes: "At least they must have a schoolhouse." (I shall not repeat how he described the "quarters" they were renting for a school.) He thought therefore it might be best to cooperate by building the church and the school together. But they did not want what is usually resorted to in such cases—a school c'.apel in which the school-room is used for church too, with only foldin͜ doors that can be opened to reveal the choir and altar.

They wanted a room for the church by itself, but it could be under the same roof as the school. That's what they wanted in Makkaur.

An administrator is apt to figure coldly and quickly. It took me just one second to put down the plan as impossible. At the same time, that occasion when I had failed to land there had made a strong impression upon me, and something also remained in my mind from correspondence with people in the place. . . . "And the Bishop will be the first to acknowledge," wrote the minister, "that for those who have children to baptize or who wish to go to church, the landing conditions are difficult. And no one can expect that people in their circumstances can get a boat and go to the school chapel at Båtsfjord—which means rowing eleven kilometers up the open fjord and perhaps returning a week later."

That bit into me. But how about the money? We cannot let one hundred and two people go ahead of thousands in other places who have been working for decades. "Well," said the minister, "now they have gathered together 800 crowns. A women's society has been working for years. The school authorities will produce 3,000 crowns for a much needed school building. If we then could obtain from the Nordland Church and School Fund some 1,500 crowns, the people themselves would contribute another 700 crowns and then we should have 6,000 crowns in all, and for that we can build," wrote the minister.

At this point I awoke. Of all the building projects that I had helped to plan every year right up to this last one, this was the maximum estimate in the direction of a minimum budget. I should have rejected it at once as nonsense had not the minister himself been a carpenter. "We shall make it all right," he assured me. "We'll all help."

Now I shall not trace the development of the fairy tale, and still less shall I apportion the honors for the undertaking, but in part at least the honors belong to the minister. Without him I should have declared the whole thing impossible. The Governor of Finnmark became enthusiastic, and he will not be angry with me if I reveal that he and I exchanged poems at Christmas about Makkaur's projected cathedral. The whole business had put us in such a mood that prose was not enough.

In the summer of 1934 the minister reported that all was ready. Although he had eighty kilometers by sea in the open Arctic Ocean to go from Vardö to Makkaur, he had made the trip several times to look after things and to lend a hand. Now it was ready to be dedicated.

We sailed out of Vardö in a fishing smack. A fresh wind was prophesied. In the ears of a person addicted to seasickness, t e word "fresh" is anything but pleasant when used of the wind and sea I was prepared for the customary trials. But the wind soon calmed down and we coasted along the naked rocks of the shore in moderate weather, using a scant eight hours to Makkaur. Strange what different impressions the same thing can give you at different times. These mountain knolls, pale as the abode of Hel, can look so forbidding when one sees them from the sea in bad weather. Now, however, we passed near enough to discern houses and homes here and there in the inlets. We landed at Havningberg and had a meeting there with the people. As we stood in the pilot house, the commander of our boat told us many things about the place and the people. Everything came so close, grew so familiar. It was very different from passing on the steamer. Such is life always. One must come close before one can grow fond of anything.

In the evening we made a fine landing at Makkaur, climbing up the famous iron ladder. Next day the Governor, the superintendent of schools, the sheriff, the organist, the postmaster, and six or seven others were to come. They ran into bad weather—luckily, I had almost said!— but it was fun when they came and we met them at the ladder.

I was to stay at the house of the fisherman Bernhard Hansen. He was seventy years old and white-haired. The minister took me outside and showed me the property. Poor soil, I thought. "This is the only soil to be found in Makkaur," said the minister, "but it's not from around here." Mentally I made a double interrogation point—not from around here?? No, Makkaur is a rock-strewn slope leveled off with smaller stones sufficiently so that one may walk here and there. Old Hansen's father began to carry earth down from the bog on the mountain in his knapsack. Afterwards he and his wife rowed to Båtsfjord and fetched soil from there. They had to carry it up from the landing. Year after year they did this, a knapsack full now and a boatload then. At last it made pasture for a cow. But the big rocks—some of them like small houses—they could not cope with, so they covered them with sod. Now you can see that the grass grows there also. When the young people began to help, they soon had pasture for two cows. Now they could get milk. And the stone fence around this estate had to be moved farther out from time to time. Just think of it, two cows in Makkaur!

But the old wife, mother of the present Old Hansen, she did not stop when the stone fence was finished. After that Peroline—her name was really Peroline—began to go by herself and clear the stones outside of the fence. "This is where the church is to stand," she said. Of course she did not live to see it. Her son was now seventy years old. But she picked up stones on the church plot as long as she had the strength. I went around

first with the minister and later by myself. Never before had I seen soil
that "wasn't from around here." It made me think: what kind of people
are these? It seemed that they were bigger than those to which we
belonged.

The church and the schoolhouse were really built for little more than
6,000 crowns. The building was beautiful, though simple, with a fine turret and a genuine church profile. And all the people could be seated at
one time. At the dedication they say that one hundred and one were
present; the one absentee had a legitimate excuse for his absence. In
addition we had all the dignitaries—most welcome guests to the people
of Makkaur—from Vardö and Vadsö. But then there was not an inch of
floor space left. This was on September 11, 1934.

Everything I had seen, heard, and experienced since I landed had filled
me with an emotion that I can describe by no other words than humility
and reverence. I felt that there was no reason why I should come here for
a single day to enjoy the occasion, or that I should be the one to dedicate
all this which these people had created. I now learned that they had
slowly gathered öre after öre ever since Peroline had begun to pick up
stones. They all had a share in it, big and small. Even in the work of
building they had all lent a hand, man after man taking his turn. This
was really their own house of God, and they ought to dedicate it themselves. I omitted the procession of ministers to the altar to place upon it
the sacred vessels and the altar books. (After all the dedication of a
school chapel is not so strictly regulated by the ritual.) The people themselves were to dedicate this church.

My sermon was on the text which I had seen on the altar of the mother
church at Vardö: "It is finished." When I came to the point of mentioning the church and its contents, I first told its history from olden times
up till today. There had been churches in Makkaur before, the first in
Catholic times, and later a smaller one which was destroyed in an attack
by the Russians when Makkaur was still an important enough fishing
center so that there was something to plunder. But all that was ancient
history. Now we come to the memory of Peroline and the contribution
of the younger generation. I expressed the thanks of us all. "And now I
ask you, the white-haired son of Peroline, to go up to the altar with the
Word of Life and place the Bible on that ground which your mother's
labor and prayers cleared for God's house here in Makkaur."

The old man was sitting with the Bible in his lap. Now he stood up
and fumbled his way to the altar, up the two steps to the choir, and
through the choir to the altar. So reverently and carefully did he place

the Bible on the altar that we were all deeply moved. He stood there silently a few seconds as if he, like the rest of us, had difficulty in tearing himself away from that moment. The church was so still, so very still, during the old man's participation. But we must go on.

"And now I bid you, children of Makkaur, take the baptismal basin in which all the coming children of Makkaur will be christened and carry it up to the baptismal font."

Two ten-year-old girls walked up the aisle of the church with the basin between them, lifted it over the font, and set it down.

In the same way the minister of the parish walked up to the altar with the communion cup.

"Now we shall light the altar candles in Makkaur chapel. I ask you, Mr. Aasfjord, who as architect have watched and attended to the placing of every plank in this house, to step forward and light the altar candles for the first time."

His hands shook as he lifted the little flame up to the candle which came to life and grew silently. Then he went reverently outside the altar railing and we sat and watched him light the other candle. Two small flames held the eyes of all.

Later the Governor said, "That moment was almost too intense."

Yes, it was the realities that were brought home to us. It was that which lay behind it all. The life of generations, the people, the primitive force back of everything. It was the faithfulness and endurance in the midst of daily toil under which such as we would break, the courage and imagination which grow in stony soil. It was this that was "almost too intense."

Such a day is a strange experience for a government official. There we sat, we three who had worked so well and happily together in every way, the Governor, the superintendent of schools, and I; we who in a small way had been given the "authority" to allow this project to be commenced. And I think we all felt very humble. For here we met incarnate that which we officials served: the living spirit in the people, the indefinable realities on which our whole society rests. We had been allowed to be the tools and we had merely pushed aside some of the hindrances which might have prevented things from growing. Now we sat there and watched them grow.

Next came the baptism. When you remember that Makkaur has only one hundred and two inhabitants, you may think I am exaggerating when I tell you the number of children I baptized. There were thirteen. In other words more than twelve percent of the entire congregation were baptized at the dedication of the church. I set this record up and challenge all the bishops in the entire North to outdo it. The children were of all ages right up to the age of confirmation. Some of them I knew about from former correspondence with their parents at a time when we were trying to provide the small children with proper nourishment, and when an Oslo man helped me by sending some blessed casks of butter. Now the mother waited to hug me and express her thanks because the children were so well.

That night we saw, in the absolute darkness, the steamer heading towards Makkaur from the west. All the guests from Vardö and Vadsö were to get on board. First there was only a single light far away, then came the well-known triangular formation, the white top lantern and the two colored side lanterns. When we saw both the red and the green at the same time, old Hansen said, "Yes, she's coming here. The steamer is making an extra stop." There is very little light to be seen on a steamer that is coming head on. From the bridge forward all must be dimmed. But when *Finnmarken* swung around and hove to outside Makkaur there was a mass of stars, a multitude of lights, something quite dazzling against the black ocean. The big world passes by, and yet one is inclined to say, the little world and the big Makkaur.

Translated by HANNA ASTRUP-LARSEN
and EDWARD O. THORPE

Arnulf Överland

WE SHALL SURVIVE

WE HAD no sword for strife,
We put our faith in kindness,
In toil, respect for life,
Unconscious of our blindness.
We did not think the destiny
Of any land could rightfully
Be built on blood and iron
And ruthless perfidy.

And so our breast was bared.
We had no sense of peril,
Because we had no quarrel.
They caught us unprepared

They came one night, and with the dawn
We woke and found our land was gone.
Our friends, our sole reliance,
Had left us there alone.

In scattered bands a few
Fought on in distant regions
Against uncounted legions
Till they were vanquished too.
Each farm boy, Norseland bred,
Who grimly fought and bled,
Knew if his will was broken
He might as well be dead.

Free have we always been.
The fetters of the foeman
May bind our limbs, but no man
Can chain the soul within.
Oppressor's ordered might
Can not change wrong to right,
Or slinking spies persuade us
That black is the same as white.

We'll not endure this yoke.
'Tis times of stress that teach us.
They shall not over-reach us.
We'll re-unite, our folk.
In town and village, on isle and shore
We're all friends and neighbors, rich or poor,
And we all shake hands together:
We soon shall meet once more.

Though some are fallen, and others
Must follow ere the end,
We've strength that will not bend:
We shall survive, my brothers.
A holy faith in victory
Gives patience for the years to be.
In heart and soul united,
We know we must be free.

Translated by CHARLES WHARTON STORK

SWEDEN

INTRODUCTION

By Eugénie Söderberg

WHEN THE authors of the "crisis-time" generation—which is the common name for Sweden's post-war generation—grew up, the influence of Strindberg was still very strong. The honesty evinced in his work, his rebellious spirit and democratic views of society and its problems, his strong "naturalism," were widely admired and appreciated only after his death. Time caught up with his pioneering work, for which he had suffered all his life.

The writers of the "crisis-time" generation still had in their midst Hjalmar Söderberg, as a master of style and prose, still writing realistic novels on contemporary society, still leading as the artistic conscience of Swedish letters. He also cleared the way to honest and unhypocritical writing; he taught readers to require of authors that they be courageous intellectual leaders of their time. He fought for the freedom of the artist to tell his true conviction in spite of conservative and reactionary forces in society.

Selma Lagerlöf, although admired and loved, never had any influence on Swedish literature, and remains as a great, individual talent.

A large proportion of the prominent and outstanding men of today's generation—men to whom the public listens, and who have something to say—began as proletarian authors. During the post-war years, Sweden recruited much intellectual ability from ranks out of which, in earlier times, such talent had emerged only sporadically. This is the result of the great movement for popular education, organized on a large scale. Through this movement for the higher education of the common people, a reservoir of talent was discovered. Every one of the writers coming from this group started out with elementary school as his only formal education. Many of them have written autobiographies, and each one has pointed out how much he had to study to overcome his handicap, to achieve his goal, writing, and to be accepted as the voice of the people, as a serious writer—in short, to take his place in Swedish literature. It is a moving and sometimes pathetic story of a generation that found itself faced with the serious problem of the leveling-off of society after the first World War. That generation was given a chance to overcome a grave handicap—and it did not fail. These writers are the sons and daughters of workers, crofters, peasants and small craftsmen. They know Sweden—the country and its people—from the inside, and they lend to their evaluation a new and fresh background. Their tales were strange and unusual, they introduced new types of heroes, new milieux and fresh ideas—giving Swedish literature a new vitality and spontaneity.

Harry Martinson, the gifted poet and inspired writer, became an author after years as a laborer, sailor and stoker; Vilhelm Moberg, the leading peasant author, was a farm, mill and lumber worker; Eyvind Johnson, a factory hand and worker at different odd jobs; Moa Martinson, a product of the poorest working and farming class.

These authors of the newest generation follow the great tradition of analyzing society, when writing psychological or historical novels or memoirs. In so doing, they underline the problems of the time or milieu depicted. The primitive power of their creative talent and the maturity of their convictions have penetrated deep into intellectual circles. There was never a serious gap between the proletarian authors and those of the same generation who came from the upper, academic or middle classes. The latter groups, also products of the same democratic movement, accepted them with great enthusiasm and joined with them in looking for new ways to solve the problems of the individual as well as those of society. Children of well-to-do families, people with academic education, did their share in analyzing and exposing the different aspects of contemporary life, especially that of the cities. Agnes von Krusenstjerna, Olle Hedberg and Gösta Gustaf-Janson are severe critics of the life bounded by conventions that strangles individuality and kills the soul and sensitivity of a human being. Talented poets like Karin Boye, Hjalmar Gullberg, Eric Blomberg or Nils Ferlin do not write l'art-pour-l'art poetry. It is very timely and awake and deals with contemporary events and ideas. Even a highly individualistic author such as Pär Lagerkvist, whose works are influenced by his philosophical views and are replete with symbols and allegories, has a strong social stand, which forces the author to express his convictions in ardent anti-Nazi poems and plays.

More than ever, the recognized authors from all groups are the real intellectual leaders and the heartbeat of the people of today. Literary production has increased enormously during the last twenty years, and this fact may be attributed to the previously-described educational movement. It has created an army of new, serious readers from all groups. Authors who in their writings do not stand for democratic ideas and ideals are rejected by the critics and reading public, even if their style of writing is good.

Modern Swedish writers have done much to analyze our times. Together with their aim to write truthfully about the average life of a cross-section of Swedish society, the best will leave after them work of great value—not only as literature but as surveys and documents of our generation, rich in ideas and events.

Pär Lagerkvist

FATHER AND I

I REMEMBER one Sunday afternoon when I was about ten years old, Daddy took my hand and we went for a walk in the woods to hear the birds sing. We waved good-bye to mother, who was staying at home to prepare supper, and so couldn't go with us. The sun was bright and warm as we set out briskly on our way. We didn't take this bird-singing too seriously, as though it was something special or unusual. We were sensible people, Daddy and I. We were used to the woods and the creatures in them, so we didn't make any fuss about it. It was just because it was Sunday afternoon and Daddy was free. We went along the railway line where other people aren't allowed to go, but Daddy belonged to the railway and had a right to. And in this way we came direct into the woods and did not need to take a round-about way. Then the bird song and all the rest began at once. They chirped in the bushes; hedge-sparrows, thrushes, and warblers; and we heard all the noises of the little creatures as we came into the woods. The ground was thick with anemones, the birches were dressed in their new leaves, and the pines had young green shoots. There was such a pleasant smell everywhere. The mossy ground was steaming a little, because the sun was shining upon it. Everywhere there was life and noise; bumble-bees flew out of their holes, midgets circled where it was damp. The birds shot out of the bushes to catch them and then dived back again. All of a sudden a train came rushing along and we had to go down the embankment. Daddy hailed the driver with two fingers to his Sunday hat: the driver saluted and waved his hand. Everything seemed on the move. As we went on our way along the sleepers which lay and oozed tar in the sunshine, there was a smell of everything, machine oil and almond blossom, tar and heather, all mixed. We took big steps from sleeper to sleeper so as not to step among the stones, which were rough to walk on, and wore your shoes out. The rails shone in the sunshine. On both sides of the line stood the telephone poles that sang as we went by them. Yes! That was a fine day! The sky was absolutely clear. There wasn't a single cloud to be seen: there just couldn't be any on a day like this, according to what Daddy said. After a while we came to a field of oats on the right side of the line, where a farmer, whom we knew, had a clearing. The oats had grown thick and even; Daddy looked at it knowingly, and I could feel that he was satisfied. I didn't understand that sort of thing much, because I was born in town. Then we came to the bridge over the brook that mostly hadn't much water in it, but now there was plenty. We took hands so that we shouldn't fall down between the sleepers. From there it wasn't far to the railway gate-keeper's little place, which was quite buried in green. There were apple trees and gooseberry bushes right close to the house. We went in there, to pay a visit, and they offered us milk. We looked at the pigs, the hens, and the fruit trees, which were in full blossom, and then we went on again. We wanted to go to the river, because there it was prettier than anywhere else. There was something special about the river, because higher up stream it flowed past Daddy's old home. We never liked going back before we got to it, and, as usual, this time we got there after a fair walk. It wasn't far to the next station, but we didn't go on there. Daddy just looked to see whether the signals were right. He thought of everything. We stopped by the river, where it flowed broad and friendly in the sunshine, and the thick leafy trees on the banks mirrored themselves in the calm water. It was all so fresh and bright. A breeze came from the little lakes higher up. We climbed down the bank, went a little way along the very edge; Daddy showed me the fishing spots. When he was a boy he used to sit there on the stones and wait for perch all day long. Often he didn't get a single bite, but it was a delightful way to spend the day. Now he never had time. We played about for some time by the side of the river, and threw in pieces of bark that the current carried away, and we threw stones to see who could throw farthest. We were, by nature, very merry and cheerful, Daddy and I. After a while we felt a bit tired. We thought we had played enough, so we started off home again.

Then it began to get dark. The woods were changed. It wasn't quite dark yet, but almost. We made haste. Maybe mother was getting anxious, and waiting supper. She was always afraid that something might happen, though nothing had. This had been a splendid day. Everything had been just as it should, and we were satisfied with it all. It was getting darker and darker, and the trees were so queer. They stood and listened for the sound of our footsteps, as though they didn't know who we were. There was a glow-worm under one of them. It lay down there in the dark and stared at us. I held Daddy's hand tight, but he didn't seem to notice the strange light: he just went on. It was quite dark when we came to the bridge over the stream. It was roaring down underneath us as if it wanted to swallow us up, as the ground seemed to open under us. We went along the sleepers carefully, holding hands tight so that we shouldn't fall in. In

HEART OF EUROPE: *Sweden*

thought Daddy would carry me over, but he didn't say anything about it.
I suppose he wanted me to be like him, and not think anything of it. We
went on. Daddy was so calm in the darkness, walking with even steps
without speaking. He was thinking his own thoughts. I couldn't understand how he could be so calm when everything was so ghostly. I looked
round scared. It was nothing but darkness everywhere. I hardly dared to
breathe deeply, because then the darkness comes into one, and that was
dangerous, I thought. One must die soon. I remember quite well thinking
so then. The railway embankment was very steep. It finished in black
night. The telephone posts stood up ghostlike against the sky, mumbling deep inside as though someone were speaking, way down in the
earth. The white china hats sat there scared, cowering with fear, listening. It was all so creepy. Nothing was real, nothing was natural, all
seemed a mystery. I went closer to Daddy, and whispered:

'Why is it so creepy when it's dark?'

'No child, it isn't creepy,' he said, and took my hand.

'Oh, yes, but it is, Daddy.'

'No, you mustn't think that. We know there is a God, don't we?'

I felt so lonely, so abandoned. It was queer that it was only me that
was frightened, and not Daddy. It was queer that we didn't feel the same
about it. And it was queerer still that what he said didn't help, didn't stop
me being frightened. Not even what he said about God helped. The
thought of God made one feel creepy too. It was creepy to think that He
was everywhere here in the darkness, down there under the trees, and in
the telephone posts that mumbled so—probably that was Him everywhere. But all the same one could never see Him.

We went along silently, each of us thinking his own thoughts. My
heart felt cramped as though the darkness had come in and was squeez-

Then, when we were in a bend, we suddenly heard a great noise behind us. We were startled out of our thoughts. Daddy pulled me down
the embankment and held me tight, and a train rushed by; a black train.
The lights were out in all the carriages, as it whizzed past us. What could
it be? There shouldn't be any train now. We looked at it, frightened. The
furnace roared in the big engine, where they shovelled in coal, and the
sparks flew out into the night. It was terrible. The driver stood so pale
and immovable, with such a stony look in the glare. Daddy didn't recognize him—didn't know who he was. He was just looking ahead as though
he was driving straight into darkness, far into darkness, which had no

Startled and panting with fear I looked after the wild thing. It was swallowed up in the night. Daddy helped me up on to the line, and we hurried home. He said, 'That was strange! What train was that I wonder? And I didn't know the driver either.' Then he didn't say any more.

I was shaking all over. That had been for me—for my sake. I guessed what it meant. It was all the fear which would come to me, all the unknown; all that Daddy didn't know about, and couldn't save me from. That was how the world would be for me, and the strange life I should live; not like Daddy's, where everyone was known and sure. It wasn't a real world, or a real life;—it just rushed burning into the darkness which had no end.

Translated by M. EKENBERG

Harry Martinson

CALABOZA

IN CHILE, Peru, Bolivia, Ecuador and Colombia the lock-ups are really prisons, and are called "calabozas." Earthquakes give the authorities an excuse for not building central jails which would collapse, they think, when the volcano Illimani starts rumbling. Thus it is that the calaboose is as common along the Andes as mushrooms in Holaveden.

The calaboose is dreaded. Nowhere in the world except in China and Abyssinia are such squalid jails to be found. Calabooses are stinking holes devoid of ventilation, and usually without even chinks for air. In certain parts of Peru the stocks are still used, and twelve or fourteen prisoners may sometimes have to sit with their feet under the same beam.

One of the smelliest nights of my life was spent in the calaboose at Tal-Tal, Chile. When the police had shut the cell door upon me I sat soberly meditating in pitch darkness all night. They'd arrested me for drunkenness. Actually I'd had a bottle of soda-water, all told.

So there I sat in the close, musty darkness, making guesses as to what they would do with the eighty-five pesos which had been taken from me by means of whipcuts across the nose.

In the night-stillness my nose felt hot: it swelled, ourned, and I raged. I sat furiously on the same patch of floor all night, waiting for the moment when I should be considered sober once more. The cell had no chinks, and in the stench the night crept on with infinite slowness. After eternities of resentment and indignation the morning came. As I have learnt to expect almost anything of people I was not particularly surprised when the calaboza authorities kept eighty-four pesos and gave me back one, assuring me that that was all I'd had with me. I knew very well that robbers sit in the offices of Chilean lock-ups while the cell-floors groan under the weight of the harmless.

The surprise I had was of quite another sort. When the opening cell-door let in twenty-four cubic feet of morning light, there sat a young Indian girl shivering on a bench in the corner. I'd sat sulkily on one spot in the pitch darkness, uttering every manner of Scandinavian curse, and she, taking me for a rough, drunken fellow, had kept breathlessly quiet all night. Now there she was in thin cotton clothes washed threadbare, the flowered pattern bleached out of them by corrosive Peruvian soft-soap. For, as I learned later, she was from Peru; a little straw-hat-maker who had had the notion of going to Santiago to look for a post as servant. This she had been unable to find, as she had let her complexion darken under the Peruvian sun and this is not considered refined by the gentry of Santiago. They're a snobbish rabble: their fat women vibrate with fire and passion, but not even continual child-bearing can rob them of their pride—and their fertility is great. The balconies and verandas which face the snowy caps of the Andes bend and give like the forecastles of old Spanish galleons, under their offspring. The Indian girl had to take to begging and vagabondage.

Now vagabondage in itself is anything but tragic, but intolerance in Chile is practised like a black art and eats into the poor as the inland plains of saltpeter ate into the soles of the Indian girl's roving feet. She had no shoes and her feet were bleeding; from every door she was turned away. She didn't sit down and weep for days on end like some kind of Hiawatha, but, when hunger set in, she began to steal little things here and there. From henhouses she skillfully removed the eggs, and from a veranda which in the early morning widens its gaze towards a distant snowy volcano she stole a pair of paragattas for her wounded feet.

She went on like this, comparatively reconciled to the new way of living, until custom made her a little careless. Her cotton clothes, of course, she washed frequently and carefully in the mountain streams. Now and then she caught a tortoise of which she made soup in a tin she had with her. But one morning early as she was about to wring a chicken's neck, she bungled it and the bird screeched. That was why she was now here in the Tal-Tal calaboose.

When the cell-door opened, a broad stream of sunlight fell on her body like a gold curtain; there she sat, dry-eyed as Indians are, cold and miserable. I was amazed. Not six feet from her had I sat in my rage, jabbering curses. I stood now like the terracotta figure of a sailor, with fire in my cheeks and my head so full of darting thoughts and impressions that it ached. She sat in the sudden sunlight plaiting her hair, and plainly not giving a damn for me either way.

Once out I asked for a little information.

"A Peruvian tramp," the greasy head-robber told me. "She pinched a laying hen at Buena Vista de la Tarde."

I stood patiently listening as he dully and wheezily told me as much about her as he could.

"Can she be bailed out?" I asked. "I and the other marineros have money on board."

The fat face gleamed knowingly, but coldly as the moon.

"Si, señor-possiblo, possiblo."

I wished his mustache could catch fire, but said only, "Quanta costa?" We agreed on a hundred pesos. Contentedly he lit a little cigar.

"Good luck," he murmured, smiling. "Go and fetch it."

I went, crushing his memory between my teeth.

In the evening we freed the girl, who would otherwise have acted mattress to the warders, for that is the fate of women in the calaboose. And the mighty Andes look on, remotely and without pity.

We bought her a cotton dress and a good straw hat as broad as a small café table; also new paragattas, a pair of stockings of yellow artificial silk and a railway ticket via Antofagasta to Uyuni, her native place in Peru. We agreed among ourselves not to make any demands on her but to treat her as if we were mission friends: with all honor.

Ah, how happy she was, standing in the train when we waved good-by to her! She had seventy-five pesos in her purse when all was paid for, and with that she could convince the people in Uyuni that she had anyhow earned something in Santiago. We suggested this to her and she nodded and smiled very slyly, in quiet bliss. Then she was borne away, waving like mad; she was crying for joy and nearly fell out of the train as it wormed itself into a cutting.

"So long, little hat-girl," we had said to her in broken Spanish. "As you've found out, the world's a damned difficult place. You have to look out for yourself among the scheming foxes and vegetating worms that over-populate it." This is what we'd said to her in signs and bits of Spanish before the train went. Afterwards we plunged into Tal-Tal's

simple underworld of wine and bought love; but the evening seemed
empty after the girl, to our great content and happiness, had left for her
Uyuni, on the topmost ledges of the Andes.

True, we each slept with a girl, but calmly and indifferently as though
we'd been married twenty years, and the whole house wondered.

The next day was Sunday, but we went on board early. Near the
beach a few hens pecked for grass-seed and worms among water-worn
blocks of lava. They cackled irritatingly. Suddenly we were all seized
with the same idea, surrounded them, wrung the necks of the whole lot
and threw them into the water. The calm sea rose and fell because of
them in and out of the stones: dull hens of cynical Chile.

For it was through a hen that she had fallen among thieves—the girl
in Uyuni who remained in our hearts as a symbol.

While washing oneself one either goes through one's memories or looks
into the future. I wonder what she's doing now, that girl in Uyuni. If she
sitting doubled-up in the sun in front of the straw-hat shed, making hats
for export to the greedy mobs of North America? Probably, for the
world is like that. Don't tell me that everything comes right in the end.
It doesn't. Through sitting doubled-up she will get catarrh and become
as hump-backed and wizened as an old woman.

Many many millions of people are good and open-hearted, but I know
well enough what the rest are like—what most are like. They are the
evilest of the evil.

This is good soap. It lathers well. And out there a stormy sea is lather-
ing too, with salt and jelly-fish and phosphorus. I step forward naked and
soapy to the wash-room ventilator, and watch the highest coast-line in
the world vanish in cloud and ice-blue snowy space.

A few sea-pelicans which have been breeding on the Chinca Islands
fly heavily landward, to disappear gradually against the vast mantle
which tonight covers the Chilean Andes.

Translated by NAOMI WALFORD

Vilhelm Moberg

THE MIND READER OF TIVOLI

THE THRONG of visitors is increasing here every evening. It's spring, to be
sure, and people recall where Tivoli is. When anyone feels the need of a
little outlet for his youthful urge of frivolity, he goes to Tivoli. People

dance, break china, throw darts, ride on the merry-go-round, go to the dwarfs' theater, listen to the concerts of the harmonica king. There are certainly many amusements to pick from—Tivoli has combined theater, variety show, circus, concert hall, and country fair into a sort of unity. The public may choose between the various parts of the unity.

And now and then one of the Tivoli visitors chooses me. I am not one of the chief attractions of the resort. I am a mind reader and character interpreter; I represent the psychic phase of Tivoli, so to speak. My studio lies somewhat in shadow, between the big scenic railway and the huge merry-go-round. In front of it stands a sign:

URBAN BRUZELLI

MIND READING AND CHARACTER

INTERPRETATION

Originally my name was Brusén, but when I came to Tivoli I considered it necessary to give the name a more international turn. To win the confidence of the Swedish public my name had to convey a not too Swedish implication. Bruzelli—that gave the air of distant countries and foreign reputation which I required. And in addition I began to use a Christian name I had never had before. Kalle Brusén became Urban Bruzelli. I was a mind reader and character interpreter.

So now I have been reading minds and interpreting characters for some thirty years. When a man has started on a certain line, it is truly difficult to get away from it; after a while he gets rooted in it. Otherwise I might just as well have been a clerk or a policeman or a waiter. But as it is, I have become a mind reader and have kept on with it as a matter of habit. A friend of mine, who is a newspaper man, gives himself the title of perennial psychologist—for my part I am a perennial mind reader.

Of course, too, from the beginning I had a certain aptitude for the profession. In my youth, when I was playing parlor games with other young people and we made experiments in thought transference, it came out that I had certain qualities which the others lacked. I was sensitive, I was "magnetic," as they call it. If all the people in a room concentrated their thoughts on a certain object there, while I was outside, I could come in and go blindfold straight to the object. The thoughts of the others forced me toward it. So I naturally have a certain faculty for this work. Moreover, it is not as difficult as people imagine. I've had some theoretic training besides; that one has to get. I've read a whole lot of

,psychic books, so that I know their terminology. I know about the
processes of personal magnetism, which conveys thoughts between various
individuals by the same laws that govern electricity.

But beyond that the only important thing is practical experience. In
many years of activity as mind reader and character interpreter one gets
to know a whole lot about people. To see into their souls is not so essential; even if I possessed such a supernatural power, I should hardly have
occasion to use it. I have the physical side to go by. I have people's appearance and clothes and expression and behavior. I observe and take
account of them, one thing with another. There are perhaps fifty per cent
of mistakes, but in fifty per cent of the cases I am right. And that is sufficient to sustain my reputation.

What more can one ask for a krona? A krona is my price, and for such
a small outlay one can hardly be over-particular. And in the cases of
mind reading where I have obviously been wrong I announce that I am
willing to forego my fee. I merely say to the lady (or gentleman, whichever it may be): "We have the same polarity, you and I. Therefore we
are unable to make the right contact. You know how it is with electricity.
So I can't read your thoughts, because we have the same polarity. Accordingly the consultation will cost you nothing." That's what I tell them, but
it's only in exceptional cases that I fail to get my krona. The visitor feels
himself morally obliged to pay my fee. It's a good thing that people still
recognize their moral duties.

As to character interpretation, I am never forced to admit that I
have made a mistake. If the consultant protests, I simply answer that
no one can judge of his own character. But ordinarily no one does protest. I take pains to satisfy my clients. I have the elementary rule: my
interpretation must be flattering. It mustn't be crude and unmitigated
soft sawder. It should be dropped into their ears gently and cautiously
and imperceptibly. Then the recipients will believe it. And when they
pay me my fee they will think they have got full value for their money.

A man, therefore, must above all be told that he has a virile nature,
and a woman must be convinced that she has a truly feminine disposition. Beyond that one must put in certain variations. In thirty years of
practice as a character interpreter one learns how to improvise.

But it is quite a strange thing that I should have chosen this unusual
profession. I once had a good fixed position in one of our government
offices. I was an exemplary public servant with a way of life that was
far from any suggestion of charlatanry. I was married, I was in all respects a model citizen and member of the community. I was deeply and

irrevocably devoted to my wife—and therefrom was engendered the seed of my tragedy. My wife is the indirect cause of my becoming Urban Bruzelli, the mind reader of Tivoli.

People may chance to fall in love with each other simultaneously, and that is well and good. But it may also be that their love does not break off simultaneously, and that is not well and good. It is simply the grimmest of tragedies. This was the tragedy that overtook me some thirty years ago.

My wife ceased to love me, while my feeling for her was still as ardent, and vital as ever. She had met another man and given him all she had previously bestowed on me. She was unfaithful to me secretly for a year; after that she was unfaithful openly. I loved her so that I submitted to the humiliation of sharing her body with the other man. But I was in torment and betook myself to alcohol for relief. After I had come home drunk several times, my wife was able to get a divorce on the ground that I was an inebriate. She went to the other man, and I was alone.

For a long time I planned to kill the thief who had taken her from me. I knew him; we had met in society, where he treated me with a good-humored condescension that was more bitter than death. I meant to annihilate him from the world of the living. I never did so. I am wont to justify myself to my own conscience with the explanation that I failed because my rival took my wife with him and lived abroad for a while. I was alone and deserted—nothing in life seemed worth living for any more. I was no longer the model official with an assured income and an unexceptionable circle of friends. I drank; I lost my position; I lost my friends, my social prestige, my home. So at last I came to Tivoli, and here I have been for thirty years, reading minds and interpreting characters.

I became Urban Bruzelli. And, as I said before, this course of life is by no means as difficult as one might suppose. In reality I merely go through a formal process when I read people's thoughts. With most human beings there are scarcely any thoughts to read. For ordinary purposes we mortals have little need to think, as some famous authority— Schopenhauer, I believe—has said. And ordinarily I read people's thoughts with sufficient thoroughness to get a krona for my pains. On that I live, for a man must earn his bread somehow or other. So there is no special mystery connected with my peculiar profession. The whole thing is really quite simple.

✧   ✧   ✧

More and more people are coming to Tivoli every evening, as the spring advances. The buds on the trees of the park seem actually to foam up, they expand so suddenly, and there is a sort of dizziness in the air. It is now especially the young folk who come out to Tivoli—their elders do not come till further on toward summer. Youth holds almost exclusively to the dancing floor and the merry-go-round. I, who represent the psychic department, am left to one side. It is only as people get older that the majority begin to take any interest in their souls.

This evening I have had only two or three customers. That is no return for a day's business. There will hardly be anything left when I have had my usual grog and pickled pork nearby here. This trade is uncertain.

But here comes a young couple. The girl reads my sign eagerly; she turns and speaks to the young man beside her. Then they both come in.

The girl has glowing red cheeks; her coloring is a delicate pink. The young man is a trifle embarrassed, as though he were ashamed of the affair.

"What's it cost to have your character interpreted?"

"A krona. Will you sit down?"

"It's the young lady here. . . ."

This case is very simple and offers me no difficulties. I have a clear opportunity to record a triumph. A young couple preoccupied with their love for each other. The young girl asks to know what her character is with the wish of being revealed to the man she loves. Such a case is a pleasure for an experienced character interpreter to deal with.

Accordingly I take the young girl's hand and hold it a few moments. She may now hear what secrets are lying hid in her soul:

She is of a diffident and retiring nature. She is not prone to giving confidences, nor does she open her soul to every chance acquaintance. But she has the power to feel; she is gifted with deep, warm, and sincere emotions. Womanliness is the dominant quality in her temperament (that is something which must never be forgotten), and it follows therefore that she is born to make a man happy. She needs an object for her abounding tenderness, and the masculine object of this will be a truly enviable person.

Here I have to give a glance toward the young man, but he is looking away in greater embarrassment than ever. The radiance in the young girl's eyes grows deeper.

"You are also extremely constant," I add. "Any sort of fickleness is foreign to you. But, on the other hand, you are very exacting. You will make great demands on the man to whom you give your faith. You expect as much as you give. The object of your affection should keep this in mind."

The girl becomes increasingly serious. The young man now whispers something to her. Then he asks what the whole seance costs, I repeat my figure, and they are gone. In my hand I hold a two-krona note—oh, of course I got two kronor instead of one. A young pair, absorbed in their love, are the most ideal customers an old mind reader can have.

Yonder comes a new pair, an older couple. It is assuredly the man, not the woman, who is proposing a visit to me. When they come in, I see at once that they don't belong to the class which asks beforehand what the consultation will be. Whether I get one krona or five means nothing to them. Their dress and behavior inform me that they belong to the prosperous part of the community. Self-assurance and arrogance are the outstanding qualities of the man; I know already how he is accustomed to be treated in his circle. Around his lips he has the irritating smile which I sometimes see among my visitors. This smile says to me: I know you are a fraud and an impostor. But it may be amusing to study your style of trickery. I am much too well educated and informed to look for anything serious in your arts, but you may give me a bit of a sensation. I can tell a little story of my visit to the mind reader at the next dinner I give my friends. The man's smile tells me—that he is one of the customers I should like to throw out of my room. If only I didn't need their kronor.

The woman stands a couple of paces away from him. The man has taken the notion of going to the mind reader, and she has merely consented to his whim and come with him. She seems quite indifferent as I begin my exposition of the man's character.

"Shall I go?" she asks him.

"Stay here," he says with the tone of one used to being obeyed. "You may as well listen. I'm not afraid of any disclosures."

He laughs as though at a particularly good joke. But I am not listening to him any more. For I have heard the woman over there speaking. There was something very remarkable in her voice. "Shall I go?" she said. The words came to my ears like the echo of some bell I was used to as a child. *I have heard that voice before.* I have heard it by night and by day. It has been near me; I have been intoxicated by it, enraptured by it—and finally tortured by it.

I scan the woman more closely. Not that I need to, for I know who she is. My ears are already convinced, and now, as a matter of impartiality, my eyes wish to be convinced as well. Yes, it is she. Her voice is that of a middle-aged woman, but I recognized it none the less. It has a touch of sharpness. But I recognized it. The voice of a woman one has loved can never be forgotten.

Yes, she has aged decidedly. Of course not as much as I, but I have presumably lived a harder life than she has. I perceive that she hasn't recognized me. I might mention that my retreat in Tivoli is none too well lighted just now. It is dusk, and I ought to light up. But I put it off. Better for her not to recognize me.

The man repeats that under no circumstances does he fear the revelations of a character interpreter. I keep quiet a couple of minutes; I give myself to my own thoughts and pay no attention to him. And now I know what I shall do.

In this consultation I have no need to overstrain myself. I know everything about this man. I know his social position, his way of life, his interests. I have not, indeed, seen him for thirty years, and he has traveled abroad extensively, but I have followed him and never really lost sight of him.

I begin in my regular professional manner:

"You have a conspicuous place in the community. You are the head of a large business. You have an innate ability to command, to give orders, anl you are a man who knows how to make himself obeyed. Your subordinates have great respect for you. They look up to you as to a fine and lofty model. They try to fulfil your wishes, because—well, above all, because they are afraid of you."

He listens, at first with an expression of scepticism in his eyes. A trace of the irritating smile is still on his lips. But when I have uttered several pronouncements, the cast of his features alters. He listens differently. His eyes register surprise and wonder.

I continue:

"You enjoy great public confidence. You have also many friends, but most of these you have made dependent upon you, so that you can hardly call them your friends. You are completely absorbed in your work and in the exercise of the duties which the confidence of the public entails on you, so that you have little time left for domestic life. But you married thirty years ago and this marriage still continues. The woman who then became your wife was previously married to another man."

I observe a slight motion in the woman yonder but give no sign. I keep my gaze keenly fixed on the man, as though I were reading all I tell him in his eyes. At this moment I have a real claim to the title of mind reader.

I know what the other man thinks: I should never have believed this. The fellow really knows his stuff.

The irritating smile is gone completely. Never before in these thirty years have I so enjoyed the practice of my calling.

But I feel the woman's glance directed upon me and now I know: She has recognized me. It is my former wife who stands there looking at me. I do not meet her glance. I continue to interpret her husband's character. And now I find myself at a point where I am on firm ground.

I resume:

"You are a strong man. You never give up anything you have undertaken. But there is a deep vein of ruthlessness in your character." (I can dispense with flattery now, surely.) "Many times in your life you have attained your object through this very lack of consideration for others. An example of this is in the events before your marriage. I should like to dwell a moment upon these events, because they are very illuminating as to your character."

The man's mouth opens wider and wider. He seems desirous of saying something, but I anticipate him:

"You had relations with your present wife while she was still living with her former husband. You did not consider it necessary to inform him that you had stolen his wife. You never told him of that. This man was weak, because he adored his wife. In collusion with her, you took advantage of his weakness. When he began to seek consolation in drink, you attacked him. You found a legal pretext for taking his wife from him. Neither she nor you ever asked what had become of him—whether he went to pieces or not. You had what you were after; that was enough for you."

The man's mouth has opened still wider; now he's fairly gaping at me. The woman utters a low, inarticulate sound. But I haven't quite finished my characterization:

"A temperament such as yours is destined to succeed in this present life. Callousness is in many instances a prerequisite to success. You cannot feel; you are absolutely incapable of feeling. Therefore you have never loved your wife. She has never experienced anything from you but coldness. Your marriage has thus for many years been unhappy. Your wife has bitterly rued that she let herself be enticed into your arms and left the man who was truly devoted to her. . . ."

A little cry bursts from the woman. I wondered whether it would come, that cry—and it came. It tells me that the last words I spoke were true.

They were nothing more than an inference, but a character interpreter must often trust to pure inferences. Fifty per cent may be wrong—but fifty per cent remains as correctly drawn. This time I have struck the mark—that I gather from the cry of the woman who was once my wife and my beloved.

A minute later the two are gone. I hardly noticed when it was they went. The man looked as if he had suddenly found he was in a burning house and had to get out as fast as he could. And the woman tottered after him. But her cry was enough for me—it told me all I needed to know about her life since our separation.

*   *   *

Yes, I've been a genuine mind reader and character interpreter now for once. As you've heard, my profession may be an extremely easy one to practise sometimes. There is no mystery at all connected with it. The whole thing is really quite simple.

But that couple who were here last forgot to pay me my fee. This annoys me greatly, for I truly need all the kronor I can earn on such a bad evening in Tivoli as this has been.

Translated by CHARLES WHARTON STORK

FINLAND

INTRODUCTION

By Eugénie Söderberg

THE STANDING JOKE about contemporary Finnish literature is: "If it continues in like fashion, there soon won't be a single Finn who has not been described in some literary work." This is, of course, exaggerated, even for such a small population which numbers but some three and one-half millions; but it is true in so far as it indicates the degree of Finnish cultural life and the great number of writers of various kinds. There is a complete absence of illiteracy—the country supports over eight hundred newspapers and periodicals.

The country has two languages—Finnish and Swedish. The latter is spoken by ten per cent of the population. Swedish-language authors have, in spite of this, a greater audience because, if they are good, they receive immediate encouragement from readers and critics in Sweden. Finnish-language authors write for the home market and must wait until their works are translated before they are known outside the limited number of readers in their own small country.

Intellectual life in Finland has always been influenced by two of its neighboring countries: Sweden with six hundred and fifty years, and Russia with one hundred years, of political domination. Finland's acquaintance with both of these countries had the result that her cultural circles were always up to date on all their literary trends. Finnish authors, as writers of a country under a foreign yoke, have tried in nationalistic manner to save and develop her own rich culture. For the same reason, these authors were very progressive and tried to widen the outlook of their people, fighting for democracy as the only means of becoming a free nation. Most contemporary Finnish authors are trying to keep this tradition alive, in spite of current political events.

More than sixty per cent of the population of Finland are peasants, and the greater part of the rest, fishermen or workers in the forests. Finnish peasants are best described as characters in Finnish literature. The greatest masters of the last generation, Juhani Aho and Frans Eemil Sillanpää write of them. Aho has also written psychological novels dealing with the problems of his time; admired for their true and deep character delineations, these novels have a good-natured humor that enlivens the dramatic incidents in the lives of the plain but violent and passionate heroes. Aho's descriptions of nature are wonderful examples of poetic prose.

Frans Eemil Sillanpää, the Nobel prize-winner for 1939, has achieved international fame. His literary work shows great versatility. Every idea is supple clay out of which he fashions a masterpiece. Each of his great novels is written in a different mood, but with the same power—strongly colored by his own personality. Poetry and sober realism alternate in his work. If he sometimes tames the realist in him, he never does so with the poet.

Among the Swedish-language writers is Jarl Hemmer, who is the most widely read of poets and novelists. As a poet, he is possessed by a romantic longing for genuineness and for purity of soul and mind. The same ideals of truth, morality and tolerance are apparent in his psychological novels.

A writer to whom fame came overnight is Sally Salminen. Her renown dates from the time she wrote her prize-winning first novel *Katrina*. Aland, her native island, supplies her with plot and character. In her other work, she shows the same sureness, and her literary style remains as uncomplicated as it was in *Katrina*.

Hagar Olsson is one of the advance-guard group of writers belonging to the Helsingfors intelligentsia. She has written short stories, plays and novels with a modern trend, dealing with, among other subjects, contemporary erotic problems.

All the modern currents in literature are, therefore, represented in Finland. The small population means that only a limited amount of copies may be printed, thus, the large number of books published in Finnish as well as in Swedish tells much about the avidity of the reading public and the rich intellectual life of that country.

F. E. Sillanpää

SILJA

DEATH CAME to Silja, a young and beautiful country girl, a week or so after Midsummer Day, when summer is still fresh and new. In view of her station in life, she died a fairly decent death. For although she was but a fatherless and motherless farm-maid, with no other relatives either, to whom she could turn for aid, and although she had had to be cared for by others for some time, at least she had not been dependent on charity. Thus her life escaped even that slight tinge of ugliness. On the Kierikka farm, where she was then in service, a tiny room adjoined the bath-house. There she was allowed to take up her quarters and thither her food was brought, the scantiness of which was well justified in that she never ate it all. This humane treatment was in no way due to any special love for their fellow-men on the part of the Kierikka family, but rather to a kind of shiftlessness; the farm was in general not very well managed. Perhaps they had Silja's savings in mind. At any rate she had plenty of good clothes, which of course became the perquisite of the person who nursed her. The mistress had already shown a tendency to borrow Silja's clothes.

Silja, taking after her father in this, was particularly neat in her habits; she made that wretched hovel quite pretty. From it emerged the faint coughing that sounded through the ramshackle window as far as the grass of the yard, where the drabfaced Kierikka children spent their days. It was one of the little things that, with the grass and flowers, went to the making of life that summer in the Kierikka farmyard.

There, towards the end of her days, the girl was able to taste the incomparable joy of solitude. As her mood, according to the wont of consumptives, remained light to the end, this spring solitude was an admirable balm for her somewhat excited love. She was solitary only so far as human beings were concerned; sympathetic company, speechless, it is true, but all the more devoted, she had in abundance. The relative sunniness of the room and the twittering of the swallows nesting in the bath-house eaves gave her finer instincts admirable material for the creation of bright and happy fancies. Dread visions of death kept away until the end; indeed she hardly realised that it was the death so often heard of in life that now came to her. Death itself came at a moment when the speechless delights of her surroundings were at their tenderest and strongest. It came in the morning, just before five, the crowning moment of the sun and the swallows. The newborn day further chanced to be a Sunday, and at that hour there was nothing in the surroundings to spoil it.

Seen from the moment of death, the life of Man is like a brief, petrified vision, a kind of symbol evoking melancholy. Thus, Silja was twenty-two years old; she was born yonder, a score or so miles to the north, and during her life she moved ever farther southward. From the incorporeal image that death always conjures forth as it were in the air near the scene of its presence, from that picture all inessential features are shed, until one might almost declare all patterns of human fate, in the light of that moment, to be pretty much of like value. In the after-death image of this maiden, which, to be sure, there was no one to absorb with his consciousness so early that Sunday, there was not much to shed. From its secret timeless beginning onward, the whole of her being, as life went by, had grown harmoniously together. A pure unbroken skin held it with elastic bonds in its own dark fastnesses, whence, to the close-held ear of a lover, had carried the beating of a heart, and his seeking eye caught a reflected glance. During her life she had not had time to be much more than a human being who smilingly fulfilled her fate. All that concerns Silja, now lying dead in the Kierikka bath-house, is for the most part ravishingly insignificant.

True, in the distance represented by the time around her birth, events are dimly discernible in which natural Fate moves on a bolder scale, having to set the luck of this dying breed on a new foundation for its closing phase. For Silja, be it remarked, was the last of her family. The extinction of such breeds of small fame is indeed observed of none; yet in the process are repeated the same melancholy main features as in cases of greater consequence.

❊ ❊ ❊

Silja and Armas: the summer still before them.

There is a spring whence, at the Professor's express wish, his drinking-water is brought—he used to say that this little act of magic was the honour paid by him to the true superstitions of his ancestors, from which long occupation with science had divorced him. He explained also that it was excellent spiritual discipline for young maids to set off, after their work was over, with bucket on arm, for a walk down a birch-shadowed path of unsurpassed beauty. They might linger on the errand, so long as they brought the water home before midnight: whether they sat alone by the spring, reading "he loves me, he loves me not" from grasses, or with their sweethearts, was not his concern.

Silja too had to find the path: on her first occasion Sofia only gave her a general idea of where it lay. A person at Rauhala could see when the water-carrier went, first along the highway, then down a lane up to a little wooden bridge, under which a brook ran, subduedly foaming. At this point Silja lingered already on her first trip: she had been fully instructed in the Professor's views on this task. Below the bridge was a boulder-bestrewn rapid where the water mildly roared, and overhanging this, intricately interlaced, grew numerous bushes and tall reeds. The sight interested the girl; she wormed her way through them until the soft jungle suddenly ended in a tiny meadow, in which were the ruins of an old mill. The clearing was closed on all sides; the only view was the lush undergrowth that began again lower down, and the only sound that carried there was the murmur of innumerable little branches of the brook. A spider had fastened on one of her sleeves and some white sticky substance on the other, but both were as something secretly whispered to her. . . . Having dreamed to her fill in this wonderful spot, she rose to continue her way to the well, deciding to come here again on similar walks in the future.

This resolution she carried out; and then one day—in the week following the Sunday when she had been to church—she left her empty bucket under a bush at the roadside. The bucket, however, was visible, and was espied by one who a little earlier had seen the girl come in this direction with the bucket on her arm. He took the vessel and hid it more carefully, and then paused a moment, straining all his senses. The deepening evening seemed to be demanding a share of his attention: the meadowsweet glowed richly, the smell of moss from the brook mingling with its strong perfume to create an impression the like of which he could not remember ever having experienced. And as he listened to the babbling of the rapids, he began to imagine the presence of countless other sounds of nature behind it, each from its unknown source adding its own note to that dominant melody.

Perhaps, in that leafy jungle, a faint impression of a trace remained at the place whence the beautiful child had plunged onward. A desirous eye easily guided the pursuer along her tracks. There she sat, her dress more workday than on that last occasion, but at the same time intimate as the beginning of this summer night. The young man crept behind her back, the ear of the solitary sitter catching perhaps a rustle, though she did not turn her head. Her heart beat furiously. It revealed who the intruder was, who now revealed himself. In the eyes of the intruder, when the girl's glance finally met them, was a mischievous gleam, as though he had been younger than he was. That glance and those features Silja had seen before, in some past summer.

She remembered now. The memory came as a sweet immaterialised anaesthetic blow dealt by the summer night. Her companion too remembered—when at last, later, they began to exchange words.

"Oh—my water—what time is it—it can't be midnight yet?"

It was very near though.

The generous hand of life had dropped many pearls for each of them to preserve.

They went to the spring together, up the gentle rise of the last part of the journey, along the birch-lined path. On each side fine white blossoms, of a kind Silja had never seen before, glowed on long stems in the grass. She was almost afraid of the path; the flowers were a kind of enchantment. How was it possible she had not noted them before? They blossomed a little while ago—one for each of us—and now a new one will flower somewhere.

The girl bent down to regard one, but did not pluck it. The youth jumped away from the path and brought one, holding it against the girl's face to admire it. The thin fine perfume of the night-flower harmonised with the girl's expression, in which, after the first kisses in her life, was a quite special gentle assurance. She took the beautiful white cluster from the young man's hand and bore it in her own hand at her bosom, as one may sometimes see in old paintings.

Midnight had passed before Silja undressed, alone in the neat little room that was her very own. Again she went to the window and looked out towards the birch-clad point, as on her first night here after the Professor's footsteps had died away upstairs and she, Silja, was left in her own potent loneliness for the first time in this house. Sleep was loth to come now, too, but the eyes that gazed out into the night shone with a different glow. Nor did they gaze into emptiness as then, nor did her mind seek her former cabin home and the youth who rowed past on a night long past. Her gaze and mind were now turned thither where she had taken leave of her love—Armas. Nothing else existed now. Not a thought of how the Professor might be sleeping upstairs; Miss Laura was an unimportant young person whom she happened to know. No, they had all withdrawn somewhere, she alone was living this summer night, still, a little—after all—hungry for her friend over there. She did not miss him much, knowing that she would soon be with him again. He is there, in that house, in that room, and I am his.

Once again, settled in her bed, the girl thought daring thoughts, still more tumultuous than on that former occasion. She touched her own forearm with her lips, seeming by so doing to be savouring anew those recent kisses. Cautiously her instinct guided her imagination, which sought rest from its present fever in her previous experiences. At certain mind-pictures her whole being rose in opposition—Oskari Tonttila—the visit to his home—dances—and something else from which her thoughts fled in panic whenever it threatened to come near. . . . Her mind found shelter in the blossoms of the white delicate night-flower which she had laid beside her on the pillow. It was of finer texture than any flower in the gardens Silja had seen, and surely no perfume in the world could equal that which it exhaled.

How delicious to awaken like this, awaken to life and every kind of blossoming in life, awaken while others slept, after having in some fashion been asleep all one's life—even in one's waking hours.

As once before on that first night—which the present night in this room greatly resembled—Silja awoke after the lightest touch of sleep. Now too she got up and went to the window.

But this time the sun was already rising, and again she could think of "yesterday." Only now the thought of "yesterday" was calming. The early morning, in which only the birds and the sun-touched air were awake as yet, announced that a new day had begun which, sunny though it was, would contain its share of everyday, at least at first.

The girl went back to her bed. On her pillow she saw the night-flower, now a little faded and tinged with yellow in the light of the dawn. She took it, broke off part of the stem and then put it between the pages of one of her books. Sleep came.

Translated by ALEXANDER MATSON

SWITZERLAND

INTRODUCTION

By Francine B. Bradley

SWITZERLAND is one of the few countries in Europe that has not been drawn into the war either for or against the Axis powers. Politically it is still a free democracy, the oldest democracy in the world. But it is surrounded on all sides by anti-democratic powers. From the first days of the war, this little nation mobilized its relatively large army that stands ready to defend the country against aggression. Nevertheless, Switzerland has been forced, in view of its lack of raw materials, to depend economically on the Axis that dominates the European continent. This dependence, and the ever-present danger of losing its liberty, has forced Switzerland to pay close attention to world events, despite the apparently peaceful life which the neutral Swiss enjoy in the fastnesses of their high mountains.

The Swiss people cannot remain indifferent to the result of the present world conflict. The fate of every individual Swiss depends on the outcome of the war. As the great Swiss writer, Gottfried Keller, asserted almost a hundred years ago: "Today everything is politics and is bound up with politics from the soles of our shoes to the tiles on our roofs; and the smoke rising from our chimneys is politics, hanging in thick clouds over huts and palaces and drifting over cities and villages." It is therefore somewhat surprising that Swiss literature between the two world wars has rarely reflected these general problems, which are bound to have so vital an influence on the future of Switzerland.

Although Switzerland is small, it enjoys a great literary tradition. Switzerland has played an important part in every great period of European thought. Its writers have at times had an influence on the literature of greater nations, as for example Bodmer and Breitinger on the literature of Germany during the period of the young Goethe, or Rousseau and Madame de Staël on France at the time of the Revolution of 1789. Switzerland has also produced great writers of its own: Gottfried Keller, Jeremias Gotthelf, Konrad Ferdinand Meyer and Rodolphe Töpffer in the middle of the last century, and Carl Spitteler who died after the first World War, to mention only a few.

These great writers of the past are perhaps the best sources of inspiration for contemporary Swiss writers. Switzerland possesses a considerable body of literature; and in fact, the number of writers has grown since the first World War. Today they are more easily identifiable since they are forced to belong to a national group. Switzerland now has her own publishing houses, writers' league and literary publications. Moreover, the newspapers of the larger and even some of the smaller cities have a literary section, the influence of which often reaches beyond the narrow boundaries of the country. There is also a very active book trade, proportionally larger than that in most countries. Almost every Swiss, including those of peasant and worker families, has a little library at home. And because Switzerland possesses such an active reading public, books play a significant role in national life.

Nevertheless, the writers of Switzerland have always had to do their writing under particularly difficult circumstances. Their land is not only small, it is also divided into four different language groups. What bound these groups together was a common historic development and a common ideal of democracy, running like a thread through all Swiss history. But their literary heritage was divided by their different languages. That meant a restricted circle of readers, even under the most ideal circumstances. But literature needs a wide radius of expansion in order properly to develop. This is why each of the language groups has been forced to depend on cultural intercourse with the larger countries with which it is bound by linguistic ties: Germany, France and Italy. The kind of atmosphere that exists in the neighboring land is, therefore, not irrelevant, even for the development of Swiss literature. This is why Gottfried Keller, with his keen eye for political and cultural interconnections showed such a great sense of despair when the revolution of 1848 experienced brutal repression in Germany.

After the end of World War I, German Switzerland received a fresh impulse from the newly arising democratic Germany. Unfortunately, the inspiring intercourse with the more democratic neighbor did not last long. When the National Socialists came to power in 1933, those writers of German Switzerland who refused to go over to Hitlerism, were thrown back on themselves and limited to the narrow circle of readers in the German-speaking part of the country. It is to their credit that, with the exception of a few men like Jakob Schaffner, they resisted all pressure from the Third Reich. What has been the result of these necessary and meritorious self-limitations? The writers of German Switzerland have fallen back on their great forerunners. They have learned from the literary great of their country, as well as from those of pre-Nazi Germany, and have maintained a relatively high level of creative work. It is almost as if the best in pre-Hitler Germany found refuge in Switzerland.

One of the best representatives of good German Swiss writing is Hermann Hesse, a real poet, who in his early novels enriched not only Swiss but German literature with some of the most exquisite novels of growing youth. Later, in his psychological novels, he became more introspective, and his melancholy turned into despair over a time that he could no longer tolerate or understand. But, in spite of his negative attitude toward our time, he is a true exponent of the life we live today. Not so much can be said of most of the other writers, who, in withdrawing from the dangerous and confusing events of our time, throw themselves into the too secure world of the past. Alfred Huggenberger and Jakob Bosshard restrict themselves to the narrow themes of peasant life as they have already been exploited in such masterly way by their great fore-runner Jeremias Gotthelf; Emanuel Stickelberger, with complete mastery of form, adds nothing new to Konrad Ferdinand Meyer's great picture of the Italian Renaissance. Fortunately Gottfried Keller does not lend himself so easily to blind copying—those who follow his tradition are forced to draw their themes from real life, as do Hugo Marti and the talented young writer Albin Zollinger, for example, but the radius of their interest remains rather personal and small. The intellectual limitations imposed on present-day Switzerland by her strict neutrality in politics is unfortunately too noticeable in literature. One has the somehow oppressive feeling of walking in a beautiful but petrified garden.

However there is a great progressive movement in Switzerland, although it is not led by a man of letters but by a theologian, Karl Barth, of Basel. He began his career in opposition to the superficial psychologic liberalism of the Protestant Church. He was expelled from Germany in 1934 for the courageous stand he took in defense of the independence of the church. At first he thought only to defend freedom of religion but came soon to realize that freedom of religion cannot exist where political freedom has been destroyed and so, back in Switzerland, he calls upon his fellow-men to make a clear-cut "decision" between brutal force and progress in this time of great historic responsibility, calling our time the period of "great commands of God": "The times in which great commandments of God are given are usually only brief passing periods; but they decisively affect the long periods which ensue. How and what we decide, in the simple form in which it is now given to us to decide, may well prove a momentous historic responsibility." Since Gottfried Keller, no other Swiss writer has recognized so clearly the historic task of his time. For years Barth's creative interpretations of the Bible have won him renown as one of the truly great Protestant theologians of our century; but his magnificent ability in grasping political problems in their broad and essential outlines places him in the front rank as a thinker. He is German Switzerland's foremost representative in the cultural world today.

The Ticinese in "Italian Switzerland" south of the St. Gotthard are relatively few in number. As a group, they are more distinct than the rest of the Swiss in that their literature, written in Italian, expresses more of the nature of their own province than is the case with the German or French Swiss. They show a stronger love of their own soil and more sharply defined provincial characteristics than their German-speaking compatriots. The result is that most Ticinese writers are hardly more than regionalists. Their province, though beautiful, is not rich, and the Ticinese have been forced to emigrate more than the other Swiss. This theme of the "errant son" who returns from foreign lands recurs frequently in their writings. They have no really "great" literature, but the works of Francesco Chiesa and of Zoppi are the most characteristic and best known. These two writers are also read extensively in Italy. They picture a sunny little land with amiable peasants who cultivate corn, tobacco and the vine by day and who spend their evenings in simple pleasures in a wine "grotto" or on the village "piazetta."

The Rheto-Roman group is so isolated that their literature is of necessity purely regional. They have a language related to Italian but of much older origin. It is closer to Latin than any of the other Latin languages. Rheto-Roman is spoken only in the canton of Graubünden, in the Engadine.

The literary development of Western or French Switzerland took place under much more favorable conditions than that of German Switzerland. The intellectual atmosphere in neighboring France remained free much longer, with an inevitably salutary effect on the French-speaking Swiss, and the connection with France was not so abruptly broken off.

Something occurred, however, which proved a detriment, not so much to the development of individual French Swiss writers, as to the development of a French Swiss literature in general. The French Swiss were powerfully attracted by Paris as a cultural center, as was every provincial writer in France proper. Many of these younger writers—as for example, Blaise Cendrars and Guy de Pourtalès—have won a name for themselves in French letters; but they generally forgot, and the world forgot, that they were of Swiss, not French, origin. Only after the first World War did the Western Swiss turn back toward the beauties of their own homeland. Small literary groups were formed in various cities of Western Switzerland—Protestant groups in Geneva, Lausanne and Neûchatel, and Catholics in Fribourg. But here, too, one soon notices a kind of democratic smugness or self-complacency arising from the fact that these Swiss were able to steer clear of the shattering conflicts of the great powers. They seem to take even less interest in world events than their German-speaking compatriots. But in return, they have demonstrated greater vividness and originality, particularly those in the canton of Vaud. Living on a choice bit of earth and cultivating a gently intoxicating white wine, they display richly humorous qualities. Their wittiest representative in letters is Charles-Albert Cingria, who can never be taken too seriously but who, in his causeries, is light and charming as the wine growing on the shores of the divinely laughing Lac Léman.

The people of Geneva are more serious—Calvinism in its severity is still much alive there. One feels this in their literature as well as in their daily life. The writer who expresses most clearly perhaps an understanding of Swiss national life is Robert de Traz. In his interesting book *L'homme dans le rang*, he attempts to paint a picture of the Swiss citizen at his democratic best, as a member of his country's citizen army.

The greatest writer in contemporary Switzerland, of whom the Swiss may well be proud, is C. F. Ramuz, the novelist from the canton of Vaud, whose most outstanding disciple is Jean Giono. He has the unerring eye of a painter in his descriptions of the human beings and landscapes of his province. With masterly realism he recreates the primitive life of the peasants he knows, as for example in *La guérison des maladies* and *Derborence*. He is in the best tradition of Swiss story-telling. Unfortunately, he follows more the spiritual paths of the conservative Gotthelf than the progressive universalism of Gottfried Keller as he stubbornly portrays the secluded world of the Swiss peasant living in the remotest parts of the Vallais, and romantically opposes ideas of modern progress. The Swiss reading public seems determined, however, to force its greatest contemporary writer to quit his ivory tower and to forsake his self-imposed retreat into the past. Ramuz has been forced to write an entire book in justification of his remoteness from present problems. Perhaps he will be persuaded to turn his mind to the questions of our times, instead of remaining buried in a kind of mystic "back-to-the-soil" isolation. If so, Ramuz will prove himself not only a great Swiss writer, which he undoubtedly is, but also one of the beacons of contemporary world literature.

Hermann Hesse

JACOB BOEHME'S CALLING

IN THE more recent centuries we only very seldom hear of men in whose life the spiritual calling is expressed in a plain and beautiful pictorial language as in the legends from the old times of the saints, so that we think we are hearing a wonderful fairy tale in which the things of our accustomed existence come to a new life, changed and with new, radiant meanings. One such rare example is that of the calling of Jacob Boehme, shoemaker in Görlitz, the *philosophus teutonicus,* as it is reported in the chronicle of Abraham of Franckenberg.

Several times Boehme, this simple and mild man, modest and timid by nature, encountered the call to his high spiritual mission in portents and experiences that encouraged and finally compelled him to follow his star and yield to a magically pious way of thinking, the fruits of which, often in language that is hard to read and in strange garb, are laid down in the enlightened shoemaker's writings.

Jacob Boehme was born in Alt-Seidenberg near Görlitz in the Upper Lausitz, as the child of poor, honest peasant folk. As a little boy he had to herd the cattle in the fields. There, at one time, he was lured by a voice while herding, so that he ran away from the cattle and from his comrades of the village and ascended a mountain in the region that is called the Landskrone. In its solitude and desolation, however, in the rough, red rock, he found a gate standing open; in childlike trust he presently entered it and in the interior of the cave saw a treasure—namely, a large trough full of money—which caused him to be seized by horror, so that he touched none of it but hastily went out again and away. And though he later went up the mountain several times with other herders and sought and found the place where this had happened to him, there was no longer any gate or entrance and everything was wild and impenetrable. This was the first call that reached him from the other world, as a portent that he, a seeker for treasure, would enter into hidden caves and raise riches of the spirit.

Next, when he was some years older and apprenticed to a shoemaker, he met with an odd occurrence. He was quite alone in the shop one day, neither his master nor the mistress being at home, when a stranger in plain but orderly garb came in and asked to buy a pair of shoes. The boy Jacob was afraid to fulfill the man's wish, since he had no authority to do so, and refused. But the stranger urged him so earnestly and had such power in his gaze and whole being that in the end he could not but comply. So he then gave the stranger a pair of shoes, but so as not to evoke the master's displeasure he demanded an extraordinary price for them, which the stranger paid at once and without demurring. Thereupon the man left, but at a certain distance from the house he halted and called with a loud and earnest voice: "Jacob—come out!"

Boehme's heart trembled at this, that an unknown man who had never seen him should call him by his Christian name, but he pulled himself together and went out to the other into the alley. There the stranger, whose face was friendly and serious and whose eyes sparkled brightly, took his hand, looked at him forcefully and penetratingly, and said, "Jacob, you are little, but you will become great and rather another kind of man and human being, so that the world will marvel at you. Be therefore pious, fear God, and honor His word; in particular, read often in Holy Scripture, wherein you find comfort and guidance, for you will have to suffer much want and poverty and persecution. Be of good cheer, however, and remain constant, for you are dear to God and His mercy is upon you."

Whereupon the man pressed Boehme's hand, looked once again forcefully into his eyes, and went upon his way. Boehme, however, remained in his place, dismayed and embarrassed, and retained this warning in his mind as long as he lived, and from this hour onward grew more serious and attentive in all his doings.

Not much later, during his journeyman days while he began to search more seriously for truth, his eye once fell upon the saying in the Gospel according to St. Luke: "The Father in heaven will give the Holy Ghost to those that ask Him for it." Then he collected himself, felt as though awakened in his innermost soul, and did literally as the proverb said; he asked God for His spirit, and he presently found himself transported into a holy Sabbath and into such clarity and peace of soul that "for seven days he stood in God's highest contemplation and realm of joy, encompassed by the Divine light."

In the year 1600, after Boehme had become a master in Görlitz and a married man as well, he was again overcome by the Divine light. At one hour, unexpectedly, his eye fell upon a tin vessel, wherein the light was reflected. At the sight of the vessel and the light mirrored therein, a veil suddenly fell from before his inner world, and the spirit led him into the innermost heart and mystery of nature. And when he, inclined to doubt, strolled out into the green fields before the gate, in order to get this seeming phantasm out of his head, his inner eye saw the entire creation explained and represented as if in pictures, lineaments, figures and colors, transparent as it were, and the longer he looked at it, the more clearly he saw it. This was the hour of his final awakening. Filled with joy, he remained silent, praised God, and gladly carried his light within himself, without telling any one about it.

Not until ten years later—in the year of Our Lord 1610 and in the thirty-fifth year of Boehme's life—was this touch of God's light so strongly renewed in him that he began to write down the content of his first revelations in a book, lest he should ever forget it. And in the year 1612 he completed his first book, which he called *Dawn Rising*.

Translated from the German by E. B. ASHTON

C. F. Ramuz

THE WAY OF THE MOLE-CATCHER

I MUST make you understand with words that he is quite small, for at this moment there is no other way for you to realize it. Around everything and around the man himself there is a kind of shell, made half of darkness and half of mist, in which everything is hidden. He, too, is hidden there. And in the air around him there are no doubt houses, meadows, fields and gardens, but this is only for the mind and the memory: the eyes cannot distinguish any of these. Yesterday, there were houses, grass, trees; today, this morning, it's all over. Yesterday, at this very hour the same little man could be seen; today nothing remains of him except the noise he makes as he drags his hobnailed sandals.

I note here what he looks like, so that you will recognize him when the moment comes that has not yet come; at present the atmosphere around you is like a clay embankment which you must dig into like a mole digging his hole. But the man goes right on. It is October weather, one of those mid-October mornings; October has been announced in the calendars. In other regions, October grinds the wine-presses; in other regions, October announces itself by a pretty little quarter of a moon. Elsewhere, October hangs in beautiful gold against white walls and stone porticos; here people lighted their oil lamps this morning, their storm-lanterns, all in vain. Sometimes it seems that God is still asleep in His dwelling and has forgotten to light the Great Lantern; for the other lamps cannot replace it. What would happen—people wonder—if the Great Lamp should never be lighted again when Satan under your feet blows his vapors into your face through the cracks? What if the other Lamp did not come to frighten him finally with Its light?

But right now someone is saying: "So much the worse! We may have to do without daylight today."

It's the little old man who walks on, who is still unseen: he is one of those who let things go by.

Once the hour comes that is his hour for getting up, habit makes him get up. He is one of those who sleep with their clothes on.

"Present!" they say, just as in the army, for they are ready at any moment, unless, perhaps, one of their shoes is missing that the mice have dragged into a corner; fortunately the leather is too hard for their teeth and they couldn't harm it, as he realized when he felt it with his fingers, because he had no candle. When he got up this morning and completed dressing, all he had to do was to grip his basket; and he did grip it, and that was that!

For if we can't see clearly, we others, what do we care?

He thought of those who are unable to be so disinterested (and he began to laugh to himself, as he walked along).

For these others the reign of the devil is dangerous, it doesn't suit them very well, because they have possessions outside themselves; unlike me they do not carry all their belongings on their backs.

Inside his woven reed basket everything he owns has been placed, it is more convenient that way; one is not held back, one is free, one doesn't depend on anyone, on anything, no matter what happens—for example, this morning (he thinks), even if the sun doesn't come out!

But what trouble for the others! For those who have fields, who still have potatoes to gather, how I pity them! But not for me (and he continues to move on, still enveloped in the thick fog; as in must, he thinks; autumn, the must of grapes, and he opens his mouth slightly and tastes it).

October has been announced in the calendar; October, elsewhere, makes the wine-presses creak, this is the season of the vintage; he opens his mouth a little and he tastes the wine: not so sweet this year, really not sweet at all, but, then, sugar is scarce.

One sinks and flounders in this fog (he laughs) and yet he pushes one foot forward, then another; but what difference does that make to me?

He knows more or less where he is going.

One hears the old mechanism of his body creak at the joints.

Caught in the must, caught in the thickness. Caught at the very bottom of the barrel, at the very bottom of the very bottom of everything.

            ❋   ❋   ❋

It hasn't become much clearer. It has only become a little more transparent (and even this only after some time passed). Things are beginning to disentangle themselves from their shells. An apple-tree becomes an apple-tree. First its trunk appears, then the big branches, then the little ones. They look like the meshes of a net through which white air is dripping. Something like a big apartment house emerges before us: the corner of a wood, a high wall advancing toward us out of nothingness, a vertical line and a horizontal line. To right and to left other isolated trees can be seen, and all around a fairly wide expanse of meadows.

It might have been better if what we now see had remained hidden: for it is not a pretty sight at all, and the change isn't for the better.

The man who is still walking forward looks; then he doesn't look any more, he doesn't want to look any more.

He lowers his head still further, and all the upper part of his body, too, under the basket, plunges his hands still deeper into his pockets and puffs harder at his dirty old clay pipe with the broken mouthpiece.

He, too, can be seen now; his clay pipe is in his mouth (he always has it in his mouth), and his face is the same color as the pipe bowl.

Baked, rebaked, painted, repainted, tiny; and one doesn't even know where the whiskers of his beard begin under his bonnet, nor whether it is not in the beard itself, this bowl with its brass lid on a chain.

As he walks he holds in front of him something dark brown at the end of a poor little cracked neck; he wears a faded blue blouse under which there seems to be nothing at all: so tiny he is, so thin, so insignificant.

He is so sad to behold that perhaps it would have been better if he, too, had remained hidden in the larger sadness, under the sky which by now has slightly opened and grown whiter (but that is perhaps for the worse); everywhere cobwebs are hanging; everything is dirty and gray; and he, in the midst of this, is dirty and gray under his basket that is bigger than he is. The little man looks like an ant that is overloaded, with a load bigger than itself.

But he keeps on thinking: "So such the worse, so much the worse!—There's nothing that can be done about it." The apartment house is now all branches and even less pretty a sight than usual, but there's nothing that can be done about it.

There's a little remnant of life in him, as there is in old clocks that have not been wound up for a long time, that makes him walk on notwithstanding; one path turns left, he takes that path.

A little remnant of life pushes him forward in spite of everything, along the path where rails seem to shine: these are ruts full of reflected sky, and he disturbs these reflections with his foot.

He drags the whole road after him. In this part of the country the road always comes with you and clings to your soles. It rises up with your every step, and then drops back into the sticky mud. The calendars have announced the autumn; here it is a sad, wet autumn.

As for him, he drags all this wetness after him.

He drags first one foot, then the other: are you coming? he seems to ask each foot. It is as if he were calling his dog. Come on! And then: Are you coming? A crow looks down on all this from the tip of a little tree—this presence, and then nothing.

❉   ❉   ❉

And yet he keeps on walking, for after all one must work at one's trade. He still has to cross this meadow, then a little wood: this is because of the two or three francs a day he earns with his moles. Wherever a little mound of earth is in sight, all he has to do is go there, he is at home. He goes there and digs into a little mound of earth. He is Frédéric, the mole-catcher, he bends forward with his beard and his pipe with a lid. Under the mound there is a little tunnel, round as the inside of a tube. At first he must make sure that it is the right one, that it has been dug recently; he knows that this is the case when the earth that has been dug up is like coffee dregs; then he must make sure of the direction the mole has taken.

. . . And then I drive in my rod and bend it and I have only to stretch the string and put the brass trap across the hole with a flat stone to prevent it from closing . . .

Now he has arrived in the wood. The place where he is going to set his traps is on the other side. He crosses the wood.

His hands get wet; one can hear creaking branches and the rain dripping from the trees.

There is a great silence in which he hears these two noises and it is as if he were in a cave, but here and there light is breaking through. On the black ground, here and a little further on, there is a wealth of pearls as on the velvet of a jeweler's showcase. What? What's that? It's a vivid little fire between two tree trunks, yellow, then green, then red, then green again, what's this?—then the man who walks on says: "Fine!" just as he said to himself before: "So much the worse." And that's all. He walks on.

And only when he has arrived at the other side of the wood—where there is a last rise of land—

You didn't know what it concealed, it rose before you up to the sky which it touched, you saw at against the sky like a slab—

Only when he has arrived there, only when he has climbed up this rise, only when he is at the top—

But then suddenly the wind began to blow—

He was up there as on a pedestal; he had stopped, removed his basket; as usual he had removed his basket, placed it beside him, begun to rummage in it, taken out a square shovel and had just knelt down—when suddenly the sky cracked open behind him, from end to end.

Blue is coming, a vast color spreads; spaces rise everywhere.

And now an immense figure rises before you: from his left hand a whole lake is hanging; to his other hand another big package of things is attached; he lifts up the whole sky with his back when he gets up again.

*   *   *

He doesn't even suspect it as he keeps on nodding his head and spitting out curses.

He doesn't even suspect it, all this blueness suspended around him.

The blueness hangs in clusters from his fingers when he stretches them and from his arms, it flows from his legs, down each of his legs; it is close to his knees like sheets of metal, it is around and below his smock like fringes—and he is there all streaming, all dripping with blueness, all streaming with space, so big, so big!

*   *   *

Frédéric! Frédéric! Who are you? I want to know.

Nothing or everything, Frédéric, because you have been so magnificently honored?

He was the poorest, the most despised of men: no one even greeted him any more, it was space itself that greeted him.

He no longer had a place among us; things made him come, things gave him his place.

It was the best place they could find for him.

"Go there," they told him. "Just one more step, that's fine. . . . One more step, only one. . . . And now don't move. . . ."

He doesn't know, he doesn't know anything, he hasn't said anything; but the dimensions of everything have changed, the scale of things is reversed.

He who was nothing is everything.

He who was small is big.

He who was the smallest is the greatest—all the sky has put itself under the domination of man; under the domination of one man, the most despised of men—he holds a mountain six thousand feet high under his left arm.

And if he lowers his arm, the mountain won't be there any more.

Translated from the French by NORBERT GUTERMAN

BIOGRAPHICAL AND BIBLIOGRAPHICAL SKETCHES

The following pages are far from possessing either the completeness or the scientific accuracy which are demanded of a true bibliography. Such a work would not only require a staff of professional bibliographers but would far exceed the space available in this book.

Rafael *Alberti* (1903–), Spanish playwright and popular poet of the vanguard. In the Spanish Civil War he was on the side of the Republicans. He lives now in exile, in South America. He published *Fermín Galán*, play, 1931; *Poesía, 1924–1930*, 1934 in Madrid; *Poesía, 1934–1938*, 1940 in Buenos Ayres.
English translations: *A Spectre Is Haunting Europe*, Poems of Revolutionary Spain, by Rafael Alberti, introduction by Angel Flores, 1936 in New York; *Garcia Lorca, Romancero gitano*, edited by Rafael Alberti.

Louis *Aragon* (1897–), French poet and novelist. He was born at Neuilly-sur-Seine; a dadaist poet, a leader of the surrealists, he became later the secretary of the International Association of Writers for the Defense of Culture, one of the editors of *l'Humanité*, then of *Ce Soir*, which was prohibited by the government a week before war broke out in 1939. After verse, he wrote gay prose to *épater le bourgeois* and *se faire la main*, then he wrote more serious prose, *Le Paysan de Paris* and *Traité du Style*. Then he began to write still more serious prose, a series of novels, picturing Europe before and after 1914, with the general title, *The Real World*. In 1936 he received the *Prix Renaudot*. Aragon served in both wars; in 1940 he was evacuated from Dunkirk to England and returned in June 1940 to France; in 1941 he was living in Nice. His war poems, *Le Crève-Coeur*, were smuggled out of France two years ago and have been published in London and New York. (Our selection is taken from this). English translations: *Red Front*, (poem) translated by E. E. Cummings, 1933; fiction: *The Bells of Basel*, 1936; *Residential Quarter*, 1938; *The Century Was Young*, 1941.

Joaquín *Arderíus* (1890–), Spanish poet, novelist, short-story writer. He was born in Lorca, in the province of Murcia. At 8 he was sent to a school directed by monks; at 15 he went to the Ecole Technique at Liége, Belgium. He returned to Madrid, wandered around the country with gypsy horse dealers, returned again to Madrid and published his first book, *Mis Mendigos* (poems, 1915), at 25. He then went to the wild Sierras, with wife and daughter. In this period he underwent all sorts of misery. He took a job in a glass factory at Lyons, France. In 1923 he came back to Madrid, published then and later several novels. He was imprisoned for plotting against Primo de Rivera. While in jail he wrote his novel *Justo il Evangelico* (published in 1930). At the establishment of the Republic he joined the Communist Party and published his novels *Lumpenproletariado* and *Campesinos*. He left the Spanish section of the party, disapproving of the tactics of certain local leaders who were later expelled.

Isaak Emmanuilovich *Babel* (1894–), Russian short-story writer. He was born near Odessa; when he was 3, his family moved to Nicolaev. The pogroms of 1905 forced his family to flee for their lives. He studied Yiddish, the Bible, the Talmud, and at the University of Saratov. In 1915 he settled down in St. Petersburg, but like all Jews he didn't have then "right of residence", and was forced to dodge the police, living in a cellar with a waiter who was always drunk. Gorki printed Babel's first stories in his magazine Letopis (Annals) in 1916 (for which Babel was arrested!). From 1917 until 1924 he was a soldier (with the then famous Cossack general Budenny), he worked in the Commissariat for Education, he was a reporter, a printer . . . Later he visited Berlin, Paris. He has never published much.—English translations: *Red Cavalry*, 1929; *Benia Krik*, 1935.

937

Stanislaw *Balinski* (1898–), Polish poet. He has been in diplomatic service, written fantastic short stories, of which he published in 1928 a collection, *The Evening in the East,* combining classical form with romantic imagination. During the present war he has published a volume of verse *The Great Journey* (Wielka podróz) and various poems in magazines. He is now living in exile in London.

Pío *Baroja* y Nessi (1872–), Spanish novelist. He was born in San Sebastian, the son of a mining engineer, a Basque. In 1893 he received his doctor's degree in Madrid; at the time he began to write articles. He was given the municipal's doctor's post in Cestona (Guipuzcua). After two years he returned to Madrid and rented together with his brother a bakery, where he worked for seven or eight years. At 26, he went to Paris, Italy, Switzerland, Germany, the Netherlands. He wrote the trilogy *The Struggle for Life.* He has never married. In 1936 he went to Pamplona, out of sheer curiosity, to have a look at the rebel Carlist and Falangist troops entering Pamplona, they arrested him and were on the point of shooting him, they then freed him, and he escaped to France and lived in Paris. He has been a free-thinker, an anti-clerical, a great realist—"the best known, the most translated and the least read novelist of contemporary Spain." He himself proclaimed: "I am a man of liberal tendencies . . . I am original . . . the person who influenced me most was Dostoievsky." In 1940 he was still living in Paris.— English translations: *The City of the Discreet,* 1917; *Caesar or Nothing,* 1919; *Youth and Egolatry,* 1920; *The Struggle for Life,* 1922–24; *The Lord of Labraz,* 1926; *The Tree of Knowledge,* 1928; *Paradox King,* 1931.

Richard *Beer-Hofmann* (1866–), Austrian playwright and poet. Born in Vienna, the son of a Viennese lawyer, he was after the early death of his mother adopted by a cousin of his father. He studied law at the University of Vienna. He was one of the Viennese members of the general literary movement of the *fin-de-siècle,* whose liaison-agent between Vienna, Berlin and Paris was Hermann Bahr. There were Peter Altenberg, Baron Leopold Andrian, Arthur Schnitzler, Hugo von Hofmannsthal, etc. Beer-Hofmann published *Novellen,* 1893; *Schlaflied für Miriam,* 1898; *Der Tod Georgs,* novelette, 1900; *Der Graf von Charolais,* 1905 (produced by Max Reinhardt); *Gedenkrede auf Mozart; Jaakobs Traum,* play, 1918; *Der Junge David,* dramatic poem, 1933;

Vorspiel auf dem Theater zu König David, 1936 in Vienna; *Gesammelte Gedichte,* 1935; *Verse,* 1941 in Stockholm and New York. In 1939 he came to this country and lives now in New York. He adapted in Vienna Sutton Vane's *Outward Bound* for the Reinhardt theater, Goethe's *Iphigenie* for Reinhardt and the Salzburg Festspiele, and Goethe's *Faust* for the Burg theater in Vienna.

Eyvind *Berggrav* (1884–), Norwegian author. As the bishop of Oslo, the head of the Norwegian church, he opposed its intended Nazifying by the Germans and gave proof of great personal courage. He has written many books, chiefly of a religious character. His book *The Land of Tension,* from which our selection is taken, deals with conditions of life in the far out-post of Finnmark, where Berggrav was for a long time a bishop.

Georges *Bernanos* (1888–), French novelist, essayist. Born in Paris—a discovery of Léon Daudet—Bernanos is a devout Catholic and royalist. He was long active in the *Action Française,* which was affiliated with fascist groups. In 1936 he went to live in Palma, in the Balearic Islands. The Spanish Civil War turned him into an anti-clerical, although he remained devoted to Catholicism. In 1937 he returned to France. He emigrated with his "numerous children" from France to Brazil, in protest after Munich. Our selection is taken from *Lettre aux Anglais.*—English translations: *A Crime,* 1936; *The Diary of a Country Priest,* 1937; *A Diary of My Times,* non-fiction, 1938; *The Star of Satan,* 1939.

Marthe Lucie *Bibesco* (Lahovary), Princess, (1887–), Rumanian novelist and essayist. Born in Rumania, brought up in France from the age of five, she has lived most of her life in Paris. At 16 she married her cousin, at 18 she published her first book. She writes in French. Besides many novels and travel books, etc., she has written six historical novels under the pseudonym of *Lucile Decaux.* She is a devout and somewhat mystical Catholic. —English translations: Fiction: *Catherine Paris,* 1928; *The Green Parrot,* 1929; *Balloons,* 1929; *World Apart,* 1935; *Katia,* 1939; non-fiction: *The Eight Paradises,* 1923; *Isvor, the Country of Willows,* 1924 (from which our selection is taken); *Royal Portraits,* 1928; *Egyptian Day,* 1930; *Some Royalties and a Prime Minister,* 1930; *Lord Thomson of Cardington,* 1932; *Crusade for the Anemone,* 1932; *Alexander of Asia,* 1935; *A Daughter of Napoleon,* 1937; *Flowers,* 1940.

Giuseppe Antonio *Borgese* (1882–), Italian-American novelist and critic. Born in Sicily, he studied in Florence, went to Naples, Berlin and Turin, where he became the literary editor of the daily *La Stampa* and married a Florentine poetess, Maria Treschi. His first book, *A History of Romantic Criticism in Italy,* 1905, was published by Croce. He was professor of German literature at the University of Rome, 1910–1917, served in the World War as an officer and became in 1918 foreign editor of the *Corriere della Sera.* From 1919–1931 he was professor at the University of Milan. In 1931 he came to America. Since 1936 he has been professor of Italian Literature at the University of Chicago. He writes now in English. He married in 1939 a daughter of Thomas Mann.—English translations: *Rubé* (novel), 1923. English publications: *On Dante Criticism,* 1936; *Goliath: or, the March of Fascism,* 1937, (from which our selection is taken).

Menno *ter Braak* (1902–1940), Dutch essayist and historian. He was the founder and editor of the periodical *Forum.* His works consist of two novels, a play and six volumes of essays, which exerted great influence on the development of Dutch intellectual life. He has been rightly regarded as the intellectual leader of the anti-fascist movement in the Netherlands. When the Germans occupied The Hague he committed suicide.

Francine B. *Bradley* (Brüstlein), Swiss-American essayist, was born in Berne, Switzerland, the daughter of a member of the Swiss Senate. While in Paris she was a correspondent of a German news agency. She came to America in 1926, taught at New York University and published essays, chiefly on René Schickele, the great Alsatian. She is married to Professor Lyman R. Bradley of New York University.

Raul *Brandão* (1867–1930), Portuguese novelist, has written many works of fiction: *A Farsa; Os Pobres; Humus; Memórias; Teatro; El-rei Junot; Os Pescadores,* etc.

Bert *Brecht* (1898–), German poet and playwright. He adapted with Lion Feuchtwanger a historical drama by Marlowe, he adapted John Gay's *Beggar's Opera,* he wrote a radio play about the flight of Lindbergh. Since 1933 in exile, he lived on the estate of Karin Michaëlis, later on his own estate in Denmark, and in Finland. He is now living in Hollywood. He wrote poems, radio plays, plays, a novel (an adaptation of his adaptation of John Gay's *Beggar's Opera*) and many librettos for Kurt Weill, Hanns Eisler, etc. —English translations: *A Penny for the Poor,* novel, 1937; *The Trial of Lucullus,* radio play, 1943.

Hermann *Broch* (1886–), Austrian novelist and essayist. Born in Vienna, he studied philosophy and mathematics. From 1910 to 1928 he was director of a textile business. Later he published a novel, *Die Schlafwandler,* 1928–30; *Unbekannte Grösse,* (essay), 1933; *Entsühnung,* (play), 1934, (produced at Zurich); *James Joyce und die Gegenwart,* essay, 1936. He is now living at Princeton, N. J. He has been a Guggenheim and Rockefeller fellow, and received the award of the *Academy for Arts and Letters* in 1942.— English translations: *The Sleepwalkers,* 1932; *Unknown Quantity,* 1934.

Ivan Alexeyevich *Bunin* (1870–), Russian poet, novelist and short-story writer, winner of the Nobel Prize 1933. He won the Pushkin Prize in 1903, has translated Byron, Tennyson and Longfellow into Russian. His first poems were published 1888, in 1910 his novel *The Village;* he left Russia in 1919. He has lived since then in France, on the Riviera and in Paris. He wrote in 1939–40 against Nazism and Communism. He escaped in 1940 from Paris, after the Nazi conquest, to unoccupied France. He lives now in occupied France and in great distress. He wrote during World War II many short stories, of which our selection is one.— English translations: *The Gentleman from San Francisco,* 1922; *The Dreams of Chang,* 1923; *The Village,* 1923; *Mitya's Love,* 1926; *The Well of Days,* 1933.

Karel *Čapek* (1890–Dec. 24, 1938), Czech novelist, dramatist, essayist. Born in Male Svatonice, Bohemia, he was the son of a physician. He studied philosophy, read William James and John Dewey and said: "American philosophy influenced me most." He translated French poetry and wrote in collaboration with his brother Joseph short stories, articles and plays. He was a close friend of Masaryk, the first president of Czechoslovakia. He was a gardener, a journalist, a theater-manager and producer. "He almost literally died of the death of his country." He wrote humorous articles, travel books, novels, plays.—English translations: Plays: *The Makropoulos Secret,* 1922; *R.U.R.,* 1923; *The Life of the Insects,* 1923; *The Power and the Glory,* 1938; Fiction: *Krakatit,* 1925; *The Absolute at Large,* 1927; *Money and Other Stories,* 1929; *Hordubal;*

Meteor; An Ordinary Life; War with the Newts, 1937; Essays: *Letters from England,* 1925; *Letters from Italy,* 1926; *How a Play is Produced,* 1928; *Letters from Spain,* 1931; *Letters from Holland,* 1933; *President Masaryk Tells His Story,* 1934; *Intimate Things,* 1935; *Masaryk On Thought and Life,* 1938; *The First Rescue Party,* 1939; *I Had a Dog and a Cat,* 1940; *The Gardener's Year; Fairy Tales; Dashenka.*

Demetrios *Capetanakis* (1913–   ), Greek essayist. He studied at the universities of Athens, Heidelberg, Cambridge. He has published several volumes of essays. He now works in the Greek Ministry of Foreign Affairs in London.

Lusitano de *Castro,* Portuguese essayist. Lusitano de Castro is the pen-name of one of the younger Portuguese writers.

C. P. *Cavafy* (–1934), Greek poet. He was born in Alexandria, where he spent most of his life and studied in Oxford. A volume of his poems was published posthumously in 1934.

Nicola *Chiaromonte,* Italian writer. Born in Lucania, he came to this country in exile, by way of France. He is an anti-Fascist writer.

Paul *Claudel* (1868–   ), French poet and playwright. On Christmas Day 1886 he entered Notre Dame in Paris and became converted to the Roman Catholic faith. "In one moment," he says, "my heart was touched and I believed." At the age of 24 he entered the French diplomatic service. Claudel was Ambassador to Japan in 1921, later in Washington and Brussels. 1939–40 he worked in the Ministry of Propaganda. In 1941, at the age of seventy-three, he was living in his chateau near Lyons—a supporter of the Catholic Church and of Pétain. He wrote ten dramas or dramatic poems. A mystic poet, he 'invented' a verse and a metre of his own. Darius Milhaud, once his secretary, wrote the music to *The Book of Christopher Columbus.*—English translations: *The East I Know,* 1914; *Letters to a Doubter,* 1927; *Ways and Crossways,* 1933; Plays: *The Tidings Brought to Mary,* 1916; *The Hostage,* 1917; *Tête d'Or,* 1919; *The City,* 1920; *Proteus,* 1921; *The Book of Christopher Columbus,* 1930; *The Satin Slipper,* 1931; Verse: *Three Poems of the War,* 1919; *Corona,* 1943.

Jean *Cocteau* (1891–   ), French poet, novelist, playwright. He was born at Maisons Lafitte near Paris. He has been actor, director, scenario-writer, novelist, dramatist, critic. He has tried many means of escape—the Catholic Church, opium, solitude, literature—the author of *Les Enfants Terribles* being "l'enfant terrible de la littérature Française." He collaborated with Picasso, Stravinsky, Diaghilev, Satie, Bakst and the new group of composers: "The Six." His ballets: *Parade,* 1917, music by Satie; *Le Boeuf sur le Toit,* 1920, jazz; *Les Mariés de la Tour Eiffel,* 1924, music by The Six; *Le Pauvre Matelot,* 1927, music by Honegger; *Orphée; Oedipus King,* 1927, music by Stravinsky; *Antigone,* 1927, music by Honegger. He wrote the plays: *La Voix Humaine,* 1930; *The Infernal Machine,* 1934; *Les Parents Terribles,* 1939. He wrote the scenario for *The Blood of a Poet.* Since 1940 he has been living in Paris.—English translations: Novels: *Thomas the Impostor,* 1925; *The Grand Ecart,* 1925; *Enfants Terribles,* 1925; Plays: *Orphée,* 1933; *The Infernal Machine,* 1936; Essays: *A Call to Order,* 1927; *Opium: The Diary of an Addict,* 1932; *Round the World Again in Thirty Days,* 1937.

Saul *Colin,* Rumanian-American playwright and essayist. He was born in Bucharest and educated in France; he is a disciple of Pirandello and Jean Wahl. Since 1935 he has been producer and playwright in New York. He is the author of *Construction and destruction of the personality in Pirandello; La Boucle du Doubs; Naturalism and Mysticism in D. H. Lawrence;* etc.

Benedetto *Croce* (1866–   ). Italian philosopher, historian and literary critic. He came of an Abruzzese family. At seventeen he lost his parents and only sister in the 1883 earthquake and was seriously injured himself, having been buried for several hours under ruins. He went to live in Rome with an uncle. Labriola impressed him. He then discovered Marx, and in 1905, Hegel. In 1893 he had already been impressed by Vico's *New Science*—"Vico, the philosopher most akin to myself." In 1903 Croce founded the Journal *La Critica,* in which he reviewed the literature of Italy. He is averse to Fascism. Benjamin Crémieux, the French critic, wrote that Croce "transformed the spiritual physiognomy of Italy." 1920–21 he was Minister of Education. He is Secretary of the Historical Society of Naples, where he usually resides. In September 1943 he was imprisoned by the Nazis, to be freed by British soldiers. He is now in Sorrento.—English translations: *The Philosophy of Vico,* 1913; *Philosophy of the Practical,* 1913; *Historical Materialism and the Economics of Karl Marx*, 1914; *The Breviary of Aesthetic*, 1915; *What is Living and What is Dead of the Philosophy of Hegel*, 1915; *Logic as the Science of Pure Concept*, 1917; *Ariosto, Shakespeare, and Corneille*, 1920; *History: Its Theory and Practice*, 1921; *Aesthetic as Science of Expression and General Linguistic*, 1922; *The Poetry of Dante*, 1922; *Goethe*, 1923; *The Conduct of Life*, 1924; *European Literature in the Nineteenth Century* (from which our selection is taken), 1924; *Benedetto Croce: An Autobiography*, 1927; *A History of Italy from 1871–1915*, 1929; *Anti-Historical Movement*, 1930; *Theory and History of Historiography*, 1933; *History of Europe in the Nineteenth Century*, 1933; *The Defense of Poetry*, 1933; *History as the Story of Liberty*, 1939.

Thomas Quinn *Curtiss* (1902–), American critic and editor. He was formerly on the staff of *Decision* magazine and is now in the Army.

Milan *Dedinac* (1902–), Serbian poet. In Belgrade he founded with the Croatian poet Milosav Krleža the magazine *Danas* (Today), which was suppressed by the censor during the Stojadinović government. Using neither rhythm nor rhyme, he published only two small volumes of poetry. His present fate is unknown.

Alfred *Doeblin* (1878–), German novelist, essayist, playwright. He was born at Stettin; in 1905 he obtained his medical degree and later specialized in the field of nervous disorders. In 1904–11 *Der Sturm* published short stories of his. He settled in Berlin in 1911; in 1912 he married. In 1915 he published *Die drei Sprünge des Wang-lun*, a novel reflecting an admiration for Taoism; in 1920 *Wallenstein*, in 1921 *Der deutsche Maskenball*, critical journalism, in 1925 a travel book about Poland, in 1927 *Manas*, in 1929 *Alexanderplatz*, in 1931 *Die Ehe*, a play, in 1932 *Berge, Meere und Giganten*. In 1933 he left Nazi Germany and settled in Paris, becoming a French citizen; two of his sons served in the French Army; in 1940 he came to this country through the Emergency Rescue Committee. He is now living in Hollywood. In exile he has published *Babylonische Wanderung*, 1934, *Pardon wird nicht gegeben*, 1935, *Das Land ohne Tod*, 1937–38, *Bürger und Soldaten 1918*, 1939, the first volume of *Eine Deutsche Revolution* (A German Revolution). He influenced younger German writers such as Bert Brecht and Anna Seghers. He also published some ontological essays, *Das Ich über der Natur*, in

1928.—English translations: *Alexanderplatz, Berlin*, 1931; *Men without Mercy*, 1937; *The Living Thoughts of Confucius* (ed.), 1940.

Georges *Duhamel* (1884–), French novelist, playwright, poet and essayist. He was born in Paris. In 1906 he founded the "Abbaye" with the playwright Charles Vildrac (later his brother-in-law), the writer René Arcos, the painter Albert Gleizes, and Jules Romains; there they lived and worked and printed their books, such as *Des Légendes des Batailles* by Duhamel and *La Vie Unanime* by Romains; in fourteen months they printed twenty books and then left the "Abbaye." Duhamel was at the front in the first World War for fifty months as assistant surgeon-major, performing 2300 operations; in 1917 he published *The New Book of Martyrs*. Since 1936 he has been a member of the French Academy, he is also a member of the Academy of Medicine. He was president of the Alliance Française and director of the literary magazine *Mercure de France*. In September 1939 he was in charge of French radio broadcasting. After the fall of France he still lived in Paris. The Nazis have placed some of his works on their banned list. He published in Paris in 1941 *La Passion de Joseph Pasquier*.—English translations: *The Heart's Domain*, 1919; *America the Menace* (Scènes de la Vie Future—critical against U.S.A.), 1939; *In Defence of Letters*, 1938; *White War of 1938*, 1939; Fiction: *The New Book of Martyrs*, 1918; *Civilization*, 1919; *Papa Pasquier*, 1934; *The Fortunes of the Pasquiers*, 1935; *Salavin*, 1936; *Pasquier Chronicles*, 1937; *Days of Delight*, 1939; Plays: *The Light*, 1914; *In the Shadow of Statues*, 1914; *Combat*, 1915.

Ilya Grigoryevich *Ehrenburg* (1891–), Russian novelist, journalist and poet. He was born in Kiev. In 1905 he helped the Social Revolutionaries in the building of barricades. In 1906 he joined the Bolshevik party, in 1908 he was imprisoned and left for Paris. After 1909 he traveled widely over Europe. Café Rotonde in Montparnasse was from 1909 until 1941 one of his headquarters. On hearing of the Russian Revolution he rushed in 1917 to his country; he fell first into the G.P.U. prison, then into the Home for Proletarian Writers. Later he went to France, where he was expelled; he wrote in Belgium a novel *Jurenito*, 1921. He started writing poetry, then wrote many novels and short stories and "chronicles of our time" about the automobile industry, the motion-picture business, about Dollfuss, the murderer of Austrian workers in 1934, the Swedish

Strike, the Five Year Plan, the Stavisky Affair and the Civil War in Spain. He is now a war reporter in Russia.—English translations: *The Love of Jeanne Nev,* 1929; *The Extraordinary Adventures of Julio Jurenito and His Disciples,* 1930; *A Street in Moscow,* 1930; *Out of Chaos,* 1934; *A Soviet Writer Looks at Vienna,* 1934; *The Fall of Paris,* 1943.

Paul *Eluard,* French poet. He was at one time connected with the surrealists, is the author of *Capitale de la douleur, La rose publique, l'Amour de la poésie* (from which our selection is taken).—English translations: *Thorns of Thunder, Selected Poems,* 1936.

Angel *Flores* (1900–   ), American essayist. He has written extensively on European literature. His latest anthology, *Fiesta in November,* 1942, introduced to American readers some of the most gifted writers of Latin America. He has translated into Spanish T. S. Eliot's *The Waste Land,* and into English, works by Unamuno, Gómez de la Serna, Rodó, Menéndez, Subercaseaux, Echeverría, Arciniegas, Neruda and Bombal. He published *Literature and Marxism,* 1938; *Lope de Vega, Monster's Nature,* 1930; *Balzac,* 1937; *Spanish Literature in English Translations,* 1926.

Bruno *Frank* (1887–   ), German novelist, playwright. He was born in Stuttgart and studied philosophy. He has adapted about fifty plays written in foreign languages for the German stage, and himself wrote about a dozen. Bruno Frank left Hitler's Germany in 1933. In 1937 he went to work in Hollywood.—English translations: *The Days of the King,* 1927; *Trenck,* 1928; *Twelve Thousand* (play), 1928; *The Persians Are Coming* (political novel), 1929; *A Man Called Cervantes,* 1934; *Lost Heritage,* 1937; *Storm in a Teacup,* 1938; *Young Madame Conti,* 1938; *One Fair Daughter,* 1943.

Leonhard *Frank* (1882–   ), German novelist, short-story writer and playwright. He was born in Würzburg; he has been a housepainter, attendant in a hospital and chauffeur to a country doctor, later an art student in Munich. He lived during the first World War in Zurich. His first novel, *Die Räuberbande,* was published in 1914. In 1919 *Der Mensch ist gut* appeared, having been partially published already in 1917 by René Schickele's *Weisse Blätter,* (stories in opposition to the war). After the publication of *Karl und Anna* he was elected to the Prussian Academy and in 1933 rejected by the Nazis. He left Hitler's Germany in 1933, lived in London

and Paris, was twice put by the French into concentration camps (1939 and 1940) and, through the help of the Emergency Rescue Committee, Thomas Mann and Mrs. Bruno Frank, came to this country in the fall of 1940. He is now living in Hollywood. He wrote in exile a novel and a play.—English translations: *The Cause of the Crime,* 1928; *The Robber Band,* 1928; *Carl and Anna,* 1929; *Carl and Anna* (drama), 1929; *Brother and Sister,* 1930; *Clamoring Self,* 1930; *Carl and Anna and Breath,* 1930 (from which our selection is taken); *The Singers,* 1933; *In the Last Coach and Other Stories,* 1934; *Three of the Three Millions,* 1936.

Stefan *George* (1868–December 4, 1933), German poet. He was a close associate of the symbolists, especially Mallarmé, and of the English Pre-Raphaelites. He translated d'Annunzio, Verlaine, Rimbaud, Mallarmé, Regnier, Rosetti, Shakespeare's Sonnets and Dante's *Divine Comedy* into German. In 1892 he founded an esoteric magazine, *Blätter für die Kunst,* wrote about a boy called Maximin, of whom he made a kind of poetical god, and became the leader of a school of poetry and of essayists. He made no secret of his homosexual tendencies. He was a spokesman in Germany of a reactionary and confused neoromanticism, preaching a' nebulous Third Reich and writing sometimes beautiful verse. When Hitler came, he left Germany at once, and in Lugano, Switzerland, he died.—English translations: *George, Hofmannsthal, Rilke* (ed. by Martin Sommerfeld), 1938; *Poems* (text in English and German), 1943.

André Paul Guillaume *Gide* (1869–   ), French novelist and essayist. He was born in Paris. He is the nephew of the famous economist, Charles Gide; Pierre Louys, author of *Aphrodite,* was his classmate. In 1891 he printed at his own expense *Cahiers d'André Walter,* which appeared anonymously, as a posthumous work. For the next few years he was a member of the symbolist group. In 1893 he went to Biskra and wrote *Nourritures Terrestres.* In Algiers he met Oscar Wilde. After the death of his mother, in 1895, Gide inherited a large fortune, and then married his cousin. In February 1909 the first number of his magazine *Nouvelle Revue Française,* made its appearance. In 1909 he published *Strait Is the Gate,* in 1914, *The Vatican Swindle.* In the first World War Gide helped Belgian refugees for eighteen months. In the second World War Gide helped the political refugees of Germany, Austria, etc., who were put into concentration camps. In 1924 the Catholic Nationalist, Henri Massis, accused Gide of "corrupting public morals by means of his subtly mendacious art." Gide answered with *Corydon*, a defense of homosexuality. In 1926 he published his autobiography *If It Die* and his "first" novel *The Counterfeiters*. In 1927 and 1928 he published *Travels in the Congo*, a powerful exposé of the ruthless exploitation of the African colonies. Gide gradually turned to Marxism, but on his visit to the Soviet Union in 1935-36 he became disillusioned. During the Spanish Civil War, Gide helped the Loyalists. In 1941 he was living in Cannes, "true to himself." In 1943 Gide was found in Tunisia. He is an unappeasable anti-Fascist.—English translations: Fiction: *Prometheus Illbound*, 1919; *Strait Is the Gait*, 1924; *The Vatican Swindle*, 1925; *The Counterfeiters*, 1927; *The Prodigal Son*, 1928; *The School for Wives*, 1929; *The Immoralist*, 1930; *Two Symphonies*, 1931; Travel and Criticism: *Oscar Wilde*, 1905; *Dostoievsky*, 1925; *Essay on Montaigne*, 1929; *Travels in the Congo*, 1929; *Return from the U.S.R.R.*, 1937; *Afterthoughts*, 1937; *The Living Thoughts of Montaigne* (ed.), 1939; Autobiography: *If It Die*, 1935.

Marnix *Gijsen* (1899–), Belgian poet and essayist. Marnix Gijsen is the pen-name of Jan Albert Goris. He was born in Antwerp, studied in Europe and in Seattle, Washington. He is a government official, now living in New York, the Commissioner for Belgium in the U.S.A. Literary and historical publications: *Het Huis*, 1925; *Ontdele Amerika*, 1927; *Odysseus achterne*, 1930; *Peripatetisch Onderricht*, I.–II., 1940; *De Zuid Nederlandsche Letterkunde sedert 1830*, 1939.

Jean *Giraudoux* (1882–), French novelist, playwright, essayist. In Cerilly he met his first friend, Charles Louis Phillipe, author of *Bubu de Montparnasse*. In 1907 he became the private tutor of the Prince of Saxe-Meiningen. Grasset published his first book, *Provinciales*, in 1909. Giraudoux turned to diplomacy and ended his career as the chief of France's ill-fated wartime propaganda and iron censorship. After the Nazi conquest he went to Vichy. After his adaptation of his novel *Siegfried et le Limousin* he became one of the successful playwrights of Paris.—English translations: *Campaigns and Intervals*, 1918; *Suzanne and the Pacific*, 1923; *My Friend from Limousin*, 1923; *Bella*, 1926; *Siegfried*, 1930; *Amphitryon 38*, 1938; *Paris Impromptu*, 1938; *Racine*, 1938.

Yvan *Goll* (1891–), French poet and essayist. He was born in Saint Dié (France).

Bilingual like most Alsatians he played a role among the German expressionists and in Paris literary circles, before coming to this country. Yvan Goll has published several volumes of verse; our selection is taken from *Jean sans terre*. In 1921 he edited together with Theodor Däubler the *Archipenko-Album*. He published *Die drei guten Geister Frankreichs*, 1919; *Gala*, 1930. He translated into French Werfel's *The Song of Bernadette*, 1942, New York, and edits a French-English quarterly, *Hemispheres*.

Ramón *Gómez de la Serna* (1891–), Spanish humorist, short-story writer, playwright and novelist. In 1904, in celebration of his thirteenth birthday, he published his first book *Entrando en Fuego* (Coming under Fire). He has published in all more than one hundred volumes of fiction, drama and criticism. He is a literary rebel, has anticipated or participated in most of the European vanguard literary movements. His outstanding contribution has been the "greguerías," aphorisms or metaphorical maxims. During the Spanish Civil War he sympathized with Republican Spain and now lives in Buenos Aires, a voluntary "exile."—English translation: *Movieland*, 1930.

Maxim *Gorki* (1868–1936), Russian novelist, playwright, essayist and short-story writer. (Gorki, meaning in Russian "the bitter one," was a pen-name.) He was born in Nijni Novgorod. At the age of four he lost his father, at nine his mother; his grandfather sent him "out into the world." For fifteen years he wandered about as a tramp. At nineteen he tried to shoot himself. Korolenko encouraged him to write. In 1892 he published his first short story, in 1898 *Sketches and Stories*, and soon became famous and popular in Russia. He came under the influence of Tolstoy, and of Chekhov who urged him to write for the theatre. He became a member of the Russian Social Democratic Party, later joining the Bolsheviki. In January 1905 he was imprisoned. In 1906 he went to U.S.A. and was expelled for moral turpitude—the actress who accompanied him was not his legal wife. He lived in exile on Capri and exchanged letters and written disputes with Lenin. Gorki was allowed to return to Russia in 1913. After the Revolution he became the official revolutionary writer, the official friend of Lenin and Stalin. He worked much to help Russian writers and he dedicated himself to cultural work among the proletariat. A museum and his native city are named after him. His health forced him to return to Capri, although he went back to Russia before his death. There were rumors that he was poisoned by foes of the Soviet Union.—English translations: *Chelkash and Other Stories*, 1895; *Orloff and His Wife*, 1899; *Foma Gordyeeff*, 1899; *The Lower Depths*, play, 1903; *Mother*, 1905; *The Spy*, 1900; *The Confession*, 1908; *Creatures That Once Were Men and Other Stories; Through Russia; My Childhood*, autobiography, 1915; *In the World*, autobiography II, 1917; *The Outcasts*, 1902; *Comrades*, 1907; *Children of the Sun*, 1912; *Stories of the Steppe*, 1918; *Reminiscences of Tolstoy*, 1920; *Night Lodgings*, 1920; *Fragments from my Diary*, 1924; *Reminiscences of My Youth*, 1924; *The Judge*, 1924; *The Story of a Novel*, 1925; *Tales from Gorki; Decadence*, 1927; *Reminiscences of Leonid Andreyev; The Bystander*, 1930; *The Magnet*, 1931; *Book of Short Stories*, ed. by Avrahm Yarmolinsky and Moura Budberg with a foreword by Aldous Huxley (from which our selection is taken); *Days with Lenin*, 1932; *To American Intellectuals*, 1932; *On Guard for the Soviet Union*, 1933.

Julien *Green* (1900–), French novelist. He was born in Paris, the son of American parents. In 1917 he served in the American Field Service near Verdun, and the next year became a French soldier. After the World War he went to the University of Virginia. His first story, *Le Voyageur sur la Terre*, was written there and published in the university literary magazine. He thought of being a painter, wrote a pseudonymous *Pamphlet contre les Catholiques de France*, 1924. In 1926 he wrote his first novel, *Mont Cinère*. During the present war he returned to U.S.A. He has twice won prizes in Harper Bros. contests. He wrote in English his autobiography, *Memories of Happy Days*, 1942. He translated together with his sister Anne Green *Basic Verities*, prose and poetry by Charles Pierre Péguy (1873–1914), 1943, New York.—English translations: *Avarice House*, 1927; *The Closed Garden*, 1928; *The Pilgrim on the Earth*, 1929; *Dark Journey*, 1929; *Christine and Other Stories*, 1930; *The Strange River*, 1932; *The Dreamer*, 1934; *Midnight*, 1936; *Personal Record*, 1939 (from which we took some passages); *Then Shall the Dust Return*, 1941.

Jan *Greshoff* (1888–), Dutch essayist and poet. After he left the Netherlands in 1927, he lived at Brussels, then at Cape Town, and now resides in New York. His collected poems appeared in 1936 and passed through four impressions before the invasion. He wrote some ten volumes

of essays and three volumes of aphorisms.

Nordahl *Grieg* (1902–), Norwegian novelist, playwright and poet. A great-nephew of the composer Edvard Grieg, born in Bergen, Nordahl Grieg has had an adventurous and varied life: he once walked from Hamburg to Rome, was a correspondent in China in 1927, lived for several years in Moscow, fought in Spain with the International Brigade, and upon the Nazi invasion of Norway succeeded with the help of thirty soldiers in conveying the gold of the Bank of Norway to England, where he now lives. His first novel was *The Ship Sails On* (from which our selection is taken) based on his experiences as an ordinary seaman, published in 1924. In 1929 he produced an anthology of Norwegian poetry, *Norway in Our Hearts*, in 1933 a play, *Our Honor and Our Power*. Another play, *Defeat*, dealing with the Paris Commune, was successful throughout Scandinavia. His last book before the Nazi invasion was *The World Must Still Be Young* with material drawn from his experiences in Russia and Spain.

Jorge *Guillén* (1893–), Spanish poet. He is now at Wellesley, Massachusetts. *The Poetry of Jorge Guillén* (including some translations) was published in English in 1942.

František *Halas* (1901–), Czech poet. Born in Prague, he was an editor and assistant manager in the semi-official Publishing House *Orbis*. He published a number of poetical books. His best known book of verse was *Old Women*. The Nazis put him into a concentration camp in 1941. We don't know what became of him. Other books, *The Face; Sepia*.

Jaroslav *Hašek* (1883–1923), Czech novelist and short-story writer. He was born in Prague, became a bank clerk and published sixteen volumes of short stories. In the first World War he was made a prisoner and spent several years in Russian camps and fought in the Czech legion. He came back to Prague and began his *Schweik*, for which he planned six volumes. He died at forty, with only four volumes written, having liked hard liquor too well.—English translation: *Schweik, The Good Soldier*, 1930.

Frans *Hellens* (1883–), Belgian novelist. Frans Hellens is the pen-name of Frederic van Ermengem. He was born at Ghent and was a government official in Brussels. His works consist of a number of fantastic novels, among them: *Les Realités fantastiques*, 1923; *Oeil-de-Dieu*, 1925; *Le*

Naïf, 1926 (from which our selection is taken); *Le Fauteuil rouge,* 1926; *La Femme partagée,* 1929; *Les Filles du Désir,* 1930; *L'impossible adieu,* 1931; *les Magasins aux poudres,* 1936; *Sidonie-ou: La Mère criminelle,* 1936; *La Pendule empire,* 1937. In 1911 he published a book about the painter, *Gérard Terborch.*

Jenö *Heltai,* Hungarian novelist and short-story writer.

Hermann *Hesse* (1877–   ), Swiss poet and novelist. He was born in Calw, Württemberg. His father was of Estonian descent and had been for some years a missionary in India. As his father became an official in the Office of Foreign Missions at Basel, Hesse went to school there. From 1895 to 1903 he was a bookseller in Basel and in Tübingen. In 1899 he published *Romantische Lieder,* in 1902 *Gedichte,* in 1904 *Peter Camenzind,* his first novel. Since 1912 he has lived continuously in Montagnola near Lugano, Switzerland, as a Swiss citizen. A student of Hindu and Chinese civilisations, in 1911 he undertook a tour of India and published in 1913 a travel book on India, and *Siddharta,* in 1922. He has written since then many novels, poems, short stories and essays.—English translations: *In the Old Sun,* 1913; *Gertrude and I,* 1915; *Inside of Chaos,* 1923; *Demian,* 1923; *Steppenwolf,* 1929; *Death and the Lover,* 1932.

Hugo von *Hofmannsthal* (Hofmann Edler von Hofmannsthal), (1874–1929), Austrian poet, playwright and essayist. He was born in Vienna, of a wealthy Spanish-Jewish family. At 17, he was called a genius. Hofmannsthal himself denied that he was a neo-romantic. In 1891 he published *Gestern* under the pseudonym *Theophile Morren;* in 1899 *Der Tod des Tizian* and *Der Tor und der Tod,* under the pen-name of Loris. While still an undergraduate, Hofmannsthal was credited with originating the romantic school in Austria. He helped to introduce Oscar Wilde, d'Annunzio, and other foreign writers into that country. In 1903 he began a twenty-year collaboration with Richard Strauss, with *Elektra,* a tragedy adapted from Sophocles. In 1905 he adapted *Venice Preserved* of Thomas Otway. In 1907 he published his collected prose, in 1909 and 1911 his poetry. He wrote for Strauss the libretto for *Der Rosenkavalier.* In 1912 he adapted *Everyman* from the English morality play, which was produced on the stage in Salzburg until 1938. *Ariadne at Naxos* was produced in 1912, the ballet *The Legend of Joseph* was produced in London in 1914. He wrote for Richard Strauss *The*

Lady without a Shadow, 1922; and *Helen.* He was a believer in "art for life's sake," as he wrote in *Buch der Freunde,* 1929. He published in 1921 *Der Schwierige,* a comedy; in 1924 *Das Salzburger Grosse Welttheater;* in 1925 *Der Turm,* an accomplished baroque drama of the 20th century. In 1931 *Die Berührung der Sphären,* and in 1932 *Andreas,* a novel fragment, were published posthumously. Gundolf, the prophet of Stefan George, called Hofmannsthal "the founder of aestheticism."—English translations: *Elektra,* 1908; *The White Fan,* 1909; *Ariadne at Naxos,* 1912; *Everyman,* 1912; *The Rose Cavalier,* 1912; *Death and the Fool,* 1912; *Venice Preserved,* 1915; *Madonna Dianora* (The Lady at the Window), 1916; *Prologue for a Marionette Theatre,* 1916; *Christina's Homecoming,* 1917; *Lyrical Poems,* 1918; *Death of Titian,* 1920; *The Adventurer and the Singer,* 1920; *The Marriage of Sobeide.*

Josef *Hora* (1891–   ), Czech poet. He was born in Roudnice, a small town in Northern Bohemia. In his poems there is a strong social note. Besides poetry, Hora writes essays on literature and criticism. He published about twenty volumes of verse, among them: *The Flourishing Tree; The Day of Labor; The Heart and the Uproar of the World; Stormy Spring; Italy; Strings in the Wind; Ten Years.* Hora translated Russian and Polish poets into Czech. He calls "brothers of his heart" Novalis, Heine and Essenin.

Ödön von *Horvath* (1901–June 1938), German dramatist and novelist, and Hungarian citizen. He was born in Fiume, lived mostly in Munich and in the Bavarian and Austrian Alps. He published a novel *Der ewige Spiesser* in the humorous Munich tradition, half a dozen plays, among them *Italienische Nacht, Geschichten aus dem Wiener Wald,* 1931; *Die Bergbahn,* etc. In 1933 he was still living in Nazi Germany; in Berlin he wrote some stories for the movies, and in the Bavarian Alps he had scuffles with some local Nazis. In 1934 he left Germany. He lived then in Austria and wrote two anti-Nazi novels. On the liveliest street in the world, on the Champs-Elysées in Paris in 1938, an old chestnut-tree broke down as Horvath passed by and killed him instantly.—English translations: *The Age of the Fish,* 1938; *A Child of Our Time,* 1939.

Egon *Hostovský,* Czech novelist and short-story writer. Born in Hronov in Northern Bohemia, he studied and became an editor of a publishing house in Prague and a literary critic. In 1939 he left Prague and went to Brussels as a member of the Czech diplomatic service, and came then to Paris and New York, where he works in the Foreign service of Czechoslovakia.— English translation: *Letters from Exile,* 1942 (from which our selection is taken).

Jan *Huizinga* (1872–), Dutch historian in the field of the history of culture. From 1905–1915 professor at the University of Groningen, 1915–1942 at Leiden. His principal works, *Het Herfstij der Middeleeuwen,* 1919; *Mensch en Menigte in Amerika,* ˙1918; *Erasmus,* 1924; *Homo ludens,* 1939. Our selection is taken from *Schaduwen van Morgen* (In the Shadow of Tomorrow). In a four-line preface to this book he wrote: "I am an optimist."— English translation: *In the Shadow of Tomorrow,* 1936.

Panait *Istrati* (1884–1935), Rumanian novelist and short-story writer, in French. Born at Braïla in Rumania, he was the son of a Greek smuggler and a Rumanian washerwoman. At 14 he began wandering; he became a butcher's clerk, a domestic servant, an apprentice mechanic, a porter and a housepainter. In 1913 he organized with a Russian exile, Christian Rakowsky (later a Soviet ambassador in Paris), the first strikes and revolutionary uprisings in Rumania. Later he established a pork business and married a militant Socialist. In 1916 he deserted his wife and his farm and spent four years in Switzerland, doing odd jobs and reading the French classics. In 1919 he was at one time a street photographer at Nice and tried to kill himself by cutting his throat. At the end of six months in the hospital he recovered, wrote a letter of fifty pages to Romain Rolland and received an answer. In 1923 his first book *Kyra Kyralina* appeared, (our selection is taken from it). In 1928 he traveled to Russia by automobile with the Soviet ambassador to France, Rakowsky, spent sixteen months traveling through Russia and becoming disillusioned. After leaving Russia he published three anti-communist books. He suffered from tuberculosis, married again, and lived in the utmost poverty at Nice, because his French publishers arranged a contract making him a pauper. As his wife was homesick, they returned to Rumania where he applied to King Carol for a pension in return for the copyright and Rumanian translation of his books. The arrangement was made, but never fulfilled. Istrati, accused of being a traitor and philofascist, was by this time a dying man, with eight people to support. He died in complete destitution.—English translations: *Kyra, My Sister,* 1930; *Uncle*

Anghel, 1927; *The Bandits,* 1929; *Thistles of the Baragan,* 1930; *Balkan Tavern,* 1931; *Bitter Orange Tree,* 1931; *Russia Unveiled,* 1931.

Franz *Kafka* (1883–1924), German novelist, short-story writer, essayist. Born in Prague, he was a Czechoslovakian citizen. In 1906 Kafka entered a story in a contest sponsored by the Viennese periodical *Die Zeit.* In 1908 he got a semi-governmental job in a workman's accident insurance institute. He studied Czech, became a vegetarian and was even impressed by Rudolf Steiner's "anthroposophism". He read with enthusiasm Kierkegaard, Pascal and Cabbalistic books. He became a friend of Max Brod and Franz Werfel and developed symptoms of consumption and unhappy love. He received in 1915 the Fontane Prize for *Der Heizer,* the first chapter of *Amerika.* Seriously ill, in the first World War he was exempt from military service. He joined his youngest sister in a small estate in Zurau. In summer 1918 he returned to his office, then moved around from sanatorium to sanatorium and was twice in nudist camps. He met in 1923 Dora Dymant, a Polish Jewish girl, still in her teens; they settled in Prague, in 1924 they moved to Berlin. In April he was transferred to the Wiener Wald sanatorium and to the Kierling sanatorium in Klosterneuburg, where he died, on his forty-first birthday. He was buried in the Jewish cemetery in Prague-Straschnitz. In his will he left definite instructions that his novels, other unfinished works and letters were to be destroyed; Max Brod disregarded the last will and published them. Kafka published *Betrachtung,* 1912; *Der Heizer,* 1913; *Verwandlung,* 1915; *Das Urteil,* 1916; *Der Landarzt,* 1919; *Ein Hungerkünstler,* 1924. Max Brod published *Der Prozess,* novel, 1924; *Das Schloss,* novel, 1926; *Amerika,* a fragment novel, 1927; *Beim Bau der Chinesischen Mauer,* 1931.—English translations: *The Castle,* 1930; *The Great Wall of China,* 1933 (from which the "Five Parables" are taken); *The Metamorphosis,* 1937; *The Trial,* 1937; *Amerika,* 1938; *A Franz Kafka Miscellany,* 1940.

Angel *Karaliichev* (1902–), Bulgarian short-story writer. He published his first book in 1924 and has written several books for children. Up to 1939 he was with the Agricultural Co-Operative Society in Sofia.

Hermann *Kesten* (1900–), German novelist and playwright. He lived at Nürnberg, studied literature and history at the universities of Erlangen and Frankfurt, left Berlin on March 1933, and Paris on May 1940 for New York. He wrote novels, plays, poems, essays, and short stories, translated into German some French and American authors, edited in Europe four anthologies; in New York, *Heinrich Heine Works of Prose*, 1943.—English translations: Novels: *Josef Breaks Free*, 1930; *Happy Man*, 1935; *Spanish Fire*, 1937; *I The King*, 1939; *The Children of Guernika*, 1939. Plays: *Mary Baker Eddy* (in collaboration with Ernst Toller), 1935.

Annette *Kolb*, German novelist and essayist. Her father was a Bavarian, her mother was French. From the age of six to twelve she was educated in a convent. Her first novel, *Das Exemplar*, won the Fontane Prize, her second, *Daphne Herbst*, the Gerhart Hauptmann Prize, 1928. Always an anti-militarist, she published in 1916 *Letters of a Franco-German*, in 1917 went to Switzerland, collaborated on René Schickele's *Weisse Blätter*. After the war, she moved to Badenweiler, where Schickele and his family were living. In 1933 she left Nazi Germany for Paris. In 1929 her biography of Briand was published, in 1938 (in Vienna) one of Mozart, and in Stockholm in 1941 one of Schubert, in 1943 one of Richard Wagner. Her third novel, *Die Schaukel*, came out in 1935. In 1939 *Festspiele in Salzburg*, an account of the Salzburg Festival and of a trip to the U.S.A. just before the outbreak of war, was published in Amsterdam. She is now living in New York, working on a book, in English, *The Book of Dreams*, and on magazine articles. — English translation: *Mozart*, 1939.

Manfred *Kridl*, Polish essayist. He was born in Lwow, Poland, was formerly on the staffs of Warsaw, Brussels and Wilno Universities and is now at Smith College. He is the author of many works of critical literature and has contributed to American as well as European periodicals. His main publications in Warsaw: *Mickiewicz and Lamennais*, 1909; *Letters of J. Slowacki*, 1915; *History of Polish Literature in the XIX. Century*, 1925–1931; *Literary Essays*, 1939, etc.

Helge *Krog* (1889–), Norwegian playwright and novelist. He was a critic of great influence in Norway. He wrote plays and novels. He published three small comedies on erotic subjects, *Treklang*, 1933; he is now a refugee in Stockholm.

Pär *Lagerkvist* (1891–), Swedish poet, novelist and playwright. He may be considered an exponent of Swedish expressionism; many of his books and plays are anti-Nazi in spirit and purpose, among them, *The Eternal Smile; The Invisible*, (play); *Guest in Real Life; Fighting Spirit; The Hangman; The Man Without a Soul* (play).

Valéry *Larbaud* (1881–), French critic, short-story writer, novelist, poet and translator. He was born in Vichy. His greatgrandfather played a role in the revolution of 1848 and was exiled after the coup d'état of Napoleon III and settled in Geneva, where he entertained his distinguished guests, among others, Barbès, and Eugène Sue. This period is recaptured in Larbaud's story *Rachel Frutiger*, our selection taken from *Enfantines*. Larbaud's father became rich, Valéry became a great traveler. His family printed in 1899 his collected poems, *Portiques*, he translated or helped to translate Coleridge, Walter Savage Landor, Samuel Butler, Walt Whitman, James Joyce, Ramon Gómez de la Serna and Gabriel Miró; he has helped to make known the work of Samuel Butler, James Joyce and Italo Svevo. In 1908 he published his *Poèmes d'un riche Amateur, or: A. O. Barnabooth: Le Pauvre Chemisier, Les Poésies*; in 1911 his first novel, *Femina Marquez*; in 1913 *A. O. Barnabooth: Son Journal Intime*, novel; in 1918 *Enfantines*, short stories; in 1924 *Amants, Heureux Amants*; in 1927 *Ce Vice Impuni, la Lecture*.—English translation: *A. O. Barnabooth: His Diary*, 1924.

Else *Lasker-Schüler* (1876–), German poet and playwright. She was born in Elberfeld, and published poems and plays, *Styx*, poems, 1902; *Der Siebente Tag*, poems; *Das Peter-Hille-Buch*, 1906; *Die Nächte der Tino von Bagdad*, 1907; *Die Wupper*, play, 1909; *Meine Wunder*, poems, 1911; *Mein Herz*, novel, 1912; *Hebräische Balladen*, poems, 1913; *Gesichte*, stories, 1913; *Der Prinz von Theben*, 1914; *Die gesammelten Gedichte*, 1917; *Der Malik, eine Kaisergeschichte*, 1919; *Essays*, 1920; *Die Kuppel*, poems, 1920; *Der Wunderrabbiner von Barcelona*, 1921; *Theben*, poems, 1923; *Ich räume auf! Meine Anklage gegen meine Verleger*, 1925; *Konzert*, 1932; *Arthur Aronymus, die Geschichte meines Vaters*, 1932. She left Nazi Germany in 1933 and is now living in Palestine, and has published a book about that country.

Marcus *Lauesen* (1907–), Danish novelist. He was born in that part of Slesvig which was returned to Denmark after World War I. He made his reputation as a writer at 23 with the novel, *Waiting for a Ship.* His subsequent books have dealt with the Danish-German border region and the last war.—English translation: *Waiting for a Ship,* 1930.

Christopher *Lazare,* American critic and editor. He was formerly on the staff of *Decision* magazine and is working on a book about Mozart's librettist, Da Ponte.

Jan *Lechon* (1899–), Polish poet. Jan Lechon is the pen-name of Leszek Serafinowicz. Born at Warsaw, he studied at the University of Warsaw. He is a member of the Skamander group and has been for ten years in the Polish diplomatic service. He lives now in New York and is an editor of the Polish weekly *Tygodnie Polski* in New York. He wrote poems and literary criticism. Of his poems *The Crimson Poem* is the most representative.

Lise *Lindbaek* (1905–), Norwegian writer. She covered the civil war in Spain and World War II in France. Now in this country, she is finishing a book on the Norwegian merchant marine.

Federico García *Lorca* (1899–1936), Spanish poet and playwright. He was born in Fuente Vaqueros (Granada), Manuel de Falla, the Spanish composer, was his godfather. Fernando de los Ríos persuaded his parents to let Lorca go to Madrid, where he stayed for most of the next fifteen years. He published in 1921 *Libro de Poemas;* in 1927 *Canciones,* in 1928 *Romancero Gitano.* A play, *Mariana Pineda* was produced in 1927. In 1929–1930 García Lorca was at Columbia University, and his poems appeared for the first time in English in the magazine *Alhambra,* then edited by Angel Flores. Inspired by Negro spirituals Lorca wrote his *Oda al Rey de Harlem,* published in a posthumous collection, *The Poet in New York.* At the outbreak of the Civil War, in July, he was arrested by Franquist soldiers. After a few days in jail he was told to go with the soldiers to his brother-in-law, Manuel Fernández Montesinos, the Socialist ex-Mayor of Granada who had been murdered. At a cemetery García Lorca was ordered out of the car; he was struck with rifle butts and his body riddled with bullets. His books were burned and are today banned in Spain.—English translations: *Bitter Oleander,* 1935 (also translated as *Blood Wedding,* 1939); *Lament for the Death of a Bullfighter and Other Poems,* 1937; *Poems,* 1939; *The Poet in New York and Other Poems,* 1940. *From Lorca's Theatre: Five Plays,* 1941; *Selected Poems,* 1941.

Emilio *Lussu* (1890–), Italian writer and political leader. Once imprisoned on Lipari, he headed Giustizia e Libertá after the murder of the Rosellis; and now leads the Italian Action Party.—English translation: *Sardinian Brigade.*

Joachim *Maass* (1902–), German novelist. Born in Hamburg, he left Nazi Germany in 1938. He is now on the German faculty of Mt. Holyoke College, and is working on *The Time of Evil.* Other novels: *Boheme ohne Mimi, Unwiederbringliche Zeit, Der Widersacher, Testament.*

Antonio *Machado* y Ruiz (1875–1939), Spanish poet and playwright. Born at Sevilla, he taught at the universities of Baeza and Segovia. His *Obras* (collected works) were published in 1940 in Mexico. He published *Nuevas Canciones,* 1924. *Poesías completas,* 1940, and he wrote three plays in collaboration with A. Machado y Ruiz, *Desdichas de la fortuna o Julianillo Valcárel,* tragicomedy, 1926; *Juan de Mañara,* drama, 1927; *La Lolaze va a los puertos,* comedy, 1930.

Maurice *Maeterlinck,* Count (1862–), Belgian dramatist, essayist and poet, winner of the Nobel Prize in 1911. In 1887 he went to Paris and made friends with the symbolists. He soon gave up law. In 1889 he published *Serres Chaudes* (poems) and produced *La Princesse Maleine,* in 1891 *L'Intruse* and *Les Aveugles,* in 1892 *Pelléas and Mélisande,* which became the libretto for the opera by Debussy. At 78 he fled in 1940 with his wife to New York.— English translations: Plays: *The Princess Maleine,* 1892; *Pelleas and Melisande,* 1892; *Alladene and Palomedes,* 1898; *Aglavaine and Selysette,* 1899; *The Death of Tintageles,* 1899; *Mary Madgalen,* 1909; *The Blue Bird,* 1909; *Betrothal,* 1912; *The Wrack of the Storm,* 1916; *The Burgomaster of Stilemonde,* 1918; *The Miracle of St. Anthony,* 1919; *The Cloud That Lifted,* 1923; *The Power of the Death,* 1923; Essays: *The Treasure of the Humble,* 1897; *Wisdom and Destiny,* 1898; *The Life of the Bee,* 1901; *The Buried Temple,* 1902; *The Double Garden,* 1904; *Life and Flowers,* 1907; *Death,* 1912; *The Life of Space,* 1923; *The Life of the White Ant,* 1926; *Magic of the Stars,* 1930; *The Life of the Ants,* 1931; *Pigeons and Spiders,* 1935; *The Hour Glass,* 1936.

André *Malraux* (1895–), French novelist. He did archeological research in Indo-China, collecting Kmer statues from old temples. He joined the Young Annam League in its fight for Indo-Chinese dominion status. In 1925 he worked with the Kuomintang and played a role in the Chinese national liberation movement. He was a secretary of the Bolshevik leader in China, Borodine. He founded with Louis Aragon the International Association of Writers for the Defense of Culture, which held its first congress at Paris in 1935. In 1936 Malraux helped organize an air corps for the Spanish Loyalists and made many flights over fascist territory. He was taken prisoner while in the French army in World War II and escaped. He was living in 1941 near Nice.—English translations: *The Conquerors*, 1929; *Man's Fate*, 1934; *The Royal Way*, 1934; *Days of Wrath*, 1936; *Man's Hope*, 1938.

Heinrich *Mann* (1871–), German novelist, playwright and essayist. He was born in Lübeck. His grandmother was a Brazilian of Portuguese origin. His father, a senator of Lübeck, was a merchant. From 1895 to 1898 he lived in Rome, later alternatively in Munich and Italy. He published *Im Schlaraffenland*, 1901; *Die Göttinnen*, 1907; *Die Kleine Stadt*, 1909; *Der Untertan*, 1918 (novel), which was a sharp attack against the Germany of Kaiser Wilhelm II, finished in 1914, its publication in a newspaper was forbidden by the German General Staff. During World War I he collaborated on René Schickele's *Weisse Blätter*, an anti-militarist literary magazine published in Switzerland, and wrote essays, such as *Zola*, 1915, that had great influence among young German writers. He published many novels, short stories, plays and essays, among them *Das Bekenntnis zum Uebernationalen*, 1933 (from which our selection is taken). After World War I he became a leader of German republican writers and a protagonist for Franco-German rapprochement. He has always loved Italy and France. Many of his novels are violent satires upon Germany. He became president of the literary section of the Prussian Academy, of which some of the members were G. Hauptmann, Thomas Mann, Jakob Wassermann, Franz Werfel, Alfred Doeblin, Leonhard Frank, etc. He fought a most courageous fight against the Nazis in Germany until 1933 and since then in exile. He published *Der Hass*, dealing with the Nazi leaders, and a historical novel in two volumes about Henri Quatre. After the fall of France he was rescued by the Emergency Rescue Committee and is now living in Hollywood. The original version of his "Supernational Manifesto" appeared first in Berlin in December 1932.—English translations: *The Poor*, 1917; *The Patrioteer*, 1918; *The Goddess*, 1918; *The Chief*, 1925; *In the Land of Cockaigne*, 1925; *Diana*, 1926; *The Royal Woman*, 1930; *Mother Mary*, 1930; *The Little Town*, 1931; *The Blue Angel*, 1932; *The Hill of Lies*, 1934; *Young Henry of Navarre*, 1938; *Henry, King of France*, 1939; *The Living Thoughts of Nietzsche* (ed.), 1939.

Klaus *Mann* (1906–), German novelist, essayist, and playwright. He was born in Munich, the second child of Thomas Mann. He left the country of his birth in 1933; he was expatriated by the Nazi government in 1934. He is now a staff-sergeant in the U. S. Army. He published more than twenty books—including novels, volumes of essays and short stories, travel books, and plays. He edited *Die Sammlung* (a literary monthly of anti-Nazi tendencies, published in Amsterdam, Holland) and *Decision: A Review of Free Culture*, New York. He wrote in English *The Turning Point: Thirty-five Years in This Century*, 1942; and *André Gide: And the Crisis of Modern Thought*, 1943.—English translations: *The Fifth Child*, a novelette, 1927; *Alexander*, novel, 1930; *Journey into Freedom*, novel, 1935; *Pathetic Symphony, A Tschaikovski Novel*, 1936. He published together with Erika Mann, *Escape to Life*, 1938 and *The Other Germany*, 1939.

Thomas *Mann* (1875–), German novelist, short-story writer and essayist, Nobel Prize winner for literature, 1929. He is the younger brother of Heinrich Mann, was born in Lübeck, son of a senator of that city who died when Mann was fifteen years old. Four years later the family moved to Munich. After a brief period in an insurance office and travels for some months in Italy, he returned to Munich and a desk in the office of the satirical review *Simplizissimus*. He published in 1898 novelettes *Der kleine Herr Friedemann und andere Novellen* and in 1903 his first novel *Die Buddenbrooks*, in 1909 his second novel *Königliche Hoheit*, in 1905 his play *Fiorenza*, and from 1903–1914 several volumes of short stories or novelettes including *Tristan*, 1903, *Death in Venice*, 1913, and *Tonio Kröger*. In both World Wars Thomas Mann published political essays dealing with the German crisis, *Friedrich und die Grosse Koalition* (1915) und *Betrachtungen eines Unpolitischen* (1918) were more on the conservative side, his *Order of the Day* (1942), (including *An Exchange of Letters, The Coming Victory of Democracy*,

This War, This Peace, etc.) are in the vanguard of democratic writing and of a new humanism. In 1924 he published his third long novel, *Der Zauberberg;* a fragment of a novel, *Bekenntnisse des Hochstaplers Felix Krull* in 1922 and in the same year novelettes and many essays, especially on Goethe and Tolstoy, and an edition of collected works. Since 1933 has been issued his fourth novel (in four volumes) *Joseph und seine Brüder.* In Germany Thomas Mann wrote against the coming Nazi barbarism, left in 1933 and lived in France, in Zurich, and, since 1938, in this country, (in Princeton, N. J., and later in Los Angeles). *Goethe's Career as a Man of Letters* was delivered as an address in 1932 at Weimar; its English version (somewhat abridged in our presentation) appeared in *Freud, Goethe, Wagner,* 1937. *Lotte in Weimar* is the first chapter of *The Beloved Returns,* 1940.—English translations: Novels: *Royal Highness,* 1906; *Buddenbrooks,* 1924; *The Magic Mountain,* 1927; *A Sketch of My Life,* 1930; *Joseph and His Brothers,* 1934; *Young Joseph,* 1935; *An Exchange of Letters,* 1937; *Joseph in Egypt,* 1938; *The Beloved Returns,* 1940; Stories: *Stories of Three Decades,* 1936; *The Transposed Heads,* 1940; Essays: *Three Essays,* 1929; *Past Masters and Other Essays,* 1933; *Freud, Goethe and Wagner,* 1937; *Order of the Day,* 1942.

Valeriu *Marcu* (1898–1942), Rumanian-born German writer. He was born in Bucharest, but wrote in German. He came at an early age to Vienna, at sixteen founded together with Willi Münzenberg a vanguard magazine, *Die Jugendinternationale,* in Zurich, and met Lenin, who contributed occasionally to the magazine. Marcu went on a political mission in 1917 to Russia, fought against Rumanian fascists in 1918, was an editor of a left-wing newspaper in Vienna in 1919 and then came to Berlin writing first political, then literary, then historical essays. He wrote the first biography of Lenin (*Lenin: 30 Jahre Russland*) 1927, and biographies of Scharnhorst (*Das Grosse Kommando Scharnhorsts*), 1928, and of *Machiavelli,* 1937, and published historical essays such as *Schatten der Geschichte,* 1926; *Männer und Mächt; Die Geburt der Nationen,* 1931; *Die Vertreibung der Juden aus Spanien,* 1934. He left Nazi Germany in 1933 and lived in Nice until 1941, when he came to this country. He died in New York in December 1942 and left half finished his autobiography, the story of the three revolutions that he had seen.—English translations: *Lenin,* 1928; *Men and Forces of Our Time,* 1931; *The Expul-*

sion of the Jews from Spain, 1935; *The Birth of the Nation,* 1932; *Accent on Power: the Life and Times of Machiavelli,* 1939.

Jacques *Maritain* (1882–), French philosopher. Born in Paris, he was converted to the Roman Catholic faith in 1906. He was on the faculty of the Collège Stanislas and the Institut Catholique in Paris and was the foremost spokesman of the "Catholic Revival" in France. He called himself an "anti-modernist." He is an interpreter of Neo-Thomism and, once a disciple of Bergson, an intellectual opponent of Bergson—*La Philosophie bergsonienne* (1918) was written as a course of philosophy for the Institut Catholique in Paris. After the fall of France in 1940 Maritain and his wife (a writer, too) came to North America, where he is a professor at the Institute of Medieval Studies in Toronto and visiting professor at Columbia and Princeton. — English translations: *Prayer and Intelligence* (with Raïssa Maritain), 1928; *Three Reformers,* 1929; *Primacy of the Mind,* 1930; *Introduction to Philosophy,* 1930; *Art and Scholasticism,* 1930; *The Things That Are Not Caesar's,* 1931; *The Angelic Doctor (St. Thomas Aquinas),* 1931; *Thomas,* 1933; *Freedom in the Modern World,* 1935; *Temporal Power and Liberty,* 1935; *The Degrees of Knowledge,* 1937; *An Introduction to Logic,* 1937; *True Humanism,* 1938; *Antisemitism,* 1939; *A Preface to Metaphysics,* 1939; *Scholasticism and Politics,* 1940; *Science and Wisdom,* 1940; *Religion in the Modern World,* 1943; *Living Thoughts of St. Paul* (ed.), 1941; *France, My Country,* 1941; *Ransoming the Time,* 1941; *Religion and Culture; A Christian Looks at the Jewish Question.*

Roger *Martin du Gard* (1881–), French novelist and playwright, winner of the Nobel Prize in 1937. He was born at Neuilly-sur-Seine, was trained at the Ecole des Chartes as an archivist and paleographer. In 1908 he published his first novel *Devenir* ("un mauvais roman de jeunesse"—says Martin du Gard). From 1910 to 1913 he worked on *Jean Barois,* novel. His school-friend Gallimard (N.R.F.) published it in 1913 as a result of André Gide's laudatory remarks. Jean Schlumberger and Copeau interested him in play-writing. During World War I he was at the front. From 1920 to 1936 he wrote the ten volumes of the series *Les Thibault,* which won him the Nobel Prize. He wrote three plays and *Vieille France,* "a simple album of village sketches." He lived in Paris, fled before the Nazis in 1940 to the South of France.—English translations: *The Thibaults* (Parts I–VI), 1936; *Summer 1914*, 1940.

Harry *Martinson* (1904–), Swedish poet, novelist and short-story writer. Son of a sea-captain who died when Martinson was a small child, he was brought up by the parish. He was at sea for six years, most of the time as a stoker, and his writings reflect the adventures and miseries of these years. Counted as a proletarian writer, Martinson is one of the finest lyric poets in Sweden.—English translation: *Cape Farewell* (from which our selection is taken).

François *Mauriac* (1885–), French novelist. He was born in Bordeaux, a Roman Catholic. He published poetry, criticism, two volumes of verse in 1909 and 1911 and a third in 1925, *Orages*. In 1912 he founded *Les Cahiers*, a Catholic magazine. In 1913 he published his first novel, *L'Enfant chargé de chaînes*—and married. He was a soldier in the first World War. He became in 1933 a member of the French Academy. During the Spanish Civil War he wrote against Spanish fascism and later against nazism. He is still in France.—English translations: Novels: *Thérèse* (from which our selection is taken), 1928; *Destinies*, 1929; *The Desert of Love*, 1929; *The Family*, 1930; *Suspicion*, 1932; *The Viper's Tangle*, 1933; Plays: *Asmodée: or, The Intruder*, 1939; Essays: *Maundy-Thursday*, 1932; *God and Mammon*, 1936; *Life of Jesus*, 1937; *Communism and Christians*, 1938.

Vladimir *Mayakovsky* (1894–1930), Russian poet. He was educated at a Gymnasium and later studied painting. His literary activity dates from 1911, when he met Burliuk and Chlebnikov and helped them to compose the Futurist Manifesto. He was an active member of the Bolshevik party from the age of fourteen and gave up all his energies and talent to the revolutionary cause. In 1930 he committed suicide. A short time before he had taken pains to contradict the suicide Essenin's dying words.

Karin *Michaelis* (1872–), Danish novelist. Karin Michaelis is the partial pseudonym of Katharina Marie (Bech-Brondum) Michaelis Strangeland. Born at Randers she married the Danish novelist Sophus Michaëlis. Soon after their separation she married an American, Charles Emil Strangeland. She published *Barnet*, 1901; *Lillemar*, 1901. She has written many novels and children's books, especially the *Bibi* series. She accused in *Der Fall d'Annunzio*, 1925, the Fascist writer D'Annunzio of having stolen the villa of the widow of Thode, the German art historian. She is the author of more than fifty books. She is living now in New York in exile.—English translations: *The Dangerous Age*, 1911; *Elsie Lindtner*, 1912; *The Governor*, 1913; *Bibi*, 1927; *Venture's End*, 1927; *Bibi Goes Travelling*, 1935; *Green Island*, 1936.

Henry *Michaux* (1899–), Belgian poet, essayist and novelist. He was born in Antwerp, studied law, writes in French. His principal works are: *Le Rêve et la jambe; Fables des origines; Qui-je-fus; Ecuador; Mes propriétés* (from which our selection has been taken); *La nuit des assassinats; un certain Plume; Moi qui fus.*

José Rodrigues *Miguéis* (1901–), Portuguese novelist, short-story writer. He was born in Lisbon, started writing at twenty for newspapers and magazines and at thirty he won the prize of the Newspaper Guild of Lisbon with a novel, *Páscoa feliz*. In 1933 he obtained another prize for his short story, *A mancha não se apaga*. A volume of his short stories, *Cinzas de incêndio*, will soon be published in Brazil. Most of his works remain unpublished and only a few of his stories have appeared in recent years in Portugal. He has written school texts and given numerous lectures. After spending three years in Belgium, José Rodrigues Miguéis came to the U.S.A. in 1935 and is at present associate-editor of the Portuguese edition of *The Reader's Digest.*

Svetoslav *Minkov* (1902–), Bulgarian short-story writer. He has published many volumes of short stories, *The Blue Chrysanthemum; The House by the Last Lantern; Automats; The Heart in a Cardboard Box*, etc., and has translated German novels into Bulgarian.

Gabriel *Miró* Ferrer (1879–1930), Spanish novelist. *Obras completas de Gabriel Miró* were published in sixteen volumes. He published in 1912 *Del huerto provinciano;* in 1916 *Figuras de la pasion del Señor*, and *Dentro del arcado, La palina rota;* in 1919 *El humo dormido;* in 1921 *El ángel, el molino, el caracol del faro, Estampas rurales y de cunetos, estampas de un león y una leona, estampas del faro;* and *Nuestro padre San Daniel, novela de capellanos y devotos;* in 1922 *Nino y grande*, novela; in 1926 *Las cerezas del cementerio*, novela; and *La novela de mi amigo;* in 1927 *El libro de siguenza;* and *Del vivir, corpus y otros cuentos;* in 1928 *El obispo leproso*, novela. In 1940 *Años y leguas* was published in Madrid.

Vilhelm *Moberg* (1898–), Swedish novelist and playwright. In his autobiographical cycle (*Memory of Youth* and *The Earth Is Ours*), he describes his development from the son of farming people, in Småland, to the life of an intellectual. He is an anti-Nazi. He has written many plays and historical novels and is the author of *Raskens, a Soldier's Family* and *Man's Woman*.—English translations: *The Earth Is Ours,* 1940; *Ride This Night!,* 1943.

Ferencz *Molnár* (1878–), Hungarian playwright, novelist and short-story writer. He studied law and statistics and in 1896 became a reporter for Budapest newspapers. His first novel was published in 1901, his first play in 1904. During the World War I, Molnár was a war correspondent and later published *A War Correspondent's Diary*. A collection of Molnár's plays—twenty in all—was published in U.S.A. In 1929, about twenty have been produced here.—English translations: *Plays,* 1929; *Husbands and Lovers,* 1924 (nineteen dialogues); *Prisoners,* (novel), 1925; *Eva and the Derelict Boat* (novelette), 1926; *Paul Street Boys* (a children's book), 1927; *The Good Fairy*.

Henry de *Montherlant*, Count (1896–), French poet, novelist and essayist. He was born in Paris, scion of an old noble family. He was sent to a Jesuit school. He admired Maurice Barrès, the French nationalist poet; he killed bulls in Burgos, Spain, in 1911; he is a staunch Catholic; he served in the first World War. His earliest novel was entitled *La relève du matin;* it was followed by *Le songe,* a war novel; *Les Olympiques;* and *Les Bestiaires (The Bullfighters,* from which our selection is taken). He later condemned Barrès. He served in the second World War and now lives in Vichy.—English translations: *The Bullfighters,* 1927; *Perish in Their Pride,* 1936; *Pity for Women,* 1938; *Costals and the Hippogriff,* 1940.

Lilika *Nakos* (1903–), Greek novelist. She was born in Athens. Her first story was printed in the French liberal magazine *Europe*. She has published novels, one of them, *Lost Soul*.

Martin Andersen-*Nexø* (1869–), Danish novelist. Born in Copenhagen, his father was a pavement-layer, who brought up eleven children, and his mother sold fish in the streets. When he was 9 they moved to the island of Bornholm. Martin Andersen-Nexø studied at a public high school. At 24 he became a school-teacher. In 1898 he published *Shadows,* a collection of short stories, in 1901 his novel, *The Frank Family,* in 1903 a travel book, *Days in the Sun,* in 1910 the four volumes of his novel, *Pelle the Conqueror,* and between 1917 and 1921 his trilogy, *Ditte*. After the war he sympathized with communism and settled in Germany. He gave an account of his travels in the U.S.S.R. in *Toward Dawn,* 1923; he returned to Denmark and wrote a novel about Danish farmers, *In God's Land*. In 1932 the first volume of his memoirs was published, *Et Lille Krae* (A Small Child). He was one of the strongest anti-Nazi writers, and is now believed to be a prisoner of the Nazis.—English translations: *Pelle the Conqueror,* 1914–17; *Ditte,* 1920–22; *Days in the Sun,* 1929; *In God's Land,* 1933; *Under the Open Sky,* 1938.

Vítězlav *Nezval* (1900–), Czech poet. He was born in a small town of Moravia and died in a German concentration camp. He translated Lautréamont into Czech and was under the influence of the surrealists. His *52 Bitter Ballads of the Student Robert David* (published as an allegedly posthumous work), made a literary sensation. He published collections of poems under bizarre names: *Podivuhodny Kouzelnik* (The Marvellous Magician), *Papousek na motocyklu* (The Parrot on the Motorcycle), *Falesny Marias* (Cardsharpers), *Akrobat* (The Acrobat), and *Básne Noci* (Poems of the Night). The last-named volume contains the long reflective poem *Edison* in which Nezval's view of life expresses itself in full force. The poems published here are taken from his collection *Praha Prsty Deste* (Prague Through Fingers of Rain).

Ivan *Olbracht* (1888–1941), Czech novelist. His real name was Camil Zeman. His father, Antal Stašek, was one of the foremost "awakeners of the nation." Olbracht himself created modern Czech prose. Among his works were: *The Evil Hermits; The Strange Friendship of the Actor Jesenius; Golet in the Valley; Nicola Shuhay, the Brigand*. Olbracht died in 1941 of "causes unknown" under the Nazi occupation.

Yury Karlovich *Olesha* (1899–) Russian novelist, playwright and short-story writer. He is the son of an office worker. His first writings were critical articles in the form of verse in the Transport Worker's newspaper, "Gudok", under the pseudonym of Zubilo. His first novel was called *Envy,* in 1926, followed by *Love,* and *The Grapevine*. He wrote several plays, including *List of Benefits,* and in 1934, *The Severe Young Man*. In 1937 he wrote the scenario for a movie called *Walter,* and in 1928 a children's book, *The Three Fat Men;* Olesha adapted it for stage production.

José *Ortega y Gasset* (1883–), Spanish essayist and philosopher. He was born in Madrid, son of a famous journalist, and went to a Jesuit school; he spent several years at German universities, especially at Marburg, where Hermann Cohen, the neo-Kantian philosopher, was his teacher. Ortega y Gasset then became professor of philosophy at the University of Madrid. In 1908 he founded the magazine *Faro* (The Beacon), a few years later, *Europa,* another magazine concerned with the spiritual crisis of Spain. On March 23, 1914, he pronounced his speech on "Old and New Politics" in which he denounced as old the Restoration, the Regency and Alfonso XIII. In 1915 he founded the magazine *España,* with the collaboration of Baroja, Azorin, d'Ors and Pérez de Ayala. In *El Sol,* a liberal newspaper which he founded, on November 15, 1930, he published an article "El Error Berenguer" with the cry: "Spaniards! Our state does not exist! Let us build one! Delenda est monarchia!" which led indirectly to the establishment of the Republic, April 14, 1931. In 1931 he became a deputy from the province of Leon. During the Spanish Civil War he fled to Paris and became later a voluntary exile in the Argentine. In 1941, he was appointed professor of philosophy at the University, Lima, Peru.—English translations: *The Revolt of the Masses* (from which our selection is taken), 1932; *The Modern Theme,* 1933; *Invertebrate Spain,* 1937; *Toward a Philosophy of History,* 1941.

Paul van *Ostayen* (1896–1928), Belgian poet. He was born in Antwerp and died at Miavoye-Anhée. He wrote in Flemish, published *Music Hall; Het Sienjaal; Bezette Stad; Gedichten;* as well as a number of essays, *Krities Proza,* and some short stories among which *Het Bordeel van Ika Loch* is outstanding.

Arnulf *Överland* (1889–), Norwegian poet. Överland matured early as a lyric poet; his first book was published in 1911. The first World War and the ensuing twenty years of ominous peace influenced Överland deeply as a writer as well as an individual. He took a vigorous stand against injustice in his own country as well as abroad. His prophetic insight is reflected in his poem, *You Must Not Sleep.* After the Nazi invasion, Överland continued to write, "anonymously." The poem *We Shall Survive* has become the anthem of national resistance. His refusal to leave or to keep silent led to his being put in a German concentration camp.

Boris *Pasternak* (1890–), Russian poet. The son of an Academy painter, he studied philosophy at Moscow and in Germany. His literary activity began in 1913; he became well known after the Russian revolution. Although an innovator in verse, he has not concerned himself with political innovations in his themes and has maintained a good deal of independence and influence as a poet, in spite of being criticized for his aloofness. He published in 1925 a collection of tales, *Kasskazy.*

Elin-Pelin (1878–), Bulgarian poet and short-story writer. Elin-Pelin is the penname of Dimitur Ivanov. He was for years a schoolteacher and edited many children's magazines. At present he is director of the Vazov Museum, Sofia. He has published short stories and poems for both children and adults. Some titles are: *Black Roses,* (poems); *Under the Monastery's Vine Tree,* (short stories); *I, You, He,* (short stories); *Land,* (novel); *Pizho and Pendo* (humoristic pieces).

Saint-John Perse (1887–), French poet. His real name is Alexis St. Léger-Léger. He was born in Saint Léger-les-Feuilles, Guadeloupe, and went to France at 11. He prepared for and entered the diplomatic service, was a close collaborator with Briand and for years held important posts in the French Foreign Office. He published some early poems, *Eloges,* later *Anabase* (translated into English by T. S. Eliot) and *Exil,* written since coming to this country in the summer of 1941. He is a Fellow of the Library of Congress.—English translation: *Anabasis,* 1930.

Rastko *Petrovich* (1898–), Yugoslav poet and novelist. Born in Belgrade, widely traveled in Europe, having lived for years in Paris and in Italy, Rastko Petrovich came to this country six years ago and is now on the staff of the Royal Yugoslav Embassy. His first book was a novel-history of the Slavs in the Balkans from the sixth to the eleventh centuries *(The Burlesque of Perun,* God of the Storm). A collection of his verse was published under the title *Apocalypse,* and his poem "Great Friend" (part of a longer one) was read on May 10, 1943, in New York at the international commemoration of the Tenth Anniversary of the (Nazi) Burning of Books. He is the author of the following fiction: *The People Speaks; Immeasurable Force's; Eight Weeks in 1915;* and a book of travel, *Africa.*

Robert *Pick* (1898–), Austrian novelist. He was born in Vienna, where he published under the pen-name Valentin Richter a novel, *Ein Leben und ein Augenblick und Ein Tag*. He is now working as a free-lance writer in this country.

Luigi *Pirandello* (1867–1936), Italian dramatist, novelist, short-story writer, Nobel prize-winner in 1934. He was born in Agrigento, Sicily, his name being of Hellenic origin. He became a teacher of Italian literature at the women's normal school in Rome, where he remained for some thirty years. He published more than twenty volumes of short stories and three novels, in 1904 his novel, *Il fu Mattia Pascal*. In 1912, at forty-five, he wrote his first one-act play, *La Morsa; Se non cosi* was produced in 1913. These early plays were written and produced in the Sicilian dialect of Agrigento. *Six Characters in Search of an Author* was produced in Rome in 1931, *Enrico IV* in 1922. In 1921 he retired as a teacher, later in 1925, he founded his own theater in Rome and took his company on summer tours through Europe. He became a member of the Fascist literary academy, but was not a "Fascist writer".—English translations: Plays: *Sicilian Limes*, 1922; *Three Plays*, 1923; *Each in His Own Way*, and two other plays, 1925; *One-Act Plays*, 1928; *As You Desire Me*, 1931; Novels: *The Late Mattia Pascal*, 1923; *The Outcast*, 1925; *Shoot!*, 1927; *The Old and the Young*, 1928; Short Stories: *Horse in the Moon*, 1931; *One, No One and Hundred Thousand*, 1933; *Naked Truth*, 1934; *The Medals and Other Stories*, 1939.

Charles *Plisnier*, Belgian novelist and short-story writer. He writes in French. He got the Prize Goncourt for *Faux Passeports* (short stories, from which our selection is taken). In 1936 he published a novel *Mariages*. — English translation: *Marriages*, novel.

Renato *Poggioli* (1907–), Italian essayist. He was formerly instructor in Russian at the University of Florence, and in Italian at the Universities of Warsaw and Wilno and formerly visiting lecturer at Smith College. He is now professor of Roman Languages and Literature at Brown University. He published *La Violetta Notturna*, an anthology of modern Russian poetry translated into Italian, 1933; *Pietre di Paragone*, a book of critical essays on modern European writers, 1938. He translated into Italian the works of Bunin, Babel, Essenin, Blok, Remizov, Hašek, etc.

Pantelis *Prevalakis*, Greek poet. He was born in Crete, studied in Paris, traveled through Spain. He published *Chronicle of a Town* and a collection of poems *The Naked Poetry*.

Marcel *Proust* (1871–1922), French novelist. He was born in Paris. His father Adrien Proust, a Roman Catholic, was a public hygienist; through his Jewish mother Marcel Proust was a cousin of Henri Bergson. At 9 Marcel suffered his first attack of asthma, the disease that tortured him to the end of his life. On finishing his baccalaureate he enlisted as volunteer in an infantry regiment at Orléans. Proust was attracted by the literary salons and the aristocratic life of the Faubourg St. Germain. In 1896 he published *Les Plaisirs et les Jours*, a collection of sketches, with a preface by, or signed by, Anatole France. Between 1900 and 1905 he was a kind of gossip writer for *le Figaro*, describing the salons which he frequented such as those of Madame Strauss and Princesse Mathilde, Princesse de Polignac and Madame de Caillavet where he met often Anatole France. After the death of his father in 1903 and of his mother in 1905, Proust moved to 102 Boulevard Haussmann and wrote in a dark, cork-lined room for the next seventeen years a long novel in many volumes *A la Recherche du Temps Perdu*. At very rare intervals he left his room and kept in touch with the world through countless letters, which now fill a dozen volumes. He completed in 1911 the first 700 pages of his novel and, tired of publishers' refusals, he printed them at his own expense in 1913. In 1918 appeared *A l'Ombre des Jeunes Filles en Fleurs*. Proust won the Goncourt Prize for 1919, after his forty-eighth birthday. When he died, three years later, he had completed *A la Recherche du Temps Perdu*, but had proofread only half the entire work, which was published in completion in 1927. On the day of his death, Proust asked for the pages of "The Death of Bergotte," which is our selection, and made certain revisions.—English translations: *Remembrance of Things Past*, 1922–1932; (2-volume complete edition), 1941.

Charles Ferdinand *Ramuz* (1878–), Swiss novelist and essayist. Ramuz writes in French. He is "the poet of the Vaudland." He published many novels, short stories, and essays, among them: *Aline*, novel, 1927; *La beauté sur la terre*, 1928; *Derborence*, récit, 1936; *Farinet: ou, La Fausse monnaie*, 1932; *Le garçon Savoyard*, novel, 1937; *La grande peur dans la montagne; Joie dans le ciel*, 1935.

Gustav *Regler* (1898–), German novelist. Born in the Saar region of Germany, he is the son of a bookseller, was a soldier in World War I, studied in Munich and Heidelberg, wrote his thesis on "Goethe's Irony", went through half a dozen professions in the post-war years and became a novelist. He published *Zug der Hirten; Wasser, Brot und blaue Bohnen*, 1932; *Der verlorene Sohn*, 1934 (published by Querido, Amsterdam, the biggest anti-Nazi publishing house in Europe). In spring 1933 Regler left Nazi Germany and went to the Saar before the plebiscite to combat the Nazis; he fled to Paris, then went to Spain in 1936 to fight against the Nazis; a member of the International Brigade, he was wounded, came back to France and in September 1939 was put, with most German political refugees and anti-Nazi writers, into French concentration camps. He was released (through the help of English friends) in May 1940 and came through this country to Mexico City, where he lives. He published in Paris a novel, *Die Saat*, and in 1940 *The Great Crusade*, a novel about the International Brigade (with a preface by Ernest Hemingway).—English translations: *The Prodigal Son*, 1934; *The Great Crusade*, 1940.

Alexei Mikhailovich *Remisov* (1877–), Russian essayist, novelist and playwright. He was banished from the University of Moscow when a student for his noncomformist activities. In 1905 he was business manager of *Voprossy Zhizni*, which published a novel of his in serial form. He published *La Russie dans ses inscriptions* and *La Passion de l'Univers*, a series of legends; *La Foi Russe*, a cycle of twenty-five tales; *Les Femmes Russes*, twenty-four portraits. From 1910 to 1912 his collected work in eight volumes were published in Petersburg. He has published studies of Gogol and Turgenev, literary reminiscences, works on Russian history, and has frequently illustrated his own books, as he is an accomplished calligrapher. His play, *Le Tzar Maximilien*, was performed during the Revolution by soldiers of the Red Army. In 1924 he escaped from Russia and made his home on the Avenue Mozart in Paris.—English translations: *The Clock*, short stories, 1924; *The Fifth Pestilence*, 1927.

Aquilino *Ribeiro* (1877–), Portuguese novelist. He is the author of *Filhas de Babilonia* (from which our selection was translated); *Terras do Demo; Via Sinuosa*, and of many short stories and essays.

Rainer Maria *Rilke* (1875–1926), German poet. He was born in Prague. His father came of a Catholic aristocratic family, his mother was Jewish. At 10 he was sent to a military school at St. Pölten, where life was a nightmare to him. ("What I suffered at that time is tantamount to the world's worst anguish . . ."). In 1890 he returned to Prague and was "condemned" to a business career, went to the Handelsakademie at Linz and eloped with a governess. Expelled from the business school he studied at the University of Vienna. In 1894 the first verses of Rilke were published, *Leben und Lieder: Bilder und Tagebuchblätter*. He then went to the University of Prague and decided to become a popular poet. Between 1895 and 1896 he published at his own expense two cheaply printed volumes of verse under the general title *Wegwarten*, then, in 1896 and 1897, *Larenopfer* and *Traumgekrönt*. In 1899 he spent a year in Russia—"Russia has made me what I am." He then joined a colony of landscape painters in Worpswede (1901–1902) where he met and married Clara Westhoff, a former pupil of Rodin. Rilke went to Paris to write a critical work about Rodin, whom he idolized. He lived for a while in Italy, Scandinavia and Germany; he learned Danish in order to read everything written by the Danish writer, Jens Peter Jacobsen (1847–1885). He began in Rome in 1903 and finished in 1910 *Die Aufzeichnungen des Malte Laurids Brigge* (The Journal of My Other Self) which appeared in 1910. He was a friend of the Danish writer Hermann Bang. About 1905 Rilke became Rodin's secretary; by March 1906 Rilke was writing from Meudon "as from a jail"—Rilke left the sculptor. He revised and sent to press a narrative poem begun in 1899, *Die Weise von Liebe und Tod des Cornets Christoph Rilke*, and wrote two volumes of poems, *Neue Gedichte* and *Der Neuen Gedichte Anderer Teil*. He visited in 1910 Algeria, Tunis and Egypt, and spent part of 1911 and 1912 in a castle in Duino, a seaport on the Adriatic, and in 1914 toured Spain. At the beginning of the first World War he joined the Austrian army but broke down under the strain of military life, and then lived in Vienna and Munich. In 1919, he went to Switzerland, where the last part of his life was spent in the Château de Muzot, near Montreux. In 1923 he finished his *Duineser Elegien*, begun in 1911. He died in 1926 of blood poisoning. He translated poems and prose of Petrarch, Mallarmé, Gide, Valéry and Elizabeth Barrett Browning.—English translations: *Poems*, 1918; *Auguste Rodin*, 1919; *The Life of the Virgin Mary*, 1925; *The Journal of My Other Self*, 1930; *Elegies from the Castle of Duino*, 1931;

The Tale of the Love and Death of Cornet Christopher Rilke, 1932; *Stories of God*, 1932; *Letters to a Young Poet*, 1934; *Requiem and Other Poems*, 1935; *Later Poems*, 1938; *Translations from the Poetry of Rainer Maria Rilke*, 1938; *Duiner Elegies*, 1939; *Fifty Selected Poems*, 1940; *Wartime Letters*, 1940; *The Book of Hours*, 1941; *Sonnets to Orpheus*, 1942.

Henriette *Roland Holst*, (née van der Schalk), (1869–   ), Dutch poet. She is the author of about twelve volumes, of which *De Nieuwe Geboort* (1902), *De Vrouw in het Woud* (1912) and *Vernieuwingen* (1929) are the most important. Further publications: an epic poem, *Heldensage*, 1927; a series of lyric dramas, *De Opstandelingen*, 1910; *Thomas More*, 1912; three biographical studies, *Jean Jacques Rousseau*, 1912, one on Garibaldi, *De Held en de Schare*, 1920, and *Leo Tolstoi*, 1930. In addition to her extensive literary work, Henriette Roland Holst took an active part in Netherlands political life. She was originally a Social Democrat, then changed to the Communist Party. She wrote approximately ten large works on political economy, the best known of which are *Geschiedenis van den Proletarischen Klassenstrijd*, 1909, and *Communisme en Moraal*, 1925. She earlier devoted much attention to the German philosopher Dietzgen.

Romain *Rolland* (1866–1943), French novelist, playwright and essayist, winner of the Nobel Prize in 1917. He was born at Clamecy and determined to devote himself to music. He was a schoolmate of Paul Claudel. At 20 he entered the Ecole Normale Supérieure in Paris. In 1889 he went to Rome and wrote a play *Orsino*. Later he became professor of the history of art at the Ecole Normale Supérieure. He also joined the faculty of the Sorbonne. In 1898 *Alert* was produced at Paris. He determined to write a dramatic commentary on the French Revolution, about which he wrote a cycle of eight plays. In Rome he became a friend of Malvida von Meysenbug, who had been the friend of many political refugees as Richard Wagner, Nietzsche, Mazzini, Alexander Herzen. *Jean Christophe*, the life-story of a musical genius, was first published in *Cahiers de la Quinzaine*, the magazine of Charles Péguy. Rolland published *Des Vies des Hommes Illustres*. 1914 found him in Switzerland and he became unpopular in France because of a series of pacifist articles published in the *Journal de Genève*. The articles were collected in book form under the title *Au Dessus de la Mêlée*, in 1915. He lived from 1922 to 1937 at Villeneuve, on the shore of Lake Geneva. In 1935 he was the guest of Maxim Gorki in Moscow. In 1937 he established himself at Vézelay in France, where he worked on his memoirs. Vichy imposed house arrest on him in 1941 and in 1943 the Nazis put him (and twenty other French writers) in a concentration camp; Rolland's death there has just been reported. He called himself "a republican with advanced socialist sympathies, an internationalist at heart and . . . a citizen of the world." It was Anatole France who recommended him for the Nobel Prize. The essay printed here is from *Goethe and Beethoven.*—English translations: *Jean Christophe*, 1910–13; *Michelangelo*, 1915; *Handel*, 1916; *The People's Theatre*, 1918; *Colas Breugnon*, 1919; *Clerambault*, 1921; *Pierre and Luce*, 1922; *Gandhi*, 1924; *The Soul Enchanted*, 1925–27; *Beethoven the Creator*, 1929; *Prophets of New India*, 1930; *Goethe and Beethoven*, 1931; *Letters of Romain Rolland and Malvida von Meysenbug 1890–91*, 1933; *I Will Not Rest*, 1935; *The Wolves* (play), 1937; *The Living Thoughts of Rousseau* (ed.), 1939.

Jules *Romains* (1885–   ), French novelist, playwright, poet and essayist. Jules Romains is the pen-name of Louis Farigoule. He spent much of his youth in Montmartre; at 18 he sponsored "Unanism," a literary school of his own. His first book of verse was *L'Ame des Hommes*, 1904. *La Vie Unanime* was published in 1908 by the Abbaye, (see note on Duhamel). After 1909 Romains was professor at Laon, Brest, Nice, Paris. In 1911 his first play was produced, *L'armée dans la ville*. Before the World War he was against war, during that war he wrote for an American magazine *Pour que l'Europe soit*, which was not published till 1930—it was a plea for Pan-Europeanism. After the World War he worked for a spiritual union of France and Germany. In this war Romains wrote and broadcast vigorously against Hitler. After the fall of France he came to this country. He now lives in Mexico. Romains considers his novels and successful plays only a preparation for his series *Men of Good Will*.—English translations: *The Death of a Nobody*, 1914; *Eyeless Sight* ("a study of the extra-retinal vision and the paroptic sense"), 1924; *Doctor Knock* (play), 1925; *Lucienne*, 1925; *Six Gentlemen in a Row*, 1927; *The Body's Rapture*, 1933; *Men of Good Will*, a series of novels, published here from 1933 on; *The Seven Mysteries of Europe*, 1941; *Stefan Zweig, Great European*, 1941; *Salsette Discovers America*, 1942.

Joseph *Roth* (1894–1939), Austrian novelist, short-story writer and essayist. He was born in Schwabendorf, Volynia, studied at Vienna, was an Austrian soldier in World War I; the Russian Revolution surprised him in Shmirinka; and after many detours he got back to Vienna. He wrote for Vienna and Berlin newspapers, later for the *Frankfurter Zeitung*. After 1924 he began writing novels. On the day Hitler became Chancellor, Roth left Berlin for Paris, where he lived in exile until his death on May 1939. While reading in a newspaper in Paris that his friend Ernst Toller had hanged himself in New York, he suffered a stroke of apoplexy and died a week later of pneumonia. Our selection is Roth's last work, finished several months before his death.—English translations: *Flight without End*, 1930; *Job: The Story of a Simple Man*, 1931; *Radetzky March*, 1933; *Tarabas, a Guest on Earth*, 1934; *Antichrist*, 1935; *The 100 Days*, 1936; *Confession of a Murderer: Told in One Night*, 1938.

Mihail *Sadoveanu*, Rumanian novelist. A modern writer of Rumanian prose, his *The Land Beyond the Dark; A Mill on the Sereth; The Realm of the Waters* (from which our selection is taken) are particularly representative.

Antoine de *Saint Exupéry* (1900–), French essayist. Born in Lyon, he went to school in Fribourg, Switzerland, studied flying in Strasbourg and went to Morocco as a cadet. To satisfy a passion for aviation he began in 1926 flying on commercial routes to Africa and South America. He was a captain in the French air force in World War II and had an adventurous escape from France. He came to this country in 1940 and is now flying for the Free French.—English translations: *Night Flight*, 1932; *Southern Mail*, 1933; *Wind, Sand and Stars*, 1939; *Flight to Arras*, 1942; *The Little Prince* (children's book), 1943.

Gaetano *Salvemini* (1873–), Italian essayist. Born in Molfetta, he was professor of history at the Universities of Messina, Pisa and Florence. He was a member of the Italian parliament, 1919–1921, and in 1925 imprisoned for anti-Fascist activities, later leaving that country. He has been a lecturer at Harvard since 1934. He is a Corresponding Fellow of the Medieval Academy, and a Fellow of the American Academy of Arts and Sciences. He is the author of *Magrati e Popolani in Firenze*, 1899; *Rivoluzione Francese*, 1905; *Mazzini*, 1905; *Riforma della Scuola Media*, 1908; *Questione dell' Adriatico*, 1918; *Partito Popolare e Questione Romana*, 1922; *Dall Patto di Londra alla Pace di Roma*, 1925.—Books available in English: *Fascist Dictatorship in Italy*, 1927; *Under the Axe of Fascism*, 1935; *Historian and Scientist*, 1939; *What to Do with Italy?* (written with George La Piana), 1943.

Axel *Sandemose* (1897–), Norwegian writer. Born in Denmark, he moved as a child to Norway. He was once a Danish author, but changed to become a Norwegian writer—an easy procedure as the two languages are similar.—English translations: *Horns for Our Adornment; A Fugitive Crosses His Tracks* (from which our selection is taken).

Arthur van *Schendel* (1874–), Dutch novelist. He was born in Batavia, the son of a high-ranking officer. From 1919 he lived in Italy, the last twelve years at Sestre Levante. His principal work is a trilogy consisting of the novels *Een Hollandsch Drama*, *De Rijke Man* and *Grauwe Vogels*. The first and third of these have been translated into English.—*A House in Haarlem; Grey Birds*.

René *Schickele* (1883–January 1940), German novelist, poet, playwright and essayist. He was born in Oberehnheim in Alsace. His father was a German, his mother French. He studied at Strasbourg and brought out at 19 a magazine *Der Stürmer*, and in 1904–05 another magazine *Das Neue Magazin*. In 1901 he published his first poems, *Sommernächte*, in 1907 his first novel, *Der Fremde*, in 1912 *Meine Freundin Lo*, a novelette, and in 1914 the novel, *Benkal der Frauentröster*, a prophetic picture of the coming war. In 1913 he collected his best pieces, written for an Alsatian paper from Paris in *Schreie auf dem Boulevard*. Schickele with a group of writers settled in 1915 in Zurich. Hating the war, he made *Die Weissen Blätter* (founded by Franz Blei), an anti-militarist, anti-imperialist magazine and published in it the work of Franz Kafka, Leonhard Frank, Carl Sternheim, Franz Werfel, Heinrich Mann, Henri Barbusse, Duhamel, and Latzko (*Men at War*). Schickele's play, *Hans im Schnakenloch*, was produced in 1916. After the war he settled down in Badenweiler. He published his trilogy, *Der Erbe am Rhein*, 1925–1931. He was a member of the Prussian Academy and a French citizen. When Hitler came to power, he went to France. He published then two novels, *Die Witwe Bosca* (1934) and *Flaschenpost* (1937). His last book was first written in French, *Le Retour;* at the same time a German translation was published (with a preface by

Hermann Kesten). Suffering during the latter part of his life from asthma he died in 1940 before the fall of France. *Angelica* is printed here for the first time in English.—English translations: *Maria Capponi,* 1928; *Heart of Alsace,* 1929.

Arthur *Schnitzler* (1862–1931), Austrian playwright, novelist,. short-story writer. He was born in Vienna, became a doctor and at about the age of thirty gave up his medical career and wrote his first play *Das Märchen.* It was produced in Vienna but was withdrawn as being "immoral." His first work to be published was *Anatol,* 1893. *Liebelei* was produced in 1895. *Reigen* (1900), a series of dialogues, could not be performed until 1920 because of its subject matter. Influenced by a "pleasant naturalism" and by Freudianism, he published many plays, short stories and novels.—English translations: Plays: *Anatol,* 1911; *Liebelei,* 1914; *Comedies of Words,* 1917; *Intermezzo, Countess Mizzi and The Lonely Way,* 1926; *Professor Bernhardi,* 1928; Novels and Stories: *Viennese Idylls,* 1913; *Bertha Garlan,* 1918; *Casanova's Homecoming,* 1921; *The Shepherd's Pipe and Other Stories,* 1922; *Road to the Open,* 1923; *Dr. Graesler,* 1923; *Fräulein Else,* 1925; *Beatrice,* 1926; *None but the Brave,* 1926; *Rhapsody,* 1927; *Daybreak,* 1928; *Theresa,* 1928; *Flight into Darkness,* 1931; *Six Viennese Novelettes,* 1931; *The Green Cockatoo,* 1933; *A Farewell Supper,* 1934.

Franz *Schoenberner* (1892–), German essayist. Born in Berlin, he was a soldier in the first World War, and after 1919 an editor of Musarion publishing house, Munich, and consecutively chief editor of *Auslandspost, Jugend* and the satirical magazine *Simplizissimus.* As his magazine attacked Hitler and the Nazis until the Reichstag fire, Schoenberner was forced to flee the country; he crossed the mountains and came to Switzerland and then France. In 1941 he came to this country. He lives in New York, is now Research Associate and Lecturer for the Council for Social Action. He is working on his autobiography.

Ramón J. *Sender* (1901–), Spanish novelist, playwright. The son of a small farmer, he was sent at 11 to a Catholic school, worked then as a clerk in a drug-store, studied at Madrid University, "was active in revolutionary movements." At 20 he served his military term fighting in Morocco, in the so-called "War of Reconquest", recounted in *Imam,* 1930. He joined the editorial staff of *El Sol* in Madrid and remained there during the dictatorship of Primo de Rivera, "taking part in many revolutionary movements." At one time he was in danger of execution in Segovia; he managed to escape, although he was later arrested and imprisoned in Madrid. His book *O.P.* (orden publica), 1931, deals with his experiences in prison. He published an antireligious fictional biography, *El Verbo se Hizo Sexo.* With the fall of the dictatorship of Primo de Rivera he abandoned *El Sol,* became a member of the National Confederation of Labor. He is proud to be called a proletarian writer. He escaped from Spain after the fall of the Loyalists and is now in Mexico.—English translations: *Pro Patria: or, Earmarked for Hell,* 1935; *Seven Red Sundays,* 1936; *Dark Wedding; Mr. Witt Among the Rebels,* 1937; *Counter-attack in Spain,* 1937; *A Man's Place* (from which our selection is taken), 1940.

Victor *Sharenkoff* (1892–), Bulgarian-American essayist. Born in Tserovo, Bulgaria, he studied philology and law at the University of Sofia. In 1927 he obtained a Ph.D. from Columbia University. He was first published in 1915, was editor of the *Zemledelska Pravda* (Agrarian Justice) in Sofia, lectured at Columbia for five years and now is on the staff of New York Public Library. He contributes to the *Narodna Volya* (Detroit) and to Serbian and Croatian newspapers. He has translated a number of short stories from Bulgarian into English, also from English and Russian into Bulgarian.—English publications: *Manichaeism in Bulgaria, with special reference to the Bogumils,* 1927, and numerous articles in various publications.

Mikhail *Sholokhov* (1895–), Russian novelist. He comes from a middle-class Cossack family, his mother being of Turkish origin. At 16 he worked with the Bolsheviks, in 1922 he fought against bandits in the Don region. In 1925 he published *Tales of the Don.* In 1941 he became one of the "fighting correspondents" in Soviet Russia.—English translations: *And Quiet Flows the Don* (from which our selection is taken), 1934; *Seeds of Tomorrow,* 1935; *The Don Flows Home to the Sea,* 1941.

Frans Eemil *Sillanpää* (1888–), Finnish novelist, winner of the Nobel Prize in 1939. He was born in Haemeenkyroe. His first novel was *Life and Sun* (1916). He was closely associated with the free community of artists in Southern Finland, among them the composer Jan Sibelius, the author Juhani Aho and the painter

Eero Järnefelt. He was influenced by Strindberg, Maeterlinck, Hamsun.—English translations: *The Maid Silja*, 1931 (from which our selection is taken); *A Man's Road*, 1932; *People in a Summer Night*, 1934; *Meek Heritage*, 1938.

Ignazio *Silone* (1900–   ), Italian novelist and essayist. Ignazio Silone is the penname of Secondo Tranquilli. Like Croce, he lost his parents in an earthquake in Southern Italy. He early joined the Peasant League, opposed the last war and, after the setting-up of the Fascist regime, lived for three years illegally in Italy, doing highly dangerous anti-Fascist organizational work. He has been imprisoned in Italy and Spain and since 1930 has lived in Switzerland; in this latter period he began writing books, which reflect his knowledge of the political circumstances of Fascist Italy.—English translations: *Fontamara* (from which our selection is taken), 1934; *Mr. Aristotle* (stories), 1935; *Bread and Wine*, 1936; *The School for Dictators* (essay), 1938; *The Living Thoughts of Mazzini* (ed.), 1939; *The Seed Beneath the Snow*, 1942.

Jan *Slauerhoff* (1897–1936), Dutch poet, short-story writer, and essayist. He roamed all over the world as a ship's doctor and spent a long time in the Far East and in South America. His collected works comprise three volumes of verse, one of short stories and one of short essays and a play.

Antoni *Slonimski* (1895–   ), Polish poet and playwright. Born in Warsaw, he was trained as a painter, gave up painting to become a free-lance journalist. He was an active member of the Skamander group of poets. He has published poems, literary reviews and plays, in 1932 *Journey to Russia*. Some plays were produced in Poland, *The Negro of Warsaw* and *The Family*. Slonimski is also a translator. During the present war a verse collection has been brought out, *The Alarm*. He is an editor of the magazine *Nowa Polska* (New Poland) in London, where he lives in exile.

Eugénie *Söderberg*, Swedish novelist and essayist. She wrote several books, scenarios and radio scripts. (*Studentfabriken*—The Student Factory—a novel about Swedish youth of our time). She has been a special correspondent in Russia, North Africa, Greece and the Near East, publishing articles, essays and a travel book. She came to this country as a correspondent of Swedish newspapers and periodicals. At present she is finishing a book about the United States, for Swedish readers, and a novel.

Borivoje *Stanković* (1876–1927), Yugoslav novelist and playwright. He wrote in Serbian, author of a popular play, *Koštana*, concerning a young gypsy, and a novel, *Impure Blood*, describing the degeneracy of a family.

Italo Svevo (1861–1928), Italian novelist and short-story writer. Italo Svevo is the pen-name of Ettore Schmitz. Born in Trieste of an Austrian father and Italian mother, he lived from 12 to 17 in Würzburg and became a successful businessman hiding his writing under a pseudonym. In 1892 appeared his first novel, *Una Vita*, in 1898 *Senilità*. In 1907 he took an English teacher, "a lean, tallish, highly excitable fellow of 25 who wanted to be a writer but meanwhile had to live from hand to mouth by teaching English," James Joyce. During the World War, Svevo became a rich man and retired. In 1923 he published his third novel, *Coscienza di Zeno*. He was working on a sequel to this novel when, as a result of an automobile accident at Motta di Livenza, he died. Some short stories were posthumously published, *The Story of the Nice Old Man and the Pretty Girl* and *The Hoax*. James Joyce never tired of singing his praises.—English translations: *The Hoax*, 1930; *The Nice Old Man and the Pretty Girl and Other Stories*, 1930; *Confessions of Zeno*, 1930; *As a Man Grows Older*, 1932.

Ernst *Toller* (1893–1939), German playwright, poet, essayist. He was born at Samotschin on the German Polish frontier. His father, a merchant, died when Toller was 16. He studied at Grenoble; at the outbreak of the World War he reached Munich via Switzerland, and reported as a volunteer; he was at the front for thirteen months, was wounded and discharged. He studied at Munich and Heidelberg, where he met war-weary students. The General Staff suppressed their small organization; Toller escaped to Berlin, where he met Kurt Eisner, and followed him to Munich. Toller was arrested at the strike of the munition workers and sent to a military prison. The November (1918) Revolution released him; he went to Berlin, was recalled to Bavaria by Eisner and led the socialist workers against counter-revolutionary Prussian troops. He saved the lives of many hostages and fought against the barbarisms of both sides. When the Revolution was suppressed, a price of 10,000 marks was set on his head and he was imprisoned for five years. When in prison he wrote and published plays and poems. *The Swallow Book* and other manuscripts had to be smuggled out. Toller later visited the Soviet Union, the U.S.A. and North Africa. He published *Justiz-Erlebnisse* (sketches), 1927. In 1933 the Nazis sent some of their official killers to Toller's apartment. But he was at this time on a lecture tour in Switzerland. Toller then lived in London, New York, lectured all over Europe and U.S.A. against Hitler and the Nazis. He spent much time and effort in collecting several million dollars for the Spanish children of both sides in the Civil War. During the international P.E.N. Congress in 1939 Toller, who had bought already a ticket for London for the following week, committed suicide in a New York hotel-room.—English translations: *The Swallow Book* (poems), 1924; *Which World—Which Way* (essays), 1931; *I Was a German* (autobiography), 1934; *Seven Plays* (and *Mary Baker Eddy*, with Hermann Kesten), 1934.

Alexei Nicolaevich *Tolstoi*, formerly Count, (1882–), Russian novelist and playwright. His mother was a Turgenev and he is a descendant, though not direct, of Leo Tolstoi. In 1908 he published his first poems, in 1909 his *Magpie Tales*, in 1910 his first novel, *The Left Bank of the Volga* and in 1914 and 1915 two other novels, *Lame Esquire* and *Old People*. During the first World War he was a military correspondent for the *Russian News*. In the Revolution he fought on the White side, but left Russia after the evacuation of Odessa and settled in France. In 1921 he returned to Soviet Russia, published in 1922 *Nikita's Childhood* and other novels, *Aelita*, 1922–23; *The Death Box*, 1925, and a play, *The Revolt of the Machines*, and his chief work, *Peter the Great*, 1929–1934. He and Sholokhov are the most popular and most official Soviet novelists.—English translations: *The Road to Cavalry*, 1923; *Peter the Great*, 1936; *Darkness and Dawn*, 1936; *The Death Box*, 1937; *Bread*, 1938.

Juljan *Tuwim* (1894–), Polish poet. Born at Lodz, he studied at a Russian grammar school and during the first World War he read law at the University of Warsaw. He published many volumes of poetry, *The Fair of Rhymes* (Jarmark rymów). He is a great student of the Polish language and its resources and has translated Russian poetry, especially Pushkin's poems. He escaped before the Nazis to Paris and after the fall of France to Brazil; now lives in New York.

His *Selected Poems* were published in Polish by Roy Publishers in New York, 1942. He is now working on an extensive poem, *Polish Flowers*, of an epic-lyrical character.

Miguel de *Unamuno* y Yugo (1864–1936), Spanish poet, novelist and essayist. He was born in Bilbao, studied in Madrid, became in 1892 professor of Greek language and literature at Salamanca University and in 1900 was made rector of the university. Throughout his life he took a fearless stand on public questions. He was so outspoken in his newspaper articles and speeches against government corruption that he was removed from the rectorship. Primo de Rivera's coup d'état of 1923 aroused him to such vehement denunciation that in February 1924 he was exiled to one of the Canary Islands. The government granted an amnesty in July 1924, but he refused to return to Spain. He went to live in Paris where Valéry Larbaud, André Gide, the Comtesse de Noailles welcomed him. He later returned to Salamanca and the rectorship of the University at the time of the setting-up of the Spanish Republic. Although the Franco Rebels tried to claim him in the Civil War, he dissociated himself from them before his death in 1936. He published many novels, short stories and essays.—English translations: *The Tragic Sense of Life*, 1921; *Essays and Soliloquies*, 1925; *The Life of Don Quixote and Sancho*, 1927; *The Agony of Christianity*, 1928; *Mist*, 1928; *Three Exemplary Novels and a Prologue*, 1930.

Sigrid *Undset* (1882–), Norwegian novelist, winner of the Nobel Prize for Literature in 1928. She was born in Kallundborg in Denmark. Her father was a prominent Norwegian archæologist and her mother was Danish. At 16 she got a job in the office of a lawyer; there she worked ten years. She wrote her first novel in secret, *Fru Marta Oulie*, 1907. In 1910 a small collection of poems appeared. She published many novels and short stories and married the Norwegian painter, Anders Avarstad. In 1921–22 she published her medieval trilogy, *Kristin Lavransdatter*. Sigrid Undset was received into the Roman Catholic Church in 1924. In 1925 her marriage was annulled. She lived with her four children in a medieval house near Lillehammer in Norway. She was in Oslo, lecturing to a student group on the night of April 7, 1940, when the German invasion began. On the ninth, her two sons Anders and Hans escaped from occupied Oslo; next morning they both joined the Norwegian army near

Lillehammer. Three weeks later Anders was killed in action. Hans finally joined his mother in Sweden, went with her all the way through Russia, Siberia, Japan to America, and returned later to the Norwegian forces in Great Britain. Sigrid Undset now lives in Brooklyn.—English translations: *Jenny*, 1921; *Kristin Lavransdatter*, 1929; *Olaf Audunssön*, 1928–30; *The Wild Orchid*, 1931; *The Master of Hestviken*, 1932; *The Burning Bush*, 1932; *Ida Elizabeth*, 1933; *Saga of the Saints*, 1934; *Stages on the Road*, 1934; *The Longest Year*, 1935; *Sunnar's Daughter*, 1936; *The Faithful Wife*, 1937; *Images in a Mirror*, 1938; *Madame Dorothea*, 1940; *Happy Times in Norway*, 1942, (from which our selection is taken).

Paul *Valéry* (1871–), French poet and essayist. Born in Cette, his father was French, his mother Italian. He left the University of Montpellier at 18 to take his military training. At a café he met Pierre Louys, who encouraged him to write and printed some of Valéry's poems in 1889 in his literary review *La Conque*. At 20 he went to Paris and became one of the followers of the great symbolist poet, Mallarmé. In 1895 he published *Introduction à la méthode de Leonardo da Vinci* and *La soirée avec Monsieur Teste*. He was then no longer a symbolist. During the next twenty years Valéry, living in Paris, published one poem. At the insistence of Pierre Louys and André Gide he reappeared with *La Jeune Parque* in 1917; then he published *Odes*, 1920; *L'Album des vers anciens*, 1920; *Charmes*, 1922; *Fragments du Narcisse*, 1922; *Poésies*, 1923; *Variété*, 1924, (this book is a collection of essays). In 1925 he was elected to the French Academy. Valéry was for long years an official of the *Agence Havas*. It was by accident, he says, that he became a poet. He is living still in Paris. "The completed work of art," he says, "I consider without interest. The only thing that arouses my curiosity is its actual creation."—English translations: *The Serpent*, 1924; *An Evening with Mr. Teste*, 1925; *Variety*, 1927; *Introduction to the Method of Leonardo da Vinci*, 1929; *Eupalinos or the Architect*, 1932; *The Graveyard by the Sea*, 1932; *Variety*, (*Second Series*), 1938.

Vladislav *Vančura* (1891–1942), Czech novelist. He wrote novels, *Jan Marhoul, the Baker*; *The Plough Fields and the Fields of War* (from which our selection is taken); *Marketa Lazarova*; *Flight to Budapest*. He was shot as a hostage by the Nazis after the assassination of Heydrich.

Dragisha *Vasić* (1885–), Yugoslav novelist and journalist. He was born at Gornji Milanovac in pre-war Serbia. He was a young lawyer when World War I broke out, served in the war and came out with a revolutionary point of view; he edited a progressive daily paper and was the chief columnist of the main organ of the republican movement. He wrote novels and a book about the 1903 revolution in Belgrade and the epoch between the Balkan and the World Wars. When the invasion of the Germans came, he placed himself on the side of General Mihailović. The fragment of a novel translated here is from his first collection of novels.

Adriaan *van der Veen* (1915–), Dutch writer. Before he came to America, he was a newspaperman in Brussels. He published among other works: *Geld speelt de Grootste Rol*; *Ofeningen Tuschen Archief en Kantoor*; *Idylle in New York*.

Simon *Vestdijk* (1898–), Dutch novelist, poet and essayist, a physician by training. Of his novels, one of the most outstanding is *Het Vijste Zegel*, with El Greco as the principal character. His collected essays, entitled *Lier en Lancet*, include a study of Emily Dickinson; he is also the author of one play.

Gerard *Walschap* (1898–), Belgian novelist and short-story writer. Born in Londerzeel-St. Jozef, he was the editor of a weekly before he became an independent writer. His main works are: the trilogy, *De familie Roothooft*; *Trouwen*; *Celibaat*; *Sybille*; *Een Mensch van goeden Wil*; *Het Kind*; *Houtekiet*; *de vierde Koning* and the short stories, *Volk and De Dood in het Dorp*. He lives in Antwerp and writes in Flemish.

Franz Carl *Weiskopf* (1900–), Czechoslovak novelist, poet, short-story writer (in German). He was born in Prague, studied philosophy and wrote his first play, *Föhn*, in 1919. It was produced at Prague in 1920. He wrote some more plays. In 1924 his first collection of poetry was published, *Tschechische Lieder*, in 1926 his first collection of short stories, *Flucht nach Frankreich*, in 1931 his first novel *Das Slawenlied*. Weiskopf lived from 1927 to March 1933 in Berlin. Then he left Nazi Germany and lived in Prague and later in Paris. Besides work for newspapers, he published a novel *Die Versuchung* (1936) in Zurich and translated and edited a collection of modern Czechoslovak poetry, *Das Herz ein Schild* (1937). He received the Herder Prize in 1937. He had lived since 1939 in New York. He has just completed a new novel, *The Firing Squad.*—English translation: *Dawn Breaks* (novel), 1942

Ernst *Weiss* (1848–1940), Czechoslovak novelist, playwright. He wrote in German. Born in Moravia, he was an Austrian by tradition, a Czechoslovak by citizenship, a German writer by misfortune, by nature a misogynist always in love, and a slanderous friend of the whole school of Bohemian poets in Prague, Kafka, Werfel, Egon Erwin Kisch, Max Brod, Rainer Maria Rilke, the blind Baum and the dead Meyrink. By first profession he was a ship's doctor. He lived in Berlin and went, in Germany's worst spring (1933), to Prague, then to Paris. On the day Hitler's army was marching into Paris, Weiss drowned himself in his bathtub. He considered his diaries his masterwork, which he wanted published after his death. The Nazis destroyed them. He died with nothing in the world except his fame among the 200 best readers of German literature and a movie-writer's contract in Hollywood. He was one of the outstanding European novelists of our time. He published many novels, *Die Galeere*, 1913; *Franziska*, 1915; *Tiere in Ketten*, 1918; *Mensch gegen Mensch*, 1919; *Stern der Dämonen*, 1921; *Nahar*, 1921; *Feuerprobe*, 1923; *Männer in der Nacht*, 1925; *Boëtius von Orlamünde* (an Olympic Prize novel), 1928; *Georg Letham, Arzt und Mörder*, 1931; *Der arme Verschwender*, 1937. He published some plays (which were produced), short stories, essays and poetry.—English translations: No English translations.

Franz *Werfel* (1890–), Austrian novelist, playwright, poet, essayist. Born in Prague, he studied philosophy in Prague and Hamburg, where he wrote his first volume of poetry, *Der Weltfreund*, in 1911. He translated into German the poems of the great Czech poet, Otakar Brezina, in *Winde von Mittag bis Mitternacht*. In 1913 he published *Wir sind* and in 1915 *Einander* (poems). He served in the World War from 1915 to 1917, afterwards settled in Vienna, participated there in the revolution, worked at Leipzig as an editor for the publisher Kurt Wolff. He married the widow of Gustav Mahler. Once a leading expressionist, he left this literary movement. He published many plays, novels, and poems. When the Nazis came to Austria, Werfel left for France and came in October 1940 through the help of his publisher Ben Huebsch and the Emergency Rescue Committee to this country. He lives now in Hollywood.—English translations: *Verdi*, 1925; *The Goat Song* (drama), 1926; *Juarez and Maximilian*, (a dramatic history), 1926; *The Man Who Conquered Death*, 1927; *The Class Reunion*, 1929; *The Pure in Heart*, 1931; *The Forty Days of Musa Dagh*, 1934; *Twilight of a World*, 1937; *Hearken Unto the Voice*, 1938; *Embezzled Heaven*, 1940; *The Song of Bernadette*, 1942.

Kazimierz *Wierzynski* (1894–), Polish poet. Born at Drohobycz in Galicia, he studied philosophy and history of literature at the universities of Cracow, Lwow and Vienna. He fought during World War I in the Pilsudski Legion, then in the Austrian army, spent three years as prisoner of war in Russia. He received the first international prize for poetry at the Ninth Olympiad in 1928. He was a member of the Polish Academy of Literature. At present he is an editor of the Polish weekly *Tygodnik Polski* in New York. He has published several volumes of poetry—*Spring and Wine*, 1919; *The Great Bear*, 1923; *The Olympic Laurel* (see above), 1928; in 1942 his volume of poems, *Windrose (Róza wiatrów)*, was published in Polish by Roy Publishers in New York.

Joseph *Wittlin* (1896–), Polish novelist, poet, essayist. Born at Dmytrow in Podolia, he studied at the universities of Vienna and Lwow, volunteered for the Polish Legion, served in the Austrian army in the first World War, for a time together with his university friend, Joseph Roth (see above). After the war Wittlin became professor of Polish literature at Lwow. In 1923 he became the literary director of the state theater in Lodz and directed a theater school there for two years. In 1927 he went to Warsaw. In 1920 he published a collection of poems, *Hymns*, which was the first literary work to appear in Poland after the war in protest against nationalism, militarism and war. He worked for long years on a translation into Polish of Homer's *Odyssey*. He collected two volumes of essays, in 1925 *War, Peace and a Poet's Soul,* in 1932 *Etapes*. In 1925–26 Wittlin lived in France and wrote a *Life of St. Francis of Assisi*, from which parts were published, likewise in 1928 an essay, *The Memories of a Post-Pacifist*. He translated about twenty novels and plays from the Italian, German and French into Polish and published new editions of *Gilgamesh, Don Quixote* and *The Tales of 1001 Nights*. He has been working for years on a trilogy *The Story of the Patient Infantry Soldier*. The first volume, *Salt of the Earth*, was published in Poland in 1934, in New

York, 1941. Wittlin went in summer 1939 to France, and came in 1941 to New York. He received several Polish literary prizes, of the Polish Academy, etc., and in New York from the *Academy for Arts and Letters*, in 1943.—English translation: *Salt of the Earth* (novel), 1941.

Karel *van de Woestijne* (1878–1929), Belgian poet. He writes in Flemish. Born at Ghent, he studied at the University there, was active as correspondent for Dutch newspapers, as official in the Ministry of Education and later as professor of Flemish literature at Ghent University. His work consists mainly of poetry: *Gulden Schaduw; Interludien; Modderen Man; God an Zee, Het Berg-meer.* Some of his essays were published in *Kunst en Geest in Vlaanderen* and *De Schroeflin*.

Jiří *Wolker* (1900–1925), Czech poet. Born at Prostejov, in Moravia, he died of tuberculosis. He wrote a volume of ballads, *A Guest Coming into the House*, and other verse.

Mikhail Mikhailovich *Zostchenko* (1895–), Russian novelist and short-story writer. He is a Soviet writer of satirical sketches, many of which have appeared in English; our selection comes from the volume, *Russia Laughs*.

Carl *Zuckmayer* (1896–), German playwright, poet, novelist. Born at Nackenheim-on-the-Rhine, he is a Roman Catholic. He studied at Heidelberg, served in the World War 1914–18. His first play *Kreuzweg* was produced in Berlin in 1920. In 1925 he received the Kleist Prize for his play *Der fröhliche Weinberg*, in 1929 the Georg Büchner Prize, and later himself gave the Kleist Prize to Ödön von Horvath (see above). He left Germany in 1933, left Austria in 1938 and has lived since then in this country. He adapted for the German theater plays by Maxwell Anderson and Ernest Hemingway. He collected his poems, *Der Baum* (1926), a volume of short stories, *Ein Bauer aus dem Taunus* (1927), and published plays and novels.—English translations: *The Captain of Koepenick* (play), 1932; *The Moons Ride Over* (novel), 1937; *Second Wind* (autobiography), 1940.

Stefan *Zweig* (1881–1942), Austrian short-story writer, essayist, and playwright. Born in Vienna, he published two volumes of verse, before his university career was over. He travelled through Europe, became the friend of many outstanding European writers, translated some of their work and introduced it in Germany and Austria (Verhaeren, Verlaine, Romain Rolland). In 1917 he wrote *Jeremiah*, a pacifist drama, and went to Zurich, where his play was staged in 1917. After the war he returned to Austria and settled in Salzburg. He wrote the libretto of the Richard Strauss' opera *Die schweigsame Frau,* (produced in 1935). Zweig left Austria and settled in London and Bath, and became an English citizen, then went to this country and to Brazil, where he committed suicide, shortly after his sixtieth birthday.—English translations: *Paul Verlaine*, 1913; *Emile Verhaeren*, 1914; *Romain Rolland*, 1921; *Jeremiah*, 1922; *Passion and Pain*, 1925; *The Invisible Collection*, (from which our selection is taken), 1926; *Conflicts*, 1927; *Adepts in Self-Portraiture*, 1928; *Volpone* (adaptation of the Ben Jonson play), 1928; *Joseph Fouché*, 1930; *Three Masters*, 1930; *Amok*, 1931; *A Letter from an Unknown Woman*, 1932; *Mental Healers*, 1932; *Kaleidoscope*, 1933; *Marie Antoinette*, 1933; *Erasmus of Rotterdam*, 1934; *Mary, Queen of Scotland and the Isles*, 1935; *The Right to Heresy: Castellio against Calvin*, 1936; *The Buried Candelabrum*, 1937; *Conqueror of the Seas: The Story of Magellan*, 1938; *Masterbuilders*, 1939; *Beware of Pity* (his first and last novel), 1939; *The Tide of Fortune*, 1940; *Brazil, Land of the Future*, 1941; *Amerigo, a Comedy of Errors in History*, 1942; *The World of Yesterday*, 1943.

ACKNOWLEDGMENTS

The Editors wish to express their gratitude to publishers and individuals for reprint permissions, as listed below in the order in which selections appear in the Anthology. The titles of published volumes from which selections have been taken are printed in italics; when selections have been made from other sources, or are printed here for the first time, the titles appear within quotation marks. When dates are mentioned, they refer to United States copyright registration, not necessarily to the publication dates of the volumes concerned. Every endeavor has been made to trace the owners of copyright, but present conditions of communication have in some cases prevented successful investigation. Apologies are offered to anyone whose rights appear to have been overlooked.

Variety II, by Paul Valéry, translated by Malcolm Cowley, Copyright, 1927, by Harcourt, Brace & Co., by permission of the publishers.

Goethe and Beethoven, by Romain Rolland, Copyright, 1931, by Harper & Bros., by permission of the publishers.

Les nouvelles nourritures, by André Gide, courtesy of the author.

Remembrance of Things Past, Vol. II, "The Captive," by Marcel Proust, Copyright, 1927, 1929, 1930, 1932, by Random House, Inc., reprinted by permission of Random House, Inc.

The Thibaults, by Roger Martin du Gard, Copyright, 1939, by permission of The Viking Press, Inc.

The Catholic Anthology, edited by Thomas Walsh, ("Shadows" by Paul Claudel), by permission of Miss Walsh and The Macmillan Co.

Aftermath, by Jules Romains, by permission of Alfred A. Knopf, Inc.

The Bullfighters, by Henry de Montherlant, by permission of The Dial Press, Inc.

Personal Record, by Julian Green, Copyright, 1939, by Julian Green, by permission of Harper & Bros.

"Written on the Door," by Saint-John Perse, courtesy of the author.

Thérèse, by François Mauriac, by permission of Liveright Publishing Corp.

"After Twenty Years," by Louis Aragon, by permission of the publishers, Duell, Sloan and Pearce, Inc.

"Preface to Faulkner," by André Malraux, courtesy of the author.

"Pablo Picasso," by Paul Eluard, courtesy of *Decision.*

"John Landless Leads the Caravan," by Yvan Goll, courtesy of the author and of *Decision.*

Southern Mail, by Antoine de Saint Exupéry, Copyright, 1933, by Harrison Smith and Robert Haas, by permission of Random House, Inc.

Art and Scholasticism, by Jacques Maritain, by permission of Charles Scribner's Sons.

"The Ruins of Paris," by Jean Cocteau, and "Return to Humanity," by Georges Bernanos, courtesy of *Decision.*

Essays and Soliloquies, by Miguel de Unamuno, by permission of Alfred A. Knopf, Inc.

Stories by Joaquin Arderíus and Gabriel Miró, "Strange Cases" and "Greguerías," by Ramón Goméz de la Serna, courtesy of Angel Flores.

"The Crime Took Place in Granada," by Antonio Machado, courtesy of *Left Review.*

The Revolt of the Masses, by José Ortega y Gasset, by permission of W. W. Norton and Co., Inc.

A Man's Place, by Ramón J. Sender, by permission of the publishers, Duell, Sloan and Pearce, Inc.

"Terrestrial Sphere," by Jorge Guillén, courtesy of the author.

"Proud Beauty," by José Rodrigues Miguéis, courtesy of the author.

"Italian Literature in Exile," by Renato Poggioli, courtesy of the author and of *Decision.*

"Better Think Twice About It," by Luigi Pirandello, by permission of E. P. Dutton & Co.

Fontamara, by Ignazio Silone, Copyright, 1934, by Harrison Smith and Robert Haas, by permission of Random House, Inc.

Sardinian Brigade, by Emilio Lussu, by permission of Alfred A. Knopf, Inc.

"Lost Italians," by Nicola Chiaromonte, by permission of *The Commonweal.*

"Two Good Europeans," by Gaetano Salvemini, courtesy of the author.

Goliath, by G. A. Borgese, Copyright, 1937, by the author, by permission of The Viking Press, Inc.

"Expecting the Barbarians," by C. P. Cavafy and "Maternity," by Lilika Nakos, courtesy of *Decision.*

The Realm of the Waters, by Mihail Sadoveanu, courtesy of Saul Colin.

Kyra Kyralina, by Panaït Istrati, by permission of Alfred A. Knopf, Inc.

"The Stone Bridge of the Rossitsa," by Angel Karaliichev, and "Guest," by Elin-Pelin, by permission of The Dial Press, Inc.

"The Man Who Came from America," by Svetoslav Minkov, courtesy of Victor Sharenkoff.

"Borromeo," by Ferencz Molnár, courtesy of the author.

Hungaria, by Jenö Heltai, by permission of Ivor Nicolson & Watson, Ltd., London.

The Age of the Fish, by Ödön von Horvath, by permission of The Dial Press, Inc.

"On a Visit," by Dragisha Vasic, and "How Silent They Who Die," by Milan Dedinac, courtesy of Rastko Petrovich.

Salt of the Earth, by Joseph Wittlin, courtesy of the author.

Poems by Juljan Tuwim, Stanislaw Balinski, Kazimierz Wierzynski, Antoni Slonimski and Jan Lechon, courtesy of the authors.

A Book of Short Stories of Maxim Gorki, by permission of Henry Holt & Co., Inc.

Bonfire 1932 ("Gedali," by Isaak Babel and "Vasily Suchkov," by Alexei Tolstoi), by permission of Ernest Benn, Ltd., London.

"The Zaddik," by Ilya Ehrenburg, reprinted from *Opinion*.

Russia Laughs, by Mikhail Zostchenko, Copyright, 1935, by Helena Clayton, by permission of Lothrop, Lee & Shepard Co.

"The Cherry Stone," by Yury Olesha, courtesy of the author.

And Quiet Flows the Don, by Mikhail Sholokhov, by permission of Putnam and Co., Ltd., London.

"Natalie," by Ivan Bunin, by permission of *New Review*.

Intimate Things, by Karel Čapek, by permission of George Allen & Unwin, Ltd., London.

Schweik, the Good Soldier, by Jaroslav Hašek, Copyright, 1930, by Doubleday, Doran & Co., Inc., by permission of Curtis Brown, Ltd.

Letters from Exile ("Vertigo," by Egon Hostovský), by permission of George Allen & Unwin, Ltd., London.

Poems by Vítězval Nezval, Jiří Wolker and František Halas, stories by Ivan Olbracht, and Vladislav Vančura, courtesy of Egon Hostovský.

"Cardiac Suture," by Ernst Weiss, by permission of the author.

"The Little Golden Apple," by F. C. Weiskopf, courtesy of the author.

Sonnets to Orpheus, Duino Elegies, by Rainer Maria Rilke, by permission of W. W. Norton and Co., Inc.; "Letter to Lisa Heise," by permission of *Twice a Year*.

"The Bulletproof Hidalgo," by Franz Werfel, courtesy of the author.

"Cavalry Tale," by Hugo von Hofmannsthal, courtesy of Christiane Zimmer-von Hofmannsthal.

Poems by Richard Beer-Hofmann, courtesy of the author.

"Pierrette," by Arthur Schnitzker, courtesy of Heinrich Schnitzler.

Kaleidoscope, by Stefan Zweig, Copyright, 1934, by permission of The Viking Press, Inc.

Freud, Goethe, Wagner and *The Beloved Returns,* by Thomas Mann, by permission of Alfred A. Knopf, Inc.

"To a Young Leader of the First World War," by Stefan George, courtesy of *Decision*.

"My People," by Else Lasker-Schüler, courtesy of the translator, Babette Deutsch.

"Angelica," by René Schickele, courtesy of the translator, Elizabeth Reynolds Hapgood.

"Convent Life," by Annette Kolb, courtesy of the author.

"The Chief," by Alfred Doeblin, courtesy of the author.

"Breathe!" by Leonhard Frank, courtesy of the author.

"The Suitcase," by Bruno Frank, courtesy of the author.

"Farewell from the Unknown," from an unfinished novel, *The Time of Evil,* by Joachim Maass, courtesy of the author.

"Clair de Lune," from an unfinished novel, *Thou Day and Night,* by Gustav Regler, courtesy of the author.

"Yes, I Live in a Dark Age," by Bert Brecht, courtesy of *Decision*.

"My Death," by Carl Zuckmayer, courtesy of the author.

"Colonel Kock," by Hermann Kesten, courtesy of the author.

"The Supernational Manifesto," by Heinrich Mann, courtesy of the author.

"Notes," by Maurice Maeterlinck, courtesy of the author.

Poems by Karel van de Woestijne, Paul van Ostayen, story by Gerard Walshap, courtesy of J. A. Goris.

In the Shadow of Tomorrow, by Johan Huizinga, by permission of W. W. Norton and Co., Inc.

Happy Times in Norway, by Sigrid Undset, by permission of Alfred A. Knopf, Inc.

A Fugitive Crosses His Tracks, by Aksel Sandemose, by permission of Alfred A. Knopf, Inc.

"Makkaur," by Eyvind Berggrav, courtesy of the *American-Scandinavian Review.*

"We Shall Survive," by Arnulf Överland, courtesy of the *American-Scandinavian Review.*

Onda Sagor, by Pär Lagerkvist, by permission of Jonathan Cape, Ltd., London.

Cape Farewell, by Harry Martinson, by permission of G. P. Putnam's Sons.

"The Mind Reader of Tivoli," by Vilhelm Moberg, courtesy of the *American-Scandinavian Review.*

The Maid Silja, by F. E. Sillanpää, by permission of The Macmillan Co.

"Jacob Boehme's Calling," by Hermann Hesse, courtesy of the author.

ALPHABETICAL LIST OF AUTHORS